TI worldwide sales offices

ALABAMA

304 Wynn Drive
Huntsville, Alabama 35806
205-837-7530

ARIZONA

4820 N. Black Canyon Hwy.
Suite 202
Phoenix, Arizona 85017
602-249-1313

CALIFORNIA

3186J Airway
Costa Mesa, California 92626
714-540-7311

831 S. Douglas St.
El Segundo, California 90245
213-973-2571

Balboa Towers Bldg., Suite 805
5252 Balboa Avenue
San Diego, California 92117
714-279-2622

776 Palomar Avenue
Sunnyvale, California 94086
408-732-1840

COLORADO

9725 E. Hampden St., Suite 301
Denver, Colorado 80231
303-751-1780

CONNECTICUT

35 Worth Avenue
Hamden, Connecticut 06518
203-281-0074

FLORIDA

4600 West Commercial Blvd.
Fort Lauderdale, Florida 33319
305-733-3300

2221 Lee Road, Suite 108
Winter Park, Florida 32789
305-644-3535

ILLINOIS

1701 E. Lake Avenue, Suite 300
Glenview, Illinois 60025
312-729-5710

INDIANA

3705 Rupp Drive
Arch Building
Fort Wayne, Indiana 46805
219-484-0606

2346 S. Lynhurst Dr., Suite 101
Indianapolis, Indiana 46241
317-248-8555

MASSACHUSETTS

504 Totten Pond Road
Waltham, Mass. 02154
617-890-7400

MICHIGAN

Central Park Plaza
26211 Central Park Blvd., Suite 215
Southfield, Michigan 48076
313-353-0830

MINNESOTA

A.I.C. Bldg., Suite 202
7615 Metro Blvd.
Edina, Minn. 55435
612-835-2900

NEW JERSEY

1245 Westfield Ave., P.O. Box 885
Clark, New Jersey 07066
201-574-9800

NEW MEXICO

1101 Cardenas Drive, N.E.,
Room 215
Albuquerque, New Mexico 87110
505-265-8491

NEW YORK

144 Metro Park
Rochester, New York 14623
716-461-1800

6700 Old Collamer Rd.
East Syracuse, New York 13057
315-463-9291

P.O. Box 618, 112 Nanticoke Ave.
Endicott, New York 13760
607-785-9987

167 Main Street
Fishkill, New York 12524
914-896-6793

1 Huntington Quadrangle, Suite 1C01
Melville, New York 11746
516-293-2560

NORTH CAROLINA

1001 East Blvd.
Charlotte, N.C. 28203
704-333-1519

OHIO

Belmont Bldg., Suite 120
28790 Chagrin Blvd.
Cleveland, Ohio 44122
216-464-2990

Hawley Bldg., Suite 101
4140 Linden Avenue
Dayton, Ohio 45432
513-253-3121

OREGON

10700 S.W. Beaverton Hwy.
Suite 11
Beaverton, Oregon 97005
503-643-6750

PENNSYLVANIA

275 Commerce Drive, Suite 300
Fort Washington, Pa. 19034
215-643-6450

TEXAS

6000 Denton Drive
P.O. Box 5012, M/S 366
Dallas, Texas 75222
214-238-6805

P.O. Box 5012, M/S 7
Dallas, Texas 75222
214-238-4881

P.O. Box 5012, M/S 288
Dallas, Texas 75222
214-238-2616

3939 Ann Arbor
Houston, Texas 77042
713-785-6906

VIRGINIA

8512 Trabue Road
Richmond, Virginia 23235
804-320-3830

WASHINGTON

700 112th N.E., Suite 101
Bellevue, Washington 98004
206-455-3480

WASHINGTON, D.C.

1500 Wilson Blvd., Suite 1100
Arlington, Virginia 22209
703-525-0336

ARGENTINA

Texas Instruments Argentina S.A.I.C.F.

C.C. Box 2296—Correo Central
Buenos Aires, Argentina
748-1141

ASIA

Texas Instruments Asia Limited

5F Aoyama Tower Bldg.
24-15 Minami Aoyama Chome
Minato-ku, Tokyo 107, Japan
402-6171

11A-15 Chatham Road
First Floor, Kowloon
Hong Kong
3-670061

Texas Instruments Singapore (PTE) Ltd.
27 Kallang Place
Singapore 1, Rep. of Singapore
258-1122

Texas Instruments Taiwan Limited
P.O. Box 3999
Taipei, Chung Ho, Taiwan
921 623

Texas Instruments Malaysia SDN. BHD.
Number 1 Lorong Enggang 33
Kuala Lampur 15-07, Malaysia
647 911

AUSTRALIA

Texas Instruments Australia Ltd.

Suite 205, 118 Great North Road
Five Dock N.S.W. 2046 Australia
831-2555

Box 63, Post Office
171-175 Philip Highway
Elizabeth 5112 South Australia
255-2066

BELGIUM

Texas Instruments Belgium

21 Avenue Ed.Lacomble
1040 Brussels
2/733 96 23

BRAZIL

Texas Instrumentos Electronicos
do Brasil Ltda.

Rua Joao Annes, 153-Lapa
Caixa Postal 30.103, CEP 01.000
Sao Paulo, SP, Brasil
260-2956

CANADA

Texas Instruments Incorporated

935 Montee De Liesse
St. Laurent H4T 1R2
Quebec, Canada
514-341-3232

280 Centre Str. East
Richmond Hill (Toronto)
Ontario, Canada
716-856-4453

DENMARK

Texas Instruments Denmark

46D, Marielundvej
2730 Herlev, Denmark
(01) 91 74 00

FINLAND

Texas Instruments Finland OY

Fredrikinkatu 75, A7
Helsinki 10, Finland
44 71 71

FRANCE

Texas Instruments France

Boite Postale 5
06 Villeneuve-Loubet, France
31 03 64

La Boursidiere, Bloc A
R.N. 186, 92350 Le Plessis Robinson
630.23.43

30-31 Quai Rambaud
69 Lyon, France
42 78 50

GERMANY

Texas Instruments Deutschland GmbH

Haggerty Str. 1
8050 Freising, Germany
08161/80-1

Frankfurter Ring 243
8000 Munich 40, Germany
089/325011-15

Lazarettstrasse, 19
4300 Essen, Germany
02141/20916

Krugerstrasse 24
1000 Berlin 49, Germany
0311/74 44 041

Akazlenstrasse 22-26
6230 Frankfurt — Griesheim
Germany
0611/39 90 61

Steimbker Hof 8A
3000 Hannover, Germany
0511/55 60 41

Krefelderstrasse 11-15
7000 Stuttgart 50, Germany
0711/54 70 01

ITALY

Texas Instruments Italia SpA

Via Della Giustizia 9
20125 Milan, Italy
02-688 31 41

Via L. Mancinella 65
00199 Roma, Italy
06-83 77 45

Via Montebello 27
10124 Torino, Italy
011-83 22 76

MEXICO

Texas Instruments de Mexico S.A.

Poniente 116 #489
Col. Industrial Vallejo
Mexico City, D.F., Mexico
567-92-00

NETHERLANDS

Texas Instruments Holland N.V.

Entrepot Gebouw-Kamer 225
P.O. Box 7603
Schiphol-Centrum
020-17 36 36

NORWAY

Texas Instruments Norway A/S
Sentrumskontorene
Brugaten 1
Oslo 1, Norway
33 18 80

SWEDEN

Texas Instruments Sweden AB

S-104 40 Stockholm 14
Skeppargatan 26
67 98 35

UNITED KINGDOM

Texas Instruments Limited

Manton Lane
Bedford, England
0234-67466

The
TTL
Data Book

for

Design Engineers

Second Edition

TEXAS INSTRUMENTS
INCORPORATED

LCC4112
74062-116 -AI

Printed in U.S.A.

IMPORTANT NOTICES

Texas Instruments reserves the right to make changes at any time in order to improve design and to supply the best product possible.

TI cannot assume any responsibility for any circuits shown or represent that they are free from patent infringement.

Information contained herein supercedes previously published data on TTL products including data books CC-411 and CC-416.

THE TTL DATA BOOK

Second Edition

In this 832-page data book, Texas Instruments is pleased to present important technical information on the industry's broadest and most advanced families of TTL integrated circuits.

You'll find complete specifications on standard-technology TTL circuits (Series 54/74, Series 54H/74H, Series 54L/74L) and on TI's high-technology TTL circuits such as the Schottky-clamped[†] Series 54LS/74LS and Series 54S/74S. Information on radiation-hardened and beam-lead circuits has not been included in this book, but TI has a broad line of these devices, and information is available upon request.

The indexes are designed for ease of circuit selection with margin tabs to guide you quickly to general circuit catagories, and the alphanumeric and functional indexes will let you locate specific circuit types quickly. In addition, a section showing pin assignments, package availability, and a brief description of the circuit type arranged in type-number order is included for quick reference. Whenever practical, the MSI functions are arranged in sequence by type number to further simplify the task of locating a particular function.

High-reliability TTL IC's are covered in a section devoted to the latest revision of the MACH IV Procurement Specification in accordance with MIL-M-38510, a program initiated by TI to ensure that quality and reliability are built into, not tested into, integrated circuits. Another section is devoted to JAN IC's and provides a table of recommended usage and cross-references from TI type number to 38510 slash sheet and 38510 slash sheet to TI type number.

Another handy reference for the design engineer is the section on IC sockets and interconnection panels from TI.

Although this volume offers design and specification data only for TTL integrated circuits, complete technical data for any TI semiconductor/component products are available from your nearest TI field sales office, local authorized TI distributor, or by writing direct to: Marketing Information Services, Texas Instruments Incorporated, P. O. Box 5012, MS 308, Dallas, Texas 75222.

We sincerely hope you will find the new TTL Data Book for Design Engineers a meaningful addition to your technical library.

[†]Integrated Schottky-Barrier diode-clamped transistor is patented by Texas Instruments. U.S. Patent Number 3,463,975.

Indexes

- **Alphanumeric**
- **Functional/Selection Guide**

TYPE NUMBERS		ELECTRICAL PAGE[†]	PIN ASSIGNMENTS PAGE	TYPE NUMBERS		ELECTRICAL PAGE[†]	PIN ASSIGNMENTS PAGE[†]
SN5400	SN7400	6-2	5-6	SN54LS14	SN74LS14	6-14	5-9
SN54H00	SN74H00	6-2	5-6	SN54H15	SN74H15	6-12	5-10
SN54L00	SN74L00	6-2	5-6	SN54LS15	SN74LS15	6-12	5-10
SN54LS00	SN74LS00	6-2	5-6	SN54S15	SN74S15	6-12	5-10
SN54S00	SN74S00	6-2	5-6	SN5416	SN7416	6-24	5-10
SN5401	SN7401	6-4	5-6	SN5417	SN7417	6-24	5-10
SN54H01	SN74H01	6-4	5-6	SN5420	SN7420	6-2	5-10
SN54L01		6-4	5-6	SN54H20	SN74H20	6-2	5-10
SN54LS01	SN74LS01	6-4	5-6	SN54L20	SN74L20	6-2	5-10
SN5402	SN7402	6-8	5-6	SN54LS20	SN74LS20	6-2	5-10
SN54L02	SN74L02	6-8	5-6	SN54S20	SN74S20	6-2	5-10
SN54LS02	SN74LS02	6-8	5-6	SN54H21	SN74H21	6-10	5-11
SN54S02	SN74S02	6-8	5-6	SN54LS21	SN74LS21	6-10	5-11
SN5403	SN7403	6-4	5-7	SN5422	SN7422	6-4	5-11
SN54L03	SN74L03	6-4	5-7	SN54H22	SN74H22	6-4	5-11
SN54LS03	SN74LS03	6-4	5-7	SN54LS22	SN74LS22	6-4	5-11
SN54S03	SN74S03	6-4	5-7	SN54S22	SN74S22	6-4	5-11
SN5404	SN7404	6-2	5-7	SN5423	SN7423	6-39	5-11
SN54H04	SN74H04	6-2	5-7	SN5425	SN7425	6-8	5-11
SN54L04	SN74L04	6-2	5-7	SN5426	SN7426	6-24	5-12
SN54LS04	SN74LS04	6-2	5-7	SN54LS26	SN74LS26	6-26	5-12
SN54S04	SN74S04	6-2	5-7	SN5427	SN7427	6-8	5-12
SN5405	SN7405	6-4	5-7	SN54LS27	SN74LS27	6-8	5-12
SN54H05	SN74H05	6-4	5-7	SN5428	SN7428	6-20	5-12
SN54LS05	SN74LS05	6-4	5-7	SN54LS28	SN74LS28	6-20	5-12
SN54S05	SN74S05	6-4	5-7	SN5430	SN7430	6-2	5-12
SN5406	SN7406	6-24	5-7	SN54H30	SN74H30	6-2	5-12
SN5407	SN7407	6-24	5-8	SN54L30	SN74L30	6-2	5-12
SN5408	SN7408	6-10	5-8	SN54LS30	SN74LS30	6-2	5-12
SN54LS08	SN74LS08	6-10	5-8	SN54S30	SN74S30	6-2	5-12
SN54S08	SN74S08	6-10	5-8	SN5432	SN7432	6-28	5-13
SN5409	SN7409	6-12	5-8	SN54LS32	SN74LS32	6-28	5-13
SN54LS09	SN74LS09	6-12	5-8	SN54S32	SN74S32	6-28	5-13
SN54S09	SN74S09	6-12	5-8	SN5433	SN7433	6-24	5-13
SN5410	SN7410	6-2	5-8	SN54LS33	SN74LS33	6-26	5-13
SN54H10	SN74H10	6-2	5-8	SN5437	SN7437	6-20	5-13
SN54L10	SN74L10	6-2	5-8	SN54LS37	SN74LS37	6-20	5-13
SN54LS10	SN74LS10	6-2	5-8	SN54S37	SN74S37	6-20	5-13
SN54S10	SN74S10	6-2	5-8	SN5438	SN7438	6-24	5-13
SN54H11	SN74H11	6-10	5-9	SN54LS38	SN74LS38	6-26	5-13
SN54LS11	SN74LS11	6-10	5-9	SN54S38	SN74S38	6-26	5-13
SN54S11	SN74S11	6-10	5-9	SN5440	SN7440	6-20	5-14
SN5412	SN7412	6-4	5-9	SN54H40	SN74H40	6-20	5-14
SN54LS12	SN74LS12	6-4	5-9	SN54LS40	SN74LS40	6-20	5-14
SN5413	SN7413	6-14	5-9	SN54S40	SN74S40	6-20	5-14
SN54LS13	SN74LS13	6-14	5-9	SN5442A	SN7442A	7-15	7-15
SN5414	SN7414	6-14	5-9	SN54L42	SN74L42	7-15	7-15

[†]See Bipolar Microcomputer Components Data Book, LCC4270.

6

TEXAS INSTRUMENTS
INCORPORATED
POST OFFICE BOX 5012 • DALLAS, TEXAS 75222

ALPHANUMERIC INDEX

TYPE NUMBERS		ELECTRICAL PAGE[†]	PIN ASSIGNMENTS PAGE[†]	TYPE NUMBERS		ELECTRICAL PAGE[†]	PIN ASSIGNMENTS PAGE[†]
SN54LS42	SN74LS42	7-15	7-15	SN54L73	SN74L73	6-54	5-22
SN5443A	SN7443A	7-15	7-15	SN54LS73A	SN74LS73A	6-56	5-22
SN54L43	SN74L43	7-15	7-15	SN5474	SN7474	6-46	5-22
SN5444A	SN7444A	7-15	7-15	SN54H74	SN74H74	6-50	5-22
SN54L44	SN74L44	7-15	7-15	SN54L74	SN74L74	6-54	5-22
SN5445	SN7445	7-20	7-20	SN54LS74A	SN74LS74A	6-56	5-22
SN5446A	SN7446A	7-22	7-22	SN54S74	SN74S74	6-58	5-22
SN54L46	SN74L46	7-22	7-22	SN5475	SN7475	7-35	7-35
SN54447A	SN74447A	7-22	7-22	SN54L75	SN74L75	7-35	7-35
SN54L47	SN74L47	7-22	7-22	SN54LS75	SN74LS75	7-35	7-35
SN54LS47	SN74LS47	7-22	7-22	SN5476	SN7476	6-46	5-23
SN5448	SN7448	7-22	7-22	SN54H76	SN74H76	6-50	5-23
SN54LS48	SN74LS48	7-22	7-22	SN54LS76A	SN74LS76A	6-56	5-23
SN5449		7-22	7-22	SN5477		7-35	7-35
SN54LS49	SN74LS49	7-22	7-22	SN54L77		7-35	7-35
SN5450	SN7450	6-39	5-16	SN54LS77		7-35	7-35
SN54H50	SN74H50	6-39	5-16	SN54H78	SN74H78	6-50	5-24
SN5451	SN7451	6-30	5-16	SN54L78	SN74L78	6-54	5-24
SN54H51	SN74H51	6-30	5-16	SN54LS78A	SN74LS78A	6-56	5-24
SN54L51	SN74L51	6-30	5-16	SN5480	SN7480	7-41	7-41
SN54LS51	SN74LS51	6-30	5-16	SN5481A	SN7481A	7-44	7-44
SN54S51	SN74S51	6-30	5-16	SN5482	SN7482	7-49	7-49
SN54H52	SN74H52	6-39	5-17	SN5483A	SN7483A	7-53	7-53
SN5453	SN7453	6-39	5-17	SN54LS83A	SN74LS83A	7-53	7-53
SN54H53	SN74H53	6-39	5-17	SN5484A	SN7484A	7-44	7-44
SN5454	SN7454	6-30	5-18	SN5485	SN7485	7-57	7-57
SN54H54	SN74H54	6-30	5-18	SN54L85	SN74L85	7-57	7-57
SN54L54	SN74L54	6-30	5-18	SN54LS85	SN74LS85	7-57	7-57
SN54LS54	SN74LS54	6-30	5-18	SN54S85	SN74S85	7-57	7-57
SN54H55	SN74H55	6-39	5-19	SN5486	SN7486	7-65	7-65
SN54L55	SN74L55	6-30	5-19	SN54L86	SN74L86	7-65	7-65
SN54LS55	SN74LS55	6-30	5-19	SN54LS86	SN74LS86	7-65	7-65
SN5460	SN7460	6-43	5-19	SN54S86	SN74S86	7-65	7-65
SN54H60	SN74H60	6-44	5-19	SN54H87	SN74H87	7-70	7-70
SN54H61	SN74H61	6-45	5-19	SN5488A	SN7488A	†	5-27
SN54H62	SN74H62	6-44	5-20		SN7489	†	5-27
SN54LS63	SN74LS63	6-62	5-20				
SN54S64	SN74S64	6-30	5-20	SN5490A	SN7490A	7-72	7-72
SN54S65	SN74S65	6-32	5-20	SN54L90	SN74L90	7-72	7-72
SN5470	SN7470	6-46	5-21	SN54LS90	SN74LS90	7-72	7-72
SN54H71	SN74H71	6-50	5-21	SN5491A	SN7491A	7-81	7-81
SN54L71	SN74L71	6-54	5-21	SN54L91	SN74L91	7-81	7-81
SN5472	SN7472	6-46	5-22	SN54LS91	SN74LS91	7-81	7-81
SN54H72	SN74H72	6-50	5-22	SN5492A	SN7492A	7-72	7-72
SN54L72	SN74L72	6-54	5-22	SN54LS92	SN74LS92	7-72	7-72
SN5473	SN7473	6-46	5-22	SN5493A	SN7493A	7-72	7-72
SN54H73	SN74H73	6-50	5-22	SN54L93	SN74L93	7-72	7-72
				SN54LS93	SN74LS93	7-72	7-72

[†]See Bipolar Microcomputer Components Data Book, LCC4270.

TEXAS INSTRUMENTS
INCORPORATED
POST OFFICE BOX 5012 • DALLAS, TEXAS 75222

TYPE NUMBERS		ELECTRICAL PAGE†	PIN ASSIGNMENTS PAGE†	TYPE NUMBERS		ELECTRICAL PAGE†	PIN ASSIGNMENTS PAGE†
SN5494	SN7494	7-86	7-86	SN54S132	SN74S132	6-14	5-32
SN5495A	SN7495A	7-89	7-89	SN54S133	SN74S133	6-2	5-38
SN54L95	SN74L95	7-89	7-89	SN54S134	SN74S134	6-33	5-38
SN54LS95B	SN74LS95B	7-89	7-89	SN54S135	SN74S135	7-129	7-129
SN5496	SN7496	7-95	7-95	SN54136	SN74136	7-131	7-131
SN54L96	SN74L96	7-95	7-95	SN54LS136	SN74LS136	7-131	7-131
SN54LS96	SN74LS96	7-95	7-95	SN54LS138	SN74LS138	7-134	7-134
SN5497	SN7497	7-102	7-102	SN54S138	SN74S138	7-134	7-134
SN54L98	SN74L98	7-107	7-107	SN54LS139	SN74LS139	7-134	7-134
SN54L99	SN74L99	7-109	7-109	SN54S139	SN74S139	7-134	7-134
SN54100	SN74100	7-113	7-113	SN54S140	SN74S140	6-22	5-39
SN54H101	SN74H101	6-52	5-31		SN74141	7-138	7-138
SN54H102	SN74H102	6-52	5-31		SN74142	7-140	7-140
SN54H103	SN74H103	6-52	5-31	SN54143	SN74143	7-143	7-143
SN54H106	SN74H106	6-52	5-32	SN54144	SN74144	7-143	7-143
SN54107	SN74107	6-46	5-32	SN54145	SN74145	7-148	7-148
SN54LS107A	SN74LS107A	6-56	5-32	SN54LS145	SN74LS145	7-148	7-148
SN54H108	SN74H108	6-52	5-32	SN54147	SN74147	7-151	7-151
SN54109	SN74109	6-46	5-33	SN54LS147	SN74LS147	7-151	7-151
SN54LS109A	SN74LS109A	6-56	5-33	SN54148	SN74148	7-151	7-151
SN54110	SN74110	6-46	5-33	SN54LS148	SN74LS148	7-151	7-151
SN54111	SN74111	6-46	5-33	SN54150	SN74150	7-157	7-157
SN54LS112A	SN74LS112A	6-56	5-34	SN54151A	SN74151A	7-157	7-157
SN54S112	SN74S112	6-58	5-34	SN54LS151	SN74LS151	7-157	7-157
SN54LS113A	SN74LS113A	6-56	5-34	SN54S151	SN74S151	7-157	7-157
SN54S113	SN74S113	6-58	5-34	SN54152A		7-157	7-157
SN54LS114A	SN74LS114A	6-56	5-34	SN54LS152		7-157	7-157
SN54S114	SN74S114	6-56	5-34	SN54153	SN74153	7-165	7-165
SN54116	SN74116	7-115	7-115	SN54L153	SN74L153	7-165	7-165
SN54120	SN74120	7-118	7-118	SN54LS153	SN74LS153	7-165	7-165
SN54121	SN74121	6-64	5-35	SN54S153	SN74S153	7-165	7-165
SN54L121	SN74L121	6-64	5-35	SN54154	SN74154	7-171	7-171
SN54122	SN74122	6-76	5-36	SN54L154	SN74L154	7-171	7-171
SN54L122	SN74L122	6-76	5-36	SN54155	SN74155	7-175	7-175
SN54LS122	SN74LS122	6-76	5-36	SN54LS155	SN74LS155	7-175	7-175
SN54123	SN74123	6-76	5-36	SN54156	SN74156	7-175	7-175
SN54L123	SN74L123	6-76	5-36	SN54LS156	SN74LS156	7-175	7-175
SN54LS123	SN74LS123	6-76	5-36	SN54157	SN74157	7-181	7-181
SN54LS124	SN74LS124	7-123	7-123	SN54L157	SN74L157	7-181	7-181
SN54S124	SN74S124	7-123	7-123	SN54LS157	SN74LS157	7-181	7-181
SN54125	SN74125	6-33	5-37	SN54S157	SN74S157	7-181	7-181
SN54LS125A	SN74LS125A	6-33	5-37	SN54LS158	SN74LS158	7-181	7-181
SN54126	SN74126	6-33	5-37	SN54S158	SN74S158	7-181	7-181
SN54LS126A	SN74LS126A	6-33	5-37	SN54159	SN74159	7-188	7-188
SN54128	SN74128	6-22	5-37	SN54160	SN74160	7-190	7-190
SN54132	SN74132	6-14	5-37	SN54LS160A	SN74LS160A	7-190	7-190
SN54LS132	SN74LS132	6-14	5-37	SN54161	SN74161	7-190	7-190

†See Bipolar Microcomputer Components Data Book, LCC4270.

TEXAS INSTRUMENTS
INCORPORATED
POST OFFICE BOX 5012 • DALLAS, TEXAS 75222

ALPHANUMERIC INDEX

[†]See Bipolar Microcomputer Components Data Book, LCC4270.

TEXAS INSTRUMENTS
INCORPORATED
POST OFFICE BOX 5012 • DALLAS, TEXAS 75222

TYPE NUMBERS		ELECTRICAL PAGE[†]	PIN ASSIGNMENTS PAGE[†]	TYPE NUMBERS		ELECTRICAL PAGE[†]	PIN ASSIGNMENTS PAGE[†]
SN54LS244	SN74LS244	6-83	5-55	SN54293	SN74293	7-423	7-423
SN54LS245	SN74LS245	7-349	7-349	SN54LS293	SN74LS293	7-423	7-423
SN54246	SN74246	7-351	7-351	SN54LS295B	SN74LS295B	7-429	7-429
SN54247	SN74247	7-351	7-351	SN54298	SN74298	7-432	7-432
SN54LS247	SN74LS247	7-351	7-351	SN54LS298	SN74LS298	7-432	7-432
SN54248	SN74248	7-351	7-351	SN54LS299	SN74S299	7-437	7-437
SN54LS248	SN74LS248	7-351	7-351	SN54S299	SN74S299	7-437	7-437
SN54249	SN74249	7-351	7-351	SN54LS300A	SN74LS300A	†	5-64
SN54LS249	SN74LS249	7-351	7-351	SN54S300A	SN74S300A	†	5-64
SN54251	SN74251	7-362	7-362	SN54S301	SN74S301	†	5-64
SN54LS251	SN74LS251	7-362	7-362	SN54S302	SN74S302	†	5-64
SN54S251	SN74S251	7-362	7-362	SN54LS314	SN74LS314	†	5-64
SN54LS253	SN74LS253	7-369	7-369	SN54S314	SN74S314	†	5-65
SN54LS257A	SN74LS257A	7-372	7-372	SN54LS315	SN74LS315	†	5-65
SN54S257	SN74S257	7-372	7-372	SN54LS323	SN74LS323	7-443	7-443
SN54LS258A	SN74LS258A	7-372	7-372	SN54LS324	SN74LS324	7-445	7-445
SN54S258	SN74S258	7-372	7-372	SN54LS325	SN74LS325	7-445	7-445
SN54259	SN74259	7-376	7-376	SN54LS326	SN74LS326	7-445	7-445
SN54LS259	SN74LS259	7-376	7-376	SN54LS327	SN74LS327	7-445	7-445
SN54S260	SN74S260	6-8	5-58	SN54LS348	SN74LS348	7-448	7-448
SN54LS261	SN74LS261	7-380	7-380		SN74351	7-451	7-451
SN54265	SN74265	6-89	5-58	SN54LS352	SN74LS352	7-454	7-454
SN54LS266	SN74LS266	7-386	7-386	SN54LS353	SN74LS353	7-457	7-457
SN54S270	SN74S270	†	5-59		SN74LS362	7-460	7-460
SN54S271	SN74S271	†	5-59	SN54LS363	SN74LS363	7-467	7-467
SN54273	SN74273	7-388	7-388	SN54LS364	SN74LS364	7-467	7-467
SN54LS273	SN74LS273	7-388	7-388	SN54365A	SN74365A	6-36	5-68
SN54S274	SN74S274	7-388	7-391	SN54LS365A	SN74LS365A	6-36	5-68
SN54LS275	SN74LS275	7-391	7-391	SN54366A	SN74366A	6-36	5-68
SN54S275	SN74S275	7-391	7-391	SN54LS366A	SN74LS366A	6-36	5-68
SN54276	SN74276	7-401	7-401	SN54367A	SN74367A	6-36	5-69
SN54278	SN74278	7-403	7-403	SN54LS367A	SN74LS367A	6-36	5-69
SN54279	SN74279	6-60	5-60	SN54368A	SN74368A	6-36	5-69
SN54LS279	SN74LS279	6-60	5-60	SN54LS368A	SN74LS368A	6-36	5-69
SN54LS280	SN74LS280	7-406	7-406	SN54S370	SN74S370	†	5-69
SN54S280	SN74S280	7-406	7-406	SN54S371	SN74S371	†	5-69
SN54S281	SN74S281	7-410	7-410	SN54LS373	SN74LS373	7-471	7-471
SN54283	SN74283	7-415	7-415	SN54S373	SN74S373	7-471	7-471
SN54LS283	SN74LS283	7-415	7-415	SN54LS374	SN74LS374	7-471	7-471
SN54S283	SN74S283	7-415	7-415	SN54S374	SN74S374	7-471	7-471
SN54284	SN74284	7-420	7-420	SN54LS375	SN74LS375	7-478	7-478
SN54285	SN74285	7-420	7-420	SN54376	SN74376	7-479	7-479
SN54S287	SN74S287	†	5-62	SN54LS377	SN74LS377	7-481	7-481
SN54S288	SN74S288	†	5-62	SN54LS378	SN74LS378	7-481	7-481
SN54S289	SN74S289	†	5-62	SN54LS379	SN74LS379	7-481	7-481
SN54290	SN74290	7-423	7-423	SN54S381	SN74S381	7-484	7-484
SN54LS290	SN74LS290	7-423	7-423	SN54LS386	SN74LS386	7-487	7-487

[†]See Bipolar Microcomputer Components Data Book, LCC4270.

ALPHANUMERIC INDEX

†See Bipolar Microcomputer Components Data Book, LCC4270.

TEXAS INSTRUMENTS
INCORPORATED
POST OFFICE BOX 5012 • DALLAS, TEXAS 75222

The following pages contain functional indexes and selection guides designed to simplify the choice of a particular function to fit a specific application. Essential characteristics of similar or like functions are grouped for comparative analysis, and the electrical specifications are referenced by page number. The following categories of functions are covered:

1

TEXAS INSTRUMENTS
INCORPORATED
POST OFFICE BOX 5012 • DALLAS, TEXAS 75222

1

POSITIVE-NAND GATES AND INVERTERS WITH TOTEM-POLE OUTPUTS
ELECTRICAL TABLES — PAGE 6-2

DESCRIPTION	TYPICAL PROPAGATION DELAY TIME	TYP POWER DISSIPATION PER GATE	DEVICE TYPE AND PACKAGE				PIN ASSIGNMENTS PAGE NO.
			−55°C to 125°C		0°C to 70°C		
HEX INVERTERS	3 ns	19 mW	SN54S04	J, W	SN74S04	J, N	
	6 ns	22 mW	SN54H04	J, W	SN74H04	J, N	
	9.5 ns	2 mW	SN54LS04	J, W	SN74LS04	J, N	5-7
	10 ns	10 mW	SN5404	J, W	SN7404	J, N	
	33 ns	1 mW	SN54L04	J, T	SN74L04	J, N	
QUADRUPLE 2-INPUT POSITIVE-NAND GATES	3 ns	19 mW	SN54S00	J, W	SN74S00	J, N	
	6 ns	22 mW	SN54H00	J, W	SN74H00	J, N	
	9.5 ns	2 mW	SN54LS00	J, W	SN74LS00	J, N	5-6
	10 ns	10 mW	SN5400	J, W	SN7400	J, N	
	33 ns	1 mW	SN54L00	J, T	SN74L00	J, N	
TRIPLE 3-INPUT POSITIVE-NAND GATES	3 ns	19 mW	SN54S10	J, W	SN74S10	J, N	
	6 ns	22 mW	SN54H10	J, W	SN74H10	J, N	
	9.5 ns	2 mW	SN54LS10	J, W	SN74LS10	J, N	
	10 ns	10 mW	SN5410	J, W	SN7410	J, N	
	33 ns	1 mW	SN54L10	J, T	SN74L10	J, N	
DUAL 4-INPUT POSITIVE-NAND GATES	3 ns	19 mW	SN54S20	J, W	SN74S20	J, N	
	6 ns	22 mW	SN54H20	J, W	SN74H20	J, N	
	9.5 ns	2 mW	SN54LS20	J, W	SN74LS20	J, N	5-10
	10 ns	10 mW	SN5420	J, W	SN7420	J, N	
	33 ns	1 mW	SN54L20	J, T	SN74L20	J, N	
8-INPUT POSITIVE-NAND GATES	3 ns	19 mW	SN54S30	J, W	SN74S30	J, N	
	6 ns	22 mW	SN54H30	J, W	SN74H30	J, N	
	17 ns	2.4 mW	SN54LS30	J, W	SN74LS30	J, N	5-12
	10 ns	10 mW	SN5430	J, W	SN7430	J, N	
	33 ns	1 mW	SN54L30	J, T	SN74L30	J, N	
13-INPUT POSITIVE-NAND GATES	3 ns	19 mW	SN54S133	J, W	SN74S133	J, N	5-38

POSITIVE-NAND GATES AND INVERTERS WITH OPEN-COLLECTOR OUTPUTS
ELECTRICAL TABLES — PAGE 6-4

DESCRIPTION	TYPICAL PROPAGATION DELAY TIME	TYP POWER DISSIPATION PER GATE	DEVICE TYPE AND PACKAGE				PIN ASSIGNMENTS PAGE NO.
			−55°C to 125°C		0°C to 70°C		
HEX INVERTERS	5 ns	17.5 mW	SN54S05	J, W	SN74S05	J, N	
	8 ns	22 mW	SN54H05	J, W	SN74H05	J, N	5-7
	16 ns	2 mW	SN54LS05	J, W	SN74LS05	J, N	
	24 ns	10 mW	SN5405	J, W	SN7405	J, N	
QUADRUPLE 2-INPUT POSITIVE-NAND GATES	5 ns	17.5 mW	SN54S03	J, W	SN74S03	J, N	5-7
	8 ns	22 mW	SN54H01	J, W	SN74H01	J, N	5-6
	16 ns	2 mW	SN54LS01	J, W	SN74LS01	J, N	5-6
	16 ns	2 mW	SN54LS03	J, W	SN74LS03	J, N	5-7
	22 ns	10 mW	SN5401	J, W	SN7401	J, N	5-6
	22 ns	10 mW	SN5403	J	SN7403	J, N	5-7
	46 ns	1 mW	SN54L01	T			5-6
	46 ns	1 mW	SN54L03	J	SN74L03	J, N	5-7
TRIPLE 3-INPUT POSITIVE-NAND GATES	16 ns	2 mW	SN54LS12	J, W	SN74LS12	J, N	5-9
	22 ns	10 mW	SN5412	J, W	SN7412	J, N	
DUAL 4-INPUT POSITIVE-NAND GATES	5 ns	17.5 mW	SN54S22	J, W	SN74S22	J, N	
	8 ns	22 mW	SN54H22	J, W	SN74H22	J, N	5-11
	16 ns	2 mW	SN54LS22	J, W	SN74LS22	J, N	
	22 ns	10 mW	SN5422	J, W	SN7422	J, N	

TEXAS INSTRUMENTS
INCORPORATED
POST OFFICE BOX 5012 • DALLAS, TEXAS 75222

POSITIVE-NOR GATES WITH TOTEM-POLE OUTPUTS
ELECTRICAL TABLES — PAGE 6-8

DESCRIPTION	TYPICAL PROPAGATION DELAY TIME	TYP POWER DISSIPATION PER GATE	DEVICE TYPE AND PACKAGE				PIN ASSIGNMENTS PAGE NO.
			−55°C to 125°C		0°C to 70°C		
QUADRUPLE 2-INPUT POSITIVE-NOR GATES	3.5 ns	29 mW	SN54S02	J, W	SN74S02	J, N	5-6
	10 ns	2.75 mW	SN54LS02	J, W	SN74LS02	J, N	
	10 ns	14 mW	SN5402	J, W	SN7402	J, N	
	33 ns	1.5 mW	SN54L02	J, T	SN74L02	J, N	
TRIPLE 3-INPUT POSITIVE-NOR GATES	8.5 ns	22 mW	SN5427	J, W	SN7427	J, N	5-12
	10 ns	4.5 mW	SN54LS27	J, W	SN74LS27	J, N	
DUAL 4-INPUT POSITIVE-NOR GATES WITH STROBE	10.5 ns	23 mW	SN5425	J, W	SN7425	J, N	5-11
DUAL 5-INPUT POSITIVE-NOR GATES	4 ns	54 mW	SN54S260	J, W	SN74S260	J, N	5-58

POSITIVE-AND GATES WITH TOTEM-POLE OUTPUTS
ELECTRICAL TABLES — PAGE 6-10

DESCRIPTION	TYPICAL PROPAGATION DELAY TIME	TYP POWER DISSIPATION PER GATE	DEVICE TYPE AND PACKAGE				PIN ASSIGNMENTS PAGE NO.
			−55°C to 125°C		0°C to 70°C		
QUADRUPLE 2-INPUT POSITIVE-AND GATES	4.75 ns	32 mW	SN54S08	J, W	SN74S08	J, N	5-8
	12 ns	4.25 mW	SN54LS08	J, W	SN74LS08	J, N	
	15 ns	19 mW	SN5408	J, W	SN7408	J, N	
TRIPLE 3-INPUT POSITIVE-AND GATES	4.75 ns	31 mW	SN54S11	J, W	SN74S11	J, N	5-9
	8.2 ns	40 mW	SN54H11	J, W	SN74H11	J, N	
	12 ns	4.25 mW	SN54LS11	J, W	SN74LS11	J, N	
DUAL 4-INPUT POSITIVE-AND GATES	8.2 ns	40 mW	SN54H21	J, W	SN74H21	J, N	5-11
	12 ns	4.25 mW	SN54LS21	J, W	SN74LS21	J, N	

POSITIVE-AND GATES WITH OPEN-COLLECTOR OUTPUTS
ELECTRICAL TABLES — PAGE 6-12

DESCRIPTION	TYPICAL PROPAGATION DELAY TIME	TYP POWER DISSIPATION PER GATE	DEVICE TYPE AND PACKAGE				PIN ASSIGNMENTS PAGE NO.
			−55°C to 125°C		0°C to 70°C		
QUADRUPLE 2-INPUT POSITIVE-AND GATES	6.5 ns	32 mW	SN54S09	J, W	SN74S09	J, N	5-8
	18.5 ns	19.4 mW	SN5409	J, W	SN7409	J, N	
	20 ns	4.25 mW	SN54LS09	J, W	SN74LS09	J, N	
TRIPLE 3-INPUT POSITIVE-AND GATES	6 ns	28 mW	SN54S15	J, W	SN74S15	J, N	5-10
	10.5 ns	38 mW	SN54H15	J, W	SN74H15	J, N	
	20 ns	4.25 mW	SN54LS15	J, W	SN74LS15	J, N	

SCHMITT-TRIGGER POSITIVE-NAND GATES AND INVERTERS WITH TOTEM-POLE OUTPUTS
ELECTRICAL TABLES — PAGE 6-14

DESCRIPTION	TYPICAL HYSTERESIS	TYPICAL DELAY TIME	DEVICE TYPE AND PACKAGE				PIN ASSIGNMENTS PAGE NO.
			−55°C to 125°C		0°C to 70°C		
HEX SCHMITT TRIGGER INVERTERS	0.8 V	15 ns	SN5414	J, W	SN7414	J, N	5-9
	0.8 V	15 ns	SN54LS14	J, W	SN74LS14	J, N	
QUADRUPLE 2-INPUT POSITIVE-NAND SCHMITT TRIGGERS	0.55 V	8 ns	SN54S132	J, W	SN74S132	J, N	5-37
	0.8 V	15 ns	SN54132	J, W	SN74132	J, N	
	0.8 V	15 ns	SN54LS132	J, W	SN74LS132	J, N	
DUAL 4-INPUT POSITIVE-NAND SCHMITT TRIGGERS	0.8 V	16.5 ns	SN5413	J, W	SN7413	J, N	5-9
	0.8 V	16.5 ns	SN54LS13	J, W	SN74LS13	J, N	

1

TEXAS INSTRUMENTS
INCORPORATED
POST OFFICE BOX 5012 • DALLAS, TEXAS 75222

BUFFERS/CLOCK DRIVERS WITH TOTEM-POLE OUTPUTS
(ALSO SEE 3-STATE BUFFERS AND DRIVERS ON PAGE 1-13)
ELECTRICAL TABLES — PAGE 6-20

DESCRIPTION	LOW-LEVEL OUTPUT CURRENT	HIGH-LEVEL OUTPUT CURRENT	TYPICAL DELAY TIME	TYP POWER PER GATE	DEVICE TYPE AND PACKAGE		PIN ASSIGNMENTS PAGE NO.
					−55°C to 125°C	0°C to 70°C	
QUADRUPLE 2-INPUT POSITIVE-NOR BUFFERS	48 mA	−2.4 mA	7 ns	28 mW	SN5428 J, W	SN7428 J, N	
	24 mA	−1.2 mA	12 ns	5.5 mW		SN74LS28 J, N	5-12
	12 mA	−1.2 mA	12 ns	5.5 mW	SN54LS28 J, W		
QUADRUPLE 2-INPUT POSITIVE-NAND BUFFERS	60 mA	−3 mA	4 ns	41 mW	SN54S37 J, W	SN74S37 J, N	
	48 mA	−1.2 mA	10.5 ns	27 mW	SN5437 J, W	SN7437 J, N	
	24 mA	−1.2 mA	12 ns	4.3 mW		SN74LS37 J, N	5-13
	12 mA	−1.2 mA	12 ns	4.3 mW	SN54LS37 J, W		
DUAL 4-INPUT POSITIVE-NAND BUFFERS	60 mA	−3 mA	4 ns	44 mW	SN54S40 J, W	SN74S40 J, N	
	60 mA	−1.5 mA	7.5 ns	44 mW	SN54H40 J, W	SN74H40 J, N	
	48 mA	−1.2 mA	10.5 ns	26 mW	SN5440 J, W	SN7440 J, N	5-14
	24 mA	−1.2 mA	12 ns	4.3 mW		SN74LS40 J, N	
	12 mA	−1.2 mA	12 ns	4.3 mW	SN54LS40 J, W		

50-OHM/75-OHM LINE DRIVERS
ELECTRICAL TABLES — PAGE 6-22

DESCRIPTION	LOW-LEVEL OUTPUT CURRENT	HIGH-LEVEL OUTPUT CURRENT	TYPICAL DELAY TIME	TYP POWER PER GATE	DEVICE TYPE AND PACKAGE		PIN ASSIGNMENTS PAGE NO.
					−55°C to 125°C	0°C to 70°C	
DUAL 4-INPUT POSITIVE-NAND LINE DRIVERS	60 mA	−40 mA	4 ns	44 mW	SN54S140 J, W	SN74S140 J, N	5-39
QUADRUPLE 2-INPUT POSITIVE-NOR LINE DRIVERS	48 mA	−42.4 mA	7 ns	28 mW		SN74128 J, N	
	48 mA	−29 mA	7 ns	28 mW	SN54128 J, W		5-37

BUFFER AND INTERFACE GATES WITH OPEN-COLLECTOR OUTPUTS
ELECTRICAL TABLES — PAGES 6-24 AND 6-26

DESCRIPTION	HIGH-LEVEL OUTPUT VOLTAGE	LOW-LEVEL OUTPUT CURRENT	TYPICAL DELAY TIME	TYP POWER PER GATE	DEVICE TYPE AND PACKAGE		PIN ASSIGNMENTS PAGE NO.
					−55°C to 125°C	0°C to 70°C	
HEX BUFFERS/DRIVERS	30 V	40 mA	13 ns	21 mW		SN7407 J, N	5-8
	30 V	30 mA	13 ns	21 mW	SN5407 J, W		5-8
	15 V	40 mA	13 ns	21 mW		SN7417 J, N	5-10
	15 V	30 mA	13 ns	21 mW	SN5417 J, W		5-10
HEX INVERTER BUFFERS/DRIVERS	30 V	40 mA	12.5 ns	26 mW		SN7406 J, N	5-7
	30 V	30 mA	12.5 ns	26 mW	SN5406 J, W		5-7
	15 V	40 mA	12.5 ns	26 mW		SN7416 J, N	5-10
	15 V	30 mA	12.5 ns	26 mW	SN5416 J, W		5-10
QUADRUPLE 2-INPUT POSITIVE-NAND BUFFERS	15 V	16 mA	13.5 ns	10 mW	SN5426 J	SN7426 J, N	5-12
	15 V	8 mA	16 ns	2 mW		SN74LS26 J, N	5-12
	15 V	4 mA	16 ns	2 mW	SN54LS26 J, W		5-12
	5.5 V	60 mA	6.5 ns	41 mW	SN54S38 J, W	SN74S38 J, N	5-13
	5.5 V	48 mA	12.5 ns	24.4 mW	SN5438 J, W	SN7438 J, N	5-13
	5.5 V	24 mA	19 ns	4.3 mW		SN74LS38 J, N	5-13
	5.5 V	12 mA	19 ns	4.3 mW	SN54LS38 J, W		5-13
QUADRUPLE 2-INPUT POSITIVE-NOR BUFFERS	5.5 V	48 mA	11 ns	28 mW	SN5433 J, W	SN7433 J, N	5-13
	5.5 V	24 mA	19 ns	5.45 mW		SN74LS33 J, N	
	5.5 V	12 mA	19 ns	5.45 mW	SN54LS33 J, W		5-13

TEXAS INSTRUMENTS
INCORPORATED
POST OFFICE BOX 5012 • DALLAS, TEXAS 75222

GATES, BUFFERS, DRIVERS, AND BUS TRANSCEIVERS WITH 3-STATE OUTPUTS

DESCRIPTION	TYPICAL PROPAGATION DELAY TIME	MAXIMUM SOURCE CURRENT	MAXIMUM SINK CURRENT	DEVICE TYPE AND PACKAGE −55°C to 125°C		DEVICE TYPE AND PACKAGE 0°C to 70°C		PIN ASSIGNMENTS PAGE NO.	ELECTRICAL CHARACTERISTICS PAGE NO.
12-INPUT NAND GATE	4.5 ns	−6.5 mA	20 mA			SN74S134	J, N	5-38	6-33
	4.5 ns	−2 mA	20 mA	SN54S134	J, W				
QUADRUPLE BUS BUFFERS/DRIVERS WITH INDEPENDENT OUTPUT CONTROLS	8 ns	−2.6 mA	24 mA			SN74LS125A	J, N	5-37	6-33
	8 ns	−1 mA	12 mA	SN54LS125A	J, W			5-37	
	8.5 ns	−2.6 mA	24 mA			SN74LS126A	J, N	5-37	
	8.5 ns	−1 mA	12 mA	SN54LS126A	J, W			5-37	
	10 ns	−5.2 mA	16 mA			SN74125	J, N	5-37	
	10 ns	−2 mA	16 mA	SN54125	J, W			5-37	
	10 ns	−5.2 mA	16 mA			SN74126	J, N	5-37	
	10 ns	−2 mA	16 mA	SN54126	J, W			5-37	
	10 ns	−5.2 mA	16 mA			SN74425	J, N	5-74	
	10 ns	−2 mA	16 mA	SN54425	J, W			5-74	
	10 ns	−5.2 mA	16 mA			SN74426	J, N	5-75	
	10 ns	−2 mA	16 mA	SN54426	J, W			5-75	
HEX BUS BUFFERS/DRIVERS	9.5 ns	−2.6 mA	24 mA			SN74LS365A	J, N	5-68	6-36
	9.5 ns	−1 mA	12 mA	SN54LS365A	J, W			5-68	
	9.5 ns	−2.6 mA	24 mA			SN74LS366A	J, N	5-68	
	9.5 ns	−1 mA	12 mA	SN54LS366A	J, W			5-68	
	9.5 ns	−2.6 mA	24 mA			SN74LS367A	J, N	5-69	
	9.5 ns	−1 mA	12 mA	SN54LS367A	J, W			5-69	
	9.5 ns	−2.6 mA	24 mA			SN74LS368A	J, N	5-69	
	9.5 ns	−1 mA	12 mA	SN54LS368A	J, W			5-69	
	11 ns	−5.2 mA	32 mA			SN74366A	J, N	5-68	
	11 ns	−2 mA	32 mA	SN54366A	J, W			5-68	
	11 ns	−5.2 mA	32 mA			SN74368A	J N	5-69	
	11 ns	−2 mA	32 mA	SN54368A	J, W			5-69	
	12 ns	−5.2 mA	32 mA			SN74366A	J, N	5-68	
	12 ns	−2 mA	32 mA	SN54365A	J, W			5-68	
	12 ns	−5.2 mA	32 mA			SN74367A	J, N	5-69	
	12 ns	−2 mA	32 mA	SN54367A	J, W			5-69	
OCTAL BUS BUFFERS/DRIVERS	5 ns	−15 mA	64 mA			SN74S240	J, N	5-54	6-83
	5 ns	−12 mA	48 mA	SN54S240	J			5-54	
	5 ns	−15 mA	64 mA			SN74S241	J, N	5-55	
	5 ns	−12 mA	48 mA	SN54S241	J			5-55	
	10 ns	−15 mA	24 mA			SN74LS240	J, N	5-54	
	10 ns	−12 mA	12 mA	SN54LS240	J			5-54	
	10 ns	−15 mA	24 mA			SN74LS241	J, N	5-55	
	10 ns	−12 mA	12 mA	SN54LS241	J			5-55	
	10 ns	−15 mA	24 mA			SN74LS244	J, N	5-55	
	10 ns	−12 mA	12 mA	SN54LS244	J			5-55	
CONTROLLER AND BUS DRIVER FOR 8080A SYSTEMS (MSI)		−1 mA	10 mA			SN74S428	N	7-514	7-514
		−1 mA	10 mA			SN74S438	N		
QUADRUPLE TRANSCEIVERS	11 ns	−15 mA	24 mA			SN74LS242	J, N	5-55	6-87
	11 ns	−12 mA	12 mA	SN54LS242	J, W				
	12 ns	−15 mA	24 mA			SN74LS243	J, N		
	12 ns	−12 mA	12 mA	SN54LS243	J, W				
QUADRUPLE TRANSCEIVERS WITH STORAGE (MSI)	10 ns	−10.3 mA	20 mA			SN74S226	J, N	7-345	7-345
	10 ns	−6.5 mA	20 mA	SN54S226	J, W				
OCTAL TRANSCEIVERS (MSI)	12 ns	−15 mA	24 mA			SN74LS245	J, N	7-349	7-349
	12 ns	−12 mA	12 mA	SN54LS245	J				

TEXAS INSTRUMENTS
INCORPORATED
POST OFFICE BOX 5012 • DALLAS, TEXAS 75222

POSITIVE-OR GATES WITH TOTEM-POLE OUTPUTS
ELECTRICAL TABLES — PAGE 6-28

DESCRIPTION	TYPICAL PROPAGATION DELAY TIME	TYP POWER DISSIPATION PER GATE	DEVICE TYPE AND PACKAGE				PIN ASSIGNMENTS PAGE NO.
			−55°C to 125°C		0°C to 70°C		
QUADRUPLE 2-INPUT POSITIVE-OR GATES	4 ns	35 mW	SN54S32	J, W	SN74S32	J, N	5-13
	12 ns	24 mW	SN5432	J, W	SN7432	J, N	
	12 ns	5 mW	SN54LS32	J, W	SN74LS32	J, N	

AND-OR-INVERT GATES WITH TOTEM-POLE OUTPUTS
ELECTRICAL TABLES — PAGE 6-30

DESCRIPTION	TYPICAL PROPAGATION DELAY TIME	TYP POWER DISSIPATION PER GATE	DEVICE TYPE AND PACKAGE				PIN ASSIGNMENTS PAGE NO.
			−55°C to 125°C		0°C to 70°C		
2-WIDE 4-INPUT	12.5 ns	2.75 mW	SN54LS55	J, W	SN74LS55	J, N	5-19
	43 ns	1.5 mW	SN54L55	J, T	SN74L55	J, N	
4-WIDE 4-2-3-2-INPUT	3.5 ns	29 mW	SN54S64	J, W	SN74S64	J, N	5-20
4-WIDE 2-2-3-2-INPUT	6.6 ns	41 mW	SN54H54	J, W	SN74H54	J, N	5-18
4-WIDE 2-INPUT	10.5 ns	23 mW	SN5454	J, W	SN7454	J, N	5-18
4-WIDE 2-3-3-2-INPUT	12.5 ns	4.5 mW	SN54LS54	J, W	SN74LS54	J, N	5-18
4-WIDE 2-3-3-2-INPUT	43 ns	1.5 mW	SN54L54	J, T	SN74L54	J, N	5-18
DUAL 2-WIDE 2-INPUT	3.5 ns	28 mW	SN54S51	J, W	SN74S51	J, N	5-16
	6.5 ns	29 mW	SN54H51	J, W	SN74H51	J, N	
	10.5 ns	14 mW	SN5451	J, W	SN7451	J, N	
	12.5 ns	2.75 mW	SN54LS51	J, W	SN74LS51	J, N	
	43 ns	1.5 mW	SN54L51	J, T	SN74L51	J, N	

AND-OR-INVERT GATES WITH OPEN-COLLECTOR OUTPUTS
ELECTRICAL TABLES — PAGE 6-32

DESCRIPTION	TYPICAL PROPAGATION DELAY TIME	TYP POWER DISSIPATION PER GATE	DEVICE TYPE AND PACKAGE				PIN ASSIGNMENTS PAGE NO.
			−55°C to 125°C		0°C to 70°C		
4-WIDE 4-2-3-2-INPUT	5.5 ns	36 mW	SN54S65	J, W	SN74S65	J, N	5-20

EXPANDABLE GATES
ELECTRICAL TABLE — PAGE 6-39

DESCRIPTION	TYPICAL PROPAGATION DELAY TIME	TYP POWER DISSIPATION PER GATE	DEVICE TYPE AND PACKAGE				PIN ASSIGNMENTS PAGE NO.
			−55°C to 125°C		0°C to 70°C		
DUAL 4-INPUT POSITIVE-NOR GATES WITH STROBE	10.5 ns	23 mW	SN5423	J, W	SN7423	J, N	5-11
4-WIDE AND-OR GATES	9.9 ns	88 mW	SN54H52	J, W	SN74H52	J, N	5-17
4-WIDE AND-OR-INVERT GATES	6.6 ns	41 mW	SN54H53	J, W	SN74H53	J, N	5-17
	10.5 ns	23 mW	SN5453	J, W	SN7453	J, N	
2-WIDE AND-OR-INVERT GATES	6.8 ns	30 mW	SN54H55	J, W	SN74H55	J, N	5-19
DUAL 2-WIDE AND-OR-INVERT GATES	6.5 ns	29 mW	SN54H50	J, W	SN74H50	J, N	5-16
	10.5 ns	14 mW	SN5450	J, W	SN7450	J, N	

EXPANDERS
ELECTRICAL TABLES — PAGES 6-43, 6-44, AND 6-45

DESCRIPTION	TYP POWER DISSIPATION PER GATE	DEVICE TYPE AND PACKAGE				PIN ASSIGNMENTS PAGE NO.
		−55°C to 125°C		0°C to 70°C		
DUAL 4-INPUT EXPANDERS	4 mW	SN5460	J, W	SN7460	J, N	5-19
	6 mW	SN54H60	J, W	SN74H60	J, N	
TRIPLE 3-INPUT EXPANDERS	13 mW	SN54H61	J, W	SN74H61	J, N	5-19
3-2-2-3-INPUT AND-OR EXPANDERS	25 mW	SN54H62	J, W	SN74H62	J, N	5-20

TEXAS INSTRUMENTS
INCORPORATED
POST OFFICE BOX 5012 • DALLAS, TEXAS 75222

DUAL J-K EDGE-TRIGGERED FLIP-FLOPS

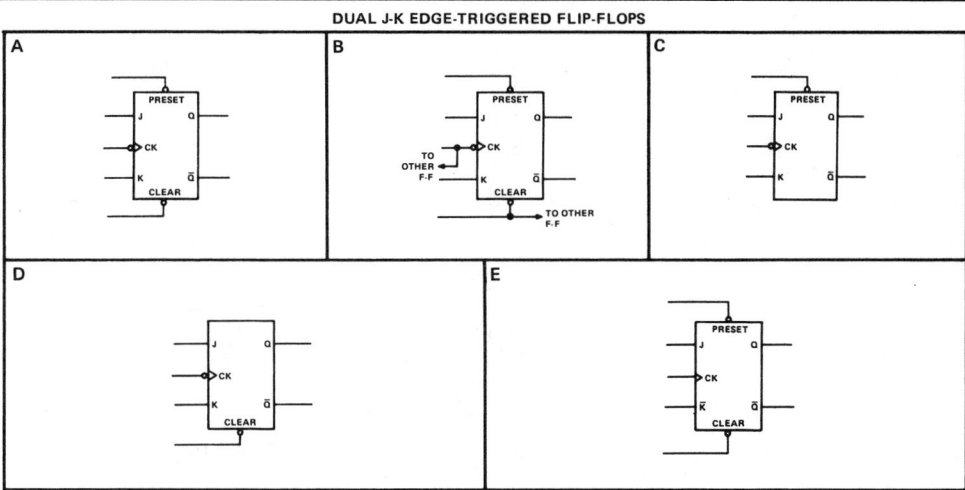

SINGLE J-K EDGE-TRIGGERED FLIP-FLOPS

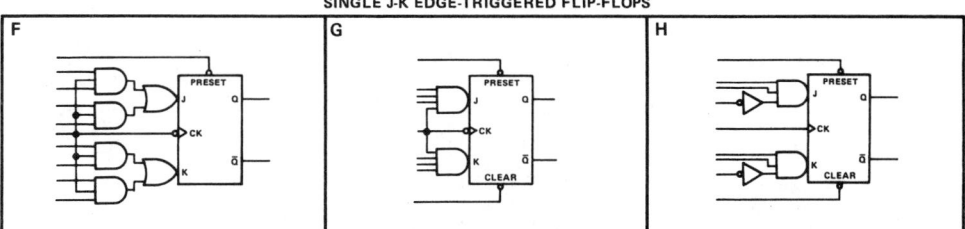

DWG REF.	TYPICAL CHARACTERISTICS		DATA TIMES		DEVICE TYPE AND PACKAGE				PAGE REFERENCES	
	f_{max} (MHz)	Pwr/F-F (mW)	SETUP (ns)	HOLD (ns)	−55°C to 125°C		0°C to 70°C		PIN ASSIGNMENTS	ELECTRICAL
A	125	75	3↓	0↓	SN54S112	J, W	SN74S112	J, N	5-34	6-58
	50	100	13↓	0↓	SN54H106	J, W	SN74H106	J, N	5-32	6-52
	45	10	20↓	0↓	SN54LS76A	J, W	SN74LS76A	J, N	5-23	6-58
	45	10	20↓	0↓	SN54LS112A	J, W	SN74LS112A	J, N	5-34	6-56
B	125	75	3↓	0↓	SN54S114	J, W	SN74S114	J, N	5-34	6-58
	50	100	13↓	0↓	SN54H108	J, W	SN74H108	J, N	5-32	6-52
	45	10	20↓	0↓	SN54LS78A	J, W	SN74LS78A	J, N	5-24	6-56
	45	10	20↓	0↓	SN54LS114A	J, W	SN74LS114A	J, N	5-34	6-56
C	125	75	3↓	0↓	SN54S113	J, W	SN74S113	J, N	5-34	6-58
	45	10	20↓	0↓	SN54LS113A	J, W	SN74LS113A	J, N	5-34	6-56
D	50	100	13↓	0↓	SN54H103	J, W	SN74H103	J, N	5-31	6-52
	45	10	20↓	0↓	SN54LS73A	J, W	SN74LS73A	J, N	5-22	6-56
	45	10	20↓	0↓	SN54LS107A	J	SN74LS107A	J, N	5-32	6-56
E	33	10	20↑	5↑	SN54LS109A	J, W	SN74LS109A	J, N	5-33	6-56
	33	45	10↑	6↑	SN54109	J, W	SN74109	J, N	5-33	6-46
F	50	100	13↓	0↓	SN54H101	J, W	SN74H101	J, N	5-31	6-52
G	50	100	13↓	0↓	SN54H102	J, W	SN74H102	J, N	5-31	6-52
H	35	65	20↑	5↑	SN5470	J, W	SN7470	J, N	5-21	6-46

↑↓ The arrow indicates the edge of the clock pulse used for reference: ↑ for the rising edge, ↓ for the falling edge.

SSI FUNCTIONS
FUNCTIONAL INDEX/SELECTION GUIDE

PULSE-TRIGGERED DUAL FLIP-FLOPS

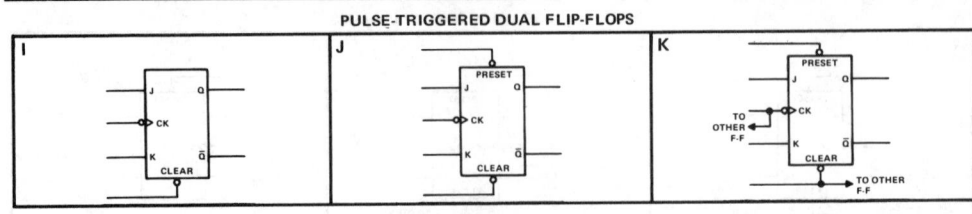

PULSE-TRIGGERED SINGLE FLIP-FLOPS

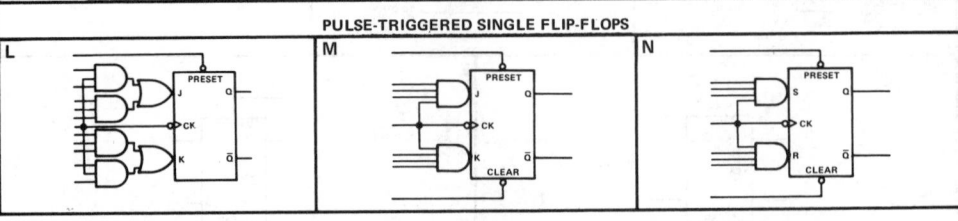

DWG. REF.	TYPICAL CHARACTERISTICS		DATA TIMES		DEVICE TYPE AND PACKAGE				PAGE REFERENCES	
	f_{max} (MHz)	Pwr/F-F (mW)	SETUP (ns)	HOLD (ns)	−55°C to 125°C		0°C to 70°C		PIN ASSIGNMENTS	ELECTRICAL
I	30	80	0↑	0↓	SN54H73	J, W	SN74H73	J, N	5-22	6-50
	20	50	0↑	0↓	SN5473	J, W	SN7473	J, N	5-22	6-46
	20	50	0↑	0↓	SN54107	J	SN74107	J, N	5-32	6-46
	3	3.8	0↑	0↓	SN54L73	J, T	SN74L73	J, N	5-22	6-54
J	30	80	0↑	0↓	SN54H76	J, W	SN74H76	J, N	5-23	6-50
	20	50	0↑	0↓	SN5476	J, W	SN7476	J, N	5-23	6-46
K	30	80	0↑	0↓	SN54H78	J, W	SN74H78	J, N	5-24	6-50
	3	3.8	0↑	0↓	SN54L78	J, T	SN74L78	J, N	5-24	6-54
L	30	80	0↑	0↓	SN54H71	J, W	SN74H71	J, N	5-21	6-50
M	30	80	0↑	0↓	SN54H72	J, W	SN74H72	J, N	5-22	6-50
	20	50	0↑	0↓	SN5472	J, W	SN7472	J, N	5-22	6-46
	3	3.8	0↑	0↓	SN54L72	J, T	SN74L72	J, N	5-22	6-54
N	3	3.8	0↑	0↓	SN54L71	J, T	SN74L71	J, N	5-21	6-54

J-K FLIP-FLOPS WITH DATA LOCKOUT
DUAL   SINGLE

D-TYPE FLIP-FLOPS
DUAL

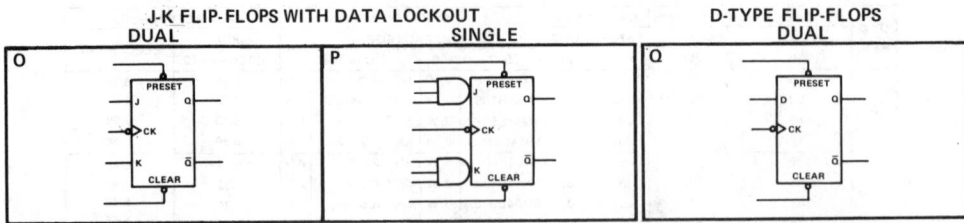

DWG. REF.	TYPICAL CHARACTERISTICS		DATA TIMES		DEVICE TYPE AND PACKAGE				PAGE REFERENCES	
	f_{max} (MHz)	Pwr/F-F (mW)	SETUP (ns)	HOLD (ns)	−55°C to 125°C		0°C to 70°C		PIN ASSIGNMENTS	ELECTRICAL
O	25	70	0↑	30↑	SN54111	J, W	SN74111	J, N	5-33	6-46
P	25	100	20↑	5↑	SN54110	J, W	SN74110	J, N	5-33	6-46
Q	110	75	3↑	2↑	SN54S74	J, W	SN74S74	J, N	5-22	6-58
	43	75	15↑	5↑	SN54H74	J, W	SN74H74	J, N	5-22	6-50
	33	10	25↑	5↑	SN54LS74A	J, W	SN74LS74A	J, N	5-22	6-56
	25	43	20↑	5↑	SN5474	J, W	SN7474	J, N	5-22	6-46
	3	4	50↑	15↑	SN54L74	J, T	SN74L74	J, N	5-22	6-54

↑↓The arrow indicates the edge of the clock pulse used for reference: ↑ for the rising edge, ↓ for the falling edge.

10

1-16

TEXAS INSTRUMENTS
INCORPORATED
POST OFFICE BOX 5012 • DALLAS, TEXAS 75222

S̄-R̄ LATCHES
ELECTRICAL TABLES — PAGE 6-60

DESCRIPTION	TYPICAL PROPAGATION DELAY TIME	TYP TOTAL POWER DISSIPATION	DEVICE TYPE AND PACKAGE				PIN ASSIGNMENTS PAGE NO.
			−55°C to 125°C		0°C to 70°C		
QUADRUPLE S̄-R̄ LATCHES	12 ns	19 mW	SN54LS279	J, W	SN74LS279	J, N	5-60
	12 ns	90 mW	SN54279	J, W	SN74279	J, N	

CURRENT-SENSING-GATES
ELECTRICAL TABLES — PAGE 6-62

DESCRIPTION	TYPICAL PROPAGATION DELAY TIME	TYP POWER DISSIPATION PER GATE	DEVICE TYPE AND PACKAGES				PIN ASSIGNMENTS PAGE NO.
			−55°C to 125°C		0°C to 70°C		
HEX	21 ns	3.3 mW	SN54LS63	J, W	SN74LS63	J, N	5-20

MONOSTABLE MULTIVIBRATORS WITH SCHMITT-TRIGGER INPUTS
ELECTRICAL TABLES — PAGES 6-64 AND 6-68

DESCRIPTION	NO. OF INPUTS		OUTPUT PULSE RANGE	TYP TOTAL POWER DISSIPATION	DEVICE TYPE AND PACKAGE				PIN ASSIGNMENTS PAGE NO.
	POSITIVE	NEGATIVE			−55°C to 125°C		0°C to 70°C		
SINGLE	1	2	40 ns−28 s	90 mW	SN54121	J, W	SN74121	J, N	5-35
	1	2	40 ns−28 s	40 mW	SN54L121	J, T	SN74L121	J, N	
DUAL	1	1	20 ns−70 s	23 mW			SN74LS221	J, N	5-54
	1	1	20 ns−49 s	23 mW	SN54LS221	J, W			
	1	1	20 ns−28 s	130 mW			SN74221	J, N	
	1	1	20 ns−21 s	130 mW	SN54221	J, W			

RETRIGGERABLE MONOSTABLE MULTIVIBRATORS
ELECTRICAL TABLES — PAGE 6-76

DESCRIPTION	NO. OF INPUTS		DIRECT CLEAR	OUTPUT PULSE RANGE	TYP TOTAL POWER	DEVICE TYPE AND PACKAGE				PIN ASSIGNMENTS PAGE NO.
	POSITIVE	NEGATIVE				−55°C to 125°C		0°C to 70°C		
SINGLE	2	2	Yes	45 ns−∞	115 mW	SN54122	J, W	SN74122	J, N	5-36
	2	2	Yes	90 ns−∞	55 mW	SN54L122	J, T	SN74L122	J, N	
	2	2	Yes	45 ns−∞	30 mW	SN54LS122	J, W	SN74LS122	J, N	
DUAL	1	1	Yes	45 ns−∞	230 mW	SN54123	J, W	SN74123	J, N	5-36
	1	1	Yes	90 ns−∞	115 mW	SN54L123	J	SN74L123	J, N	
	1	1	Yes	45 ns−∞	60 mW	SN54LS123	J, W	SN74LS123	J, N	

CLOCK GENERATOR CIRCUITS
ELECTRICAL TABLES — PAGES 6-89 AND 7-123

DESCRIPTION	TYP TOTAL POWER DISSIPATION	DEVICE TYPE AND PACKAGE				PIN ASSIGNMENTS PAGE NO.
		−55°C to 125°C		0°C to 70°C		
QUADRUPLE COMPLEMENTARY-OUTPUT LOGIC ELEMENTS	125 mW	SN54265	J, W	SN74265	J, N	5-58
DUAL VOLTAGE-CONTROLLED OSCILLATORS (MSI)	90 mW	SN54LS124	J, W	SN74LS124	J, N	7-123
	525 mW	SN54S124	J, W	SN74S124	J, N	

ADDERS

DESCRIPTION	TYPICAL CARRY TIME	TYPICAL ADD TIME	TYP POWER DISSIPATION PER BIT	DEVICE TYPE AND PACKAGE				PAGE NO.
				−55°C to 125°C		0°C to 70°C		
SINGLE 1-BIT GATED FULL ADDERS	10.5 ns	52 ns	105 mW	SN5480	J, W	SN7480	J, N	7-41
SINGLE 2-BIT FULL ADDERS	14.5 ns	25 ns	87 mW	SN5482	J, W	SN7482	J, N	7-49
SINGLE 4-BIT FULL ADDERS	10 ns	15 ns	24 mW	SN54LS83A	J, W	SN74LS83A	J, N	7-53
	10 ns	15 ns	24 mW	SN54LS283	J, W	SN74LS283	J, N	7-415
	11 ns	7 ns	124 mW	SN54S283	J	SN74S283	J, N	7-415
	10 ns	16 ns	76 mW	SN5483A	J, W	SN7483A	J, N	7-53
	10 ns	16 ns	76 mW	SN54283	J, W	SN74283	J, N	7-415
DUAL 1-BIT CARRY-SAVE FULL ADDERS	11 ns	11 ns	110 mW	SN54H183	J, W	SN74H183	J, N	7-287
	15 ns	15 ns	23 mW	SN54LS183	J, W	SN74LS183	J, N	7-287

ACCUMULATORS, ARITHMETIC LOGIC UNITS, LOOK-AHEAD CARRY GENERATORS

DESCRIPTION	TYPICAL CARRY TIME	TYPICAL ADD TIME	TYP TOTAL POWER DISSIPATION	DEVICE TYPE AND PACKAGE				PAGE NO.
				−55°C to 125°C		0°C to 70°C		
4-BIT PARALLEL BINARY ACCUMULATORS	10 ns	20 ns	720 mW	SN54S281	J, W	SN74S281	J, N	7-410
4-BIT ARITHMETIC LOGIC UNITS/ FUNCTION GENERATORS	11 ns	20 ns	525 mW			SN74S381	N	7-484
	7 ns	11 ns	600 mW	SN54S181	J, W	SN74S181	J, N	7-271
	12.5 ns	24 ns	455 mW	SN54181	J, W	SN74181	J, N	7-271
	16 ns	24 ns	102 mW	SN54LS181	J, W	SN74LS181	J, N	7-271
LOOK-AHEAD CARRY GENERATORS	7 ns		260 mW	SN54S182	J, W	SN74S182	J, N	7-282
	13 ns		180 mW	SN54182	J, W	SN74182	J, N	7-282

MULTIPLIERS

DESCRIPTION	DEVICE TYPE AND PACKAGE				PAGE NO.
	−55°C to 125°C		0°C to 70°C		
2-BIT-BY-4-BIT PARALLEL BINARY MULTIPLIERS	SN54LS261	J, W	SN74LS261	J, N	7-380
4-BIT-BY-4-BIT PARALLEL BINARY MULTIPLIERS	SN54284, SN54285	J, W	SN74284, SN74285	J, N	7-420
	SN54S274	J	SN74S274	J, N	7-391
7-BIT-SLICE WALLACE TREES	SN54LS275	J	SN74LS275	J, N	7-391
	SN54S275	J	SN74S275	J, N	7-391
25-MHz 6-BIT-BINARY RATE MULTIPLIERS	SN5497	J, W	SN7497	J, N	7-102
25-MHz DECADE RATE MULTIPLIERS	SN54167	J, W	SN74167	J, N	7-222

COMPARATORS

DESCRIPTION	TYPICAL COMPARE TIME	TYP TOTAL POWER DISSIPATION	DEVICE TYPE AND PACKAGE				PAGE NO.
			−55°C to 125°C		0°C to 70°C		
4-BIT MAGNITUDE COMPARATORS	11.5 ns	365 mW	SN54S85	J, W	SN74S85	J, N	7-57
	21 ns	275 mW	SN5485	J, W	SN7485	J, N	7-57
	23.5 ns	52 mW	SN54LS85	J, W	SN74LS85	J, N	7-57
	82 ns	20 mW	SN54L85	J	SN74L85	J, N	7-57

TEXAS INSTRUMENTS
INCORPORATED
POST OFFICE BOX 5012 • DALLAS, TEXAS 75222

PARITY GENERATORS/CHECKERS

DESCRIPTION	TYPICAL DELAY TIME	TYP TOTAL POWER DISSIPATION	DEVICE TYPE				PAGE NO.
			−55°C to 125°C		0°C to 70°C		
9-BIT ODD/EVEN PARITY GENERATORS/CHECKERS	31 ns	80 mW	SN54LS280	J, W	SN74LS280	J, N	7-406
	13 ns	335 mW	SN54S280	J, W	SN74S280	J, N	
8-BIT ODD/EVEN PARITY GENERATORS/CHECKERS	35 ns	170 mW	SN54180	J, W	SN74180	J, N	7-269

OTHER ARITHMETIC OPERATORS

DESCRIPTION	TYPICAL DELAY TIME	TYP TOTAL POWER DISSIPATION	DEVICE TYPE AND PACKAGE				PAGE NO.
			−55°C to 125°C		0°C to 70°C		
QUADRUPLE 2-INPUT EXCLUSIVE-OR GATES WITH TOTEM-POLE OUTPUTS	7 ns	250 mW	SN54S86	J, W	SN74S86	J, N	7-65
	10 ns	30 mW	SN54LS86	J, W	SN74LS86	J, N	7-65
	10 ns	30 mW	SN54LS386	J, W	SN74LS386	J, N	7-487
	14 ns	150 mW	SN5486	J, W	SN7486	J, N	7-65
	55 ns	15 mW	SN54L86	J, T	SN74L86	J, N	7-65
QUADRUPLE 2-INPUT EXCLUSIVE-OR GATES WITH OPEN-COLLECTOR OUTPUTS	18 ns	30 mW	SN54LS136	J, W	SN74LS136	J, N	7-131
	27 ns	150 mW	SN54136	J, W	SN74136	J, N	
QUADRUPLE 2-INPUT EXCLUSIVE-NOR GATES	18 ns	40 mW	SN54LS266	J, W	SN74LS266	J, N	7-386
QUADRUPLE EXCLUSIVE OR/NOR GATES	8 ns	325 mW	SN54S135	J, W	SN74S135	J, N	7-129
4-BIT TRUE/COMPLEMENT, ZERO/ONE ELEMENT	14 ns	270 mW	SN54H87	J, W	SN74H87	J, N	7-70

QUAD, HEX, AND OCTAL FLIP-FLOPS

DESCRIPTION	F-F PER PKG	FREQ	POWER PER FLIP-FLOP	DATA TIMES SETUP ns	DATA TIMES HOLD ns	DEVICE TYPE AND PACKAGE				PAGE NO.
						−55°C to 125°C		0°C to 70°C		
D TYPE 3-STATE WITH ENABLE	8	50 MHz	26 mW	20↑	0↑	SN54LS364*	J	SN74LS364*	J, N	7-467
		50 MHz	17 mW	20↑	0↑	SN54LS374'	J	SN74LS374	J, N	7-471
		100 MHz	56 mW	5↑	2↑	SN54S374	J	SN74S374	J, N	7-471
D TYPE WITH ENABLE	8	40 MHz	10.6 mW	20↑	5↑	SN54LS377	J	SN74LS377	J, N	7-481
	6	40 MHz	10.6 mW	20↑	5↑	SN54LS378	J, W	SN74LS378	J, N	7-481
	4	40 MHz	10.6 mW	20↑	5↑	SN54LS379	J	SN74LS379	J, N	7-481
	8	40 MHz	39 mW	20↑	5↑	SN54273	J	SN74273	J, N,	7-388
		40 MHz	10.6 mW	20↑	5↑	SN54LS273	J	SN74LS273	J, N	
D TYPE WITH CLEAR	6	35 MHz	38 mW	20↑	5↑	SN54174	J, W	SN74174	J, N	7-253
		40 MHz	10.6 mW	20↑	5↑	SN54LS174	J, W	SN74LS174	J, N	
		110 MHz	75 mW	5↑	3↑	SN54S174	J, W	SN74S174	J, N	
	4	35 MHz	38 mW	20↑	5↑	SN54175	J, W	SN74175	J, N	7-253
		40 MHz	10.6 mW	20↑	5↑	SN54LS175	J, W	SN74LS175	J, N	
		110 MHz	75 mW	5↑	3↑	SN54S175	J, W	SN74S175	J, N	
J-K TYPE WITH SEPARATE CLOCK	4	50 MHz	75 mW	3↓	10↓	SN54276	J	SN74276	J, N	7-401
J-K TYPE WITH COMMON CLOCK	4	45 MHz	65 mW	0↑	20↑	SN54376	J, W	SN74376	J, N	7-479

REGISTER FILES

DESCRIPTION	TYPICAL ADDRESS TIME	TYP READ ENABLE TIME	DATA INPUT RATE	TYP TOTAL POWER DISSIPATION	DEVICE TYPE AND PACKAGE				PAGE NO.
					−55°C to 125°C		0°C to 70°C		
EIGHT WORDS OF TWO BITS	33 ns	15 ns	20 MHz	560 mW			SN74172	J, N	7-245
FOUR WORDS OF FOUR BITS	27 ns	15 ns	20 MHz	125 mW	SN54LS170	J, W	SN74LS170	J, N	7-237
	30 ns	15 ns	20 MHz	635 mW	SN54170	J, W	SN74170	J, N	
FOUR WORDS OF FOUR BITS (3-STATE OUTPUTS)	24 ns	19 ns	20 MHz	135 mW	SN54LS670	J, W	SN74LS670	J, N	7-526

*New product in development as of October 1976.

TEXAS INSTRUMENTS
INCORPORATED
POST OFFICE BOX 5012 • DALLAS, TEXAS 75222

SHIFT REGISTERS

DESCRIPTION	NO. OF BITS	SHIFT FREQ	SERIAL DATA INPUT	ASYNC CLEAR	S-R‡	S-L‡	LOAD	HOLD	TYP TOTAL POWER DISSIPATION	−55°C to 125°C		0°C to 70°C		PAGE NO.
PARALLEL-IN, PARALLEL-OUT (BIDIRECTIONAL)	8	50 MHz	D	Low	X	X	X	X	750 mW	SN54S299	J, W	SN74S299*	J, N	7-437
		35 MHz	D	Low	X	X	X	X	175 mW	SN54LS299*	J	SN74LS299*	J, N	7-437
		35 MHz	D	Sync L	X	X	X	X	175 mW	SN54LS323*	J	SN74LS323*	J, N	7-443
		25 MHz	D	Low	X	X	X	X	360 mW	SN54198	J, W	SN74198	J, N	7-338
	4	70 MHz	D	Low	X	X	X	X	450 mW	SN54S194	J, W	SN74S194	J, N	7-316
		25 MHz	D	Low	X	X	X	X	75 mW	SN54LS194A	J, W	SN74LS194A	J, N	
		25 MHz	D	Low	X	X	X	X	195 mW	SN54194	J, W	SN74194	J, N	
PARALLEL-IN, PARALLEL-OUT	8	25 MHz	J-K̄	Low	X		X	X	360 mW	SN54199	J, W	SN74199	J, N	7-338
	5	10 MHz	D	Low	X		X		60 mW	SN54LS96	J, W	SN74LS96	J, N	7-95
		10 MHz	D	Low	X		X		240 mW	SN5496	J, W	SN7496	J, N	
		5 MHz	D	Low	X		X		120 mW	SN54L96	J	SN74L96	J, N	
	4	70 MHz	J-K̄	Low	X		X		375 mW	SN54S195	J, W	SN74S195	J, N	7-324
		30 MHz	J-K̄	Low	X		X		195 mW	SN54195	J, W	SN74195	J, N	7-324
		30 MHz	D	Low	X		X		75 mW	SN54LS395A	J, W	SN74LS395A	J, N	7-496
		25 MHz	D	None	X		X		195 mW	SN5495A	J, W	SN7495A	J, N	7-89
		25 MHz	D	Low	X		X	X	230 mW	SN54179	J, W	SN74179	J, N	7-265
		25 MHz	D	None	X		X	X	230 mW	SN54178	J, W	SN74178	J, N	7-265
		30 MHz	J-K̄	Low	X		X		70 mW	SN54LS195A	J, W	SN74LS195A	J, N	7-324
		30 MHz	D	None	X		X		65 mW	SN54LS95B	J, W	SN74LS95B	J, N	7-89
		25 MHz	D	None	X		X		70 mW	SN54LS295B	J, W	SN74LS295B	J, N	7-429
		3 MHz	J-K̄	None	X		X		19 mW	SN54L99	J	SN74L99	J, N	7-109
		3 MHz	D	None	X		X		19 mW	SN54L95	J, T	SN74L95	J, N	7-89
SERIAL-IN, PARALLEL-OUT	8	25 MHz	Gated D	Low	X				80 mW	SN54LS164	J, W	SN74LS164	J, N	7-206
		25 MHz	Gated D	Low	X				167 mW	SN54164	J, W	SN74164	J, N	
		12 MHz	Gated D	Low	X				84 mW	SN54L164	J, T	SN74L164	J, N	
PARALLEL-IN, SERIAL-OUT	8	25 MHz	D	None	X		X	X	210 mW	SN54165	J, W	SN74165	J, N	7-212
		35 MHz	D	None	X		X	X	105 mW	SN54LS165	J, W	SN74LS165	J, N	7-212
		20 MHz	D	Low	X		X	X	360 mW	SN54166	J, W	SN74166	J, N	7-217
		35 MHz	D	Low	X		X	X	110 mW	SN54LS166	J, W	SN74LS166	J, N	7-217
	4	10 MHz	D	High	X		X		175 mW	SN5494	J, W	SN7494	J, N	7-86
SERIAL-IN, SERIAL-OUT	8	25 MHz	Gated D	None	X				60 mW	SN54LS91	J, W	SN74LS91	J, N	7-81
		10 MHz	Gated D	None	X				175 mW	SN5491A	J, W	SN7491A	J, N	
		3 MHz	Gated D	None	X				17.5 mW	SN54L91	J, T	SN74L91	J, N	

‡S-R ≡ shift right, S-L ≡ shift left

OTHER REGISTERS

DESCRIPTION	FREQ	ASYNC CLEAR	TYP TOTAL POWER DISSIPATION	−55°C to 125°C		0°C to 70°C		PAGE NO.
QUADRUPLE MULTIPLEXERS WITH STORAGE	30 MHz	None	36.5 mW	SN54LS398	J	SN74LS398	J, N	7-499
	30 MHz	None	36.5 mW	SN54LS399	J, W	SN74LS399	J, N	7-499
	25 MHz	None	65 mW	SN54LS298	J, W	SN74LS298	J, N	7-432
	25 MHz	None	195 mW	SN54298	J, W	SN74298	J, N	7-432
	3 MHz	None	25 mW	SN54L98	J	SN74L98	J, N	7-107
8-BIT UNIVERSAL SHIFT/STORAGE REGISTERS	35 MHz	Low	175 mW	SN54LS299*	J	SN74LS299*	J, N	7-437
	50 MHz	Low	750 mW	SN54S299	J, W	SN74S299	J, N	
QUADRUPLE BUS-BUFFER REGISTERS	25 MHz	High	250 mW	SN54173	J, W	SN74173	J, N	7-249
	50 MHz	High	85 mW	SN54LS173*	J, W	SN74LS173*	J, N	

*New product in development as of October 1976.

TEXAS INSTRUMENTS
INCORPORATED
POST OFFICE BOX 5012 • DALLAS, TEXAS 75222

LATCHES

DESCRIPTION	NO. OF BITS	CLEAR	OUTPUTS	TYPICAL DELAY TIME	TYP TOTAL POWER DISSIPATION	DEVICE TYPE AND PACKAGE −55°C to 125°C		DEVICE TYPE AND PACKAGE 0°C to 70°C		PAGE NO.
MULTI-MODE BUFFERED	8	Low	Q	11 ns	410 mW	SN54S412	J	SN74S412	J, N	7-502
ADDRESSABLE	8	Low	Q	12 ns	300 mW	SN54259	J, W	SN74259	J, N	7-376
		Low	Q	17 ns	110 mW	SN54LS259	J, W	SN74LS259	J, N	7-376
TRANSPARENT	8	None	Q	17 ns	210 mW	SN54LS363*	J	SN74LS363*	J, N	7-467
		None	Q	19 ns	120 mW	SN54LS373	J	SN74LS373	J, N	7-471
		None	Q	7 ns	525 mW	SN54S373	J	SN74S373	J, N	7-471
DUAL 4-BIT WITH INDEPENDENT ENABLE	8	Low	Q	11 ns	250 mW	SN54116	J, W	SN74116	J, N	7-115
		None	Q	15 ns	320 mW	SN54100	J, W	SN74100	J, N	7-113
DUAL 2-BIT WITH INDEPENDENT ENABLE	4	None	Q, Q̄	15 ns	160 mW	SN5475	J, W	SN7475	J, N	7-35
		None	Q, Q̄	30 ns	80 mW	SN54L75	J	SN74L75	J, N	7-35
		None	Q, Q̄	11 ns	32 mW	SN54LS75	J, W	SN74LS75	J, N	7-35
		None	Q	15 ns	160 mW	SN5477	W			7-35
		None	Q	30 ns	80 mW	SN54L77	T			7-35
		None	Q	10 ns	35 mW	SN54LS77	W			7-35
		None	Q, Q̄	12 ns	32 mW	SN54LS375	J, W	SN74LS375	J, N	7-478
QUAD S̄-R̄ (SSI)	4	None	Q	12 ns	90 mW	SN54279	J, W	SN74279	J, N	6-60
		None	Q	12 ns	19 mW	SN54LS279	J, W	SN74LS279	J, N	6-60

CLOCK GENERATOR CIRCUITS

DESCRIPTION		TYP TOTAL POWER DISSIPATION	DEVICE TYPE AND PACKAGE −55°C to 125°C		DEVICE TYPE AND PACKAGE 0°C to 70°C		PAGE NO.
CLOCK GENERATOR/DRIVERS	(FOR TMS 9900)	669 mW			SN74LS362	J, N	7-460
	(FOR TMS 8080A)	719 mW			SN74LS424	J, N	7-507
DUAL VOLTAGE-CONTROLLED OSCILLATOR WITH ENABLE		90 mW	SN54LS124	J, W	SN74LS124	J, N	7-123
		525 mW	SN54S124	J, W	SN74S124	J, N	7-123
		90 mW	SN54LS326	J, W	SN74LS326	J, N	7-445
DUAL VOLTAGE-CONTROLLED OSCILLATOR		150 mW	SN54LS325	J, W	SN74LS325	J, N	7-445
		150 mW	SN54LS327	J, W	SN74LS327	J, N	7-445
VOLTAGE-CONTROLLED OSCILLATOR WITH ENABLE		90 mW	SN54LS324	J, W	SN74LS324	J, N	7-445
DUAL 30-MHz PULSE SYNCHRONIZERS/DRIVERS		255 mW	SN54120	J, W	SN74120	J, N	7-118
QUAD COMPLIMENTARY GATES (CLOCK/CLOCK) [SSI]		125 mW	SN54265	J, W	SN74265	J, N	6-89

CODE CONVERTERS

DESCRIPTION	TYPICAL DELAY TIME PER PACKAGE LEVEL	TYPICAL TOTAL POWER DISSIPATION	DEVICE TYPE AND PACKAGE −55°C to 125°C		DEVICE TYPE AND PACKAGE 0°C to 70°C		PAGE NO.
6-LINE-BCD TO 6-LINE BINARY, OR 4-LINE TO 4-LINE BCD 9's/BCD 10's CONVERTERS	25 ns	280 mW	SN54184	J, W	SN74184	J, N	7-290
6-BIT-BINARY TO 6-BIT-BCD CONVERTERS	25 ns	280 mW	SN54185A	J, W	SN74185A	J, N	7-290

*New product in development as of October 1976.

877

TEXAS INSTRUMENTS
INCORPORATED
POST OFFICE BOX 5012 • DALLAS, TEXAS 75222

MSI/LSI FUNCTIONS
FUNCTIONAL INDEX/SELECTION GUIDE

PRIORITY ENCODERS/REGISTERS

DESCRIPTION	TYPICAL DELAY TIME	TYP TOTAL POWER DISSIPATION	DEVICE TYPE AND PACKAGE −55°C to 125°C		DEVICE TYPE AND PACKAGE 0°C to 70°C		PAGE NO.
FULL BCD PRIORITY ENCODERS	10 ns	225 mW	SN54147	J, W	SN74147	J, N	7-151
	15 ns	60 mW	SN54LS147	J, W	SN74LS147	J, N	
CASCADABLE OCTAL PRIORITY ENCODERS	12 ns	190 mW	SN54148	J, W	SN74148	J, N	7-151
	15 ns	60 mW	SN54LS148	J, W	SN74LS148	J, N	
CASCADABLE OCTAL PRIORITY ENCODERS WITH 3-STATE OUTPUTS	16 ns	63 mW	SN54LS348	J, W	SN74LS348	J, N	7-448
4-BIT CASCADABLE PRIORITY REGISTERS	35 ns	275 mW	SN54278	J, W	SN74278	J, N	7-403

DATA SELECTORS/MULTIPLEXERS

DESCRIPTION	TYPE OF OUTPUT	DATA TO INV OUTPUT	DATA TO NON-INV OUTPUT	FROM ENABLE	TYP TOTAL POWER DISSIPATION	DEVICE TYPE AND PACKAGE −55°C to 125°C		DEVICE TYPE AND PACKAGE 0°C to 70°C		PAGE NO.
16-LINE-TO-1-LINE	2-State	11 ns		18 ns	200 mW	SN54150	J, W	SN74150	J, N	7-157
DUAL 8-LINE-TO-1-LINE	3-State	10 ns		17 ns	220 mW			SN74351	N	7-451
8-LINE-TO-1-LINE	3-State	4.5 ns	8 ns	14 ns	275 mW	SN54S251	J, W	SN74S251	J, N	7-362
	3-State	17 ns	21 ns	21 ns	250 mW	SN54251	J, W	SN74251	J, N	7-362
	3-State	17 ns	21 ns	21 ns	35 mW	SN54LS251	J, W	SN74LS251	J, N	7-362
	2-State	4.5 ns	8 ns	9 ns	225 mW	SN54S151	J, W	SN74S151	J, N	7-157
	2-State	8 ns	16 ns	22 ns	145 mW	SN54151A	J, W	SN74151A	J, N	7-157
	2-State	8 ns			130 mW	SN54152A	W			7-157
	2-State	11 ns	18 ns	27 ns	30 mW	SN54LS151	J, W	SN74LS151	J, N	7-157
	2-State	11 ns		18 ns	28 mW	SN54LS152	W			7-157
DUAL 4-LINE-TO-1-LINE	3-State		12 ns	16 ns	35 mW	SN54LS253	J, W	SN74LS253	J, N	7-369
	2-State	15 ns		22 ns	31 mW	SN54LS352	J, W	SN74LS352	J, N	7-454
	3-State	12 ns		21 ns	43 mW	SN54LS353	J, W	SN74LS353	J, N	7-457
	2-State		6 ns	9.5 ns	225 mW	SN54S153	J, W	SN74S153	J, N	7-165
	2-State		14 ns	17 ns	180 mW	SN54153	J, W	SN74153	J, N	7-165
	2-State		14 ns	17 ns	31 mW	SN54LS153	J, W	SN74LS153	J, N	7-165
	2-State		27 ns	34 ns	90 mW	SN54L153	J	SN74L153	J, N	7-165
QUADRUPLE 2-LINE-TO-1-LINE WITH STORAGE	2-State		20 ns†		65 mW	SN54LS298	J, W	SN74LS298	J, N	7-432
	2-State		20 ns†		195 mW	SN54298	J, W	SN74298	J, N	7-432
	2-State		20 ns†		32 mW	SN54LS398	J	SN74LS398	J, N	7-499
	2-State	20 ns†	20 ns†		37 mW	SN54LS399	J, W	SN74LS399	J, N	7-499
	2-State		120 ns†		25 mW	SN54L98	J	SN74L98	J, N	7-107
QUADRUPLE 2-LINE-TO-1-LINE	3-State	4 ns		14 ns	280 mW	SN54S258	J, W	SN74S258	J, N	7-372
	3-State		5 ns	14 ns	320 mW	SN54S257	J, W	SN74S257	J, N	7-372
	2-State	4 ns		7 ns	195 mW	SN54S158	J, W	SN74S158	J, N	7-181
	2-State		5 ns	8 ns	250 mW	SN54S157	J, W	SN74S157	J, N	7-181
	3-State	12 ns		20 ns	60 mW	SN54LS258A*	J, W	SN74LS258A*	J, N	7-372
	3-State		12 ns	20 ns	60 mW	SN54LS257A*	J, W	SN74LS257A*	J, N	7-372
	2-State	7 ns		12 ns	24 mW	SN54LS158	J, W	SN74LS158	J, N	7-181
	2-State		9 ns	14 ns	49 mW	SN54LS157	J, W	SN74LS157	J, N	7-181
	2-State		9 ns	14 ns	150 mW	SN54157	J, W	SN74157	J, N	7-181
	2-State		18 ns	27 ns	75 mW	SN54L157	J	SN74L157	J, N	7-181

†From clock.
*New product in development as of October 1976.

TEXAS INSTRUMENTS
INCORPORATED
POST OFFICE BOX 5012 • DALLAS, TEXAS 75222

DECODERS/DEMULTIPLEXERS

DESCRIPTION	TYPE OF OUTPUT	TYPICAL SELECT TIME	TYPICAL ENABLE TIME	TYP TOTAL POWER DISSIPATION	DEVICE TYPE AND PACKAGE −55°C to 125°C		DEVICE TYPE AND PACKAGE 0°C to 70°C		PAGE NO.
4-LINE-TO-16-LINE	Totem-Pole	23 ns	19 ns	170 mW	SN54154	J, W	SN74154	J, N	7-171
	Totem-Pole	46 ns	38 ns	85 mW	SN54L154	J	SN74L154	J, N	7-171
	Open-Collector	24 ns	19 ns	170 mW	SN54159	J, W	SN74159	J, N	7-188
4-LINE-TO-10-LINE, BCD-TO-DECIMAL	Totem-Pole	17 ns		35 mW	SN54LS42	J, W	SN54LS42	J, N	
	Totem-Pole	17 ns		140 mW	SN5442A	J, W	SN7442A	J, N	7-15
	Totem-Pole	34 ns		70 mW	SN54L42	J	SN74L42	J, N	
4-LINE-TO-10-LINE, EXCESS-3-TO-DECIMAL	Totem-Pole	17 ns		140 mW	SN5443A	J, W	SN7443A	J, N	7-15
	Totem-Pole	34 ns		70 mW	SN54L43	J	SN74L43	J, N	
4-LINE-TO-10-LINE EXCESS-3-GRAY-TO-DECIMAL	Totem-Pole	17 ns		140 mW	SN5444A	J, W	SN7444A	J, N	7-15
	Totem-Pole	34 ns		70 mW	SN54L44	J	SN74L44	J, N	
3-LINE-TO-8-LINE	Totem-Pole	8 ns	7 ns	245 mW	SN54S138	J, W	SN74S138	J, N	7-134
	Totem-Pole	22 ns	21 ns	31 mW	SN54LS138	J, W	SN74LS138	J, N	7-134
DUAL 2-LINE-TO-4-LINE	Totem-Pole	7.5 ns	6 ns	300 mW	SN54S139	J, W	SN74S139	J, N	7-134
	Totem-Pole	22 ns	19 ns	34 mW	SN54LS139	J, W	SN74LS139	J, N	7-134
	Totem-Pole	18 ns	15 ns	30 mW	SN54LS155	J, W	SN74LS155	J, N	7-175
	Totem-Pole	21 ns	16 ns	125 mW	SN54155	J, W	SN74155	J, N	7-175
	Open-Collector	23 ns	18 ns	125 mW	SN54156	J, W	SN74156	J, N	7-175
	Open-Collector	33 ns	26 ns	31 mW	SN54LS156	J, W	SN74LS156	J, N	7-175

OPEN-COLLECTOR DISPLAY DECODERS/DRIVERS WITH COUNTERS/LATCHES

DESCRIPTION	OUTPUT SINK CURRENT	OFF-STATE OUTPUT VOLTAGE	TYP TOTAL POWER DISSIPATION	BLANKING	DEVICE TYPE AND PACKAGE −55°C to 125°C		DEVICE TYPE AND PACKAGE 0°C to 70°C		PAGE NO.
BCD COUNTER/ 4-BIT LATCH/ BCD-TO-DECIMAL DECODER/DRIVER	7 mA	55 V	340 mW				SN74142	J, N	7-140
BCD COUNTER/ 4-BIT LATCH/ BCD-TO-SEVEN-SEGMENT DECODER/ LED DRIVER	Constant Current 15 mA	7 V	280 mW	Ripple	SN54143	J, W	SN74143	J, N	7-143
BCD COUNTER/ 4-BIT LATCH/ BCD-TO-SEVEN-SEGMENT DECODER/ LAMP DRIVER	20 mA 25 mA	15 V 15 V	280 mW 280 mW	Ripple Ripple	SN54144	J, W	SN74144	J, N	7-143

RESULTANT DISPLAYS USING '143, '144

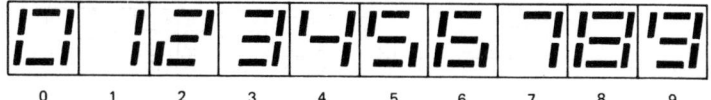

0 1 2 3 4 5 6 7 8 9

1

OPEN-COLLECTOR DISPLAY DECODERS/DRIVERS

DESCRIPTION	OUTPUT SINK CURRENT	OFF-STATE OUTPUT VOLTAGE	TYP TOTAL POWER DISSIPATION	BLANKING	DEVICE TYPE AND PACKAGE				PAGE NO.
					−55°C to 125°C		0°C to 70°C		
BCD-TO-DECIMAL DECODERS/DRIVERS	80 mA	30 V	215 mW	Invalid Codes	SN5445	J, W	SN7445	J, N	7-20
	80 mA	15 V	35 mW	Invalid Codes			SN74LS145	J, N	7-148
	12 mA	15 V	35 mW	Invalid Codes	SN54LS145	J, W			7-148
	80 mA	15 V	215 mW	Invlaid Codes	SN54145	J, W	SN74145	J, N	7-148
	7 mA	60 V	80 mW	Invalid Codes			SN74141	J, N	7-138
BCD-TO- SEVEN-SEGMENT DECODERS/DRIVERS	40 mA	30 V	320 mW	Ripple	SN5446A	J, W	SN7446A	J, N	7-22
	40 mA	30 V	320 mW	Ripple	SN54246	J, W	SN74246	J, N	7-22
	40 mA	15 V	320 mW	Ripple	SN5447A	J, W	SN7447A	J, N	7-22
	40 mA	15 V	320 mW	Ripple	SN54247	J, W	SN74247	J, N	7-351
	24 mA	15 V	35 mW	Ripple			SN74LS47	J, N	7-22
	24 mA	15 V	35 mW	Ripple			SN74LS247	J, N	7-351
	12 mA	15 V	35 mW	Ripple	SN54LS47	J, W			7-22
	12 mA	15 V	35 mW	Ripple	SN54LS247	J, W			7-351
	20 mA	30 V	133 mW	Ripple	SN54L46	J	SN74L46	J, N	7-22
	20 mA	15 V	133 mW	Ripple	SN54L47	J	SN74L47	J, N	7-22
	6.4 mA	5.5 V	265 mW	Ripple	SN5448	J, W	SN7448	J, N	7-22
	6.4 mA	5.5 V	265 mW	Ripple	SN54248	J, W	SN74248	J, N	7-351
	6 mA	5.5 V	125 mW	Ripple			SN74LS48	J, N	7-22
	6 mA	5.5 V	125 mW	Ripple			SN74LS248	J, N	7-351
	2 mA	5.5 V	125 mW	Ripple	SN54LS48	J, W			7-22
	2 mA	5.5 V	125 mW	Ripple	SN54LS248	J, W			7-351
	10 mA	5.5 V	165 mW	Direct	SN5449	W			7-22
	10 mA	5.5 V	265 mW	Direct	SN54249	J, W	SN74249	J, N	7-351
	8 mA	5.5 V	40 mW	Direct			SN74LS249	J, N	7-351
	8 mA	5.5 V	40 mW	Direct			SN74LS49	J, N	7-22
	4 mA	5.5 V	40 mW	Direct	SN54LS49	J, W			7-22
	4 mA	5.5 V	40 mW	Direct	SN54LS249	J, W			7-351

RESULTANT DISPLAYS USING '46A, '47A, '48, '49, 'L46, 'L47, 'LS47, 'LS48, 'LS49

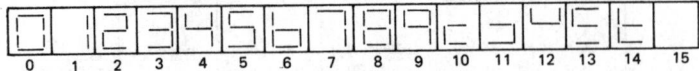

RESULTANT DISPLAYS USING '246, '247, '248, '249, 'LS247, 'LS248, 'LS249

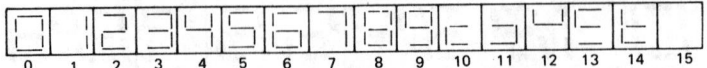

TEXAS INSTRUMENTS
INCORPORATED
POST OFFICE BOX 5012 • DALLAS, TEXAS 75222

BUS TRANSCEIVERS AND DRIVERS

DESCRIPTION	TYPICAL PROPAGATION DELAY TIMES	MAXIMUM SOURCE CURRENT	MAXIMUM SINK CURRENT	DEVICE TYPE AND PACKAGE				PAGE NO.
				−55°C to 125°C		0°C to 70°C		
CONTROLLER AND BUS DRIVER		−1 mA	10 mA			SN74S428	N	7-514
FOR 8080A SYSTEMS		−1 mA	10 mA			SN74S438	N	
OCTAL BUS TRANSCEIVERS	8 ns	−12 mA	12 mA	SN54LS245	J	SN74LS245	J, N	7-349
4-BIT BUS TRANSCEIVERS WITH STORAGE	10 ns	−6.5 mA	20 mA	SN54S226	J, W	SN74S226	J, N	7-345

ASYNCHRONOUS COUNTERS (RIPPLE CLOCK)—NEGATIVE-EDGE TRIGGERED

DESCRIPTION	COUNT FREQ	PARALLEL LOAD	CLEAR	TYP TOTAL POWER DISSIPATION	DEVICE TYPE AND PACKAGE				PAGE NO.
					−55°C to 125°C		0°C to 70°C		
DECADE	50 MHz	Yes	Low	240 mW	SN54196	J, W	SN74196	J, N	7-331
	100 MHz	Yes	Low	375 mW	SN54S196	J, W	SN74S196	J, N	7-331
	35 MHz	Yes	Low	150 mW	SN54176	J, W	SN74176	J, N	7-259
	32 MHz	Set-to-9	High	40 mW	SN54LS90	J, W	SN74LS90	J, N	7-72
	32 MHz	Set-to-9	High	40 mW	SN54LS290	J, W	SN74LS290	J, N	7-423
	32 MHz	Set-to-9	High	160 mW	SN5490A	J, W	SN7490A	J, N	7-72
	32 MHz	Set-to-9	High	160 mW	SN54290	J, W	SN74290	J, N	7-423
	30 MHz	Yes	Low	60 mW	SN54LS196	J, W	SN74LS196	J, N	7-331
	3 MHz	Set-to-9	High	20 mW	SN54L90	J, T	SN74L90	J, N	7-72
4-BIT BINARY	50 MHz	Yes	Low	240 mW	SN54197	J, W	SN74197	J, N	7-331
	100 MHz	Yes	Low	375 mW	SN54S197	J, W	SN74S197	J, N	7-331
	35 MHz	Yes	Low	150 mW	SN54177	J, W	SN74177	J, N	7-259
	32 MHz	None	High	39 mW	SN54LS93	J, W	SN74LS93	J, N	7-72
	32 MHz	None	High	39 mW	SN54LS293	J, W	SN74LS293	J, N	7-423
	32 MHz	None	High	160 mW	SN5493A	J, W	SN7493A	J, N	7-72
	32 MHz	None	High	160 mW	SN54293	J, W	SN74293	J, N	7-423
	30 MHz	Yes	Low	60 mW	SN54LS197	J, W	SN74LS197	J, N	7-331
	3 MHz	None	High	20 mW	SN54L93	J, T	SN74L93	J, N	7-72
DIVIDE-BY-12	32 MHz	None	High	39 mW	SN54LS92	J, W	SN74LS92	J, N	7-72
	32 MHz	None	High	160 mW	SN5492A	J, W	SN7492A	J, N	
DUAL DECADE	25 MHz	None	High	210 mW	SN54390	J, W	SN74390	J, N	7-489
	35 MHz	None	High	75 mW	SN54LS390	J, W	SN74LS390	J, N	7-489
	25 MHz	Set-to-9	High	225 mW	SN54490	J, W	SN74490	J, N	7-520
	35 MHz	Set-to-9	High	75 mW	SN54LS490	J, W	SN74LS490	J, N	7-520
DUAL 4-BIT BINARY	25 MHz	None	High	190 mW	SN54393	J, W	SN74393	J, N	7-489
	35 MHz	None	High	75 mW	SN54LS393	J, W	SN74LS393	J, N	7-489

1

MSI/LSI FUNCTIONS
FUNCTIONAL INDEX/SELECTION GUIDE

SYNCHRONOUS COUNTERS—POSITIVE-EDGE TRIGGERED

DESCRIPTION	COUNT FREQ	PARALLEL LOAD	CLEAR	TYP TOTAL POWER DISSIPATION	DEVICE TYPE AND PACKAGE				PAGE NO.
					−55°C to 125°C		0°C to 70°C		
DECADE	40 MHz	Sync	Sync-L	475 mW	SN54S162	J, W	SN74S162	J, N	
	25 MHz	Sync	Sync-L	93 mW	SN54LS162A	J, W	SN74LS162A	J, N	
	25 MHz	Sync	Async-L	93 mW	SN54LS160A	J, W	SN74LS160A	J, N	7-190
	25 MHz	Sync	Sync-L	305 mW	SN54162	J, W	SN74162	J, N	
	25 MHz	Sync	Async-L	305 mW	SN54160	J, W	SN74160	J, N	
DECADE UP/DOWN	40 MHz	Sync	None	500 mW	SN54S168	J, W	SN74S168	J, N	7-226
	25 MHz	Sync	None	100 mW	SN54LS168A	J, W	SN74LS168A	J, N	7-226
	25 MHz	Async	Async-H	85 mW	SN54LS192	J, W	SN74LS192	J, N	7-306
	25 MHz	Async	Async-H	325 mW	SN54192	J, W	SN74192	J, N	7-306
	20 MHz	Async	None	100 mW	SN54LS190	J, W	SN74LS190	J, N	7-296
	20 MHz	Async	None	325 mW	SN54190	J, W	SN74190	J, N	7-296
	3 MHz	Async	Async-H	42 mW	SN54L192	J	SN74L192	J, N	7-306
DECADE RATE MULTIPLIER, $\frac{1}{N_{10}}$	25 MHz	Set-to-9	Async-H	270 mW	SN54167	J, W	SN74167	J, N	7-222
4-BIT BINARY	40 MHz	Sync	Sync-L	475 mW	SN54S163	J, W	SN74S163	J, N	
	25 MHz	Sync	Sync-L	93 mW	SN54LS163A	J, W	SN74LS163A	J, N	
	25 MHz	Sync	Async-L	93 mW	SN54LS161A	J, W	SN74LS161A	J, N	7-190
	25 MHz	Sync	Sync-L	305 mW	SN54163	J, W	SN74163	J, N	
	25 MHz	Sync	Async-L	305 mW	SN54161	J, W	SN74161	J, N	
4-BIT BINARY UP/DOWN	40 MHz	Sync	None	500 mW	SN54S169	J, W	SN74S169	J, N	7-226
	25 MHz	Sync	None	100 mW	SN54LS169A	J, W	SN74LS169A	J, N	7-226
	25 MHz	Async	Async-H	85 mW	SN54LS193	J, W	SN74LS193	J, N	7-306
	25 MHz	Async	Async-H	325 mW	SN54193	J, W	SN74193	J, N	7-306
	20 MHz	Async	None	90 mW	SN54LS191	J, W	SN74LS191	J, N	7-296
	20 MHz	Async	None	325 mW	SN54191	J, W	SN74191	J, N	7-296
	3 MHz	Async	Async-H	42 mW	SN54L193	J	SN74L193	J, N	7-306
6-BIT BINARY RATE MULTIPLIER, $\frac{1}{N_2}$	25 MHz		Async-H	345 mW	SN5497	J, W	SN7497	J, N	7-102

BIPOLAR BIT-SLICE PROCESSOR ELEMENTS[†]

DESCRIPTION	CASCADABLE TO N-BITS	TYPICAL μ-OPERATION TIME	TECHNOLOGY	DEVICE TYPE AND PACKAGE			
				−55°C to 125°C		0°C to 70°C	
4-BIT SLICE	Yes	100 ns	STTL	SN54S481	J	SN74S481	J, N
	Yes	230 ns	I²L	SBP0400AM	J	SBP0400AC	J, N
	Yes	230 ns	I²L	SBP0401AM	J	SBP0401AC	J, N

FIRST-IN FIRST-OUT MEMORIES (FIFO'S)[†]

DESCRIPTION	TYPE OF OUTPUT	DELAY TIME FROM CLOCK	TYP TOTAL POWER DISSIPATION	DEVICE TYPE AND PACKAGE			
				−55°C to 125°C		0°C to 70°C	
ASYNCHRONOUS 16 X 5	3-State	50 ns	400 mW			SN74S225	J

[†]See Bipolar Microcomputer Components Data Book, LCC4270.

TEXAS INSTRUMENTS
INCORPORATED
POST OFFICE BOX 5012 • DALLAS, TEXAS 75222

1

RANDOM-ACCESS READ-WRITE MEMORIES (RAM'S)

DESCRIPTION	ORGANI-ZATION	TYPE OF OUTPUT	TYPICAL ADDRESS TIME	TYPICAL ENABLE TIME	TYP POWER DISSIPATION PER BIT	DEVICE TYPE AND PACKAGE				PAGE NO.
						−55°C to 125°C		0°C to 70°C		
1024-BIT ARRAYS	1024 X 1	3-State	65 ns	20 ns	0.2/0.07 mW	SN54LS215	JD	SN74LS215	JD, N	†
WITH POWER-DOWN	1024 X 1	O-C	65 ns	20 ns	0.2/0.07 mW	SN54LS315	JD	SN74LS315	JD, N	†
	1024 X 1	3-State	65 ns	20 ns	0.2 mW	SN54LS214	JD	SN74LS214	JD, N	†
	1024 X 1	3-State	30 ns	15 ns	0.51 mW	SN54S214	JD	SN74S214	JD, N	†
	1024 X 1	O-C	65 ns	20 ns	0.2 mW	SN54LS314	JD	SN74LS314	JD, N	†
1024-BIT ARRAYS	1024 X 1	O-C	30 ns	15 ns	0.51 mW	SN54S314	JD	SN74S314	JD, N	†
	256 X 4	3-State	60 ns	20 ns	0.3 mW	SN54LS207	J	SN74LS207	J, N	†
	256 X 4	3-State	40 ns	15 ns	0.59 mW	SN54S207	J	SN74S207	J, N	†
	256 X 4	3-State	60 ns	20 ns	0.3 mW	SN54LS208	J	SN74LS208	J, N	†
	256 X 4	3-State	40 ns	15 ns	0.59 mW	SN54S208	J	SN74S208	J, N	†
256-BIT ARRAYS	256 X 1	3-State	35 ns	15 ns	1.1/0.39 mW	SN54LS202	J, W	SN74LS202	J, N	†
WITH POWER-DOWN	256 X 1	O-C	35 ns	15 ns	1.1/0.39 mW	SN54LS302	J, W	SN74LS302	J, N	†
	256 X 1	3-State	35 ns	15 ns	1.1 mW	SN54LS200A	J, W	SN74LS200A	J, N	†
	256 X 1	3-State	25 ns	15 ns	1.9 mW	SN54S200A	J, W	SN74S200A	J, N	†
	256 X 1	3-State	42 ns	17 ns	1.9 mW	SN54S201	J, W	SN74S201	J, N	†
256-BIT ARRAYS	256 X 1	O-C	35 ns	15 ns	1.1 mW	SN54LS300A	J, W	SN74LS300A	J, N	†
	256 X 1	O-C	25 ns	15 ns	1.9 mW	SN54S300A	J, W	SN74S300A	J, N	†
	256 X 1	O-C	42 ns	13 ns	1.9 mW	SN54S301	J, W	SN74S301	J, N	†
	16 X 4	3-State	25 ns	12 ns	5.9 mW	SN54S189	J, W	SN74S189	J, N	†
64-BIT ARRAYS	16 X 4	O-C	25 ns	12 ns	5.9 mW	SN54S289	J, W	SN74S289	J, N	†
	16 X 4	O-C	32 ns	30 ns	5.9 mW			SN7489	J, N	†
16-BIT ARRAYS	16 X 1	O-C	15 ns	15 ns	14 mW	SN5481A	J, W	SN7481A	J, N	†
	16 X 1	O-C	15 ns	15 ns	14 mW	SN5484A	J, W	SN7484A	J, N	†
16-BIT MULTIPLE-PORT REGISTER FILE	8 X 2	3-State	33 ns	15 ns	35 mW			SN74172	J, N	7-245
	4 X 4	O-C	27 ns	15 ns	7.8 mW	SN54LS170	J, W	SN74LS170	J, N	7-237
16-BIT REGISTER FILE	4 X 4	O-C	30 ns	15 ns	40 mW	SN54170	J, W	SN74170	J, N	7-237
	4 X 4	3-State	24 ns	19 ns	9.3 mW	SN54LS670	J, W	SN74LS670	J, N	7-526

READ-ONLY MEMORIES (ROM'S)†

DESCRIPTION	ORGANI-ZATION	TYPE OF OUTPUT	TYPICAL ADDRESS TIME	TYPICAL ENABLE TIME	TYP POWER DISSIPATION PER BIT	DEVICE TYPE AND PACKAGE			
						−55°C to 125°C		0°C to 70°C	
2048-BIT ARRAYS	512 X 4	O-C	45 ns	15 ns	0.26 mW	SN54S270	J	SN74S270	J, N
	256 X 8	O-C	45 ns	15 ns	0.26 mW	SN54S271	J	SN74S271	J, N
	512 X 4	3-State	45 ns	15 ns	0.26 mW	SN54S370	J	SN74S370	J, N
	256 X 8	3-State	45 ns	15 ns	0.26 mW	SN54S371	J	SN74S371	J, N
1024-BIT ARRAYS	256 X 4	O-C	40 ns	20 ns	0.46 mW	SN54187	J, W	SN74187	J, N
256-BIT ARRAYS	32 X 8	O-C	26 ns	22 ns	1.1 mW	SN5488A	J, W	SN7488A	J, N

†See Bipolar Microcomputer Components Data Book, LCC4270.

076

PROGRAMMABLE READ-ONLY MEMORIES (PROM'S)[†]

DESCRIPTION	ORGANI-ZATION	TYPE OF OUTPUT	TYPICAL ADDRESS TIME	TYPICAL ENABLE TIME	TYP POWER DISSIPATION PER BIT	DEVICE TYPE AND PACKAGE −55°C to 125°C		DEVICE TYPE AND PACKAGE 0°C to 70°C	
4096-BIT ARRAYS	512 X 8	3-State	55 ns	20 ns	0.14 mW	SN54S472	J	SN74S472	J, N
	512 X 8	O-C	55 ns	20 ns	0.14 mW	SN54S473	J	SN74S473	J, N
	512 X 8	3-State	55 ns	20 ns	0.14 mW	SN54S474	J, W	SN74S474	J, N
	512 X 8	O-C	55 ns	20 ns	0.14 mW	SN54S475	J, W	SN74S475	J, N
2048-BIT ARRAYS	256 X 8	O-C	50 ns	20 ns	0.24 mW	SN54S470	J	SN74S470	J, N
	256 X 8	3-State	50 ns	20 ns	0.27 mW	SN54S471	J	SN74S471	J, N
1024-BIT ARRAYS	256 X 4	3-State	40 ns	15 ns	0.49 mW	SN54S287	J, W	SN74S287	J, N
	256 X 4	O-C	40 ns	15 ns	0.49 mW	SN54S387	J, W	SN74S387	J, N
512-BIT ARRAYS	64 X 8	O-C	50 ns	47 ns	0.6 mW	SN54186	J, W	SN74186	J, N
256-BIT ARRAYS	32 X 8	O-C	29 ns	28 ns	1.3 mW	SN54188A	J, W	SN74188A	J, N
	32 X 8	O-C	25 ns	12 ns	1.56 mW	SN54S188	J, W	SN74S188	J, N
	32 X 8	3-State	25 ns	12 ns	1.56 mW	SN54S288	J, W	SN74S288	J, N

MICROPROCESSOR CONTROLLERS AND SUPPORT FUNCTIONS

DESCRIPTION	SYSTEM APPLICATION	TYP TOTAL POWER DISSIPATION	DEVICE TYPE AND PACKAGE −55°C to 125°C		DEVICE TYPE AND PACKAGE 0°C to 70°C		PAGE NO.
SYSTEM CONTROLLERS	8080A	700 mW			SN74S428 (TIM8228)	N	7-514
	8080A	700 mW			SN74S438 (TIM8238)	N	7-514
	Universal	450 mW	SN54S482	J	SN74S482	J, N	†
REGISTERS	TMS 9900	110 mW	SN54LS259	J, W	SN74LS259 (TIM9906)	J, N	7-376
	MOS	210 mW	SN54LS363*	J	SN74LS363*	J, N	7-467
		210 mW	SN54LS364*	J	SN74LS364*	J, N	7-467
MULTI-MODE LATCHES	8080A	410 mW	SN54S412	J, W	SN74S412 (TIM8212)	J, N	7-502
TRANSCEIVERS AND BUS DRIVERS		625 mW	SN54S226*	J, W	SN74S226*	J, N	7-345
		207 mW	SN54LS245	J	SN74LS245	J, N	7-349
TRANSCEIVERS AND BUS DRIVERS (SSI)		98 mW	SN54LS240	J	SN74LS240	J, N	6-83
		450 mW	SN54S240	J	SN74S240	J, N	6-83
		100 mW	SN54LS241	J	SN74LS241	J, N	6-83
		538 mW	SN54S241	J	SN74S241	J, N	6-83
		128 mW	SN54LS242	J, W	SN74LS242	J, N	6-87
		128 mW	SN54LS243	J, W	SN74LS243	J, N	6-87
		100 mW	SN54LS244	J	SN74LS244	J, N	6-83
CLOCK ELEMENTS	TMS 9900	669 mW			SN74LS362 (TIM9904)	J, N	7-460
	8080A	719 mW			SN74S424 (TIM8224)	J, N	7-507
LOGIC ELEMENTS	TMS 9900	190 mW	SN54148	J, W	SN74148 (TIM9907)	J, N	7-151
	TMS 9900	35 mW	SN54LS251	J, W	SN74LS251 (TIM9905)	J, N	7-362
	TMS 9900	63 mW	SN54LS348	J, W	SN74LS348 (TIM9908)	J, N	7-448

*New product in development as of October 1976.
[†]See Bipolar Microcomputer Components Data Book, LCC4270.

TEXAS INSTRUMENTS
INCORPORATED
POST OFFICE BOX 5012 • DALLAS, TEXAS 75222

Interchangeability
Guide

TTL INTERCHANGEABILITY GUIDE

<u>Direct Replacements</u> were selected as pin-for-pin equivalent circuits based on similarity of electrical and mechanical characteristics as shown in currently published data. Interchangability in any particular application is not necessarily guaranteed. Before using a substitute, the user should compare the specifications of the substitute device with the detailed specifications of the original device.

TI makes no warranty as to the information furnished and buyer assumes all risk in the use thereof. No liability is assumed for damages resulting from the use of the information contained in this list.

<u>Recommendation for New Designs</u> lists devices performing a similar (sometimes identical) function. Most are pin-for-pin equivalents for the competitor's part. However, the recommended part may have different pin-outs or organizations, as later technologies are listed in some cases to ensure that current high-performance components are recommended.

Only the basic circuit numbers are cross referenced. As the pin-out sometimes varies between a flat-package part and the equivalent DIP part, it is recommended that the manufacturer's specifications be consulted prior to specifying a direct replacement. Other than parts offered only in a flat package, the dual-in-line pin-outs were used as a guide in preparing the following cross references.

This list is intended to give TI replacements for competitors' parts not using the 54/74 numbering system. For a complete listing of parts in the 54 and 74 families, see the functional index, pages 1-9 through 1-28.

ADVANCED MICRO DEVICES

Example of AMD ordering code:

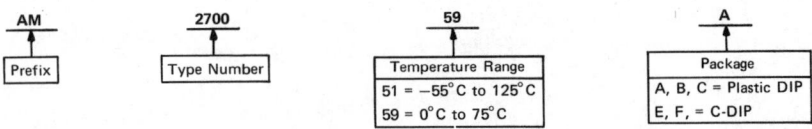

AMD TYPE	TI DIRECT REPLACEMENT	RECOMMENDED FOR NEW DESIGN	AMD TYPE	TI DIRECT REPLACEMENT	RECOMMENDED FOR NEW DESIGN
2501		SN54192/SN74191	27S09	SN54S288/SN74S288	SN54S288/SN74S288
2505		SN54284/SN74284	27S10	SN54S387/SN74S387	SN54S387/SN74S387
		SN54285/SN74285	27S11	SN54S287/SN74S287	SN54S287/SN74S287
2506		SN54S181/SN74S181	3101	SN7489	SN7489
25LS07	SN54LS378/SN74LS378	SN54LS378/SN74LS378	3101A	SN54S289/SN74S289	SN54S289/SN74S289
25LS08	SN54LS379/SN74LS379	SN54LS379/SN74LS379	9300	SN54195/SN74195	SN54195/SN74195
25LS09	SN54LS399/SN74LS399	SN54LS399/SN74LS399	9301	SN29301/SN39301	SN5442A/SN7442A
25LS22	SN54LS322/SN74LS322	SN54LS322/SN74LS322	9308	SN29308/SN39308	SN54116/SN74116
25LS23	SN54LS323/SN74LS323	SN54LS323/SN74LS323	9309	SN29309/SN39309	SN54153/SN74153
2600		SN54121/SN74121	9310	SN54160/SN74160	SN54160/SN74160
2602		SN54123/SN74123	9311	SN54154/SN74154	SN54154/SN74154
26123	SN54123/SN74123	SN54123/SN74123	9312	SN29312/SN39312	SN54151A/SN74151A
2700	SN54S200A/SN74S200A	SN54S200A/SN74S200A	9316	SN54161/SN74161	SN54161/SN74161
	SN54S201/SN74S201	SN54S201/SN74S201	9318	SN54148/SN74148	SN54148/SN74148
27LS00	SN54LS200A/SN74LS200A	SN54LS200A/SN74LS200A	9322	SN54157/SN74157	SN54157/SN74167
2701	SN54S300A/SN74S300A	SN54S300A/SN74S300A	9334	SN54259/SN74259	SN54259/SN74259
	SN54S301/SN74S301	SN54S301/SN74S301	9341	SN54181/SN74181	SN54181/SN74181
27S02	SN54S289/SN74S289	SN54S289/SN74S289	9342	SN54182/SN74182	SN54182/SN74182
27S03	SN54S189/SN74S189	SN54S189/SN74S189	9601	SN29601	
27S08	SN54S188/SN74S188	SN54S188/SN74S188	93415	SN54S314/SN74S314	SN54S314/SN74S314

FAIRCHILD

Example of order code:

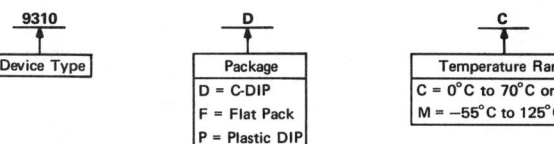

	9310		D		C
	Device Type		Package		Temperature Range
			D = C-DIP		C = 0°C to 70°C or 75°C
			F = Flat Pack		M = −55°C to 125°C
			P = Plastic DIP		

2

FSC TYPE	TI DIRECT REPLACEMENT	RECOMMENDED FOR NEW DESIGN	FSC TYPE	TI DIRECT REPLACEMENT	RECOMMENDED FOR NEW DESIGN
9000	SN29000	SN54276/SN74276	9014		SN54S135/SN74S135
9H00	SN54H00/SN74H00	SN54S00/SN74S00	9N14	SN5414/SN7414	SN5414/SN7414
9L00	SN54LS00/SN74LS00	SN54LS00/SN74LS00	9015		SN5402/SN7402
9N00	SN5400/SN7400	SN5400/SN7400	9S15	SN54S15/SN74S15	SN54S15/SN74S15
9S00	SN54S00/SN74S00	SN54S00/SN74S00	9016	SN29016/SN7404, SN5404	SN54S240/SN74S240
9001	SN29001	SN54276/SN74276	9N16	SN5416/SN7416	SN5416/SN7416
		SN54376/SN74376	9017	SN5405/SN7405	SN54S241/SN74S241
9H01	SN54H01/SN74H01	SN54S03/SN74S03	9N17	SN5417/SN7417	SN5417/SN7417
9N01	SN5401/SN7401	SN5403/SN7403	9020		SN74276
9002	SN29002/SN7400, SN5400	SN5400/SN7400	9H20	SN54H20/SN74H20	SN54S20/SN74S20
9N02	SN5402/SN7402	SN5402/SN7402	9N20	SN5420/SN7420	SN5420/SN7420
9S02	SN54S02/SN74S02	SN54S02/SN74S02	9S20	SN54S20/SN74S20	SN54S20/SN74S20
9003	SN29003/SN7410, SN5410	SN5410/SN7410	9H21	SN54H21/SN74H21	SN54S15/SN74S15
9N03	SN5403/SN7403	SN5403/SN7403	9022		SN74376
9S03	SN54S03/SN74S03	SN54S03/SN74S03	9H22	SN54H22/SN74H22	SN54S22/SN74S22
9004	SN29004/SN7420, SN5420	SN5420/SN7420	9S22	SN54S22/SN74S22	SN54S22/SN74S22
9H04	SN54H04/SN74H04	SN54S04/SN74S04	9N23	SN5423/SN7423	SN5423/SN7423
9L04	SN54LS04/SN74LS04	SN54LS04/SN74LS04	9024	SN29024/SN74109, SN54109	SN54276/SN74276
9N04	SN5404/SN7404	SN5404/SN7404			SN54376/SN74376
9S04	SN54S04/SN74S04	SN54S04/SN74S04	9L24	SN54LS109A/SN74LS109A	SN54LS109A/SN74LS109A
9005	SN29005/SN7450, SN5450	SN5450/SN7450	9N25	SN5425/SN7425	SN5425/SN7425
9H05	SN54S05/SN74S05	SN54S05/SN74S05	9N26	SN5426/SN7426	SN5426/SN7426
9S05	SN54S05/SN74S05	SN54S05/SN74S05	9N27	SN5427/SN7427	SN5427/SN7427
9006	SN5460/SN7460	SN5460/SN7460	9H30	SN54H30/SN74H30	SN54S30/SN74S30
9N06	SN5406/SN7406	SN5406/SN7406	9N30	SN5430/SN7430	SN5430/SN7430
9007	SN29007	SN54S133/SN74S133	9S30	SN54S30/SN74S30	SN54S30/SN74S30
9N07	SN5407/SN7407	SN5407/SN7407	9N32	SN5432/SN7432	SN5432/SN7432
9008	SN29008	SN54S65/SN74S65	9S32	SN54S32/SN74S32	SN54S32/SN74S32
9N08	SN5408/SN7408	SN5408/SN7408	9033	SN83433, SN93433	SN54S189/SN74S189
9S08	SN54S08/SN74S08	SN54S08/SN74S08	9034	SN5488A/SN7488A	SN54S371/SN74S371
9009	SN29009/SN7440, SN5440	SN54S140/SN74S140	9037	SN5437/SN7437	SN5437/SN7437
9N09	SN5409/SN7409	SN5409/SN7409	9N38	SN5438/SN7438	SN5438/SN7438
9S09	SN54S09/SN74S09	SN54S09/SN74S09	9H40	SN54H40/SN74H40	SN54S40/SN74S40
9H10	SN54H10/SN74H10	SN54S10/SN74S10	9N40	SN5440/SN7440	SN5440/SN7440
9N10	SN5410/SN7410	SN5410/SN7410	9S40	SN54S40/SN74S40	SN54S40/SN74S40
9S10	SN54S10/SN74S10	SN54S10/SN74S10	9H50	SN54H50/SN74H50	SN54S51/SN74S51
9H11	SN54H11/SN74H11	SN54S11/SN74S11	9N50	SN5450/SN7450	SN5450/SN7450
9S11	SN54S11/SN74S11	SN54S11/SN74S11	9H51	SN54H51/SN74H51	SN54S51/SN74S51
9012	SN2901/SN7403, SN5403	SN5403/SN7403	9N51	SN5451/SN7451	SN5451/SN7451
9N12	SN5412/SN7412	SN5412/SN7412	9S51	SN54S51/SN74S51	SN54S51/SN74S51
9N13	SN5413/SN7413	SN5413/SN7413	9H52	SN54H52/SN74H52	SN54S51/SN74S51

FAIRCHILD

FSC TYPE	TI DIRECT REPLACEMENT	RECOMMENDED FOR NEW DESIGN	FSC TYPE	TI DIRECT REPLACEMENT	RECOMMENDED FOR NEW DESIGN
9H53	SN54H53/SN74H53	SN54H53/SN74H53	93L00	SN54LS195A/SN74LS195A	SN54LS195A/SN74LS195A
9N53	SN5453/SN7453	SN5453/SN7453	93S00	SN54S195/SN74S195	SN54S195/SN74S195
9H54	SN54H54/SN74H54	SN54H54/SN74H54	9301	SN39301/SN29301	SN5442A/SN7442A
9L54	SN54L54/SN74L54	SN54LS54/SN74LS54	93L01		SN54L42/SN74L42
9N54	SN5454/SN7454	SN5454/SN7454	9302		SN5442A/SN7442A
9H55	SN54H55/SN74H55	SN54S65/SN74S65	9304		SN54H183/SN74H183
9H60	SN54H60/SN74H60	SN54S11/SN74S11	9305		SN54S169/SN74S169
9N60	SN5460/SN7460	SN5460/SN7460	93S05		SN54S169/SN74S169
9H61	SN54H61/SN74H61	SN54S11/SN74S11	9307	SN5448A/SN7448A	SN5448A/SN7448A
9H62	SN54H62/SN74H62	SN54H62/SN74H62	9308	SN39308/SN54116	SN54116/SN74116
9S64	SN54S64/SN74S64	SN54S64/SN74S64		SN29308/SN74116	
9S65	SN54S65/SN74S65	SN54S65/SN74S65	9309	SN39309/SN29309	SN54153/SN74153
9N70	SN5470/SN7470	SN5470/SN7470	93L09		SN54L153/SN74L153
9H71	SN54H71/SN74H71	SN54S112/SN74S112	9310	SN39310/SN54160	SN54S162/SN74S162
9H72	SN54H72/SN74H72	SN54S112/SN74S112		SN29310/SN74160	
9N72	SN5472/SN7472	SN5472/SN7472	93S10		SN54S162/SN74S162
9H73	SN54H73/SN74H73	SN54S113/SN74S113	9311	SN39311/SN54154	SN54154/SN74154
9N73	SN5473/SN7473	SN5473/SN7473		SN29311/SN74154	
9H74	SN54H74/SN74H74	SN54S74/SN74S74	93L11	SN54L154/SN74L154	SN54L154/SN74L154
9N74	SN5474/SN7474	SN5474/SN7474	9312	SN39312/SN29312	SN54151A/SN74151A
9S74	SN54S74/SN74S74	SN54S74/SN74S74	93S12		SN54S151/SN74S151
9N75	SN5475/SN7475	SN5475/SN7475	9313		SN54251/SN74251
9H76	SN54H76/SN74H76	SN54S112/SN74S112	9314		SN54273/SN74273
9N76	SN5476/SN7476	SN5476/SN7476	93L14		SN54L75/SN74L75
9H78	SN54H78/SN74H78	SN54S114/SN74S114	9315	SN54141	SN74141
9L86	SN54L86/SN74L86	SN54LS86/SN74LS86	9316	SN39316/SN54161	SN54S163/SN74S163
9N86	SN5486/SN7486	SN5486/SN7486		SN29316/SN74161	
9S86	SN54S86/SN74S86	SN54S86/SN74S86	93S16		SN54S163/SN74S163
9H101	SN54H101/SN74H101	SN54S112/SN74S112	9317B	SN5446A/SN7446A	SN5446A/SN7446A
9H102	SN54H102/SN74H102	SN54S112/SN74S112	9317C	SN5446A/SN7446A	SN5446A/SN7446A
9H103	SN54H103/SN74H103	SN54S113/SN74S113	9318	SN39318/SN54148	SN54148/SN74148
9H106	SN54H106/SN76H106	SN54S112/SN74S112		SN29318/SN74148	
9H107	SN54107/SN74107	SN54107/SN74107	93L21	SN54LS139/SN74LS139	SN54LS139/SN74LS139
9N107	SN54107/SN74107	SN54107/SN74107	9321	SN54S139/SN74S139	SN54S139/SN74S139
9H108	SN54H108/SN74H108	SN54S114/SN74S114	9322	SN39322/SN54157	SN54157/SN74157
9S112	SN54S112/SN74S112	SN54S112/SN74S112		SN29322/SN74157	
9S113	SN54S113/SN74S113	SN54S113/SN74S113	93L22	SN54L157/SN74L157	SN54L157/SN74L157
9S114	SN54S114/SN74S114	SN54S114/SN74S114	93S22	SN54S157/SN74S157	SN54S157/SN74S157
9N122	SN54122/SN74122	SN54122/SN74122	9324		SN54S85/SN74S85
9N123	SN54123/SN74123	SN54123/SN74123	93L24		SN54L85/SN74L85
9N132	SN54132/SN74132	SN54132/SN74132	9325	SN74141	SN74141
9S132	SN54S132/SN74S132	SN54S132/SN74S132	9328		SN5491A/SN7491A
9S133	SN54S133/SN74S133	SN94S133/SN74S133	93L28		SN54L91/SN74L91
9S134	SN54S134/SN74S134	SN54S134/SN74S134	9334	SN54259/SN74259	SN54259/SN74259
9S135	SN54S135/SN74S135	SN54S135/SN74S135	9338		SN74172
9S140	SN54S140/SN74S140	SN54S140/SN74S140	9340		SN54S281/SN74S281
9N279	SN54279/SN74279	SN54279/SN74279	93L40		SN54LS181/SN74LS181
9300	SN39300/SN54195	SN54S299/SN74S299	9341	SN54181/SN74181	SN54181/SN74181
	SN29300/SN74195		93S41	SN54S181/SN74S181	SN54S181/SN74S181
93H00	SN54S195/SN74S195	SN54S195/SN74S195	9342	SN54182/SN74182	SN54182/SN74182

FAIRCHILD

FSC TYPE	TI DIRECT REPLACEMENT	RECOMMENDED FOR NEW DESIGN	FSC TYPE	TI DIRECT REPLACEMENT	RECOMMENDED FOR NEW DESIGN
93S42	SN54S182/SN74S182	SN54S182/SN74S182	93155	SN54155/SN74155	SN54155/SN74155
93S43		SN74S274	93156	SN54156/SN74156	SN54156/SN74156
9344		SN74S274	93157	SN54157/SN74157	SN54157/SN74157
9345	SN5445/SN7445	SN5445/SN7445	93S157	SN54S157/SN74S157	SN54S157/SN74S157
93S46		SN54S85/SN74S85	93S158	SN54S158/SN74S158	SN54S158/SN74S158
93S47		SN54S85/SN74S85	93160	SN54160/SN74160	SN54160/SN74160
9348		SN54S280/SN74S280	93161	SN54161/SN74161	SN54161/SN74161
9349	SN54180/SN74180	SN54180/SN74180	93162	SN54162/SN74162	SN54162/SN74162
9350	SN54290/SN74290	SN54290/SN74290	93163	SN54163/SN74163	SN54163/SN74163
9352	SN5442A/SN7442A	SN5442A/SN7442A	93164	SN54164/SN74164	SN54164/SN74164
9353	SN5443A/SN7443A	SN5443A/SN7443A	93165	SN54165/SN74165	SN54165/SN74165
9354	SN5444A/SN7444A	SN5444A/SN7444A	93166	SN54166/SN74166	SN54166/SN74166
9356	SN54293/SN74293	SN54293/SN74293	93170	SN54170/SN74170	SN54170/SN74170
9357A	SN5446A/SN7446A	SN5446A/SN7446A	93174	SN54174/SN74174	SN54174/SN74174
9357B	SN5447A/SN7447A	SN5447A/SN7447A	93175	SN54175/SN74175	SN54175/SN74175
9358	SN5448/SN7448	SN5448/SN7448	93S175	SN54S175/SN74S175	SN54S175/SN74S175
9359	SN5449/SN7449	SN5449/SN7449	93176	SN54176/SN74176	SN54176/SN74176
9360	SN54192/SN74192	SN54192/SN74192	93177	SN54177/SN74177	SN54177/SN74177
93S62		SN54S280/SN74S280	93178	SN54178/SN74178	SN54178/SN74178
9366	SN54193/SN74193	SN54193/SN74193	93179	SN54179/SN74179	SN54179/SN74179
9368C		SN54143/SN74143	93180	SN54180/SN74180	SN54180/SN74180
9370C		SN54144/SN74144	93H183	SN54H183/SN74H183	SN54H183/SN74H183
93H72		SN54S194/SN74S194	93190	SN54190/SN74190	SN54190/SN74190
9374C		SN54143/SN74143	93191	SN54191/SN74191	SN54191/SN74191
9375	SN5475/SN7475	SN54175/SN74175	93194	SN54194/SN74194	SN54194/SN74194
9377	SN5477/SN7477	SN54175/SN74175	93S194	SN54S194/SN74S194	SN54S194/SN74S194
9380	SN5480/SN7480	SN5480/SN7480	93195	SN54195/SN74195	SN54195/SN74195
9382	SN5482/SN7482	SN5482/SN7482	93196	SN54196/SN74196	SN54196/SN74196
9383	SN5483A/SN7483A	SN54283/SN74283	93197	SN54197/SN74197	SN54197/SN74197
9386	SN54LS266/SN74LS266	SN54LS266/SN74LS266	93198	SN54198/SN74198	SN54198/SN74198
93H87	SN54H87/SN74H87	SN54H87/SN74H87	93199	SN54199/SN74199	SN54199/SN74199
9390	SN5490A/SN7490A	SN54290/SN74290	93S251	SN54S251/SN74S251	SN54S251/SN74S251
9391	SN5491A/SN7491A	SN5491A/SN7491A	93S257	SN54S257/SN74S257	SN54S257/SN74S257
9392	SN5492A/SN7492A	SN5492A/SN7492A	93S258	SN54S258/SN74S258	SN54S258/SN74S258
9393	SN5493A/SN7493A	SN54293/SN74293	93400		SN54S201/SN74S201
9394	SN5494/SN7494	SN5494/SN7494	93403	SN54S289/SN74S289	SN54S289/SN74S289
9395	SN5495A/SN7495A	SN5495A/SN7495A	93404		SN54S289/SN74S289
9396	SN5496/SN7496	SN5496/SN7496	93405		SN54S189/SN74S189
93S137		SN54S138/SN74S138	93406	SN54187/SN74187	SN54187/SN74187
93S138	SN54S138/SN74S138	SN54S138/SN74S138	93407	SN5481A/SN7481A	SN5481A/SN7481A
93S139	SN54S139/SN74S139	SN54S139/SN74S139	93410	SN54S300A/SN74S300A	SN54S300A/SN74S300A
93141C	SN74141	SN74141		SN54S301/SN74S301	SN54S301/SN74S301
93145	SN54145/SN74145	SN54145/SN74145	93411	SN54S200A/SN74S200A	SN54S200A/SN74S200A
93150	SN54150/SN74150	SN54150/SN74150		SN54S201/SN74S201	SN54S201/SN74S201
93151	SN54151/SN74151	SN54151A/SN74151A	93412	SN54S214/SN74S214	SN54S214/SN74S214
93S151	SN54S139/SN74S139	SN54S139/SN74S139	93415A	SN54S314/SN74S314	SN54S314/SN74S314
93152	SN54152/SN74152	SN54151A/SN74151A	93415	SN54S314/SN74S314	SN54S314/SN74S314
93153	SN54153/SN74153	SN54153/SN74153	93416	SN54S387/SN74S387	SN54S387/SN74S387
93S153	SN54S153/SN74S153	SN54S153/SN74S153	93417	SN54S387/SN74S387	SN54S387/SN74S378

FAIRCHILD

FSC TYPE	TI DIRECT REPLACEMENT	RECOMMENDED FOR NEW DESIGN	FSC TYPE	TI DIRECT REPLACEMENT	RECOMMENDED FOR NEW DESIGN
93421	SN54S200A/SN74S200A	SN54S200A/SN74S200A	93436	SN54S270/SN74S270	SN54S270/SN74S270
	SN54S201/SN74S201	SN54S201/SN74S201	93438	SN54S475/SN74S475	SN54S475/SN74S475
93425A	SN54S214/SN74S214	SN54S214/SN74S214	93446		SN54S472/SN74S472
93425	SN54S214/SN74S214	SN54S214/SN74S214	93448	SN54S474/SN74S474	SN54S474/SN74S474
93426	SN54S287/SN74S287	SN54S287/SN74S287	9600		SN54221/SN74221
93427	SN54S287/SN74S287	SN54S287/SN74S287	9601	SN29601	SN54122/SN74122
93433	SN83433, SN93433	SN5481A/SN7481A	9602		SN54123/SN74123
93434	SN5488A/SN7488A	SN5488A/SN7488A	9603	SN54121/SN74121	SN54221/SN74221
93435	SN7489	SN7489			

HARRIS

Example of Harris order code:

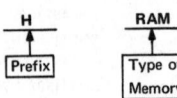 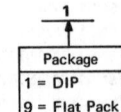 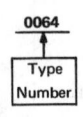 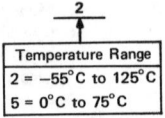 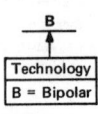 

H	**RAM**	**1**
Prefix	Type of Memory	Package 1 = DIP 9 = Flat Pack

0064	**2**	**B**
Type Number	Temperature Range 2 = −55°C to 125°C 5 = 0°C to 75°C	Technology B = Bipolar

HARRIS TYPE	TI DIRECT REPLACEMENT	RECOMMENDED FOR NEW DESIGNS	HARRIS TYPE	TI DIRECT REPLACEMENT	RECOMMENDED FOR NEW DESIGNS
M 7602	SN54S188/SN74S188	SN54S188/SN74S188	M 7640	SN54S475/SN74S475	SN54S475/SN74S475
M 7603	SN54S288/SN74S288	SN54S288/SN74S288	M 7641	SN54S474/SN74S474	SN54S474/SN74S474
M 7610	SN54S387/SN74S387	SN54S387/SN74S387	RAM 1-0064	SN7489	SN7489
M 7611	SN54S287/SN74S287	SN54S287/SN74S287	PROM 1-0512	SN54186/SN74186	SN54S470/SN74S470
		SN54S470/SN74S470	PROM 1-1024	SN54S287/SN74S287	SN54S287/SN74S287
M 7620		SN54S473/SN74S473	PROM 1-1024A	SN54S387/SN74S387	SN54S387/SN74S387
		SN54S471/SN74S471	ROM 1-1024	SN54187/SN74187	SN54187/SN74187
M 7621		SN54S472/SN74S472	PROM 1-8256	SN54S188/SN74S188	SN54S188/SN74S188

TEXAS INSTRUMENTS
INCORPORATED
POST OFFICE BOX 5012 • DALLAS, TEXAS 75222

INTEL

Example of Intel order code:

INTEL TYPE	TI DIRECT REPLACEMENT	RECOMMENDED FOR NEW DESIGNS	INTEL TYPE	TI DIRECT REPLACEMENT	RECOMMENDED FOR NEW DESIGNS
3101	SN54S289/SN74S289	SN54S289/SN74S289	3301A	SN54187/SN74187	SN54187/SN74187
3101A	SN54S289/SN74S289	SN54S289/SN74S289	3304		SN54S473/SN74S473
3102		SN54S200A/SN74S200A	3404A		SN54S373/SN74S373
3106A	SN54S200A/SN74S200A	SN54S200A/SN74S200A	3601	SN54S387/SN74S387	SN54S387/SN74S387
	SN54S201/SN74S201	SN54S201/SN74S201	3604	SN54S475/SN74S475	SN54S475/SN74S475
3107A	SN54S300A/SN74S300A	SN54S300A/SN74S300A	3621	SN54S287/SN74S287	SN54S287/SN74S287
	SN54S301/SN74S301	SN54S301/SN74S301	3624	SN54S474/SN74S474	SN54S474/SN74S474
3110	SN74S214, SN74S314	SN74S214/SN74S314	8212	SN54S412/SN74S412	SN54S412/SN74S412
3205		SN54S138/SN74S138	8224	SN74LS424 (TIM8224)	SN74LS424 (TIM8224)
3212	SN54S412/SN74S412	SN54S412/SN74S412	8228	SN74S428 (TIM8228)	SN74S428 (TIM8228)
			8338	SN74S438 (TIM8238)	SN74S438 (TIM8238)

INTERSIL

Example of Intersil ordering code:

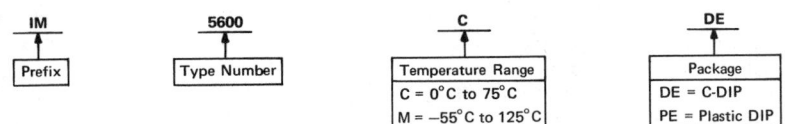

INTERSIL TYPE	TI DIRECT REPLACEMENT	RECOMMENDED FOR NEW DESIGNS	INTERSIL TYPE	TI DIRECT REPLACEMENT	RECOMMENDED FOR NEW DESIGNS
5501	SN54S289/SN74S289	SN54S289/SN74S289	5543	SN54S300A/SN74S300A	SN54S300A/SN74S300A
5502	SN5481A/SN7481A	SN5481A/SN7481A		SN54S301/SN74S301	SN54S301/SN74S301
5503	SN54S300A/SN74S300A	SN54S300A/SN74S300A	5553	SN54S200A/SN74S200A	SN54S200A/SN74S200A
	SN54S301/SN74S301	SN54S301/SN74S301	5600	SN54S188/SN74S188	SN54S188/SN74S188
5508	SN54S214/SN74S214	SN54S214/SN74S214	5602	SN54S475/SN74S475	SN54S475/SN74S475
	SN54S314/SN74S314	SN54S314/SN74S314	5603	SN54S387/SN74S387	SN54S387/SN74S387
55S08	SN54S314/SN74S314	SN54S314/SN74S314	5604		SN54S470/SN74S470
5512	SN5481A/SN7481A	SN5481A/SN7481A	5610	SN54S288/SN74S288	SN54S288/SN74S288
55S18	SN54S214/SN74S214	SN54S214/SN74S214	5623	SN54S287/SN74S287	SN54S287/SN74S287
5523	SN54S200A/SN74S200A	SN54S200A/SN74S200A	5624	SN54S370/SN74S370	SN54S370/SN74S370
	SN54S201/SN74S201	SN54S201/SN74S201	5625	SN54S474/SN74S474	SN54S474/SN74S474
5533	SN54S300A/SN74S300A	SN54S300A/SN74S300A			
	SN54S301/SN74S301	SN54S301/SN74S301			

MONOLITHIC MEMORIES

Example of Monolithic Memories ordering code:

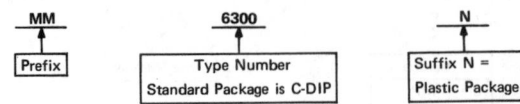

MONOLITHIC MEMORIES TYPE	TI DIRECT REPLACEMENT	RECOMMENDED FOR NEW DESIGNS	MONOLITHIC MEMORIES TYPE	TI DIRECT REPLACEMENT	RECOMMENDED FOR NEW DESIGNS
A5200		SN54S473/SN74S473	5335		SN54S470/SN74S470
A5240		SN54S473/SN74S473	5340	SN54S475/SN74S475	SN54S475/SN74S475
A5241		SN54S472/SN74S472	5341	SN54S474/SN74S474	SN54S474/SN74S474
A5280		SN54S473/SN74S473	5348	SN54S473/SN74S473	SN54S473/SN74S473
A5281		SN54S472/SN74S472	5349	SN54S472/SN74S472	SN54S472/SN74S472
A6240		SN54S473/SN74S473	5530	SN54S301/SN74S301	SN54S301/SN74S301
A6241		SN54S472/SN74S472	5531	SN54S201/SN74S201	SN54S201/SN74S201
A6280		SN54S473/SN74S473	5560	SN54S289/SN74S289	SN54S289/SN74S289
A6281		SN54S472/SN74S472	5561	SN54S189/SN74S189	SN54S189/SN74S189
H5200	SN54187/SN74187	SN54187/SN74187	6200	SN54187/SN74187	SN54187/SN74187
H5201	SN54S287/SN74S287	SN54S287/SN74S287	6201	SN54S387/SN74S387	SN54S387/SN74S387
H5240		SN54S473/SN74S473	6205	SN54S270/SN74S270	SN54S270/SN74S270
H5241		SN54S472/SN74S472	6206	SN54S370/SN74S370	SN54S370/SN74S370
H6200		SN54S473/SN74S473	6210		SN54S470/SN74S470
H6201	SN54S287/SN74S287	SN54S287/SN74S287	6225		SN54S473/SN74S473
H6240	'	SN54S473/SN74S473	6230	SN5488A/SN7488A	SN5488A/SN7488A
H6241		SN54S472/SN74S472	6231		SN54S473/SN74S473
5200	SN54187/SN74187	SN54187/SN74187	6235		SN54S470/SN74S470
5201	SN54S387/SN74S387	SN54S387/SN74S387	6260		SN54S473/SN74S473
5205	SN54S270/SN74S270	SN54S270/SN74S270	6300	SN54S387/SN74S387	SN54S387/SN74S387
5206	SN54S370/SN74S370	SN54S370/SN74S370	6301	SN54S287/SN74S287	SN54S287/SN74S287
5210		SN54S470/SN74S470	6305		SN54S470/SN74S470
5225		SN54S470/SN74S470	6306		SN54S471/SN74S471
5230	SN5488A/SN7488A	SN5488A/SN7488A	6308	SN54S470/SN74S470	SN54S470/SN74S470
5231	SN54S188A/SN74S188A	SN54S188A/SN74S188A	6309	SN54S471/SN74S471	SN54S471/SN74S471
5235		SN54S470/SN74S470	6330	SN54S188A/SN74S188A	SN54S188A/SN74S188A
5255		SN54S473/SN74S473	6331	SN54S288/SN74S288	SN54S288/SN74S288
5260		SN54S473/SN74S473	6335		SN54S470/SN74S470
5300	SN54S387/SN74S387	SN54S387/SN74S387	6340	SN54S475/SN74S475	SN54S475/SN74S475
5301	SN54S287/SN74S287	SN54S287/SN74S287	6341	SN54S474/SN74S474	SN54S474/SN74S474
5305	SN54S270/SN74S270	SN54S270/SN74S270	6348	SN54S473/SN74S473	SN54S473/SN74S473
5306	SN54S370/SN74S370	SN54S370/SN74S370	6349	SN54S472/SN74S472	SN54S472/SN74S472
5308	SN54S470/SN74S470	SN54S470/SN74S470	6530	SN54S301/SN74S301	SN54S301/SN74S301
5309	SN54S471/SN74S471	SN54S471/SN74S471	6531	SN54S201/SN74S201	SN54S201/SN74S201
5330	SN54S188A/SN74S188A	SN54S188A/SN74S188A	6560	SN54S289/SN74S289	SN54S289/SN74S289
5331	SN54S288/SN74S288	SN54S288/SN74S288	6561	SN54S189/SN74S189	SN54S189/SN74S189

MOTOROLA

Example of Motorola order code:

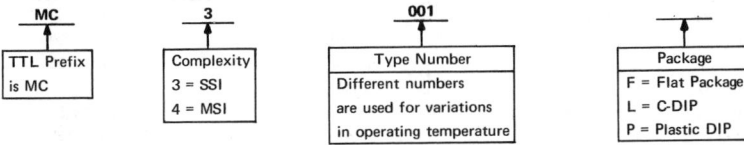

MC	**3**	**001**	
TTL Prefix is MC	Complexity 3 = SSI 4 = MSI	Type Number Different numbers are used for variations in operating temperature	Package F = Flat Package L = C-DIP P = Plastic DIP

MOTOROLA TYPE	TI DIRECT REPLACEMENT	RECOMMENDED FOR NEW DESIGNS	MOTOROLA TYPE	TI DIRECT REPLACEMENT	RECOMMENDED FOR NEW DESIGNS
MC3000	SN74H00	SN74S00	MC3107		SN54S15
MC3001	SN7408	SN74S11	MC3108	SN54H04	SN54S04
MC3002		SN74S02	MC3109	SN54H05	SN54S05
MC3003	SN7432	SN7432	MC3110	SN54H20	SN54S20
MC3004	SN74H01	SN74S03	MC3111	SN54H21	SN54S11
MC3005	SN74H10	SN74S10	MC3112	SN54H22	SN54S22
MC3006	SN74H11	SN74S11	MC3115		SN54S133, SN54S134
MC3007		SN74S15	MC3116	SN54H30	SN54S133
MC3008	SN74H04	SN74S04	MC3118	SN54H62	SN54S11
MC3009	SN74H05	SN74S05	MC3119	SN54H61	SN54S11
MC3010	SN74H20	SN74S20	MC3120	SN54H50	SN54S51
MC3011	SN74H21	SN74S11	MC3121	SN54S86	SN54S86
MC3012	SN74H22	SN74S22	MC3122		SN54S135
MC3015		SN74S133, SN74S134	MC3123	SN54H51	SN54S51
MC3016	SN74H30	SN74S133	MC3124	SN54H40	SN54S40
MC3018	SN74H62	SN74S11	MC3125	SN54H40	SN54S40
MC3019	SN74H61	SN74S11	MC3126		SN54S37, SN54S38
MC3020	SN74H50	SN74S51	MC3128		SN54S37, SN54S38
MC3021	SN74S86	SN74S86	MC3129		SN54S37, SN54S38
MC3022		SN74S135	MC3130	SN54H60	SN54S11
MC3023	SN74H51	SN74S51	MC3131	SN54H52	SN54S64
MC3024	SN74H40	SN74S40	MC3132	SN54H53	SN54S64
MC3025	SN74H40	SN74S40	MC3133	SN54H54	SN54S64
MC3026		SN74S140	MC3134	SN54H55	SN54S64
MC3028		SN74S240, SN74S241	MC3150		SN54S373, SN54S374
MC3029		SN74S240, SN74S241	MC3151		SN54S373, SN54S374
MC3030	SN74H60	SN74S11	MC3152		SN54S373, SN54S374
MC3031	SN74H52	SN74S64	MC3154	SN54H71	SN54S112
MC3032	SN74H53	SN74S64	MC3155	SN54H72	SN54S112
MC3033	SN74H54	SN74S64	MC3160	SN54H74	SN54S74
MC3034	SN74H55	SN74S64	MC3161	SN54S114	SN54S114
MC3050		SN74S373, SN74S374	MC3162	SN54S113	SN54S113
MC3051		SN74S373, SN74S374	MC3163	SN54H73	SN54S112
MC3052		SN74S373, SN74S374	MC4000		SN74S139
MC3053		SN74S374	MC4001		SN74184/SN74185A
MC3054	SN74H71	SN74S112	MC4002		SN74S139
MC3055	SN74H72	SN74S112	MC4004	SN7481A	SN7481A
MC3060	SN74H74	SN74S74	MC4005	SN7481A	SN7481A
MC3061	SN74S114	SN74S114	MC4006		SN74S138
MC3062	SN74S113	SN74S113	MC4007		SN74S139
MC3063	SN74H73	SN74S112	MC4008		SN74S280

MOTOROLA

MOTOROLA TYPE	TI DIRECT REPLACEMENT	RECOMMENDED FOR NEW DESIGNS	MOTOROLA TYPE	TI DIRECT REPLACEMENT	RECOMMENDED FOR NEW DESIGNS
MC3100	SN54H00	SN54S00	MC4010		SN74S135
MC3101	SN5408	SN54S11	MC4012		SN74S299
MC3102		SN54S02	MC4015		SN74S195
MC3103	SN5432	SN5432	MC4016		SN74S168
MC3104	SN54H01	SN54S03	MC4017		SN74S168
MC3105	SN54H10	SN54S10	MC4018		SN74S169
MC3106	SN54H11	SN54S11	MC4019		SN74S169
MC4021		SN74S85	MC4306		SN54S138
MC4022		SN74S85	MC4307		SN54S138, SN54S139
MC4023		SN74S260	MC4308		SN54S280
MC4025		SN74S124	MC4310		SN54S280
MC4026		SN74S381	MC4316		SN54S168
MC4027		SN74S381	MC4317		SN54S168
MC4028		SN74S281	MC4318		SN54S169
MC4029		SN74S281	MC4319		SN54S169
MC4029		SN74S281	MC4324		SN54S124
MC4030		SN74S281	MC4326		SN54S381
MC4031		SN74S281	MC4327		SN54S381
MC4032		SN74S182	MC4328		SN54S281
MC4035		SN74S373, SN74S374	MC4329		SN54S281, SN54S281
MC4037		SN74S373, SN74S374	MC4330		SN54S281, SN74S381
MC4038		SN74S138	MC4331		SN54S281
MC4039		SN74S143, SN74S144	MC4332		SN54S182
MC4040		SN74S139	MC4335		SN54S373, SN54S374
MC4042		SN74S240, SN74S241	MC4337		SN54S373, SN54S374
MC4043		SN74S240, SN74S241	MC4350		SN54143
MC4048		SN74S138	MC9310	SN54160	SN54160
MC4050		SN74143	MC9311	SN54154	SN54154
MC4051		SN74144	MC9316	SN54161	SN54161
MC4062		SN74S64	MCM4002	SN7488A	SN7488A
MC4300		SN54S139	MCM4004	SN7481A	SN7481A
MC4304	SN5481A	SN5481A	MCM4005	SN7481A	SN7481A
MC4305	SN5481A	SN5481A	MCM4006	SN74S387	SN74S387

NATIONAL

Example of National order code:

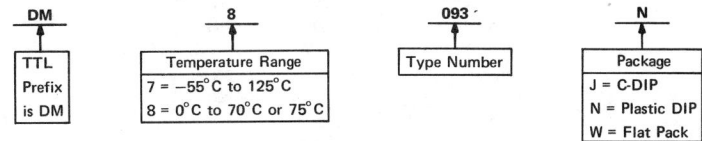

DM	8	093	N
TTL Prefix is DM	Temperature Range 7 = −55°C to 125°C 8 = 0°C to 70°C or 75°C	Type Number	Package J = C-DIP N = Plastic DIP W = Flat Pack

NATIONAL TYPE	TI DIRECT REPLACEMENT	RECOMMENDED FOR NEW DESIGNS	NATIONAL TYPE	TI DIRECT REPLACEMENT	RECOMMENDED FOR NEW DESIGNS
7091		SN5437	7553		SN54S163
7093	SN54125	SN54125	7554		SN54S373, SN54S374
7094	SN54126	SN54126	7555		SN54S168
7095	SN54365	SN54365	7556		SN54S169
7096	SN54366	SN54366	7560	SN54192	SN54192
7097	SN54367	SN54367	75L60	SN54L192	SN54L192
7098	SN54368	SN54368	7563	SN54193	SN54193
7121	SN54251	SN54251	75L63	SN54L193	SN54L193
71L22	SN54L157	SN54L157	7570	SN54164	SN54164
7123	SN54S257	SN54S257	7573	SN54S387	SN54S387
7130		SN54S85	7574	SN54S188	SN54S188
7131		SN54S85	7577	SN54S188	SN54S188
7136		SN5485	7578	SN54S288	SN54S288
7160		SN54S85	7582	SN54S301	SN54S301
7200		SN54S85	7588	SN54S188	SN54S188
7210		SN54151A, SN54351	7590	SN54165	SN54165
7211		SN54151A, SN54351	7594		SN54S200A
7213	SN54154	SN54154	7595	SN54S473	SN54S473
7214	SN54LS253	SN54LS253	7596		SN54S472
7219		SN54150	7597	SN54S287, SN54S370	SN54S287, SN54S370
7220		SN54S280	7598		SN54S471
7223		SN54S139	7599	SN54S189	SN54S189
7230		SN54S257	7600		SN54194
7280	SN54176	SN54176	7613		SN54376
7281	SN54177	SN54177	76L70	SN54L164	SN54L164
7283	SN5483A	SN5483A	7795		SN54S473
7288		SN5492A	7796		SN54S472
7290	SN54196	SN54196	7810	5426	5426
7291	SN54197	SN54197	7811		SN5426
7511		SN54376	7812	SN5416	SN5416
7512		SN54376	7819		SN54S240, SN54S241
7520		SN5497	7853		SN54221
7544		SN54265	7875A		SN54284
7551	SN54173	SN54173	7875B		SN54285
7552		SN54S162	8091		SN74240, SN74241
8093	SN74125	SN74125	8551	SN74173	SN74173
8094	SN74126	SN74126	8552		SN74S162
8095	SN74365	SN74365	8553		SN74S163
8096	SN74366	SN74366	8554		SN74S373, SN74S374
8097	SN74367	SN74367	8555		SN74S168
8098	SN74368	SN74368	8556		SN74S169

NATIONAL

NATIONAL TYPE	TI DIRECT REPLACEMENT	RECOMMENDED FOR NEW DESIGNS	NATIONAL TYPE	TI DIRECT REPLACEMENT	RECOMMENDED FOR NEW DESIGNS
8121	SN74251	SN74251	8560	SN74192	SN74192
81L22	SN74L157	SN74L157	85L60	SN74L192	SN74LS192
8123	SN74S257	SN74S257	8563	SN74193	SN74193
8130		SN74S85	85L63	SN74L193	SN74LS193
8131		SN74S85	8570	SN74164	SN74164
8136		SN7485	8573	SN74S387	SN74S387
8160		SN74S85	8574	SN74S287	SN74S287
8200		SN74S85	8577	SN74S188	SN74S188
8210		SN74151A, SN74351	8578	SN74S288	SN74S288
8211		SN74151A, SN74351	8579	SN74164	SN74164
8213	SN74154	SN74154	8580	SN7495A	SN7495A
8214	SN74LS253	SN74LS253	8582	SN74S301	SN74S301
8219		SN74150	8588	SN7488A	SN7488A
8220		SN74S280	8590	SN74165	SN74165
8223		SN74S139	8597	SN74S287, SN74S370	SN74S287, SN74S370
8230		SN74S257	8598		SN7488A
8280	SN74176	SN74176	8599	SN74S189	SN74S189
8281	SN74177	SN74177	8640	SN74141	SN74141
8283	SN7483A	SN7483A	86L70	SN74L164	SN74L164
8288		SN7492A	8810	SN7426	SN7426
8290	SN74196	SN74196	8811		SN7426
8291	SN74197	SN74197	8812		SN7416
8296	SN74196	SN74196	8819		SN7426
8500	SN7476	SN7476	8842	SN7442A	SN7442A
8501	SN7473	SN7473	8846	SN7446A	SN7446A
8510	SN7474	SN7474	8847	SN7447A	SN7447A
8511		SN74276	8848	SN7448	SN7448
8512		SN74276	8853		SN74221
8520		SN7497	8875A		SN74S274
8530	SN7490A	SN7490A	8875B		SN74S274
8532	SN7492A	SN7492A			
8533	SN7493A	SN7493A			
8544		SN74265			

SIGNETICS

Example of Signetics order code:

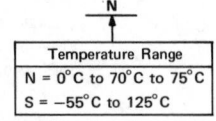

Temperature Range
N = 0°C to 70°C to 75°C
S = −55°C to 125°C

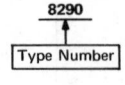

Type Number

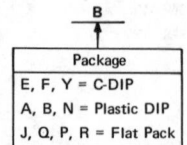

Package
E, F, Y = C-DIP
A, B, N = Plastic DIP
J, Q, P, R = Flat Pack

SIGNETICS TYPE	TI DIRECT REPLACEMENT	RECOMMENDED FOR NEW DESIGNS	SIGNETICS TYPE	TI DIRECT REPLACEMENT	RECOMMENDED FOR NEW DESIGNS
8H16		SN54S20/SN74S20	8201		SN54174/SN74174
8H20		SN54S112/SN74S112	8202		SN54174/SN74174
8H21		SN54S112/SN74S112	8203		SN54174/SN74174
8H22		SN54S112/SN74S112	8204		SN54S471/SN74S471
8H70	SN54H11/SN74H11	SN54S11/SN74S11	8205		SN54S472/SN74S472

SIGNETICS

SIGNETICS TYPE	TI DIRECT REPLACEMENT	RECOMMENDED FOR NEW DESIGNS
8H80	SN54H00/SN74H00	SN54S00/SN74S00
8H90	SN54H04/SN74H04	SN54S04/SN74S04
8T01		SN74141
8T04		SN547A/SN7447A
8T05		SN5448/SN7448
8T06		SN54143/SN74143
8T09		SN54128/SN74128
8T10	SN54173/SN74173	SN74173
8T13		SN54128/SN74128
8T18		SN5426/SN5426
8T20		SN54121/SN74121
8T22	SN54122/SN74122	SN54122/SN74122
8T23		SN54128/SN74128
8T24		
8T26		SN54125/SN74125
8T28		SN54S240/SN74S240
		SN54S241/SN74S241
8T51		SN54143/SN74143
		SN54144/SN74144
8T54		SN54143/SN74143
		SN54144/SN74144
8T59		SN54143/SN74143
		SN54144/SN74144
8T71		SN54143/SN74143
		SN54144/SN74144
8T74		SN54143/SN74143
		SN54144/SN74144
8T75		SN54143/SN74143
		SN54144/SN74144
8T79		SN54143/SN74143
		SN54144/SN74144
8T80		SN5426/SN7426
8T90		SN5406/SN7406
8T93		SN54125/SN74125
		SN54425/SN74425
8T94		SN54125/SN74125
		SN54425/SN74425
8T95		SN54365/SN74365
8T96		SN54366/SN74366
8T97		SN54367/SN74367
8T98		SN54368/SN74368
8162		SN54121/SN74121
8200		SN54174/SN74174
8260		SN54S281/SN74S281
8261		SN54S182/SN74S182
8262		SN54180/SN74180
82S63		SN54S280/SN74S280
8263		SN54153/SN74153
8264		SN54153/SN74153
8266		SN54157/SN74157
82S66		SN54S157/SN74S157

SIGNETICS TYPE	TI DIRECT REPLACEMENT	RECOMMENDED FOR NEW DESIGNS
8206	SN54S200A/SN74S200A	SN54S200A/SN74S200A
	SN54S201/SN74S201	SN54S201/SN74S201
82S06	SN54S200A/SN74S200A	SN54S200A/SN74S200A
	SN54S201/SN74S201	SN54S201/SN74S201
8207	SN54S300A/SN74S300A	SN54S300A/SN74S300A
	SN54S301/SN74S301	SN54S301/SN74S301
82S07	SN54S300A/SN74S300A	SN54S300A/SN74S300A
	SN54S301/SN74S301	SN54S301/SN74S301
82S08	SN54S314/SN74S314	SN54S314/SN74S314
82S10	SN54S314/SN74S314	SN54S314/SN74S314
82S11	SN54S214/SN74S214	SN54S214/SN74S214
82S16	SN54S200A/SN74S200A	SN54S200A/SN74S200A
	SN54S201/SN74S201	SN54S201/SN74S201
82S17	SN54S300A/SN74S300A	SN54S300A/SN74S300A
	SN54S301/SN74S301	SN54S301/SN74S301
8223	SN54S188/SN74S188	SN54S188/SN74S188
8224	SN5488A/SN7488A	SN5488A/SN7488A
8225	SN54S289/SN74S289	SN54S289/SN74S289
82S25	SN54S289/SN74S289	SN54S289/SN74S289
82S26	SN54S387/SN74S387	SN54S387/SN74S387
8228		SN54S471/SN74S471
82S29	SN54S287/SN74S287	SN54S287/SN74S287
8230	SN39312/SN29312	SN54151A/SN74151A
82S30		SN54S151A/SN74S151A
8231		SN54S251/SN74S251
82S31		SN54S151/SN74S151
8232		SN54151A/SN74151A
82S32		SN54S151/SN74S151
8233		SN54157/SN74157
82S33		SN54S157/SN74S157
8234		SN54S258/SN74S258
82S34		SN54S258/SN74S258
8235		SN4H87/SN74H87
8241		SN5486/SN7486
82S41		SN54S86/SN74S86
8242	SN54LS266/SN74LS266	SN54LS266/SN74LS266
82S42		SN54S135/SN74S135
8243		SN54198/SN74198
8250		SN5442A/SN7442A
82S50		SN54138/SN74138
8252	SN39301/SN29301	SN5442A/SN7442A
82S52		SN54S280/SN74S280
8255	SN54S289/SN74S289	SN54S289/SN74S289
82147	SN54147/SN74147	SN54147/SN74147
82148	SN54148/SN74148	SN54148/SN74148
8415		SN5420/SN7420
8416		SN5420/SN7420
8417		SN5410/SN7410
8424		SN54111/SN74111
8425		SN54111/SN74111
8440		SN5450/SN7450

2

SIGNETICS

SIGNETICS TYPE	TI DIRECT REPLACEMENT	RECOMMENDED FOR NEW DESIGNS	SIGNETICS TYPE	TI DIRECT REPLACEMENT	RECOMMENDED FOR NEW DESIGNS
8267		SN54157/SN74157	8455	SN5440/SN7440	SN5440/SN7440
8268	SN5480/SN7480	SN54181/SN74181	8470	SN5410/SN7410	SN5410/SN7410
8269		SN5485/SN7485	8471	SN5412/SN7412	SN5412/SN7412
8270	SN54178/SN74178	SN54194/SN74194	8480	SN5400/SN7400	SN5400/SN7400
82S70		SN54S299/SN74S299	8481	SN5403/SN7403	SN5403/SN7403
8271	SN54179/SN74179	SN54194/SN74194	8490	SN5404/SN7404	SN5404/SN7404
82S71		SN54S299/SN74S299	8706		SN5460/SN7460
8273		SN54198/SN74198	8731		SN5460/SN7460
8274		SN54198/SN74198	8806	SN5460/SN7460	SN5460/SN7460
8275		SN54174/SN74174	8808	SN5430/SN7430	SN5430/SN7430
8276		SN5491A/SN7491A	8815	SN5425/SN7425	SN5425/SN7425
8277		SN5491A/SN7491A	8816		SN5420/SN7420
8280	SN54176/SN74176	SN54176/SN74176	8821		SN5476/SN7476
8281	SN54177/SN74177	SN54177/SN74177	8822		SN54107/SN74107
8283		SN54S169/SN74S169	8824		SN5476/SN7476
8284		SN54S169/SN74S169	8825		SN5470/SN7470
8285		SN54S168/SN74S169	8826		SN54107/SN74107
8288		SN54163/SN74163	8827		SN5476/SN7476
8290	SN54196/SN74196	SN54196/SN74196	8828	SN5474/SN7474	SN5474/SN7474
82S90	SN54S196/SN74S196	SN54S196/SN74S196	8829	SN54110/SN74110	SN54110/SN74110
8291	SN54197/SN74197	SN54LS197/SN74LS197	8840	SN5450/SN7450	SN5450/SN7450
82S91	SN54S197/SN74S197	SN54S197/SN74S197	8848	SN54H54/SN74H74	SN54S64/SN74S64
8292	SN54LS196/SN74S196	SN54LS196/SN74LS196	8855		SN5440/SN7440
8293	SN54LS197/SN74LS197	SN54LS197/SN74LS197	8859	SN5450/SN7450	SN5450/SN7450
82S110	SN54S314/SN74S314	SN54S314/SN74S314	8870		SN5410/SN7410
82S111	SN54S214/SN74S214	SN54S214/SN74S214	8875	SN5427/SN7427	SN5427/SN7427
82S116	SN54S200A/SN74S200A	SN54S200A/SN74S200A	8879	SN5410/SN7410	SN5410/SN7410
	SN54S201/SN74S201	SN54S201/SN74S201	8880		SN5400/SN7400
82S117	SN54S300A/SN74S300A	SN54S300A/SN74S300A	8881	SN5401/SN7401	SN5401/SN7401
	SN54S301/SN74S301	SN54S301/SN74S301	8885		SN5402/SN7402
82S123	SN54S288/SN74S288	SN54S288/SN74S288	8889		SN5401/SN7401
82S124	SN54S387/SN74S387	SN54S387/SN74S387	8890	SN5404/SN7404	SN5404/SN7404
82S126	SN54S387/SN74S387	SN54S387/SN74S387	8891	SN5405/SN7405	SN5405/SN7405
82S129	SN54S287/SN74S287	SN54S287/SN74S287			
82S130	SN54170/SN74170	SN54170/SN74170			

2

General Information

3

Fuels and Combustion

INTRODUCTION

These symbols, terms, and definitions are in accordance with those currently agreed upon by the JEDEC Council of the Electronic Industries Association (EIA) for use in the USA and by the International Electrotechnical Commission (IEC) for international use.

PART I — OPERATING CONDITIONS AND CHARACTERISTICS (INCLUDING LETTER SYMBOLS)

Clock Frequency

Maximum clock frequency, f_{max}
The highest rate at which the clock input of a bistable circuit can be driven through its required sequence while maintaining stable transitions of logic level at the output with input conditions established that should cause changes of output logic level in accordance with the specification.

Current

High-level input current, I_{IH}
The current into* an input when a high-level voltage is applied to that input.

High-level output current, I_{OH}
The current into* an output with input conditions applied that according to the product specification will establish a high level at the output.

Low-level input current, I_{IL}
The current into* an input when a low-level voltage is applied to that input.

Low-level output current, I_{OL}
The current into* an output with input conditions applied that according to the product specification will establish a low level at the output.

Off-state output current, $I_{O(off)}$
The current flowing into* an output with input conditions applied that according to the product specification will cause the output switching element to be in the off state.

Note: This parameter is usually specified for open-collector outputs intended to drive devices other than logic circuits.

Off-state (high-impedance-state) output current (of a three-state output), I_{OZ}
The current into* an output having three-state capability with input conditions applied that according to the product specification will establish the high-impedance state at the output.

Short-circuit output current, I_{OS}
The current into* an output when that output is short-circuited to ground (or other specified potential) with input conditions applied to establish the output logic level farthest from ground potential (or other specified potential).

Supply current, I_{CC}
The current into* the V_{CC} supply terminal of an integrated circuit.

---

*Current out of a terminal is given as a negative value.

TEXAS INSTRUMENTS
INCORPORATED
POST OFFICE BOX 5012 • DALLAS, TEXAS 75222

GLOSSARY
TTL TERMS AND DEFINITIONS

Hold Time

Hold time, t_h
The interval during which a signal is retained at a specified input terminal after an active transition occurs at another specified input terminal.

NOTES: 1. The hold time is the actual time between two events and may be insufficient to accomplish the intended result. A minimum value is specified that is the shortest interval for which correct operation of the logic element is guaranteed.
2. The hold time may have a negative value in which case the minimum limit defines the longest interval (between the release of data and the active transition) for which correct operation of the logic element is guaranteed.

Output Enable and Disable Time

Output enable time (of a three-state output) to high level, t_{PZH} (or low level, t_{PZL})[†]
The propagation delay time between the specified reference points on the input and output voltage waveforms with the three-state output changing from a high-impedance (off) state to the defined high (or low) level.

Output enable time (of a three-state output) to high or low level, t_{PZX}[†]
The propagation delay time between the specified reference points on the input and output voltage waveforms with the three-state output changing from a high-impedance (off) state to either of the defined active levels (high or low).

Output disable time (of a three-state output) from high level, t_{PHZ} (or low level, t_{PLZ})[†]
The propagation delay time between the specified reference points on the input and output voltage waveforms with the three-state output changing from the defined high (or low) level to a high-impedance (off) state.

Output disable time (of a three-state output) from high or low level, t_{PXZ}[†]
The propagation delay time between the specified reference points on the input and output voltage waveforms with the three-state output changing from either of the defined active levels (high or low) to a high-impedance (off) state.

Propagation Time

Propagation delay time, t_{PD}
The time between the specified reference points on the input and output voltage waveforms with the output changing from one defined level (high or low) to the other defined level.

Propagation delay time, low-to-high-level output, t_{PLH}
The time between the specified reference points on the input and output voltage waveforms with the output changing from the defined low level to the defined high level.

Propagation delay time, high-to-low-level output, t_{PHL}
The time between the specified reference points on the input and output voltage waveforms with the output changing from the defined high level to the defined low level.

[†]On older data sheets, similar symbols without the P subscript were used; i.e. t_{ZH}, t_{ZL}, t_{HZ}, and t_{LZ}.

TEXAS INSTRUMENTS
INCORPORATED
POST OFFICE BOX 5012 • DALLAS, TEXAS 75222

Pulse Width

Pulse width, t_W
The time interval between specified reference points on the leading and trailing edges of the pulse waveform.

Recovery Time

Sense recovery time, t_{SR}
The time interval needed to switch a memory from a write mode to a read mode and to obtain valid data signals at the output.

Release Time

Release time, $t_{release}$
The time interval between the release from a specified input terminal of data intended to be recognized and the occurrence of an active transition at another specified input terminal.

Note: When specified, the interval designated "release time" falls within the setup interval and constitutes, in effect, a negative hold time.

Setup Time

Setup time, t_{su}
The time interval between the application of a signal that is maintained at a specified input terminal and a consecutive active transition at another specified input terminal.

NOTES: 1. The setup time is the actual time between two events and may be insufficient to accomplish the setup. A minimum value is specified that is the shortest interval for which correct operation of the logic element is guaranteed.
2. The setup time may have a negative value in which case the minimum limit defines the longest interval (between the active transition and the application of the other signal) for which correct operation of the logic element is guaranteed.

Transition Time

Transition time, low-to-high-level, t_{TLH}
The time between a specified low-level voltage and a specified high-level voltage on a waveform that is changing from the defined low level to the defined high level.

Transition time, high-to-low-level, t_{THL}
The time between a specified high-level voltage and a specified low-level voltage on a waveform that is changing from the defined high level to the defined low level.

TEXAS INSTRUMENTS
INCORPORATED
POST OFFICE BOX 5012 • DALLAS, TEXAS 75222

GLOSSARY
TTL TERMS AND DEFINITIONS

Voltage

High-level input voltage, V_{IH}
An input voltage within the more positive (less negative) of the two ranges of values used to represent the binary variables.
NOTE: A minimum is specified that is the least positive value of high-level input voltage for which operation of the logic element within specification limits is guaranteed.

High-level output voltage, V_{OH}
The voltage at an output terminal with input conditions applied that according to the product specification will establish a high level at the output.

Input clamp voltage, V_{IK}
An input voltage in a region of relatively low differential resistance that serves to limit the input voltage swing.

Low-level input voltage, V_{IL}
An input voltage level within the less positive (more negative) of the two ranges of values used to represent the binary variables.
NOTE: A maximum is specified that is the most positive value of low-level input voltage for which operation of the logic element within specification limits is guaranteed.

Low-level output voltage, V_{OL}
The voltage at an output terminal with input conditions applied that according to the product specification will establish a low level at the output.

Negative-going threshold voltage, V_{T-}
The voltage level at a transition-operated input that causes operation of the logic element according to specification as the input voltage falls from a level above the positive-going threshold voltage, V_{T+}.

Off-state output voltage, $V_{O(off)}$
The voltage at an output terminal with input conditions applied that according to the product specification will cause the output switching element to be in the off state.

Note: This characteristic is usually specified only for outputs not having internal pull-up elements.

On-state output voltage, $V_{O(on)}$
The voltage at an output terminal with input conditions applied that according to the product specification will cause the output switching element to be in the on state.

Note: This characteristic is usually specified only for outputs not having internal pull-up elements.

Positive-going threshold voltage, V_{T+}
The voltage level at a transition-operated input that causes operation of the logic element according to specification as the input voltage rises from a level below the negative-going threshold voltage, V_{T-}.

TEXAS INSTRUMENTS
INCORPORATED
POST OFFICE BOX 5012 • DALLAS, TEXAS 75222

PART II – CLASSIFICATION OF CIRCUIT COMPLEXITY

Gate Equivalent Circuit

A basic unit-of-measure of relative digital-circuit complexity. The number of gate equivalent circuits is that number of individual logic gates that would have to be interconnected to perform the same function.

Large-Scale Integration, LSI

A concept whereby a complete major subsystem or system function is fabricated as a single microcircuit. In this context a major subsystem or system, whether digital or linear, is considered to be one that contains 100 or more equivalent gates or circuitry of similar complexity.

Medium-Scale Integration, MSI

A concept whereby a complete subsystem or system function is fabricated as a single microcircuit. The subsystem or system is smaller than for LSI, but whether digital or linear, is considered to be one that contains 12 or more equivalent gates or circuitry of similar complexity.

Small-Scale Integration, SSI

Integrated circuits of less complexity than medium-scale integration (MSI).

Very-Large-Scale Integration, VLSI

A concept whereby a complete system function is fabricated as a single microcircuit. In this context, a system, whether digital or linear, is considered to be one that contains 1000 or more gates or circuitry of similar complexity.

3

TEXAS INSTRUMENTS
INCORPORATED
POST OFFICE BOX 5012 • DALLAS, TEXAS 75222

EXPLANATION OF FUNCTION TABLES

The following symbols are now being used in function tables on TI data sheets:

H	=	high level (steady state)
L	=	low level (steady state)
↑	=	transition from low to high level
↓	=	transition from high to low level
X	=	irrelevant (any input, including transitions)
Z	=	off (high-impedance) state of a 3-state output
a..h	=	the level of steady-state inputs at inputs A through H respectively
Q_0	=	level of Q before the indicated steady-state input conditions were establsihed
$\overline{Q}_0$	=	complement of Q_0 or level of $\overline{Q}$ before the indicated steady-state input conditions were established
Q_n	=	level of Q before the most recent active transition indicated by ↓ or ↑
⊓	=	one high-level pulse
⊔	=	one low-level pulse
TOGGLE	=	each output changes to the complement of its previous level on each active transition indicated by ↓ or ↑.

If, in the input columns, a row contains only the symbols H, L, and/or X, this means the indicated output is valid whenever the input configuration is achieved and regardless of the sequence in which it is achieved. The output persists so long as the input configuration is maintained.

If, in the input columns, a row contains H, L, and/or X together with ↑ and/or ↓, this means the output is valid whenever the input configuration is achieved but the transition(s) must occur following the achievement of the steady-state levels. If the output is shown as a level (H, L, Q_0, or $\overline{Q}_0$), it persists so long as the steady-state input levels and the levels that terminate indicated transitions are maintained. Unless otherwise indicated, input transitions in the opposite direction to those shown have no effect at the output. (If the output is shown as a pulse, ⊓ or ⊔, the pulse follows the indicated input transition and persists for an interval dependent on the circuit.)

TEXAS INSTRUMENTS
INCORPORATED
POST OFFICE BOX 5012 • DALLAS, TEXAS 75222

Among the most complex function tables in this book are those of the shift registers. These embody most of the symbols used in any of the function tables, plus more. Below is the function table of a 4-bit bidirectional universal shift register, e.g., type SN74194.

FUNCTION TABLE

| CLEAR | MODE | | CLOCK | SERIAL | | PARALLEL | | | | OUTPUTS | | | |
	S1	S0		LEFT	RIGHT	A	B	C	D	Q_A	Q_B	Q_C	Q_D
L	X	X	X	X	X	X	X	X	X	L	L	L	L
H	X	X	L	X	X	X	X	X	X	Q_{A0}	Q_{B0}	Q_{C0}	Q_{D0}
H	H	H	↑	X	X	a	b	c	d	a	b	c	d
H	L	H	↑	X	H	X	X	X	X	H	Q_{An}	Q_{Bn}	Q_{Cn}
H	L	H	↑	X	L	X	X	X	X	L	Q_{An}	Q_{Bn}	Q_{Cn}
H	H	L	↑	H	X	X	X	X	X	Q_{Bn}	Q_{Cn}	Q_{Dn}	H
H	H	L	↑	L	X	X	X	X	X	Q_{Bn}	Q_{Cn}	Q_{Dn}	L
H	L	L	X	X	X	X	X	X	X	Q_{A0}	Q_{B0}	Q_{C0}	Q_{D0}

The first line of the table represents a synchronous clearing of the register and says that if clear is low, all four outputs will be reset low regardless of the other inputs. In the following lines, clear is inactive (high) and so has no effect.

The second line shows that so long as the clock input remains low (while clear is high), no other input has any effect and the outputs maintain the levels they assumed before the steady-state combination of clear high and clock low was established. Since on other lines of the table only the rising transition of the clock is shown to be active, the second line implicitly shows that no further change in the outputs will occur while the clock remains high or on the high-to-low transition of the clock.

The third line of the table represents synchronous parallel loading of the register and says that if S1 and S0 are both high then, without regard to the serial input, the data entered at A will be at output Q_A, data entered at B will be at Q_B, and so forth, following a low-to-high clock transition.

The fourth and fifth lines represent the loading of high- and low-level data, respectively, from the shift-right serial input and the shifting of previously entered data one bit; data previously at Q_A is now at Q_B, the previous levels of Q_B and Q_C are now at Q_C and Q_D respectively, and the data previously at Q_D is no longer in the register. This entry of serial data and shift takes place on the low-to-high transition of the clock when S1 is low and S0 is high and the levels at inputs A through D have no effect.

The sixth and seventh lines represent the loading of high- and low-level data, respectively, from the shift-left serial input and the shifting of previously entered data one bit; data previously at Q_B is now at Q_A, the previous levels of Q_C and Q_D are now at Q_B and Q_C, respectively, and the data previously at Q_A is no longer in the register. This entry of serial data and shift takes place on the low-to-high transition of the clock when S1 is high and S0 is low and the levels at inputs A through D have no effect.

The last line shows that as long as both mode inputs are low, no other input has any effect and, as in the second line, the outputs maintain the levels they assumed before the steady-state combination of clear high and both mode inputs low was established.

SERIES 54/74, 54H/74H, 54S/74S, AND SPECIFIED† SERIES 54L/74L DEVICES

PARAMETER MEASUREMENT INFORMATION

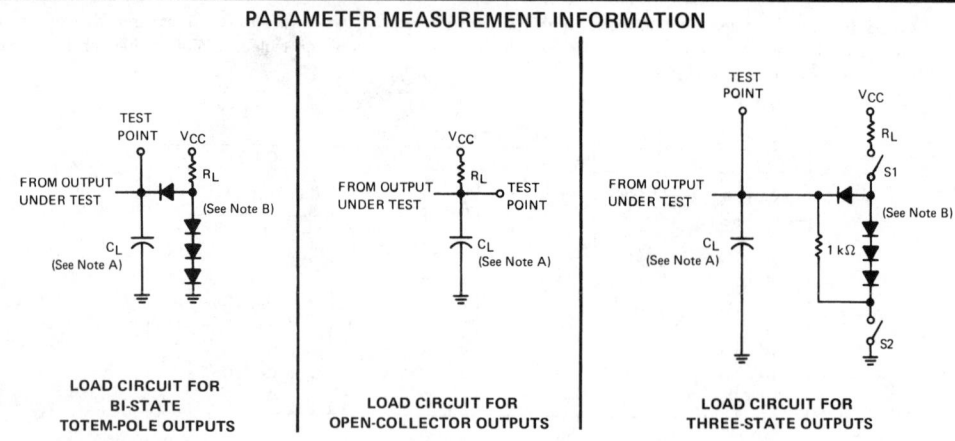

LOAD CIRCUIT FOR BI-STATE TOTEM-POLE OUTPUTS

LOAD CIRCUIT FOR OPEN-COLLECTOR OUTPUTS

LOAD CIRCUIT FOR THREE-STATE OUTPUTS

NOTES. A. C_L includes probe and jig capacitance.
B. All diodes are 1N916 or 1N3064.

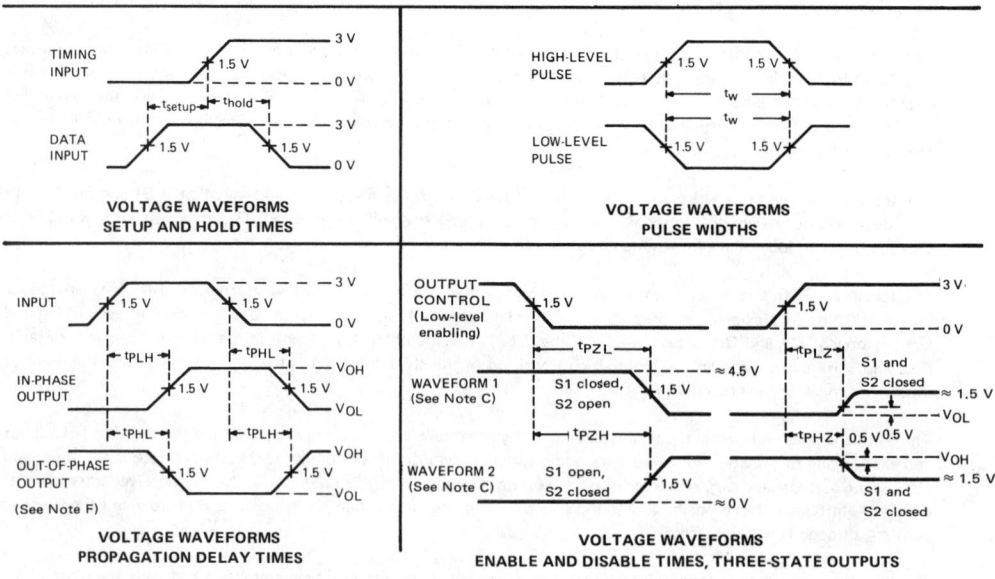

VOLTAGE WAVEFORMS SETUP AND HOLD TIMES

VOLTAGE WAVEFORMS PULSE WIDTHS

VOLTAGE WAVEFORMS PROPAGATION DELAY TIMES

VOLTAGE WAVEFORMS ENABLE AND DISABLE TIMES, THREE-STATE OUTPUTS

NOTES: C. Waveform 1 is for an output with internal conditions such that the output is low except when disabled by the output control.
Waveform 2 is for an output with internal conditions such that the output is high except when disabled by the output control.
D. In the examples above, the phase relationships between inputs and outputs have been chosen arbitrarily.
E. All input pulses are supplied by generators having the following characteristics: PRR ≤ 1 MHz, Z_{out} ≈ 50 Ω and:
For Series 54/74 and 54H/74H, t_r ≤ 7 ns, t_f ≤ 7 ns;
For Specified† Series 54L/74L devices: t_r ≤ 10 ns, t_f ≤ 10 ns;
For Series 54S/74S, t_r ≤ 2.5 ns, t_f ≤ 2.5 ns.
F. When measuring propagation delay times of 3-state outputs, switches S1 and S2 are closed.

†'L42, 'L43, 'L44, 'L46, 'L47, 'L75, 'L77, 'L96, 'L121, 'L122, 'L123, 'L153, 'L154, 'L157, 'L164

TEXAS INSTRUMENTS
INCORPORATED
POST OFFICE BOX 5012 • DALLAS, TEXAS 75222

PARAMETER MEASUREMENT INFORMATION

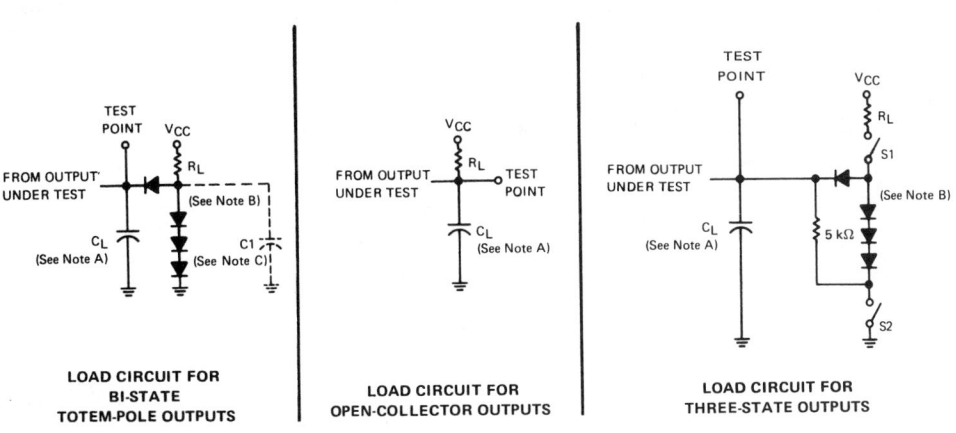

LOAD CIRCUIT FOR
BI-STATE
TOTEM-POLE OUTPUTS

LOAD CIRCUIT FOR
OPEN-COLLECTOR OUTPUTS

LOAD CIRCUIT FOR
THREE-STATE OUTPUTS

NOTES   A. C_L includes probe and jig capacitance.
B. All diodes are 1N916 or 1N3064.
C. C1 (30 pF) is used for testing Series 54L/74L devices only.

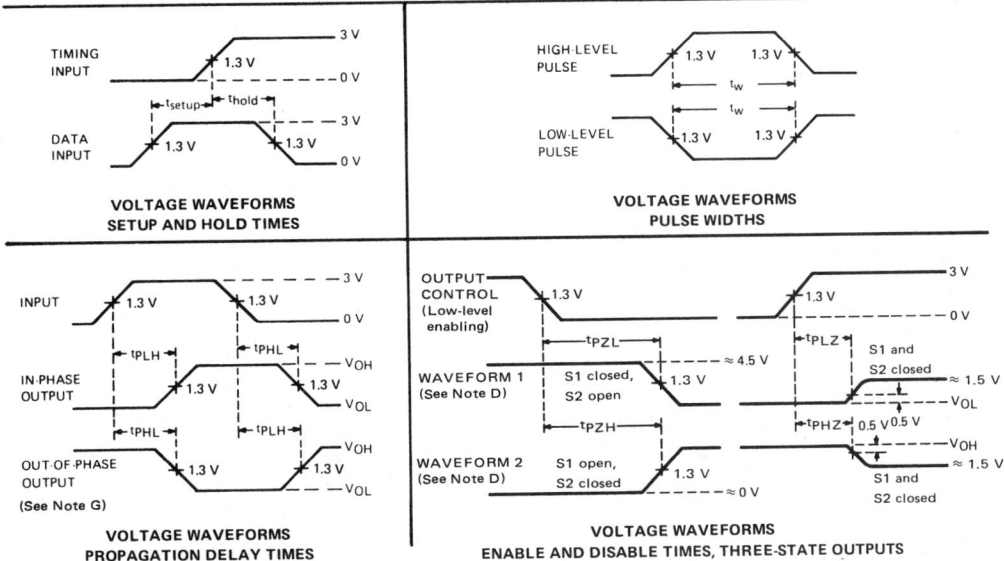

VOLTAGE WAVEFORMS
SETUP AND HOLD TIMES

VOLTAGE WAVEFORMS
PULSE WIDTHS

VOLTAGE WAVEFORMS
PROPAGATION DELAY TIMES

VOLTAGE WAVEFORMS
ENABLE AND DISABLE TIMES, THREE-STATE OUTPUTS

NOTES: D. Waveform 1 is for an output with internal conditions such that the output is low except when disabled by the output control.
Waveform 2 is for an output with internal conditions such that the output is high except when disabled by the output control.
E. In the examples above, the phase relationships between inputs and outputs have been chosen arbitrarily.
F. All input pulses are supplied by generators having the following characteristics: PRR ≤ 1 MHz, Z_{out} ≈ 50 Ω and:
For Series 54L/74L gates and inverters, t_r = 60 ns, t_f = 60 ns;
For Series 54L/74L flip-flops and MSI, t_r ≤ 25 ns, t_f ≤ 25 ns;
For Series 54LS/74LS, t_r ≤ 15 ns, t_f ≤ 6 ns.
G. When measuring propagation delay times of 3-state outputs, switches S1 and S2 are closed.

†Except 'L42, 'L43, 'L44, 'L46, 'L47, 'L75, 'L77, 'L96, 'L121, 'L122, 'L123, 'L153, 'L154, 'L157, 'L164

Ordering Instructions
and
Mechanical Data

4

4

TTL INTEGRATED CIRCUITS MECHANICAL DATA

ORDERING INSTRUCTIONS

Electrical characteristics presented in this data book, unless otherwise noted, apply for circuit type(s) listed in the page heading regardless of package. The availability of a circuit function in a particular package is denoted by an alphabetical reference above the pin-connection diagram(s). These alphabetical references refer to mechanical outline drawings shown in this section.

Factory orders for circuits described in this catalog should include a four-part type number as explained in the following example.

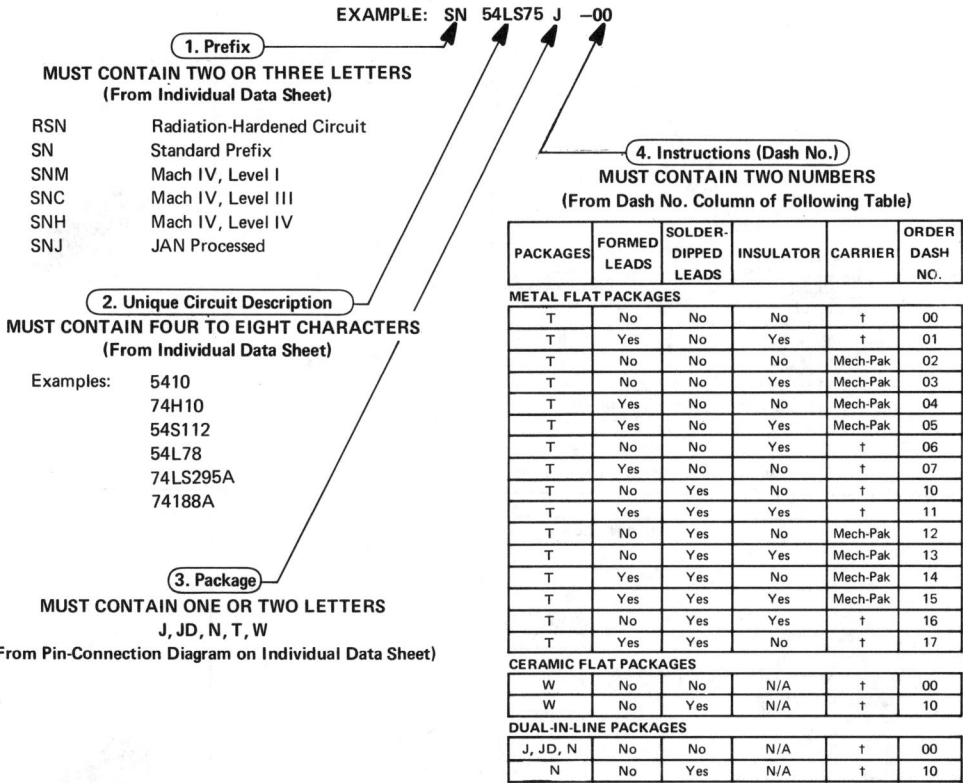

EXAMPLE: SN 54LS75 J −00

1. Prefix

MUST CONTAIN TWO OR THREE LETTERS
(From Individual Data Sheet)

RSN	Radiation-Hardened Circuit
SN	Standard Prefix
SNM	Mach IV, Level I
SNC	Mach IV, Level III
SNH	Mach IV, Level IV
SNJ	JAN Processed

2. Unique Circuit Description

MUST CONTAIN FOUR TO EIGHT CHARACTERS
(From Individual Data Sheet)

Examples: 5410
74H10
54S112
54L78
74LS295A
74188A

3. Package

MUST CONTAIN ONE OR TWO LETTERS
J, JD, N, T, W
(From Pin-Connection Diagram on Individual Data Sheet)

4. Instructions (Dash No.)

MUST CONTAIN TWO NUMBERS
(From Dash No. Column of Following Table)

PACKAGES	FORMED LEADS	SOLDER-DIPPED LEADS	INSULATOR	CARRIER	ORDER DASH NO.
METAL FLAT PACKAGES					
T	No	No	No	†	00
T	Yes	No	Yes	†	01
T	No	No	No	Mech-Pak	02
T	No	No	Yes	Mech-Pak	03
T	Yes	No	No	Mech-Pak	04
T	Yes	No	Yes	Mech-Pak	05
T	No	No	Yes	†	06
T	Yes	No	No	†	07
T	No	Yes	No	†	10
T	Yes	Yes	Yes	†	11
T	No	Yes	No	Mech-Pak	12
T	No	Yes	Yes	Mech-Pak	13
T	Yes	Yes	No	Mech-Pak	14
T	Yes	Yes	Yes	Mech-Pak	15
T	No	Yes	Yes	†	16
T	Yes	Yes	No	†	17
CERAMIC FLAT PACKAGES					
W	No	No	N/A	†	00
W	No	Yes	N/A	†	10
DUAL-IN-LINE PACKAGES					
J, JD, N	No	No	N/A	†	00
N	No	Yes	N/A	†	10

†These circuits are shipped in one of the carriers shown below. Unless a specific method of shipment is specified by the customer (with possible additional posts), circuits will be shipped in the most practical carrier. Please contact your TI sales representative for the method that will best suit your particular needs.

Flat (T, W)	Dual-in-line ((J, JD, N)
—Barnes Carrier	—Slide Magazines
—Milton Ross Carrier	—A-Channel Plastic Tubing
	—Barnes Carrier (N only)
	—Sectioned Cardboard Box
	—Individual Plastic Box

TEXAS INSTRUMENTS
INCORPORATED
POST OFFICE BOX 5012 • DALLAS, TEXAS 75222

TTL INTEGRATED CIRCUITS MECHANICAL DATA

J ceramic dual-in-line package

These hermetically sealed dual-in-line packages consist of a ceramic base, ceramic cap, and a 14-, 16-, 20-, or 24-lead frame. Hermetic sealing is accomplished with glass. The packages are intended for insertion in mounting-hole rows on 0.300 (7,62) or 0.600 (15,24) centers. Once the leads are compressed and inserted, sufficient tension is provided to secure the package in the board during soldering. Tin-plated ("bright-dipped") leads (−00) require no additional cleaning or processing when used in soldered assembly.

14-PIN J CERAMIC

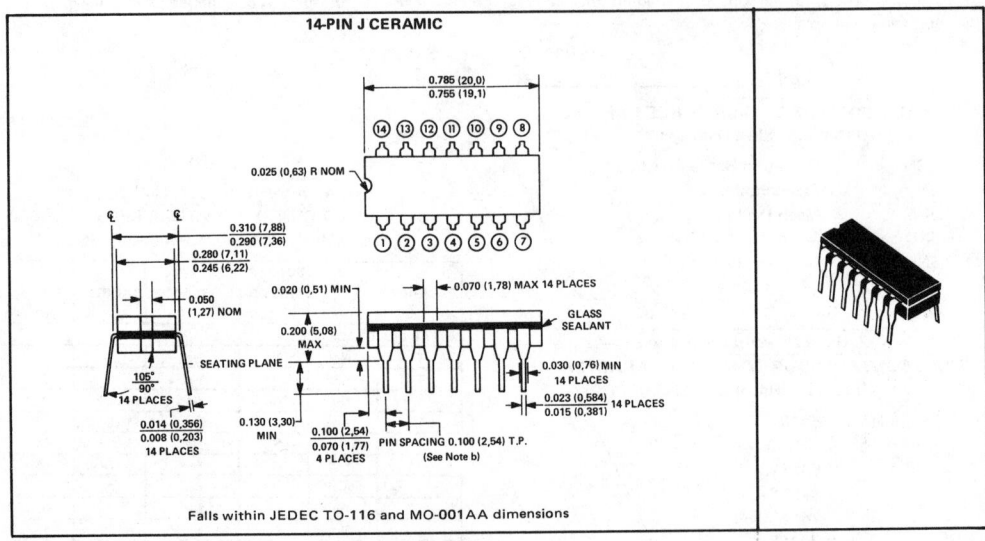

Falls within JEDEC TO-116 and MO-001AA dimensions

16-PIN J CERAMIC

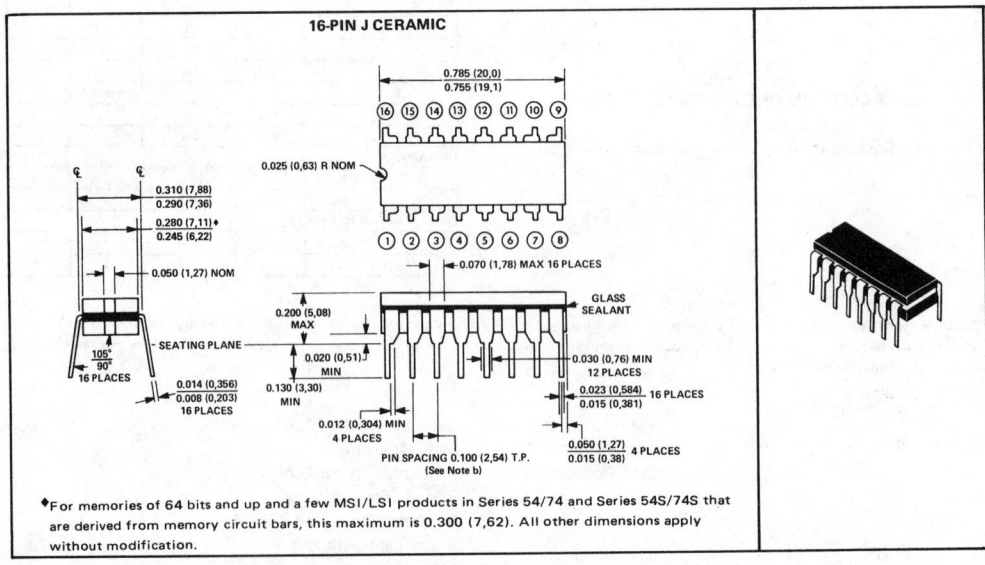

♦For memories of 64 bits and up and a few MSI/LSI products in Series 54/74 and Series 54S/74S that are derived from memory circuit bars, this maximum is 0.300 (7,62). All other dimensions apply without modification.

TEXAS INSTRUMENTS
INCORPORATED
POST OFFICE BOX 5012 • DALLAS, TEXAS 75222

J ceramic dual-in-line packages (continued)

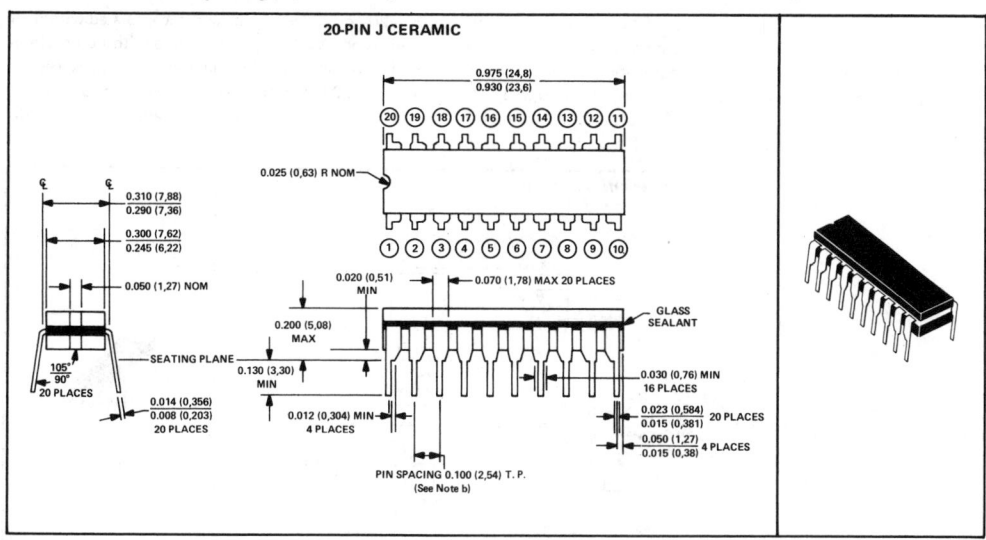

20-PIN J CERAMIC

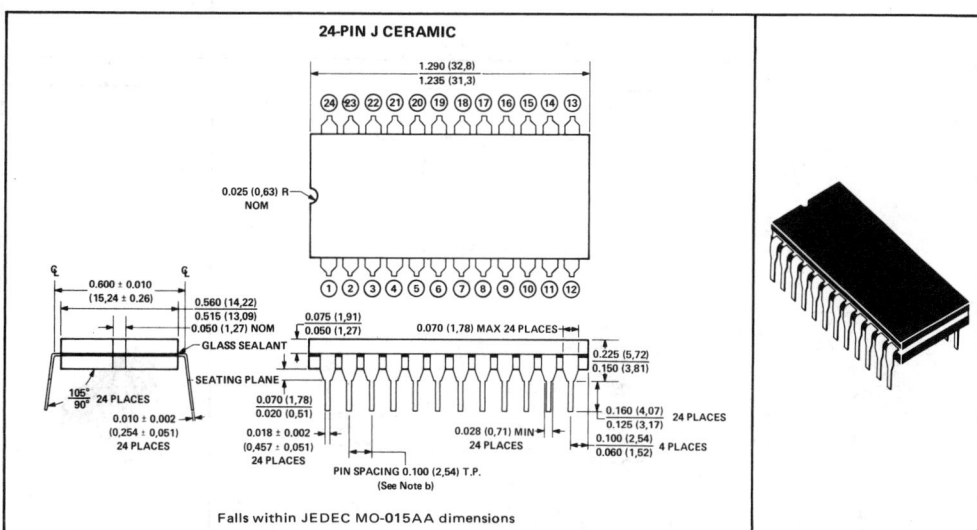

24-PIN J CERAMIC

Falls within JEDEC MO-015AA dimensions

NOTES: a. All dimensions are shown in inches (and parenthetically in millimeters for reference only). Inch dimensions govern.

b. Each pin centerline is located within 0.010 (0,26) of its true longitudinal position.

TEXAS INSTRUMENTS
INCORPORATED
POST OFFICE BOX 5012 • DALLAS, TEXAS 75222

TTL INTEGRATED CIRCUITS MECHANICAL DATA

N plastic dual-in-line packages

These dual-in-line packages consist of a circuit mounted on a 14-, 16-, 20-, or 28-lead frame and encapsulated within an electrically nonconductive plastic compound. The compound will withstand soldering temperature with no deformation and circuit performance characteristics remain stable when operated in high-humidity conditions. The packages are intended for insertion in mounting hole rows on 0.300 (7,62) or 0.600 (15,24) centers. Once the leads are compressed and inserted, sufficient tension is provided to secure the package in the board during soldering. Leads require no additional cleaning or processing when used in soldered assembly.

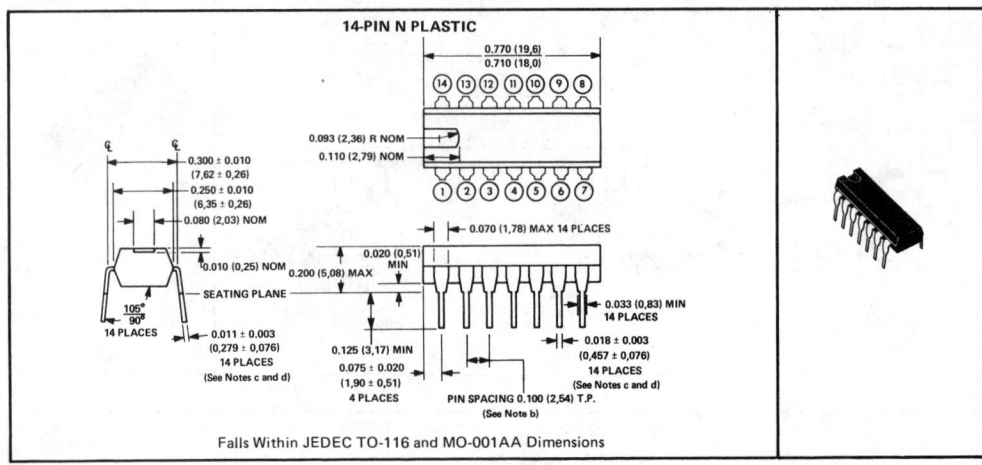

14-PIN N PLASTIC

Falls Within JEDEC TO-116 and MO-001AA Dimensions

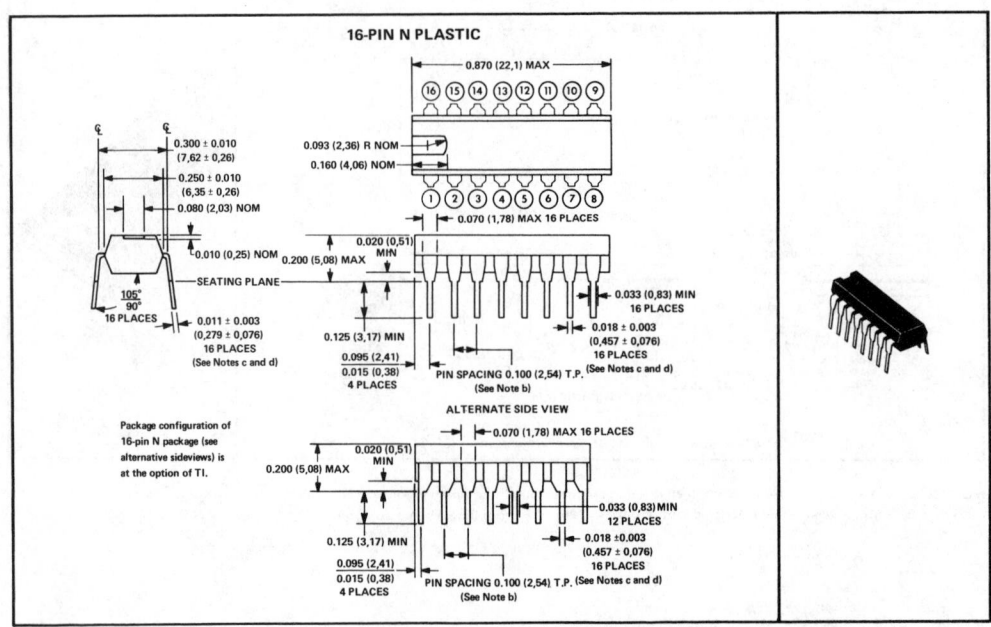

16-PIN N PLASTIC

TEXAS INSTRUMENTS
INCORPORATED
POST OFFICE BOX 5012 • DALLAS, TEXAS 75222

N plastic dual-in-line packages (continued)

20-PIN N PLASTIC

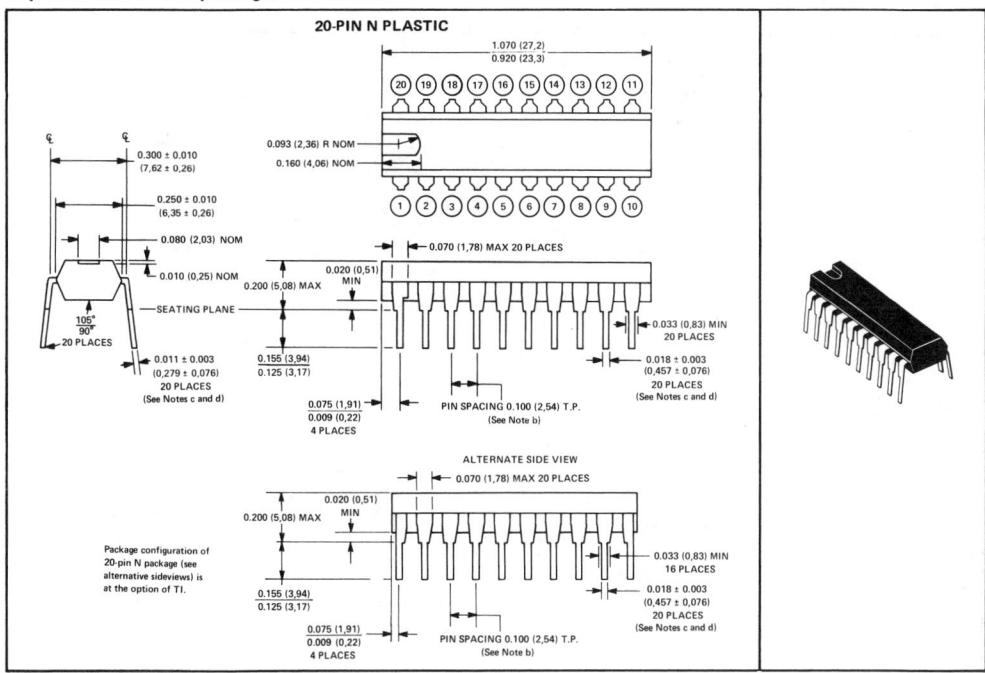

24-PIN N PLASTIC

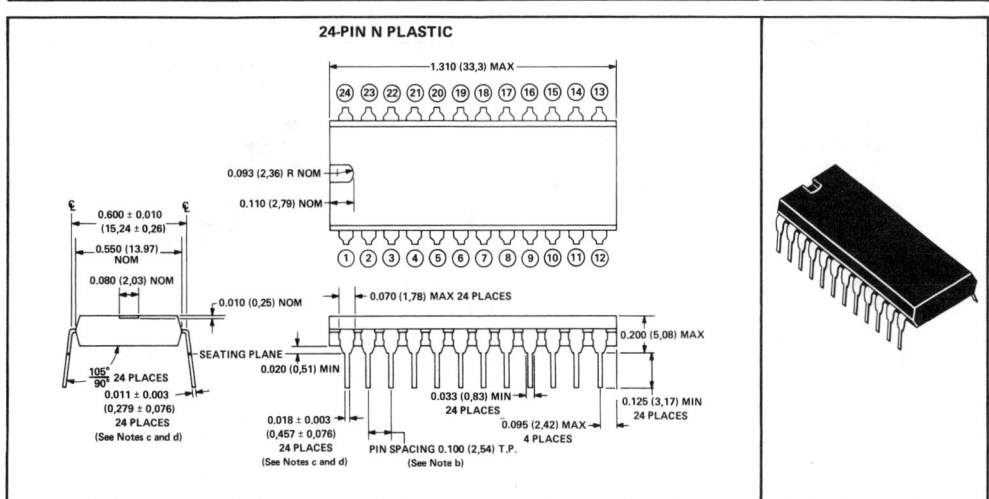

NOTES: a. All dimensions are shown in inches (and parenthetically in millimeters for reference only). Inch dimensions govern.

b. Each pin centerline is located within 0.010 (0,26) of its true longitudinal position.

c. This dimension does not apply for solder-dipped leads.

d. When solder-dipped leads are specified, dipped area of the lead extends from the lead tip to at least 0.020 (0,50) above the seating plane.

TTL INTEGRATED CIRCUITS MECHANICAL DATA

N plastic dual-in-line packages (continued)

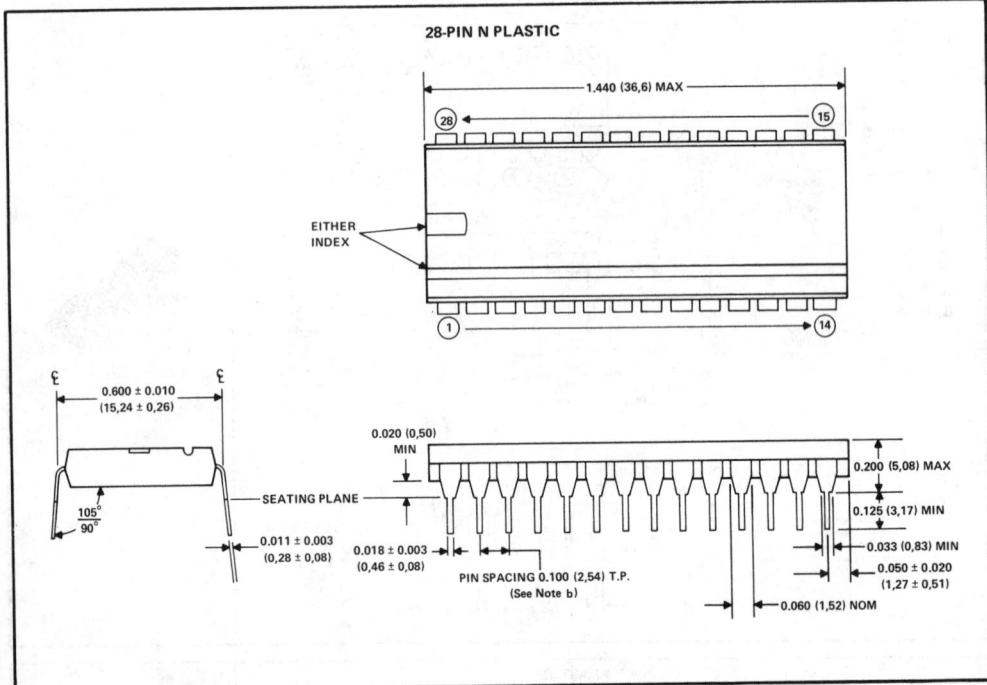

28-PIN N PLASTIC

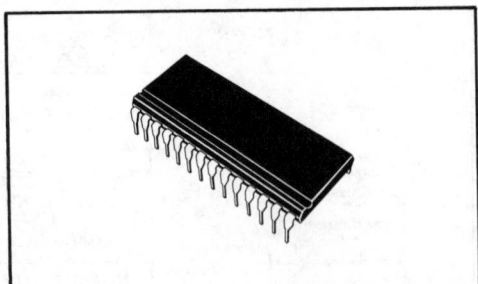

NOTES: a. All dimensions are shown in inches (and parenthetically in millimeters for reference only). Inch dimensions govern.
b. Each pin centerline is located within 0.010 (0,26) of its true longitudinal position.
c. This dimension does not apply for solder-dipped leads.
d. When solder-dipped leads are specified, dipped area of the lead extends from the lead tip to at least 0.020 (0,50) above the seating plane.

TEXAS INSTRUMENTS
INCORPORATED
POST OFFICE BOX 5012 • DALLAS, TEXAS 75222

TTL INTEGRATED CIRCUITS MECHANICAL DATA

T flat package

This hermetic package features glass-to-metal seals and welded construction. Package body and leads are gold-plated F-15 ≠ glass-sealing alloy. Approximate weight is 0.1 gram.

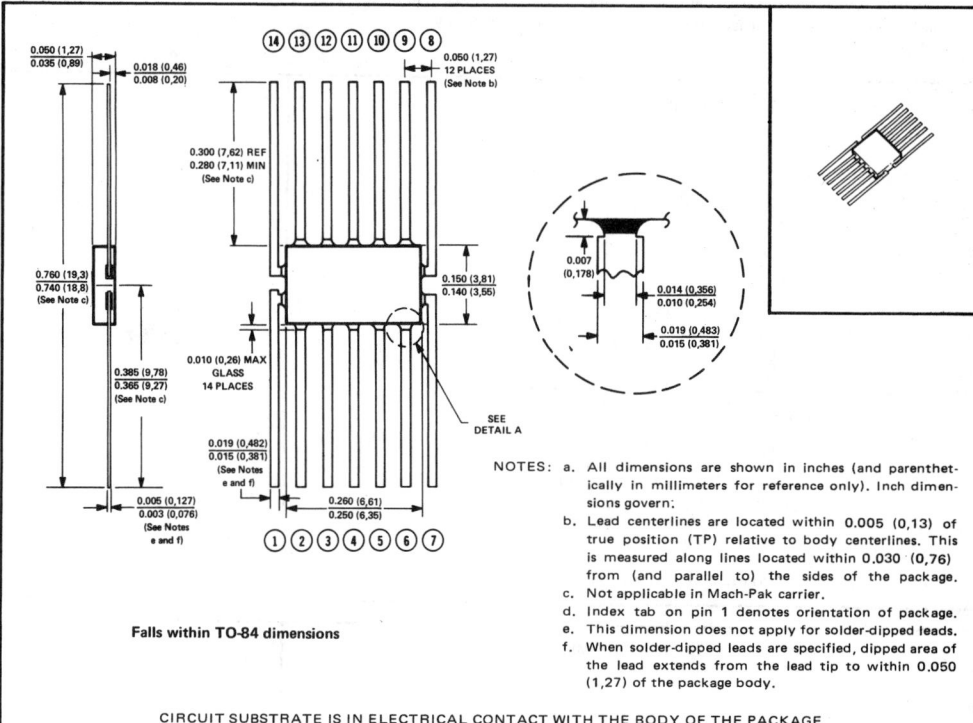

Falls within TO-84 dimensions

NOTES: a. All dimensions are shown in inches (and parenthetically in millimeters for reference only). Inch dimensions govern.
      b. Lead centerlines are located within 0.005 (0,13) of true position (TP) relative to body centerlines. This is measured along lines located within 0.030 (0,76) from (and parallel to) the sides of the package.
      c. Not applicable in Mach-Pak carrier.
      d. Index tab on pin 1 denotes orientation of package.
      e. This dimension does not apply for solder-dipped leads.
      f. When solder-dipped leads are specified, dipped area of the lead extends from the lead tip to within 0.050 (1,27) of the package body.

CIRCUIT SUBSTRATE IS IN ELECTRICAL CONTACT WITH THE BODY OF THE PACKAGE.

T package leads

Gold-plated F-15‡ leads require no additional cleaning or processing when used in soldered or welded assembly. Solder-dipped leads are also available. Formed leads are available to facilitate planar mounting of networks on flat circuit boards. Circuits can be removed from Mach-Pak carriers with lead lengths up to 0.300 (7,62).

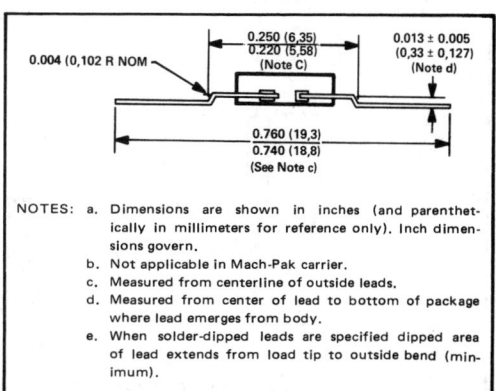

NOTES: a. Dimensions are shown in inches (and parenthetically in millimeters for reference only). Inch dimensions govern.
      b. Not applicable in Mach-Pak carrier.
      c. Measured from centerline of outside leads.
      d. Measured from center of lead to bottom of package where lead emerges from body.
      e. When solder-dipped leads are specified dipped area of lead extends from load tip to outside bend (minimum).

‡F-15 is the ASTM designation for an iron-nickel-cobalt alloy containing nominally 53% iron, 29% nickel, and 17% cobalt.

TEXAS INSTRUMENTS
INCORPORATED
POST OFFICE BOX 5012 • DALLAS, TEXAS 75222

TTL INTEGRATED CIRCUITS MECHANICAL DATA

W ceramic flat package

These hermetically sealed flat packages consist of an electrically nonconductive ceramic base and cap, and a 14-, 16-, or 24-lead frame. Hermetic sealing is accomplished with glass. Tin-plated ("bright-dipped") leads (−00) require no additional cleaning or processing when used in soldered assembly.

14 PIN W CERAMIC

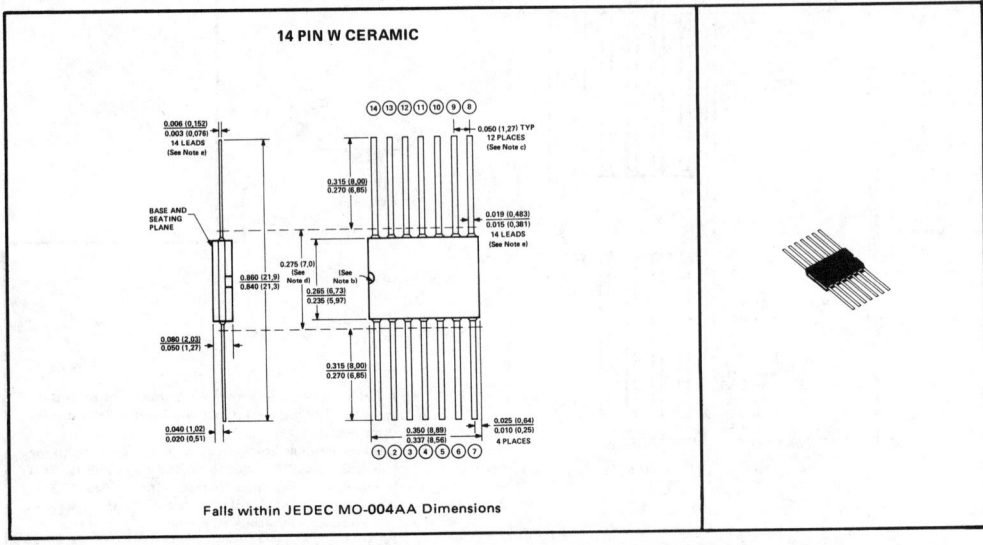

Falls within JEDEC MO-004AA Dimensions

16 PIN W CERAMIC

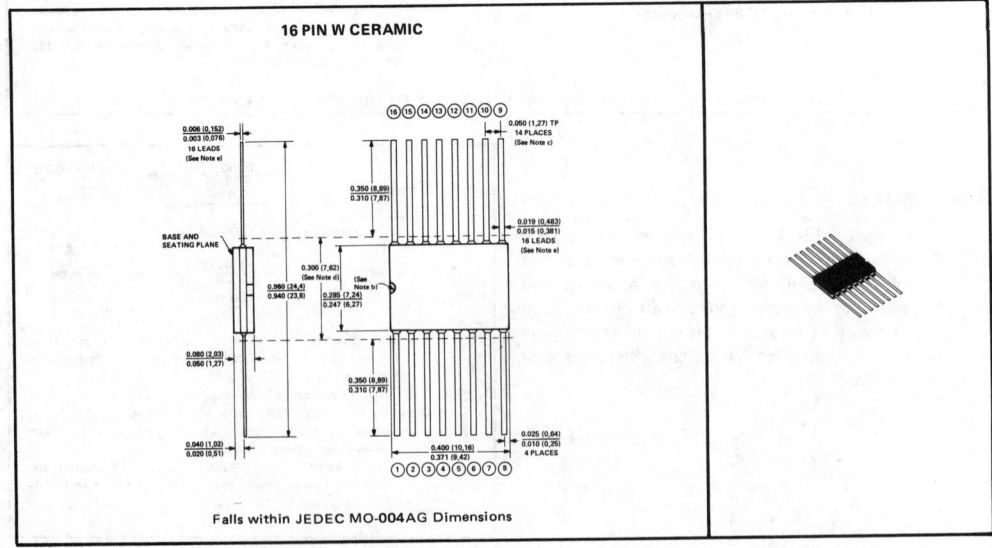

Falls within JEDEC MO-004AG Dimensions

TEXAS INSTRUMENTS
INCORPORATED
POST OFFICE BOX 5012 • DALLAS, TEXAS 75222

W ceramic flat package (continued)

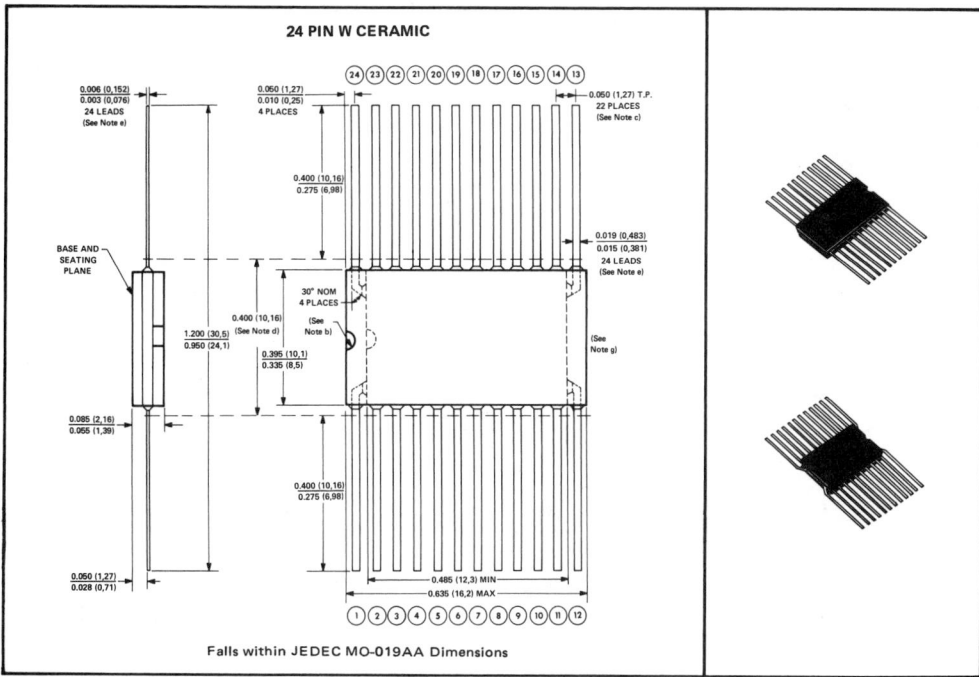

24 PIN W CERAMIC

Falls within JEDEC MO-019AA Dimensions

NOTES: a. All dimensions are shown in inches (and parenthetically in millimeters for reference only). Inch dimensions govern.

b. Index point is provided on cap for terminal identification only.

c. Leads are within 0.005 (0,13) radius of true position (T.P.) at maximum material condition.

d. This dimension determines a zone within which all body and lead irregularities lie.

e. Not applicable for solder-dipped leads.

f. When solder-dipped leads are specified, dipped area extends from lead tip to within 0.050 (1,27) of package body.

g. End configuration of 24-pin package is at the option of TI.

TEXAS INSTRUMENTS
INCORPORATED
POST OFFICE BOX 5012 • DALLAS, TEXAS 75222

54/74 Families
of Compatible
TTL Circuits

description

Texas Instruments transistor-transistor-logic (TTL) family of high-performance bipolar digital integrated circuits comprises five distinct series of compatible product lines. These product lines offer the digital systems designer a full spectrum of performance ranges in order to optimize system cost and performance. The available choices range from the very high performance of the Schottky-clamped[†] functions for systems operating typically up to 125 megahertz to low-power functions with power consumption of only one milliwatt per gate.

Typical characteristics of the five TTL series offered are shown in Table I and their respective speed/power relationships are illustrated in Figure A.

SPEED-POWER RELATIONSHIPS
OF DIGITAL IC FAMILIES‡

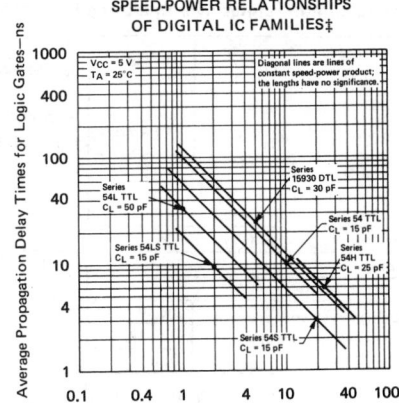

‡Typical saturated logic gate from the indicated families.

FIGURE A

TABLE I—54/74 FAMILY TYPICAL SSI PERFORMANCE CHARACTERISTICS

SERIES	GATES			FLIP-FLOPS
	Speed-Power Product	Propagation Delay Time	Power Dissipation	Clock Input Frequency Range
54LS/74LS	19 pJ	9.5 ns	2 mW	dc to 45 MHz
54L/74L	33 pJ	33 ns	1 mW	dc to 3 MHz
54S/74S	57 pJ	3 ns	19 mW	dc to 125 MHz
54/74	100 pJ	10 ns	10 mW	dc to 35 MHz
54H/74H	132 pJ	6 ns	22 mW	dc to 50 MHz

features

EASE OF SYSTEM DESIGN

- Full compatibility provides choice from five distinct performance ranges
- Broad range of functions are offered in each series
- Diode-clamped inputs are provided on all high-performance functions
- Terminated,controlled-impedance lines are not normally required with TTL
- Low output impedance:
  Provides low a-c noise susceptibility
  Drives high-capacity loads

FULL COMPATIBILITY IS DESIGNED INTO TI TTL

- All series are designed for single 5-volt power supply
- All series provide one-volt or greater typical d-c noise margins
- Power dissipation relatively insensitive to operating frequency
- Switching times are guaranteed at full d-c loading
- Compatible with most logic families such as DTL, MOS, CMOS

†Integrated Schottky-Barrier diode-clamped transistor is patented by Texas Instruments. U.S. Patent Number 3,463,975.

TEXAS INSTRUMENTS
INCORPORATED
POST OFFICE BOX 5012 • DALLAS, TEXAS 75222

54/74 FAMILIES OF COMPATIBLE TTL CIRCUITS

absolute maximum ratings over operating free-air temperature range (unless otherwise noted)

		SERIES 54 SERIES 54H	SERIES 54L	SERIES 54LS	SERIES 54LS	SERIES 54S	
	74 FAMILY	SERIES 74 SERIES 74H	SERIES 74L	SERIES 74LS WITH DIODE INPUTS	SERIES 74LS WITH EMITTER INPUTS	SERIES 74S	UNIT
Supply voltage, V$_{CC}$ (see Note 1)		7	8	7	7	7	V
Input voltage		5.5	5.5	7	5.5	5.5	V
Interemitter voltage (see Note 2)		5.5	5.5		5.5	5.5	V
Off-state (high-level) voltage applied	'06, '07	30					
to open-collector outputs of SSI	'16, '17, '26	15					V
circuits (see Note 3)	Others		8	7	7	7	
High-level voltage applied to a disabled 3-state output		5.5		5.5	5.5	5.5	V
Operating free-air temperature range	54 Family	−55 to 125					°C
	74 Family	0 to 70					
Storage temperature range		−65 to 150					°C

NOTES: 1. Voltage values, unless otherwise noted, are with respect to network ground terminal.
  2. This is the voltage between two emitters of a multiple-emitter transistor. This rating applies between inputs that go directly into the same AND or NAND gate in the functional block diagram.
  3. Ratings for MSI parts are given on the individual data sheets.

unused inputs of positive-AND/NAND gates

For optimum switching times and minimum noise susceptibility, unused inputs of AND or NAND gates should be maintained at a voltage greater than V$_{OH}$ min (see tables of electrical characteristics), but not to exceed the absolute maximum rating. This eliminates the distributed capacitance associated with the floating input, bond wire, and package lead, and ensures that no degradation will occur in the propagation delay times. Some possible ways of handling unused inputs are:

a. Connect unused inputs to an independent supply voltage. Preferably, this voltage should be between V$_{OH}$ min and 4.5 V. Series 54LS/74LS devices with diode inputs may be connected directly to V$_{CC}$.

b. Connect unused inputs to a used input if maximum drive capability of the driving output will not be exceeded. Each additional input presents a full load to the driving output at a high-level voltage but adds no loading at a low-level voltage.

c. Connect unused inputs to V$_{CC}$ through a 1-kΩ resistor so that if a transient that exceeds the input maximum rating should occur, the impedance will be high enough to protect the input. One to 25 unused inputs may be connected to each 1-kΩ resistor. Series 54LS/74LS devices with diode inputs may be connected directly to V$_{CC}$.

d. Connect unused inputs to any fixed-high-level compatible output such as the output of an inverter or NAND gate that has its input(s) grounded. Maximum high-level drive capability of the output should not be exceeded.

TEXAS INSTRUMENTS
INCORPORATED
POST OFFICE BOX 5012 • DALLAS, TEXAS 75222

input-current requirements

Input-current requirements reflect worst-case conditions over the specified recommended operating free-air temperature and V_{CC} ranges. The table below shows maximum input current requirements and nominal base resistor values for standard loads in each TTL series. A standard load is defined as an input connected to a single emitter or diode that is associated with a pull-up resistor having the value indicated in the table. However, some inputs are tied to more than one input transistor (or diode), or the base-resistor values of some inputs have been changed either to reduce input-current requirements or to improve performance. Therefore, the input-current requirements may vary. Consult the electrical characteristics table for the particular device type to determine the input-current requirements of each input.

STANDARD INPUTS (ONE LOAD)

SERIES	NOMINAL VALUE OF INPUT PULL-UP RESISTOR	MAXIMUM HIGH-LEVEL INPUT CURRENT	MAXIMUM LOW-LEVEL INPUT CURRENT
54/74	4 kΩ	40 μA	−1.6 mA
54H/74H	2.8 kΩ	50 μA	−2 mA
54L/74L‡	40 kΩ	10 μA	−0.18 mA
	8 kΩ	20 μA	−0.8 mA
54LS/74LS	18kΩ	20 μA	−0.4 mA
54S/74S	2.8 kΩ	50 μA	−2 mA

‡Series 54L/74L has two different types of standard inputs as shown.

Since low-level input current is primarily a function of the input base resistor, two or more inputs of the same NAND or AND gate may be tied together and still be considered one load at a low logic level, but at a high logic level, each input is an additional load.

Currents into input terminals are specified as positive values. Arrows on the d-c test circuits indicate the actual direction of current flow.

drive capability

The maximum value of I_{OL} given under "recommended operating conditions" reflects the ability of an output to sink current from a number of loads at a low voltage level and maximum I_{OH} reflects the ability to supply current at a high voltage level. Each standard output at a low level is capable of sinking current from 10 standard loads of its own series (20 standard loads for Series 74L and 74LS), and at a high level is capable of supplying current to either 10 or 20 loads of its own series. The fan-out of 20 at a high logic level makes it possible to tie as many as 10 unused inputs of NAND or AND gates to used inputs of the same gates (as mentioned under input-current requirements) without exceeding the fan-out capability of the output driving 10 used inputs. Certain outputs are designed for special applications and have greater or lesser drive capability. See the recommended operating conditions for each type.

The loads may be intermixed in any desired combination so long as the load totals for I_{IH} and I_{IL} are less than the maximum recommended values of I_{OH} and I_{OL}, respectively, for the driving circuit.

5

TEXAS INSTRUMENTS
INCORPORATED
POST OFFICE BOX 5012 • DALLAS, TEXAS 75222

54/74 FAMILIES OF COMPATIBLE TTL CIRCUITS

PIN ASSIGNMENTS (TOP VIEWS)

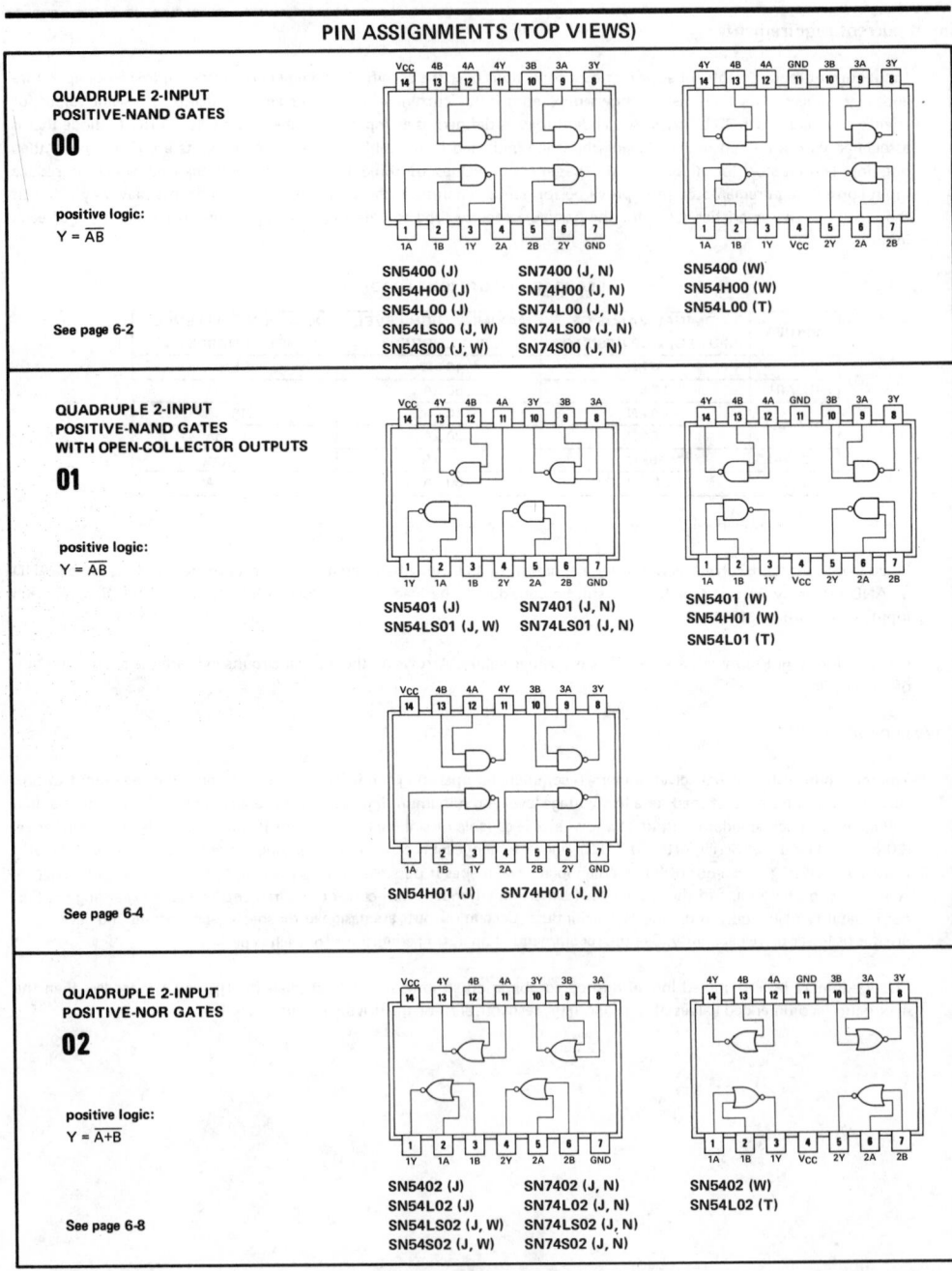

QUADRUPLE 2-INPUT POSITIVE-NAND GATES

00

positive logic:
$Y = \overline{AB}$

See page 6-2

SN5400 (J)   SN7400 (J, N)   SN5400 (W)
SN54H00 (J)   SN74H00 (J, N)   SN54H00 (W)
SN54L00 (J)   SN74L00 (J, N)   SN54L00 (T)
SN54LS00 (J, W) SN74LS00 (J, N)
SN54S00 (J, W)   SN74S00 (J, N)

QUADRUPLE 2-INPUT POSITIVE-NAND GATES WITH OPEN-COLLECTOR OUTPUTS

01

positive logic:
$Y = \overline{AB}$

SN5401 (J)   SN7401 (J, N)   SN5401 (W)
SN54LS01 (J, W) SN74LS01 (J, N) SN54H01 (W)
                                  SN54L01 (T)

SN54H01 (J)   SN74H01 (J, N)

See page 6-4

QUADRUPLE 2-INPUT POSITIVE-NOR GATES

02

positive logic:
$Y = \overline{A+B}$

See page 6-8

SN5402 (J)   SN7402 (J, N)   SN5402 (W)
SN54L02 (J)   SN74L02 (J, N)   SN54L02 (T)
SN54LS02 (J, W) SN74LS02 (J, N)
SN54S02 (J, W)   SN74S02 (J, N)

5

TEXAS INSTRUMENTS
INCORPORATED
POST OFFICE BOX 5012 • DALLAS, TEXAS 75222

PIN ASSIGNMENTS (TOP VIEWS)

QUADRUPLE 2-INPUT
POSITIVE-NAND GATES
WITH OPEN-COLLECTOR OUTPUTS

03

positive logic:
$Y = \overline{AB}$

See page 6-4

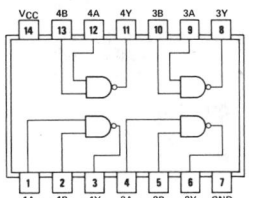

SN5403 (J)   SN7403 (J, N)
SN54L03 (J)   SN74L03 (J, N)
SN54LS03 (J, W)   SN74LS03 (J, N)
SN54S03 (J, W)   SN74S03 (J, N)

HEX INVERTERS

04

positive logic:
$Y = \overline{A}$

See page 6-2

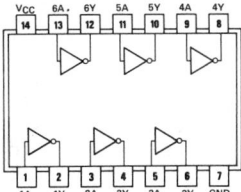

SN5404 (J)   SN7404 (J, N)
SN54H04 (J)   SN74H04 (J, N)
SN54L04 (J)   SN74L04 (J, N)
SN54LS04 (J, W)   SN74LS04 (J, N)
SN54S04 (J, W)   SN74S04 (J, N)

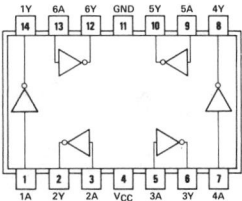

SN5404 (W)
SN54H04 (W)
SN54L04 (T)

HEX INVERTERS
WITH OPEN-COLLECTOR OUTPUTS

05

positive logic:
$Y = \overline{A}$

See page 6-4

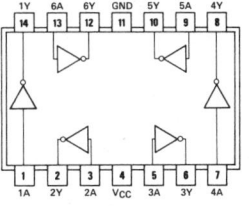

SN5405 (J)   SN7405 (J, N)
SN54H05 (J)   SN74H05 (J, N)
SN54LS05 (J, W)   SN74LS05 (J, N)
SN54S05 (J, W)   SN74S05 (J, N)

SN5405 (W)
SN54H05 (W)

HEX INVERTER BUFFERS/DRIVERS
WITH OPEN-COLLECTOR
HIGH-VOLTAGE OUTPUTS

06

positive logic:
$Y = \overline{A}$

See page 6-24

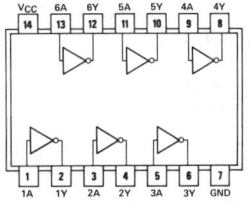

SN5406 (J, W)   SN7406 (J, N)

TEXAS INSTRUMENTS
INCORPORATED
POST OFFICE BOX 5012 • DALLAS, TEXAS 75222

5

PIN ASSIGNMENTS (TOP VIEWS)

**HEX BUFFERS/DRIVERS
WITH OPEN-COLLECTOR
HIGH-VOLTAGE OUTPUTS**

07

positive logic:

Y = A

See page 6-24

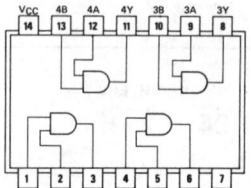

SN5407 (J, W)   SN7407 (J, N)

**QUADRUPLE 2-INPUT
POSITIVE-AND GATES**

08

positive logic:

Y = AB

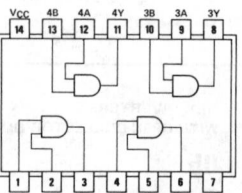

SN5408 (J, W)   SN7408 (J, N)
SN54LS08 (J, W)   SN74LS08 (J, N)
SN54S08 (J, W)   SN74S08 (J, N)

See page 6-10

**QUADRUPLE 2-INPUT
POSITIVE-AND GATES
WITH OPEN-COLLECTOR OUTPUTS**

09

positive logic:

Y = AB

SN5409 (J, W)   SN7409 (J, N)
SN54LS09 (J, W)   SN74LS09 (J, N)
SN54S09 (J, W)   SN74S09 (J, N)

See page 6-12

**TRIPLE 3-INPUT
POSITIVE-NAND GATES**

10

positive logic:

Y = $\overline{ABC}$

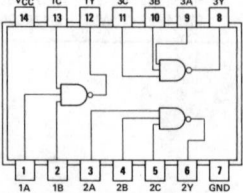 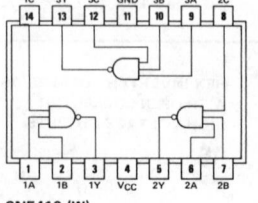

SN5410 (J)   SN7410 (J, N)   SN5410 (W)
SN54H10 (J)   SN74H10 (J, N)   SN54H10 (W)
SN54L10 (J)   SN74L10 (J, N)   SN54L10 (T)
SN54LS10 (J, W)   SN74LS10 (J, N)
SN54S10 (J, W)   SN74S10 (J, N)

See page 6-2

TEXAS INSTRUMENTS
INCORPORATED
POST OFFICE BOX 5012 • DALLAS, TEXAS 75222

PIN ASSIGNMENTS (TOP VIEWS)

TRIPLE 3-INPUT POSITIVE-AND GATES

11

positive logic:

Y = ABC

See page 6-10

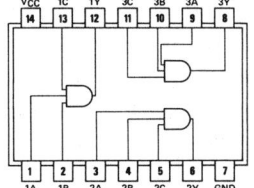

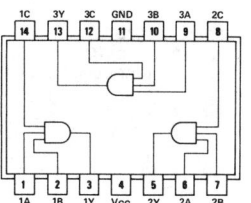

SN54H11 (J)   SN74H11 (J, N)   SN54H11 (W)
SN54LS11 (J, W) SN74LS11 (J, N)
SN54S11 (J, W)   SN74S11 (J, N)

TRIPLE 3-INPUT POSITIVE-NAND GATES WITH OPEN-COLLECTOR OUTPUTS

12

positive logic:

Y = $\overline{ABC}$

See page 6-4

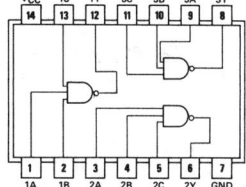

SN5412 (J, W)   SN7412 (J, N)
SN54LS12 (J, W)   SN74LS12 (J, N)

DUAL 4-INPUT POSITIVE-NAND SCHMITT TRIGGERS

13

positive logic:

Y = $\overline{ABCD}$

See page 6-14

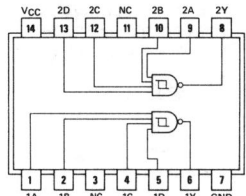

SN5413 (J, W)   SN7413 (J, N)
SN54LS13 (J, W)   SN74LS13 (J, N)

NC—No internal connection

HEX SCHMITT-TRIGGER INVERTERS

14

positive logic:

Y = $\overline{A}$

See page 6-14

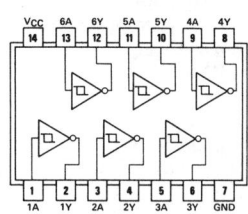

SN5414 (J, W)   SN7414 (J, N)
SN54LS14 (J, W)   SN74LS14 (J, N)

TEXAS INSTRUMENTS
INCORPORATED
POST OFFICE BOX 5012 • DALLAS, TEXAS 75222

54/74 FAMILIES OF COMPATIBLE TTL CIRCUITS

PIN ASSIGNMENTS (TOP VIEWS)

**TRIPLE 3-INPUT
POSITIVE-AND GATES
WITH OPEN-COLLECTOR OUTPUTS**

15

positive logic:

Y = ABC

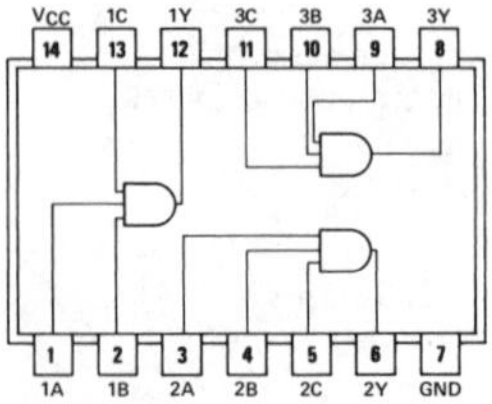

See page 6-12

SN54H15 (J, W)   SN74H15 (J, N)
SN54LS15 (J, W)   SN74LS15 (J, N)
SN54S15 (J, W)   SN74S15 (J, N)

**HEX INVERTER BUFFERS/DRIVERS
WITH OPEN-COLLECTOR
HIGH-VOLTAGE OUTPUTS**

16

positive logic:

Y = $\overline{A}$

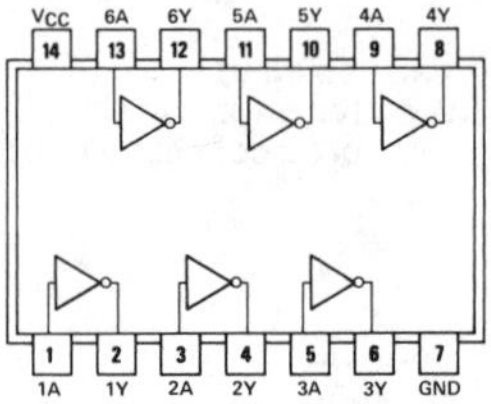

See page 6-24

SN5416 (J, W)   SN7416 (J, N)

**HEX BUFFERS/DRIVERS
WITH OPEN-COLLECTOR
HIGH-VOLTAGE OUTPUTS**

17

positive logic:

Y = A

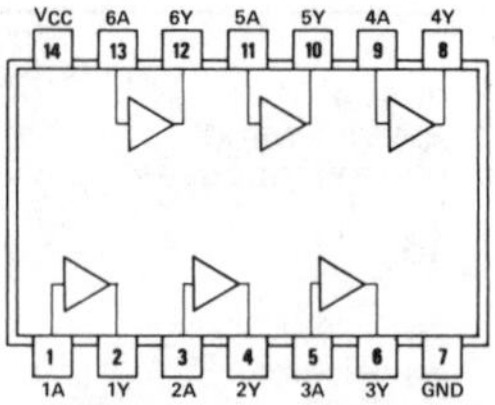

See page 6-24

SN5417 (J, W)   SN7417 (J, N)

**DUAL 4-INPUT
POSITIVE-NAND GATES**

20

positive logic:

Y = $\overline{ABCD}$

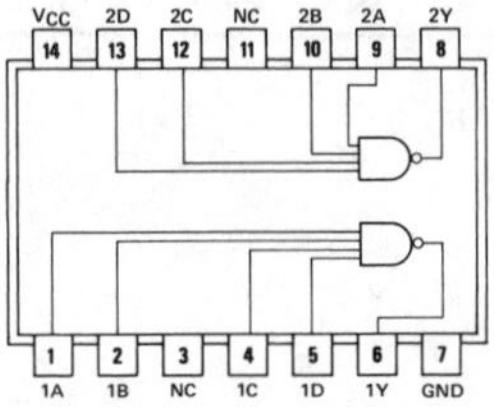

See page 6-2

SN5420 (J)   SN7420 (J, N)   SN5420 (W)
SN54H20 (J)   SN74H20 (J, N)   SN54H20 (W)
SN54L20 (J)   SN74L20 (J, N)   SN54L20 (T)
SN54LS20 (J, W)   SN74LS20 (J, N)
SN54S20 (J, W)   SN74S20 (J, N)   NC—No internal connection

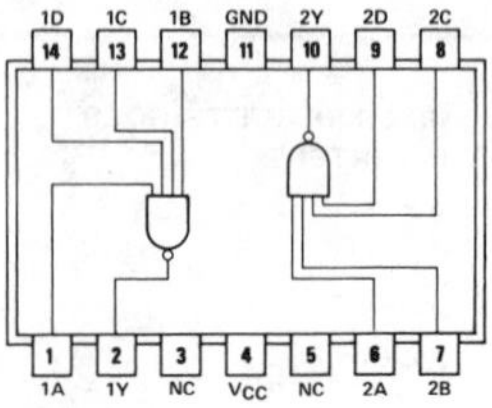

TEXAS INSTRUMENTS
INCORPORATED
POST OFFICE BOX 5012 • DALLAS, TEXAS 75222

PIN ASSIGNMENTS (TOP VIEWS)

DUAL 4-INPUT POSITIVE-AND GATES

21

positive logic:

Y = ABCD

See page 6-10

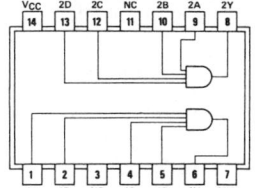

SN54H21 (J)   SN74H21 (J, N)   SN54H21 (W)
SN54LS21 (J, W)   SN74LS21 (J, N)

NC—No internal connection

DUAL 4-INPUT POSITIVE-NAND GATES WITH OPEN-COLLECTOR OUTPUTS

22

positive logic:

Y = $\overline{ABCD}$

See page 6-4

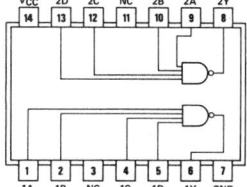

SN5422 (J, W)   SN7422 (J, N)   SN54H22 (W)
SN54H22 (J)   SN74H22 (J, N)
SN54LS22 (J, W)   SN74LS22 (J, N)
SN54S22 (J, W)   SN74S22 (J, N)

NC—No internal connection

EXPANDABLE DUAL 4-INPUT POSITIVE-NOR GATES WITH STROBE

23

positive logic:

1Y = $\overline{1G(1A+1B+1C+1D)+X}$
2Y = $\overline{2G(2A+2B+2C+2D)}$
   X = output of SN5460/SN7460

See page 6-39

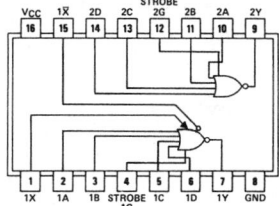

SN5423 (J, W)   SN7423 (J, N)

DUAL 4-INPUT POSITIVE-NOR GATES WITH STROBE

25

positive logic:

Y = $\overline{G(A+B+C+D)}$

See page 6-8

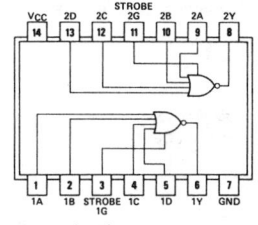

SN5425 (J, W)   SN7425 (J, N)

5

TEXAS INSTRUMENTS
INCORPORATED
POST OFFICE BOX 5012 • DALLAS, TEXAS 75222

54/74 FAMILIES OF COMPATIBLE TTL CIRCUITS

**QUADRUPLE 2-INPUT
HIGH-VOLTAGE INTERFACE
POSITIVE-NAND GATES**

26

positive logic:

$Y = \overline{AB}$

See pages 6-24 and 6-26

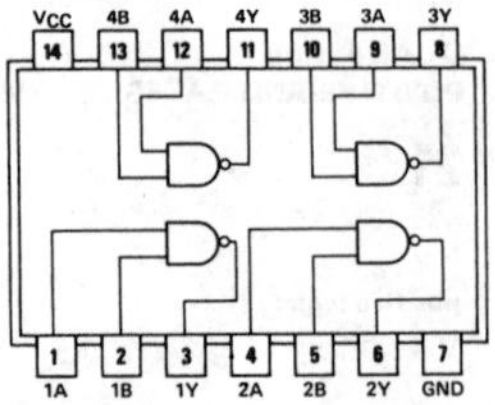

SN5426 (J)   SN7426 (J, N)
SN54LS26 (J, W)   SN74LS26 (J, N)

**TRIPLE 3-INPUT
POSITIVE-NOR GATES**

27

positive logic:

$Y = \overline{A+B+C}$

See page 6-8

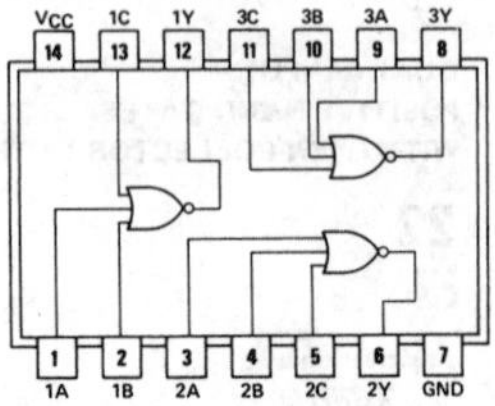

SN5427 (J, W)   SN7427 (J, N)
SN54LS27 (J, W)   SN74LS27 (J, N)

**QUADRUPLE 2-INPUT
POSITIVE-NOR BUFFERS**

28

positive logic:

$Y = \overline{A+B}$

See page 6-20

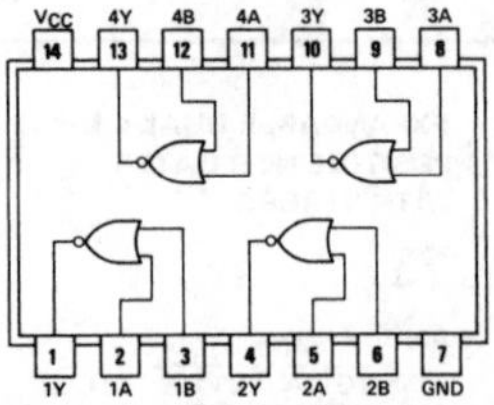

SN5428 (J, W)   SN7428 (J, N)
SN54LS28 (J, W)   SN74LS28 (J, N)

**8-INPUT
POSITIVE-NAND GATES**

30

positive logic:

$Y = \overline{ABCDEFGH}$

See page 6-2

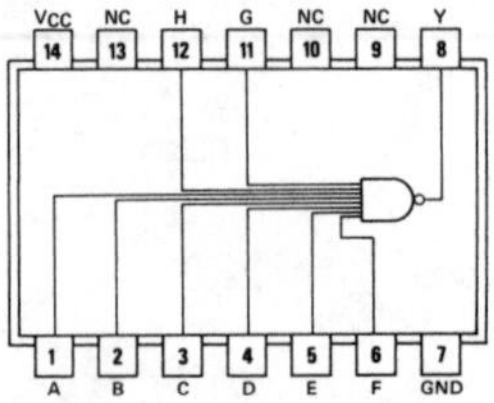

SN5430 (J)   SN7430 (J, N)
SN54H30 (J)   SN74H30 (J, N)
SN54L30 (J)   SN74L30 (J, N)
SN54LS30 (J, W)   SN74LS30 (J, N)
SN54S30 (J, W)   SN74S30 (J, N)

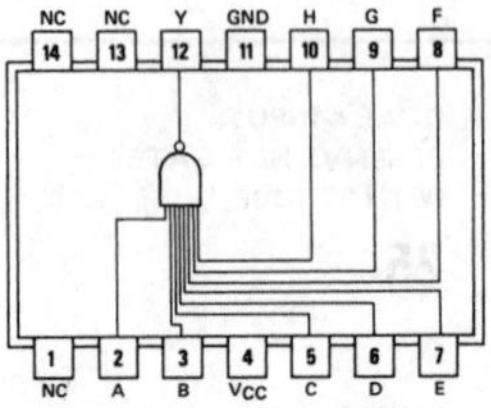

SN5430 (W)
SN54H30 (W)
SN54L30 (T)

NC—No internal connection

TEXAS INSTRUMENTS
INCORPORATED
POST OFFICE BOX 5012 • DALLAS, TEXAS 75222

PIN ASSIGNMENTS (TOP VIEWS)

**QUADRUPLE 2-INPUT
POSITIVE-OR GATES**

32

positive logic:
$Y = A+B$

See page 6-28

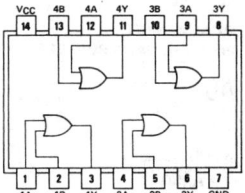

SN5432 (J, W)   SN7432 (J, N)
SN54LS32 (J, W)   SN74LS32 (J, N)
SN54S32 (J, W)   SN74S32 (J, N)

**QUADRUPLE 2-INPUT
POSITIVE-NOR BUFFERS
WITH OPEN-COLLECTOR OUTPUTS**

33

positive logic:
$Y = \overline{A+B}$

See pages 6-24 and 6-26

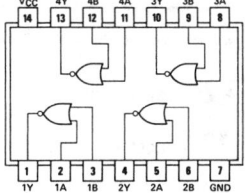

SN5433 (J, W)   SN7433 (J, N)
SN54LS33 (J, W)   SN74LS33 (J, N)

**QUADRUPLE 2-INPUT
POSITIVE-NAND BUFFERS**

37

positive logic:
$Y = \overline{AB}$

See page 6-20

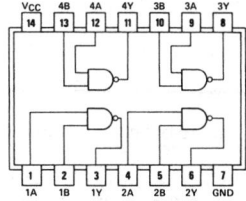

SN5437 (J, W)   SN7437 (J, N)
SN54LS37 (J, W)   SN74LS37 (J, N)
SN54S37 (J, W)   SN74S37 (J, N)

**QUADRUPLE 2-INPUT
POSITIVE-NAND BUFFERS
WITH OPEN-COLLECTOR OUTPUTS**

38

positive logic:
$Y = \overline{AB}$

See pages 6-24 and 6-26

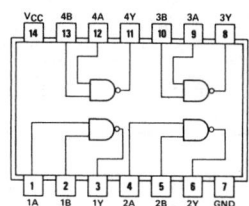

SN5438 (J, W)   SN7438 (J, N)
SN54LS38 (J, W)   SN74LS38 (J, N)
SN54S38 (J, W)   SN74S38 (J, N)

5

TEXAS INSTRUMENTS
INCORPORATED
POST OFFICE BOX 5012 • DALLAS, TEXAS 75222

PIN ASSIGNMENTS (TOP VIEWS)

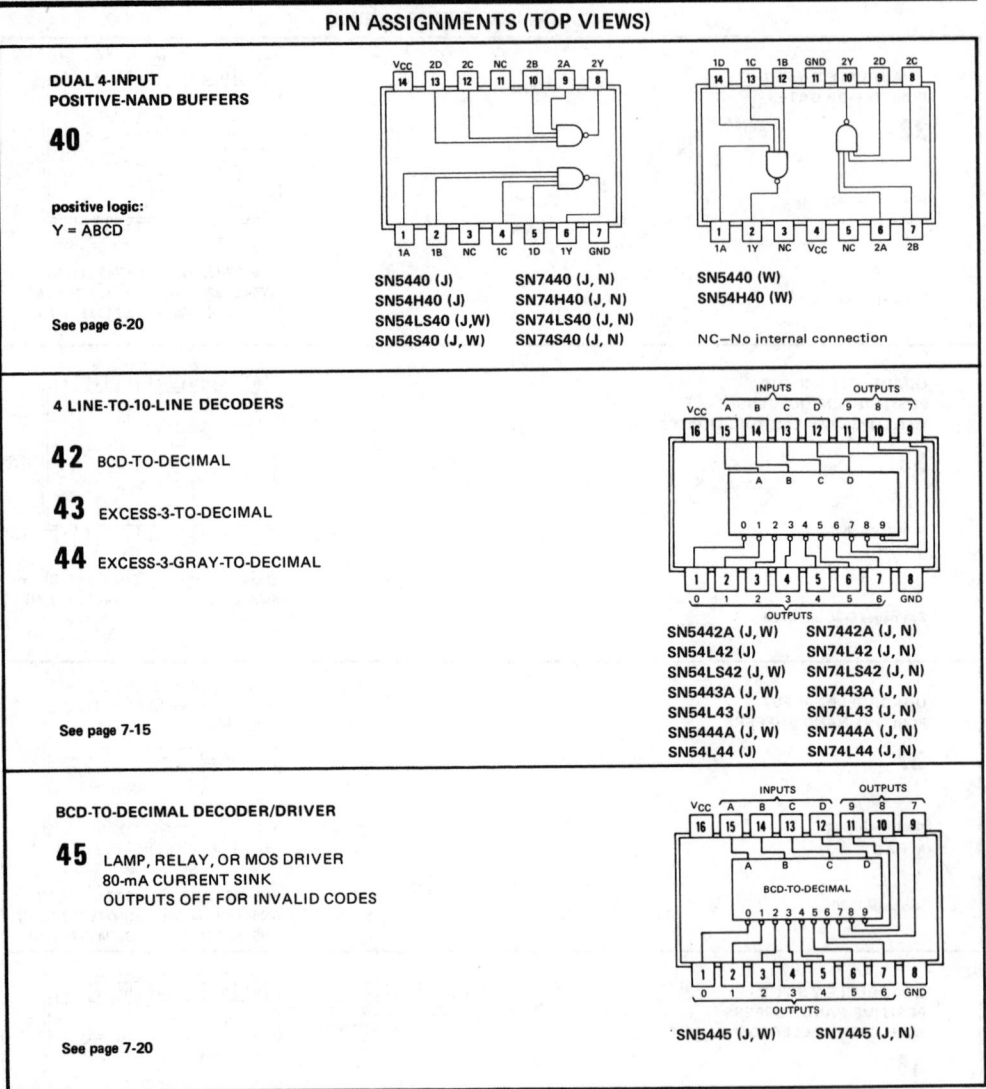

DUAL 4-INPUT POSITIVE-NAND BUFFERS

40

positive logic:
$Y = \overline{ABCD}$

See page 6-20

SN5440 (J)   SN7440 (J, N)
SN54H40 (J)   SN74H40 (J, N)
SN54LS40 (J,W) SN74LS40 (J, N)
SN54S40 (J, W) SN74S40 (J, N)

SN5440 (W)
SN54H40 (W)

NC—No internal connection

---

4 LINE-TO-10-LINE DECODERS

42 BCD-TO-DECIMAL

43 EXCESS-3-TO-DECIMAL

44 EXCESS-3-GRAY-TO-DECIMAL

See page 7-15

SN5442A (J, W)   SN7442A (J, N)
SN54L42 (J)   SN74L42 (J, N)
SN54LS42 (J, W) SN74LS42 (J, N)
SN5443A (J, W)   SN7443A (J, N)
SN54L43 (J)   SN74L43 (J, N)
SN5444A (J, W)   SN7444A (J, N)
SN54L44 (J)   SN74L44 (J, N)

BCD-TO-DECIMAL DECODER/DRIVER

45 LAMP, RELAY, OR MOS DRIVER
80-mA CURRENT SINK
OUTPUTS OFF FOR INVALID CODES

See page 7-20

SN5445 (J, W)   SN7445 (J, N)

TEXAS INSTRUMENTS
INCORPORATED
POST OFFICE BOX 5012 • DALLAS, TEXAS 75222

PIN ASSIGNMENTS (TOP VIEWS)

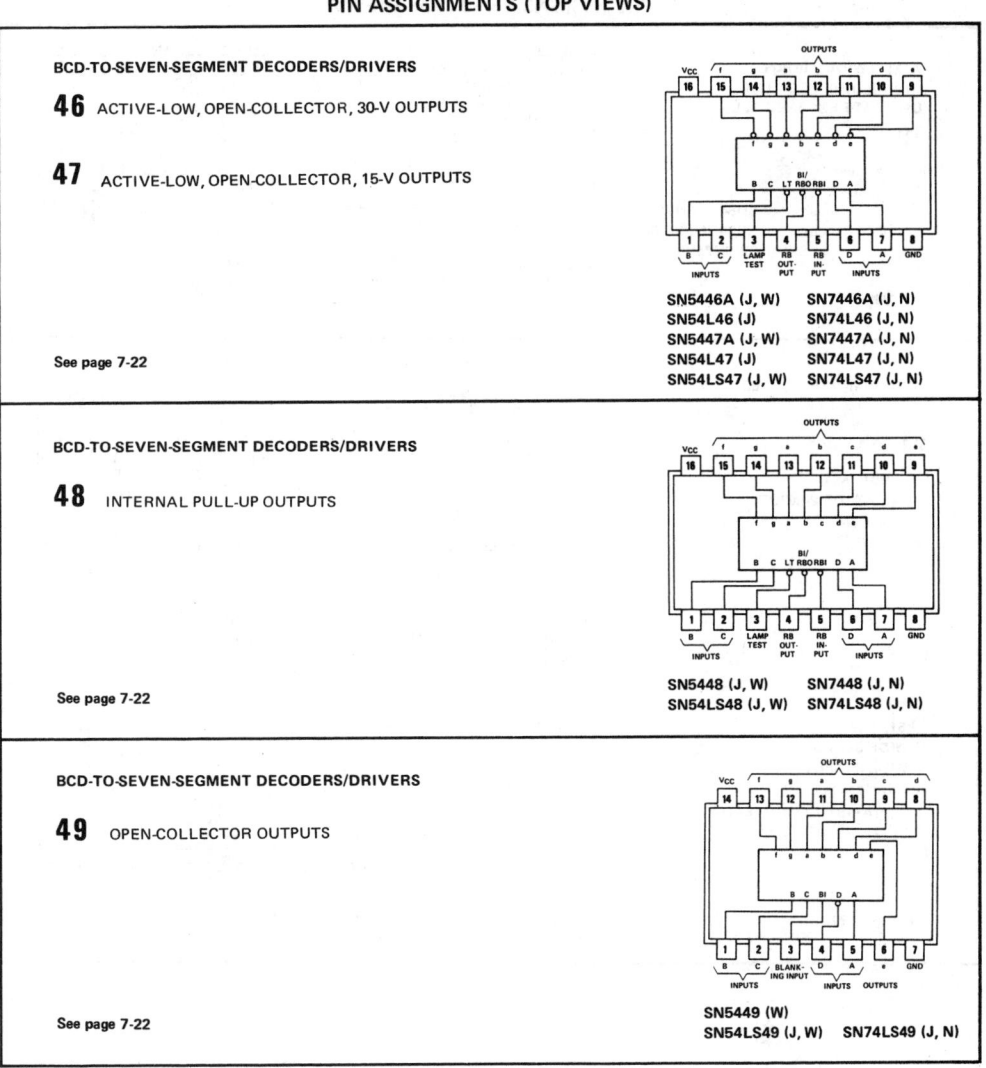

BCD-TO-SEVEN-SEGMENT DECODERS/DRIVERS

46 ACTIVE-LOW, OPEN-COLLECTOR, 30-V OUTPUTS

47 ACTIVE-LOW, OPEN-COLLECTOR, 15-V OUTPUTS

See page 7-22

SN5446A (J, W)   SN7446A (J, N)
SN54L46 (J)   SN74L46 (J, N)
SN5447A (J, W)   SN7447A (J, N)
SN54L47 (J)   SN74L47 (J, N)
SN54LS47 (J, W)   SN74LS47 (J, N)

BCD-TO-SEVEN-SEGMENT DECODERS/DRIVERS

48 INTERNAL PULL-UP OUTPUTS

See page 7-22

SN5448 (J, W)   SN7448 (J, N)
SN54LS48 (J, W)   SN74LS48 (J, N)

BCD-TO-SEVEN-SEGMENT DECODERS/DRIVERS

49 OPEN-COLLECTOR OUTPUTS

See page 7-22

SN5449 (W)
SN54LS49 (J, W)   SN74LS49 (J, N)

5

076

PIN ASSIGNMENTS (TOP VIEWS)

**DUAL 2-WIDE 2-INPUT
AND-OR-INVERT GATES
(ONE GATE EXPANDABLE)**

50

positive logic:

$Y = \overline{AB+CD+X}$

'50: X = output of SN5460/SN7460
'H50: X = output of SN54H60/SN74H60
or SN54H62/SN74H62

See page 6-39

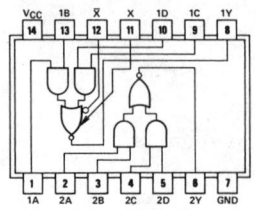

SN5450 (J)   SN7450 (J, N)
SN54H50 (J)   SN74H50 (J, N)

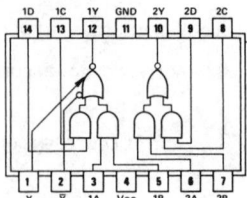

SN5450 (W)
SN54H50 (W)

AND-OR-INVERT GATES

51

'51, 'H51, 'S51
DUAL 2-WIDE 2-INPUT
positive logic:

$Y = \overline{AB+CD}$

MAKE NO EXTERNAL CONNECTION

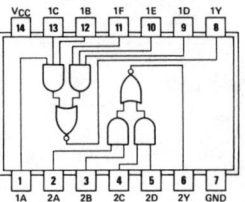

MAKE NO EXTERNAL CONNECTION

SN5451 (J)   SN7451 (J, N)
SN54H51 (J)   SN74H51 (J, N)
SN54S51 (J, W)   SN74S51 (J, N)

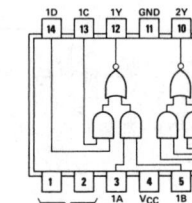

SN5451 (W)
SN54H51 (W)

'L51, 'LS51
**2-WIDE 3-INPUT,
2-WIDE 2-INPUT**
positive logic:

$1Y = \overline{(1A \cdot 1B \cdot 1C)+(1D \cdot 1E \cdot 1F)}$
$2Y = \overline{(2A \cdot 2B)+(2C \cdot 2D)}$

See page 6-30

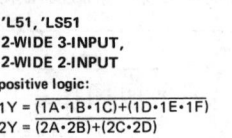

SN54L51 (J)   SN74L51 (J, N)
SN54LS51 (J, W)   SN74LS51 (J, N)

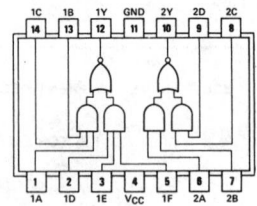

SN54L51 (T)

TEXAS INSTRUMENTS
INCORPORATED
POST OFFICE BOX 5012 • DALLAS, TEXAS 75222

PIN ASSIGNMENTS (TOP VIEWS)

EXPANDABLE 4-WIDE AND-OR GATES

52

'H52(J, N)
positive logic:
Y = AB+CDE+FG+HI+X
    X = output of SN54H61/SN74H61

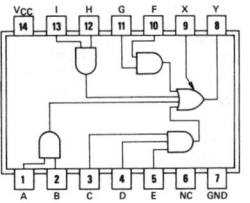

SN54H52 (J)   SN74H52 (J, N)

'H52(W)
positive logic:
Y = AB+CD+EF+GHI+X
    X = output of SN54H61/SN74H61

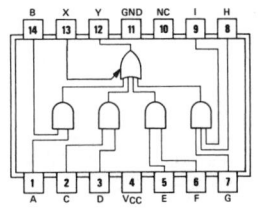

SN54H42 (W)

See page 6-39

NC—No internal connection

EXPANDABLE 4-WIDE AND-OR-INVERT GATES

53

'53
positive logic:
Y = $\overline{AB+CD+EF+GH+X}$
    X = output of SN5460/SN7460

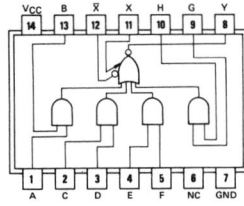

SN5453 (J)   SN7453 (J, N)

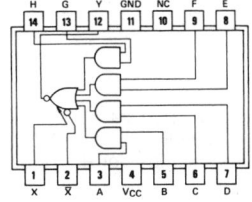

SN5453 (W)

'H53
positive logic:
Y = $\overline{AB+CD+EFG+HI+X}$
    X = output of SN54H60/SN74H60
    or SN54H62/SN74H62

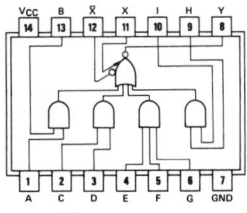

SN54H53 (J)   SN74H53 (J,N)

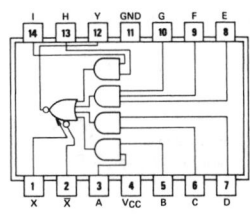

SN54H53 (W)

See page 6-39

NC—No internal connection

5

PIN ASSIGNMENTS (TOP VIEWS)

4-WIDE AND-OR-INVERT GATES

54

'54
positive logic:
$Y = \overline{AB+CD+EF+GH}$

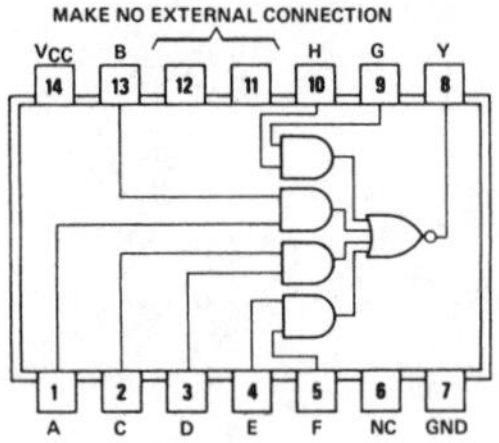

SN5454 (J)   SN7454 (J, N) 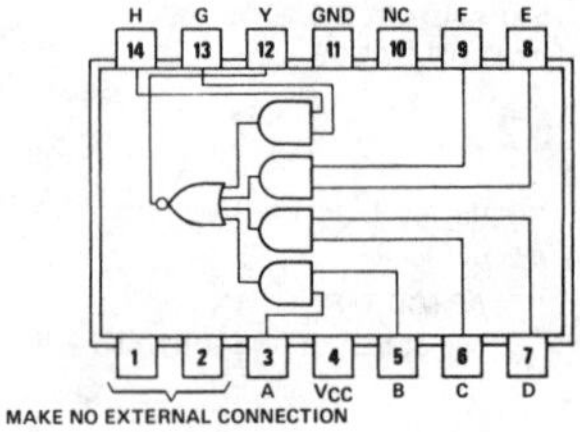   SN5454 (W)

'H54
positive logic:
$Y = \overline{AB+CD+EFG+HI}$

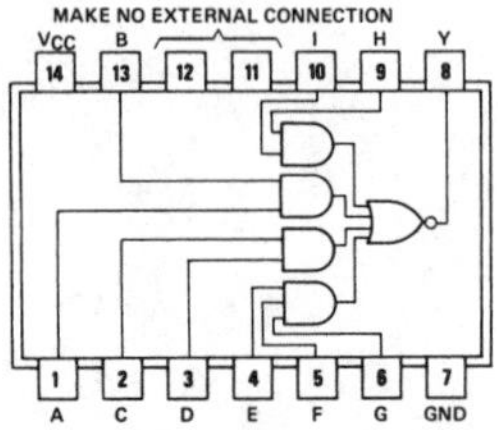

SN54H54 (J)   SN74H54 (J, N) 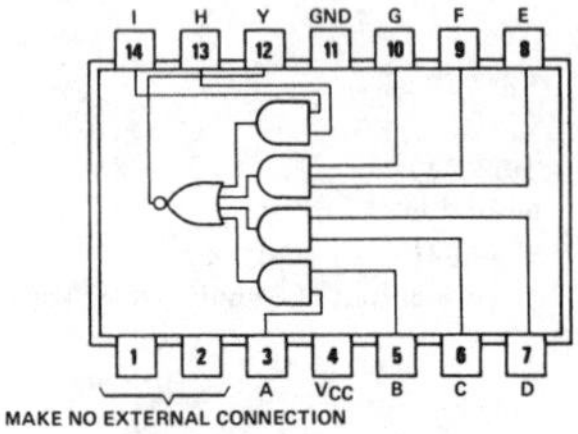   SN54H54 (W)

'L54(J, N), 'LS54
positive logic:
$Y = \overline{AB+CDE+FGH+IJ}$

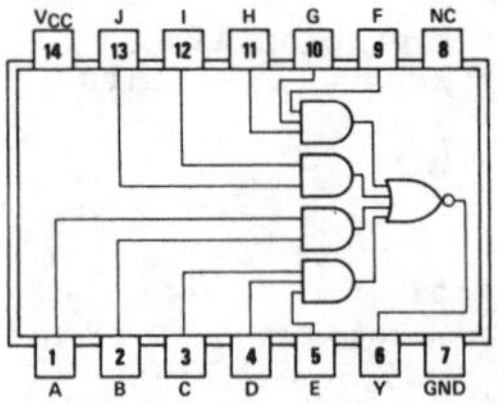

SN54L54 (J)   SN74L54 (J, N)
SN54LS54 (J, W)   SN74LS54 (J, N)

'L54(T)
positive logic:
$Y = \overline{ABC+DE+FG+HIJ}$

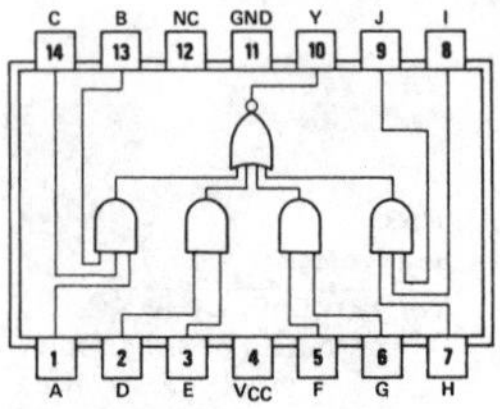

SN54L54 (T)

See page 6-30

NC—No internal connection

TEXAS INSTRUMENTS
INCORPORATED
POST OFFICE BOX 5012 • DALLAS, TEXAS 75222

PIN ASSIGNMENTS (TOP VIEWS)

**2-WIDE 4-INPUT
AND-OR-INVERT GATES**

55

'H55 (EXPANDABLE)
positive logic:
$$Y = \overline{ABCD + EFGH + X}$$
X = output of SN54H60/SN74H60
or SN54H62/SN74H62

See page 6-39

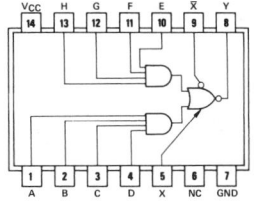

SN54H55 (J)   SN74H55 (J, N)

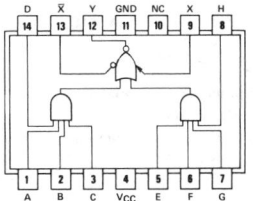

SN54H55 (W)

'L55, 'LS55
positive logic:
$$Y = \overline{ABCD + EFGH}$$

See page 6-30

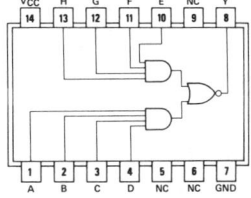

SN54L55 (J)   SN74L55 (J, N)
SN54LS55 (J, W)   SN74LS55 (J, N)

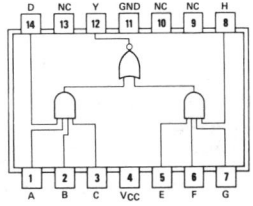

SN54L55 (T)

NC—No internal connection

DUAL 4-INPUT EXPANDERS

60

positive logic:
X = ABCD when connected to X and $\overline{X}$ inputs
of SN5423/SN7423, SN5450/SN7450, or
SN5453/SN7453

'H60
positive logic:
X = ABCD when connected to X and $\overline{X}$
inputs of SN54H50/SN74H50,
SN54H53/SN74H53, or
SN54H55/SN74H55

See pages 6-43 and 6-44

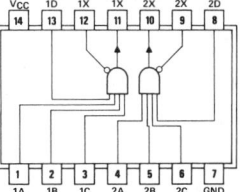

SN5460 (J)   SN7460 (J, N)
SN54H60 (J)   SN74H60 (J, N)

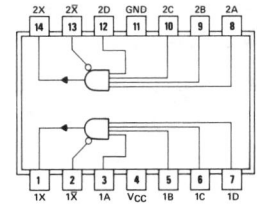

SN5460 (W)
SN54H60 (W)

NC—No internal connection

**TRIPLE 3-INPUT
EXPANDERS**

61

positive logic:
X = ABC when connected to X input of
SN54H52/SN74H52

See page 6-45

SN54H61 (J)   SN74H61 (J, N)

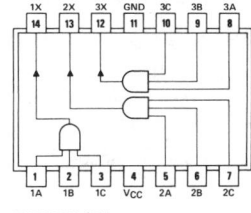

SN54H61 (W)

5

TEXAS INSTRUMENTS
INCORPORATED
POST OFFICE BOX 5012 • DALLAS, TEXAS 75222

54/74 FAMILIES OF COMPATIBLE TTL CIRCUITS

PIN ASSIGNMENTS (TOP VIEWS)

4-WIDE AND-OR EXPANDERS

62

'H62(J, N) (2-3-3-2 INPUT)
positive logic:

X = AB+CDE+FGH+IJ when connected
to X and X̄ inputs of SN54H50/SN74H50,
SN54H53/SN74H53, or SN54H55/SN74H55

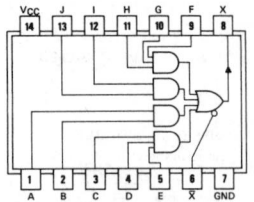

SN54H62 (J)   SN74H62 (J, N)

'H62(W) (3-2-2-3 INPUT)
positive logic:

X = ABC+DE+FG+HIJ when connected to
X and X̄ inputs of SN54H50/SN74H50,
SN54H53/SN74H53, or SN54H55/SN74H55

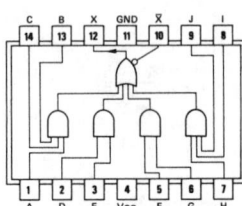

SN54H62 (W)

See page 6-44

HEX CURRENT-SENSING INTERFACE GATES

63

TRANSLATES LOW-LEVEL INPUT CURRENT TO LOW-LEVEL VOLTAGE
AND
HIGH-LEVEL CURRENT TO HIGH-LEVEL VOLTAGE

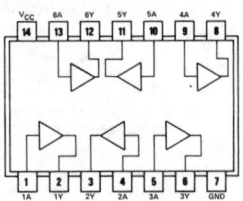

SN54LS63(J,W) SN74LS63(J,N)

See page 6-62

4-2-3-2 INPUT AND-OR-INVERT GATES

64

TOTEM-POLE OUTPUT

65

OPEN-COLLECTOR OUTPUT

positive logic: $\overline{Y = ABCD+EF+GHI+JK}$

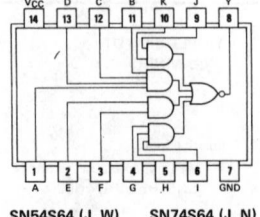

SN54S64 (J, W)   SN74S64 (J, N)
SN54S65 (J, W)   SN74S65 (J, N)

See pages 6-30 and 6-32

TEXAS INSTRUMENTS
INCORPORATED
POST OFFICE BOX 5012 • DALLAS, TEXAS 75222

PIN ASSIGNMENTS (TOP VIEWS)

AND-GATED J-K POSITIVE-EDGE-TRIGGERED FLIP-FLOPS WITH PRESET AND CLEAR

70 FUNCTION TABLE

INPUTS					OUTPUTS	
PRESET	CLEAR	CLOCK	J	K	Q	$\bar{Q}$
L	H	L	X	X	H	L
H	L	L	X	X	L	H
L	L	X	X	X	L*	L*
H	H	↑	L	L	Q_0	$\bar{Q}_0$
H	H	↑	H	L	H	L
H	H	↑	L	H	L	H
H	H	↑	H	H	TOGGLE	
H	H	L	X	X	Q_0	$\bar{Q}_0$

positive logic: $J = J1 \cdot J2 \cdot \bar{J}$
$K = K1 \cdot K2 \cdot \bar{K}$
If inputs $\bar{J}$ and $\bar{K}$ are not used, they must be grounded.
See page 6-46   Preset or clear function can occur only when the clock input is low.

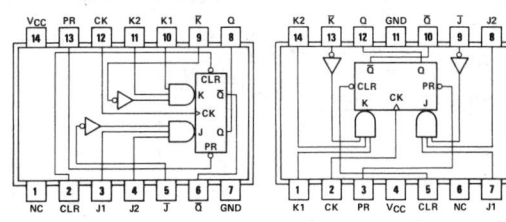

SN5470 (J)   SN7470 (J, N)   SN5470 (W)

NC—No internal connection

AND-OR-GATED J-K MASTER-SLAVE FLIP-FLOPS WITH PRESET

H71

FUNCTION TABLE

INPUTS				OUTPUTS	
PRESET	CLOCK	J	K	Q	$\bar{Q}$
L	X	X	X	H	L
H	⊓	L	L	Q_0	$\bar{Q}_0$
H	⊓	H	L	H	L
H	⊓	L	H	L	H
H	⊓	H	H	TOGGLE	

positive logic: $J = (J1A \cdot J1B) + (J2A \cdot J2B)$
$K = (K1A \cdot K1B) + (K2A \cdot K2B)$

See page 6-50

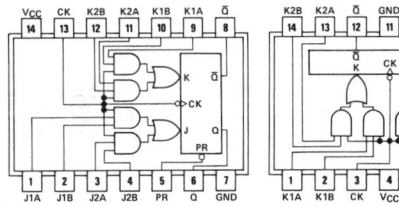

SN54H71 (J)   SN74H71 (J, N)   SN54H71 (W)

AND-GATED R-S MASTER-SLAVE FLIP-FLOPS WITH PRESET AND CLEAR

L71
FUNCTION TABLE

INPUTS					OUTPUTS	
PRESET	CLEAR	CLOCK	S	R	Q	$\bar{Q}$
L	H	X	X	X	H	L
H	L	X	X	X	L	H
L	L	X	X	X	H*	H*
H	H	⊓	L	L	Q_0	$\bar{Q}_0$
H	H	⊓	H	L	H	L
H	H	⊓	L	H	L	H
H	H	⊓	H	H	INDETERMINATE	

positive logic: $R = R1 \cdot R2 \cdot R3$
$S = S1 \cdot S2 \cdot S3$

See page 6-54

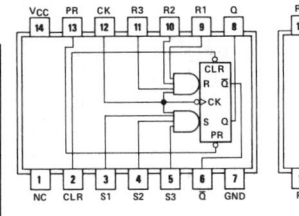 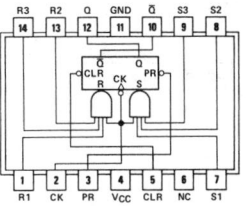

SN54L71 (J)   SN74L71 (J, N)   SN54L71 (T)

NC—No internal connection

See explanation of function tables on page 3-8.
*This configuration is nonstable; that is, it will not persist when preset and clear inputs return to their inactive (high) level.

TEXAS INSTRUMENTS
INCORPORATED
POST OFFICE BOX 5012 • DALLAS, TEXAS 75222

5

54/74 FAMILIES OF COMPATIBLE TTL CIRCUITS

PIN ASSIGNMENTS (TOP VIEWS)

AND-GATED J-K MASTER-SLAVE FLIP-FLOPS WITH PRESET AND CLEAR

72

FUNCTION TABLE

INPUTS					OUTPUTS	
PRESET	CLEAR	CLOCK	J	K	Q	$\bar{Q}$
L	H	X	X	X	H	L
H	L	X	X	X	L	H
L	L	X	X	X	H*	H*
H	H	⊓	L	L	Q_0	$\bar{Q}_0$
H	H	⊓	H	L	H	L
H	H	⊓	L	H	L	H
H	H	⊓	H	H	TOGGLE	

positive logic: J = J1·J2·J3; K1·K2·K3

See pages 6-46, 6-50, and 6-54

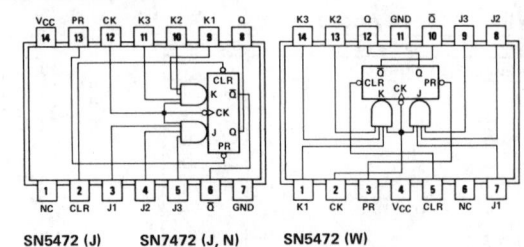

SN5472 (J)   SN7472 (J, N)   SN5472 (W)
SN54H72 (J) SN74H72 (J, N) SN54H72 (W)
SN54L72 (J) SN74L72 (J, N) SN54L72 (T)

NC—No internal connection

DUAL J-K FLIP-FLOPS WITH CLEAR

73

'73, 'H73, 'L73
FUNCTION TABLE

INPUTS				OUTPUTS	
CLEAR	CLOCK	J	K	Q	$\bar{Q}$
L	X	X	X	L	H
H	⊓	L	L	Q_0	$\bar{Q}_0$
H	⊓	H	L	H	L
H	⊓	L	H	L	H
H	⊓	H	H	TOGGLE	

'LS73A
FUNCTION TABLE

INPUTS				OUTPUTS	
CLEAR	CLOCK	J	K	Q	$\bar{Q}$
L	X	X	X	L	H
H	↓	L	L	Q_0	$\bar{Q}_0$
H	↓	H	L	H	L
H	↓	L	H	L	H
H	↓	H	H	TOGGLE	
H	H	X	X	Q_0	$\bar{Q}_0$

See pages 6-46, 6-50, 6-54, and 6-56

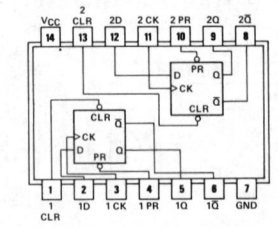

SN5473 (J, W)   SN7473 (J, N)
SN54H73 (J, W)   SN74H73 (J, N)
SN54L73 (J, T)   SN74L73 (J, N)
SN54LS73A (J, W)   SN74LS73A (J, N)

DUAL D-TYPE POSITIVE-EDGE-TRIGGERED FLIP-FLOPS WITH PRESET AND CLEAR

74

FUNCTION TABLE

INPUTS				OUTPUTS	
PRESET	CLEAR	CLOCK	D	Q	$\bar{Q}$
L	H	X	X	H	L
H	L	X	X	L	H
L	L	X	X	H*	H*
H	H	↑	H	H	L
H	H	↑	L	L	H
H	H	L	X	Q_0	$\bar{Q}_0$

See pages 6-46, 6-50, 6-54, and 6-56

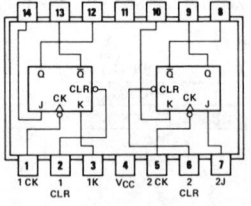

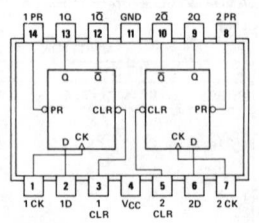

SN5474 (J)   SN7474 (J, N)   SN5474 (W)
SN54H74 (J)   SN74H74 (J, N)   SN54H74 (W)
SN54L74 (J)   SN74L74 (J, N)   SN54L74 (T)
SN54LS74A (J, W)   SN74LS74A (J, N)
SN54S74 (J, W)   SN74S74 (J, N)

See explanation of function tables on page 3-8.
*This configuration is nonstable; that is, it will not persist when preset and clear inputs return to their inactive (high) level.

TEXAS INSTRUMENTS
INCORPORATED
POST OFFICE BOX 5012 • DALLAS, TEXAS 75222

PIN ASSIGNMENTS (TOP VIEWS)

4-BIT BISTABLE LATCHES

75

FUNCTION TABLE
(Each Latch)

INPUTS		OUTPUTS	
D	G	Q	$\bar{Q}$
L	H	L	H
H	H	H	L
X	L	Q_0	$\bar{Q}_0$

H = high level, L = low level, X = irrelevant

Q_0 = the level of Q before the high-to-low transistion of G

See page 7-35

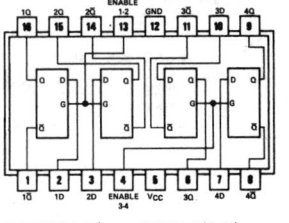

SN5475 (J, W)   SN7475 (J, N)
SN54L75 (J)   SN74L75 (J, N)
SN54LS75 (J, W)   SN74LS75 (J, N)

DUAL J-K FLIP-FLOPS WITH PRESET AND CLEAR

76

'76, 'H76 FUNCTION TABLE

INPUTS					OUTPUTS	
PRESET	CLEAR	CLOCK	J	K	Q	$\bar{Q}$
L	H	X	X	X	H	L
H	L	X	X	X	L	H
L	L	X	X	X	H*	H*
H	H	⊓	L	L	Q_0	$\bar{Q}_0$
H	H	⊓	H	L	H	L
H	H	⊓	L	H	L	H
H	H	⊓	H	H	TOGGLE	

'LS76A FUNCTION TABLE

INPUTS					OUTPUTS	
PRESET	CLEAR	CLOCK	J	K	Q	$\bar{Q}$
L	H	X	X	X	H	L
H	L	X	X	X	L	H
L	L	X	X	X	H*	H*
H	H	↓	L	L	Q_0	$\bar{Q}_0$
H	H	↓	H	L	H	L
H	H	↓	L	H	L	H
H	H	↓	H	H	TOGGLE	
H	H	H	X	X	Q_0	$\bar{Q}_0$

See pages 6-46, 6-50, and 6-56

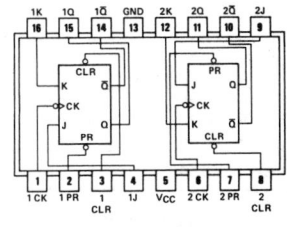

SN5476 (J, W)   SN7476 (J, N)
SN54H76 (J, W)   SN74H76 (J, N)
SN54LS76A (J, W)   SN74LS76A (J, N)

4-BIT BISTABLE LATCHES

77

FUNCTION TABLE
(Each Latch)

INPUTS		OUTPUTS	
D	G	Q	$\bar{Q}$
L	H	L	H
H	H	H	L
X	L	Q_0	$\bar{Q}_0$

H = high level, L = low level, X = irrelevant

Q_0 = the level of Q before the high-to-low transistion of G

See page 7-35

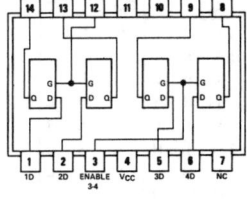

SN5477 (W)
SN54L77 (T)
SN54LS77 (W)

See explanation of function tables on page 3-8.

*This configuration is nonstable; that is, it will not persist when preset and clear inputs return to their inactive (high) level.

PIN ASSIGNMENTS (TOP VIEWS)

DUAL J-K FLIP-FLOPS WITH PRESET, COMMON CLEAR, AND COMMON CLOCK

78   'H78, 'L78
FUNCTION TABLE

INPUTS					OUTPUTS	
PRESET	CLEAR	CLOCK	J	K	Q	Q̄
L	H	X	X	X	H	L
H	L	X	X	X	L	H
L	L	X	X	X	H*	H*
H	H	⊓	L	L	Q₀	Q̄₀
H	H	⊓	H	L	H	L
H	H	⊓	L	H	L	H
H	H	⊓	H	H	TOGGLE	

See pages 6-50 and 6-54

'LS78A
FUNCTION TABLE

INPUTS					OUTPUTS	
PRESET	CLEAR	CLOCK	J	K	Q	Q̄
L	H	X	X	X	H	L
H	L	X	X	X	L	H
L	L	X	X	X	H*	H*
H	H	∣	L	L	Q₀	Q̄₀
H	H	∣	H	L	H	L
H	H	∣	L	H	L	H
H	H	∣	H	H	TOGGLE	
H	H	H	X	X	Q₀	Q̄₀

See page 6-56

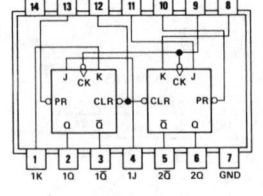

SN54H78(J,W) SN74H78(J,N)

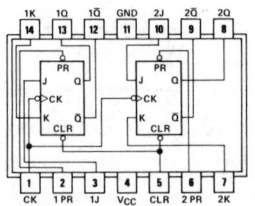

SN54L78(J,T) SN74L78(J,N)
SN54LS78A(J,W) SN74LS78A(J,N)

GATED FULL ADDERS

80   GATED COMPLEMENTARY INPUTS
COMPLEMENTARY SUM OUTPUTS

FUNCTION TABLE
(See Notes 1, 2, and 3)

INPUTS			OUTPUTS		
Cₙ	B	A	C̄ₙ₊₁	Σ̄	Σ
L	L	L	H	H	L
L	L	H	H	L	H
L	H	L	H	L	H
L	H	H	L	H	L
H	L	L	H	L	H
H	L	H	L	H	L
H	H	L	L	H	L
H	H	H	L	L	H

H = high level, L = low level

NOTES: 1. $A = \overline{A}_C + \overline{A}☆ + A1 \cdot A2$, $B = \overline{B}_C + B☆ + B1 \cdot B2$.
2. When A☆ is used as an input, A1 or A2 must be low. When B☆ is used as an input, B1 or B2 must be low.
3. When A1 and A2 or B1 and B2 are used as inputs, A☆ or B☆, respectively, must be open or used to perform dot-AND logic.

See page 7-41

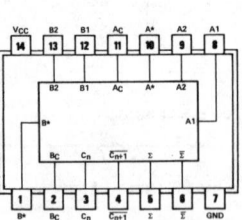

SN5480(J) SN7480(J,N)

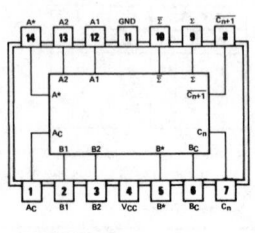

SN5480(W)

See explanation of function tables on page 3-8.
* This configuration is nonstable; that is, it will not persist when preset and clear inputs return to their inactive (high) level.

TEXAS INSTRUMENTS
INCORPORATED
POST OFFICE BOX 5012 • DALLAS, TEXAS 75222

PIN ASSIGNMENTS (TOP VIEWS)

16-BIT RANDOM-ACCESS MEMORIES

81

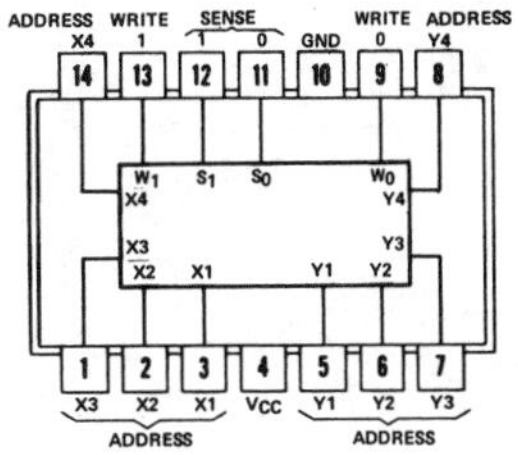

See page 7-44

SN5481A (J, W) SN7481A (J, N)

2-BIT BINARY FULL ADDERS

82

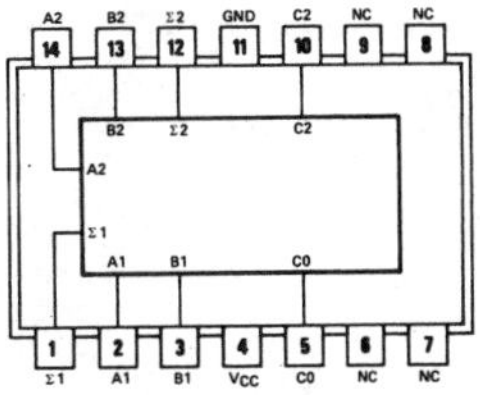

See page 7-49

SN5482 (J, W) SN7482 (J, N)

NC—No internal connection

4-BIT BINARY FULL ADDERS WITH FAST CARRY

83

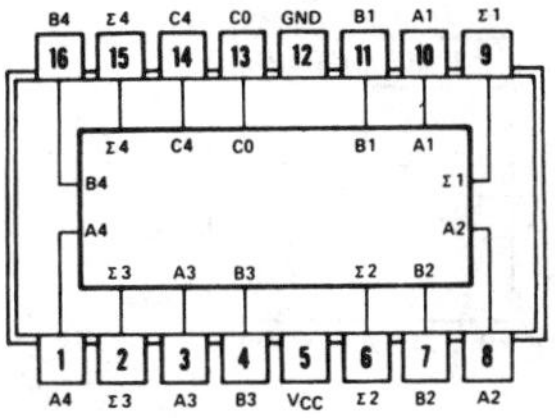

See page 7-53

SN5483A (J, W)   SN74 83A (J, N)
SN54LS83A (J, W)   SN74LS83A (J, N)

16-BIT RANDOM-ACCESS MEMORIES

84

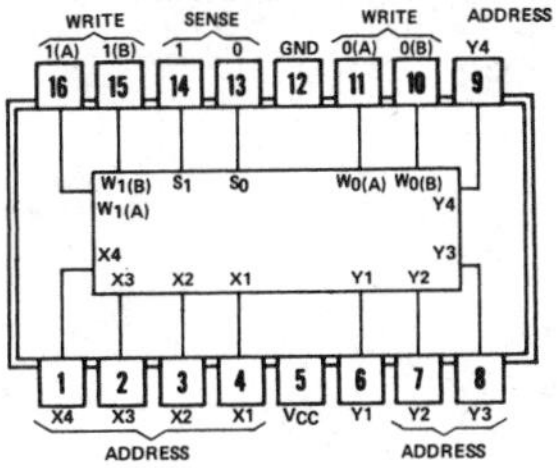

See page 7-44

SN5484A (J, W)   SN7484A (J, N)

TEXAS INSTRUMENTS
INCORPORATED
POST OFFICE BOX 5012 • DALLAS, TEXAS 75222

54/74 FAMILIES OF COMPATIBLE TTL CIRCUITS

PIN ASSIGNMENTS (TOP VIEWS)

4-BIT MAGNITUDE COMPARATORS

85

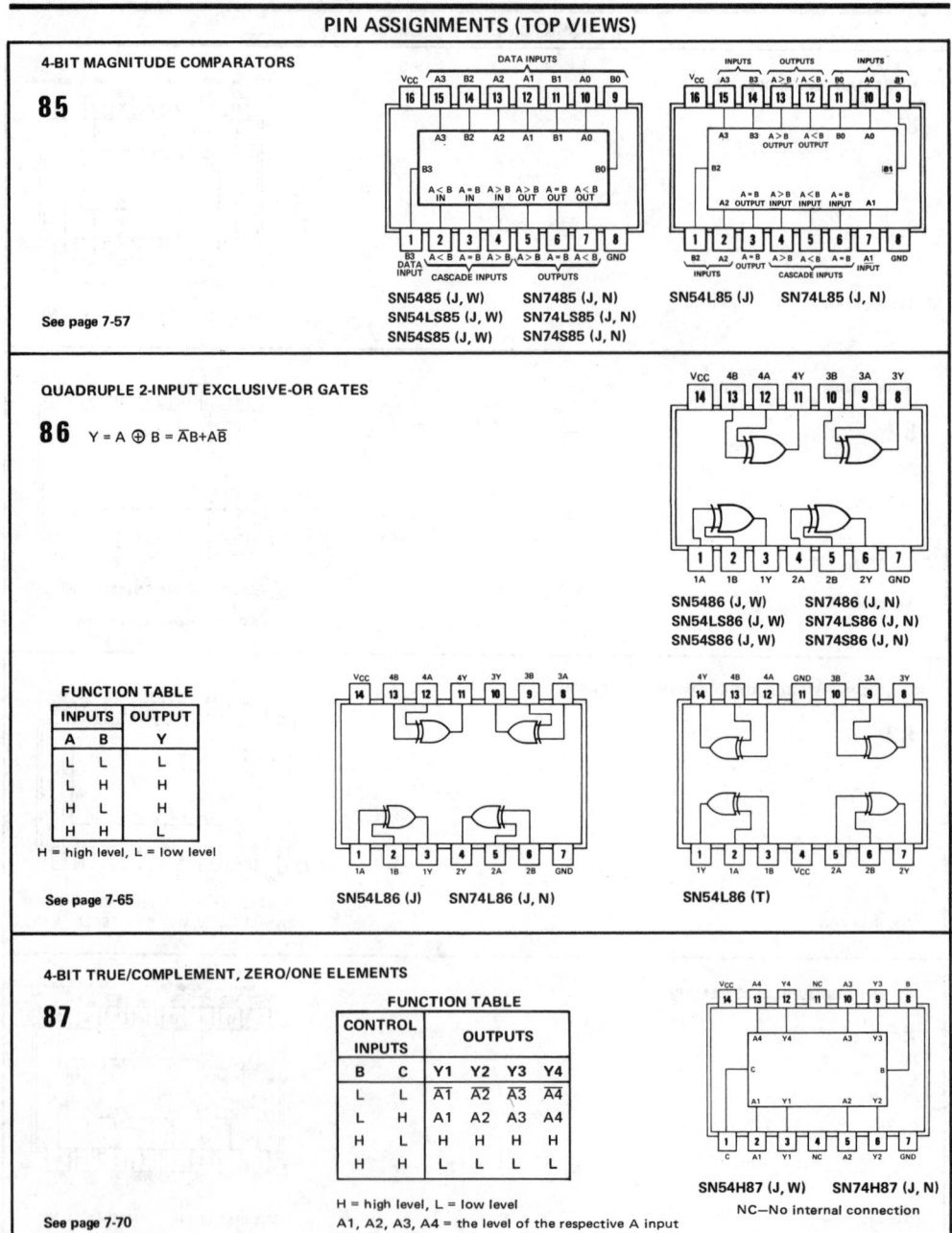

SN5485 (J, W)   SN7485 (J, N)
SN54LS85 (J, W) SN74LS85 (J, N)
SN54S85 (J, W)   SN74S85 (J, N)

SN54L85 (J)   SN74L85 (J, N)

See page 7-57

QUADRUPLE 2-INPUT EXCLUSIVE-OR GATES

86 $Y = A \oplus B = \overline{A}B + A\overline{B}$

SN5486 (J, W)   SN7486 (J, N)
SN54LS86 (J, W) SN74LS86 (J, N)
SN54S86 (J, W)   SN74S86 (J, N)

FUNCTION TABLE

INPUTS		OUTPUT
A	B	Y
L	L	L
L	H	H
H	L	H
H	H	L

H = high level, L = low level

See page 7-65

SN54L86 (J)   SN74L86 (J, N)

SN54L86 (T)

4-BIT TRUE/COMPLEMENT, ZERO/ONE ELEMENTS

87

FUNCTION TABLE

CONTROL INPUTS		OUTPUTS			
B	C	Y1	Y2	Y3	Y4
L	L	$\overline{A1}$	$\overline{A2}$	$\overline{A3}$	$\overline{A4}$
L	H	A1	A2	A3	A4
H	L	H	H	H	H
H	H	L	L	L	L

H = high level, L = low level
A1, A2, A3, A4 = the level of the respective A input

See page 7-70

SN54H87 (J, W)   SN74H87 (J, N)
NC—No internal connection

TEXAS INSTRUMENTS
INCORPORATED
POST OFFICE BOX 5012 • DALLAS, TEXAS 75222

PIN ASSIGNMENTS (TOP VIEWS)

256-BIT READ-ONLY MEMORIES

88 32 8-BIT WORDS
OPEN-COLLECTOR OUTPUTS

See Bipolar Microcomputer Components Data Book, LCC4270

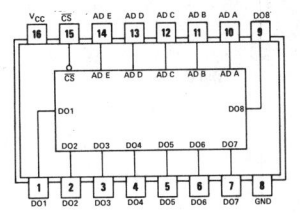

·SN5488A (J, W)   SN7488A (J, N)

64-BIT READ/WRITE MEMORIES

89 16 4-BIT WORDS

See Bipolar Microcomputer Components Data Book, LCC4270

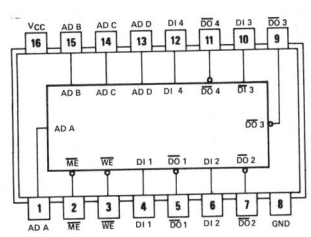

SN7489 (J, N)

DECADE COUNTERS

90 DIVIDE-BY-TWO AND DIVIDE-BY FIVE

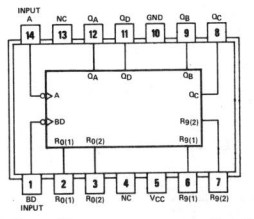

SN5490A (J, W)   SN7490A (J, N)
SN54L90 (J, T)   SN74L90 (J, N)
SN54LS90 (J, W)   SN74LS90 (J, N)

NC — No internal connection

See Page 7-72

TEXAS INSTRUMENTS
INCORPORATED
POST OFFICE BOX 5012 • DALLAS, TEXAS 75222

PIN ASSIGNMENTS (TOP VIEWS)

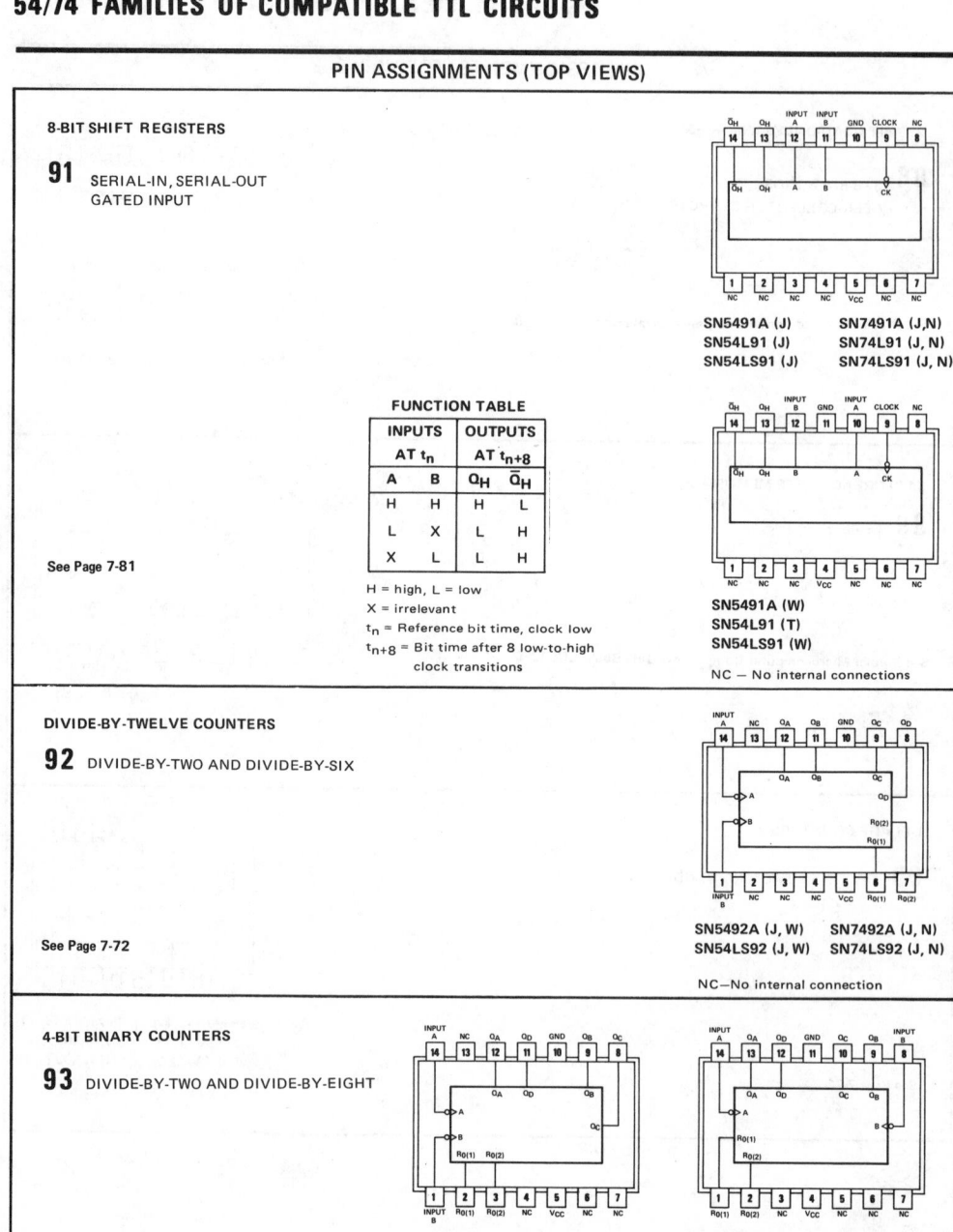

8-BIT SHIFT REGISTERS

91 SERIAL-IN, SERIAL-OUT
GATED INPUT

SN5491A (J)   SN7491A (J,N)
SN54L91 (J)   SN74L91 (J, N)
SN54LS91 (J)   SN74LS91 (J, N)

FUNCTION TABLE

INPUTS AT t_n		OUTPUTS AT t_{n+8}	
A	B	Q_H	$\overline{Q}_H$
H	H	H	L
L	X	L	H
X	L	L	H

See Page 7-81

H = high, L = low
X = irrelevant
t_n = Reference bit time, clock low
t_{n+8} = Bit time after 8 low-to-high
clock transitions

SN5491A (W)
SN54L91 (T)
SN54LS91 (W)

NC — No internal connections

DIVIDE-BY-TWELVE COUNTERS

92 DIVIDE-BY-TWO AND DIVIDE-BY-SIX

See Page 7-72

SN5492A (J, W)   SN7492A (J, N)
SN54LS92 (J, W)   SN74LS92 (J, N)

NC—No internal connection

4-BIT BINARY COUNTERS

93 DIVIDE-BY-TWO AND DIVIDE-BY-EIGHT

See Page 7-72

SN5493A (J, W)   SN7493A (J, N)
SN54LS93 (J, W)   SN74LS93 (J, N)

SN54L93 (J, T)   SN74L93 (J, N)

NC—No internal connection

TEXAS INSTRUMENTS
INCORPORATED
POST OFFICE BOX 5012 • DALLAS, TEXAS 75222

PIN ASSIGNMENTS (TOP VIEWS)

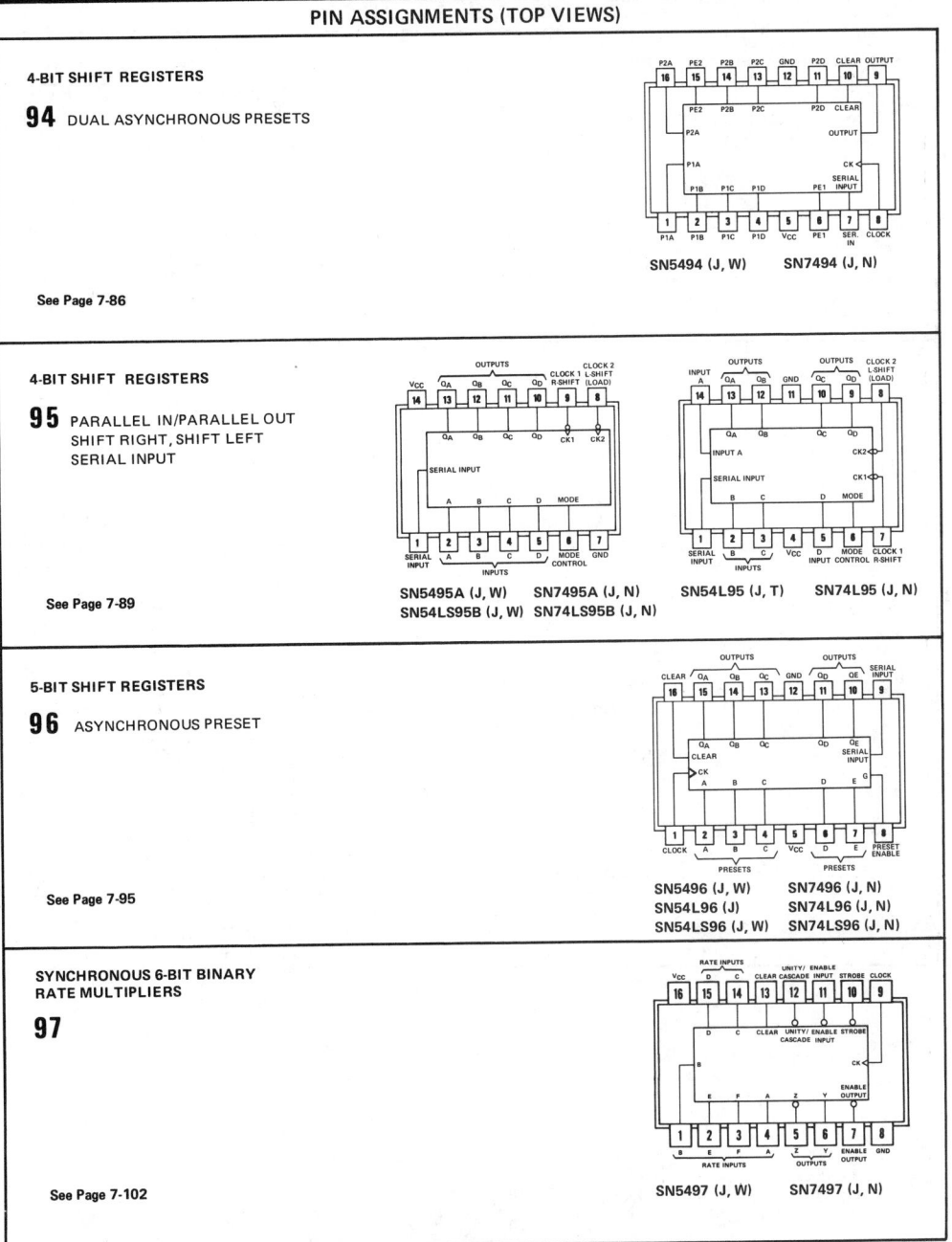

4-BIT SHIFT REGISTERS

94 DUAL ASYNCHRONOUS PRESETS

SN5494 (J, W)   SN7494 (J, N)

See Page 7-86

4-BIT SHIFT REGISTERS

95 PARALLEL IN/PARALLEL OUT
SHIFT RIGHT, SHIFT LEFT
SERIAL INPUT

See Page 7-89

SN5495A (J, W)   SN7495A (J, N)
SN54LS95B (J, W) SN74LS95B (J, N)

SN54L95 (J, T)   SN74L95 (J, N)

5-BIT SHIFT REGISTERS

96 ASYNCHRONOUS PRESET

See Page 7-95

SN5496 (J, W)   SN7496 (J, N)
SN54L96 (J)   SN74L96 (J, N)
SN54LS96 (J, W) SN74LS96 (J, N)

**SYNCHRONOUS 6-BIT BINARY
RATE MULTIPLIERS**

97

See Page 7-102

SN5497 (J, W)   SN7497 (J, N)

54/74 FAMILIES OF COMPATIBLE TTL CIRCUITS

PIN ASSIGNMENTS (TOP VIEWS)

4-BIT DATA SELECTOR/STORAGE REGISTERS

98 SELECTS 1 OF 2 4-BIT WORDS
PARALLEL IN/OUT

See Page 7-107

SN54L98 (J)   SN74L98 (J, N)

4-BIT BIDIRECTIONAL UNIVERSAL SHIFT REGISTERS

99 SERIAL J-$\overline{K}$ INPUTS

See Page 7-109

SN54L99 (J)   SN74L99 (J, N)

8-BIT BISTABLE LATCHES

100

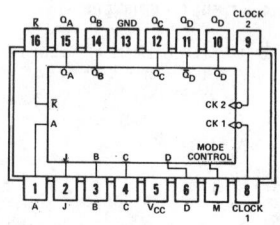

FUNCTION TABLE
(Each Latch)

INPUTS		OUTPUTS	
D	G	Q	$\overline{Q}$
L	H	L	H
H	H	H	L
X	L	Q_0	$\overline{Q}_0$

H = high level, X = irrelevant
Q_0 = the level of Q before the
high-to-low transition of G

See Page 7-113

SN54100 (J, W)   SN74100 (J, N)
NC — No internal connection

TEXAS INSTRUMENTS
INCORPORATED
POST OFFICE BOX 5012 • DALLAS, TEXAS 75222

PIN ASSIGNMENTS (TOP VIEWS)

AND-OR-GATED J-K NEGATIVE-EDGE-TRIGGERED FLIP-FLOPS WITH PRESET

FUNCTION TABLE

INPUTS				OUTPUTS	
PRESET	CLOCK	J	K	Q	$\bar{Q}$
L	X	X	X	H	L
H	↓	L	L	Q_0	$\bar{Q}_0$
H	↓	H	L	H	L
H	↓	L	H	L	H
H	↓	H	H	TOGGLE	
H	H	X	X	Q_0	$\bar{Q}_0$

positive logic: J = (J1A·J1B)+(J2A·J2B)
K = (K1A·K1B)+(K2A·K2B)

See page 6-52

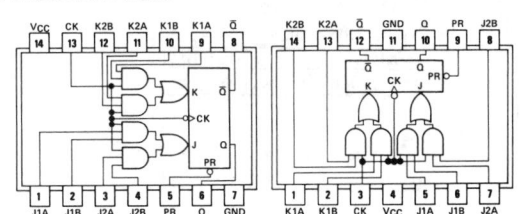

SN54H101 (J)   SN74H101 (J, N)   SN54H101 (W)

AND-GATED J-K NEGATIVE-EDGE-TRIGGERED FLIP-FLOPS WITH PRESET AND CLEAR

102

FUNCTION TABLE

INPUTS					OUTPUTS	
PRESET	CLEAR	CLOCK	J	K	Q	$\bar{Q}$
L	H	X	X	X	H	L
H	L	X	X	X	L	H
L	L	X	X	X	H*	H*
H	H	↓	L	L	Q_0	$\bar{Q}_0$
H	H	↓	H	L	H	L
H	H	↓	L	H	L	H
H	H	↓	H	H	TOGGLE	
H	H	H	X	X	Q_0	$\bar{Q}_0$

positive logic: J = J1·J2·J3
K = K1·K2·K3

See page 6-52

SN54H102 (J)   SN74H102 (J,N)   SN54H102 (W)

NC—No internal connection

DUAL J-K NEGATIVE-EDGE-TRIGGERED FLIP-FLOPS WITH CLEAR

103

FUNCTION TABLE

INPUTS				OUTPUTS	
CLEAR	CLOCK	J	K	Q	$\bar{Q}$
L	X	X	X	L	H
H	↓	L	L	Q_0	$\bar{Q}_0$
H	↓	H	L	H	L
H	↓	L	H	L	H
H	↓	H	H	TOGGLE	
H	H	X	X	Q_0	$\bar{Q}_0$

See page 6-52

SN54H103 (J, W)   SN74H103 (J, N)

See explanation of function tables on page 3-8.
*This configuration is nonstable; that is, it will not persist when preset and clear inputs return to their inactive (high) level.

TEXAS INSTRUMENTS
INCORPORATED
POST OFFICE BOX 5012 • DALLAS, TEXAS 75222

54/74 FAMILIES OF COMPATIBLE TTL CIRCUITS

PIN ASSIGNMENTS (TOP VIEWS)

DUAL J-K NEGATIVE-EDGE-TRIGGERED FLIP-FLOPS WITH PRESET AND CLEAR

106

FUNCTION TABLE

INPUTS					OUTPUTS	
PRESET	CLEAR	CLOCK	J	K	Q	$\bar{Q}$
L	H	X	X	X	H	L
H	L	X	X	X	L	H
L	L	X	X	X	H*	H*
H	H	↓	L	L	Q_0	$\bar{Q}_0$
H	H	↓	H	L	H	L
H	H	↓	L	H	L	H
H	H	↓	H	H	TOGGLE	
H	H	H	X	X	Q_0	$\bar{Q}_0$

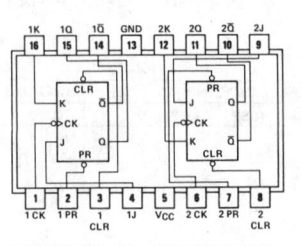

SN54H106 (J, W)   SN74H106 (J, N)

See page 6-52

DUAL J-K FLIP-FLOPS WITH CLEAR

107

'107
FUNCTION TABLE

INPUTS				OUTPUTS	
CLEAR	CLOCK	J	K	Q	$\bar{Q}$
L	X	X	X	L	H
H	⊓	L	L	Q_0	$\bar{Q}_0$
H	⊓	H	L	H	L
H	⊓	L	H	L	H
H	⊓	H	H	TOGGLE	

'LS107A
FUNCTION TABLE

INPUTS				OUTPUTS	
CLEAR	CLOCK	J	K	Q	$\bar{Q}$
L	X	X	X	L	H
H	↓	L	L	Q_0	$\bar{Q}_0$
H	↓	H	L	H	L
H	↓	L	H	L	H
H	↓	H	H	TOGGLE	
H	H	X	X	Q_0	$\bar{Q}_0$

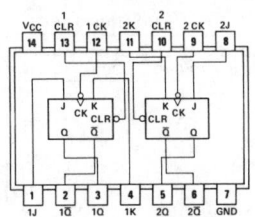

SN54107 (J)   SN74107 (J, N)
SN54LS107A (J)   SN74LS107A (J, N)

See pages 6-46 and 6-56

DUAL J-K NEGATIVE-EDGE-TRIGGERED FLIP-FLOPS WITH PRESET, COMMON CLEAR, AND COMMON CLOCK

108

FUNCTION TABLE

INPUTS					OUTPUTS	
PRESET	CLEAR	CLOCK	J	K	Q	$\bar{Q}$
L	H	X	X	X	H	L
H	L	X	X	X	L	H
L	L	X	X	X	H*	H*
H	H	↓	L	L	Q_0	$\bar{Q}_0$
H	H	↓	H	L	H	L
H	H	↓	L	H	L	H
H	H	↓	H	H	TOGGLE	
H	H	H	X	X	Q_0	$\bar{Q}_0$

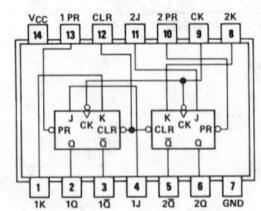

SN54H108 (J, W)   SN74H108 (J, N)

See page 6-52

See explanation of function tables on page 3-8.

*This configuration is nonstable; that is, it will not persist when preset and clear inputs return to their inactive (high) level.

TEXAS INSTRUMENTS
INCORPORATED
POST OFFICE BOX 5012 • DALLAS, TEXAS 75222

PIN ASSIGNMENTS (TOP VIEWS)

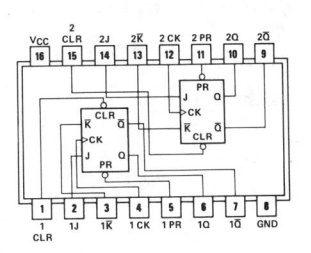

DUAL J-K̄ POSITIVE-EDGE-TRIGGERED FLIP-FLOPS WITH PRESET AND CLEAR

109

FUNCTION TABLE

INPUTS					OUTPUTS	
PRESET	CLEAR	CLOCK	J	K̄	Q	Q̄
L	H	X	X	X	H	L
H	L	X	X	X	L	H
L	L	X	X	X	H*	H*
H	H	↑	L	L	L	H
H	H	↑	H	L	TOGGLE	
H	H	↑	L	H	Q_0	$\bar{Q}_0$
H	H	↑	H	H	H	L
H	H	L	X	X	Q_0	$\bar{Q}_0$

See pages 6-46 and 6-56

SN54109 (J, W)   SN74109 (J, N)
SN54LS109A (J, W)   SN74LS109A (J, N)

AND-GATED J-K MASTER-SLAVE FLIP-FLOPS WITH DATA LOCKOUT

110

FUNCTION TABLE

INPUTS					OUTPUTS	
PRESET	CLEAR	CLOCK	J	K	Q	Q̄
L	H	X	X	X	H	L
H	L	X	X	X	L	H
L	L	X	X	X	H*	H*
H	H	⊓	L	L	Q_0	$\bar{Q}_0$
H	H	⊓	H	L	H	L
H	H	⊓	L	H	L	H
H	H	⊓	H	H	TOGGLE	

positive logic: J = J1•J2•J3
                 K = K1•K2•K3

See page 6-46

SN54110 (J, W)   SN74110 (J, N)

NC—No internal connection

DUAL J-K MASTER-SLAVE FLIP-FLOPS WITH DATA LOCKOUT

111

FUNCTION TABLE

INPUTS					OUTPUTS	
PRESET	CLEAR	CLOCK	J	K	Q	Q̄
L	H	X	X	X	H	L
H	L	X	X	X	L	H
L	L	X	X	X	H*	H*
H	H	⊓	L	L	Q_0	$\bar{Q}_0$
H	H	⊓	H	L	H	L
H	H	⊓	L	H	L	H
H	H	⊓	H	H	TOGGLE	

See page 6-46

SN54111 (J, W)   SN74111 (J, N)

See explanation of function tables on page 3-8.
*This configuration is nonstable; that is, it will not persist when preset and clear inputs return to their inactive (high) level.

TEXAS INSTRUMENTS
INCORPORATED
POST OFFICE BOX 5012 • DALLAS, TEXAS 75222

54/74 FAMILIES OF COMPATIBLE TTL CIRCUITS

PIN ASSIGNMENTS (TOP VIEWS)

DUAL J-K NEGATIVE-EDGE-TRIGGERED FLIP-FLOPS WITH PRESET AND CLEAR

112

FUNCTION TABLE

INPUTS					OUTPUTS	
PRESET	CLEAR	CLOCK	J	K	Q	$\bar{Q}$
L	H	X	X	X	H	L
H	L	X	X	X	L	H
L	L	X	X	X	H*	H*
H	H	↓	L	L	Q_0	$\bar{Q}_0$
H	H	↓	H	L	H	L
H	H	↓	L	H	L	H
H	H	↓	H	H	TOGGLE	
H	H	H	X	X	Q_0	$\bar{Q}_0$

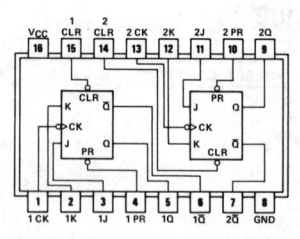

SN54LS112A (J, W)   SN74LS112A (J,N)
SN54S112 (J, W)   SN74S112 (J, N)

See pages 6-56 and 6-58

DUAL J-K NEGATIVE-EDGE-TRIGGERED FLIP-FLOPS WITH PRESET

113

FUNCTION TABLE

INPUTS				OUTPUTS	
PRESET	CLOCK	J	K	Q	$\bar{Q}$
L	X	X	X	H	L
H	↓	L	L	Q_0	$\bar{Q}_0$
H	↓	H	L	H	L
H	↓	L	H	L	H
H	↓	H	H	TOGGLE	
H	H	X	X	Q_0	$\bar{Q}_0$

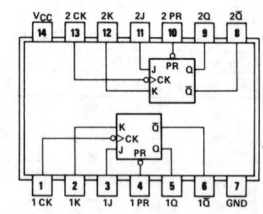

SN54LS113A (J, W) SN74LS113A (J, N)
SN54S113 (J, W)   SN74S113 (J, N)

See pages 6-56 and 6-58

DUAL J-K NEGATIVE-EDGE-TRIGGERED FLIP-FLOPS WITH PRESET, COMMON CLEAR, AND COMMON CLOCK

114

FUNCTION TABLE

INPUTS					OUTPUTS	
PRESET	CLEAR	CLOCK	J	K	Q	$\bar{Q}$
L	H	X	X	X	H	L
H	L	X	X	X	L	H
L	L	X	X	X	H*	H*
H	H	↓	L	L	Q_0	$\bar{Q}_0$
H	H	↓	H	L	H	L
H	H	↓	L	H	L	H
H	H	↓	H	H	TOGGLE	
H	H	H	X	X	Q_0	$\bar{Q}_0$

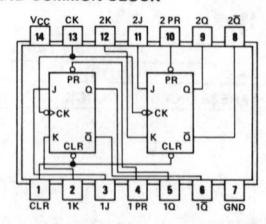

SN54LS114A (J, W) SN74LS114A (J,N)
SN54S114 (J, W)   SN74S114 (J,N)

See pages 6-56 and 6-58

See explanation of function tables on page 3-8.

*This configuration is nonstable; that is, it will not persist when preset and clear inputs return to their inactive (high) level.

TEXAS INSTRUMENTS
INCORPORATED
POST OFFICE BOX 5012 • DALLAS, TEXAS 75222

PIN ASSIGNMENTS (TOP VIEWS)

DUAL 4-BIT LATCHES

116

FUNCTION TABLE
(EACH LATCH)

INPUTS			OUTPUT
CLEAR	ENABLE	DATA	Q
	$\overline{G1}$ $\overline{G2}$		
H	L L	L	L
H	L L	H	H
H	X H	X	Q_0
H	H X	X	Q_0
L	X X	X	L

See page 7-115

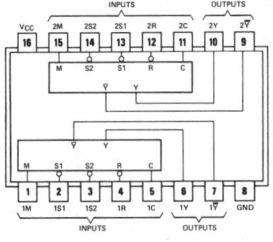

SN54116 (J, W)   SN74116 (J, N)

DUAL PULSE SYNCHRONIZERS/DRIVERS

120

FUNCTION TABLE

INPUTS			FUNCTION
R	S1	S2	
X	L	X	Pass Output Pulses
X	X	L	Pass Output Pulses
L	H	H	Inhibit Output Pulses
H	↓	H	Start Output Pulses
H	H	↓	Start Output Pulses
↓	H	H	Stop Output Pulses
H	H	H	Continue†

†Operation initiated by last ↓ transition continues.

See page 7-118

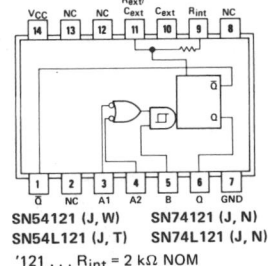

SN54120 (J, W)   SN74120 (J, N)

MONOSTABLE MULTIVIBRATORS

121

FUNCTION TABLE

INPUTS			OUTPUTS	
A1	A2	B	Q	$\overline{Q}$
L	X	H	L	H
X	L	H	L	H
X	X	L	L	H
H	H	X	L	H
H	↓	H	⊓	⊔
↓	H	H	⊓	⊔
↓	↓	H	⊓	⊔
L	X	↑	⊓	⊔
X	L	↑	⊓	⊔

See page 6-64

NOTES: 1. An external capacitor may be connected between C_{ext} (positive) and R_{ext}/C_{ext}.

2. To use the internal timing resistor, connect R_{int} to V_{CC}. For improved pulse width accuracy and repeatability, connect an external resistor between R_{ext}/C_{ext} and V_{CC} with R_{int} open-circuited.

SN54121 (J, W)   SN74121 (J, N)
SN54L121 (J, T)   SN74L121 (J, N)

'121 . . . R_{int} = 2 kΩ NOM
'L121 . . . R_{int} = 4 kΩ NOM

NC—No internal connection

See explanation of function tables on page 3-8.

076

PIN ASSIGNMENTS (TOP VIEWS)

RETRIGGERABLE MONOSTABLE MULTIVIBRATORS WITH CLEAR

122   FUNCTION TABLE

INPUTS					OUTPUTS	
CLEAR	A1	A2	B1	B2	Q	Q̄
L	X	X	X	X	L	H
X	H	H	X	X	L	H
X	X	X	L	X	L	H
X	X	X	X	L	L	H
H	L	X	↑	H	⊓	⊔
H	L	X	H	↑	⊓	⊔
H	X	L	↑	H	⊓	⊔
H	X	L	H	↑	⊓	⊔
H	H	↓	H	H	⊓	⊔
H	↓	↓	H	H	⊓	⊔
H	↓	H	H	H	⊓	⊔
↑	L	X	H	H	⊓	⊔
↑	X	L	H	H	⊓	⊔

NOTES: 1. An external timing capacitor may be connected between C_{ext} and R_{ext}/C_{ext} (positive).

2. For accurate repeatable pulse widths, connect an external resistor between R_{ext}/C_{ext} and V_{CC} with R_{int} open-circuited.

See page 6-76

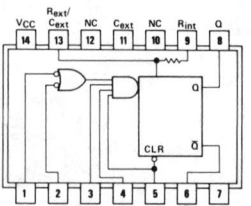

SN54122 (J, W)   SN74122 (J, N)
SN54L122 (J, T)   SN74L122 (J, N)
SN54LS122 (J, W)   SN74LS122 (J, N)
'122 . . . R_{int} = 10 kΩ NOM
'L122 . . . R_{int} = 20 kΩ NOM
'LS122 . . . R_{int} = 10 kΩ NOM

NC—No internal connection

DUAL RETRIGGERABLE MONOSTABLE MULTIVIBRATORS WITH CLEAR

123   FUNCTION TABLE

INPUTS			OUTPUTS	
CLEAR	A	B	Q	Q̄
L	X	X	L	H
X	H	X	L	H
X	X	L	L	H
H	L	↑	⊓	⊔
H	↓	H	⊓	⊔
↑	L	H	⊓	⊔

See page 6-76

SN54123 (J, W)   SN74123 (J, N)
SN54L123 (J)   SN74L123 (J, N)
SN54LS123 (J, W) SN74LS123 (J, N)

DUAL VOLTAGE-CONTROLLED OSCILLATORS

124

See page 7-123

SN54LS124 (J, W)   SN74LS124 (J, N)
SN54S124 (J, W)   SN74S124 (J, N)

NC—No internal connection

†See explanation of function tables on page 3-8.

TEXAS INSTRUMENTS
INCORPORATED
POST OFFICE BOX 5012 • DALLAS, TEXAS 75222

PIN ASSIGNMENTS (TOP VIEWS)

QUADRUPLE BUS BUFFER GATES WITH THREE-STATE OUTPUTS

125

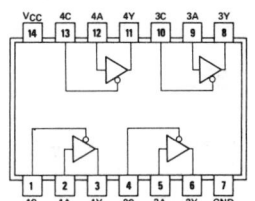

positive logic:

Y = A

Output is off (disabled) when C is high.

See page 6-33

SN54125 (J, W)   SN74125 (J, N)
SN54LS125A(J, W) SN74LS125A (J, N)

QUADRUPLE BUS BUFFER GATES WITH THREE-STATE OUTPUTS

126

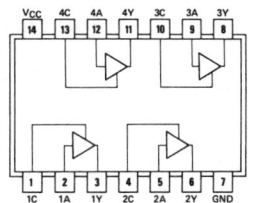

positive logic:

Y = A

Output is off (disabled) when C is low.

See page 6-33

SN54126 (J, W)   SN74126 (J, N)
SN54LS126A(J, W) SN74LS126A (J, N)

SN54128 . . . 75-OHM LINE DRIVER
SN74128 . . . 50-OHM LINE DRIVER

128

positive logic:

$Y = \overline{A+B}$

See page 6-22

SN54128 (J, W)   SN74128 (J, N)

QUADRUPLE 2-INPUT POSITIVE-NAND SCHMITT TRIGGERS

132

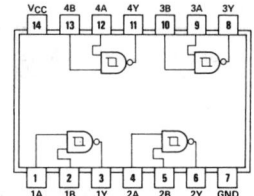

positive logic:

$Y = \overline{AB}$

See page 6-14

SN54132 (J, W)   SN74132 (J, N)
SN54LS132 (J, W) SN74LS132 (J, N)
SN54S132 (J, W)   SN74S132 (J, N)

TEXAS INSTRUMENTS
INCORPORATED
POST OFFICE BOX 5012 • DALLAS, TEXAS 75222

5

PIN ASSIGNMENTS (TOP VIEWS)

13-INPUT POSITIVE-NAND GATES

133

positive logic:
$$Y = \overline{ABCDEFGHIJKLM}$$

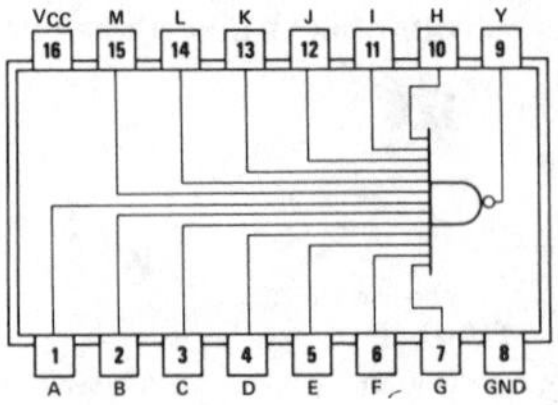

SN54S133 (J, W)   SN74S133 (J, N)

See page 6-2

12-INPUT POSITIVE-NAND GATES WITH THREE-STATE OUTPUTS

134

positive logic:
$$Y = \overline{ABCDEFGHIJKL}$$
Output is off (disabled) when output control is high.

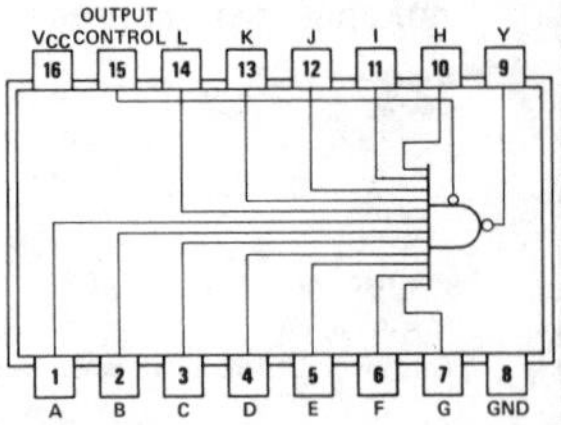

SN54S134 (J, W)   SN74S134 (J, N)

See page 6-33

QUAD EXCLUSIVE-OR/NOR GATES

135

positive logic: $Y = (A \oplus B) \oplus C = A\overline{B}\overline{C} + \overline{A}B\overline{C} + \overline{A}\overline{B}C + ABC$

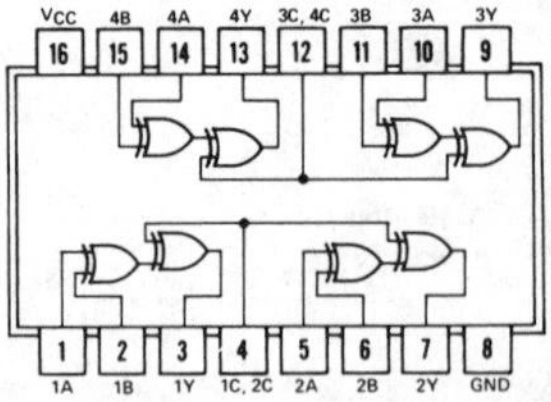

SN54S135 (J, W)   SN74S135(J, N)

See page 7-129

NC—No internal connection

QUAD EXCLUSIVE-OR GATES

136

positive logic: $Y = A \oplus B = A\overline{B} + \overline{A}B$

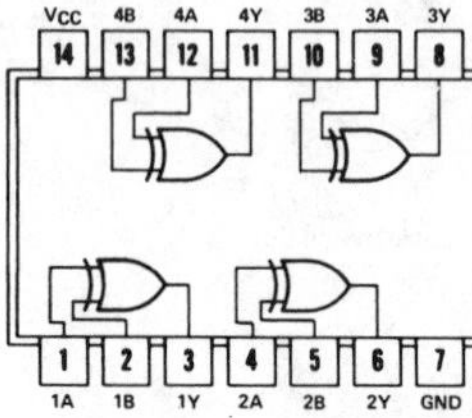

SN54136 (J, W)   SN74136 (J, N)
SN54LS136 (J, W) SN74LS136 (J, N)

See page 7-131

TEXAS INSTRUMENTS
INCORPORATED
POST OFFICE BOX 5012 • DALLAS, TEXAS 75222

PIN ASSIGNMENTS (TOP VIEW)

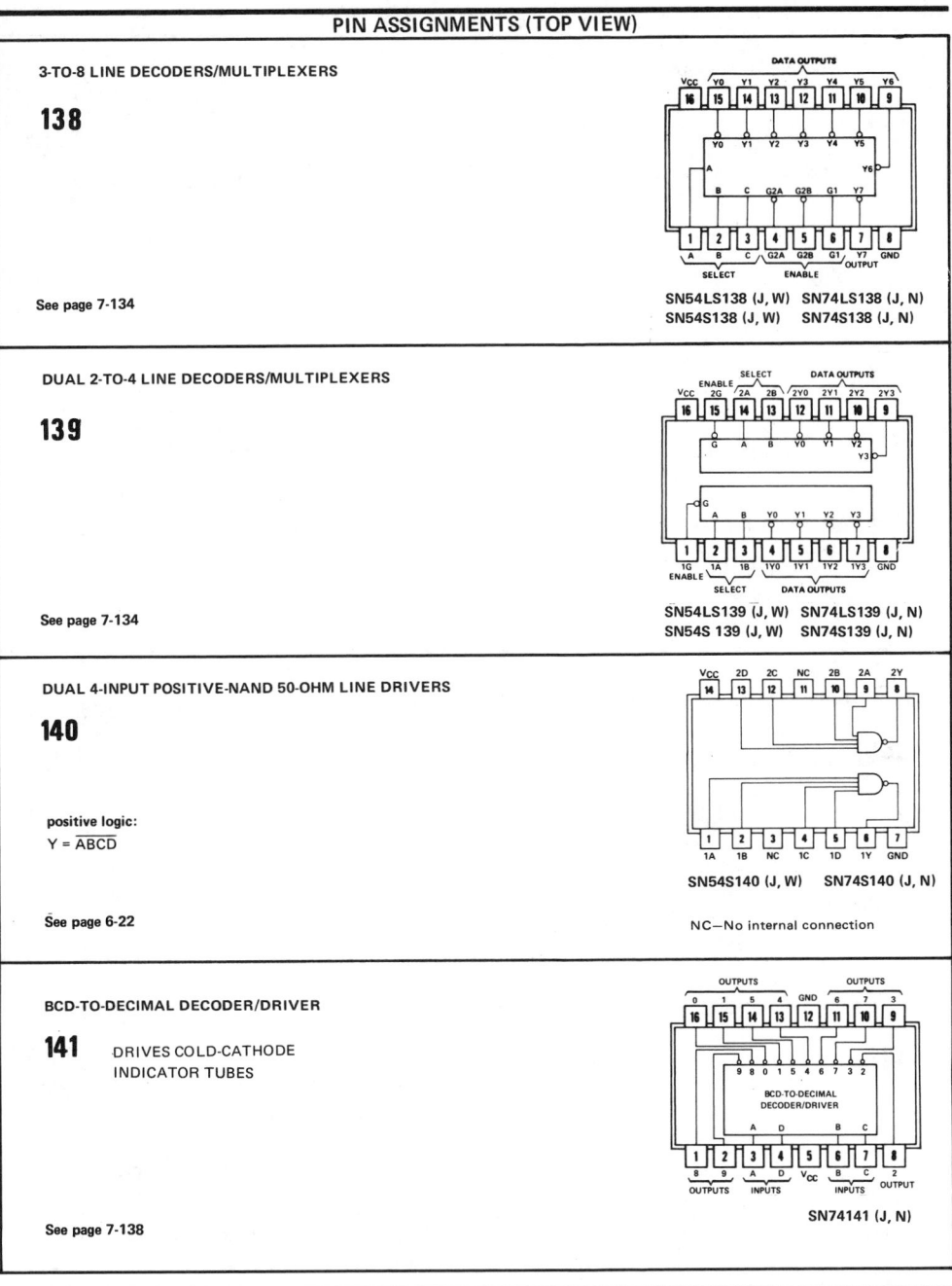

3-TO-8 LINE DECODERS/MULTIPLEXERS

138

See page 7-134

SN54LS138 (J, W) SN74LS138 (J, N)
SN54S138 (J, W)   SN74S138 (J, N)

DUAL 2-TO-4 LINE DECODERS/MULTIPLEXERS

139

See page 7-134

SN54LS139 (J, W) SN74LS139 (J, N)
SN54S 139 (J, W) SN74S139 (J, N)

DUAL 4-INPUT POSITIVE-NAND 50-OHM LINE DRIVERS

140

positive logic:
Y = $\overline{ABCD}$

See page 6-22

SN54S140 (J, W)   SN74S140 (J, N)

NC—No internal connection

BCD-TO-DECIMAL DECODER/DRIVER

141   DRIVES COLD-CATHODE
INDICATOR TUBES

See page 7-138

SN74141 (J, N)

TEXAS INSTRUMENTS
INCORPORATED
POST OFFICE BOX 5012 • DALLAS, TEXAS 75222

076

5

54/74 FAMILIES OF COMPATIBLE TTL CIRCUITS

PIN ASSIGNMENTS (TOP VIEWS)

COUNTER/LATCH/DECODER/DRIVER

142
DIVIDE-BY-10 COUNTER
4-BIT LATCH
4-BIT TO 7-SEGMENT DECODER
NIXIE ‡ TUBE DRIVER

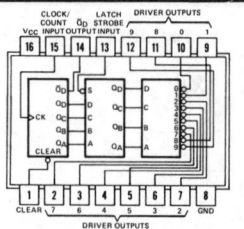

See page 7-140

SN74142 (J, N)

‡ Nixie is a registered trademark of the Borroughs Corp.

COUNTERS/LATCHES/DECODERS/DRIVERS

143
15 mA CONSTANT CURRENT
1- TO 5-V OUTPUT RANGE

144
UP TO 15-V INDICATORS
UP TO 25 mA
OPEN-COLLECTOR OUTPUT

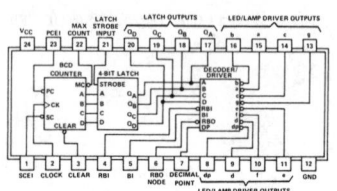

SN54143 (J, W)	SN74143 (J, N)
SN54144 (J, W)	SN74144 (J, N)

See page 7-143

BCD-TO-DECIMAL DECODERS/DRIVERS FOR LAMPS, RELAYS, MOS

145
BCD-TO-DECIMAL

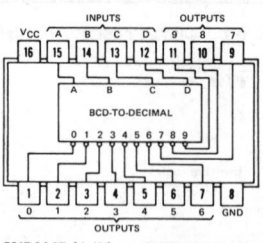

SN54145 (J, W)	SN74145 (J, N)
SN54LS145 (J, W)	SN74LS145 (J, W)

See page 7-148

10-LINE DECIMAL TO 4-LINE BCD PRIORITY ENCODERS

147

SN54147 (J, W)	SN74147 (J, N)
SN54LS147 (J, W)	SN74LS147 (J, N)
NC — No internal connection	

See page 7-151

TEXAS INSTRUMENTS
INCORPORATED
POST OFFICE BOX 5012 • DALLAS, TEXAS 75222

PIN ASSIGNMENTS (TOP VIEWS)

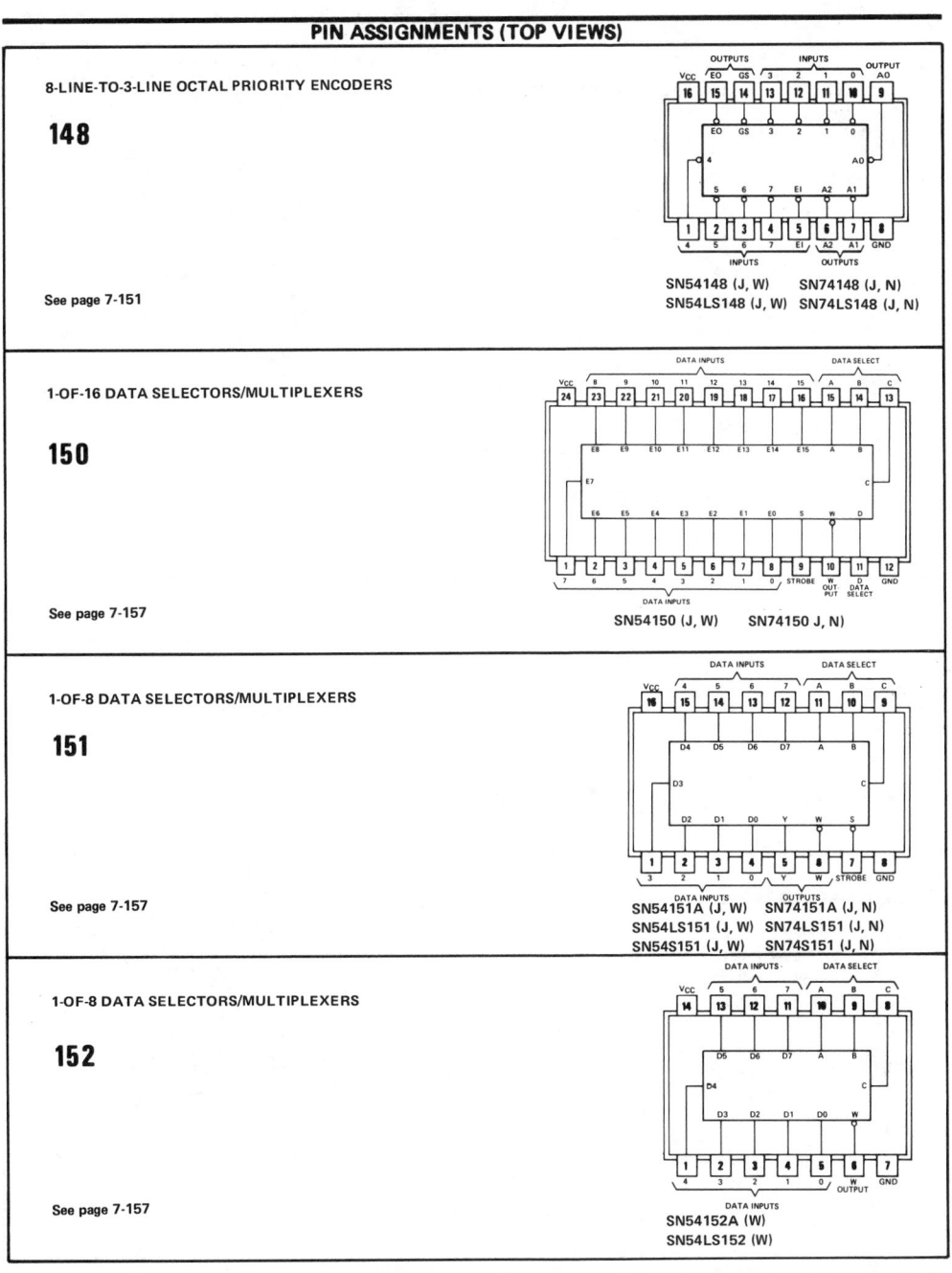

8-LINE-TO-3-LINE OCTAL PRIORITY ENCODERS

148

See page 7-151

SN54148 (J, W)   SN74148 (J, N)
SN54LS148 (J, W) SN74LS148 (J, N)

1-OF-16 DATA SELECTORS/MULTIPLEXERS

150

See page 7-157

SN54150 (J, W)   SN74150 J, N)

1-OF-8 DATA SELECTORS/MULTIPLEXERS

151

See page 7-157

SN54151A (J, W)   SN74151A (J, N)
SN54LS151 (J, W) SN74LS151 (J, N)
SN54S151 (J, W)   SN74S151 (J, N)

1-OF-8 DATA SELECTORS/MULTIPLEXERS

152

See page 7-157

SN54152A (W)
SN54LS152 (W)

5

PIN ASSIGNMENTS (TOP VIEW)

DUAL 4-LINE TO 1-LINE DATA SELECTORS/MULTIPLEXERS

153

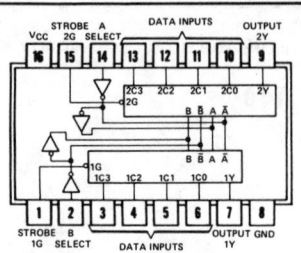

SN54153 (J, W)   SN74153 (J, N)
SN54L153 (J)   SN74L153 (J, N)
SN54LS153 (J, W)   SN74LS153 (J, N)
SN54S153 (J, W)   SN74S153 (J, N)

See page 7-165

4-LINE TO 16-LINE DECODERS/DEMULTIPLEXERS

154

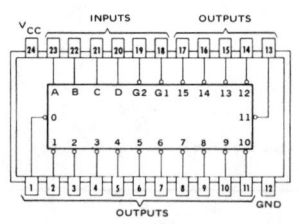

SN54154 (J, W)   SN74154 (J, N)
SN54L154 (J)   SN74L154 (J, N)

See page 7-171

DECODERS/DEMULTIPLEXERS

DUAL 2- TO 4-LINE DECODER
DUAL 1- TO 4-LINE DEMULTIPLEXER
3- TO 8-LINE DECODER
1- TO 8-LINE DEMULTIPLEXER

155   TOTEM-POLE OUTPUTS

156   OPEN-COLLECTOR OUTPUTS

See page 7-175

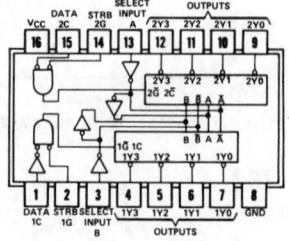

SN54155 (J, W)   SN74155 (J, N)
SN54LS155 (J, W)   SN74LS155 (J, N)
SN54156 (J, W)   SN74156 (J, N)
SN54LS156 (J, W)   SN74LS156 (J, N)

TEXAS INSTRUMENTS
INCORPORATED
POST OFFICE BOX 5012 • DALLAS, TEXAS 75222

PIN ASSIGNMENTS (TOP VIEW)

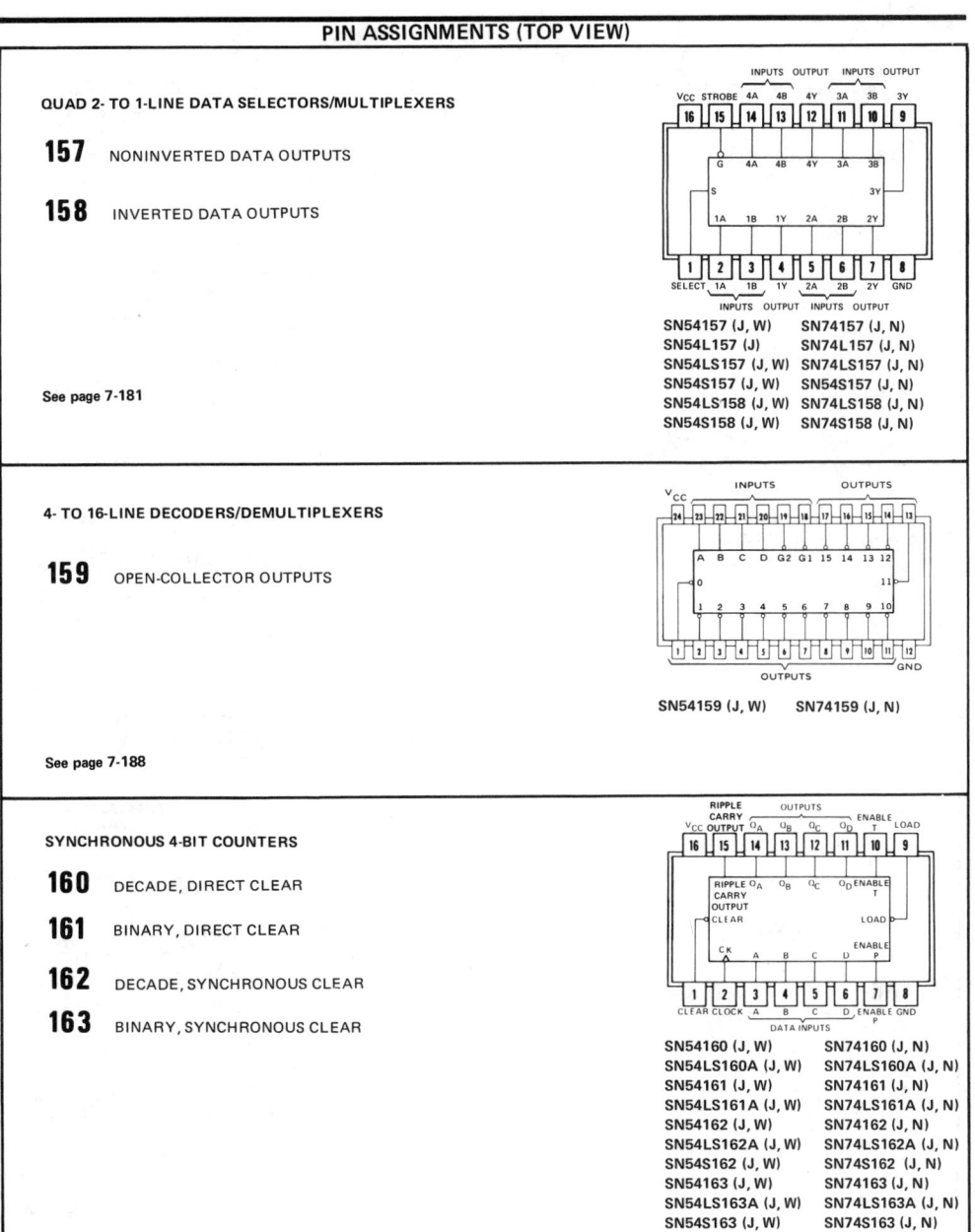

QUAD 2- TO 1-LINE DATA SELECTORS/MULTIPLEXERS

157 NONINVERTED DATA OUTPUTS

158 INVERTED DATA OUTPUTS

See page 7-181

SN54157 (J, W) SN74157 (J, N)
SN54L157 (J) SN74L157 (J, N)
SN54LS157 (J, W) SN74LS157 (J, N)
SN54S157 (J, W) SN54S157 (J, N)
SN54LS158 (J, W) SN74LS158 (J, N)
SN54S158 (J, W) SN74S158 (J, N)

4- TO 16-LINE DECODERS/DEMULTIPLEXERS

159 OPEN-COLLECTOR OUTPUTS

See page 7-188

SN54159 (J, W) SN74159 (J, N)

SYNCHRONOUS 4-BIT COUNTERS

160 DECADE, DIRECT CLEAR

161 BINARY, DIRECT CLEAR

162 DECADE, SYNCHRONOUS CLEAR

163 BINARY, SYNCHRONOUS CLEAR

See page 7-190

SN54160 (J, W) SN74160 (J, N)
SN54LS160A (J, W) SN74LS160A (J, N)
SN54161 (J, W) SN74161 (J, N)
SN54LS161A (J, W) SN74LS161A (J, N)
SN54162 (J, W) SN74162 (J, N)
SN54LS162A (J, W) SN74LS162A (J, N)
SN54S162 (J, W) SN74S162 (J, N)
SN54163 (J, W) SN74163 (J, N)
SN54LS163A (J, W) SN74LS163A (J, N)
SN54S163 (J, W) SN74S163 (J, N)

76

54/74 FAMILIES OF COMPATIBLE TTL CIRCUITS

PIN ASSIGNMENTS (TOP VIEWS)

8-BIT PARALLEL OUTPUT SERIAL SHIFT REGISTERS

164 ASYNCHRONOUS CLEAR

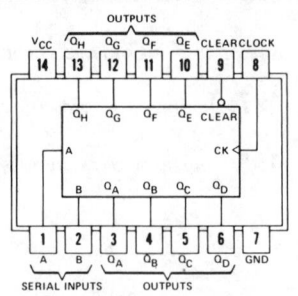

See page 7-206

SN54164 (J, W)   SN74164 (J, N)
SN54L164 (J, T)   SN74L164 (J, N)
SN54LS164 (J, W)   SN74LS164 (J, N)

**PARALLEL-LOAD 8-BIT SHIFT REGISTERS WITH
COMPLEMENTARY OUTPUTS**

165

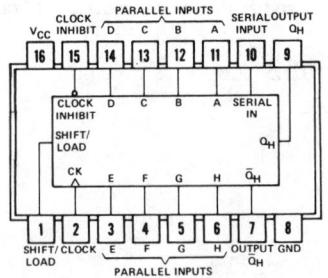

See page 7-212

SN54165 (J, W)   SN74165 (J, N)
SN54LS165 (J, W)   SN74LS165 (J, N)

8-BIT SHIFT REGISTERS

166 PARALLEL/SERIAL INPUT
SERIAL OUTPUT

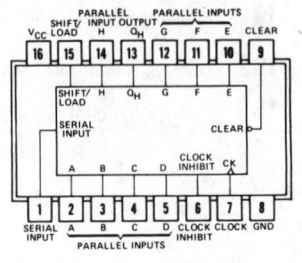

See page 7-217

SN54166 (J, W)   SN74166 (J, N)
SN54LS166 (J, W)   SN74LS166 (J, N)

TEXAS INSTRUMENTS
INCORPORATED
POST OFFICE BOX 5012 • DALLAS, TEXAS 75222

PIN ASSIGNMENTS (TOP VIEW)

SYNCHRONOUS DECADE RATE MULTIPLIERS

167

See page 7-222

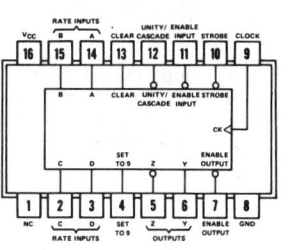

SN54167 (J, W)   SN74167 (J, N)

NC — No internal connection

4-BIT UP/DOWN SYNCHRONOUS COUNTERS

168   DECADE

169   BINARY

See page 7-226

SN54LS168A (J, W)   SN74LS168A (J, N)
SN54S168 (J, W)   SN74S168 (J, N)
SN54LS169A (J, W)   SN74LS169A (J, N)
SN54S169 (J, W)   SN74S169 (J, N)

4-BY-4 REGISTER FILES

170   SEPARATE READ/WRITE ADDRESSING
SIMULTANEOUS READ AND WRITE
OPEN-COLLECTOR OUTPUTS
EXPANDABLE TO 1024 WORDS

SN54170 (J, W)   SN74170 (J, N)
SN54LS170 (J, W)   SN74LS170 (J, N)

See page 7-237

5

TEXAS INSTRUMENTS
INCORPORATED
POST OFFICE BOX 5012 • DALLAS, TEXAS 75222

PIN ASSIGNMENTS (TOP VIEWS)

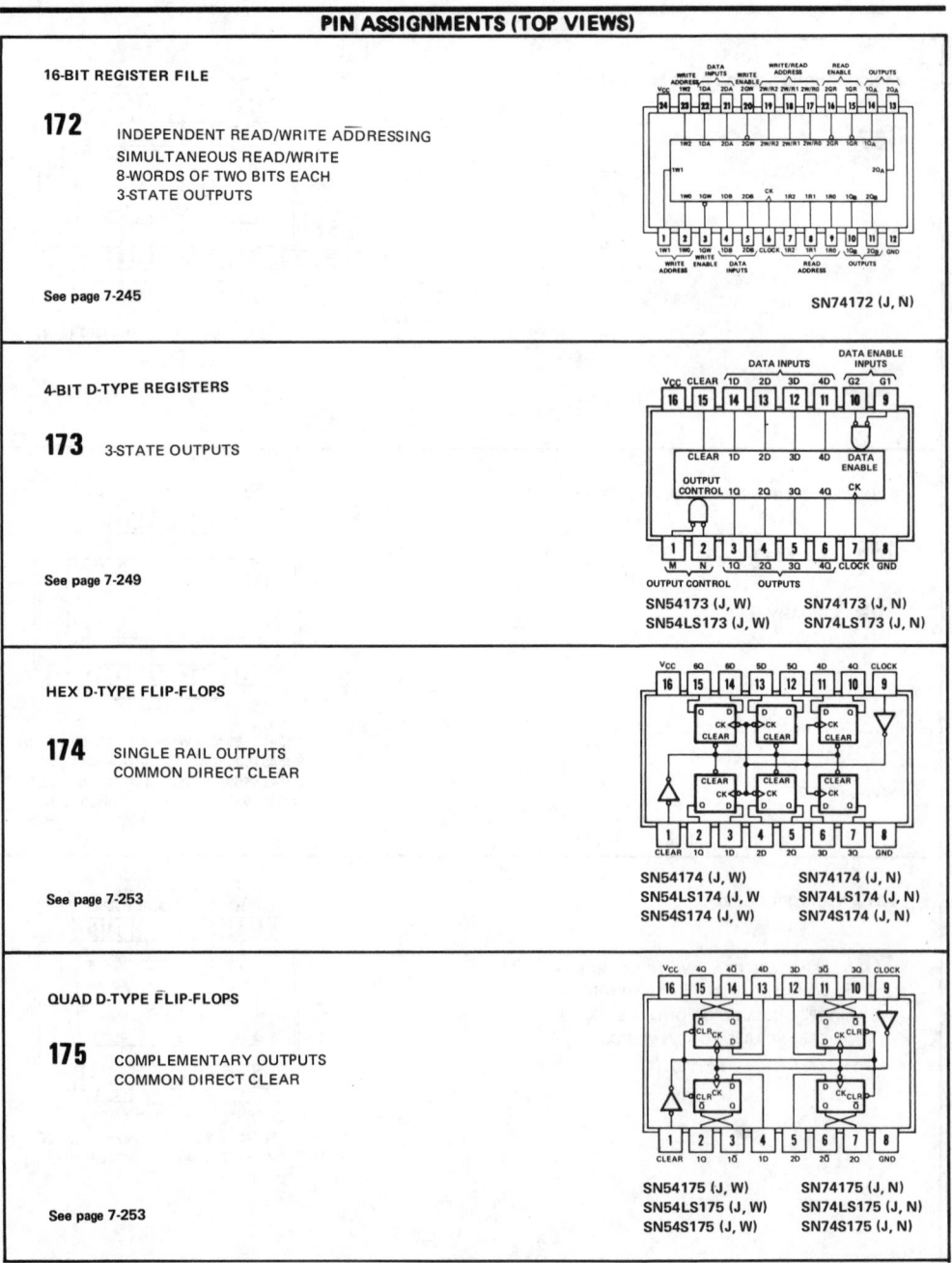

16-BIT REGISTER FILE

172
    INDEPENDENT READ/WRITE ADDRESSING
SIMULTANEOUS READ/WRITE
8-WORDS OF TWO BITS EACH
3-STATE OUTPUTS

See page 7-245

SN74172 (J, N)

4-BIT D-TYPE REGISTERS

173   3-STATE OUTPUTS

See page 7-249

SN54173 (J, W)   SN74173 (J, N)
SN54LS173 (J, W)   SN74LS173 (J, N)

HEX D-TYPE FLIP-FLOPS

174   SINGLE RAIL OUTPUTS
COMMON DIRECT CLEAR

See page 7-253

SN54174 (J, W)   SN74174 (J, N)
SN54LS174 (J, W   SN74LS174 (J, N)
SN54S174 (J, W)   SN74S174 (J, N)

QUAD D-TYPE FLIP-FLOPS

175   COMPLEMENTARY OUTPUTS
COMMON DIRECT CLEAR

See page 7-253

SN54175 (J, W)   SN74175 (J, N)
SN54LS175 (J, W)   SN74LS175 (J, N)
SN54S175 (J, W)   SN74S175 (J, N)

TEXAS INSTRUMENTS
INCORPORATED
POST OFFICE BOX 5012 • DALLAS, TEXAS 75222

PIN ASSIGNMENTS (TOP VIEWS)

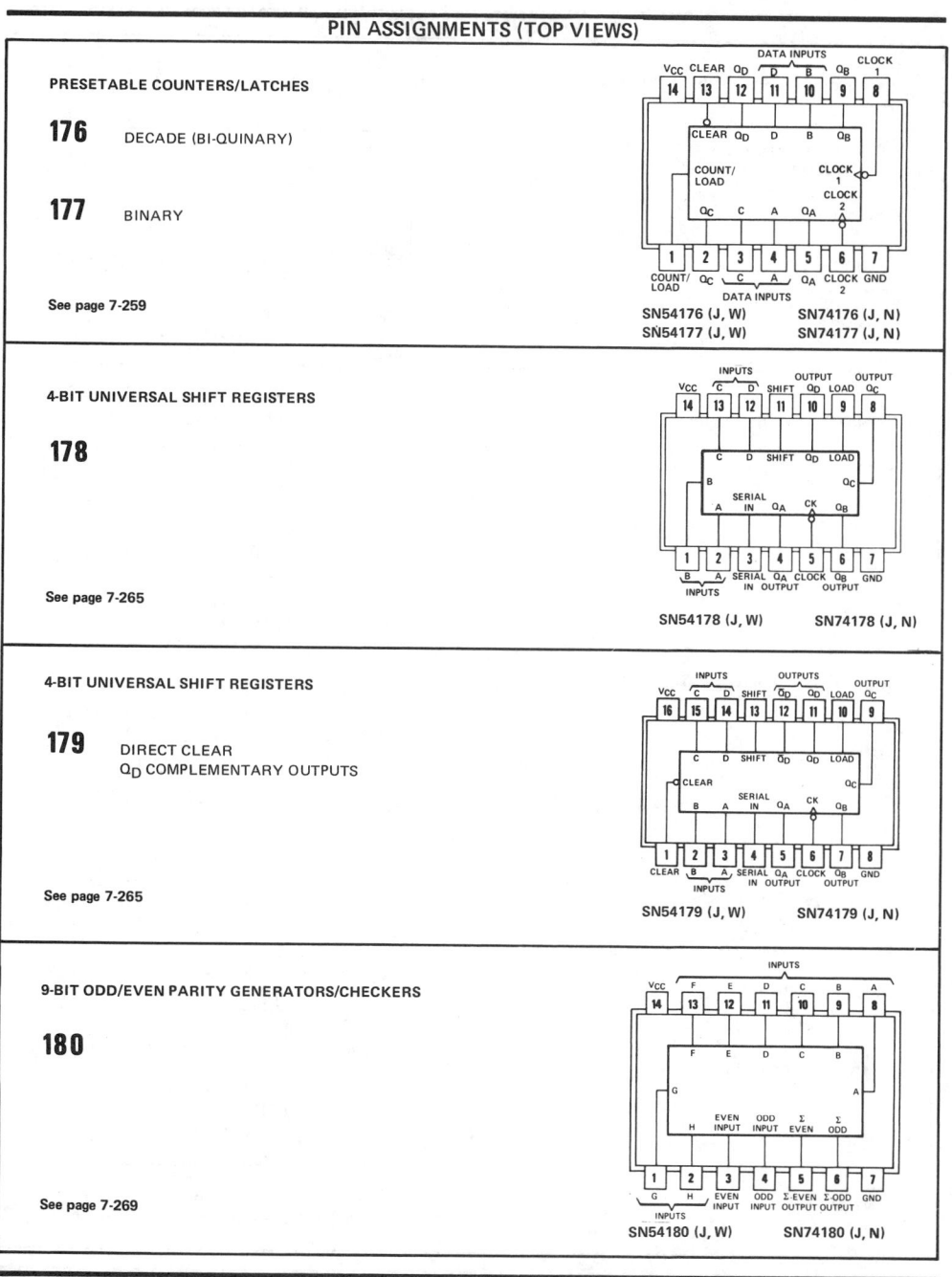

PRESETABLE COUNTERS/LATCHES

176 DECADE (BI-QUINARY)

177 BINARY

See page 7-259

SN54176 (J, W) SN74176 (J, N)
SN54177 (J, W) SN74177 (J, N)

4-BIT UNIVERSAL SHIFT REGISTERS

178

See page 7-265

SN54178 (J, W) SN74178 (J, N)

4-BIT UNIVERSAL SHIFT REGISTERS

179 DIRECT CLEAR
Q_D COMPLEMENTARY OUTPUTS

See page 7-265

SN54179 (J, W) SN74179 (J, N)

9-BIT ODD/EVEN PARITY GENERATORS/CHECKERS

180

See page 7-269

SN54180 (J, W) SN74180 (J, N)

5

PIN ASSIGNMENTS (TOP VIEWS)

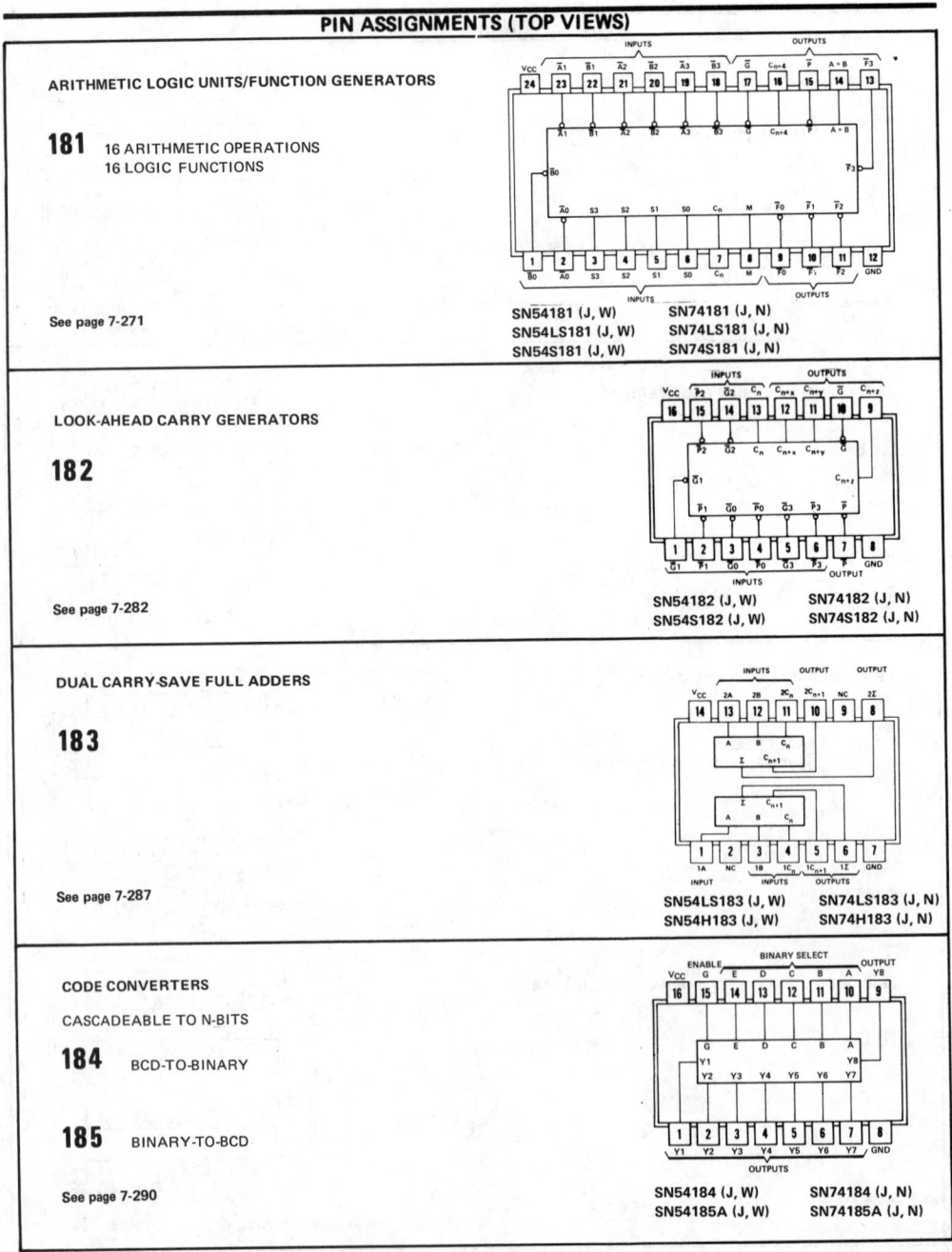

ARITHMETIC LOGIC UNITS/FUNCTION GENERATORS

181 16 ARITHMETIC OPERATIONS
16 LOGIC FUNCTIONS

See page 7-271

SN54181 (J, W) SN74181 (J, N)
SN54LS181 (J, W) SN74LS181 (J, N)
SN54S181 (J, W) SN74S181 (J, N)

LOOK-AHEAD CARRY GENERATORS

182

See page 7-282

SN54182 (J, W) SN74182 (J, N)
SN54S182 (J, W) SN74S182 (J, N)

DUAL CARRY-SAVE FULL ADDERS

183

See page 7-287

SN54LS183 (J, W) SN74LS183 (J, N)
SN54H183 (J, W) SN74H183 (J, N)

CODE CONVERTERS

CASCADEABLE TO N-BITS

184 BCD-TO-BINARY

185 BINARY-TO-BCD

See page 7-290

SN54184 (J, W) SN74184 (J, N)
SN54185A (J, W) SN74185A (J, N)

TEXAS INSTRUMENTS
INCORPORATED
POST OFFICE BOX 5012 • DALLAS, TEXAS 75222

54/74 FAMILIES OF COMPATIBLE TTL CIRCUITS

PIN ASSIGNMENTS (TOP VIEWS)

512-BIT PROGRAMMABLE READ-ONLY MEMORIES

186 64 8-BIT WORDS
OPEN-COLLECTOR OUTPUTS

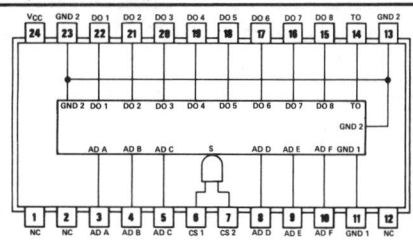

See Bipolar Microcomputer Components Data Book, LCC4270

SN54186 (J, W)   SN74186 (J, N)

NC — No internal connection

1024-BIT READ-ONLY MEMORIES

187 256 4-BIT WORDS
OPEN-COLLECTOR OUTPUTS

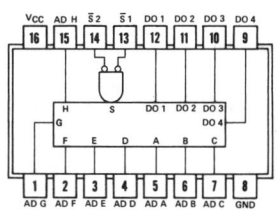

See Bipolar Microcomputer Components Data Book, LCC4270

SN54187 (J, W)   SN74187 (J, N)

256-BIT PROGRAMMABLE READ-ONLY MEMORIES

188 32 8-BIT WORDS
OPEN-COLLECTOR OUTPUTS

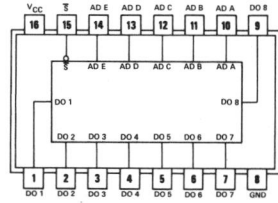

See Bipolar Microcomputer Components Data Book, LCC4270

SN54188A (J, W)   SN74188A (J, N)
SN54S188 (J, W)   SN74S188 (J, N)

64-BIT RANDOM-ACCESS MEMORIES

189 16 4-BIT WORDS
THREE-STATE OUTPUTS

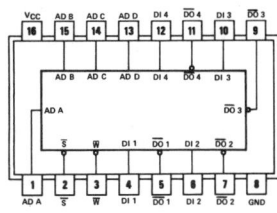

See Bipolar Microcomputer Components Data Book, LCC4270

SN54S189 (J, W)   SN74S189 (J, N)

5

54/74 FAMILIES OF COMPATIBLE TTL CIRCUITS

PIN ASSIGNMENTS (TOP VIEWS)

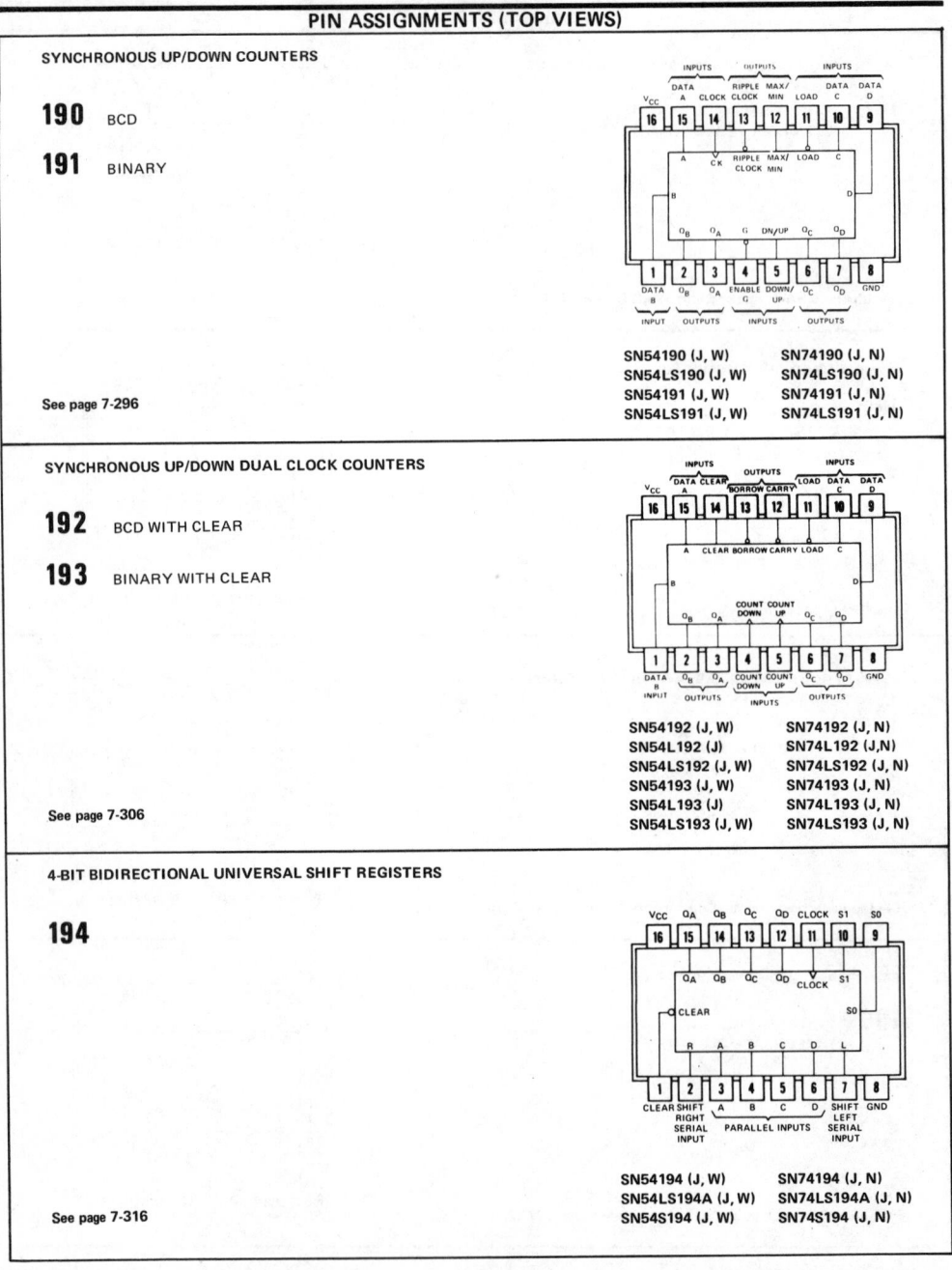

SYNCHRONOUS UP/DOWN COUNTERS

190 BCD

191 BINARY

See page 7-296

SN54190 (J, W)   SN74190 (J, N)
SN54LS190 (J, W)   SN74LS190 (J, N)
SN54191 (J, W)   SN74191 (J, N)
SN54LS191 (J, W)   SN74LS191 (J, N)

SYNCHRONOUS UP/DOWN DUAL CLOCK COUNTERS

192 BCD WITH CLEAR

193 BINARY WITH CLEAR

See page 7-306

SN54192 (J, W)   SN74192 (J, N)
SN54L192 (J)   SN74L192 (J,N)
SN54LS192 (J, W)   SN74LS192 (J, N)
SN54193 (J, W)   SN74193 (J, N)
SN54L193 (J)   SN74L193 (J, N)
SN54LS193 (J, W)   SN74LS193 (J, N)

4-BIT BIDIRECTIONAL UNIVERSAL SHIFT REGISTERS

194

See page 7-316

SN54194 (J, W)   SN74194 (J, N)
SN54LS194A (J, W)   SN74LS194A (J, N)
SN54S194 (J, W)   SN74S194 (J, N)

TEXAS INSTRUMENTS
INCORPORATED
POST OFFICE BOX 5012 • DALLAS, TEXAS 75222

PIN ASSIGNMENTS (TOP VIEWS)

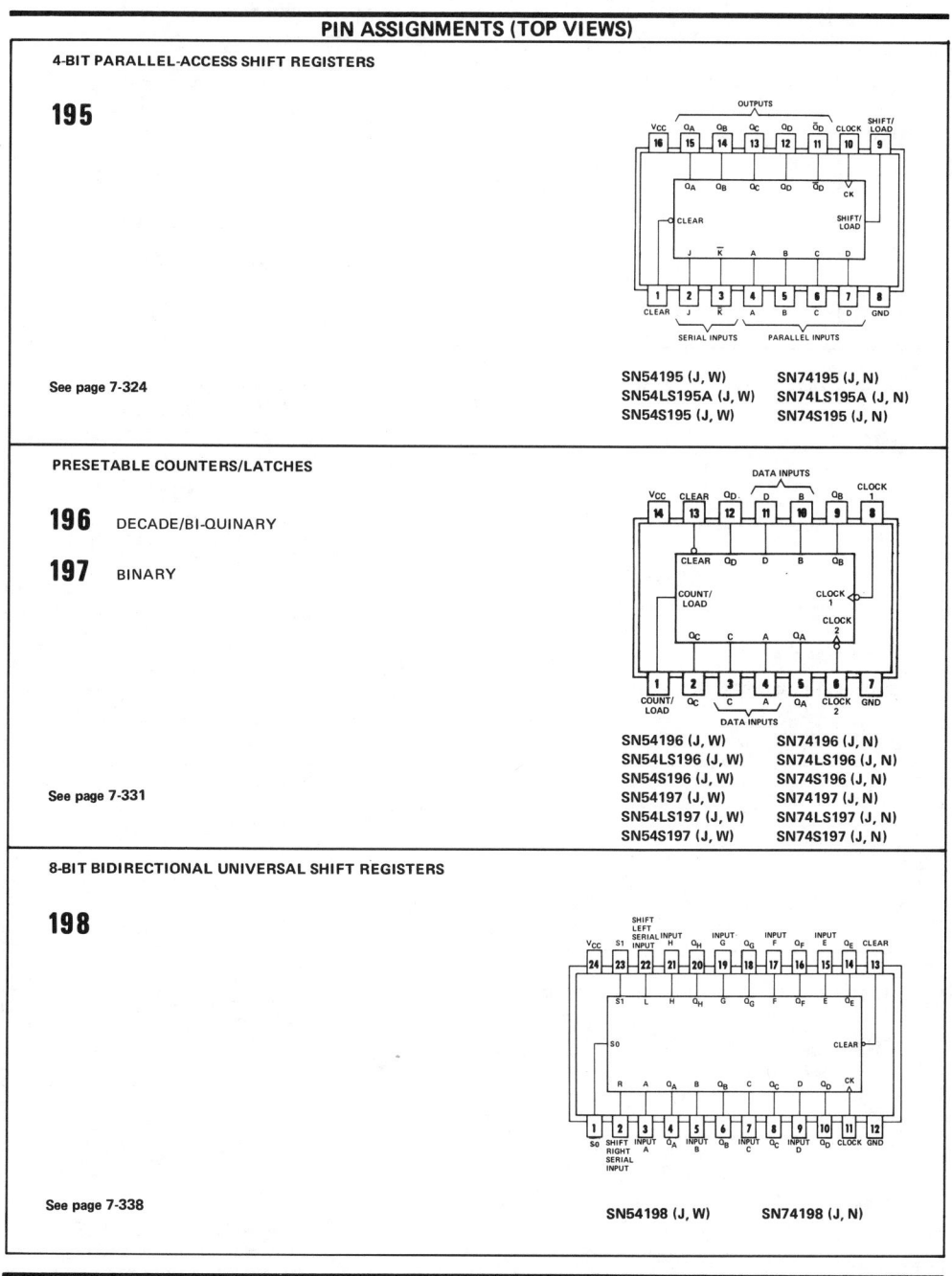

4-BIT PARALLEL-ACCESS SHIFT REGISTERS

195

See page 7-324

SN54195 (J, W)   SN74195 (J, N)
SN54LS195A (J, W)   SN74LS195A (J, N)
SN54S195 (J, W)   SN74S195 (J, N)

PRESETABLE COUNTERS/LATCHES

196 DECADE/BI-QUINARY

197 BINARY

See page 7-331

SN54196 (J, W)   SN74196 (J, N)
SN54LS196 (J, W)   SN74LS196 (J, N)
SN54S196 (J, W)   SN74S196 (J, N)
SN54197 (J, W)   SN74197 (J, N)
SN54LS197 (J, W)   SN74LS197 (J, N)
SN54S197 (J, W)   SN74S197 (J, N)

8-BIT BIDIRECTIONAL UNIVERSAL SHIFT REGISTERS

198

See page 7-338

SN54198 (J, W)   SN74198 (J, N)

5

076

TEXAS INSTRUMENTS
INCORPORATED
POST OFFICE BOX 5012 • DALLAS, TEXAS 75222

54/74 FAMILIES OF COMPATIBLE TTL CIRCUITS

PIN ASSIGNMENTS (TOP VIEWS)

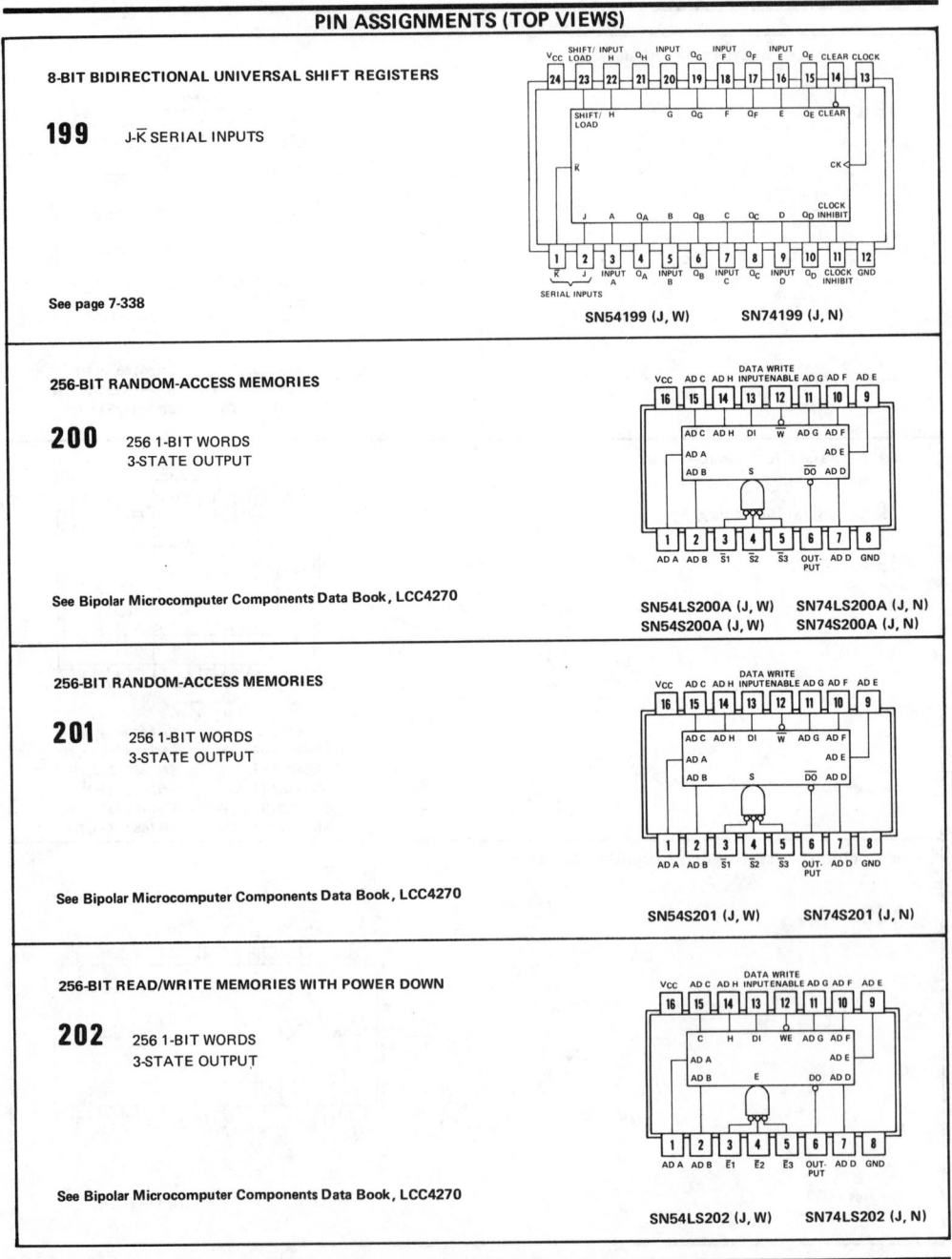

8-BIT BIDIRECTIONAL UNIVERSAL SHIFT REGISTERS

199 J-$\overline{\text{K}}$ SERIAL INPUTS

See page 7-338

SN54199 (J, W)   SN74199 (J, N)

256-BIT RANDOM-ACCESS MEMORIES

200 256 1-BIT WORDS
3-STATE OUTPUT

See Bipolar Microcomputer Components Data Book, LCC4270

SN54LS200A (J, W)   SN74LS200A (J, N)
SN54S200A (J, W)   SN74S200A (J, N)

256-BIT RANDOM-ACCESS MEMORIES

201 256 1-BIT WORDS
3-STATE OUTPUT

See Bipolar Microcomputer Components Data Book, LCC4270

SN54S201 (J, W)   SN74S201 (J, N)

256-BIT READ/WRITE MEMORIES WITH POWER DOWN

202 256 1-BIT WORDS
3-STATE OUTPUT

See Bipolar Microcomputer Components Data Book, LCC4270

SN54LS202 (J, W)   SN74LS202 (J, N)

TEXAS INSTRUMENTS
INCORPORATED
POST OFFICE BOX 5012 • DALLAS, TEXAS 75222

54/74 FAMILIES OF COMPATIBLE TTL CIRCUITS

PIN ASSIGNMENTS (TOP VIEWS)

RANDOM-ACCESS MEMORIES

207 EDGE-TRIGGERED WRITE CONTROL
256 4-BIT WORDS
COMMON I/O PORTS

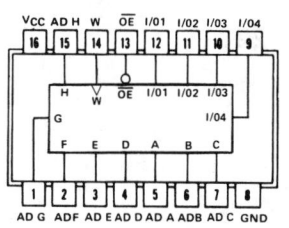

SN54LS207 (J)   SN74LS207 (J, N)
SN54S207 (J)   SN74S207 (J, N)

See Bipolar Microcomputer Components Data Book, LCC4270

RANDOM-ACCESS MEMORIES

208 256 4-BIT WORDS
3-STATE OUTPUTS
EDGE-TRIGGERED WRITE CONTROL

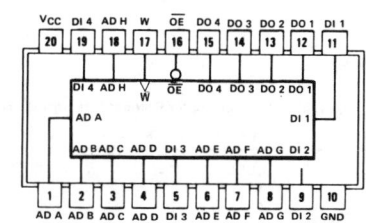

SN54LS208 (J)   SN74LS208 (L, N)
SN54S208 (J)   SN74S208 (J, N)

See Bipolar Microcomputer Components Data Book, LCC4270

RANDOM-ACCESS MEMORIES

1024 1-BIT WORDS
3-STATE OUTPUTS

214 CHIP SELECT ($\overline{S}$) SIMPLIFIES EXPANSION

215 CHIP ENABLE ($\overline{E}$) SIMPLIFIES EXPANSION
AND CONTROLS POWER DOWN

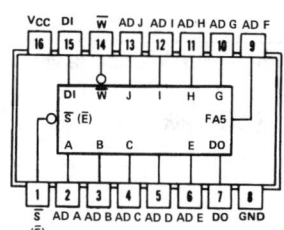

SN54LS214 (JD)   SN74LS214 (JD, N)
SN54S214 (JD)   SN74S214 (JD, N)
SN54LS215 (JD)   SN74LS215 (JD, N)

See Bipolar Microcomputer Components Data Book, LCC4270

TEXAS INSTRUMENTS
INCORPORATED
POST OFFICE BOX 5012 • DALLAS, TEXAS 75222

PIN ASSIGNMENTS (TOP VIEWS)

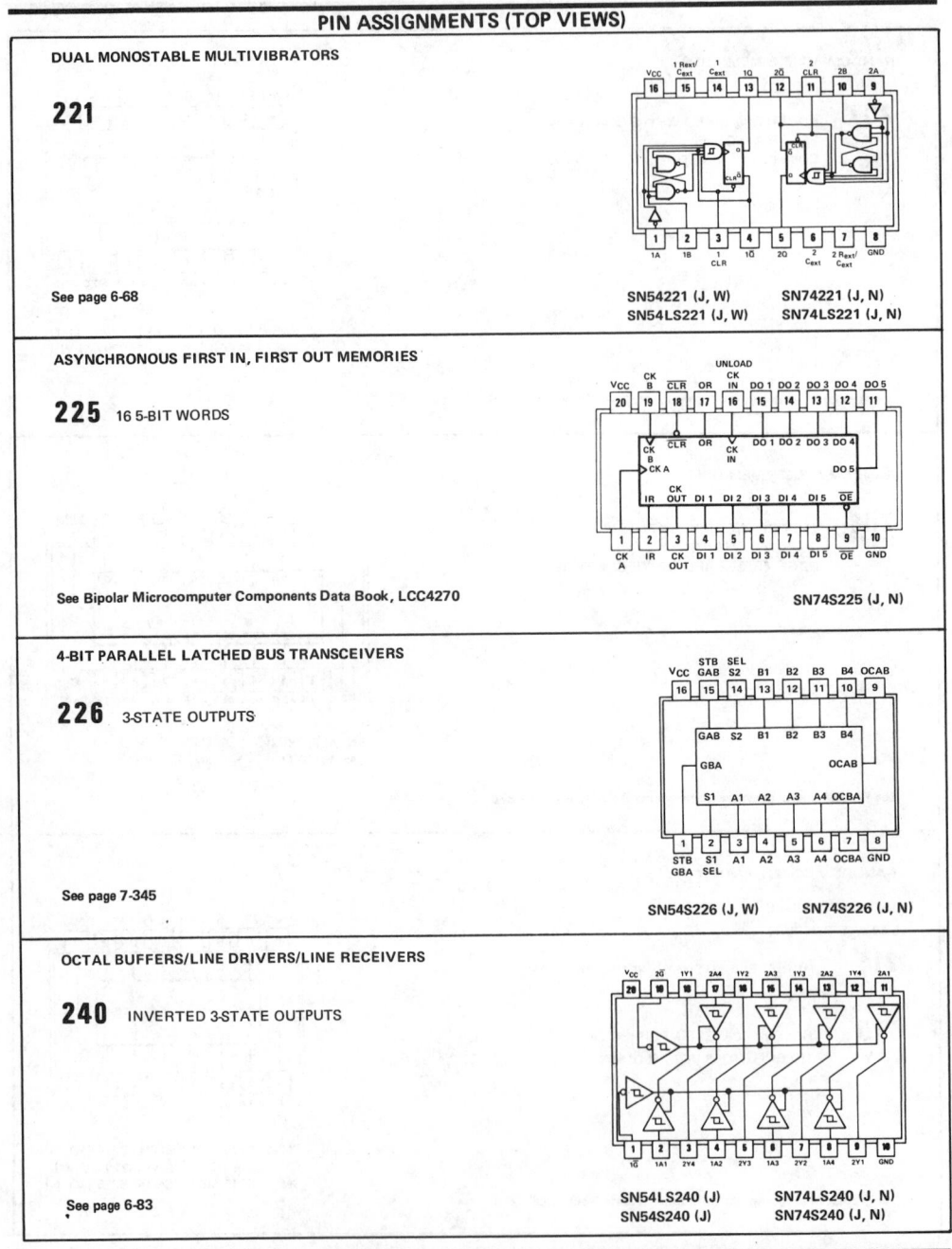

DUAL MONOSTABLE MULTIVIBRATORS

221

See page 6-68

SN54221 (J, W)   SN74221 (J, N)
SN54LS221 (J, W)   SN74LS221 (J, N)

ASYNCHRONOUS FIRST IN, FIRST OUT MEMORIES

225 16 5-BIT WORDS

See Bipolar Microcomputer Components Data Book, LCC4270

SN74S225 (J, N)

4-BIT PARALLEL LATCHED BUS TRANSCEIVERS

226 3-STATE OUTPUTS

See page 7-345

SN54S226 (J, W)   SN74S226 (J, N)

OCTAL BUFFERS/LINE DRIVERS/LINE RECEIVERS

240 INVERTED 3-STATE OUTPUTS

See page 6-83

SN54LS240 (J)   SN74LS240 (J, N)
SN54S240 (J)   SN74S240 (J, N)

TEXAS INSTRUMENTS
INCORPORATED
POST OFFICE BOX 5012 • DALLAS, TEXAS 75222

54/74 FAMILIES OF COMPATIBLE TTL CIRCUITS

PIN ASSIGNMENTS (TOP VIEWS)

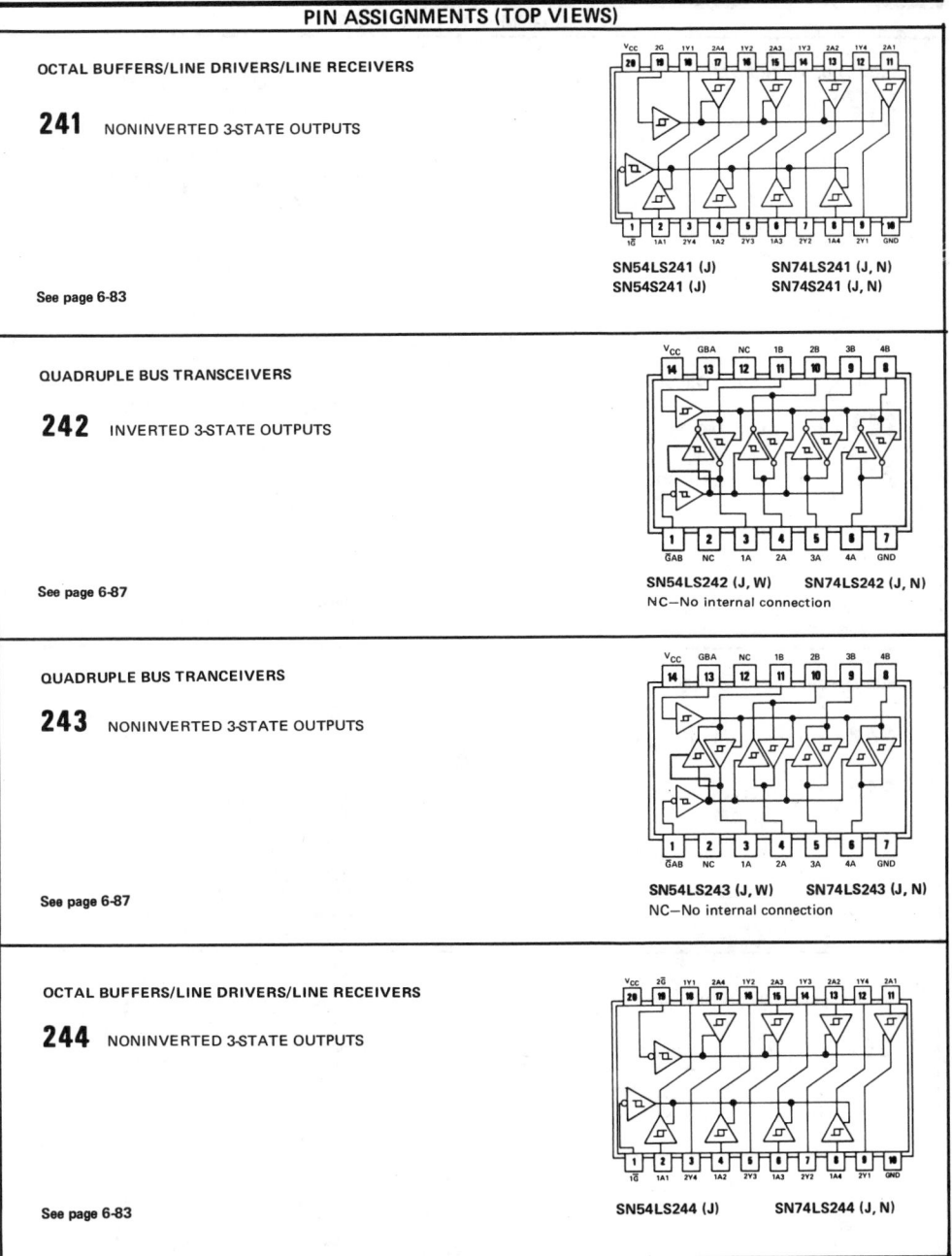

OCTAL BUFFERS/LINE DRIVERS/LINE RECEIVERS

241 NONINVERTED 3-STATE OUTPUTS

See page 6-83

SN54LS241 (J)   SN74LS241 (J, N)
SN54S241 (J)   SN74S241 (J, N)

QUADRUPLE BUS TRANSCEIVERS

242 INVERTED 3-STATE OUTPUTS

See page 6-87

SN54LS242 (J, W)   SN74LS242 (J, N)
NC—No internal connection

QUADRUPLE BUS TRANCEIVERS

243 NONINVERTED 3-STATE OUTPUTS

See page 6-87

SN54LS243 (J, W)   SN74LS243 (J, N)
NC—No internal connection

OCTAL BUFFERS/LINE DRIVERS/LINE RECEIVERS

244 NONINVERTED 3-STATE OUTPUTS

See page 6-83

SN54LS244 (J)   SN74LS244 (J, N)

5

PIN ASSIGNMENTS (TOP VIEWS)

OCTAL BUS TRANCEIVERS

245 NONINVERTED 3-STATE OUTPUTS

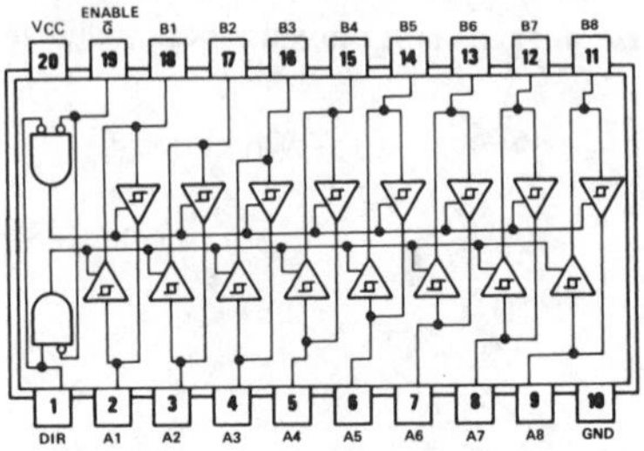

See page 7-349

SN54LS245 (J)   SN74LS245 (J, N)

BCD-TO-SEVEN-SEGMENT DECODERS/DRIVERS

246 ACTIVE-LOW, OPEN-COLLECTOR, 30-V OUTPUTS

247 ACTIVE-LOW, OPEN-COLLECTOR, 15-V OUTPUTS

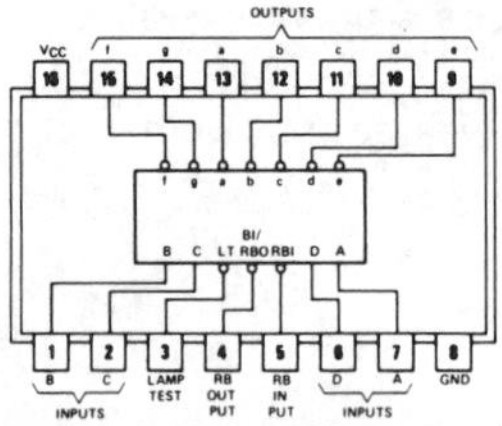

See page 7-351

SN54246 (J, W)	SN74246 (J, N)
SN54247 (J, W)	SN74247 (J, N)
SN54LS247 (J, W)	SN74LS247 (J, N)

BCD-TO-SEVEN-SEGMENT DECODERS/DRIVERS

248 INTERNAL PULL-UP OUTPUTS

249 OPEN-COLLECTOR OUTPUTS

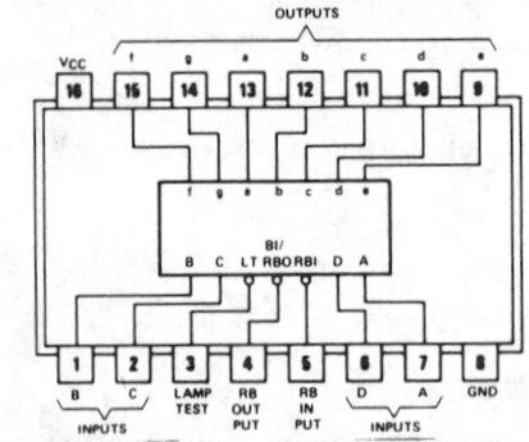

See page 7-351

SN54248 (J, W)	SN74248 (J, N)
SN54LS248 (J, W)	SN74LS248 (J, N)
SN54249 (J, W)	SN74249 (J, N)
SN54LS249 (J, W)	SN74LS249 (J, N)

DATA SELECTORS/MULTIPLEXERS

251 TRUE AND INVERTED 3-STATE OUTPUTS

See page 7-362

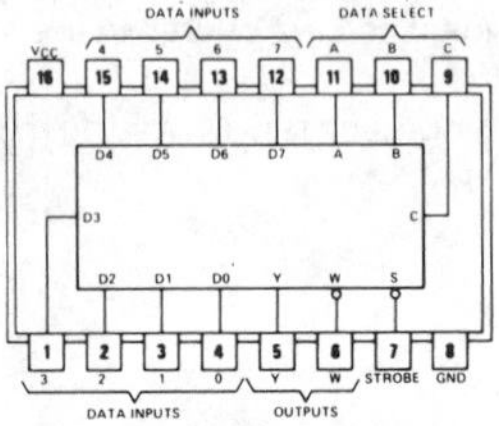

SN54251 (J, W)	SN74251 (J, N)
SN54LS251 (J, W)	SN74LS251 (J, N)
SN54S251 (J, W)	SN74S251 (J, N)

TEXAS INSTRUMENTS
INCORPORATED
POST OFFICE BOX 5012 • DALLAS, TEXAS 75222

PIN ASSIGNMENTS (TOP VIEWS)

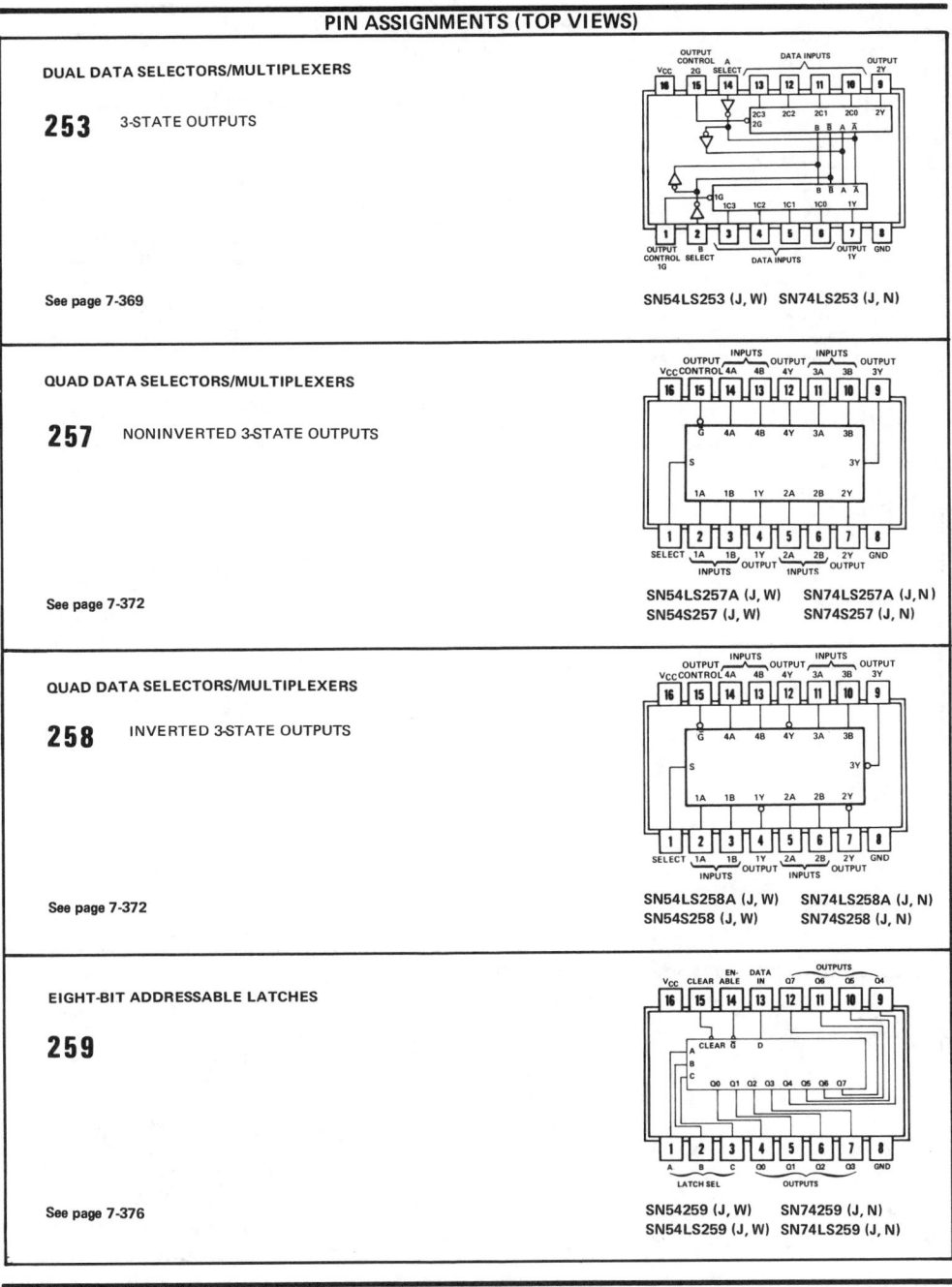

DUAL DATA SELECTORS/MULTIPLEXERS

253   3-STATE OUTPUTS

See page 7-369

SN54LS253 (J, W)   SN74LS253 (J, N)

QUAD DATA SELECTORS/MULTIPLEXERS

257   NONINVERTED 3-STATE OUTPUTS

See page 7-372

SN54LS257A (J, W)   SN74LS257A (J, N)
SN54S257 (J, W)   SN74S257 (J, N)

QUAD DATA SELECTORS/MULTIPLEXERS

258   INVERTED 3-STATE OUTPUTS

See page 7-372

SN54LS258A (J, W)   SN74LS258A (J, N)
SN54S258 (J, W)   SN74S258 (J, N)

EIGHT-BIT ADDRESSABLE LATCHES

259

See page 7-376

SN54259 (J, W)   SN74259 (J, N)
SN54LS259 (J, W)   SN74LS259 (J, N)

5

54/74 FAMILIES OF COMPATIBLE TTL CIRCUITS

PIN ASSIGNMENTS (TOP VIEWS)

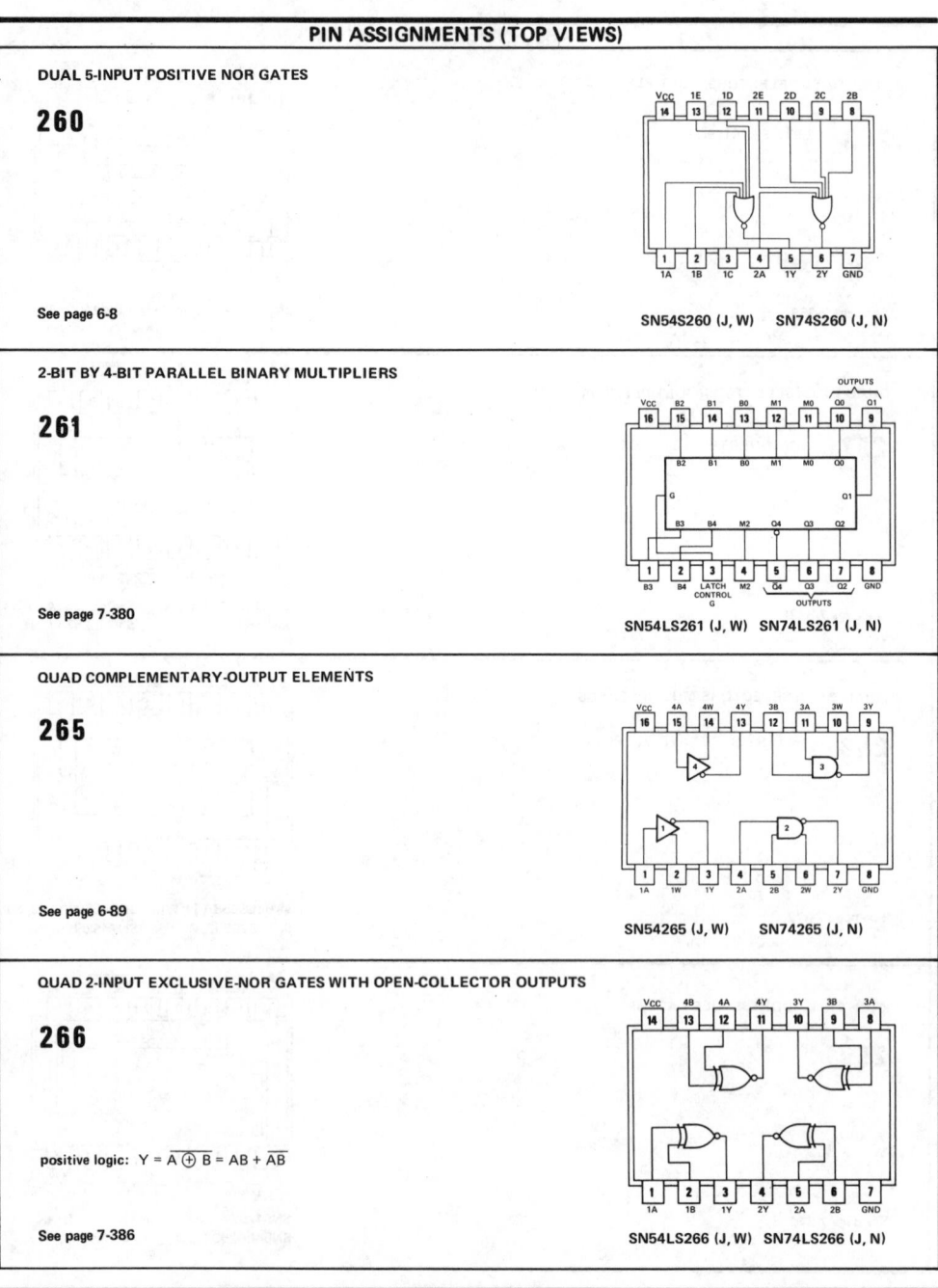

DUAL 5-INPUT POSITIVE NOR GATES

260

See page 6-8

SN54S260 (J, W)   SN74S260 (J, N)

2-BIT BY 4-BIT PARALLEL BINARY MULTIPLIERS

261

See page 7-380

SN54LS261 (J, W) SN74LS261 (J, N)

QUAD COMPLEMENTARY-OUTPUT ELEMENTS

265

See page 6-89

SN54265 (J, W)   SN74265 (J, N)

QUAD 2-INPUT EXCLUSIVE-NOR GATES WITH OPEN-COLLECTOR OUTPUTS

266

positive logic: $Y = \overline{A \oplus B} = AB + \overline{AB}$

See page 7-386

SN54LS266 (J, W) SN74LS266 (J, N)

TEXAS INSTRUMENTS
INCORPORATED
POST OFFICE BOX 5012 • DALLAS, TEXAS 75222

8

PIN ASSIGNMENTS (TOP VIEWS)

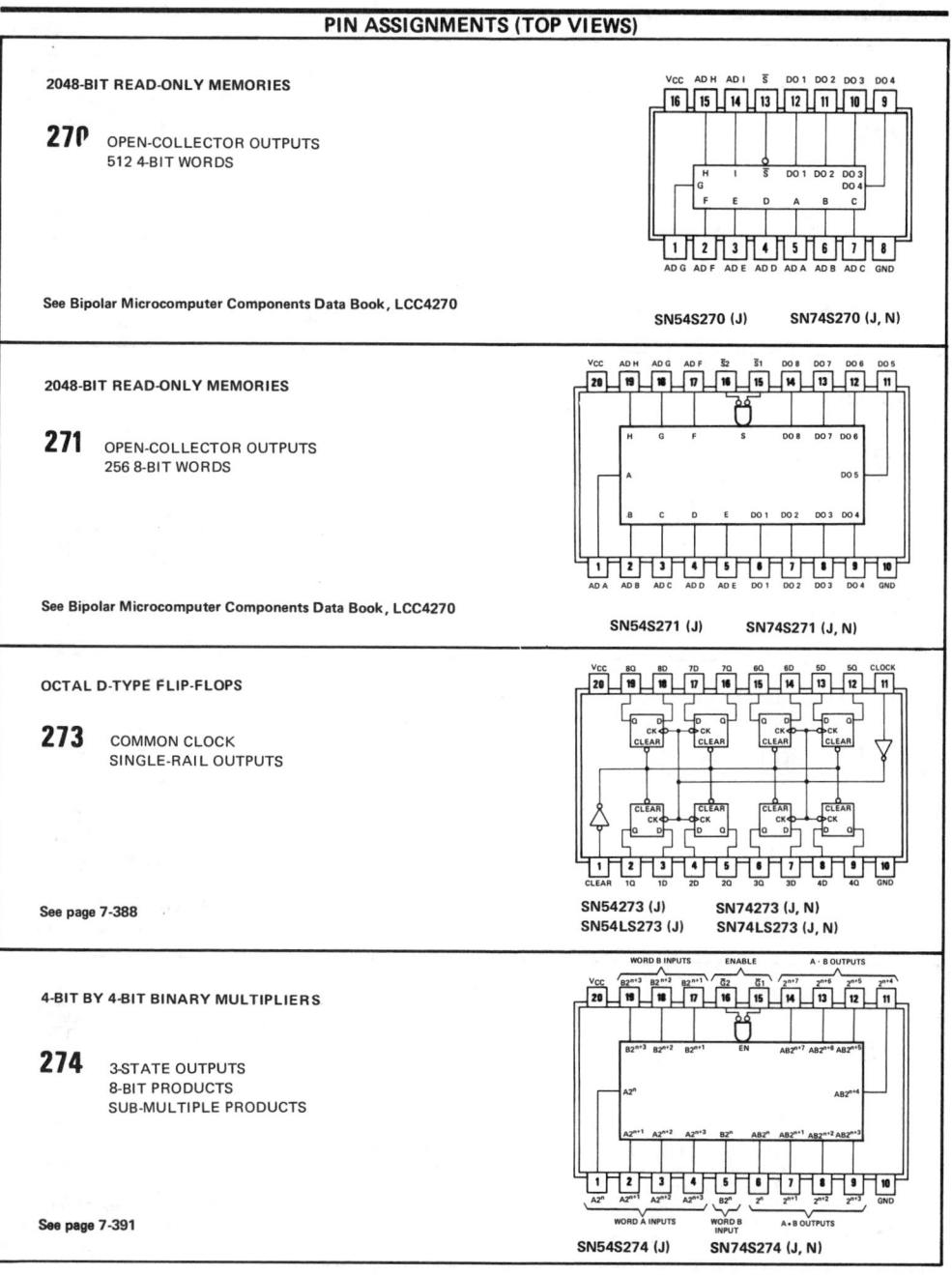

2048-BIT READ-ONLY MEMORIES

270 OPEN-COLLECTOR OUTPUTS
512 4-BIT WORDS

See Bipolar Microcomputer Components Data Book, LCC4270

SN54S270 (J)   SN74S270 (J, N)

2048-BIT READ-ONLY MEMORIES

271 OPEN-COLLECTOR OUTPUTS
256 8-BIT WORDS

See Bipolar Microcomputer Components Data Book, LCC4270

SN54S271 (J)   SN74S271 (J, N)

OCTAL D-TYPE FLIP-FLOPS

273 COMMON CLOCK
SINGLE-RAIL OUTPUTS

See page 7-388

SN54273 (J)   SN74273 (J, N)
SN54LS273 (J)   SN74LS273 (J, N)

4-BIT BY 4-BIT BINARY MULTIPLIERS

274 3-STATE OUTPUTS
8-BIT PRODUCTS
SUB-MULTIPLE PRODUCTS

See page 7-391

SN54S274 (J)   SN74S274 (J, N)

54/74 FAMILIES OF COMPATIBLE TTL CIRCUITS

PIN ASSIGNMENTS (TOP VIEW)

7-BIT SLICE WALLACE TREES

275 3-STATE OUTPUTS

See page 7-391

SN54LS275 (J)   SN74LS275 (J, N)
SN54S275 (J)   SN74S275 (J, N)

QUAD J-$\overline{\text{K}}$ FLIP-FLOPS

276 SEPARATE CLOCKS
EDGE-TRIGGERING
COMMON DIRECT CLEAR

See page 7-401

SN54276 (J)   SN74276 (J, N)

4-BIT CASCADEABLE PRIORITY REGISTERS

278 LATCHED DATA INPUTS
PRIORITY OUTPUT GATING

See page 7-403

SN54278 (J, W)   SN74278 (J, N)

NC — No internal connection

QUAD $\overline{\text{S}}$-$\overline{\text{R}}$ LATCHES

279 DIODE-CLAMPED INPUTS
TOTEM-POLE OUTPUTS

FUNCTION TABLE

INPUTS		OUTPUT
$\overline{\text{S}}$[†]	$\overline{\text{R}}$	Q
H	H	Q_0
L	H	H
H	L	L
L	L	H*

H = high level
L = low level
Q_0 = the level of Q before the indicated input conditions were established.
*This output level is pseudo stable; that is, it may not persist when the $\overline{\text{S}}$ and $\overline{\text{R}}$ inputs return to their inactive (high) level.
[†]For latches with double $\overline{\text{S}}$ inputs:
   H = both $\overline{\text{S}}$ inputs high
   L = one or both $\overline{\text{S}}$ inputs low

See page 6-60

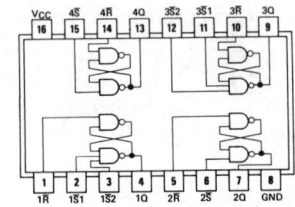

SN54279 (J, W)   SN74279 (J, N)
SN54LS279 (J, W) SN74LS279 (J, N)

TEXAS INSTRUMENTS
INCORPORATED
POST OFFICE BOX 5012 • DALLAS, TEXAS 75222

PIN ASSIGNMENTS (TOP VIEWS)

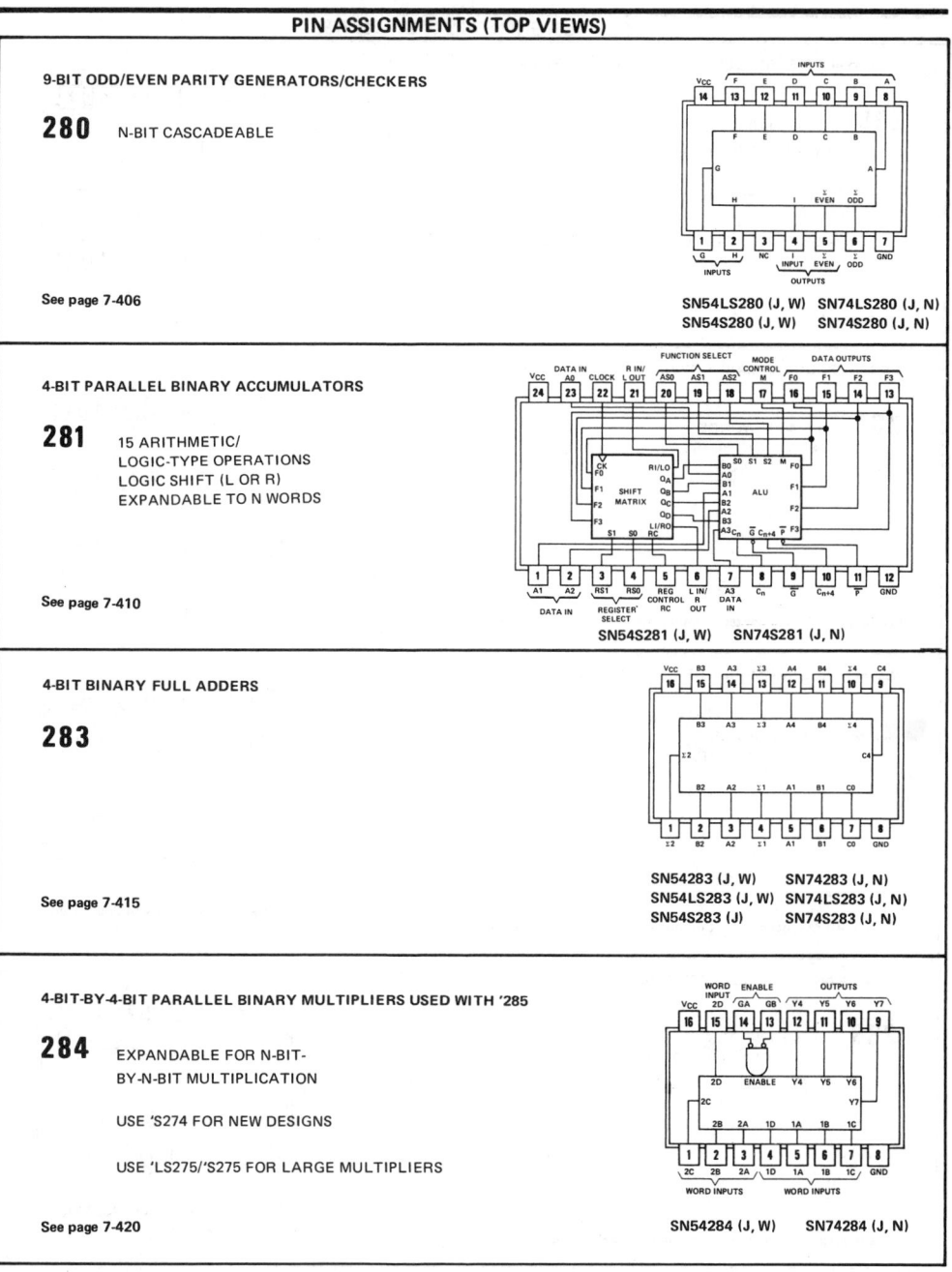

9-BIT ODD/EVEN PARITY GENERATORS/CHECKERS

280 N-BIT CASCADEABLE

See page 7-406

SN54LS280 (J, W) SN74LS280 (J, N)
SN54S280 (J, W) SN74S280 (J, N)

4-BIT PARALLEL BINARY ACCUMULATORS

281 15 ARITHMETIC/
LOGIC-TYPE OPERATIONS
LOGIC SHIFT (L OR R)
EXPANDABLE TO N WORDS

See page 7-410

SN54S281 (J, W) SN74S281 (J, N)

4-BIT BINARY FULL ADDERS

283

See page 7-415

SN54283 (J, W) SN74283 (J, N)
SN54LS283 (J, W) SN74LS283 (J, N)
SN54S283 (J) SN74S283 (J, N)

4-BIT-BY-4-BIT PARALLEL BINARY MULTIPLIERS USED WITH '285

284 EXPANDABLE FOR N-BIT-
BY-N-BIT MULTIPLICATION

USE 'S274 FOR NEW DESIGNS

USE 'LS275/'S275 FOR LARGE MULTIPLIERS

See page 7-420

SN54284 (J, W) SN74284 (J, N)

5

54/74 FAMILIES OF COMPATIBLE TTL CIRCUITS

PIN ASSIGNMENTS (TOP VIEWS)

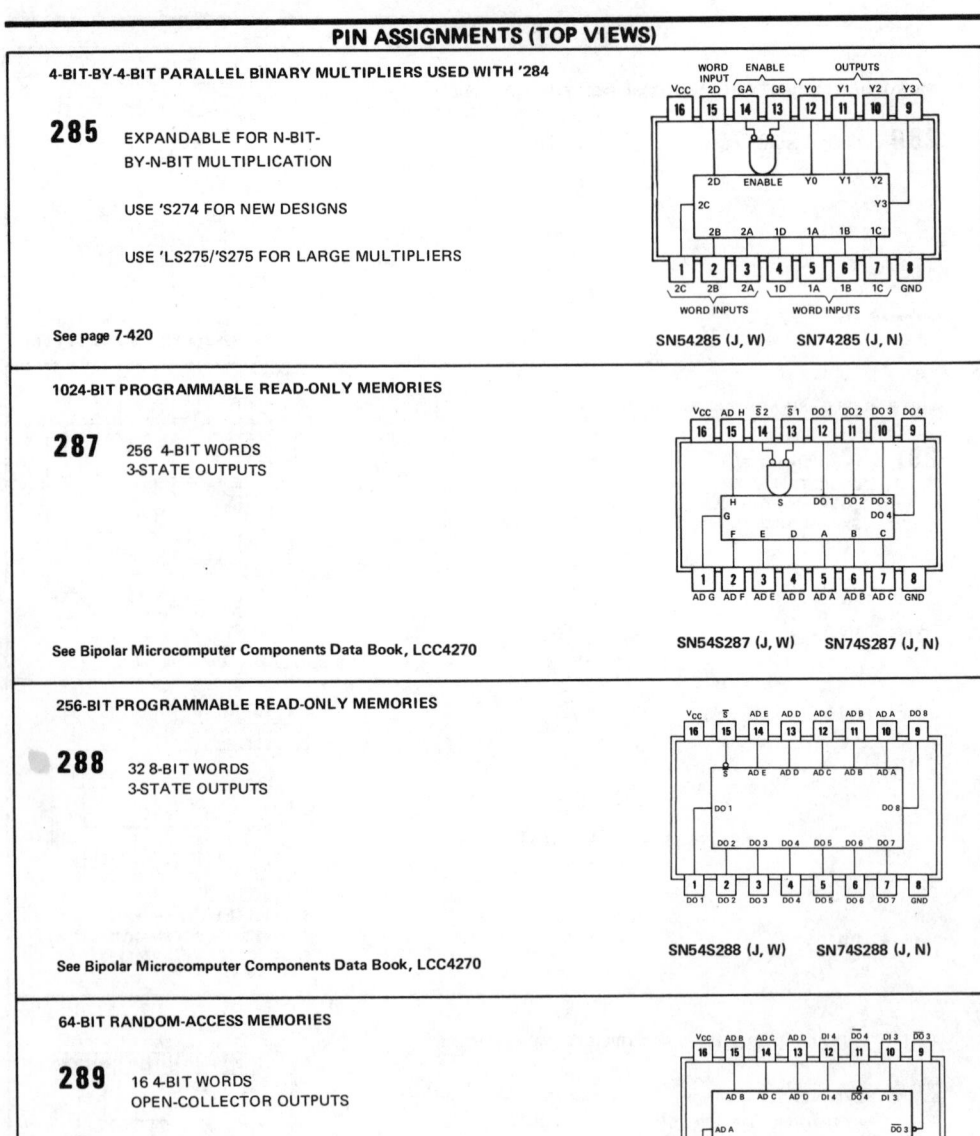

4-BIT-BY-4-BIT PARALLEL BINARY MULTIPLIERS USED WITH '284

285 EXPANDABLE FOR N-BIT-
BY-N-BIT MULTIPLICATION

USE 'S274 FOR NEW DESIGNS

USE 'LS275/'S275 FOR LARGE MULTIPLIERS

See page 7-420

SN54285 (J, W)   SN74285 (J, N)

1024-BIT PROGRAMMABLE READ-ONLY MEMORIES

287 256 4-BIT WORDS
3-STATE OUTPUTS

See Bipolar Microcomputer Components Data Book, LCC4270

SN54S287 (J, W)   SN74S287 (J, N)

256-BIT PROGRAMMABLE READ-ONLY MEMORIES

288 32 8-BIT WORDS
3-STATE OUTPUTS

See Bipolar Microcomputer Components Data Book, LCC4270

SN54S288 (J, W)   SN74S288 (J, N)

64-BIT RANDOM-ACCESS MEMORIES

289 16 4-BIT WORDS
OPEN-COLLECTOR OUTPUTS

See Bipolar Microcomputer Components Data Book, LCC4270

SN54S289 (J, W)   SN74S289 (J, N)

TEXAS INSTRUMENTS
INCORPORATED
POST OFFICE BOX 5012 • DALLAS, TEXAS 75222

54/74 FAMILIES OF COMPATIBLE TTL CIRCUITS

PIN ASSIGNMENTS (TOP VIEWS)

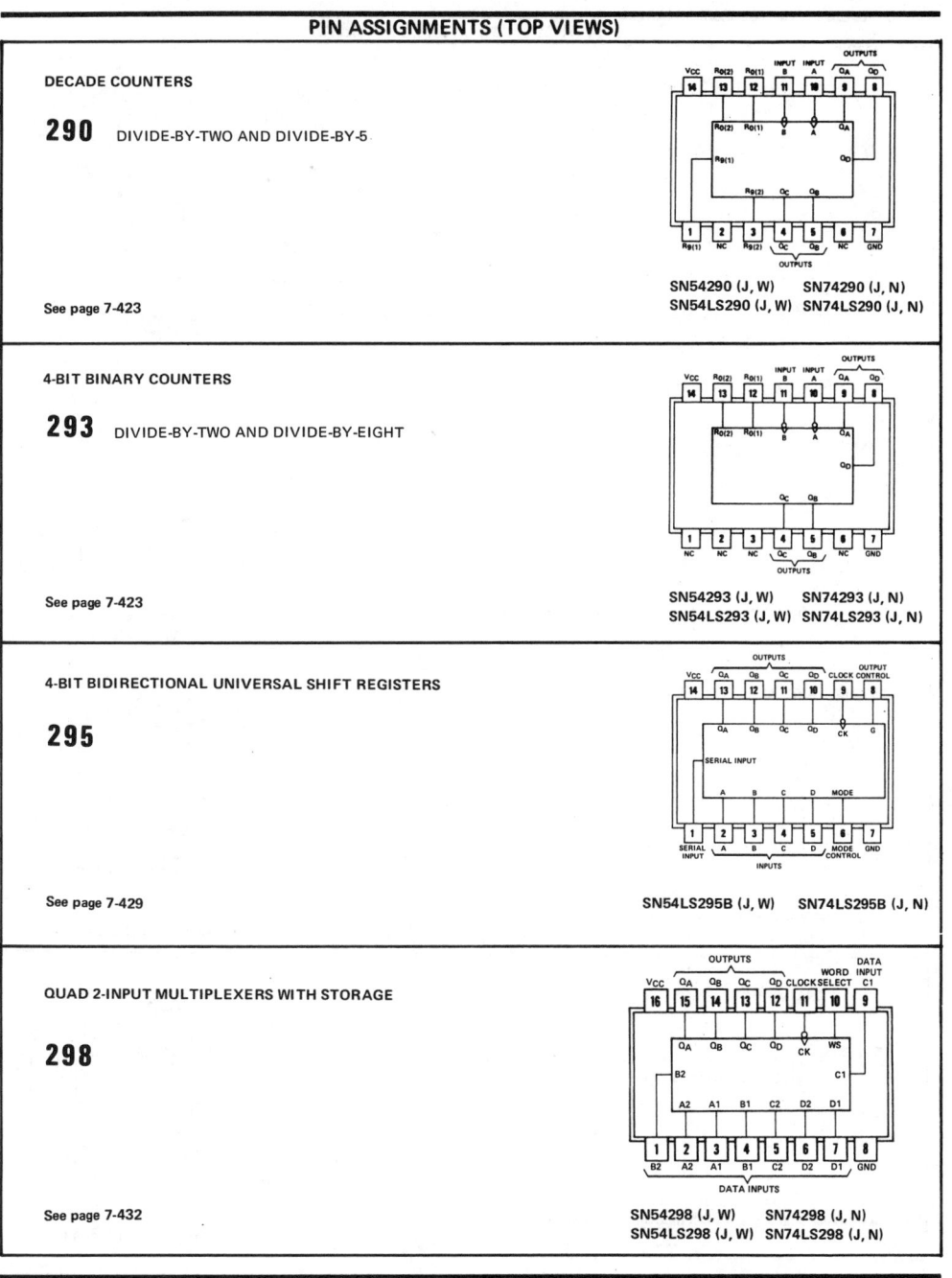

DECADE COUNTERS

290 DIVIDE-BY-TWO AND DIVIDE-BY-5

See page 7-423

SN54290 (J, W)   SN74290 (J, N)
SN54LS290 (J, W) SN74LS290 (J, N)

4-BIT BINARY COUNTERS

293 DIVIDE-BY-TWO AND DIVIDE-BY-EIGHT

See page 7-423

SN54293 (J, W)   SN74293 (J, N)
SN54LS293 (J, W) SN74LS293 (J, N)

4-BIT BIDIRECTIONAL UNIVERSAL SHIFT REGISTERS

295

See page 7-429

SN54LS295B (J, W)   SN74LS295B (J, N)

QUAD 2-INPUT MULTIPLEXERS WITH STORAGE

298

See page 7-432

SN54298 (J, W)   SN74298 (J, N)
SN54LS298 (J, W) SN74LS298 (J, N)

54/74 FAMILIES OF COMPATIBLE TTL CIRCUITS

PIN ASSIGNMENTS (TOP VIEWS)

8-BIT BIDIRECTIONAL UNIVERSAL SHIFT/STORAGE REGISTERS

299 3-STATE OUTPUTS

See page 7-437

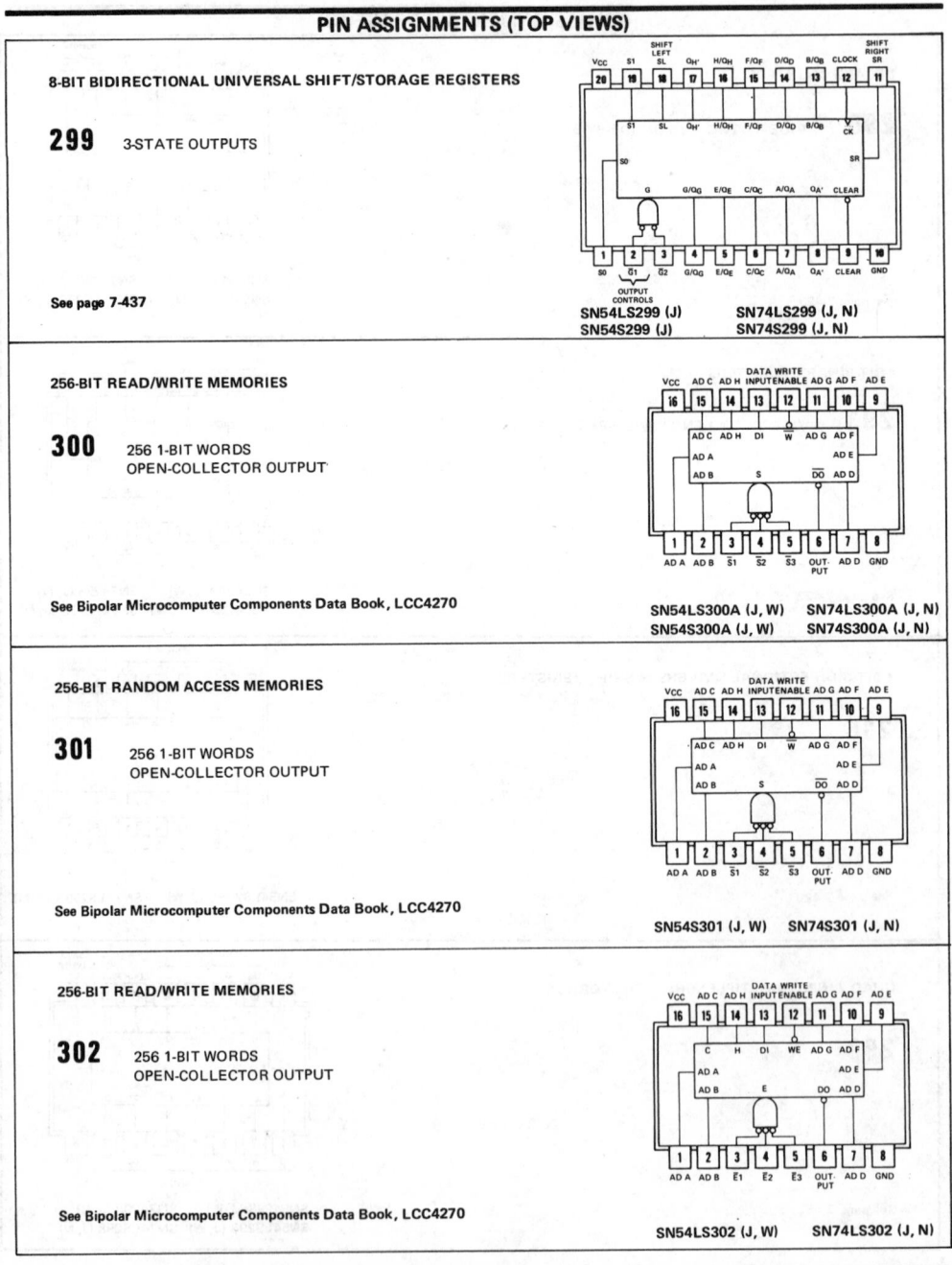

SN54LS299 (J)   SN74LS299 (J, N)
SN54S299 (J)   SN74S299 (J, N)

256-BIT READ/WRITE MEMORIES

300 256 1-BIT WORDS
OPEN-COLLECTOR OUTPUT

See Bipolar Microcomputer Components Data Book, LCC4270

SN54LS300A (J, W)   SN74LS300A (J, N)
SN54S300A (J, W)   SN74S300A (J, N)

256-BIT RANDOM ACCESS MEMORIES

301 256 1-BIT WORDS
OPEN-COLLECTOR OUTPUT

See Bipolar Microcomputer Components Data Book, LCC4270

SN54S301 (J, W)   SN74S301 (J, N)

256-BIT READ/WRITE MEMORIES

302 256 1-BIT WORDS
OPEN-COLLECTOR OUTPUT

See Bipolar Microcomputer Components Data Book, LCC4270

SN54LS302 (J, W)   SN74LS302 (J, N)

TEXAS INSTRUMENTS
INCORPORATED
POST OFFICE BOX 5012 • DALLAS, TEXAS 75222

54/74 FAMILIES OF COMPATIBLE TTL CIRCUITS

PIN ASSIGNMENTS (TOP VIEWS)

1024-BIT RANDOM-ACCESS MEMORIES

1024 1-BIT WORDS
OPEN-COLLECTOR OUTPUT

314 CHIP SELECT ($\bar{S}$)
SIMPLIFIES EXPANSION

315 CHIP ENABLE ($\bar{E}$) SIMPLIFIES EXPANSION
AND CONTROLS POWER DOWN

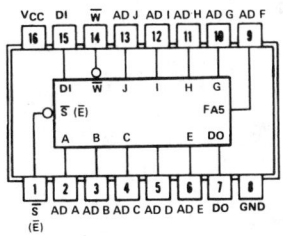

See Bipolar Microcomputer Components Data Book, LCC4270

SN54LS314 (JD)   SN74LS314 (JD, N)
SN54S314 (JD)   SN74S314 (JD, N)
SN54LS315 (JD)   SN74LS315 (JD, N)

8-BIT BIDIRECTIONAL UNIVERSAL SHIFT/STORAGE REGISTERS

323 3-STATE OUTPUTS

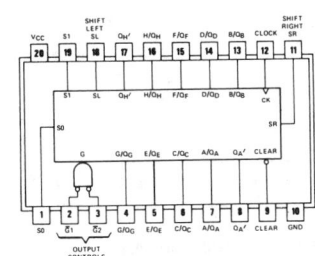

SN54LS323 (J)   SN74LS323 (J, N)

See page 7-443

VOLTAGE-CONTROLLED OSCILLATORS

324 TWO-PHASE OUTPUTS
ENABLE CONTROL

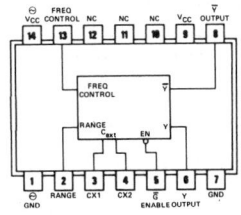

SN54LS324 (J, W)   SN74LS324 (J, N)

See page 7-445

TEXAS INSTRUMENTS
INCORPORATED
POST OFFICE BOX 5012 • DALLAS, TEXAS 75222

54/74 FAMILIES OF COMPATIBLE TTL CIRCUITS

PIN ASSIGNMENTS (TOP VIEWS)

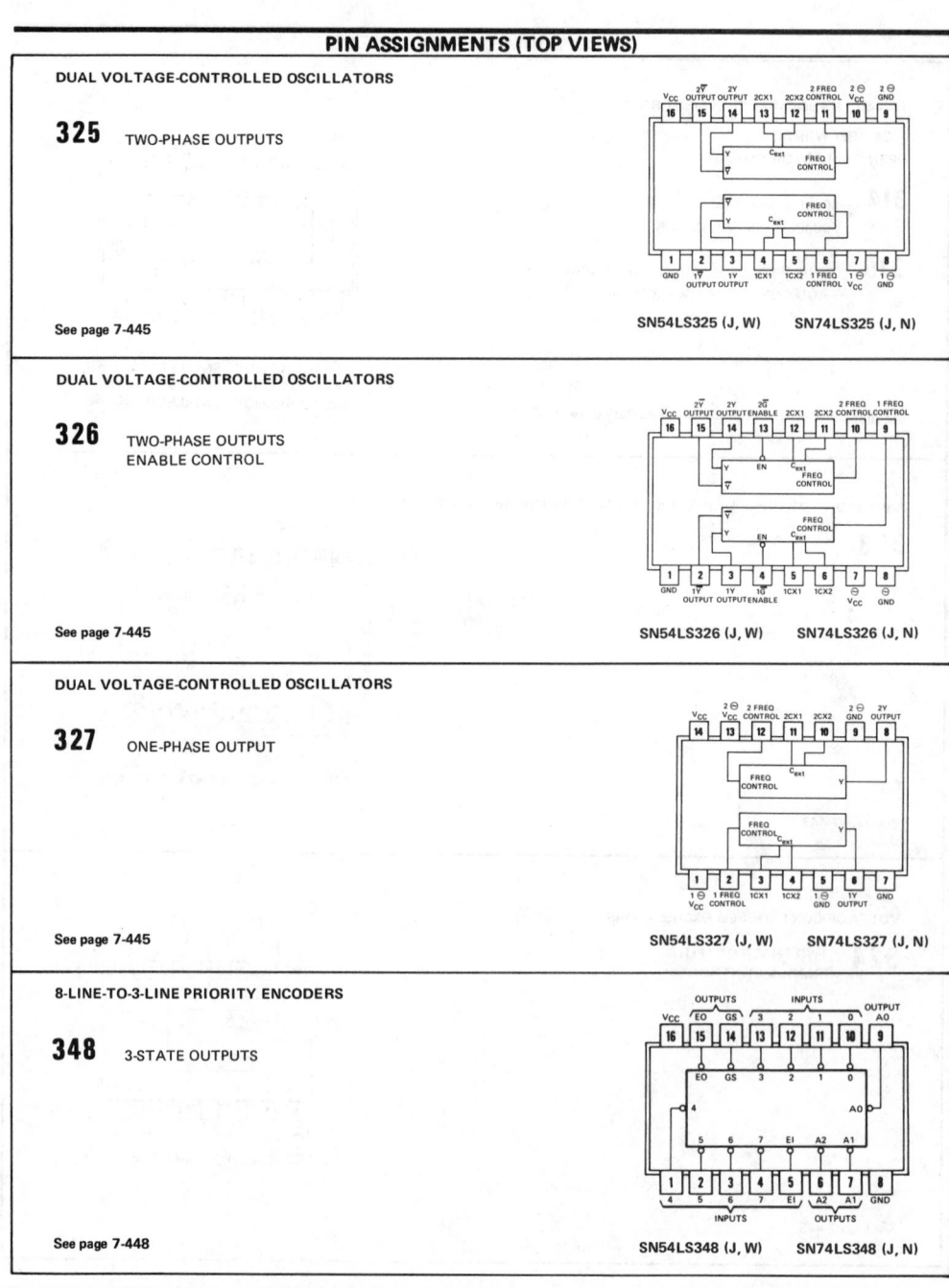

DUAL VOLTAGE-CONTROLLED OSCILLATORS

325 TWO-PHASE OUTPUTS

See page 7-445

SN54LS325 (J, W)   SN74LS325 (J, N)

DUAL VOLTAGE-CONTROLLED OSCILLATORS

326 TWO-PHASE OUTPUTS
ENABLE CONTROL

See page 7-445

SN54LS326 (J, W)   SN74LS326 (J, N)

DUAL VOLTAGE-CONTROLLED OSCILLATORS

327 ONE-PHASE OUTPUT

See page 7-445

SN54LS327 (J, W)   SN74LS327 (J, N)

8-LINE-TO-3-LINE PRIORITY ENCODERS

348 3-STATE OUTPUTS

See page 7-448

SN54LS348 (J, W)   SN74LS348 (J, N)

TEXAS INSTRUMENTS
INCORPORATED
POST OFFICE BOX 5012 • DALLAS, TEXAS 75222

PIN ASSIGNMENTS (TOP VIEWS)

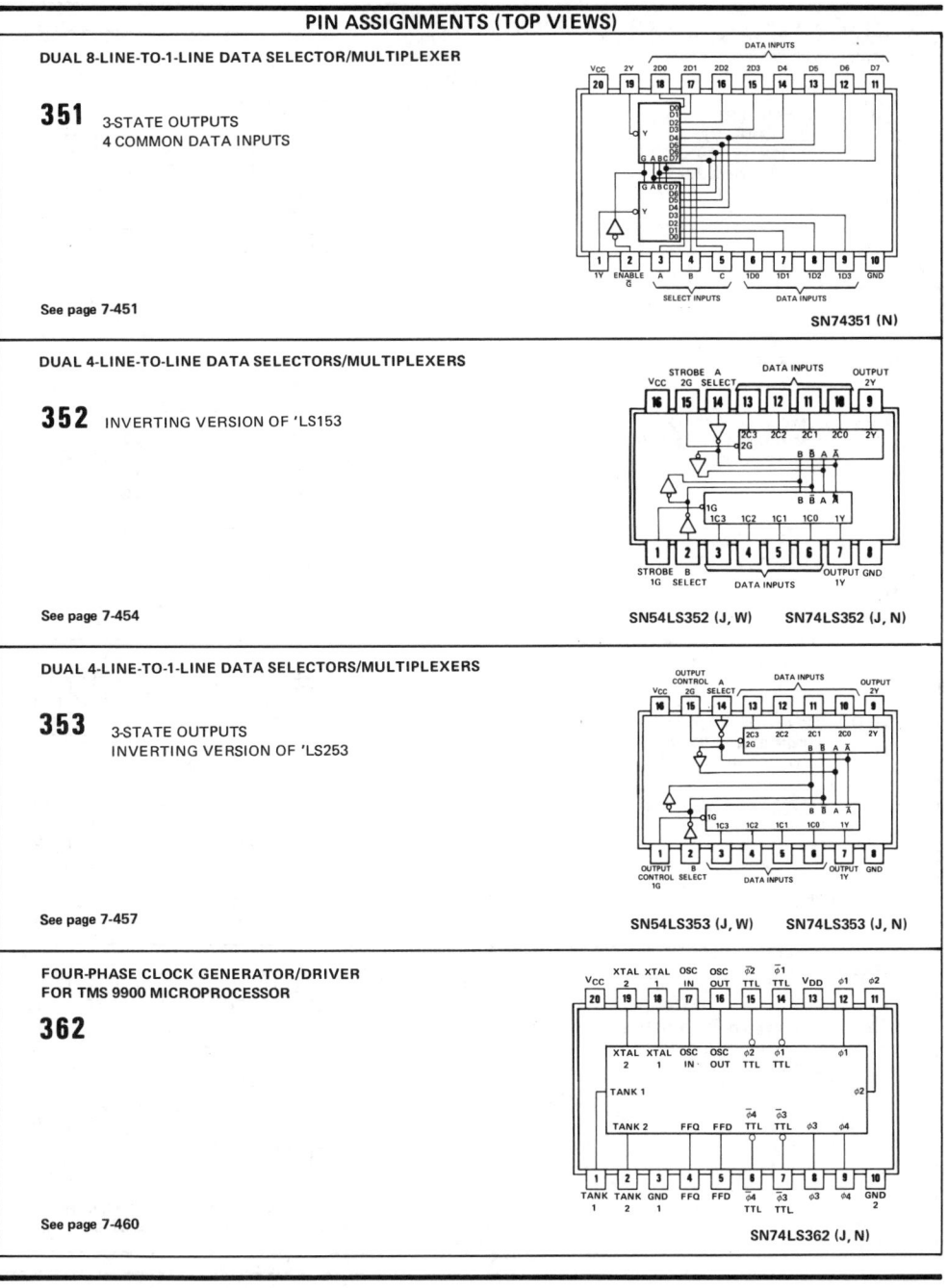

DUAL 8-LINE-TO-1-LINE DATA SELECTOR/MULTIPLEXER

351 3-STATE OUTPUTS
4 COMMON DATA INPUTS

See page 7-451

SN74351 (N)

DUAL 4-LINE-TO-LINE DATA SELECTORS/MULTIPLEXERS

352 INVERTING VERSION OF 'LS153

See page 7-454

SN54LS352 (J, W)   SN74LS352 (J, N)

DUAL 4-LINE-TO-1-LINE DATA SELECTORS/MULTIPLEXERS

353 3-STATE OUTPUTS
INVERTING VERSION OF 'LS253

See page 7-457

SN54LS353 (J, W)   SN74LS353 (J, N)

**FOUR-PHASE CLOCK GENERATOR/DRIVER
FOR TMS 9900 MICROPROCESSOR**

362

See page 7-460

SN74LS362 (J, N)

54/74 FAMILIES OF COMPATIBLE TTL CIRCUITS

PIN ASSIGNMENTS (TOP VIEWS)

OCTAL D-TYPE LATCHES

363 TRANSPARENT LATCH
3-STATE OUTPUTS
COMMON OUTPUT CONTROL
COMMON ENABLE

See page 7-467

SN54LS363 (J)   SN74LS363 (J, N)

OCTAL D-TYPE FLIP-FLOPS

364 COMMON CLOCK
COMMON OUTPUT CONTROL
3-STATE OUTPUTS

See page 7-467

SN54LS364 (J)   SN74LS364 (J, N)

HEX BUS DRIVERS

365 3-STATE OUTPUTS
NONINVERTED DATA OUTPUTS
GATED ENABLE INPUTS

See page 6-36

SN54365A (J, W)   SN74365A (J, N)
SN54LS365A (J, W)   SN74LS365A (J, N)

HEX BUS DRIVERS

366 INVERTED DATA OUTPUTS
GATED ENABLE INPUTS
3-STATE OUTPUTS

See page 6-36

SN54366A (J, W)   SN74366A (J, N)
SN54LS366A (J, W)   SN74LS366A (J, N)

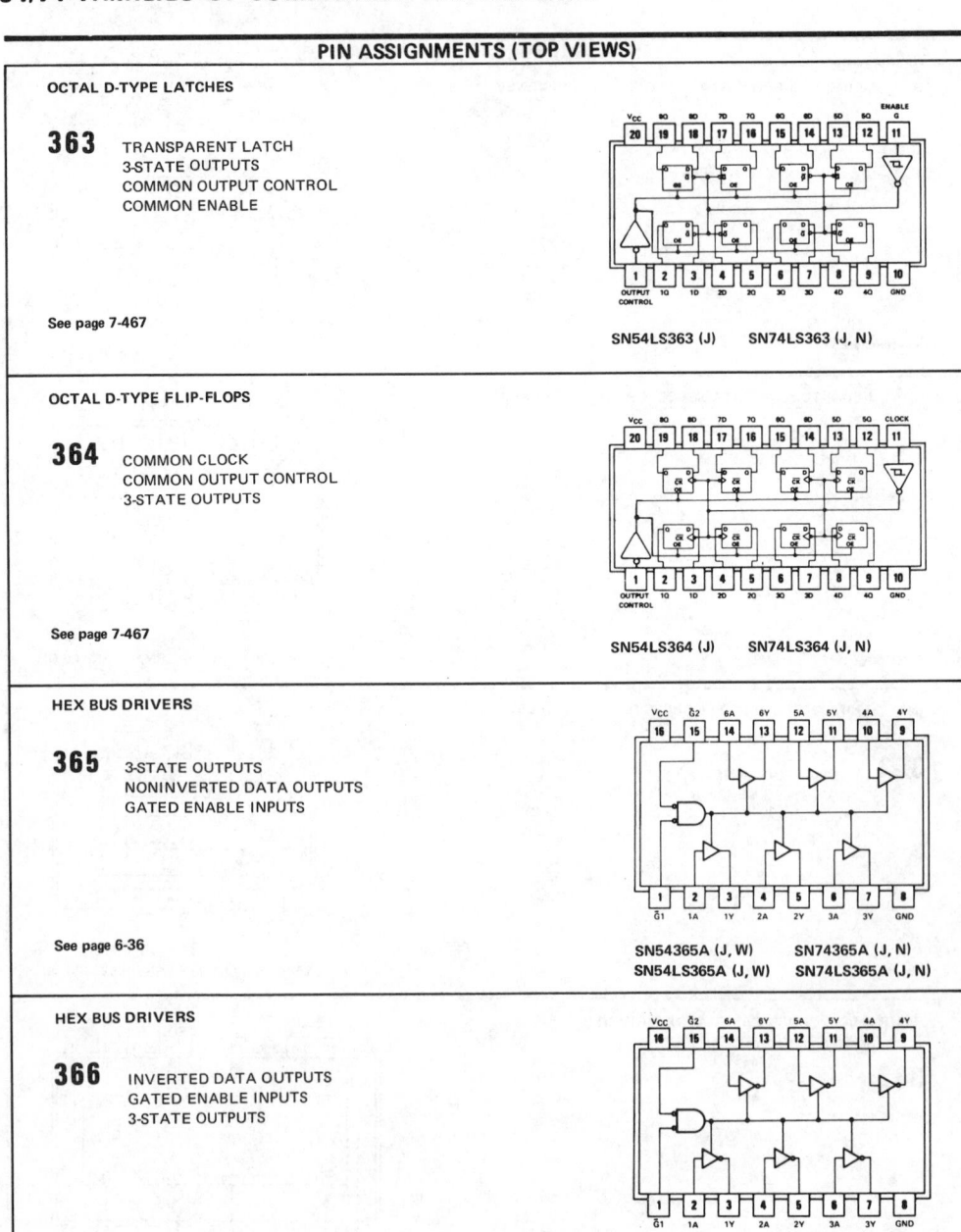

TEXAS INSTRUMENTS
INCORPORATED
POST OFFICE BOX 5012 • DALLAS, TEXAS 75222

8

54/74 FAMILIES OF COMPATIBLE TTL CIRCUITS

PIN ASSIGNMENTS (TOP VIEWS)

HEX BUS DRIVERS

367
NONINVERTED DATA OUTPUTS
4-LINE AND 2-LINE ENABLE INPUTS
3-STATE OUTPUTS

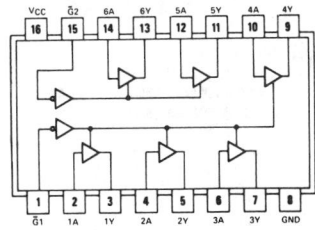

See page 6-36

SN54367A (J, W)   SN74367A (J, N)
SN54LS367A (J, W)   SN74LS367A (J, N)

HEX BUS DRIVERS

368
INVERTED DATA OUTPUTS
4-LINE AND 2-LINE ENABLE INPUTS
3-STATE OUTPUTS

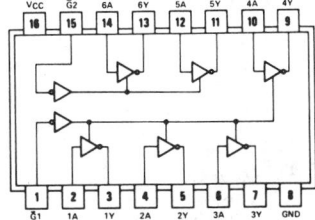

See page 6-36

SN54368A (J, W)   SN74368A (J, N)
SN54LS368A (J, W)   SN74LS368A (J, N)

2048-BIT READ-ONLY MEMORIES

370
512 4-BIT WORDS
3-STATE OUTPUTS

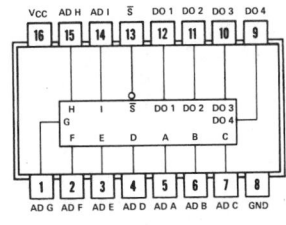

See Bipolar Microcomputer Components Data Book, LCC4270

SN54S370 (J)   SN74S370 (J, N)

2048-BIT READ-ONLY MEMORIES

371
256 8-BIT WORDS
3-STATE OUTPUTS

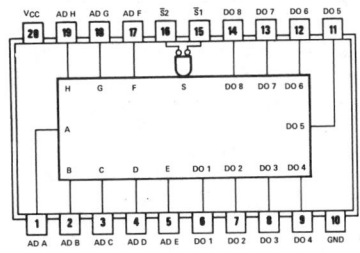

See Bipolar Microcomputer Components Data Book, LCC4270

SN54S371 (J)   SN74S371 (J, N)

5

TEXAS INSTRUMENTS
INCORPORATED
POST OFFICE BOX 5012 • DALLAS, TEXAS 75222

PIN ASSIGNMENTS (TOP VIEWS)

OCTAL D-TYPE LATCHES

373

3-STATE OUTPUTS
COMMON OUTPUT CONTROL
COMMON ENABLE

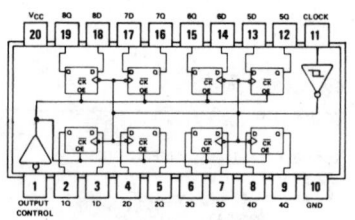

See page 7-471

SN54LS373 (J)   SN74LS373 (J, N)
SN54S373 (J)   SN74S373 (J, N)

OCTAL D-TYPE FLIP-FLOPS

374

3-STATE OUTPUTS
COMMON OUTPUT CONTROL
COMMON CLOCK

See page 7-471

SN54LS374 (J)   SN74LS374 (J, N)
SN54S374 (J)   SN74S374 (J, N)

4-BIT BISTABLE LATCHES

375

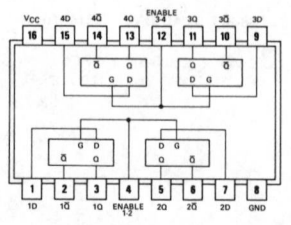

See page 7-478

SN54LS375 (J, W) SN74LS375 (J, N)

TEXAS INSTRUMENTS
INCORPORATED
POST OFFICE BOX 5012 • DALLAS, TEXAS 75222

PIN ASSIGNMENTS (TOP VIEWS)

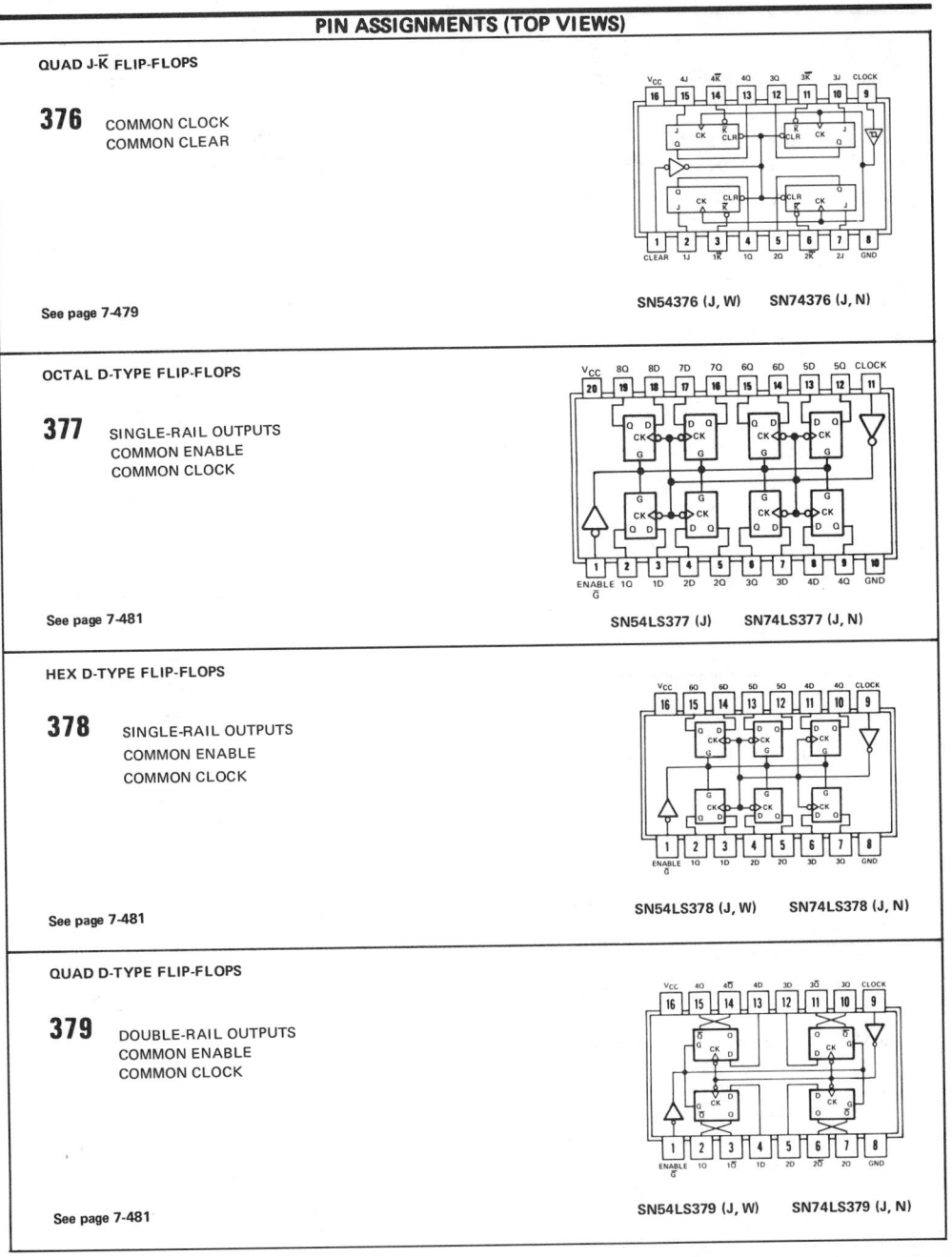

QUAD J-K̄ FLIP-FLOPS

376 COMMON CLOCK
COMMON CLEAR

See page 7-479

SN54376 (J, W)   SN74376 (J, N)

OCTAL D-TYPE FLIP-FLOPS

377 SINGLE-RAIL OUTPUTS
COMMON ENABLE
COMMON CLOCK

See page 7-481

SN54LS377 (J)   SN74LS377 (J, N)

HEX D-TYPE FLIP-FLOPS

378 SINGLE-RAIL OUTPUTS
COMMON ENABLE
COMMON CLOCK

See page 7-481

SN54LS378 (J, W)   SN74LS378 (J, N)

QUAD D-TYPE FLIP-FLOPS

379 DOUBLE-RAIL OUTPUTS
COMMON ENABLE
COMMON CLOCK

See page 7-481

SN54LS379 (J, W)   SN74LS379 (J, N)

TEXAS INSTRUMENTS
INCORPORATED
POST OFFICE BOX 5012 • DALLAS, TEXAS 75222

54/74 FAMILIES OF COMPATIBLE TTL CIRCUITS

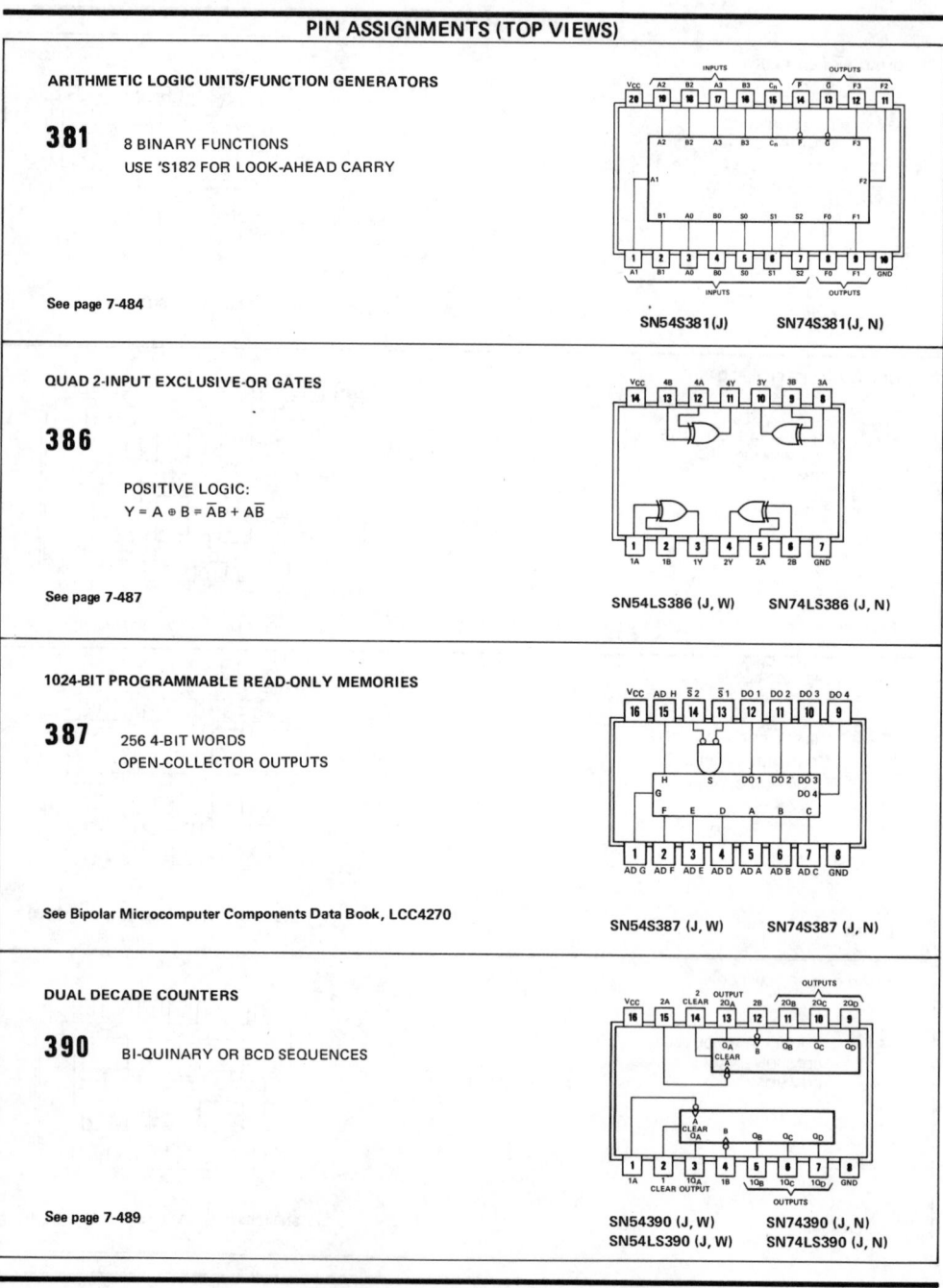

ARITHMETIC LOGIC UNITS/FUNCTION GENERATORS

381   8 BINARY FUNCTIONS
USE 'S182 FOR LOOK-AHEAD CARRY

See page 7-484

SN54S381(J)   SN74S381(J, N)

QUAD 2-INPUT EXCLUSIVE-OR GATES

386

POSITIVE LOGIC:
$Y = A \oplus B = \bar{A}B + A\bar{B}$

See page 7-487

SN54LS386 (J, W)   SN74LS386 (J, N)

1024-BIT PROGRAMMABLE READ-ONLY MEMORIES

387   256 4-BIT WORDS
OPEN-COLLECTOR OUTPUTS

See Bipolar Microcomputer Components Data Book, LCC4270

SN54S387 (J, W)   SN74S387 (J, N)

DUAL DECADE COUNTERS

390   BI-QUINARY OR BCD SEQUENCES

See page 7-489

SN54390 (J, W)   SN74390 (J, N)
SN54LS390 (J, W)   SN74LS390 (J, N)

TEXAS INSTRUMENTS
INCORPORATED
POST OFFICE BOX 5012 • DALLAS, TEXAS 75222

PIN ASSIGNMENTS (TOP VIEWS)

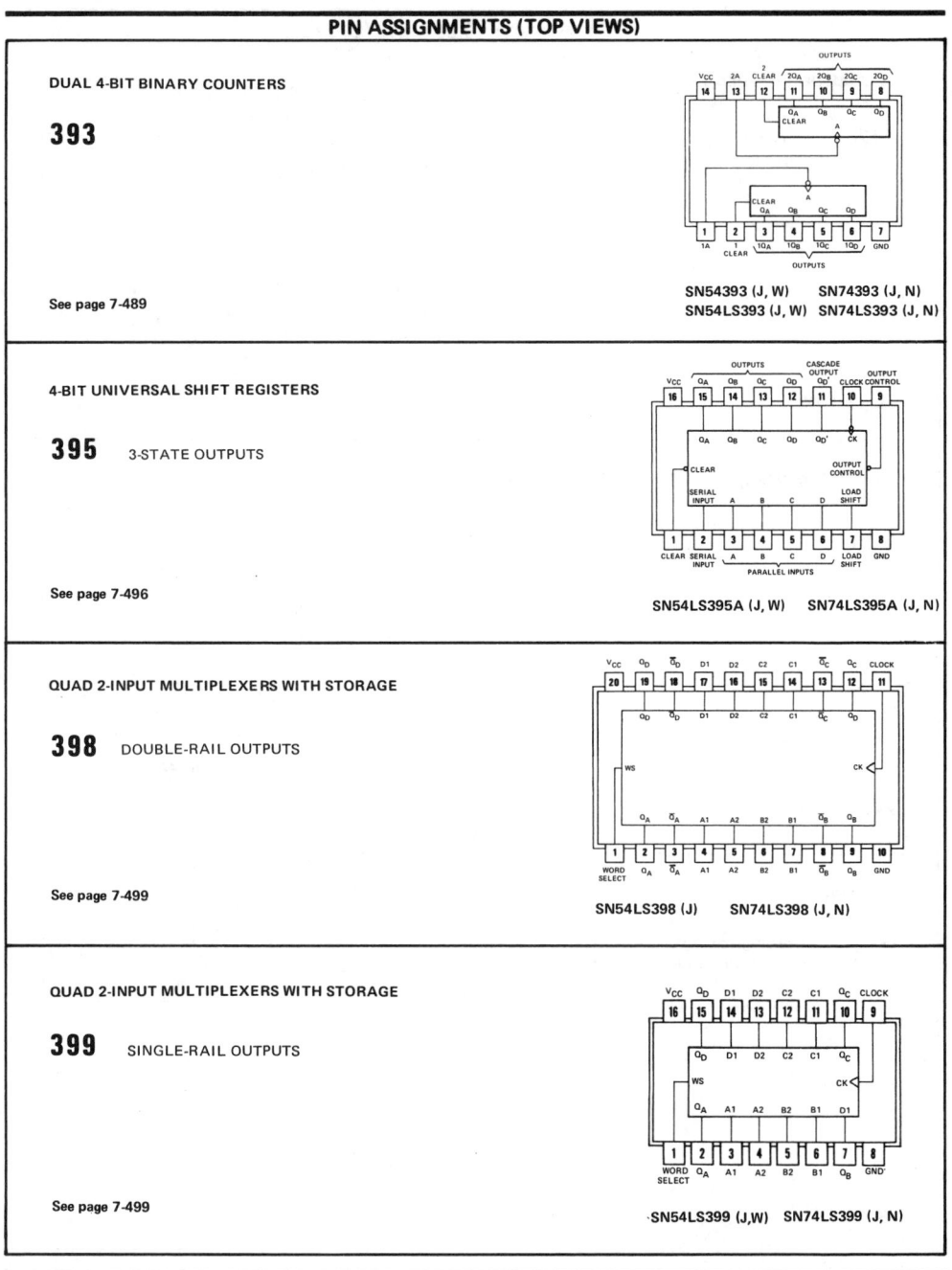

DUAL 4-BIT BINARY COUNTERS

393

See page 7-489

SN54393 (J, W)   SN74393 (J, N)
SN54LS393 (J, W) SN74LS393 (J, N)

4-BIT UNIVERSAL SHIFT REGISTERS

395   3-STATE OUTPUTS

See page 7-496

SN54LS395A (J, W)   SN74LS395A (J, N)

QUAD 2-INPUT MULTIPLEXERS WITH STORAGE

398   DOUBLE-RAIL OUTPUTS

See page 7-499

SN54LS398 (J)   SN74LS398 (J, N)

QUAD 2-INPUT MULTIPLEXERS WITH STORAGE

399   SINGLE-RAIL OUTPUTS

See page 7-499

SN54LS399 (J,W)   SN74LS399 (J, N)

076

54/74 FAMILIES OF COMPATIBLE TTL CIRCUITS

PIN ASSIGNMENTS (TOP VIEWS)

MULTI-MODE BUFFERED 8-BIT LATCHES

412 3-STATE OUTPUTS
DIRECT CLEAR

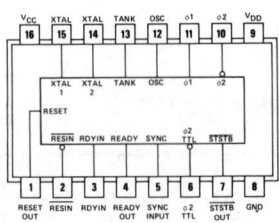

SN54S412 (J)   SN74S412 (J, N)

See page 7-502

TWO-PHASE CLOCK GENERATOR/DRIVER FOR 8080A

424

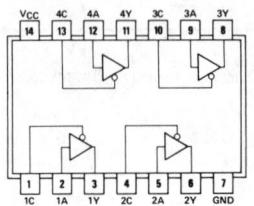

SN74LS424 (J, N)

See page 7-507

QUAD GATES

425 3-STATE OUTPUTS
ACTIVE-HIGH ENABLING

positive logic: Y = A

SN54425 (J, W)   SN74425 (J, N)

See page 6-33

TEXAS INSTRUMENTS
INCORPORATED
POST OFFICE BOX 5012 • DALLAS, TEXAS 75222

PIN ASSIGNMENTS (TOP VIEWS)

QUAD GATES

426 3-STATE OUTPUTS
ACTIVE-LOW ENABLING

positive logic: Y = A

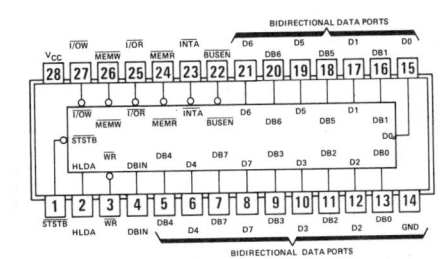

SN54426 (J, W)   SN74426 (J, N)

See page 6-33

SYSTEM CONTROLLER FOR 8080A

428 BIDIRECTIONAL DATA PORTS

438 BIDIRECTIONAL DATA PORTS

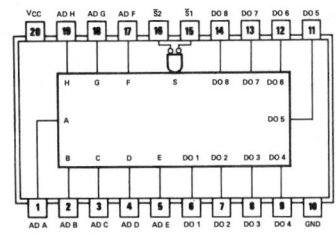

SN74S428 (N)
SN74S438 (N)

See page 7-514

PROGRAMMABLE READ-ONLY MEMORIES

256 8-BIT WORDS

470 OPEN-COLLECTOR OUTPUTS

471 3-STATE OUTPUTS

SN54S470 (J)   SN74S470 (J, N)
SN54S471 (J)   SN74S471 (J, N)

See Bipolar Microcomputer Components Data Book, LCC4270

54/74 FAMILIES OF COMPATIBLE TTL CIRCUITS

PIN ASSIGNMENTS (TOP VIEWS)

PROGRAMMABLE READ-ONLY MEMORIES

472 3-STATE OUTPUTS

473 OPEN-COLLECTOR OUTPUTS

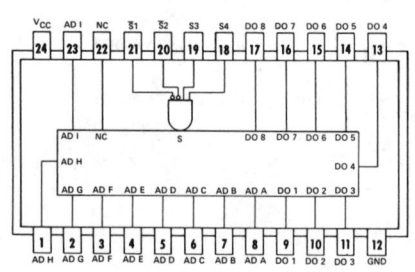

See Memory and Microprocessor Data Book, LCC 4270

SN54S472 (J)	SN74S472 (J, N)
SN54S473 (J)	SN74S473 (J, N)

PROGRAMMABLE READ-ONLY MEMORIES

474 3-STATE OUTPUTS

475 OPEN-COLLECTOR OUTPUTS

See Memory and Microprocessor Data Book, LCC 4270

SN54S474 (J)	SN74S474 (J, N)
SN54S475 (J)	SN74S475 (J, N)

NC — No internal connection

4-BIT SLICE PROCESSOR ELEMENTS

481

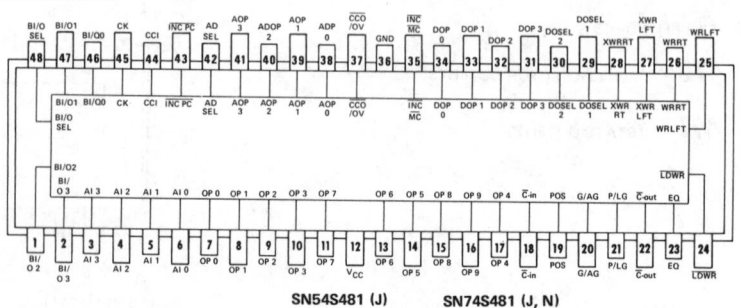

SN54S481 (J)   SN74S481 (J, N)

See Memory and Microprocessor Data Book, LCC 4270

TEXAS INSTRUMENTS
INCORPORATED
POST OFFICE BOX 5012 • DALLAS, TEXAS 75222

PIN ASSIGNMENTS (TOP VIEWS)

4-BIT-SLICE EXPANDABLE CONTROL ELEMENTS

482 CASCADABLE TO N-BITS

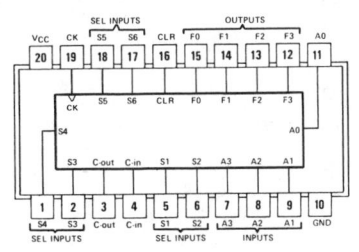

SN54S482 (J)   SN74S482 (J, N)

See Bipolar Microcomputer Components Data Book, LCC4270

DUAL DECADE COUNTERS

490

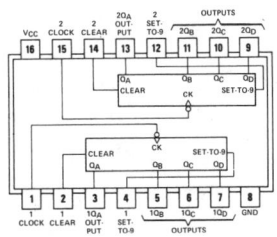

SN54490 (J, W)   SN74490 (J, N)
SN54LS490 (J, W) SN74LS490 (J, N)

See page 7-520

4-BY-4 REGISTER FILES

670 3-STATE OUTPUTS
SIMULTANEOUS READ/WRITE
EXPANDABLE TO 1024 WORDS

SN54LS670 (J, W)   SN74LS670 (J, N)

See page 7-526

5

TEXAS INSTRUMENTS
INCORPORATED
POST OFFICE BOX 5012 • DALLAS, TEXAS 75222

54/74 Family
SSI Circuits

recommended operating conditions

PARAMETER		SERIES 54 / SERIES 74 '00, '04, '10, '20, '30 MIN NOM MAX			SERIES 54H / SERIES 74H 'H00, 'H04, 'H10, 'H20, 'H30 MIN NOM MAX			SERIES 54L / SERIES 74L 'L00, 'L04, 'L10, 'L20, 'L30 MIN NOM MAX			SERIES 54LS / SERIES 74LS 'LS00, 'LS04, 'LS10, 'LS20, 'LS30 MIN NOM MAX			SERIES 54S / SERIES 74S 'S00, 'S04, 'S10, 'S20, 'S30, 'S133 MIN NOM MAX			UNIT
Supply voltage, V_{CC}	54 Family	4.5	5	5.5	4.5	5	5.5	4.5	5	5.5	4.5	5	5.5	4.5	5	5.5	V
	74 Family	4.75	5	5.25	4.75	5	5.25	4.75	5	5.25	4.75	5	5.25	4.75	5	5.25	
High-level output current, I_{OH}	54 Family			−400			−500			−100			−400			−1000	µA
	74 Family			−400			−500			−200			−400			−1000	
Low-level output current, I_{OL}	54 Family			16			20			2			4			20	mA
	74 Family			16			20			3.6			8			20	
Operating free-air temperature, T_A	54 Family	−55		125	−55		125	−55		125	−55		125	−55		125	°C
	74 Family	0		70	0		70	0		70	0		70	0		70	

electrical characteristics over recommended operating free-air temperature range (unless otherwise noted)

PARAMETER	TEST FIGURE	TEST CONDITIONS†		SERIES 54 / SERIES 74 '00, '04, '10, '20, '30 MIN TYP‡ MAX			SERIES 54H / SERIES 74H 'H00, 'H04, 'H10, 'H20, 'H30 MIN TYP‡ MAX			SERIES 54L / SERIES 74L 'L00, 'L04, 'L10, 'L20, 'L30 MIN TYP‡ MAX			SERIES 54LS / SERIES 74LS 'LS00, 'LS04, 'LS10, 'LS20, 'LS30 MIN TYP‡ MAX			SERIES 54S / SERIES 74S 'S00, 'S04, 'S10, 'S20, 'S30, 'S133 MIN TYP‡ MAX			UNIT
V_{IH} High-level input voltage	1, 2			2			2			2			2			2			V
V_{IL} Low-level input voltage	1, 2		54 Family			0.8			0.8			0.7			0.7			0.8	V
			74 Family			0.8			0.8			0.7			0.8			0.8	
V_{IK} Input clamp voltage	3	V_{CC} = MIN, I_I = §				−1.5			−1.5						−1.5			−1.2	V
V_{OH} High-level output voltage	1	V_{CC} = MIN, V_{IH} = MIN, V_{IL} = V_{IL} max, I_{OH} = MAX	54 Family	2.4	3.4		2.4	3.5		2.4	3.3		2.5	3.4		2.5	3.4		V
			74 Family	2.4	3.4		2.4	3.5		2.4	3.2		2.7	3.4		2.7	3.4		
V_{OL} Low-level output voltage	2	V_{CC} = MIN, V_{IH} = 2 V, I_{OL} = MIN	54 Family		0.2	0.4		0.2	0.4		0.15	0.3		0.25	0.4			0.5	V
			74 Family		0.2	0.4		0.2	0.4		0.2	0.4		0.25	0.5			0.5	
		I_{OL} = 4 mA Series 74LS													0.4				
I_I Input current at maximum input voltage	4	V_I = 5.5 V, V_I = 7 V				1			1			0.1			0.1			1	mA
I_{IH} High-level input current	4	V_{CC} = MAX, V_{IH} = 2.4 V, V_{IH} = 2.7 V				40			50			10			20			50	µA
I_{IL} Low-level input current	5	V_{CC} = MAX, V_{IL} = 0.3 V, V_{IL} = 0.4 V, V_{IL} = 0.5 V				−1.6			−2			−0.18			−0.4			−2	mA
I_{OS} Short-circuit output current♦	6	V_{CC} = MAX	54 Family	−20		−55	−40		−100	−3		−15	−20		−100	−40		−100	mA
			74 Family	−18		−55	−40		−100	−3		−15	−20		−100	−40		−100	
I_{CC} Supply current	7	V_{CC} = MAX																		mA

See table on next page

†For conditions shown as MIN or MAX, use the appropriate value specified under recommended operating conditions.
‡All typical values are at V_{CC} = 5 V, T_A = 25°C.
§I_I = −12 mA for SN54'/SN74', −8 mA for SN54H'/SN74H', and −18 mA for SN54LS'/SN74LS' and SN54S'/SN74S'.
♦Not more than one output should be shorted at a time, and for SN54H'/SN74H', SN54LS'/SN74LS', and SN54S'/SN74S', duration of short-circuit should not exceed 1 second.

TEXAS INSTRUMENTS
INCORPORATED
POST OFFICE BOX 5012 • DALLAS, TEXAS 75222

POSITIVE-NAND GATES AND INVERTERS WITH TOTEM-POLE OUTPUTS

switching characteristics at $V_{CC} = 5$ V, $T_A = 25°C$

TYPE	TEST CONDITIONS#	t_{PLH} (ns) Propagation delay time, low-to-high-level output			t_{PHL} (ns) Propagation delay time, high-to-low-level output		
		MIN	TYP	MAX	MIN	TYP	MAX
'00, '10	$C_L = 15$ pF, $R_L = 400 \Omega$		11	22		7	15
'04, 20			12	22		8	15
'30			13	22		8	15
'H00	$C_L = 25$ pF, $R_L = 280 \Omega$		5.9	10		6.2	10
'H04			6	10		6.5	10
'H10			5.9	10		6.3	10
'H20			6	10		7	10
'H30			6.8	10		8.9	12
'L00, 'L04, 'L10, L20	$C_L = 50$ pF, $R_L = 4 k\Omega$		35	60		31	60
'L30			35	60		70	100
'LS00, 'LS04	$C_L = 15$ pF, $R_L = 2 k\Omega$		9	15		10	15
'LS10, 'LS20			8	15		13	20
'LS30			3	4.5		3	5
'S00, 'S04	$C_L = 15$ pF, $R_L = 280 \Omega$		4.5			5	
'S10, 'S20	$C_L = 50$ pF, $R_L = 280 \Omega$		4	6		4.5	
'S30, 'S133	$C_L = 15$ pF, $R_L = 280 \Omega$ / $C_L = 50$ pF, $R_L = 280 \Omega$		5.5			6.5	7

#Load circuits and voltage waveforms are shown on pages 3-10 and 3-11.

supply current¶

TYPE	I_{CCH} (mA) Total with outputs high		I_{CCL} (mA) Total with outputs low		I_{CC} (mA) Average per gate (50% duty cycle)
	TYP	MAX	TYP	MAX	TYP
'00	4	8	12	22	2
'04	6	12	18	33	2
'10	3	6	9	16.5	2
'20	2	4	6	11	2
'30	1	2	3	6	2
'H00	10	16.8	26	40	4.5
'H04	16	26	40	58	4.5
'H10	7.5	12.6	19.5	30	4.5
'H20	5	8.4	13	20	4.5
'H30	2.5	4.2	6.5	10	4.5
'L00	0.44	0.8	1.16	2.04	0.20
'L04	0.66	1.2	1.74	3.06	0.20
'L10	0.33	0.6	0.87	1.53	0.20
'L20	0.22	0.4	0.58	1.02	0.20
SN54L30	0.11	0.33	0.29	0.51	0.20
SN74L30	0.11	0.2	0.29	0.51	0.20
'LS00	0.8	1.6	2.4	4.4	0.4
'LS04	1.2	2.4	3.6	6.6	0.4
'LS10	0.6	1.2	1.8	3.3	0.4
'LS20	0.4	0.8	1.2	2.2	0.4
'LS30	0.35	0.5	0.6	1.1	0.48
'S00	10	16	20	36	3.75
'S04	15	24	30	54	3.75
'S10	7.5	12	15	27	3.75
'S20	5	8	10	18	3.75
'S30	3	5	5.5	10	4.25
'S133	3	5	5.5	10	4.25

¶Maximum values of I_{CC} are over the recommended operating ranges of V_{CC} and T_A; typical values are at $V_{CC} = 5$ V, $T_A = 25°C$.

schematics (each gate)

CIRCUIT	R1	R2	R3	R4
'00, '04, '10, '20, '30	4 k	1.6 k	130	1 k
'L00, 'L04, 'L10, 'L20, 'L30	40 k	20 k	500	12 k

'00, '04, '10, '20, '30, 'L00, 'L04, 'L10, 'L20, 'L30, CIRCUITS
Input clamp diodes are not on SN54L'/SN74L' circuits.

'S00, 'S04, 'S10, 'S20, 'S30, 'S133 CIRCUITS

'LS00, 'LS04, 'LS10, 'LS20, 'LS30 CIRCUITS
*The 12-kΩ resistor is not on 'LS30.
Resistor values shown are nominal and in ohms.

'H00, 'H04, 'H10, 'H20, 'H30 CIRCUITS

6

POSITIVE-NAND GATES AND INVERTERS WITH OPEN-COLLECTOR OUTPUTS

recommended operating conditions

PARAMETER		54 FAMILY / 74 FAMILY	SERIES 54 / SERIES 74 '01, '03, '05, '12, '22			SERIES 54H / SERIES 74H 'H01, 'H05, 'H22			SERIES 54L / SERIES 74L 'L01, 'L03			SERIES 54LS / SERIES 74LS 'LS01, 'LS03, 'LS05, 'LS12, 'LS22			SERIES 54S / SERIES 74S 'S03, 'S05, 'S22			UNIT
			MIN	NOM	MAX	MIN	NOM	MAX	MIN	NOM	MAX	MIN	NOM	MAX	MIN	NOM	MAX	
Supply voltage, V_{CC}		54 Family	4.5	5	5.5	4.5	5	5.5	4.5	5	5.5	4.5	5	5.5	4.5	5	5.5	V
		74 Family	4.75	5	5.25	4.75	5	5.25	4.75	5	5.25	4.75	5	5.25	4.75	5	5.25	V
High-level output voltage, V_{OH}		54 Family			5.5			5.5			5.5			5.5			5.5	V
		74 Family			5.5			5.5			5.5			5.5			5.5	V
Low-level output current, I_{OL}		54 Family			16			20			2			4			20	mA
		74 Family			16			20			3.6			8			20	mA
Operating free-air temperature, T_A		54 Family	-55		125	-55		125	-55		125	-55		125	-55		125	°C
		74 Family	0		70	0		70	0		70	0		70	0		70	°C

electrical characteristics over recommended operating free-air temperature range (unless otherwise noted)

PARAMETER	TEST FIGURE	TEST CONDITIONS[†]	SERIES 54 / 74 '01, '03, '05, '12, '22			SERIES 54H / 74H 'H01, 'H05, 'H22			SERIES 54L / 74L 'L01, 'L03			SERIES 54LS / 74LS 'LS01, 'LS03, 'LS05, 'LS12, 'LS22			SERIES 54S / 74S 'S03, 'S05, 'S22			UNIT
			MIN	TYP[‡]	MAX	MIN	TYP[‡]	MAX	MIN	TYP[‡]	MAX	MIN	TYP[‡]	MAX	MIN	TYP[‡]	MAX	
V_{IH} High-level input voltage	1, 2		2			2			2			2			2			V
V_{IL} Low-level input voltage	1, 2	54 Family			0.8			0.8			0.6			0.7			0.8	V
		74 Family			0.8			0.8			0.6			0.8			0.8	V
V_{IK} Input clamp voltage	3	V_{CC} = MIN, I_I = §[§]			-1.5			-1.5			-1.5			-1.5			-1.2	V
I_{OH} High-level output current	1	V_{CC} = MIN, V_{IL} = V_{IL} max, V_{OH} = 5.5 V			250			250			50			100			250	µA
V_{OL} Low-level output voltage	2	V_{CC} = MIN, V_{IH} = 2 V (54 Family)		0.2	0.4		0.2	0.4		0.15	0.3		0.25	0.4			0.5	V
		V_{IH} = 2 V (74 Family)		0.2	0.4		0.2	0.4		0.2	0.4		0.35	0.5			0.5	V
		I_{OL} = 4 mA (Series 74LS)											0.25	0.4				V
I_I Input current at maximum input voltage	4	V_I = 5.5 V / V_I = 7 V			1			1			0.1			0.1			1	mA
I_{IH} High-level input current	4	V_{CC} = MAX, V_{IH} = 2.4 V / 2.7 V			40			50			10			20			50	µA
I_{IL} Low-level input current	5	V_{CC} = MAX, V_{IL} = 0.3/0.4/0.5 V			-1.6			-2			-0.18			-0.4			-2	mA
I_{CC} Supply current	7	V_{CC} = MAX			See table on next page													mA

[†] For conditions shown as MIN or MAX, use the appropriate value specified under recommended operating conditions.
[‡] All typical values are at V_{CC} = 5 V, T_A = 25°C.
[§] I_I = -12 mA for SN54'/SN74', -8 mA for SN54H'/SN74H', and -18 mA for SN54LS'/SN74LS' and SN54S'/SN74S'.

TEXAS INSTRUMENTS
INCORPORATED
POST OFFICE BOX 5012 • DALLAS, TEXAS 75222

schematics (each gate)

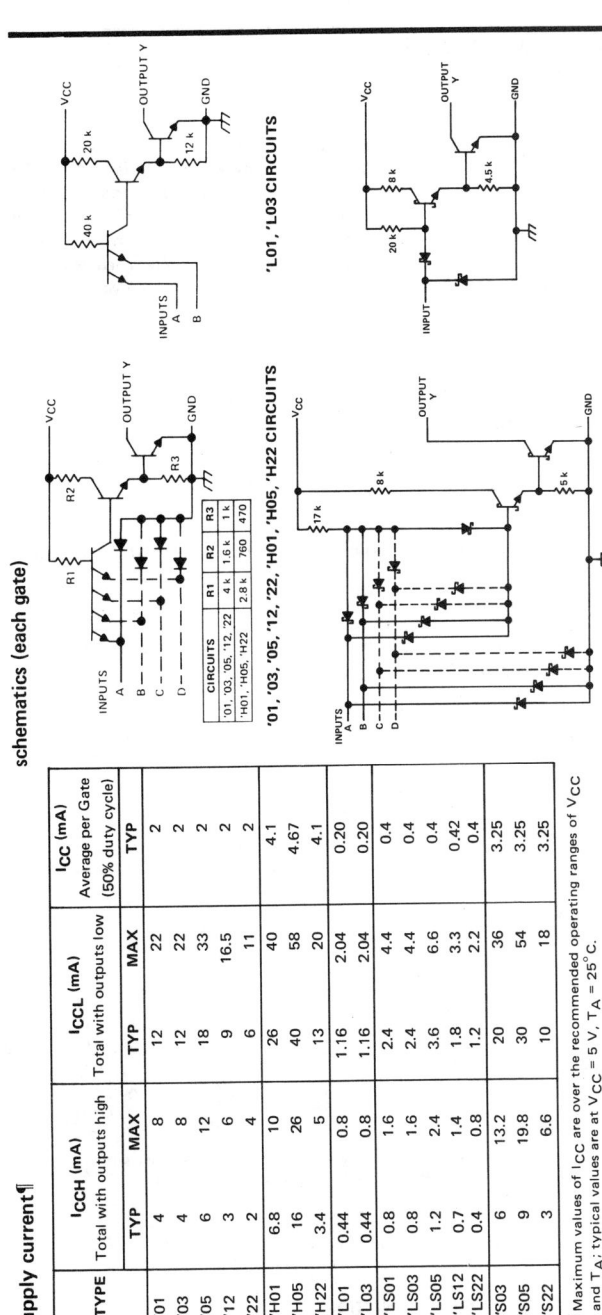

'L01, 'L03 CIRCUITS

'LS05 CIRCUITS

'S03, 'S05, 'S22 CIRCUITS

Resistor values shown are nominal and in ohms.

'01, '03, '05, '12, '22, 'H01, 'H05, 'H22 CIRCUITS

CIRCUITS	R1	R2	R3
'01, '03, '05, '12, '22	4 k	1.6 k	1 k
'H01, 'H05, 'H22	2.8 k	760	470

'LS01, 'LS03, 'LS12, 'LS22 CIRCUITS

supply current¶

TYPE	ICCH (mA) Total with outputs high TYP	MAX	ICCL (mA) Total with outputs low TYP	MAX	ICC (mA) Average per Gate (50% duty cycle) TYP
'01	4	8	12	22	2
'03	4	8	12	22	2
'05	6	12	18	33	2
'12	3	6	9	16.5	2
'22	2	4	6	11	2
'H01	6.8	10	26	40	4.1
'H05	16	26	40	58	4.67
'H22	3.4	5	13	20	4.1
'L01	0.44	0.8	1.16	2.04	0.20
'L03	0.44	0.8	1.16	2.04	0.20
'LS01	0.8	1.6	2.4	4.4	0.4
'LS03	0.8	1.6	2.4	4.4	0.4
'LS05	1.2	2.4	3.6	6.6	0.4
'LS12	0.7	1.4	1.8	3.3	0.42
'LS22	0.4	0.8	1.2	2.2	0.4
'S03	6	13.2	20	36	3.25
'S05	9	19.8	30	54	3.25
'S22	3	6.6	10	18	3.25

¶ Maximum values of I_{CC} are over the recommended operating ranges of V_{CC} and T_A; typical values are at V_{CC} = 5 V, T_A = 25°C.

switching characteristics at V_{CC} = 5 V, T_A = 25°C

TYPE	TEST CONDITIONS#	tPLH (ns) Propagation delay time, low-to-high-level output MIN	TYP	MAX	tPHL (ns) Propagation delay time, high-to-low-level output MIN	TYP	MAX
'01, '03	CL = 15 pF, RL = 4 kΩ for tPLH, 400 Ω for tPHL		35	45		8	15
'05			40	55		8	15
'12, '22			35	45		8	15
'H01, 'H05, 'H22	CL = 25 pF, RL = 280 Ω		10	15		7.5	12
'L01, 'L03	CL = 50 pF, RL = 4 kΩ		60	90		33	60
'LS01, 'LS03,	CL = 15 pF, RL = 2 kΩ		17	32		15	28
'LS05, 'LS12, 'LS22		2	5	7.5	2	4.5	7
'S03, 'S05, 'S22	CL = 50 pF, RL = 280 Ω		7.5			7	

Load circuits and voltage waveforms are shown on pages 3-10 and 3-11.

OPEN-COLLECTOR OUTPUT APPLICATION DATA

APPLICATION DATA

combined fan-out and wire-AND capabilities

The open-collector TTL gate, when supplied with a proper load resistor (R_L), may be paralleled with other similar TTL gates to perform the wire-AND function, and simultaneously, will drive from one to nine standard loads of its own series. When no other open-collector gates are paralleled, this gate may be used to drive ten loads. For any of these conditions an appropriate load resistor value must be determined for the desired circuit configuration. A maximum resistor value must be determined which will ensure that sufficient load current (to TTL loads) and off current (through paralleled outputs) will be available while the output is high. A minimum resistor value must be determined which will ensure that current through this resistor and sink current from the TTL loads will not cause the output voltage to rise above the low level even if only one of the paralleled outputs is sinking all the currents.

In both conditions (low and high level) the value of R_L is determined by:

$$R_L = \frac{V_{RL}}{I_{RL}}$$

where V_{RL} is the voltage drop in volts, and I_{RL} is the current in amperes.

high-level (off-state) circuit calculations (see figure A)

The allowable voltage drop across the load resistor (V_{RL}) is the difference between V_{CC} applied and the V_{OH} level required at the load:

$$V_{RL} = V_{CC} - V_{OH\,min}$$

The total current through the load resistor (I_{RL}) is the sum of the load currents (I_{IH}) and off-state reverse currents (I_{OH}) through each of the wire-AND-connected outputs:

$$I_{RL} = \eta \cdot I_{OH} + N \cdot I_{IH} \text{ to TTL loads}$$

Therefore, calculations for the maximum value of R_L would be:

$$R_{L(max)} = \frac{V_{CC} - V_{OH\,min}}{\eta \cdot I_{OH} + N \cdot I_{IH}}$$

where η = number of gates wire-AND-connected, and N = number of standard loads.

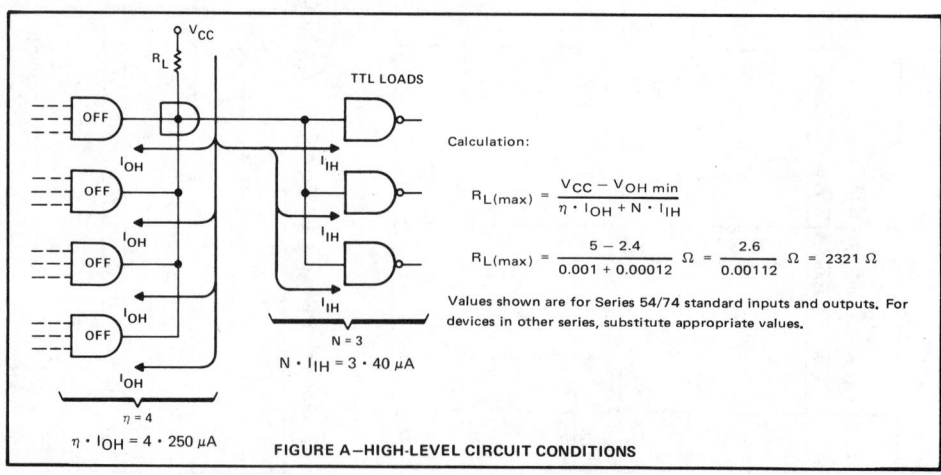

Calculation:

$$R_{L(max)} = \frac{V_{CC} - V_{OH\,min}}{\eta \cdot I_{OH} + N \cdot I_{IH}}$$

$$R_{L(max)} = \frac{5 - 2.4}{0.001 + 0.00012}\ \Omega = \frac{2.6}{0.00112}\ \Omega = 2321\ \Omega$$

Values shown are for Series 54/74 standard inputs and outputs. For devices in other series, substitute appropriate values.

$N = 3$

$N \cdot I_{IH} = 3 \cdot 40\ \mu A$

$\eta = 4$

$\eta \cdot I_{OH} = 4 \cdot 250\ \mu A$

FIGURE A—HIGH-LEVEL CIRCUIT CONDITIONS

6

TEXAS INSTRUMENTS
INCORPORATED
POST OFFICE BOX 5012 • DALLAS, TEXAS 75222

APPLICATION DATA

low-level (on-state) circuit calculations (see figure B)

The current through the resistor must be limited to the maximum sink current of one output transistor. Note that if several output transistors are wire-AND connected, the current through R_L may be shared by those paralleled transistors. However, unless it can be absolutely guaranteed that more than one transistor will be on during low-level periods, the current must be limited to the recommended maximum I_{OL}, the maximum current which will ensure that the low-level output voltage, V_{OL}, will be below V_{OL} max.

Also, fan-out must be considered. Part of I_{OL} will be supplied from the inputs which are being driven. This reduces the amount of current which can be allowed through R_L.

Therefore, the equation used to determine the minimum value of R_L would be:

$$R_{L(min)} = \frac{V_{CC} - V_{OL} \text{ max}}{I_{OL} \text{ capability} - N \cdot I_{IL}}$$

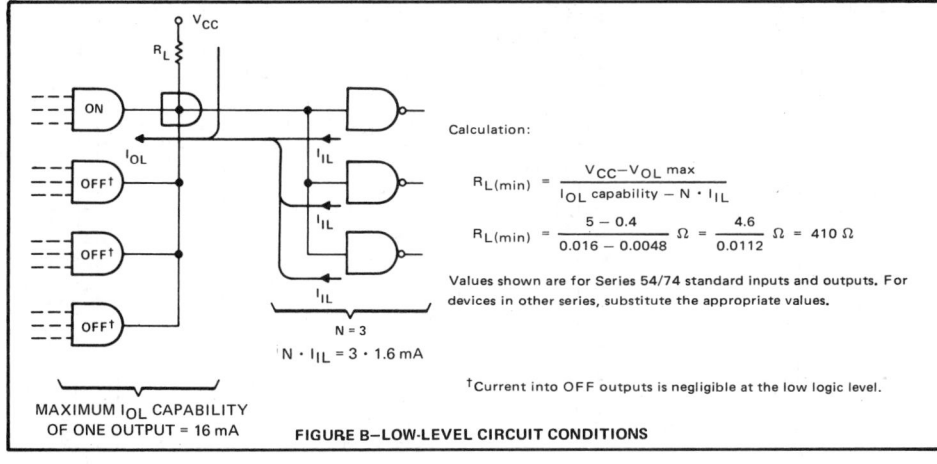

Calculation:

$$R_{L(min)} = \frac{V_{CC} - V_{OL} \text{ max}}{I_{OL} \text{ capability} - N \cdot I_{IL}}$$

$$R_{L(min)} = \frac{5 - 0.4}{0.016 - 0.0048} \Omega = \frac{4.6}{0.0112} \Omega = 410 \Omega$$

Values shown are for Series 54/74 standard inputs and outputs. For devices in other series, substitute the appropriate values.

$N = 3$

$N \cdot I_{IL} = 3 \cdot 1.6 \text{ mA}$

†Current into OFF outputs is negligible at the low logic level.

MAXIMUM I_{OL} CAPABILITY OF ONE OUTPUT = 16 mA

FIGURE B—LOW-LEVEL CIRCUIT CONDITIONS

6

recommended operating conditions

		SERIES 54 FAMILY / 74 FAMILY '02			SERIES 54 / SERIES 74 '25, '27			SERIES 54L / SERIES 74L 'L02			SERIES 54LS / SERIES 74LS 'LS02, 'LS27			SERIES 54S / SERIES 74S 'S02, 'S260			UNIT
		MIN	NOM	MAX	MIN	NOM	MAX	MIN	NOM	MAX	MIN	NOM	MAX	MIN	NOM	MAX	
Supply voltage, V_{CC}	54 Family	4.5	5	5.5	4.5	5	5.5	4.5	5	5.5	4.5	5	5.5	4.5	5	5.5	V
	74 Family	4.75	5	5.25	4.75	5	5.25	4.75	5	5.25	4.75	5	5.25	4.75	5	5.25	
High-level output current, I_{OH}	54 Family			-400			-800			-100			-400			-1000	µA
	74 Family			-400			-800			-200			-400			-1000	
Low-level output current, I_{OL}	54 Family			16			16			2			4			20	mA
	74 Family			16			16			3.6			8			20	
Operating free-air temperature, T_A	54 Family	-55		125	-55		125	-55		125	-55		125	-55		125	°C
	74 Family	0		70	0		70	0		70	0		70	0		70	

electrical characteristics over recommended operating free-air temperature range (unless otherwise noted)

PARAMETER	TEST FIGURE	TEST CONDITIONS†	SERIES 54 / SERIES 74 '02, '25, '27 MIN	TYP‡	MAX	SERIES 54L / SERIES 74L 'L02 MIN	TYP‡	MAX	SERIES 54LS / SERIES 74LS 'LS02, 'LS27 MIN	TYP‡	MAX	SERIES 54S / SERIES 74S 'S02, 'S260 MIN	TYP‡	MAX	UNIT
V_{IH} High-level input voltage	1, 2		2			2			2			2			V
V_{IL} Low-level input voltage	1, 2	54 Family			0.8			0.7			0.7			0.8	V
		74 Family			0.8			0.7			0.8			0.8	
V_{IK} Input clamp voltage	3	V_{CC} = MIN, I_I = §			-1.5			-1.5			-1.5			-1.2	V
V_{OH} High-level output voltage	1	V_{CC} = MIN, V_{IL} = V_{IL} max, I_{OH} = MAX, 54 Family	2.4	3.4		2.4	3.3		2.5	3.4		2.5	3.4		V
		74 Family	2.4	3.4		2.4	3.2		2.7	3.4		2.7	3.4		
V_{OL} Low-level output voltage	2	V_{CC} = MIN, I_{OL} = MAX, 54 Family		0.2	0.4		0.15	0.3		0.25	0.4			0.5	V
		V_{IH} = 2 V, 74 Family		0.2	0.4		0.2	0.4		0.35	0.5			0.5	
		I_{OL} = 4 mA, Series 74LS								0.25	0.4				
I_I Input current at maximum input voltage	4	V_{CC} = MAX, V_I = 5.5 V			1									1	mA
		V_I = 7 V						0.1			0.1				
I_{IH} High-level input current	4	V_{CC} = MAX, V_{IH} = 2.4 V, Data inputs			40			10							µA
		Strobe of '25			160										
		V_{IH} = 2.7 V, All inputs									20			50	
I_{IL} Low-level input current	5	V_{CC} = MAX, V_{IL} = 0.3 V						-0.18							mA
		V_{IL} = 0.4 V, Data inputs			-1.6						-0.4				
		Strobe of '25			-6.4										
		V_{IL} = 0.5 V, All inputs												-2	
I_{OS} Short-circuit output current♦	6	V_{CC} = MAX, 54 Family	-20		-55	-3		-15	-20		-100	-40		-100	mA
		74 Family	-18		-55	-3		-20	-20		-100	-40		-100	
I_{CC} Supply current	7	V_{CC} = MAX							See table on next page						mA

†For conditions shown as MIN or MAX, use the appropriate value specified under recommended operating conditions.
‡All typical values are at V_{CC} = 5 V, T_A = 25°C.
§I_I = -12 mA for SN54'/SN74' and -18 mA for SN54LS'/SN74LS' and SN54S'/SN74S'.
♦Not more than one output should be shorted at a time, and for SN54LS'/SN74LS' and SN54S'/SN74S', duration of output short-circuit should not exceed one second.

TEXAS INSTRUMENTS
INCORPORATED
POST OFFICE BOX 5012 • DALLAS, TEXAS 75222

6

schematics (each gate)

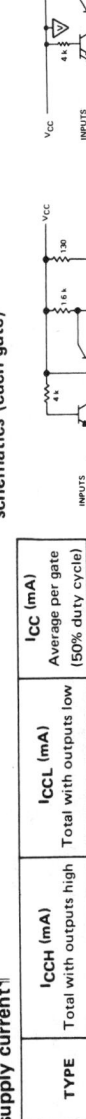

'25 CIRCUITS

'02, '27 CIRCUITS

The portion of the schematic within the dashed lines is repeated for the C input of the '27.

Resistor values are nominal and in ohms.

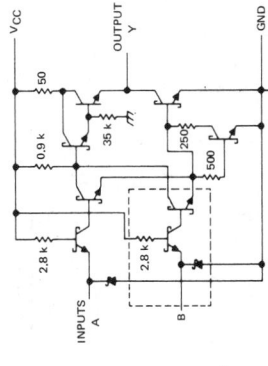

'S02, 'S260 CIRCUITS

The portion of the schematic within the dashed lines is repeated for each additional input of the 'S260, and the 0.9-kΩ resistor is changed to 0.6 kΩ.

'LS02, 'LS27 CIRCUITS

The portion of the schematic within the dashed lines applies only to the 'LS27.

'L02 CIRCUITS

supply current¶

TYPE	I_{CCH} (mA) Total with outputs high		I_{CCL} (mA) Total with outputs low		I_{CC} (mA) Average per gate (50% duty cycle)
	TYP	MAX	TYP	MAX	TYP
'02	8	16	14	27	2.75
'25	8	16	10	19	2.25
'27	10	16	16	26	4.34
'L02	0.8	1.6	1.4	2.6	0.275
'LS02	1.6	3.2	2.8	5.4	0.55
'LS27	2.0	4	3.4	6.8	0.9
'S02	17	29	26	45	5.38
'S260	17	29	26	45	10.75

¶Maximum values of I_{CC} are over the recommended operating ranges of V_{CC} and T_A; typical values are at V_{CC} = 5 V, T_A = 25°C.

switching characteristics at V_{CC} = 5 V, T_A = 25°C

TYPE	TEST CONDITIONS#	t_{PLH} (ns) Propagation delay time, low-to-high-level output			t_{PHL} (ns) Propagation delay time, high-to-low-level output		
		MIN	TYP	MAX	MIN	TYP	MAX
'02	C_L = 15 pF, R_L = 400 Ω		12	15		8	15
'25			13	22		8	15
'27			10	15		7	11
'L02	C_L = 50 pF, R_L = 4 kΩ		31	60		35	60
'LS02, 'LS27	C_L = 15 pF, R_L = 2 kΩ		10	15		10	15
'S02	C_L = 15 pF, R_L = 280 Ω		3.5	5.5		3.5	5.5
	C_L = 50 pF, R_L = 280 Ω		5			5	
'S260	C_L = 15 pF, R_L = 280 Ω		4	5.5		4	6

#Load circuit and voltage waveforms are shown on pages 3-10 and 3-11.

6

076

POSITIVE-AND GATES WITH TOTEM-POLE OUTPUTS

recommended operating conditions

		SERIES 54 / SERIES 74 '08			SERIES 54H / SERIES 74H 'H11, 'H21			SERIES 54LS / SERIES 74LS 'LS08, 'LS11, 'LS21			SERIES 54S / SERIES 74S 'S08, 'S11			UNIT
		MIN	NOM	MAX	MIN	NOM	MAX	MIN	NOM	MAX	MIN	NOM	MAX	
Supply Voltage, V_{CC}	54 Family	4.5	5	5.5	4.5	5	5.5	4.5	5	5.5	4.5	5	5.5	V
	74 Family	4.75	5	5.25	4.75	5	5.25	4.75	5	5.25	4.75	5	5.25	V
High-level output current, I_{OH}				−800			−500			−400			−1000	µA
Low-level output current, I_{OL}	54 Family			16			20			4			20	mA
	74 Family			16			20			8			20	mA
Operating free-air temperature, T_A	54 Family	−55		125	−55		125	−55		125	−55		125	°C
	74 Family	0		70	0		70	0		70	0		70	°C

electrical characteristics over recommended operating free-air temperature range (unless otherwise noted)

PARAMETER	TEST FIGURE	TEST CONDITIONS[†]		SERIES 54 / SERIES 74 '08			SERIES 54H / SERIES 74H 'H11, 'H21			SERIES 54LS / SERIES 74LS 'LS08, 'LS11, 'LS21			SERIES 54S / SERIES 74S 'S08, 'S11			UNIT
				MIN	TYP[‡]	MAX	MIN	TYP[‡]	MAX	MIN	TYP[‡]	MAX	MIN	TYP[‡]	MAX	
V_{IH} High-level input voltage	1, 2			2			2			2			2			V
V_{IL} Low-level input voltage	1, 2		54 Family			0.8			0.8			0.7			0.8	V
			74 Family			0.8			0.8			0.8			0.8	V
V_{IK} Input clamp voltage	3	V_{CC} = MIN, I_I = §[§]				−1.5			−1.5			−1.5			−1.2	V
V_{OH} High-level output voltage	1	V_{CC} = MIN, V_{IH} = 2 V, I_{OH} = MAX	54 Family	2.4	3.4		2.4	3.4		2.5	3.4		2.5	3.4		V
			74 Family	2.4	3.4		2.4	3.4		2.7	3.4		2.7	3.4		V
V_{OL} Low-level output voltage	2	V_{CC} = MIN, V_{IH} = 2 V, I_{OL} = MAX	54 Family		0.2	0.4		0.15	0.3		0.25	0.4			0.5	V
			74 Family		0.2	0.4		0.2	0.4		0.35	0.5			0.5	V
		I_{OL} = 4 mA	Series 74LS								0.25	0.4				V
I_I Input current at maximum input voltage	4	V_I = 5.5 V / V_I = 7 V				1			0.1			0.1			1	mA
I_{IH} High-level input current	4	V_{CC} = MAX, V_{IH} = 2.4 V / V_{IH} = 2.7 V				40			50			20			50	µA
I_{IL} Low-level input current	5	V_{CC} = MAX, V_{IL} = 0.4 V / V_{IL} = 0.5 V				−1.6			−2			−0.4			−2	mA
I_{OS} Short circuit output current[♦]	6	V_{CC} = MAX	54 Family	−20		−55	−40		−100	−20		−100	−40		−100	mA
			74 Family	−18		−55	−40		−100	−20		−100	−40		−100	mA
I_{CC} Supply current	7	V_{CC} = MAX											See table on next page			mA

[†] For conditions shown as MIN or MAX, use the appropriate values specified under recommended operating conditions.
[‡] All typical values are at V_{CC} = 25°C.
[§] I_I = −12 mA for SN54/SN74', −8 mA for SN54H'/SN74H', and −18 mA for SN54LS'/SN74LS' and SN54S'/SN74S'.
[♦] Not more than one output should be shorted at a time, and for SN54H'/SN74H', SN54LS'/SN74LS' and SN54S'/SN74S', duration of output short circuit should not exceed one second.

TEXAS INSTRUMENTS
INCORPORATED
POST OFFICE BOX 5012 • DALLAS, TEXAS 75222

schematics (each gate)

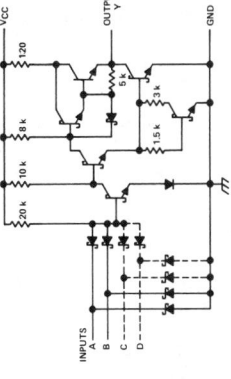

'08 CIRCUITS   'H11, 'H21 CIRCUITS   'LS08, 'LS11, 'LS21 CIRCUITS   'S08, 'S11 CIRCUITS

Resistor values shown are nominal and in ohms.

supply current¶

TYPE	I_{CCH} (mA) Total with outputs high		I_{CCL} (mA) Total with outputs low		I_{CC} (mA) Average per gate (50% duty cycle)
	TYP	MAX	TYP	MAX	TYP
'08	11	21	20	33	3.88
'H11	18	30	30	48	8
'H21	12	20	20	32	8
'LS08	2.4	4.8	4.4	8.8	0.85
'LS11	1.8	3.6	3.3	6.6	0.85
'LS21	1.2	2.4	2.2	4.4	0.85
'S08	18	32	32	57	6.25
'S11	13.5	24	24	42	6.25

¶ Maximum values of I_{CC} are over the recommended operating ranges of V_{CC} and T_A; typical values are at V_{CC} = 5 V, T_A = 25°C.

switching characteristics at V_{CC} = 5 V, T_A = 25°C

TYPE	TEST CONDITIONS#	t_{PLH} (ns) Propagation delay time, low-to-high-level output			t_{PHL} (ns) Propagation delay time, high-to-low-level output		
		MIN	TYP	MAX	MIN	TYP	MAX
'08	C_L = 15 pF, R_L = 400 Ω		17.5	27		12	19
'H11, 'H21	C_L = 25 pF, R_L = 280 Ω		7.6	12		8.8	12
'LS08, 'LS11	C_L = 15 pF, R_L = 2 kΩ		8	15		10	20
'LS21	C_L = 15 pF, R_L = 280 Ω		4.5	7		5	7.5
'S08, 'S11	C_L = 50 pF, R_L = 280 Ω		6			7.5	

#Load circuit and voltage waveforms are shown on pages 3-10 and 3-11.

6

TEXAS INSTRUMENTS
INCORPORATED
POST OFFICE BOX 5012 • DALLAS, TEXAS 75222

recommended operating conditions

PARAMETER		SERIES 54 / SERIES 74 '09			SERIES 54H / SERIES 74H 'H15			SERIES 54LS / SERIES 74LS 'LS09, 'LS15			SERIES 54S / SERIES 74S 'S09, 'S15			UNIT
		MIN	NOM	MAX	MIN	NOM	MAX	MIN	NOM	MAX	MIN	NOM	MAX	
Supply Voltage, V_{CC}	54 Family	4.5	5	5.5	4.5	5	5.5	4.5	5	5.5	4.5	5	5.5	V
	74 Family	4.75	5	5.25	4.75	5	5.25	4.75	5	5.25	4.75	5	5.25	
High-level output voltage, V_{OH}	54 Family			5.5			5.5			5.5			5.5	V
	74 Family			5.5			5.5			5.5			5.5	
Low-level output current, I_{OL}	54 Family			16			20			4			20	mA
	74 Family			16			20			8			20	
Operating free-air temperature, T_A	54 Family	−55		125	−55		125	−55		125	−55		125	°C
	74 Family	0		70	0		70	0		70	0		70	

electrical characteristics over recommended operating free-air temperature range (unless otherwise noted)

PARAMETER	TEST FIGURE	TEST CONDITIONS†	SERIES 54 / SERIES 74 '09			SERIES 54H / SERIES 74H 'H15			SERIES 54LS / SERIES 74LS 'LS09, 'LS15			SERIES 54S / SERIES 74S 'S09, 'S15			UNIT
			MIN	TYP‡	MAX	MIN	TYP‡	MAX	MIN	TYP‡	MAX	MIN	TYP‡	MAX	
V_{IH} High-level input voltage	1, 2		2			2			2			2			V
V_{IL} Low-level input voltage	1, 2	54 Family			0.8			0.8			0.7			0.8	V
		74 Family			0.8			0.8			0.8			0.8	
V_{IK} Input clamp voltage	3	V_{CC} = MIN, I_I = §			−1.5			−1.5			−1.5			−1.2	V
I_{OH} High-level output current	1	V_{CC} = MIN, V_{IH} = 2 V, V_{OH} = 5.5 V			250			250			100			250	µA
V_{OL} Low-level output voltage	2	V_{CC} = MIN, V_{IH} = 2 V, I_{OL} = MAX (54 Family)		0.2	0.4		0.15	0.3		0.25	0.4			0.5	V
		I_{OL} = MAX, V_{IH} = 2 V (74 Family)		0.2	0.4		0.2	0.4		0.35	0.5			0.5	
		I_{OL} = 4 mA (Series 74LS)								0.25	0.4				
I_I Input current at maximum input voltage	4	V_{CC} = MAX, V_I = 5.5 V / V_I = 7 V			1			1			0.1			1	mA
I_{IH} High-level input current	4	V_{CC} = MAX, V_{IH} = 2.4 V / V_{IH} = 2.7 V			40			50			20			50	µA
I_{IL} Low-level input current	5	V_{CC} = MAX, V_{IL} = 0.4 V / V_{IL} = 0.5 V			−1.6			−2			−0.4			−2	mA
I_{CC} Supply current	7	V_{CC} = MAX					See table on next page								mA

†For conditions shown as MIN or MAX, use the appropriate value specified under recommended operating conditions.
‡All typical values are at V_{CC} = 5 V, T_A = 25°C.
§I_I = −12 mA for SN54S'/SN74S', −8 mA for SN54'/SN74', and −18 mA for SN54H'/SN74H'.

6

TEXAS INSTRUMENTS
INCORPORATED
POST OFFICE BOX 5012 • DALLAS, TEXAS 75222

schematics (each gate)

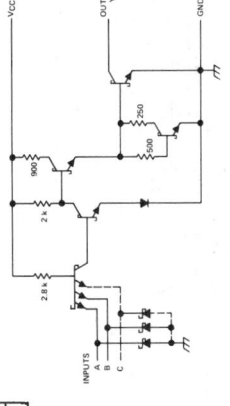

'09 CIRCUITS

'H15 CIRCUITS

'LS09, 'LS15 CIRCUITS

'S09, 'S15 CIRCUITS

Resistor values shown are nominal and in ohms.

supply current¶

TYPE	I$_{CCH}$ (mA) Total with outputs high		I$_{CCL}$ (mA) Total with outputs low		I$_{CC}$ (mA) Average per gate (50% duty cycle)
	TYP	MAX	TYP	MAX	TYP
'09	11	21	20	33	3.88
'H15	15	25	30	48	7.5
'LS09	2.4	4.8	4.4	8.8	0.85
'LS15	1.8	3.6	3.3	6.6	0.85
'S09	18	32	32	57	6.25
'S15	10.5	19.5	24	42	5.75

¶Maximum values of I$_{CC}$ are over the recommended operating ranges of V$_{CC}$ and T$_A$; typical values are at V$_{CC}$ = 5 V, T$_A$ = 25°C.

switching characteristics at V$_{CC}$ = 5 V, T$_A$ = 25°C

TYPE	TEST CONDITIONS#	t$_{PLH}$ (ns) Propagation delay time, low-to-high-level output			t$_{PHL}$ (ns) Propagation delay time, high-to-low-level output		
		MIN	TYP	MAX	MIN	TYP	MAX
'09	C$_L$ = 15 pF, R$_L$ = 400 Ω		21	32		16	24
'H15	C$_L$ = 25 pF, R$_L$ = 280 Ω		12	18		9	13
'LS09, 'LS15	C$_L$ = 15 pF, R$_L$ = 2 kΩ		20	35		17	35
'S09	C$_L$ = 15 pF, R$_L$ = 280 Ω		6.5	10		6.5	10
	C$_L$ = 50 pF, R$_L$ = 280 Ω		9			9	
'S15	C$_L$ = 15 pF, R$_L$ = 280 Ω		5.5	8.5		6	9
	C$_L$ = 50 pF, R$_L$ = 280 Ω		8.5			8	

#Load circuit and voltage waveforms are shown on pages 3-10 and 3-11.

6

SCHMITT-TRIGGER POSITIVE-NAND GATES AND INVERTERS WITH TOTEM-POLE OUTPUTS

recommended operating conditions

	54 FAMILY / 74 FAMILY	SERIES 54 / SERIES 74 '13, '14, '132			SERIES 54LS / SERIES 74LS 'LS13, 'LS14, 'LS132			SERIES 54S / SERIES 74S 'S132			UNIT
		MIN	NOM	MAX	MIN	NOM	MAX	MIN	NOM	MAX	
Supply voltage, V_{CC}	54 Family	4.5	5	5.5	4.5	5	5.5	4.5	5	5.5	V
	74 Family	4.75	5	5.25	4.75	5	5.25	4.75	5	5.25	V
High level output current, I_{OH}				−800			−400			−1000	µA
Low-level output current, I_{OL}	54 Family			16			4			20	mA
	74 Family			16			8			20	mA
Operating free-air temperature, T_A	54 Family	−55		125	−55		125	−55		125	°C
	74 Family	0		70	0		70	0		70	°C

electrical characteristics over recommended operating free-air temperature range (unless otherwise noted)

PARAMETER	TEST FIGURE	TEST CONDITIONS†		SERIES 54 / SERIES 74 '13, '14, '132			SERIES 54LS / SERIES 74LS 'LS13, 'LS14, 'LS132			SERIES 54S / SERIES 74S 'S132			UNIT
				MIN	TYP‡	MAX	MIN	TYP‡	MAX	MIN	TYP‡	MAX	
V_{T+} Positive-going threshold voltage	8	V_{CC} = 5 V		1.5	1.7	2	1.4	1.6	1.9	1.6	1.77	1.9	V
V_{T-} Negative-going threshold voltage	9	V_{CC} = 5 V		0.6	0.9	1.1	0.5	0.8	1	1.1	1.22	1.4	V
Hysteresis (V_{T+}–V_{T-})	8,9	V_{CC} = 5 V		0.4	0.8		0.4	0.8		0.2	0.55		V
V_{IK} Input clamp voltage	3	V_{CC} = MIN, I_I = §				−1.5			−1.5			−1.2	V
V_{OH} High-level output voltage	9	V_{CC} = MIN, I_{OH} = MAX, V_I = $V_{T-\ min}$	54 Family	2.4	3.4		2.5	3.4		2.5	3.4		V
			74 Family	2.4	3.4		2.7	3.4		2.7	3.4		V
V_{OL} Low-level output voltage	8	V_{CC} = MIN, V_I = $V_{T+\ max}$, I_{OL} = MAX	54 Family		0.2	0.4		0.25	0.4			0.5	V
		I_{OL} = MAX	74 Family		0.2	0.4		0.35	0.5			0.5	V
		I_{OL} = 4 mA	Series 74LS					0.25	0.4				V
I_{T+} Input current at positive-going threshold	8	V_{CC} = 5 V, V_I = V_{T+}			−0.65			−0.14			−0.9		mA
I_{T-} Input current at negative-going threshold	9	V_{CC} = 5 V, V_I = V_{T-}			−0.85			−0.18			−1.1		mA
I_I Input current at maximum input voltage	4	V_{CC} = MAX, V_I = 5.5 V / V_I = 7 V				1			0.1			1	mA
I_{IH} High-level input current	4	V_{CC} = MAX, V_I = 2.4 V / V_I = 2.7 V				40			20			50	µA
I_{IL} Low-level input current	5	V_{CC} = MAX, V_{IL} = 0.4 V / V_{IL} = 0.5 V			−1	−1.6		−0.8	−0.4			−2	mA
I_{OS} Short-circuit output current◆	6	V_{CC} = MAX		−18		−55	−20		−100	−40		−100	mA

† For conditions shown as MIN or MAX, use the appropriate value specified under recommended operating conditions.
‡ All typical values are at V_{CC} = 5 V, T_A = 25°C.
§ I_I = −12 mA for SN54'/SN74' and −18 mA for 'LS13', 'LS14, 'LS132, and 'S132.
◆ Not more than one output should be shorted at a time, and for SN54LS'/SN74LS' and 'S132, duration of output short-circuit should not exceed one second.

6

TEXAS INSTRUMENTS
INCORPORATED
POST OFFICE BOX 5012 • DALLAS, TEXAS 75222

switching characteristics, $V_{CC} = 5$ V, $T_A = 25°C$

TYPE	TEST CONDITIONS	t_{PLH} (ns) Propagation delay time, low-to-high-level output			t_{PHL} (ns) Propagation delay time, high-to-low-level output		
		MIN	TYP	MAX	MIN	TYP	MAX
'13	$C_L = 15$ pF, $R_L = 400\ \Omega$		18	27		15	22
'14, '132			15	22		15	22
'LS13	$C_L = 15$ pF, $R_L = 2\ k\Omega$		15	22		18	27
'LS14			15	22		15	22
'LS132			15	22		15	22
'S132	$C_L = 15$ pF, $R_L = 280\ \Omega$		7	10.5		8.5	13

supply current[¶]

TYPE	I_{CCH} (mA) Total with outputs high		I_{CCL} (mA) Total with outputs low		I_{CC} (mA) Average per gate (50% duty cycle)
	TYP	MAX	TYP	MAX	TYP
'13	14	23	20	32	8.5
'14	22	36	39	60	5.1
'132	15	24	26	40	5.1
'LS13	2.9	6	4.1	7	1.75
'LS14	8.6	16	12	21	1.72
'LS132	5.9	11	8.2	14	1.76
'S132	28	44	44	68	9

[¶]Maximum values of I_{CC} are over the recommended operating ranges of V_{CC} and T_A; typical values are at $V_{CC} = 5$ V, $T_A = 25°C$.

PARAMETER MEASUREMENT INFORMATION

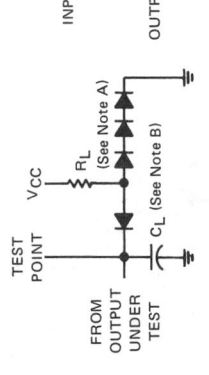

LOAD CIRCUIT

VOLTAGE WAVEFORMS

NOTES: A. All diodes are 1N916 or 1N3064.
B. C_L includes probe and jig capacitance.
C. Generator characteristics and reference voltages are:

	Generator Characteristics				Reference Voltages		
	Z_{out}	PRR	t_r	t_f	$V_{I\,ref(H)}$	$V_{I\,ref(L)}$	$V_{O\,ref}$
SN54'/SN74'	50 Ω	1 MHz	10 ns	10 ns	1.7 V	0.9 V	1.5 V
SN54LS'/SN74LS'	50 Ω	1 MHz	15 ns	6 ns	1.6 V	0.8 V	1.3 V
'S132	50 Ω	1 MHz	2.5 ns	2.5 ns	1.8 V	1.2 V	1.5 V

6

SCHMITT-TRIGGER POSITIVE-NAND GATES AND INVERTERS WITH TOTEM-POLE OUTPUTS

schematics (each gate)

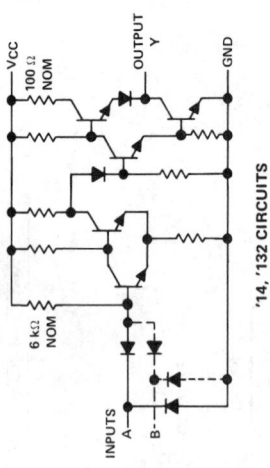

'14, '132 CIRCUITS

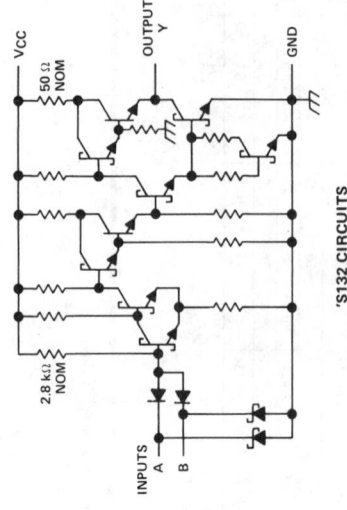

'S132 CIRCUITS

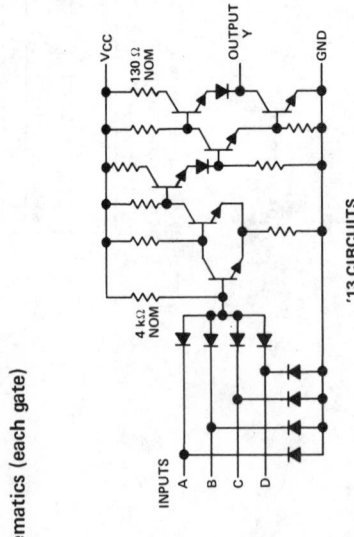

'13 CIRCUITS

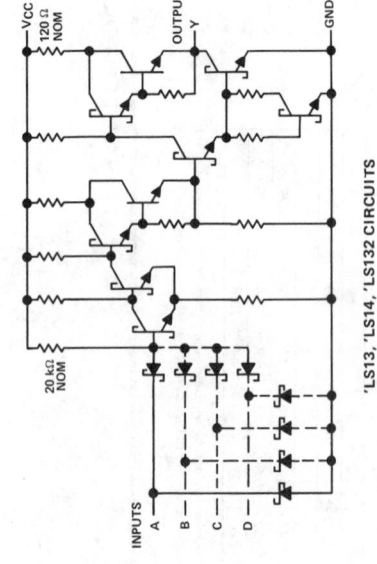

'LS13, 'LS14, 'LS132 CIRCUITS

Resistor values shown are nominal.

TEXAS INSTRUMENTS
INCORPORATED
POST OFFICE BOX 5012 • DALLAS, TEXAS 75222

107

SCHMITT-TRIGGER POSITIVE-NAND GATES AND INVERTERS
WITH TOTEM-POLE OUTPUTS

TYPICAL CHARACTERISTICS OF '13, '14, AND '132 CIRCUITS[†]

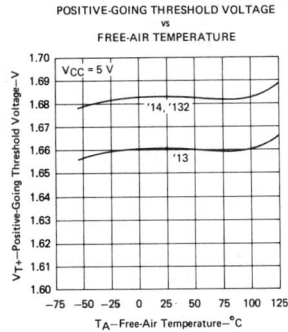

POSITIVE-GOING THRESHOLD VOLTAGE
vs
FREE-AIR TEMPERATURE

FIGURE 1

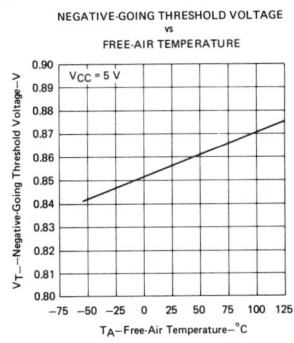

NEGATIVE-GOING THRESHOLD VOLTAGE
vs
FREE-AIR TEMPERATURE

FIGURE 2

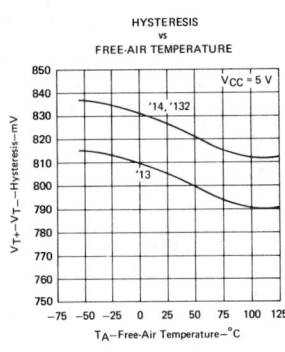

HYSTERESIS
vs
FREE-AIR TEMPERATURE

FIGURE 3

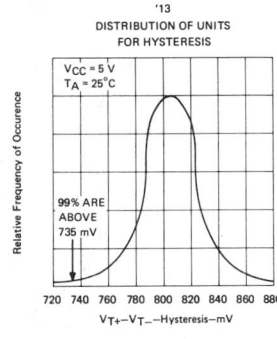

'13
DISTRIBUTION OF UNITS
FOR HYSTERESIS

FIGURE 4

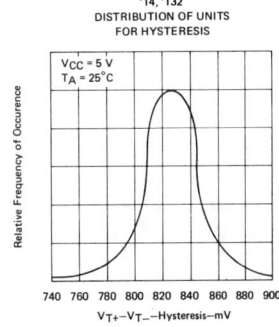

'14, '132
DISTRIBUTION OF UNITS
FOR HYSTERESIS

FIGURE 5

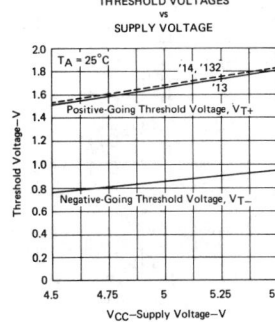

THRESHOLD VOLTAGES
vs
SUPPLY VOLTAGE

FIGURE 6

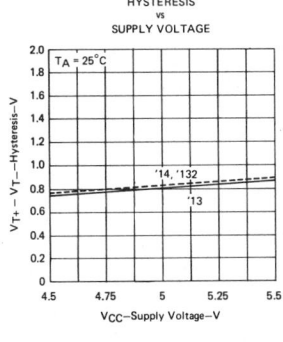

HYSTERESIS
vs
SUPPLY VOLTAGE

FIGURE 7

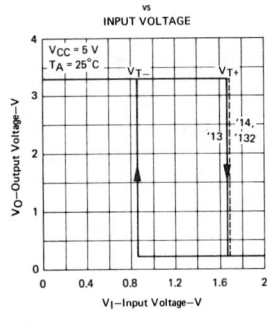

OUTPUT VOLTAGE
vs
INPUT VOLTAGE

FIGURE 8

[†]Data for temperatures below 0°C and 70°C and supply voltages below 4.75V and above 5.25 V are applicable for SN5413, SN5414, and SN54132 only.

TEXAS INSTRUMENTS
INCORPORATED
POST OFFICE BOX 5012 • DALLAS, TEXAS 75222

6

SCHMITT-TRIGGER POSITIVE-NAND GATES AND INVERTERS WITH TOTEM-POLE OUTPUTS

TYPICAL CHARACTERISTICS OF 'LS13, 'LS14, AND 'LS132 CIRCUITS[†]

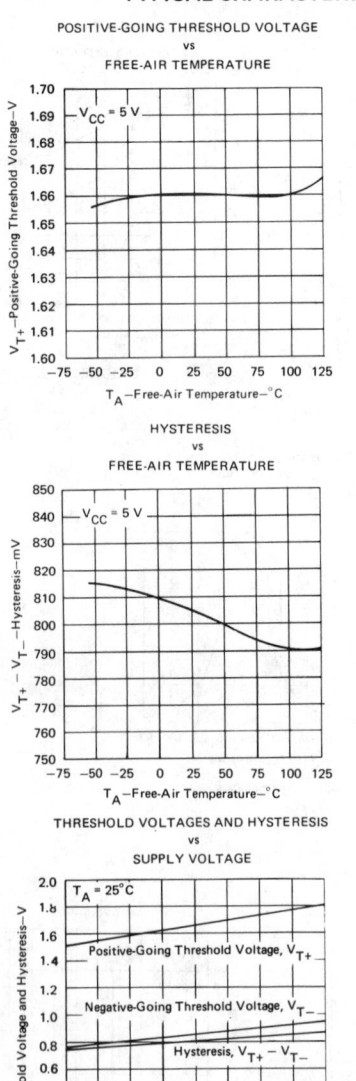

POSITIVE-GOING THRESHOLD VOLTAGE
vs
FREE-AIR TEMPERATURE

HYSTERESIS
vs
FREE-AIR TEMPERATURE

THRESHOLD VOLTAGES AND HYSTERESIS
vs
SUPPLY VOLTAGE

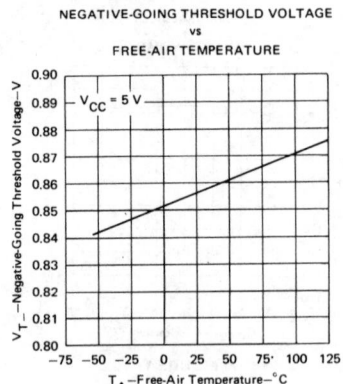

NEGATIVE-GOING THRESHOLD VOLTAGE
vs
FREE-AIR TEMPERATURE

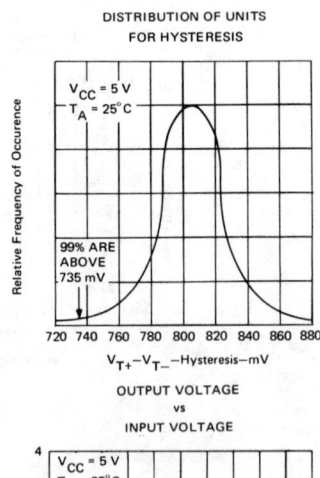

DISTRIBUTION OF UNITS
FOR HYSTERESIS

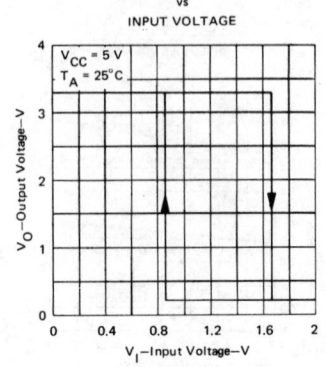

OUTPUT VOLTAGE
vs
INPUT VOLTAGE

[†]Data for temperatures below 0°C and above 70°C and supply voltages below 4.75 V and above 5.25 are applicable for SN54LS13, SN54LS14, and SN54LS132 only.

TEXAS INSTRUMENTS
INCORPORATED
POST OFFICE BOX 5012 • DALLAS, TEXAS 75222

SCHMITT-TRIGGER POSITIVE-NAND GATES AND INVERTERS WITH TOTEM-POLE OUTPUTS

TYPICAL APPLICATION DATA

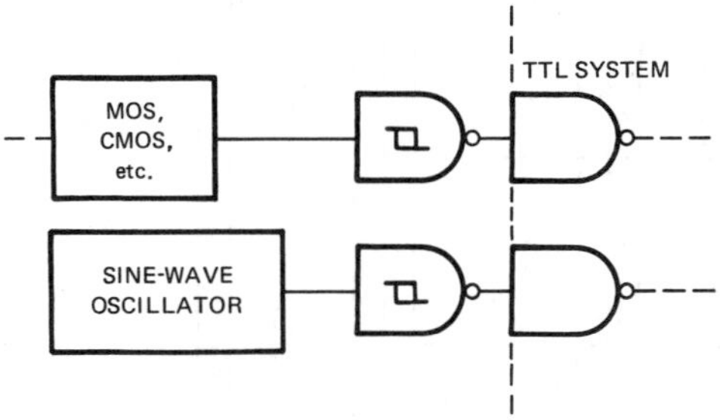

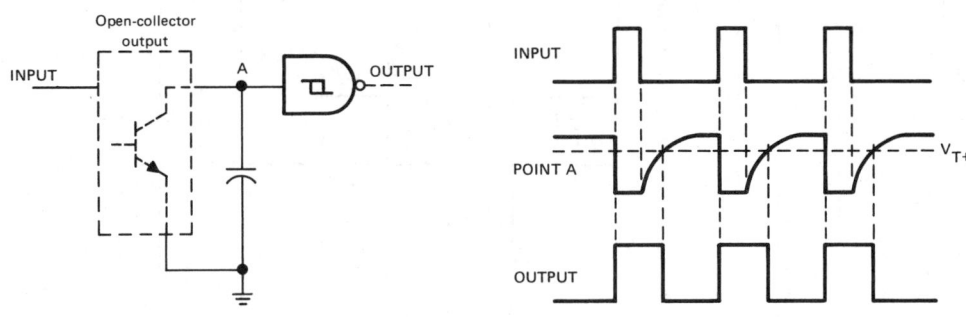

TTL SYSTEM INTERFACE FOR SLOW INPUT WAVEFORMS

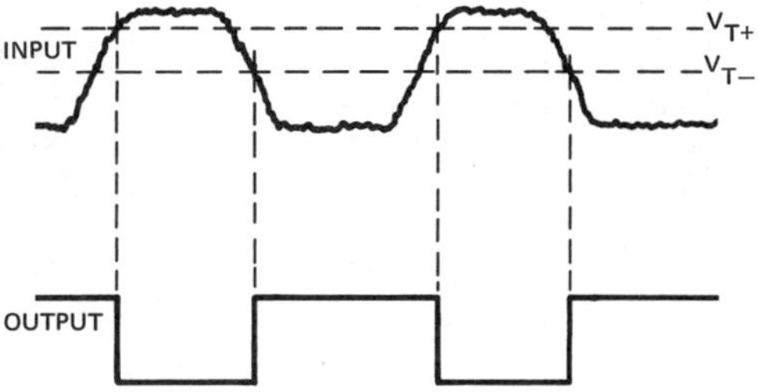

PULSE SHAPER

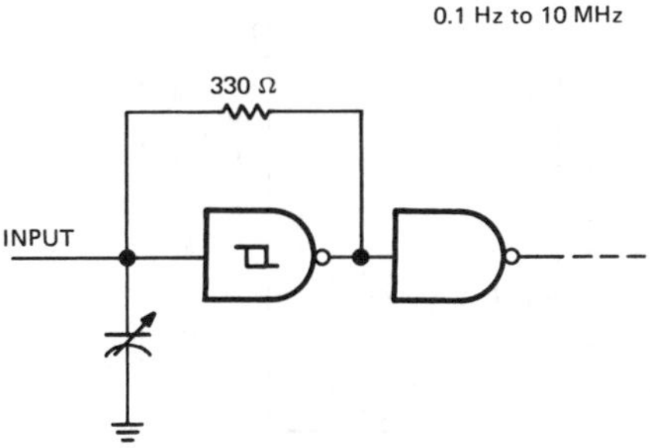

0.1 Hz to 10 MHz

330 Ω

INPUT

MULTIVIBRATOR

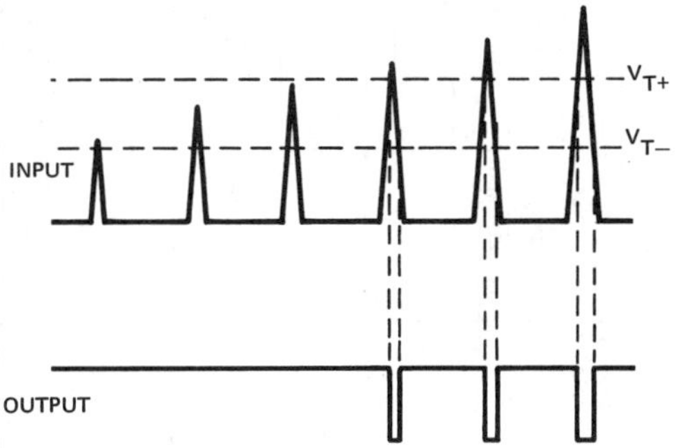

V_{T+}
V_{T-}
INPUT

OUTPUT

THRESHOLD DETECTOR

Open-collector output

INPUT

A

OUTPUT

INPUT

POINT A — V_{T+}

OUTPUT

PULSE STRETCHER

TEXAS INSTRUMENTS
INCORPORATED
POST OFFICE BOX 5012 • DALLAS, TEXAS 75222

recommended operating conditions

54 FAMILY / 74 FAMILY		SERIES 54 / SERIES 74 ('28)			'37, '40			SERIES 54H / SERIES 74H ('H40)			SERIES 54LS / SERIES 74LS ('LS28, 'LS37, 'LS40)			SERIES 54S / SERIES 74S ('S37, 'S40)			UNIT
		MIN	NOM	MAX	MIN	NOM	MAX	MIN	NOM	MAX	MIN	NOM	MAX	MIN	NOM	MAX	
Supply voltage, V_CC	54 Family	4.5	5	5.5	4.5	5	5.5	4.5	5	5.5	4.5	5	5.5	4.5	5	5.5	V
	74 Family	4.75	5	5.25	4.75	5	5.25	4.75	5	5.25	4.75	5	5.25	4.75	5	5.25	
High-level output current, I_OH				-2.4			-1.2			-1.5			-1.2			-3	mA
Low-level output current, I_OL	54 Family			48			48			60			12			60	mA
	74 Family			48			48			60			24			60	
Operating free-air temperature, T_A	54 Family	-55		125	-55		125	-55		125	-55		125	-55		125	°C
	74 Family	0		70	0		70	0		70	0		70	0		70	

electrical characteristics over recommended operating free-air temperature range (unless otherwise noted)

PARAMETER	TEST FIGURE	TEST CONDITIONS†		SERIES 54 / SERIES 74 ('28)			'37, '40			SERIES 54H / SERIES 74H ('H40)			SERIES 54LS / SERIES 74LS ('LS28, 'LS37, 'LS40)			SERIES 54S / SERIES 74S ('S37, 'S40)			UNIT
				MIN	TYP‡	MAX	MIN	TYP‡	MAX	MIN	TYP‡	MAX	MIN	TYP‡	MAX	MIN	TYP‡	MAX	
V_IH High-level input voltage	1, 2			2			2			2			2			2			V
V_IL Low-level input voltage	1, 2		54 Family			0.8			0.8			0.8			0.7			0.8	V
			74 Family			0.8			0.8			0.8			0.8			0.8	
V_IK Input clamp voltage	3	V_CC = MIN, I_I = §				-1.5			-1.5			-1.5			-1.5			-1.2	V
V_OH High-level output voltage	1	V_CC = MIN, V_IL = V_IL max, I_OH = MAX	54 Family	2.4	3.4		2.4	3.3		2.4	3.4		2.5	3.4		2.5	3.4		V
			74 Family	2.4	3.4		2.4	3.3		2.4	3.4		2.7	3.4		2.7	3.4		
V_OL Low-level output voltage	2	V_CC = MIN, I_OL = MAX / V_IH = 2 V	54 Family		0.2	0.4		0.2	0.4		0.15	0.3		0.25	0.4			0.5	V
			74 Family		0.2	0.4		0.2	0.4		0.2	0.4		0.35	0.5			0.5	
		I_OL = 12 mA Series 74LS												0.25	0.4				
I_I Input current at maximum input voltage	4	V_I = 5.5 V / V_I = 7 V				1			1			0.1			0.1			1	mA
I_IH High-level input current	4	V_CC = MAX, V_IH = 2.4 V / V_IH = 2.7 V				40			40			100			20			100	µA
I_IL Low-level input current	5	V_CC = MAX, V_IL = 0.4 V / V_IL = 0.5 V				-1.6			-1.6			-4			-0.4			-4	mA
I_OS Short-circuit output current◆	6	V_CC = MAX	54 Family	-70		-180	-20		-70	-40		-125	-30		-130	-50		-225	mA
			74 Family	-70		-180	-18		-70	-40		-125	-30		-130	-50		-225	
I_CC Supply current	7	V_CC = MAX		See table on next page															mA

†For conditions shown as MIN or MAX, use the appropriate value specified under recommended operating conditions.
‡All typical values are at V_CC = 5 V, T_A = 25°C.
§I_I = -12 mA for SN54'/SN74', -8 mA for SN54H'/SN74H', and -18 mA for SN54LS'/SN74LS' and SN54S'/SN74S'.
◆Not more than one output should be shorted at a time, and duration of the short-circuit should not exceed one second for all of these circuits except 'S37 and 'S40, or 100 milliseconds for 'S37 and 'S40.

6

TEXAS INSTRUMENTS
INCORPORATED
POST OFFICE BOX 5012 • DALLAS, TEXAS 75222

switching characteristics, VCC = 5 V, TA = 25°C

TYPE	TEST CONDITIONS#	tPLH (ns) Propagation delay time, low-to-high-level output			tPHL (ns) Propagation delay time, high-to-low output		
		MIN	TYP	MAX	MIN	TYP	MAX
'28	$C_L = 50$ pF, $R_L = 133\,\Omega$		6	9		8	12
	$C_L = 150$ pF, $R_L = 133\,\Omega$		10	15		12	18
'37	$C_L = 45$ pF, $R_L = 133\,\Omega$		13	22		8	15
'40	$C_L = 15$ pF, $R_L = 133\,\Omega$		13	22		8	15
'H40	$C_L = 25$ pF, $R_L = 93\,\Omega$		8.5	12		6.5	12
'LS28			12	24		12	24
'LS37	$C_L = 45$ pF, $R_L = 667\,\Omega$		12	24		12	24
'LS40			12	24		12	24
'S37,	$C_L = 50$ pF, $R_L = 93\,\Omega$		4	6.5		4	6.5
'S40	$C_L = 150$ pF, $R_L = 93\,\Omega$		6			6	

#Load circuit and voltage waveforms are shown on pages 3-10 and 3-11.

supply current¶

TYPE	ICCH (mA) Total with outputs high		ICCL (mA) Total with outputs low		ICC (mA) Average per gate (50% duty cycle)
	TYP	MAX	TYP	MAX	TYP
'28	12	21	33	57	5.63
'37	9	15.5	34	54	5.38
'40	4	8	17	27	5.25
'H40	10.4	16	25	40	8.85
'LS28	1.8	3.6	6.9	13.8	1.09
'LS37	0.9	2	6	12	0.86
'LS40	0.45	1	3	6	0.86
'S37	20	36	46	80	8.25
'S40	10	18	25	44	8.75

¶ Maximum values of I_{CC} are over the recommended operating ranges of V_{CC} and T_A; typical values are at $V_{CC} = 5$ V, $T_A = 25°C$.

schematics (each gate)

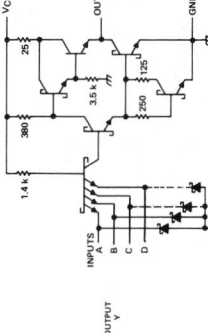

	'37	'40	'H40
R1	4 k	4 k	1.4 k
R2	600	600	390
R3	100	100	45
R4	400	400	250
R5	4 k	4 k	2 k

'37, '40, 'H40 CIRCUITS

'S37, 'S40 CIRCUITS

'28 CIRCUITS

'LS37, 'LS40 CIRCUITS

'LS28 CIRCUITS

Resistor values shown are nominal and in ohms.

TEXAS INSTRUMENTS
INCORPORATED
POST OFFICE BOX 5012 • DALLAS, TEXAS 75222

50-OHM/75-OHM LINE DRIVERS

recommended operating conditions

	54 FAMILY / 74 FAMILY	SERIES 54 / SERIES 74 '128 MIN	NOM	MAX	SERIES 54S / SERIES 74S 'S140 MIN	NOM	MAX	UNIT
Supply voltage, V_{CC}	54 Family	4.5	5	5.5	4.5	5	5.5	V
	74 Family	4.75	5	5.25	4.75	5	5.25	
High-level output current, I_{OH}	54 Family			-29			-40	mA
	74 Family			-42.4			-40	
Low-level output current, I_{OL}	54 Family			48			60	mA
	74 Family							
Operating free-air temperature, T_A	54 Family	-55		125	-55	0	125	°C
	74 Family	0		70	0		70	

electrical characteristics over recommended operating free-air temperature range (unless otherwise noted)

PARAMETER	TEST FIGURE	TEST CONDITIONS†	SERIES 54 / SERIES 74 '128 MIN	TYP‡	MAX	SERIES 54S / SERIES 74S 'S140 MIN	TYP‡	MAX	UNIT
V_{IH} High-level input voltage	1, 2		2			2			V
V_{IL} Low-level input voltage	1, 2				0.8			0.8	V
V_{IK} Input clamp voltage	3	V_{CC} = MIN, I_I = §			-1.5			-1.2	V
V_{OH} High-level output voltage	1	V_{CC} = MIN, V_{IL} = 0.8 V, I_{OH} = -2.4 mA 54 Family	2.4	3.4		2.5	3.4		V
		V_{CC} = MIN, V_{IL} = 0.4 V, I_{OH} = -13.2 mA 74 Family	2.4	3.4		2.7	3.4		
		V_{CC} = MIN, V_{IL} = 0.4 V, I_{OH} = MAX	2.4			2			
		V_{CC} = MIN, V_{IL} = 0.8 V, I_{OH} = -3 mA 54 Family	2						
		V_{CC} = MIN, V_{IL} = 0.5 V, R_O = 50 Ω to GND 74 Family				2			
V_{OL} Low-level output voltage	2	V_{CC} = MIN, V_{IH} = 2 V, I_{OL} = MAX		0.26	0.4			0.5	V
I_I Input current at maximum input voltage	4	V_{CC} = MAX, V_I = 5.5 V			1			1	mA
I_{IH} High-level input current	4	V_{CC} = MAX V_{IH} = 2.4 V / V_{IH} = 2.7 V			40			100	µA
I_{IL} Low-level input current	5	V_{CC} = MAX V_{IL} = 0.4 V / V_{IL} = 0.5 V			-1.6			-4	mA
I_{OS} Short-circuit output current♦	6	V_{CC} = MAX	-70		-180	-50		-225	mA
I_{CC} Supply current	7	Total, outputs high V_{CC} = MAX		12	21		10	18	mA
		Total, outputs low V_{CC} = MAX		33	57		25	44	mA
		Average per gate V_{CC} = 5 V, 50% duty cycle		5.63			8.75		

† For conditions shown as MIN or MAX, use the appropriate value specified under recommended operating conditions.
‡ All typical values are at V_{CC} = 5 V, T_A = 25°C.
§ I_I = -12 mA for '128 and -18 mA for 'S140.
♦ Not more than one output should be shorted at a time, and duration of short circuit should not exceed one second for '128 or 100 milliseconds for 'S140.

6

switching characteristics, VCC = 5 V, TA = 25°C

TYPE	TEST CONDITIONS#	tPLH (ns) Propagation delay time, low-to-high-level output			tPHL (ns) Propagation delay time, high-to-low-level output		
		MIN	TYP	MAX	MIN	TYP	MAX
'128	CL = 50 pF, RL = 133 Ω		6	9		8	12
	CL = 150 pF, RL = 133 Ω		10	15		12	18
'S140	CL = 50 pF, RL = 93 Ω		4	6.5		4	6.5
	CL = 150 pF, RL = 93 Ω		6			6	

#Load circuit and voltage waveforms are shown on page 3-10.

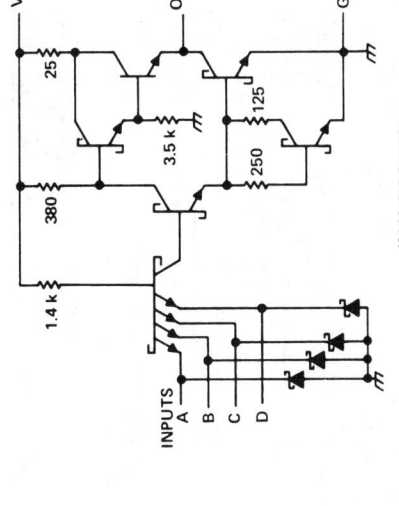

'S140 CIRCUITS

schematics (each driver)

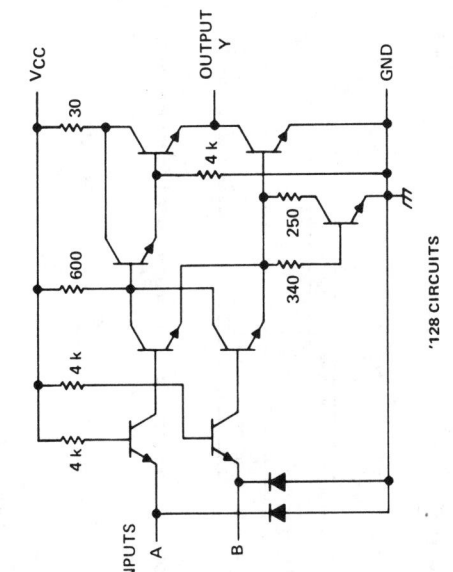

'128 CIRCUITS

Resistor values shown are nominal and in ohms.

recommended operating conditions

PARAMETER	54 FAMILY / 74 FAMILY	'06, '07 MIN	NOM	MAX	'16, '17 MIN	NOM	MAX	'26 MIN	NOM	MAX	'33, '38 MIN	NOM	MAX	UNIT
Supply voltage, V_{CC}	54 Family	4.5	5	5.5	4.5	5	5.5	4.5	5	5.5	4.5	5	5.5	V
	74 Family	4.75	5	5.25	4.75	5	5.25	4.75	5	5.25	4.75	5	5.25	V
High-level output voltage, V_{OH}	74 Family			30			30			15			15	V
Low-level output current, I_{OL}	54 Family			30			30			16			48	mA
	74 Family			40			40			16			48	mA
Operating free-air temperature, T_A	54 Family	−55		125	−55		125	−55		125	−55		125	°C
	74 Family	0		70	0		70	0		70	0		70	°C

electrical characteristics over recommended operating free-air temperature range (unless otherwise noted)

PARAMETER	TEST FIGURE	TEST CONDITIONS†	SERIES 54' / SERIES 74' '06, '07 MIN	TYP	MAX	'16, '17 MIN	TYP	MAX	'26 MIN	TYP	MAX	'33, '38 MIN	TYP	MAX	UNIT
V_{IH} High-level input voltage	1, 2		2			2			2			2			V
V_{IL} Low-level input voltage	1, 2				0.8			0.8			0.8			0.8	V
V_{IK} Input clamp voltage	3	V_{CC} = MIN, I_I = −12 mA			−1.5			−1.5			−1.5			−1.5	V
I_{OH} High-level output current	1	V_{CC} = MIN, V_I = ▲, V_{OH} = 12 V / V_{OH} = MAX			250			250		50	1000			250	μA
V_{OL} Low-level output voltage	2	V_{CC} = MIN, V_I = ▲, I_{OL} = 16 mA / I_{OL} = MAX			0.4 / 0.7			0.4 / 0.7			0.4			0.7	V
I_I Input current at maximum input voltage	4	V_{CC} = MAX, V_I = 5.5 V			1			1			1			1	mA
I_{IH} High-level input current	4	V_{CC} = MAX, V_{IH} = 2.4 V			40			40			40			40	μA
I_{IL} Low-level input current	5	V_{CC} = MAX, V_{IL} = 0.4 V			−1.6			−1.6			−1.6			−1.6	mA
I_{CC} Supply current	7	V_{CC} = MAX	See table on next page												mA

† For conditions shown as MIN or MAX, use the appropriate value specified under recommended operating conditions.

▲ The input voltage is V_{IH} = 2 V or V_{IL} = V_{IL} max, as appropriate. See tables with test figures 1 and 2.

6

TEXAS INSTRUMENTS
INCORPORATED
POST OFFICE BOX 5012 • DALLAS, TEXAS 75222

switching characteristics, V_{CC} = 5 V, T_A = 25°C

TYPE	TEST CONDITIONS#	t_{PLH} (ns) Propagation delay time, low-to-high-level output		t_{PHL} (ns) Propagation delay time, high-to-low-level output	
		TYP	MAX	TYP	MAX
'06, '16	C_L = 15 pF, R_L = 110 Ω	10	15	15	23
'07, '17	C_L = 15 pF, R_L = 1 kΩ	6	10	20	30
'26	C_L = 50 pF, R_L = 133 Ω	16	24	11	17
'33	C_L = 150 pF, R_L = 133 Ω	10	15	12	18
		15	22	16	24
'38	C_L = 45 pF, R_L = 133 Ω	14	22	11	18

#Load circuit and voltage waveforms are shown on page 3-10.

supply current¶

TYPE	I_{CCH} (mA) Total with outputs high		I_{CCL} (mA) Total with outputs low		I_{CC} (mA) Average per gate (50% duty cycle)
	TYP	MAX	TYP	MAX	TYP
'06, '16	30	48	32	51	5.17
'07, '17	29	41	21	30	4.17
'26	4	8	12	22	2.00
'33	12	21	33	57	5.63
'38	5	8.5	34	54	4.88

¶Maximum values of I_{CC} shown are over the recommended operating ranges of V_{CC} and T_A; typical values are at V_{CC} = 5 V, T_A = 25°C.

schematics (each gate)

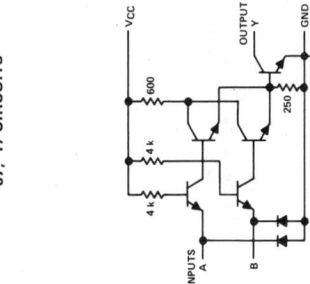

'07, '17 CIRCUITS

'33 CIRCUITS

'06, '16 CIRCUITS

'26, '38 CIRCUITS

CIRCUITS	R1	R2	R3
'26	4 kΩ	1.6 kΩ	1 kΩ
'38	4 kΩ	600 Ω	400 Ω

6

SERIES 54LS/74LS AND SERIES 54S/74S
BUFFER AND INTERFACE GATES WITH OPEN-COLLECTOR OUTPUTS

recommended operating conditions

PARAMETER		'LS26 MIN	NOM	MAX	SERIES 54LS'/74LS' 'LS33 MIN	NOM	MAX	'LS38 MIN	NOM	MAX	SERIES 54S'/74S' 'S38 MIN	NOM	MAX	UNIT
Supply voltage, V_{CC}	54 Family	4.5	5	5.5	4.5	5	5.5	4.5	5	5.5	4.5	5	5.5	V
	74 Family	4.75	5	5.25	4.75	5	5.25	4.75	5	5.25	4.75	5	5.25	V
High-level output voltage, V_{OH}	74 Family			15			5.5			5.5			5.5	V
Low-level output current, I_{OL}	54 Family			4			12			12			60	mA
	74 Family			8			24			24			60	mA
Operating free-air temperature, T_A	54 Family	-55		125	-55		125	-55		125	-55		125	°C
	74 Family	0		70	0		70	0		70	0		70	°C

electrical characteristics over recommended operating free-air temperature range (unless otherwise noted)[†]

PARAMETER	TEST FIGURE	TEST CONDITIONS[†]		'LS26 MIN	TYP[‡]	MAX	SERIES 54LS'/74LS' 'LS33 MIN	TYP[‡]	MAX	'LS38 MIN	TYP[‡]	MAX	SERIES 54S'/74S' 'S38 MIN	TYP[‡]	MAX	UNIT
V_{IH} High-level input voltage	1, 2			2			2			2			2			V
V_{IL} Low-level input voltage	1, 2		54 Family			0.7			0.7			0.7			0.8	V
			74 Family			0.8			0.8			0.8			0.8	V
V_{IK} Input clamp voltage	3	V_{CC} = MIN, I_I = §				-1.5			-1.5			-1.5			-1.2	V
I_{OH} High-level output current	1	V_{CC} = MIN, V_I = ▲	V_{OH} = 12 V		50	1000			250			250			250	µA
			V_{OH} = MAX													
V_{OL} Low-level output voltage	2	V_{CC} = MIN, V_I = ▲, I_{OL} = MAX	54 Family		0.25	0.4		0.25	0.4		0.25	0.4			0.4	V
			74 Family		0.35	0.5		0.35	0.5		0.35	0.5			0.5	
		I_{OL} = 4 mA / I_{OL} = 12 mA	Series 74LS'		0.25	0.4		0.25	0.4		0.25	0.4				
I_I Input current at maximum input voltage	4	V_{CC} = MAX, V_I = 5.5 V (V_I = 7 V)				0.1			0.1			0.1			1	mA
I_{IH} High-level input current	4	V_{CC} = MAX, V_{IH} = 2.7 V				20			20			20			100	µA
I_{IL} Low-level input current	5	V_{CC} = MAX, V_{IL} = 0.4 V (V_{IL} = 0.5 V)				-0.4			-0.4			-0.4			-4	mA
I_{CC} Supply current	7	V_{CC} = MAX							See table on next page							mA

† For conditions shown as MIN or MAX, use the appropriate value specified under recommended operating conditions.
‡ All typical values are at V_{CC} = 5 V, T_A = 25°C.
§ I_I = -18 mA for SN54LS'/SN74LS' and -12 mA for SN54S'/SN74S'.
▲ The input voltage is V_{IH} = 2 V or V_{IL} = V_{IL} max, as appropriate. See tables with test figures 1 and 2.

6

TEXAS INSTRUMENTS
INCORPORATED
POST OFFICE BOX 5012 • DALLAS, TEXAS 75222

supply current¶

TYPE	I_{CCH} (mA) Total with outputs high		I_{CCL} (mA) Total with outputs low		I_{CC} (mA) Average per gate (50% duty cycle)
	TYP	MAX	TYP	MAX	TYP
'LS26	0.8	1.6	2.4	4.4	0.4
'LS33	1.8	3.6	6.9	13.8	1.09
'LS38	0.9	2	6	12	0.86
'S38	20	36	46	80	8.25

¶Maximum values of I_{CC} shown are over the recommended operating ranges of V_{CC} and T_A; typical values are at V_{CC} = 5 V, T_A = 25°C.

switching characteristics, V_{CC} = 5 V, T_A = 25°C

TYPE	TEST CONDITIONS#		t_{PLH} (ns) Propagation delay time, low-to-high-level output		t_{PHL} (ns) Propagation delay time, high-to-low-level output	
			TYP	MAX	TYP	MAX
'LS26	C_L = 15 pF,	R_L = 2 kΩ	17	32	15	28
'LS33	C_L = 45 pF,	R_L = 667 Ω	20	32	18	28
'LS38		C_L = 50 pF	20	32	18	28
'S38	R_L = 93 Ω	C_L = 50 pF	6.5	10	6.5	10
		C_L = 150 pF	9		8.5	

#Load circuit and voltage waveforms are shown on pages 3-10 and 3-11.

schematics (each gate)

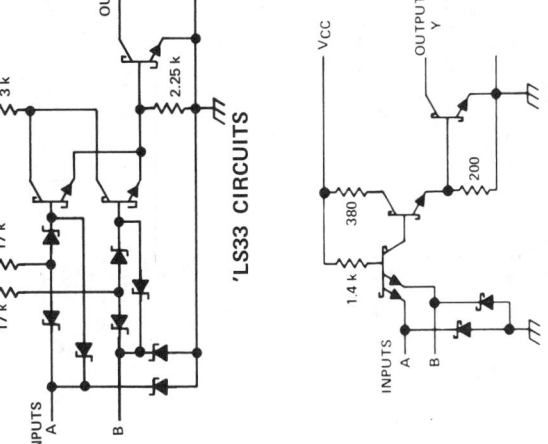

'LS33 CIRCUITS

'S38 CIRCUITS

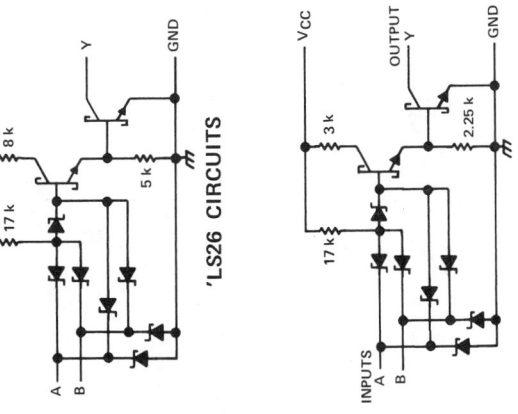

'LS26 CIRCUITS

'LS38 CIRCUITS

1076

recommended operating conditions

PARAMETER		SERIES 54 / SERIES 74 '32			SERIES 54LS / SERIES 74LS 'LS32			SERIES 54S / SERIES 74S 'S32			UNIT
		MIN	NOM	MAX	MIN	NOM	MAX	MIN	NOM	MAX	
Supply voltage, VCC	54 Family	4.5	5	5.5	4.5	5	5.5	4.5	5	5.25	V
	74 Family	4.75	5	5.25	4.75	5	5.25	4.75	5	5.25	
High-level output current, IOH	54 Family,			-800			-400			-1000	µA
Low-level output current, IOL	54 Family,			16			4			20	mA
	74 Family			16			8			20	
Operating free-air temperature, TA	54 Family	-55		125	-55		125	-55		125	C
	74 Family	0		70	0		70	0		70	

electrical characteristics over recommended free-air temperature range (unless otherwise noted)

PARAMETER	TEST FIGURE	TEST CONDITIONS†		SERIES 54 / SERIES 74 '32			SERIES 54LS / SERIES 74LS 'LS32			SERIES 54S / SERIES 74S 'S32			UNIT
				MIN	TYP‡	MAX	MIN	TYP‡	MAX	MIN	TYP‡	MAX	
VIH High-level input voltage	1, 2			2			2			2			V
VIL Low-level input voltage	1, 2	54 Family				0.8			0.7			0.8	V
		74 Family				0.8			0.8			0.8	
VIK Input clamp voltage	3	VCC = MIN, II = §, VIH = 2 V,				-1.5			-1.5			-1.2	V
VOH High-level output voltage	1	VCC = MIN, IOH = MAX	54 Family	2.4	3.4		2.5	3.4		2.5	3.4		V
			74 Family	2.4	3.4		2.7	3.4		2.7	3.4		
VOL Low-level output voltage	2	VCC = MIN, VIL = VIL max, IOL = MAX	54 Family		0.2	0.4		0.25	0.4			0.5	V
			74 Family		0.2	0.4		0.35	0.5			0.5	
		IOL = 4 mA	Series 74LS					0.25	0.4				
II Input current at maximum input voltage	4	VCC = MAX, VI = 5.5 V				1						1	mA
		VI = 7 V							0.1				
IIH High-level input current	4	VCC = MAX, VIH = 2.4 V				40							µA
		VIH = 2.7 V							20			50	
IIL Low-level input current	5	VCC = MAX, VIL = 0.4 V				-1.6			-0.4				mA
		VIL = 0.5 V										-2	
IOS Short-circuit output current♦	6	VCC = MAX	54 Family	-20		-55	-20		-100	-40		-100	mA
			74 Family	-18		-55	-20		-100	-40		-100	
ICC Supply current	7	VCC = MAX,	Total, outputs high		15	22		3.1	6.2		18	32	mA
		VCC = 5 V,	Total, outputs low		23	38		4.9	9.8		38	68	
		50% duty cycle	Average per gate		4.75			1.0			7		

† For conditions shown as MIN or MAX, use the appropriate value specified under recommended operating conditions.

‡ All typical values are at VCC = 5 V, TA = 25°C.

§ II = -12 mA for SN54'/SN74' and -18 mA for SN54LS'/SN74LS' and SN54S'/SN74S'.

♦ Not more than one output should be shorted at a time, and for SN54LS'/SN74LS' and SN54S'/SN74S', duration of the short-circuit should be less than one second.

TEXAS INSTRUMENTS
INCORPORATED
POST OFFICE BOX 5012 • DALLAS, TEXAS 75222

1076

POSITIVE-OR GATES WITH TOTEM-POLE OUTPUTS

schematics (each gate)

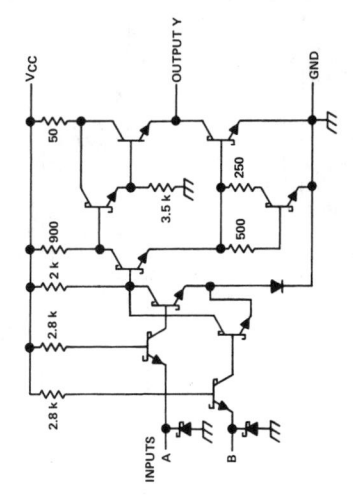

'32 CIRCUITS

'S32 CIRCUITS

switching characteristics at VCC = 5 V, TA = 25°C

TYPE	TEST CONDITIONS#	tPLH (ns) Propagation delay time, low-to-high-level output			tPHL (ns) Propagation delay time, high-to-low-level output		
		MIN	TYP	MAX	MIN	TYP	MAX
'32	CL = 15 pF, RL = 400 Ω		10	15		14	22
'LS32	CL = 15 pF, RL = 2 kΩ		14	22		14	22
'S32	CL = 15 pF, RL = 280 Ω		4	7		4	7
	CL = 50 pF, RL = 280 Ω		5			5	

#Load circuit and voltage waveforms are shown on pages 3-10 and 3-11.

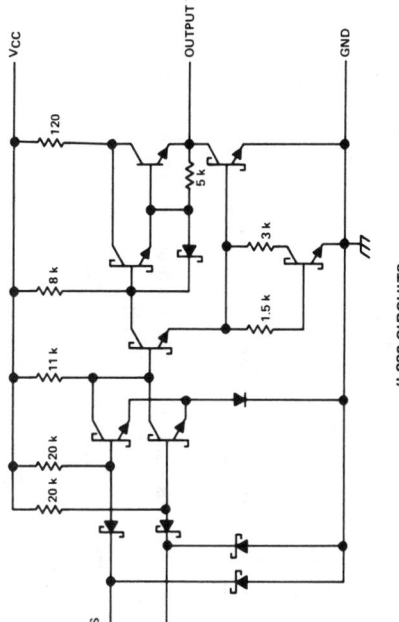

'LS32 CIRCUITS

Resistor values shown are nominal and in ohms.

6

recommended operating conditions

PARAMETER		SERIES 54 / SERIES 74 '51, '54			SERIES 54H / SERIES 74H 'H51, 'H54			SERIES 54L / SERIES 74L 'L51, 'L54, 'L55			SERIES 54LS / SERIES 74LS 'LS51, 'LS54, 'LS55			SERIES 54S / SERIES 74S 'S51, 'S64			UNIT
		MIN	NOM	MAX	MIN	NOM	MAX	MIN	NOM	MAX	MIN	NOM	MAX	MIN	NOM	MAX	
Supply voltage, VCC	54 Family	4.5	5	5.5	4.5	5	5.5	4.5	5	5.5	4.5	5	5.5	4.5	5	5.5	V
	74 Family	4.75	5	5.25	4.75	5	5.25	4.75	5	5.25	4.75	5	5.25	4.75	5	5.25	V
High-level output current, IOH	54 Family			−400			−500			−100			−400			−1000	µA
	74 Family			−400			−500			−200			−400			−1000	µA
Low-level output current, IOL	54 Family			16			20			2			4			20	mA
	74 Family			16			20			3.6			8			20	mA
Operating free-air temperature, TA	54 Family	−55		125	−55		125	−55		125	−55		125	−55		125	°C
	74 Family	0		70	0		70	0		70	0		70	0		70	°C

electrical characteristics over recommended operating free-air temperature range (unless otherwise noted)

PARAMETER	TEST FIGURE	TEST CONDITIONS†		SERIES 54 / SERIES 74 '51, '54			SERIES 54H / SERIES 74H 'H51, 'H54			SERIES 54L / SERIES 74L 'L51, 'L54, 'L55			SERIES 54LS / SERIES 74LS 'LS51, 'LS54, 'LS55			SERIES 54S / SERIES 74S 'S51, 'S64			UNIT
				MIN	TYP‡	MAX	MIN	TYP‡	MAX	MIN	TYP‡	MAX	MIN	TYP‡	MAX	MIN	TYP‡	MAX	
VIH High-level input voltage	1, 2			2			2			2			2			2			V
VIL Low-level input voltage	1, 2		54 Family			0.8			0.8			0.7			0.7			0.8	V
			74 Family			0.8			0.8			0.7			0.8			0.8	V
VIK Input clamp voltage	3	VCC = MIN, II = §				−1.5			−1.5			−1.5			−1.5			−1.2	V
VOH High-level output voltage	1	VCC = MIN, VIL = VIL max, IOH = MAX	74 Family	2.4	3.4		2.4	3.4		2.4	3.3		2.7	3.4		2.7	3.4		V
			54 Family	2.4	3.4		2.4	3.4		2.4	3.2		2.5	3.4		2.5	3.4		V
VOL Low-level output voltage	2	VCC = MIN, VIH = 2 V, IOL = MAX	54 Family		0.2	0.4		0.2	0.4		0.15	0.3		0.25	0.4			0.5	V
		IOL = MAX	74 Family		0.2	0.4		0.2	0.4		0.2	0.4		0.35	0.5			0.5	V
		IOL = 4 mA	Series 74LS											0.25	0.4				V
II Input current at maximum input voltage	4	VI = 5.5 V / VI = 7 V				1			1			0.1			0.1			1	mA
IIH High-level input current	4	VCC = MAX, VIH = 2.4 V / VIH = 2.7 V				40			50			10			20			50	µA
IIL Low-level input current	5	VCC = MAX, VIL = 0.3 V / 0.4 V / 0.5 V				−1.6			−2			−0.18			−0.4			−2	mA
IOS Short-circuit output current◆	6	VCC = MAX	54 Family	−20		−55	−40		−100	−3		−15	−20		−100	−40		−100	mA
			74 Family	−18		−55	−40		−100	−3		−15	−20		−100	−40		−100	mA
ICC Supply current	7	VCC = MAX			See table on next page														mA

† For conditions shown as MIN or MAX, use the appropriate value specified under recommended operating conditions.
‡ All typical values are at VCC = 5 V, TA = 25°C.
§ II = −12 mA for SN54'/SN74', −8 mA for SN54H'/SN74H', and −18 mA for SN54LS'/SN74LS' and SN54S'/SN74S'.
◆ Not more than one output should be shorted at a time, and for SN54LS'/SN74LS', SN54H'/SN74H', and SN54S'/SN74S', duration of the short-circuit should not exceed one second.

TEXAS INSTRUMENTS
INCORPORATED
POST OFFICE BOX 5012 • DALLAS, TEXAS 75222

switching characteristics at VCC = 5 V, TA = 25° C

TYPE	TEST CONDITIONS#	t_{PLH} (ns) Propagation delay time, low-to-high-level output			t_{PHL} (ns) Propagation delay time, high-to-low-level output		
		MIN	TYP	MAX	MIN	TYP	MAX
'51, '54	C_L = 15 pF, R_L = 400 Ω		13	22		8	15
'H51	C_L = 25 pF, R_L = 280 Ω		6.8	11		6.2	11
'H54	C_L = 25 pF, R_L = 280 Ω		7	11		6.2	11
'L51, 'L54, 'L55	C_L = 50 pF, R_L = 4 kΩ		50	90		35	60
'LS51, 'LS55	C_L = 15 pF, R_L = 2 kΩ		12	20		12.5	20
'LS54	C_L = 15 pF, R_L = 2 kΩ		12	20		12.5	20
'S51, 'S64	C_L = 15 pF, R_L = 280 Ω		3.5	5.5		3.5	5.5
	C_L = 50 pF, R_L = 280 Ω		5	5.5		5.5	5.5

#Load circuit and voltage waveforms are shown on pages 3-10 and 3-11.

supply current¶

TYPE	I_{CCH} (mA) Total with outputs high		I_{CCL} (mA) Total with outputs low		I_{CC} (mA) Average per AOI gate (50% duty cycle)
	TYP	MAX	TYP	MAX	TYP
'51	4	8	7.4	14	2.85
'54	4	8	5.1	9.5	4.55
'H51	8.2	12.8	15.2	24	5.85
'H54	7.1	11	9.4	14	8.25
'L51	0.44	0.8	0.76	1.3	0.30
'L54	0.39	0.8	0.60	0.99	0.50
'L55	0.22	0.4	0.38	0.65	0.30
'LS51	0.8	1.6	1.4	2.8	0.55
'LS54	0.8	1.6	1.0	2	0.9
'LS55	0.4	0.8	0.7	1.3	0.55
'S51	8.2	17.8	13.6	22	5.45
'S64	7	12.5	8.5	16	7.75

¶Maximum values of I_{CC} are over the recommended operating ranges of V_{CC} and T_A; typical values are at V_{CC} = 5 V, T_A = 25° C.

schematics (each gate)

The portion of the circuits within the dashed lines is repeated (with as many emitters or input diodes as applicable) for each additional AND section.

Resistor values shown are nominal and in ohms.

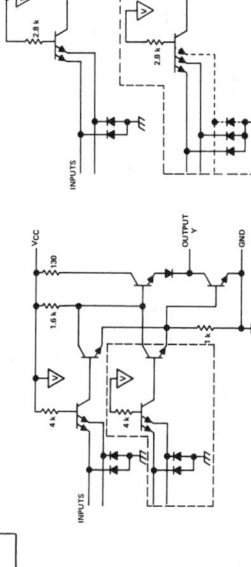

'51, '54 CIRCUITS

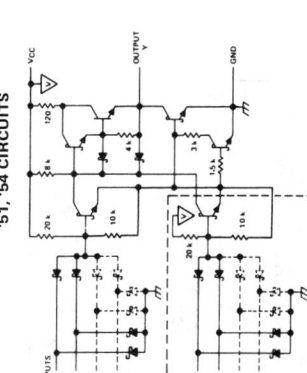

'H51, 'H54 CIRCUITS

'S51, 'S64 CIRCUITS

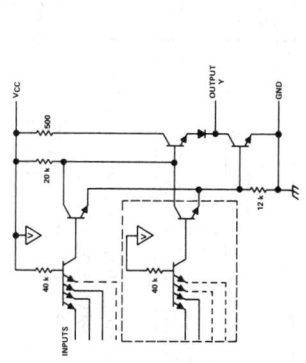

'LS51, 'LS54, 'LS55 CIRCUITS

'L51, 'L54, 'L55 CIRCUITS

TEXAS INSTRUMENTS
INCORPORATED
POST OFFICE BOX 5012 • DALLAS, TEXAS 75222

AND-OR-INVERT GATES WITH OPEN-COLLECTOR OUTPUTS

schematic

Resistor values shown are nominal and in ohms.

recommended operating conditions

	SN54S65 MIN	NOM	MAX	SN74S65 MIN	NOM	MAX	UNIT
Supply voltage, V_{CC}	4.5	5	5.5	4.75	5	5.25	V
High-level output voltage, V_{OH}			5.5			5.5	V
Low-level output current, I_{OL}			20			20	mA
Operating free-air temperature, T_A	−55		125	0		70	°C

electrical characteristics over operating free-air temperature range (unless otherwise noted)

PARAMETER	TEST FIGURE	TEST CONDITIONS†	'S65 MIN	TYP‡	MAX	UNIT
V_{IH} High-level input voltage	1, 2		2			V
V_{IL} Low-level input voltage	1, 2				0.8	V
V_{IK} Input clamp voltage	3	V_{CC} = MIN, I_I = −18 mA			−1.2	V
I_{OH} High-level output current	1	V_{CC} = MIN, V_{IH} = 0.8 V, V_{OH} = 5.5 V			250	µA
V_{OL} Low-level output voltage	2	V_{CC} = MIN, V_{IL} = 2 V, I_{OL} = 20 mA			0.5	V
I_I Input current at maximum input voltage	4	V_{CC} = MAX, V_I = 5.5 V			1	mA
I_{IH} High-level input current	4	V_{CC} = MAX, V_I = 2.7 V			50	µA
I_{IL} Low-level input current	5	V_{CC} = MAX, V_I = 0.5 V			−2	mA
I_{CCH} Supply current, output high	7	V_{CC} = MAX		6	11	mA
I_{CCL} Supply current, output low	7	V_{CC} = MAX		8.5	16	mA

†For conditions shown as MIN or MAX, use the appropriate value specified under recommended operating conditions.
‡All typical values are at V_{CC} = 5 V, T_A = 25° C.

switching characteristics, V_{CC} = 5 V, T_A = 25° C

PARAMETER	TEST CONDITIONS#	'S65 MIN	TYP	MAX	UNIT
t_{PLH} Propagation delay time, low-to-high-level output	C_L = 15 pF, R_L = 280 Ω	2	5	7.5	ns
	C_L = 50 pF, R_L = 280 Ω		5	8	ns
t_{PHL} Propagation delay time, high-to-low-level output	C_L = 15 pF, R_L = 280 Ω	2	5.5	8.5	ns
	C_L = 50 pF, R_L = 280 Ω		6.5		ns

#Load circuit and voltage waveforms are shown on page 3-10.

TEXAS INSTRUMENTS
INCORPORATED
POST OFFICE BOX 5012 • DALLAS, TEXAS 75222

recommended operating conditions

PARAMETER		54 FAMILY 74 FAMILY	SERIES 54 SERIES 74 '125, '126, '425, '426			SERIES 54LS SERIES 74LS 'LS125A, 'LS126A			SERIES 54S SERIES 74S 'S134			UNIT
			MIN	NOM	MAX	MIN	NOM	MAX	MIN	NOM	MAX	
Supply voltage, VCC		54 Family	4.5	5	5.5	4.5	5	5.5	4.5	5	5.5	V
		74 Family	4.75	5	5.25	4.75	5	5.25	4.75	5	5.25	
High-level output current, IOH		54 Family			-2			-1			-2	mA
		74 Family			-5.2			-2.6			-6.5	
Low-level output current, IOL		54 Family			16			12			20	mA
		74 Family			16			24			20	
Operating free-air temperature, TA		54 Family	-55		125	-55		125	-55		125	°C
		74 Family	0		70	0		70	0		70	

electrical characteristics over recommended operating free-air temperature range (unless otherwise noted)

PARAMETER	TEST FIGURE	TEST CONDITIONS†		SERIES 54 SERIES 74 '125, '126, '425, '426			SERIES 54LS SERIES 74LS 'LS125A, 'LS126A			SERIES 54S SERIES 74S 'S134			UNIT
				MIN	TYP‡	MAX	MIN	TYP‡	MAX	MIN	TYP‡	MAX	
VIH High-level input voltage	1, 2			2			2			2			V
VIL Low-level input voltage	1, 2	54 Family				0.8			0.7			0.8	V
		74 Family				0.8			0.8			0.8	
VIK Input clamp voltage	3	VCC = MIN,	II = §			-1.5			-1.5			-1.2	V
VOH High-level output voltage	1	VCC = MIN, VIH = 2 V,	54 Family	2.4	3.3		2.4			2.4	3.4		V
		VIL = VIL max, IOH = MAX	74 Family	2.4	3.1		2.4			2.4	3.2		
VOL Low-level output voltage	2	VCC = MIN, VIH = 2 V,	54 Family			0.4		0.25	0.4			0.5	V
		VIL = VIL max	74 Family			0.4		0.35	0.5			0.5	
		IOL = 12 mA	Series 74LS					0.25	0.4				
IOZ Off-state (high-impedance state) output current	19	VCC = MAX, VIH = 2 V, VIL = VIL max	VO = 2.4 V			40			20			50	µA
			VO = 0.4 V			-40			-20			-50	
II Input current at maximum input voltage	4	VCC = MAX	VI = 5.5 V			1						1	mA
			VI = 7 V						0.1				
IIH High-level input current	4	VCC = MAX	VIH = 2.4 V			40			20			50	µA
			VIH = 2.7 V										
IIL Low-level input current	5	VCC = MAX	VIL = 0.4 V			-1.6			-0.4			-2	mA
			VIL = 0.5 V										
IOS Short-circuit output current♦	6	VCC = MAX	54 Family	-30		-70	-40		-225	-40		-100	mA
			74 Family	-28		-70	-40		-225	-40		-100	
ICC Supply current	7	VCC = MAX						See table on next page					mA

† For conditions shown as MIN or MAX, use the appropriate value specified under recommended operating conditions.
‡ All typical values are at VCC = 5 V, TA = 25°C.
§ II = -12 mA for SN54/SN74' and -18 mA for SN54LS'/SN74LS' and SN54S'/SN74S'.
♦ Not more than one output should be shorted at a time, and for SN54LS'/SN74LS' and SN54S'/SN74S', duration of the short circuit should not exceed one second.

GATES WITH 3-STATE OUTPUTS

schematics (each gate)

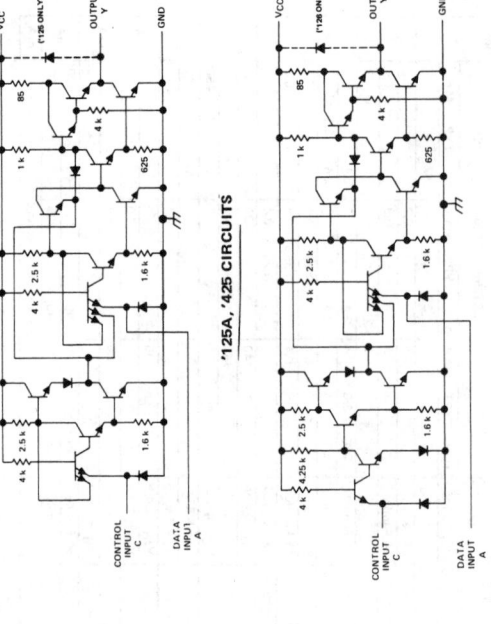

'125A, '425 CIRCUITS

'126A, '426 CIRCUITS

Resistor values shown are nominal and in ohms.

supply current ¶

TYPE	TEST CONDITIONS DATA INPUTS	TEST CONDITIONS OUTPUT CONTROLS	ICC (mA) MIN	ICC (mA) TYP	ICC (mA) MAX
'125, '425	0 V	4.5 V		32	54
'126, '426	0 V	0 V		36	62
'LS125A	0 V	4.5 V		11	20
'LS126A	0 V	0 V		12	22
'S134	0 V	0 V		7	13
	5 V	0 V		9	16
	5 V	5 V		14	25

¶ Maximum values of I_{CC} are over the recommended operating ranges of V_{CC} and T_A; typical values are at V_{CC} = 5 V, T_A = 25°C.

switching characteristics, V_{CC} = 5 V, T_A = 25°C

PARAMETER	SERIES 54/74 TEST CONDITIONS#	'125,'425 TYP	'125,'425 MAX	'126,'426 TYP	'126,'426 MAX	SERIES 54LS/74LS TEST CONDITIONS#	'LS125A TYP	'LS125A MAX	'LS126A TYP	'LS126A MAX	SERIES 54S/74S TEST CONDITIONS#	'S134 TYP	'S134 MAX	UNIT
t_{PLH} Propagation delay time, low-to-high-level output	C_L = 50 pF, R_L = 400 Ω	8	13	8	13	C_L = 45 pF, R_L = 667 Ω	9	15	9	15	C_L = 15 pF, R_L = 280 Ω	4	6	ns
											C_L = 50 pF, R_L = 280 Ω		5.5	
t_{PHL} Propagation delay time, high-to-low-level output		12	18	12	18		7	18	8	18	C_L = 15 pF, R_L = 280 Ω	5	7.5	ns
											C_L = 50 pF, R_L = 280 Ω		7	
t_{PZH} Output enable time to high level		11	17	11	18		12	20	16	25	C_L = 50 pF, R_L = 280 Ω	13	19.5	ns
t_{PZL} Output enable time to low level		16	25	16	25		15	25	21	35		14	21	ns
t_{PHZ} Output disable time from high level	C_L = 5 pF, R_L = 400 Ω	5	8	10	16	C_L = 5 pF, R_L = 667 Ω		20		25	C_L = 5 pF, R_L = 280 Ω	5.5	8.5	ns
t_{PLZ} Output disable time from low level		7	12	12	18			20		25		9	14	ns

Load circuit and voltage waveforms are shown on page 3-10 and 3-11.

schematics (each gate)

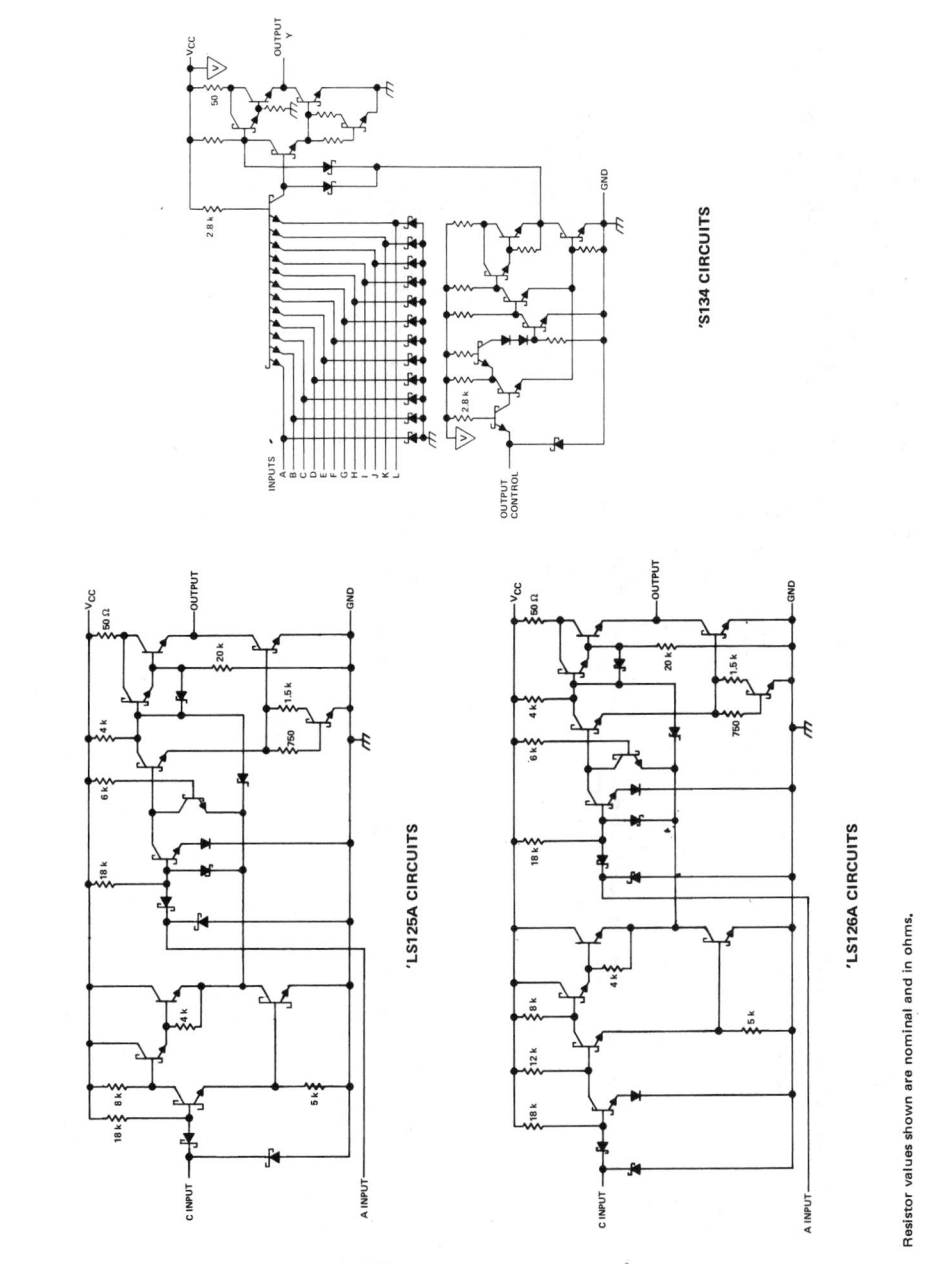

'S134 CIRCUITS

'LS125A CIRCUITS

'LS126A CIRCUITS

Resistor values shown are nominal and in ohms.

6

TEXAS INSTRUMENTS
INCORPORATED
POST OFFICE BOX 5012 • DALLAS, TEXAS 75222

recommended operating conditions

PARAMETER		SERIES 54 / SERIES 74 '365A, '366A, '367A, '368A			SERIES 54LS / SERIES 74LS 'LS365A, 'LS366A, 'LS367A, 'LS368A			UNIT
		MIN	NOM	MAX	MIN	NOM	MAX	
Supply voltage, V_{CC}	54 Family	4.5	5	5.5	4.5	5	5.5	V
	74 Family	4.75	5	5.25	4.75	5	5.25	
High-level output current, I_{OH}	54 Family			−2			−1	mA
	74 Family			−5.2			−2.6	
Low-level output current, I_{OL}	54 Family			32			12	mA
	74 Family			32			24	
Operating free-air temperature, T_A	54 Family	−55		125	−55		125	°C
	74 Family	0		70	0		70	

electrical characteristics over recommended operating free-air temperature range (unless otherwise noted)

PARAMETER		TEST FIGURE	TEST CONDITIONS†	SERIES 54 / SERIES 74 '365A, '366A, '367A, '368A			SERIES 54LS / SERIES 74LS 'LS365A, 'LS366A, 'LS367A, 'LS368A			UNIT
				MIN	TYP‡	MAX	MIN	TYP‡	MAX	
V_{IH} High-level input voltage		1, 2		2			2			V
V_{IL} Low-level input voltage		1, 2	54 Family			0.8			0.7	V
			74 Family			0.8			0.8	
V_{IK} Input clamp voltage		3	V_{CC} = MIN, I_I = §			−1.5			−1.5	V
V_{OH} High-level output voltage		1	V_{CC} = MIN, V_{IH} = 2 V, V_{IL} = V_{IL} max, I_{OH} = MAX	2.4	3.3		2.4	3.3		V
				2.4	3.1		2.4	3.1		
V_{OL} Low-level output voltage		2	V_{CC} = MIN, V_{IH} = 2 V, V_{IL} = V_{IL} max, I_{OL} = MAX			0.4		0.25	0.4	V
						0.4		0.35	0.5	
			I_{OL} = 12 mA Series 74LS					0.25	0.4	
I_{OZ} Off-state (high-impedance state) output current		19	V_{CC} = MAX, V_{IH} = 2 V, V_O = 2.4 V			40			20	µA
			V_O = 0.4 V			−40			−20	
I_I Input current at maximum input voltage		4	V_{CC} = MAX, V_I = 5.5 V			1				mA
			V_I = 7 V						0.1	
I_{IH} High-level input current		4	V_{CC} = MAX, V_I = 2.4 V			40				µA
			V_I = 2.7 V						20	
I_{IL} Low-level input current	A inputs		V_{CC} = MAX, V_I = 0.5 V, Either $\overline{G}$ input at 2 V			−40			−20	µA
			V_{CC} = MAX, V_I = 0.4 V, Both $\overline{G}$ inputs at 0.4 V			−1.6			−1.6	mA
	$\overline{G}$ inputs		V_{CC} = MAX, V_I = 0.4 V			−1.6			−0.4	mA
I_{OS} Short-circuit output current♦		6	V_{CC} = MAX	−40		−130	−40		−225	mA
I_{CC} Supply current		7	V_{CC} = MAX		See table on next page					mA

† For conditions shown as MIN or MAX, use the appropriate value specified under recommended operating conditions.
‡ All typical values are at V_{CC} = 5 V, T_A = 25°C.
§ I_I = −12 mA for SN54'/SN74' and −18 mA for SN54LS'/SN74LS'.
♦ Not more than one output should be shorted at a time, and for SN54LS'/SN74LS' and SN54S'/SN74S', duration of output short-circuit should not exceed one second.

supply current¶

TYPE	DATA INPUTS	OUTPUT CONTROLS	I_CC (mA) TYP	I_CC (mA) MAX
'365A, '367A	0 V	4.5 V	65	85
'366A, '368A	0 V	4.5 V	59	77
'LS365A, 'LS367A	0 V	4.5 V	14	24
'LS366A, 'LS368A	0 V	4.5 V	12	21

¶Maximum values of I_{CC} are over the recommended operating ranges of V_{CC} and T_A; typical values are at $V_{CC} = 5$ V, $T_A = 25°C$.

switching characteristics, $V_{CC} = 5$ V, $T_A = 25°C$, see note 1

PARAMETER*	TEST CONDITIONS	TEST CONDITIONS	SERIES 54/74 '365A, '367A TYP	SERIES 54/74 '365A, '367A MAX	SERIES 54/74 '366A, '368A TYP	SERIES 54/74 '366A, '368A MAX	SERIES 54LS/74LS 'LS365A, 'LS367A TYP	SERIES 54LS/74LS 'LS365A, 'LS367A MAX	SERIES 54LS/74LS 'LS366A, 'LS368A TYP	SERIES 54LS/74LS 'LS366A, 'LS368A MAX
tPLH	$C_L = 50$ pF,	$C_L = 45$ pF,		16		17	10	16	7	15
tPHL	$R_L = 400\ \Omega$	$R_L = 667\ \Omega$		22		16	9	22	12	18
tPZH				35		35	19	35	18	35
tPZL				37		37	24	40	28	45
tPHZ	$C_L = 5$ pF,	$C_L = 5$ pF,		11		11		30		32
tPLZ	$R_L = 400\ \Omega$	$R_L = 667\ \Omega$		27		27		35		35

*tPLH = Propagation delay time, low-to-high-level output
tPHL = Propagation delay time, high-to-low-level output
tPZH = Output enable time to high level
tPZL = Output enable time to low level
tPHZ = Output disable time from high level
tPLZ = Output disable time from low level
NOTE 1: Load circuits and voltage waveforms are shown on pages 3-10 and 3-11.

schematics

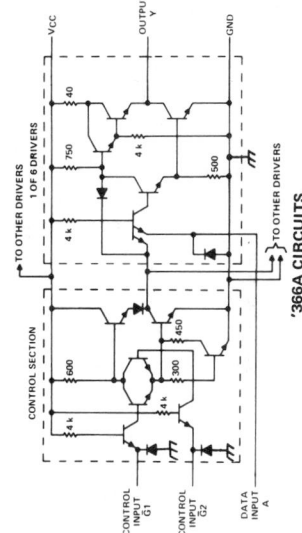

'365A CIRCUITS

'367A CIRCUITS

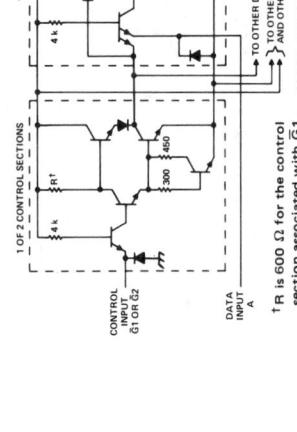

'366A CIRCUITS

'368A CIRCUITS

†R is 600 Ω for the control section associated with $\overline{G}1$ and 900 Ω for the control section associated with $\overline{G}2$.

Resistor values shown are nominal and in ohms.

6

TEXAS INSTRUMENTS
INCORPORATED
POST OFFICE BOX 5012 • DALLAS, TEXAS 75222

HEX BUS DRIVERS WITH 3-STATE OUTPUTS

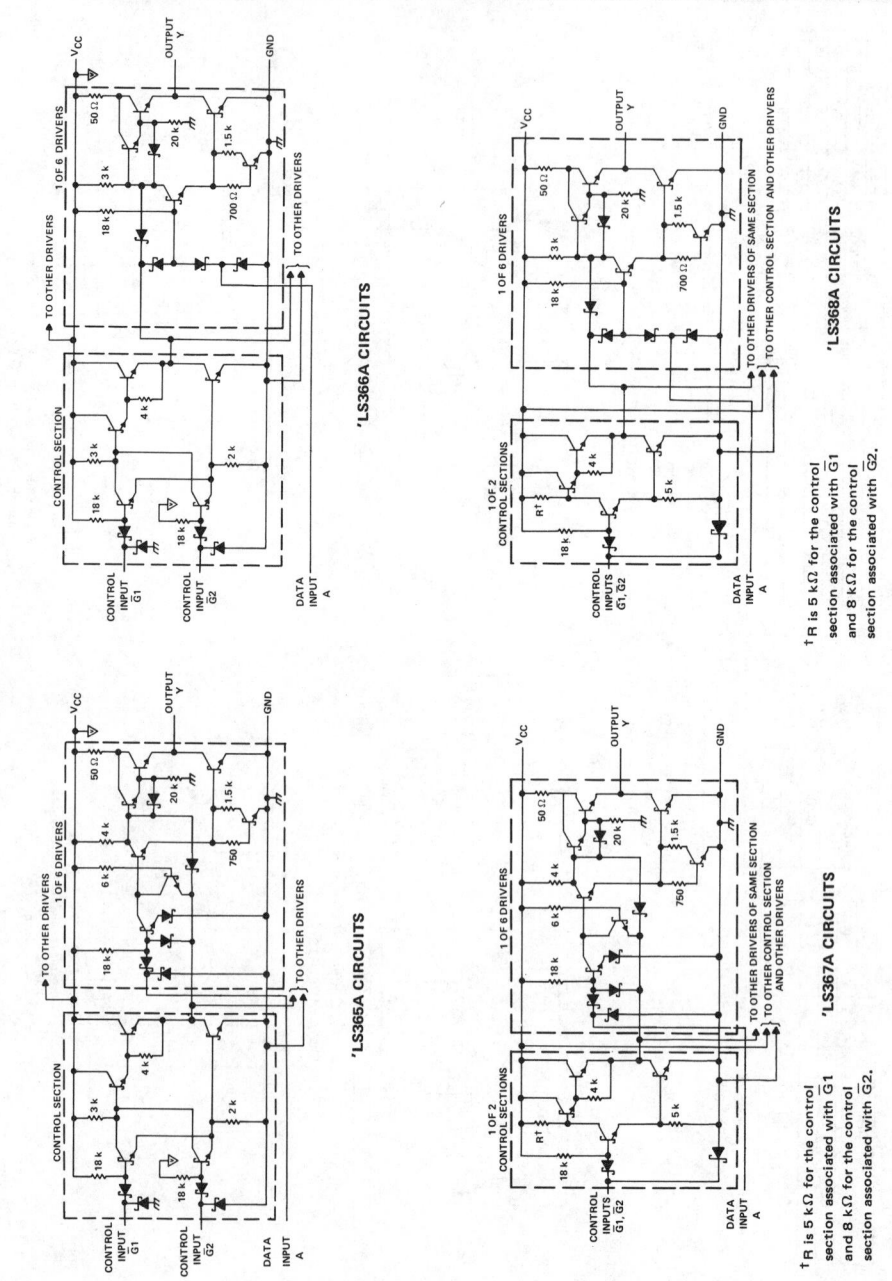

'LS366A CIRCUITS

'LS368A CIRCUITS

'LS365A CIRCUITS

'LS367A CIRCUITS

† R is 5 kΩ for the control
section associated with G̅1
and 8 kΩ for the control
section associated with G̅2.

Resistor values shown are nominal and in ohms

TEXAS INSTRUMENTS
INCORPORATED
POST OFFICE BOX 5012 • DALLAS, TEXAS 75222

recommended operating conditions

		SERIES 54 SERIES 74						SERIES 54H SERIES 74H			UNIT
	54 FAMILY 74 FAMILY	'23			'50, '53			'H50, 'H52, 'H53, 'H55			
		MIN	NOM	MAX	MIN	NOM	MAX	MIN	NOM	MAX	
Supply voltage, V_{CC}	54 Family	4.5	5	5.5	4.5	5	5.5	4.5	5	5.5	V
	74 Family	4.75	5	5.25	4.75	5	5.25	4.75	5	5.25	
High-level output current, I_{OH}				-800			-400			-500	µA
Low-level output current, I_{OL}	54 Family			16			16			20	mA
	74 Family			16			16			20	
Operating free-air temperature range, T_A	54 Family	-55		125	-55		125	-55		125	°C
	74 Family	0		70	0		70	0		70	

The '23, '50, and '53 are designed for use with up to four '60 expanders.
The 'H50, 'H53, and 'H55 are designed for use with up to four 'H60 expanders or one 'H62 expander.
The 'H52 is designed for use with up to six 'H61 expanders.

electrical characteristics over recommended operating free-air temperature range (unless otherwise noted)†

PARAMETER	TEST FIGURE	TEST CONDITIONS†	SERIES 54 SERIES 74						SERIES 54H SERIES 74H			UNIT
			'23			'50, '53			'H50, 'H52, 'H53, 'H55			
			MIN	TYP‡	MAX	MIN	TYP‡	MAX	MIN	TYP‡	MAX	
V_{IH} High-level input voltage	1, 2		2			2			2			V
V_{IL} Low-level input voltage	1, 2				0.8			0.8			0.8	V
V_{IK} Input clamp voltage	3	V_{CC} = MIN, I_I = §			-1.5			-1.5			-1.5	V
V_{OH} High-level output voltage	1	V_{CC} = MIN, V_I = ▲, I_{OH} = MAX	2.4	3.4		2.4	3.4		2.4	3.4		V
V_{OL} Low-level output voltage	2	V_{CC} = MIN, V_I = ▲, I_{OL} = MAX		0.2	0.4		0.2	0.4		0.2	0.4	V
I_I Input current at maximum input voltage	4	V_{CC} = MAX, V_I = 5.5 V			1			1			1	mA
I_{IH} High-level input current Data input	4	V_{CC} = MAX, V_{IH} = 2.4 V			40			40			50	µA
Strobe of '23					160							
I_{IL} Low-level input current Data inputs	5	V_{CC} = MAX, V_{IL} = 0.4 V			-1.6			-1.6			-2	mA
Strobe of '23					-6.4							
I_{OS} Short-circuit output current♦ 54 Family	6	V_{CC} = MAX	-20		-55	-20		-55	-40		-100	mA
74 Family			-18		-55	-18		-55	-40		-100	
I_{CC} Supply current	7	V_{CC} = MAX						See table on next page				mA

† For conditions shown as MIN or MAX, use the appropriate value specified under recommended operating conditions.
‡ All typical values are at V_{CC} = 5 V, T_A = 25° C.
§ I_I = −12 mA for SN54'/SN74' and −8 mA for SN54H'/SN74H'.
▲ The input voltage is V_{IH} = 2 V or V_{IL} = V_{IL} max, as appropriate. See tables with test figures 1 and 2.
♦ Not more than one output should be shorted at a time, and for the SN54H'/SN74H', duration of short-circuit should not exceed one second.

EXPANDABLE GATES

electrical characteristics using expander inputs, V_{CC} = MIN, T_A = MIN (unless otherwise noted)

TYPE	$I_{\bar{X}}$ (mA) (I_X for 'H52) Expander current				$V_{BE(Q)}$ (V) Base-emitter voltage of output transistor Q				V_{OH} (V) High-level output voltage				V_{OL} (V) Low-level output voltage			
	TEST CONDITIONS	MIN	TYP‡	MAX	TEST CONDITIONS	MIN	TYP‡	MAX	TEST CONDITIONS	MIN	TYP‡	MAX	TEST CONDITIONS	MIN	TYP‡	MAX
SN5423	$V_{\bar{X}\bar{X}}$ = 0.4 V, I_{OL} = 16 mA, See Figure 10			−3.5	$I_X + I_{\bar{X}}$ = 410 µA, $R_{\bar{X}\bar{X}}$ = 0, I_{OL} = 16 mA, See Figure 11			1.1	I_X = 150 µA, $I_{\bar{X}}$ = −150 µA, I_{OH} = −400 µA, See Figure 12	2.4	3.4		$I_X + I_{\bar{X}}$ = 300 µA, $R_{\bar{X}\bar{X}}$ = 114 Ω▲, I_{OL} = 16 mA, See Figure 11		0.2	0.4
SN5450				−2.9												
SN5453	See Figure 10			−2.9												
SN7423	$V_{\bar{X}\bar{X}}$ = 0.4 V, I_{OL} = 16 mA, See Figure 10			−3.8	$I_X + I_{\bar{X}}$ = 620 µA, $R_{\bar{X}\bar{X}}$ = 0, I_{OL} = 16 mA, See Figure 11			1	I_X = 270 µA, $I_{\bar{X}}$ = −270 µA, I_{OH} = −400 µA, See Figure 12	2.4	3.4		$I_X + I_{\bar{X}}$ = 430 µA, $R_{\bar{X}\bar{X}}$ = 105 Ω▲, I_{OL} = 16 mA, See Figure 11		0.2	0.4
SN7450				−3.1												
SN7453	See Figure 10			−3.1												
SN54H50, SN54H53, SN54H55	$V_{\bar{X}}$ = 1.4 V, I_X = 0, I_{OL} = 0, See Figure 10			−5.85	$I_X + I_{\bar{X}}$ = 700 µA, $R_{\bar{X}\bar{X}}$ = 0, I_{OL} = 20 mA, See Figure 11			1.1	I_X = 320 µA, $I_{\bar{X}}$ = −320 µA, I_{OH} = −500 µA, See Figure 12	2.4	3.4		$I_X + I_{\bar{X}}$ = 470 µA, $R_{\bar{X}\bar{X}}$ = 68 Ω, I_{OL} = 20 mA, See Figure 11		0.2	0.4
SN74H50, SN74H53, SN74H55	$V_{\bar{X}}$ = 1.4 V, I_X = 0, I_{OL} = 0, See Figure 10			−6.3	$I_X + I_{\bar{X}}$ = 1.1 mA, $R_{\bar{X}\bar{X}}$ = 0, I_{OL} = 20 mA, See Figure 11			1	I_X = 570 µA, $I_{\bar{X}}$ = −570 µA, I_{OH} = −500 µA, See Figure 12	2.4	3.4		$I_X + I_{\bar{X}}$ = 600 µA, $R_{\bar{X}\bar{X}}$ = 63 Ω, I_{OL} = 20 mA, See Figure 11		0.2	0.4
SN54H52	V_X = 1 V, I_{OH} = −500 µA, See Figure 13	−2.7		−4.5					V_X = 1 V, I_{OH} = −500 µA, See Figure 13	2.4	3.4		I_X = −300 µA, I_{OL} = 20 mA, T_A = MAX, See Figure 14		0.2	0.4
SN74H52		−2.9		−5.35												

‡All typical values are at V_{CC} = 5 V, T_A = 25°C.

▲$R_{\bar{X}\bar{X}}$ equals 114 Ω for SN5423, 138 Ω for SN5450 and SN5453, 105 Ω for SN7423, and 130 Ω for SN7450 and SN7453.

supply current¶

TYPE	I_{CCH} (mA) Total with outputs high		I_{CCL} (mA) Total with outputs low		I_{CC} (mA) Average per gate (50% duty cycle)
	TYP	MAX	TYP	MAX	TYP
'23	8	16	10	19	4.5
'50	4	8	7.4	14	2.85
'53	4	8	5.1	9.5	4.55
'H50	8.2	12.8	15.2	24	5.85
'H52	20	31	15.2	24	17.6
'H53	7.1	11	9.4	14	8.25
'H55	4.5	6.4	7.5	12	6.00

¶Maximum values of I_{CC} are over the recommended operating ranges of V_{CC} and T_A; typical values are at V_{CC} = 5 V, T_A = 25°C.

TEXAS INSTRUMENTS
INCORPORATED
POST OFFICE BOX 5012 • DALLAS, TEXAS 75222

schematics (each gate)

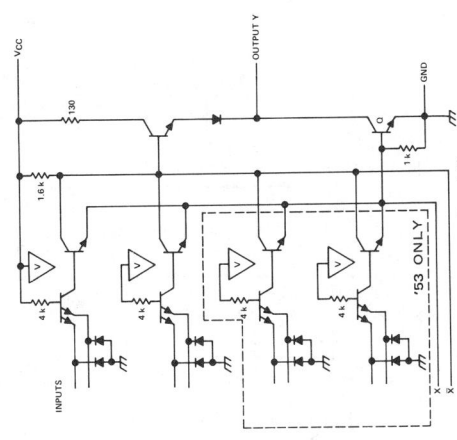

'23 CIRCUITS

If expander is not used, leave X and X̄ open.

'50, '53 CIRCUITS

If expander is not used, leave X and X̄ open.

Resistor values shown are nominal and in ohms.

switching characteristics, VCC = 5 V, TA = 25°C

TYPE	TEST CONDITIONS#	t_{PLH} (ns) Propagation delay time, low-to-high-level output		t_{PHL} (ns) Propagation delay time, high-to-low-level output	
		TYP	MAX	TYP	MAX
'23, '50, '53	$C_L = 15$ pF, $R_L = 400$ Ω, Expander pins open	13	22	8	15
'50	$C_L = 15$ pF, $R_L = 400$ Ω, From input of '60 expander	15	30	10	20
'H50	$C_L = 25$ pF, $R_L = 280$ Ω, Expander pins open	6.8	11	6.2	11
'H52		10.6	15	9.2	15
'H53		7	11	6.2	11
'H55		7	11	6.5	11
'H50	$C_L = 25$ pF, $R_L = 280$ Ω, C = 15 pF (GND to X̄ of 'H50, 'H53, or 'H55; or to X of 'H52)	11		7.4	
'H52		14.8		9.8	
'H53		11.4		7.4	
'H55		11.4		7.7	

#Load circuit and voltage waveforms are shown on page 3-10.

TYPICAL ADDED PROPAGATION DELAY TIME vs EXPANDER-NODE CAPACITANCE

$C_L = 25$ pF
$R_L = 280$ Ω
$T_A = 25°C$

SN54H50, SN74H50
SN54H53, SN74H53
SN54H52, SN74H52

Δt_{PHL} — Added Propagation Delay Time, High-to-Low-Level Output — ns

$C_{\bar{X}}$ or C_X — Expander-Node Capacitance — pF

$C_L = 25$ pF
$R_L = 280$ Ω
$T_A = 25°C$

SN54H50, SN74H50
SN54H52, SN74H52
SN54H53, SN74H53
SN54H55, SN74H55

Δt_{PLH} — Added Propagation Delay Time, Low-to-High-Level Output — ns

$C_{\bar{X}}$ or C_X — Expander-Node Capacitance — pF

6

EXPANDABLE GATES

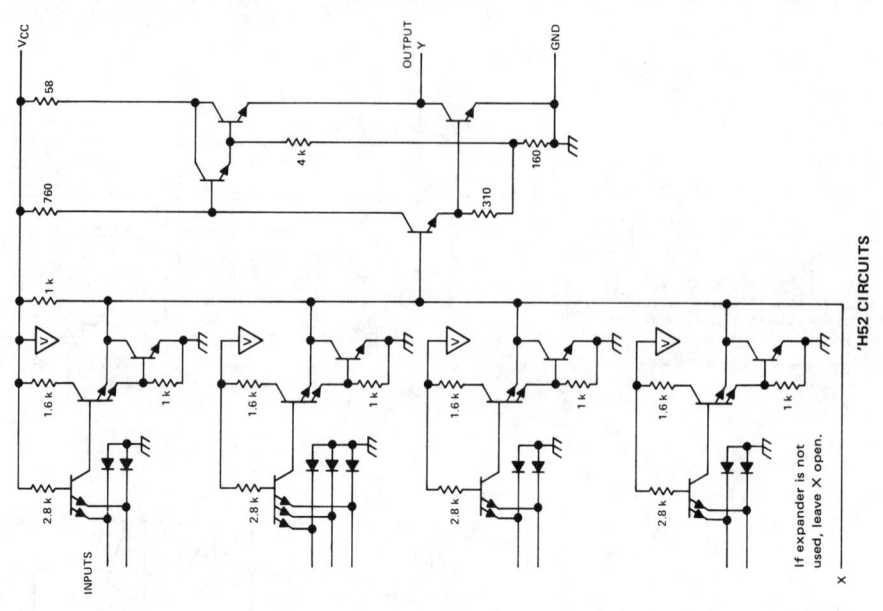

'H52 CIRCUITS

Resistor values shown are nominal and in ohms.

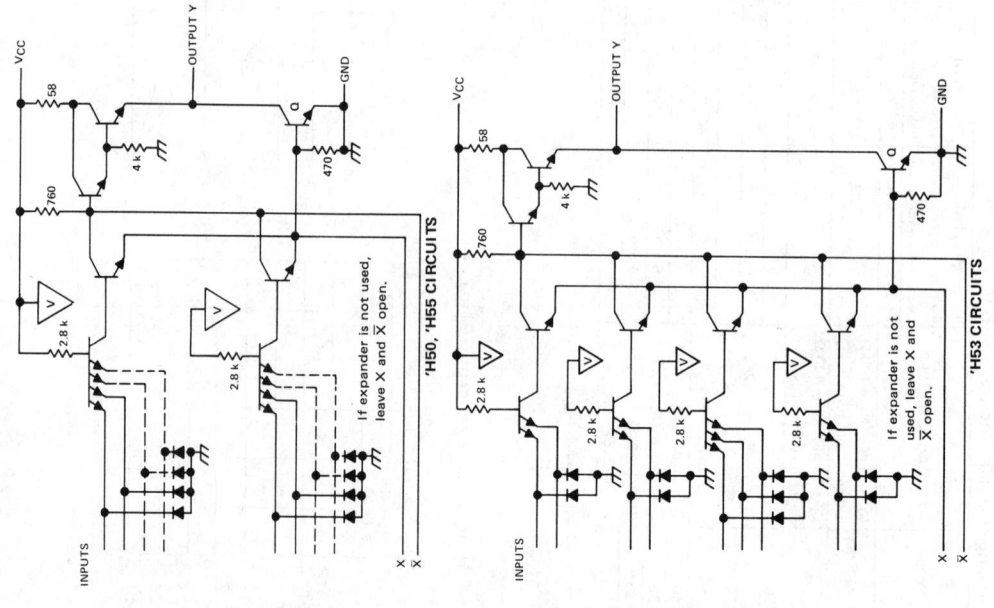

'H50, 'H55 CIRCUITS

'H53 CIRCUITS

recommended operating conditions

	SN5460			SN7460			UNIT
	MIN	NOM	MAX	MIN	NOM	MAX	
Supply voltage, V_{CC}	4.5	5	5.5	4.75	5	5.25	V
Operating free-air temperature, T_A	−55		125	0		70	°C

The '23, '50, and '53 are designed for use with up to four '60 expanders.

schematic (each gate)

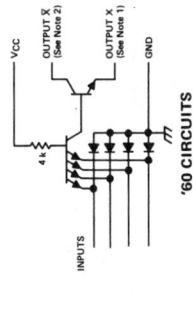

OUTPUT $\overline{X}$ (See Note 2)

OUTPUT X (See Note 1)

V_{CC}

GND

INPUTS

4 k

'60 CIRCUITS

NOTES: 1. Connect to X input of '23, '50, or '53 circuit.
2. Connect to $\overline{X}$ input of '23, '50, or '53 circuit.

Resistor value shown is nominal and in ohms.

electrical characteristics over recommended operating free-air temperature range (unless otherwise noted)

PARAMETER		TEST FIGURE	SN5460				SN7460				UNIT
			TEST CONDITIONS	MIN	TYP‡	MAX	TEST CONDITIONS	MIN	TYP‡	MAX	
V_{IH}	High-level input voltage	15		2				2			V
V_{IL}	Low-level input voltage	16				0.8				0.8	V
$V_{\overline{X}X(on)}$	On-state voltage between expander outputs	15	V_{CC} = 4.5 V, V_{IH} = 2 V, V_X = 1.1 V, $I\overline{X}$ = 3.5 mA, T_A = −55°C			0.4	V_{CC} = 4.75 V, V_{IH} = 2 V, V_X = 1 V, $I\overline{X}$ = 3.8 mA, T_A = 0°C			0.4	V
$I_{X(on)}$	On-state expander current	15	V_{CC} = 4.5 V, V_{IH} = 2 V, V_X = 1.1 V, $I\overline{X}$ = 0, T_A = −55°C	−0.3			V_{CC} = 4.75 V, V_{IH} = 2 V, V_X = 1 V, $I\overline{X}$ = 0, T_A = 0°C	−0.43			mA
$I_{\overline{X}(off)}$	Off-state expander current	16	V_{CC} = 4.5 V, V_{IL} = 0.8 V, $\overline{X}$ = 4.5 V, R_X = 1.2 kΩ, T_A = −55°C			150	V_{CC} = 4.75 V, V_{IL} = 0.8 V, $\overline{X}$ = 4.5 V, R_X = 1.2 kΩ, T_A = 0°C			270	μA
I_I	Input current at maximum input voltage	4	V_{CC} = 5.5 V, V_I = 5.5 V			1	V_{CC} = 5.25 V, V_I = 5.5 V			1	mA
I_{IH}	High-level input current	4	V_{CC} = 5.5 V, V_I = 2.4 V			40	V_{CC} = 5.25 V, V_I = 2.4 V			40	μA
I_{IL}	Low-level input current	5	V_{CC} = 5.5 V, V_I = 0.4 V			−1.6	V_{CC} = 5.25 V, V_I = 0.4 V			−1.6	mA
$I_{CC(on)}$	Supply current, expander on	7	V_{CC} = 5.5 V, V_I = 4.5 V, V_X = 0.85 V, $I\overline{X}$ = 0		1.2	2.5	V_{CC} = 5.25 V, V_I = 4.5 V, V_X = 0.85 V, $I\overline{X}$ = 0		1.2	2.5	mA
$I_{CC(off)}$	Supply current, expander off	7	V_{CC} = 5.5 V, V_I = 0, V_X = 0.85 V, $I\overline{X}$ = 0		2	4	V_{CC} = 5.25 V, V_I = 0, V_X = 0.85 V, $I\overline{X}$ = 0		2	4	mA

‡All typical values are at V_{CC} = 5 V, T_A = 25°C.

77

TEXAS INSTRUMENTS
INCORPORATED
POST OFFICE BOX 5012 • DALLAS, TEXAS 75222

6

recommended operating conditions

	SN54H60 SN54H62			SN74H60 SN74H62			UNIT
	MIN	NOM	MAX	MIN	NOM	MAX	
Supply voltage, V_{CC}	4.5	5	5.5	4.75	5	5.25	V
Operating free-air temperature, T_A	−55		125	0		70	°C

The 'H50, 'H53, and 'H55 are designed for use with up to four 'H60 expanders or one 'H62 expander.

electrical characteristics over recommended operating free-air temperature range (unless otherwise noted)

PARAMETER	TEST FIGURE	SN54H60, SN54H62 TEST CONDITIONS	MIN	TYP‡	MAX	SN74H60, SN74H62 TEST CONDITIONS	MIN	TYP‡	MAX	UNIT
V_{IH} High-level input voltage	15		2				2			V
V_{IL} Low-level input voltage	16				0.8				0.8	V
$V_{\overline{X}X(on)}$ On-state voltage between expander outputs	15	$V_{CC}=4.5\,V,\ V_{IH}=2\,V,$ $V_{\overline{X}}=1.1\,V,\ I_{\overline{X}}=5.85\,mA,$ $T_A=-55°C$ $V_{CC}=5.5\,V,\ V_{IH}=2\,V,$ $V_{\overline{X}}=1\,V,\ I_{\overline{X}}=7.85\,mA,$ $T_A=125°C$			0.4 — 0.4	$V_{CC}=4.75\,V,\ V_{IH}=2\,V,$ $V_{\overline{X}}=1\,V,\ I_{\overline{X}}=6.3\,mA,$ $T_A=0°C$ $V_{CC}=5.25\,V,\ V_{IH}=2\,V,$ $V_{\overline{X}}=1\,V,\ I_{\overline{X}}=7.4\,mA,$ $T_A=70°C$			0.4 — 0.4	V
$I_{X(on)}$ On-state expander current	15	$V_{CC}=4.5\,V,\ V_{IH}=2\,V,$ $V_{\overline{X}}=1.1\,V,\ I_{\overline{X}}=0,$ $T_A=-55°C$	−470			$V_{CC}=4.75\,V,\ V_{IH}=2\,V,$ $V_{\overline{X}}=1\,V,\ I_{\overline{X}}=0,$ $T_A=0°C$	−600			µA
$I_{\overline{X}(off)}$ Off-state expander current	16	$V_{CC}=4.5\,V,\ V_{IL}=0.8\,V,$ $V_{\overline{X}}=4.5\,V,\ R_{\overline{X}}=575\,\Omega,$ $T_A=-55°C$			320	$V_{CC}=4.75\,V,\ V_{IL}=0.8\,V,$ $V_{\overline{X}}=4.5\,V,\ R_{\overline{X}}=575\,\Omega,$ $T_A=0°C$			570	µA
I_I Input current at maximum input voltage	4	$V_{CC}=5.5\,V,\ V_I=5.5\,V$			1	$V_{CC}=5.25\,V,\ V_I=5.5\,V$			1	mA
I_{IH} High-level input current	4	$V_{CC}=5.5\,V,\ V_I=2.4\,V$			50	$V_{CC}=5.25\,V,\ V_I=2.4\,V$			50	µA
I_{IL} Low-level input current	5	$V_{CC}=5.5\,V,\ V_I=0.4\,V$			−2	$V_{CC}=5.25\,V,\ V_I=0.4\,V$			−2	mA
$I_{CC(on)}$ Supply current, expander on	7	'H60: $V_{CC}=5.5\,V,\ V_I=4.5\,V,$ 'H62: $V_{\overline{X}}=0.85\,V,\ I_{\overline{X}}=0,$		1.9 3.8	3.5 7	'H60: $V_{CC}=5.25\,V,\ V_I=4.5\,V,$ 'H62: $V_{\overline{X}}=0.85\,V,\ I_{\overline{X}}=0$		1.9 3.8	3.5 7	mA
$I_{CC(off)}$ Supply current, expander off	7	'H60: $V_{CC}=5.5\,V,\ V_I=0,$ 'H62: $V_{\overline{X}}=0.85\,V,\ I_{\overline{X}}=0$		3 6	4.5 9	'H60: $V_{CC}=5.25\,V,\ V_I=0,$ 'H62: $V_{\overline{X}}=0.85\,V,\ I_{\overline{X}}=0$		3 6	4.5 9	mA
$C_{\overline{X}}$ Expander output capacitance		'H60 'H62 V_{CC}, inputs, and X open; $f=1\,MHz$		5.4 6.0		V_{CC}, inputs, and X open; $f=1\,MHz$		5.4 6.0		pF

‡All typical values are at $V_{CC}=5\,V$ (except $C_{\overline{X}}$), $T_A=25°C$.

See schematics next page

TEXAS INSTRUMENTS
INCORPORATED
POST OFFICE BOX 5012 • DALLAS, TEXAS 75222

schematics (each gate)

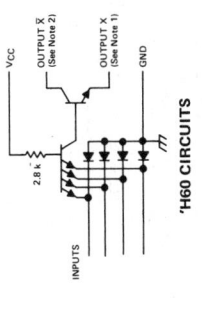

'H60 CIRCUITS

'H61 CIRCUITS

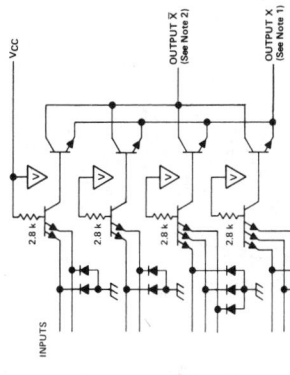

'H62 CIRCUITS

NOTES: 1. Connect to X input of 'H50, 'H53, or 'H55 circuit.
2. Connect to X̄ input of 'H50, 'H53, or 'H55 circuit.

Resistor values shown are nominal and in ohms.

recommended operating conditions

	SN54H61			SN74H61			UNIT
	MIN	NOM	MAX	MIN	NOM	MAX	
Supply voltage, V_{CC}	4.5	5	5.5	4.75	5	5.25	V
Operating free-air temperature, T_A	−55		125	0		70	°C

The 'H52 is designed for use with up to six 'H61 expanders.

electrical characteristics over recommended operating free-air temperature range (unless otherwise noted)

PARAMETER		TEST FIGURE	TEST CONDITIONS	MIN	TYP‡	MAX	UNIT
V_{IH}	High-level input voltage	17		2			V
V_{IL}	Low-level input voltage	18				0.8	V
$V_{X(on)}$	On-state expander-output voltage	17	V_{CC} = MIN, V_{IH} = 2 V, I_X = 4.5 mA for SN54H61, 5.35 mA for SN74H61, T_A = MIN			1	V
$I_{X(off)}$	Off-state expander current	18	V_{CC} = MIN, V_{IL} = 0.8 V, V_X = 2.2 V, T_A = MAX			50	μA
I_I	Input current at maximum input voltage	4	V_{CC} = 5.5 V, V_I = 5.5 V			1	mA
I_{IH}	High-level input current	4	V_{CC} = 5.5 V, V_I = 2.4 V			50	μA
I_{IL}	Low-level input current	5	V_{CC} = 5.5 V, V_I = 0.4 V			−2	mA
$I_{CC(on)}$	Supply current, expander on	7	V_{CC} = 5.5 V, V_I = 4.5 V		11	16	mA
$I_{CC(off)}$	Supply current, expander off	7	V_{CC} = 5.5 V, V_I = 0		5	7	mA
C_X	Expander output capacitance		V_{CC} and inputs open, f = 1 MHz		5.4		pF

† For conditions shown as MIN or MAX, use the appropriate value specified under recommended operating conditions.
‡ All typical values are at V_{CC} = 5 V (except C_X), T_A = 25°C.

6

SERIES 54/74 FLIP-FLOPS

recommended operating conditions

SERIES 54/74		'70			'72,'73,'76,'107			'74			'109			'110			'111			UNIT
		MIN	NOM	MAX	MIN	NOM	MAX	MIN	NOM	MAX	MIN	NOM	MAX	MIN	NOM	MAX	MIN	NOM	MAX	
Supply voltage, V_{CC}	Series 54	4.5	5	5.5	4.5	5	5.5	4.5	5	5.5	4.5	5	5.5	4.5	5	5.5	4.5	5	5.5	V
	Series 74	4.75	5	5.25	4.75	5	5.25	4.75	5	5.25	4.75	5	5.25	4.75	5	5.25	4.75	5	5.25	
High-level output current, I_{OH}				-400			-400			-400			-800			-800			-800	µA
Low-level output current, I_{OL}				16			16			16			16			16			16	mA
Pulse width, t_w	Clock high	20			20			30			20			25			25			ns
	Clock low	30			47			37			20			25			25			
	Preset or clear low	25			25			30			20			20†			0†			
Input setup time, t_{su}		20†			0†			20†			10†			20†			0†			ns
Input hold time, t_h		5†			0†			5†			6†			5†			30†			ns
Operating free-air temperature, T_A	Series 54	-55		125	-55		125	-55		125	-55		125	-55		125	-55		125	°C
	Series 74	0		70	0		70	0		70	0		70	0		70	0		70	

†↓ The arrow indicates the edge of the clock pulse used for reference; ↑ for the rising edge, ↓ for the falling edge.

electrical characteristics over recommended operating free-air temperature range (unless otherwise noted)

PARAMETER		TEST CONDITIONS†	'70		'72,'73,'76,'107		'74		'109		'110		'111		UNIT
			MIN TYP‡	MAX	MIN TYP‡	MAX	MIN TYP‡	MAX	MIN TYP‡	MAX	MIN TYP‡	MAX	MIN TYP‡	MAX	
V_{IH} High-level input voltage			2		2		2		2		2		2		V
V_{IL} Low-level input voltage				0.8		0.8		0.8		0.8		0.8		0.8	V
V_{IK} Input clamp voltage		V_{CC} = MIN, I_I = -12 mA		-1.5		-1.5		-1.5		-1.5		-1.5		-1.5	V
V_{OH} High-level output voltage		V_{CC} = MIN, V_{IH} = 2 V, V_{IL} = 0.8 V, I_{OH} = MAX	2.4 3.4		2.4 3.4		2.4 3.4		2.4 3.4		2.4 3.4		2.4 3.4		V
V_{OL} Low-level output voltage		V_{CC} = MIN, V_{IH} = 2 V, V_{IL} = 0.8 V, I_{OL} = 16 mA	0.2	0.4	0.2	0.4	0.2	0.4	0.2	0.4	0.2	0.4	0.2	0.4	V
I_I Input current at maximum input voltage		V_{CC} = MAX, V_I = 5.5 V		1		1		1		1		1		1	mA
I_{IH} High-level input current	D, J, K, or K̄	V_{CC} = MAX, V_I = 2.4 V		40		40		40		40		40		40	µA
	Clear			80		80		120		160		160		80	
	Preset			80		80		80		80		80		80	
	Clock			40		40		80		80		40		120	
I_{IL} Low-level input current	D, J, K, or K̄	V_{CC} = MAX, V_I = 0.4 V		-1.6		-1.6		-1.6		-1.6		-1.6		-1.6	mA
	Clear ★			-3.2		-3.2		-3.2		-4.8		-3.2		-3.2	
	Preset ★			-3.2		-3.2		-1.6		-3.2		-3.2		-3.2	
	Clock			-1.6		-3.2		-3.2		-3.2		-1.6		-4.8	
I_{OS} Short-circuit output current♦	Series 54	V_{CC} = MAX	-20	-57	-20	-57	-20	-57	-30	-85	-20	-57	-20	-57	mA
	Series 74		-18	-57	-18	-57	-18	-57	-30	-85	-18	-57	-18	-57	
I_{CC} Supply current (Average per flip-flop)		V_{CC} = MAX, See Note 1	13	26	10	20	8.5	15	9	15	20	34	14	20.5	mA

† For conditions shown as MIN or MAX, use the appropriate value specified under recommended operating conditions.

‡ All typical values are at V_{CC} = 5 V, T_A = 25°C.

♦ Not more than one output should be shorted at a time.

★ Clear is tested with preset high and preset is tested with clear high.

NOTE 1: With all outputs open, I_{CC} is measured with the Q and Q̄ outputs high in turn. At the time of measurement, the clock input is at 4.5 V for the '70, '72, '73, '110, and '111; and is grounded for all the others.

TEXAS INSTRUMENTS
INCORPORATED
POST OFFICE BOX 5012 • DALLAS, TEXAS 75222

switching characteristics, $V_{CC} = 5\,V$, $T_A = 25°C$

PARAMETER¶	FROM (INPUT)	TO (OUTPUT)	TEST CONDITIONS	'70 MIN	'70 TYP	'70 MAX	'72, '73 '76, '107 MIN	'72, '73 '76, '107 TYP	'72, '73 '76, '107 MAX	'74 MIN	'74 TYP	'74 MAX	'109 MIN	'109 TYP	'109 MAX	'110 MIN	'110 TYP	'110 MAX	'111 MIN	'111 TYP	'111 MAX	UNIT
f_{max}				20	35		15	20		15	25		25	33		20	25		20	25		MHz
t_{PLH}	Preset (as applicable)	Q	$C_L = 15\,pF,$			50		16	25			25		10	15		12	20		12	18	ns
t_{PHL}		Q̄	$R_L = 400\,\Omega,$			50		25	40			40		23	35		18	25		21	30	
t_{PLH}	Clear (as applicable)	Q̄	See Note 2			50		16	25			25		10	15		12	20		12	18	ns
t_{PHL}		Q				50		25	40			40		17	25		18	25		21	30	
t_{PLH}	Clock	Q or Q̄			27	50		16	25		14	25		10	16		20	30		12	17	ns
t_{PHL}					18	50		25	40		20	40		18	28		13	20		20	30	

¶ $f_{max} \equiv$ maximum clock frequency; $t_{PLH} \equiv$ propagation delay time, low-to-high-level output; $t_{PHL} \equiv$ propagation delay time, high-to-low-level output.
NOTE 2: Load circuit and voltage waveforms are shown on page 3-10.

functional block diagrams

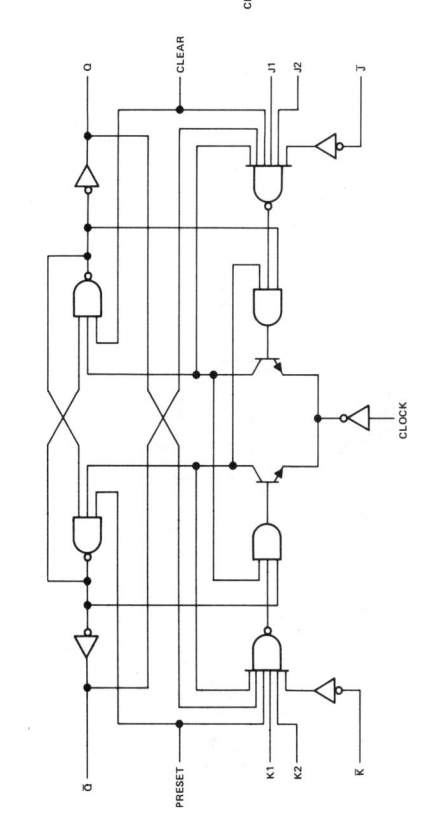

'70—GATED J-K WITH CLEAR AND PRESET

'72—GATED J-K WITH CLEAR AND PRESET

'109—DUAL J-K̄ WITH CLEAR AND PRESET
'110—GATED J-K WITH CLEAR AND PRESET
'111—DUAL J-K WITH CLEAR AND PRESET

See following pages for:
'73—DUAL J-K WITH CLEAR
'74—DUAL D WITH CLEAR AND PRESET
'76—DUAL J-K WITH CLEAR AND PRESET
'107—DUAL J-K WITH CLEAR

6

TEXAS INSTRUMENTS
INCORPORATED
POST OFFICE BOX 5012 • DALLAS, TEXAS 75222

functional block diagrams (continued)

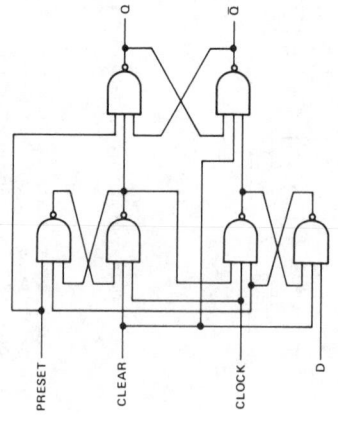

'74—DUAL D WITH CLEAR AND PRESET

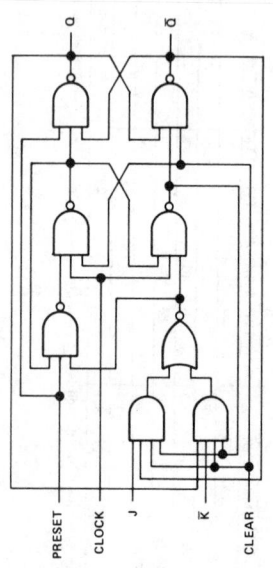

'109—DUAL J-K̄ WITH CLEAR AND PRESET

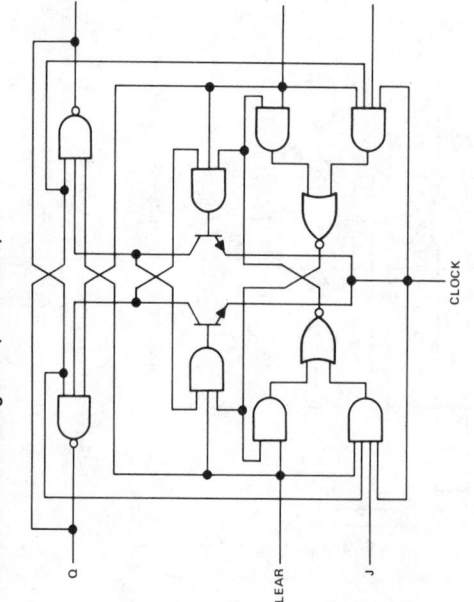

'73—DUAL J-K WITH CLEAR
'76—DUAL J-K WITH CLEAR AND PRESET
'107—DUAL J-K WITH CLEAR

TEXAS INSTRUMENTS
INCORPORATED
POST OFFICE BOX 5012 • DALLAS, TEXAS 75222

functional block diagrams (continued)

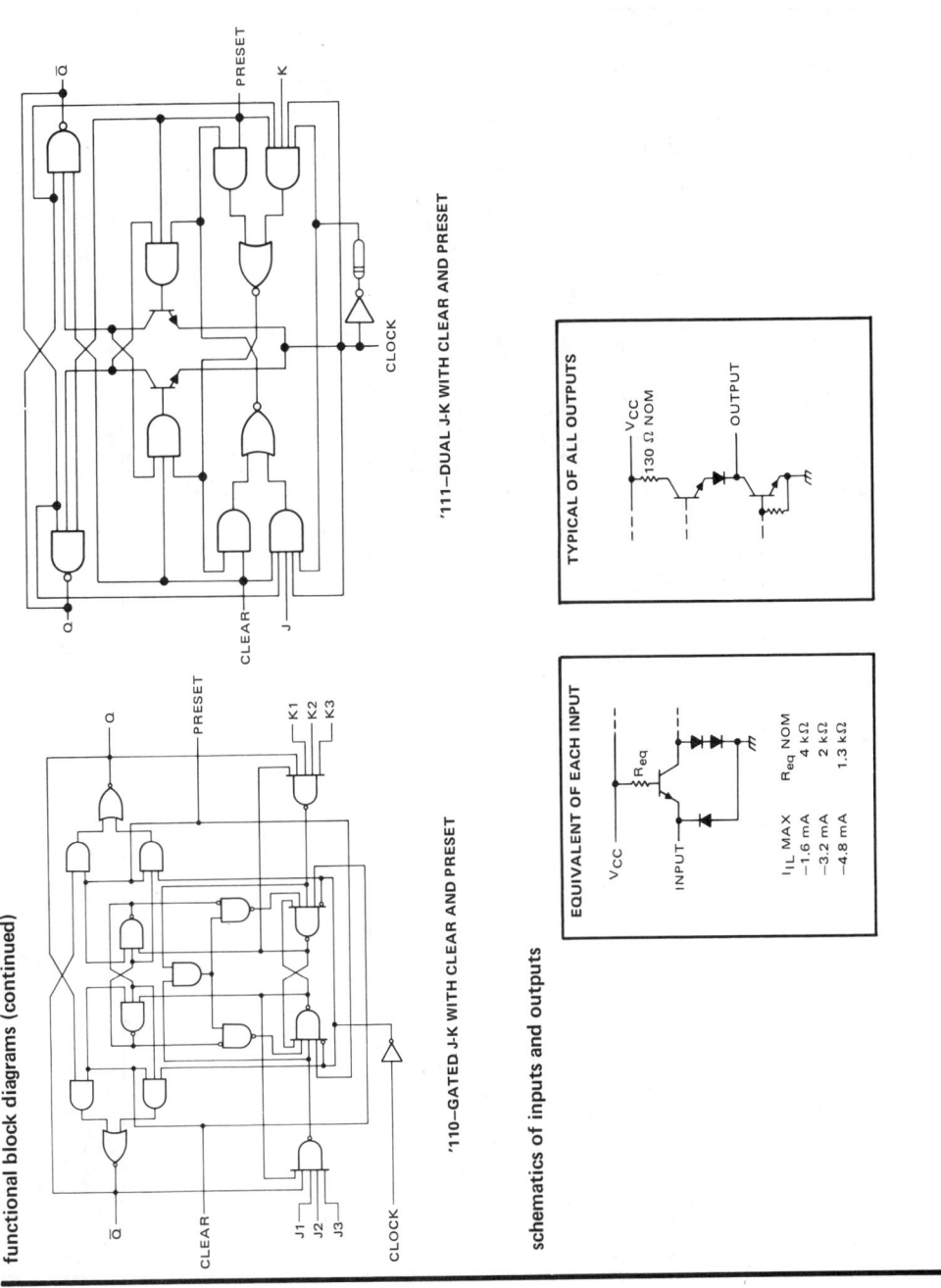

'111—DUAL J-K WITH CLEAR AND PRESET

'110—GATED J-K WITH CLEAR AND PRESET

schematics of inputs and outputs

TYPICAL OF ALL OUTPUTS

EQUIVALENT OF EACH INPUT

I_{IL} MAX	R_{eq} NOM
−1.6 mA	4 kΩ
−3.2 mA	2 kΩ
−4.8 mA	1.3 kΩ

6

TEXAS INSTRUMENTS
INCORPORATED

POST OFFICE BOX 5012 • DALLAS, TEXAS 75222

recommended operating conditions

SERIES 54H/74H		'H71 MIN	NOM	MAX	'H72,'H73,'H76 MIN	NOM	MAX	'H74 MIN	NOM	MAX	'H78 MIN	NOM	MAX	UNIT
Supply voltage, V_{CC}	Series 54H	4.5	5	5.5	4.5	5	5.5	4.5	5	5.5	4.5	5	5.5	V
	Series 74H	4.75	5	5.25	4.75	5	5.25	4.75	5	5.25	4.75	5	5.25	
High-level output current, I_{OH}				−500			−500			−1000			−500	µA
Low-level output current, I_{OL}				20			20			20			20	mA
Pulse width, t_w	Clock high	12			12			15			12			ns
	Clock low	28			28			13.5			28			
	Clear or preset low	16			16			25			16			
Setup time, t_{su}	High-level data	0↑			0↑			10↑			0↑			ns
	Low-level data	0↑			0↑			15↑			0↑			
Hold time, t_h		0↓			0↓			5↑			0↓			ns
Operating free-air temperature, T_A	Series 54H	−55		125	−55		125	−55		125	−55		125	°C
	Series 74H	0		70	0		70	0		70	0		70	

↑↓ The arrow indicates the edge of the clock pulse used for reference: ↑ for the rising edge, ↓ for the falling edge.

electrical characteristics over recommended operating free-air temperature range (unless otherwise noted)

PARAMETER	TEST CONDITIONS[†]		'H71 MIN	TYP[‡]	MAX	'H72,'H73,'H76 MIN	TYP[‡]	MAX	'H74 MIN	TYP[‡]	MAX	'H78 MIN	TYP[‡]	MAX	UNIT
V_{IH} High-level input voltage			2			2			2			2			V
V_{IL} Low-level input voltage					0.8			0.8			0.8			0.8	V
V_{IK} Input clamp voltage	V_{CC} = MIN, I_I = −8 mA				−1.5			−1.5			−1.5			−1.5	V
V_{OH} High-level output voltage	V_{CC} = MIN, V_{IH} = 2 V, V_{IL} = 0.8 V, I_{OH} = MAX		2.4	3.4		2.4	3.4		2.4	3.4		2.4	3.4		V
V_{OL} Low-level output voltage	V_{CC} = MIN, V_{IH} = 2 V, V_{IL} = 0.8 V, I_{OL} = 20 mA			0.2	0.4		0.2	0.4		0.2	0.4		0.2	0.4	V
I_I Input current at maximum input voltage	V_{CC} = MAX, V_I = 5.5 V	D, J, or K			1			1			1			1	mA
I_{IH} High-level input current	V_{CC} = MAX, V_I = 2.4 V	Clear			50			50			50			50	µA
		Preset			150			100			150			200	
		Clock			100			100			100			100	
I_{IL} Low-level input current	V_{CC} = MAX, V_I = 0.4 V	Clear ★			−2			−2			−2			−2	mA
		Preset ★			−6			−4			−4			−8	
		Clock			−4			−2			−2			−4	
I_{OS} Short-circuit output current◆	V_{CC} = MAX		−40		−100	−40		−100	−40		−100	−40		−100	mA
I_{CC} Supply current (Average per flip-flop)	V_{CC} = MAX, See Note 1	Series 54H		19	30		16	25		15	21		16	25	mA
		Series 74H		19	30		16	25		15	25		16	25	mA

[†]For conditions shown as MIN or MAX, use the appropriate value specified under recommended operating conditions.
[‡]All typical values are at V_{CC} = 5 V, T_A = 25°C.
◆Not more than one output should be shorted at a time, and duration of the short-circuit should not exceed one second.
★Clear is tested with preset high and preset is tested with clear high.
NOTE 1: With all outputs open, I_{CC} is measured with the Q and Q̄ outputs high in turn, At the time of measurement, the clock input is grounded.

TEXAS INSTRUMENTS
INCORPORATED
POST OFFICE BOX 5012 • DALLAS, TEXAS 75222

switching characteristics, VCC = 5 V, TA = 25°C

PARAMETER¶	FROM (INPUT)	TO (OUTPUT)	TEST CONDITIONS	'H71, 'H72, 'H73, 'H76, 'H78 MIN	TYP	MAX	'H74 MIN	TYP	MAX	UNIT
f_{max}			$C_L = 25$ pF, $R_L = 280\ \Omega$, See Note 2	25	30		35	43		MHz
t_{PLH}	Preset (as applicable)	Q̄			6	13			20	ns
t_{PHL}		Q̄			12	24			30	
t_{PLH}	Clear (as applicable)	Q̄			6	13			20	ns
t_{PHL}		Q			12	24			30	
t_{PLH}	Clock	Q or Q̄			14	21		8.5	15	ns
t_{PHL}					22	27		13	20	

¶$f_{max} \equiv$ maximum clock frequency; $t_{PLH} \equiv$ propagation delay time, low-to-high-level output; $t_{PHL} \equiv$ propagation delay time, high-to-low-level output.

NOTE 2: Load circuit and voltage waveforms are shown on page 3-10.

schematics of input and outputs

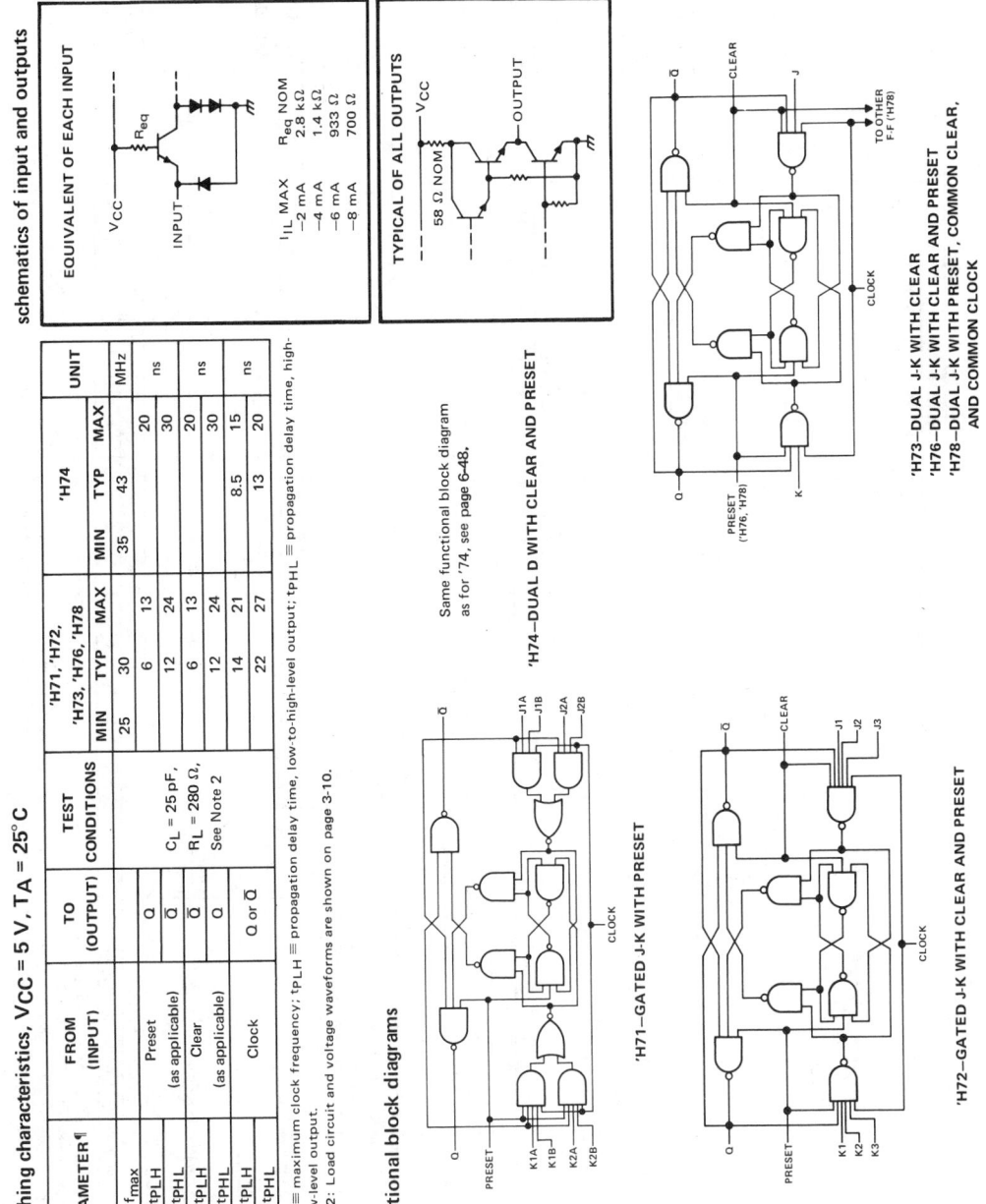

EQUIVALENT OF EACH INPUT

	R_{eq} NOM
I_{IL} MAX	
−2 mA	2.8 kΩ
−4 mA	1.4 kΩ
−6 mA	933 Ω
−8 mA	700 Ω

TYPICAL OF ALL OUTPUTS

58 Ω NOM

functional block diagrams

'H71–GATED J-K WITH PRESET

'H72–GATED J-K WITH CLEAR AND PRESET

'H74–DUAL D WITH CLEAR AND PRESET

Same functional block diagram as for '74, see page 6-48.

'H73–DUAL J-K WITH CLEAR
'H76–DUAL J-K WITH CLEAR AND PRESET
'H78–DUAL J-K WITH PRESET, COMMON CLEAR, AND COMMON CLOCK

recommended operating conditions

SERIES 54H/74H		'H101 MIN	NOM	MAX	'H102,'H106 MIN	NOM	MAX	'H103 MIN	NOM	MAX	'H108 MIN	NOM	MAX	UNIT
Supply voltage, V_{CC}	Series 54H	4.5	5	5.5	4.5	5	5.5	4.5	5	5.5	4.5	5	5.5	V
	Series 74H	4.75	5	5.25	4.75	5	5.25	4.75	5	5.25	4.75	5	5.25	
High-level output current, I_{OH}				-500			-500			-500			-500	µA
Low-level output current, I_{OL}				20			20			20			20	mA
Pulse width, t_w	Clock high	10			10			10			10			ns
	Clock low	15			15			15			15			
	Clear or preset low	16			16			16			16			
Setup time, t_{su}	High-level data	10↓			10↓			10↓			10↓			ns
	Low-level data	13↓			13↓			13↓			13↓			
Hold time, t_h		0↓			0↓			0↓			0↓			ns
Operating free-air temperature, T_A	Series 54H	-55		125	-55		125	-55		125	-55		125	°C
	Series 74H	0		70	0		70	0		70	0		70	

↓ The arrow indicates that the falling edge of the clock pulse is used for reference.

electrical characteristics over recommended operating free-air temperature range (unless otherwise noted)

PARAMETER		TEST CONDITIONS†	'H101 MIN	TYP‡	MAX	'H102,'H106 MIN	TYP‡	MAX	'H103 MIN	TYP‡	MAX	'H108 MIN	TYP‡	MAX	UNIT
V_{IH} High-level input voltage			2			2			2			2			V
V_{IL} Low-level input voltage					0.8			0.8			0.8			0.8	V
V_{IK} Input clamp voltage		V_{CC} = MIN, I_I = −8 mA			-1.5			-1.5			-1.5			-1.5	V
V_{OH} High-level output voltage		V_{CC} = MIN, V_{IH} = 2 V, V_{IL} = 0.8 V, I_{OH} = −500 µA	2.4	3.4		2.4	3.4		2.4	3.4		2.4	3.4		V
V_{OL} Low-level output voltage		V_{CC} = MIN, V_{IH} = 2 V, V_{IL} = 0.8 V, I_{OL} = 20 mA		0.2	0.4		0.2	0.4		0.2	0.4		0.2	0.4	V
I_I Input current at maximum input voltage		V_{CC} = MAX, V_I = 5.5 V			1			1			1			1	mA
I_{IH} High-level input current	Any J or K	V_{CC} = MAX, V_I = 2.4 V			50			50			50			50	µA
	Clear				100			100			100			100	
	Preset				100			100			100			100	
	Clock														
I_{IL} Low-level input current	Any J or K	V_{CC} = MAX, V_I = 0.4 V		-1	-2		-1	-2		-1	-2		-1	-2	mA
	Clear			-1	-2		-1	-2		-1	-2		-1	-2	
	Preset			-1	-2		-1	-2		-1	-2		-1	-2	
	Clock			-3	-4.8		-3	-4.8		-3	-4.8		-6	-9.6	
I_{OS} Short-circuit output current◆		V_{CC} = MAX	-40		-100	-40		-100	-40		-100	-40		-100	mA
I_{CC} Supply current (Average per flip-flop)		V_{CC} = MAX, See Note 1		20	38		20	38		20	38		20	38	mA

† For conditions shown as MIN or MAX, use the appropriate value specified under recommended operating conditions
‡ All typical values are at V_{CC} = 5 V, T_A = 25°C.
◆ Not more than one output should be shorted at a time, and duration of short-circuit should not exceed one second.
NOTE 1: With all outputs open, I_{CC} is measured with the Q and $\overline{Q}$ outputs high in turn. At the time of measurement, the clock input is grounded.

TEXAS INSTRUMENTS
INCORPORATED
POST OFFICE BOX 5012 • DALLAS, TEXAS 75222

schematics of inputs and outputs

EQUIVALENT OF EACH INPUT

V_{CC}

R_{eq}

INPUT

	R_{eq} NOM
I_{IL} MAX	
−2 mA	4 kΩ
−4.8 mA	1.3 kΩ
−9.6 mA	650 Ω

TYPICAL OF ALL OUTPUTS

V_{CC}

58 Ω NOM

OUTPUT

switching characteristics, $V_{CC} = 5$ V, $T_A = 25°C$

PARAMETER¶	FROM (INPUT)	TO (OUTPUT)	TEST CONDITIONS	MIN	TYP	MAX	UNIT
f_{max}				40	50		MHz
t_{PLH}	Preset or clear	Q or $\overline{Q}$			8	12	ns
t_{PHL}	Preset or clear (clock high)	$\overline{Q}$ or Q	$C_L = 25$ pF, $R_L = 280$ Ω, See Note 2		15	20	ns
	Preset or clear (clock low)	Q or $\overline{Q}$			23	35	
t_{PLH}	Clock	Q or $\overline{Q}$			10	15	ns
t_{PHL}					16	20	

¶ $f_{max} \equiv$ maximum clock frequency
$t_{PLH} \equiv$ propagation delay time, low-to-high-level output
$t_{PHL} \equiv$ propagation delay time, high-to-low-level output
NOTE 2: Load circuit and voltage waveforms are shown on page 3-10.

functional block diagrams

'H103–DUAL J-K WITH CLEAR
'H106–DUAL J-K WITH CLEAR AND PRESET
'H108–DUAL J-K WITH PRESET, COMMON CLEAR, AND COMMON CLOCK

CLEAR, J, $\overline{Q}$, TO OTHER FLIP-FLOP ('H108), CLOCK, Q, PRESET ('H106, 'H108), K

'H101–GATED J-K WITH PRESET

$\overline{Q}$, J1A, J1B, J2A, J2B, CLOCK, PRESET, K1A, K1B, K2A, K2B, Q

'H102–GATED J-K WITH CLEAR AND PRESET

$\overline{Q}$, CLEAR, J1, J2, J3, CLOCK, PRESET, K1, K2, K3, Q

TEXAS INSTRUMENTS
INCORPORATED
POST OFFICE BOX 5012 • DALLAS, TEXAS 75222

SERIES 54L/74L FLIP-FLOPS

recommended operating conditions

		'71			'L72,'L73			'74			'78			UNIT
		MIN	NOM	MAX	MIN	NOM	MAX	MIN	NOM	MAX	MIN	NOM	MAX	
Supply voltage, V_{CC}	Series 54L	4.5	5	5.5	4.5	5	5.5	4.5	5	5.5	4.5	5	5.5	V
	Series 74L	4.75	5	5.25	4.75	5	5.25	4.75	5	5.25	4.75	5	5.25	
High-level output current, I_{OH}	Series 54L			−100			−100			−100			−100	µA
	Series 74L			−200			−200			−200			−200	
Low-level output current, I_{OL}	Series 54L			2			2			2			2	mA
	Series 74L			3.6			3.6			3.6			3.6	
Pulse width, t_w	Clock high	200			200			200			200			ns
	Clock low	200			200			200			200			
	Clear or preset low	100			100			100			100			
Setup time, t_{su}		0↑			0↑			50↑			0↑			ns
Hold time, t_h		0↓			0↓			15↑			0↓			ns
Operating free-air temperature, T_A	Series 54L	−55		125	−55		125	−55		125	−55		125	°C
	Series 74L	0		70	0		70	0		70	0		70	

↑↓The arrow indicates the edge of the clock pulse used for reference: ↑ for the rising edge, ↓ for the falling edge.

electrical characteristics over recommended operating free-air temperature range (unless otherwise noted)

PARAMETER		TEST CONDITIONS†	'71			'L72,'L73			'74			'78			UNIT
			MIN	TYP‡	MAX	MIN	TYP‡	MAX	MIN	TYP‡	MAX	MIN	TYP‡	MAX	
V_{IH} High-level input voltage			2			2			2			2			V
V_{IL} Low-level input voltage	Clock input				0.6			0.6			0.7			0.6	V
	All other inputs				0.7			0.7			0.7			0.7	
V_{OH} High-level output voltage	Series 54L	V_{CC} = MIN, V_{IH} = 2 V,	2.4	3.3		2.4	3.3		2.4	3.3		2.4	3.3		V
	Series 74L	V_{IL} = V_{IL} max, I_{OH} = MAX	2.4	3.2		2.4	3.2		2.4	3.2		2.4	3.2		
V_{OL} Low-level output voltage	Series 54L	V_{CC} = MIN, V_{IH} = 2 V,		0.15	0.3		0.15	0.3		0.15	0.3		0.15	0.3	V
	Series 74L	V_{IL} = V_{IL} max, I_{OL} = MAX		0.2	0.4		0.2	0.4		0.2	0.4		0.2	0.4	
I_I Input current at maximum input voltage	R, S, J, K, or D	V_{CC} = MAX, V_I = 5.5 V			100			100			100			100	µA
	Clear				200			200			300			400	
	Preset				200			200			200			200	
	Clock				200			200			200			400	
I_{IH} High-level input current	R, S, J, K, or D	V_{CC} = MAX, V_I = 2.4 V			10			10			10			10	µA
	Clear				20			20			30			40	
	Preset				20			20			20			20	
	Clock				−200			−200			20			−400	
I_{IL} Low-level input current	R, S, J, K, or D	V_{CC} = MAX, V_I = 0.3 V			−0.18			−0.18			−0.18			−0.18	mA
	Clear				−0.36			−0.36			−0.72			−0.72	
	Preset				−0.36			−0.36			−0.36			−0.36	
	Clock				−0.36			−0.36			−0.72			−0.72	
I_{OS} Short-circuit output current		V_{CC} = MAX	−3		−15	−3		−15	−3		−15	−3		−15	mA
I_{CC} Supply current (Average per flip-flop)		V_{CC} = MAX, See Note 1		0.76	1.44		0.76	1.44		0.8	1.5		0.76	1.44	mA

† For conditions shown as MIN or MAX, use the appropriate value specified under recommended operating conditions.
‡ All typical values are at V_{CC} = 5 V, T_A = 25°C.
NOTE 1: With all outputs open, I_{CC} is measured with the Q and Q̄ outputs high in turn. At the time of measurement, the clock input is grounded.

TEXAS INSTRUMENTS
INCORPORATED
POST OFFICE BOX 5012 • DALLAS, TEXAS 75222

schematics of inputs and outputs

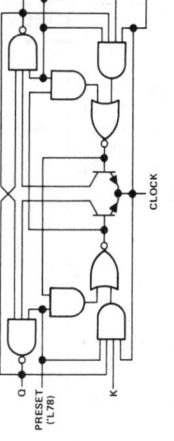

EQUIVALENT OF EACH INPUT

VCC

Req

INPUT

	Req NOM
I_{IL} MAX	
−0.18 mA	40 kΩ
−0.36 mA	20 kΩ
−0.72 mA	10 kΩ

TYPICAL OF ALL OUTPUTS

VCC

OUTPUT

500 Ω NOM

switching characteristics, V_{CC} = 5 V, T_A = 25°C

PARAMETER¶	FROM (INPUT)	TO (OUTPUT)	TEST CONDITIONS	'L71, 'L72, 'L73, 'L78			'L74			UNIT
				MIN	TYP	MAX	MIN	TYP	MAX	
f_{max}				2.5	3		2.5	3		MHz
t_{PLH}	Preset or clear	Q or Q̄	C_L = 50 pF, R_L = 4 kΩ, See Note 2		35	75		50	75	ns
t_{PHL}	Preset or clear (clock high)	Q̄ or Q			60	150		80	150	ns
t_{PHL}	Preset or clear (clock low)					200		80	150	ns
t_{PLH}	Clock	Q or Q̄		10	35	75	15	65	100	ns
t_{PHL}				10	60	150	15	65	150	ns

¶f_{max} ≡ maximum clock frequency
t_{PLH} ≡ propagation delay time, low-to-high-level output
t_{PHL} ≡ propagation delay time, high-to-low-level output
NOTE 2: Load circuit and voltage waveforms are shown on page 3-11.

functional block diagrams

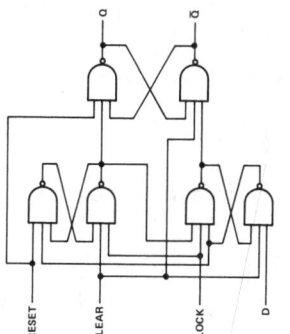

'L74—DUAL D WITH CLEAR AND PRESET

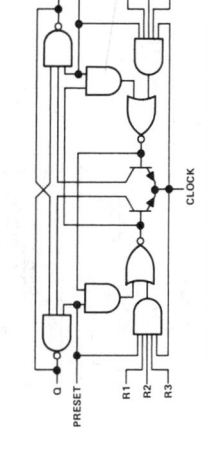

'L71—GATED R-S WITH CLEAR AND PRESET

'L73—DUAL J-K WITH CLEAR
'L78—DUAL J-K WITH PRESET, COMMON CLEAR, AND COMMON CLOCK

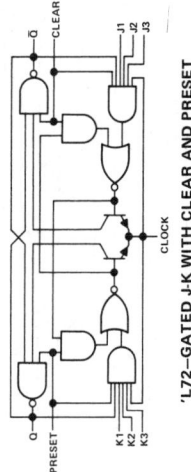

'L72—GATED J-K WITH CLEAR AND PRESET

6

6

recommended operating conditions

			SERIES 54LS/74LS			'LS73A,'LS107A,'LS113A			'LS74A			'LS76A,'LS112A			'LS78A,'LS114A			'LS109A			UNIT
						MIN	NOM	MAX	MIN	NOM	MAX	MIN	NOM	MAX	MIN	NOM	MAX	MIN	NOM	MAX	
Supply voltage, V_{CC}		Series 54LS				4.5	5	5.5	4.5	5	5.5	4.5	5	5.5	4.5	5	5.5	4.5	5	5.5	V
		Series 74LS				4.75	5	5.25	4.75	5	5.25	4.75	5	5.25	4.75	5	5.25	4.75	5	5.25	
High-level output current, I_{OH}		Series 54LS						−400			−400			−400			−400			−400	µA
Low-level output current, I_{OL}		Series 54LS						4			4			4			4			4	mA
		Series 74LS						8			8			8			8			8	
Clock frequency, f_{clock}						0		30	0		25	0		30	0		30	0		25	MHz
Pulse width, t_W	Clock high					20			25			20			20			25			ns
	Preset or clear low					25			25			25			25			25			
Setup time, t_{su}	High-level data					20↓			25↑			20↓			20↓			20↑			ns
	Low-level data					20↓			20↑			20↓			20↓			20↑			
Hold time, t_h						0↓			5↑			0↓			0↓			5↑			ns
Operating free-air temperature, T_A		Series 54LS				−55		125	−55		125	−55		125	−55		125	−55		125	°C
		Series 74LS				0		70	0		70	0		70	0		70	0		70	

† The arrow indicates the edge of the clock pulse used for reference: ↑ for the rising edge, ↓ for the falling edge.

electrical characteristics over recommended operating free-air temperature range (unless otherwise noted)

PARAMETER			TEST CONDITIONS†		'LS73A,'LS107A,'LS113A			'LS74A			'LS76A,'LS112A			'LS78A,'LS114A			'LS109A			UNIT
					MIN	TYP‡	MAX	MIN	TYP‡	MAX	MIN	TYP‡	MAX	MIN	TYP‡	MAX	MIN	TYP‡	MAX	
V_{IH}	High-level input voltage				2			2			2			2			2			V
V_{IL}	Low-level input voltage	Series 54LS					0.7			0.7			0.7			0.7			0.7	V
		Series 74LS					0.8			0.8			0.8			0.8			0.8	
V_{IK}	Input clamp voltage		V_{CC} = MIN, I_I = −18 mA				−1.5			−1.5			−1.5			−1.5			−1.5	V
V_{OH}	High-level output voltage	Series 54LS	V_{CC} = MIN, V_{IH} = 2 V,		2.5	3.4		2.5	3.4		2.5	3.4		2.5	3.4		2.5	3.4		V
		Series 74LS	V_{IL} = V_{IL} max, I_{OH} = −400 µA		2.7	3.4		2.7	3.4		2.7	3.4		2.7	3.4		2.7	3.4		
V_{OL}	Low-level output voltage	Series 54LS	V_{CC} = MIN,			0.25	0.4		0.25	0.4		0.25	0.4		0.25	0.4		0.25	0.4	V
			V_{IL} = V_{IL} max,			0.35	0.5		0.35	0.5		0.35	0.5		0.35	0.5		0.35	0.5	
		Series 74LS	V_{IH} = 2 V	I_{OL} = MAX		0.25	0.4		0.25	0.4		0.25	0.4		0.25	0.4		0.25	0.4	
				I_{OL} = 4 mA			0.1			0.1			0.1			0.1			0.1	
I_I	Input current at maximum input voltage	D, J, K, or $\overline{K}$					0.3			0.2			0.3			0.6			0.2	mA
		Clear	V_{CC} = MAX, V_I = 7 V				0.3			0.2			0.3			0.3			0.2	
		Preset					0.4			0.1			0.4			0.8			0.1	
		Clock																			
I_{IH}	High-level input current	D, J, K, or $\overline{K}$	V_{CC} = MAX, V_I = 2.7 V				20			20			20			20			20	µA
		Clear					60			40			60			120			40	
		Preset					60			40			60			60			40	
		Clock					80			20			80			160			20	
I_{IL}	Low-level input current	D, J, K, or $\overline{K}$	V_{CC} = MAX, V_I = 0.4 V				−0.4			−0.4			−0.4			−0.4			−0.4	mA
		Clear					−0.8			−0.8			−0.8			−1.6			−0.8	
		Preset					−0.8			−0.8			−0.8			−0.8			−0.8	
		Clock					−0.8			−0.4			−0.8			−1.6			−0.4	
I_{OS}	Short-circuit output current◆	Series 54LS	V_{CC} = MAX		−20		−100	−20		−100	−20		−100	−20		−100	−20		−100	mA
		Series 74LS			−20		−100	−20		−100	−20		−100	−20		−100	−20		−100	
I_{CC}	Supply current (Total)		V_{CC} = MAX, See Note 1		4		6	4		8	4		6	4		6	4		8	mA

† For conditions shown as MIN or MAX, use the appropriate value specified under recommended operating conditions.
‡ All typical values are at V_{CC} = 5 V, T_A = 25°C.
◆ Not more than one output should be shorted at a time, and duration of short circuit should not exceed one second.
NOTE 1: With all outputs open, I_{CC} is measured with the Q and $\overline{Q}$ outputs high in turn. At the time of measurement, the clock input is grounded.

TEXAS INSTRUMENTS
INCORPORATED
POST OFFICE BOX 5012 • DALLAS, TEXAS 75222

schematics of 'LS74A and 'LS109A

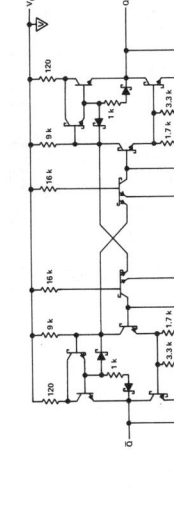

'LS74A–DUAL D WITH CLEAR AND PRESET

'LS109A–DUAL J-K̄ WITH CLEAR AND PRESET

switching characteristics, V_{CC} = 5 V, T_A = 25°C

PARAMETER¶	FROM	TO	TEST		'LS73A,'LS76A,'LS78A, 'LS107A,'LS112A, 'LS113A,'LS114A			'LS74A, 'LS109A			UNIT
	(INPUT)	(OUTPUT)	CONDITIONS		MIN	TYP	MAX	MIN	TYP	MAX	
f_{max}			C_L = 15 pF,		30	45		25	33		MHz
t_{PLH}	Clear, preset, or	Q or Q̄	R_L = 2 kΩ,			15	20		13	25	ns
t_{PHL}	clock (as appropriate)		See Note 2			15	20		25	40	ns

¶f_{max} ≡ maximum clock frequency
t_{PLH} ≡ propagation delay time, low-to-high-level output
t_{PHL} ≡ propagation delay time, high-to-low-level output
NOTE 2: Load circuit and voltage waveforms are shown on page 3-11.

functional block diagrams and schematics of inputs and outputs

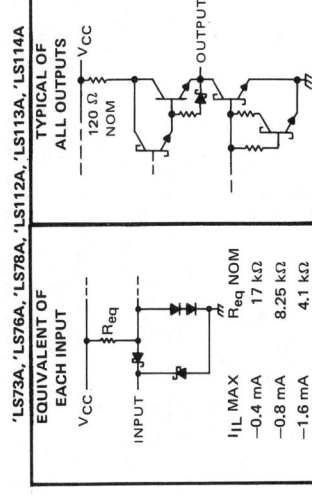

'LS73A, 'LS107A–DUAL J-K WITH CLEAR
'LS76A, 'LS112A–DUAL J-K WITH CLEAR AND PRESET
'LS78A, 'LS114A–DUAL J-K WITH PRESET, COMMON CLEAR,
AND COMMON CLOCK

'LS113A–DUAL J-K WITH PRESET

TYPICAL OF
ALL OUTPUTS

'LS73A, 'LS76A, 'LS78A, 'LS112A, 'LS113A, 'LS114A

EQUIVALENT OF
EACH INPUT

	R_{eq} NOM
I_{IL} MAX	
–0.4 mA	17 kΩ
–0.8 mA	8.25 kΩ
–1.6 mA	4.1 kΩ

TEXAS INSTRUMENTS
INCORPORATED
POST OFFICE BOX 5012 • DALLAS, TEXAS 75222

6

SERIES 54S/74S FLIP-FLOPS

recommended operating conditions

	SERIES 54S/74S	'S74 MIN	NOM	MAX	'S112 MIN	NOM	MAX	'S113 MIN	NOM	MAX	'S114 MIN	NOM	MAX	UNIT
Supply voltage, V_{CC}	Series 54S	4.5	5	5.5	4.5	5	5.5	4.5	5	5.5	4.5	5	5.5	V
	Series 74S	4.75	5	5.25	4.75	5	5.25	4.75	5	5.25	4.75	5	5.25	
High-level output current, I_{OH}				−1			−1			−1			−1	mA
Low-level output current, I_{OL}				20			20			20			20	mA
Pulse width, t_w	Clock high	6			6			6			6			ns
	Clock low	7.3			6.5			6.5			6.5			
	Clear or preset low	7			8			8			8			
Input setup time, t_{su}	High-level data	3↑			3↓			3↓			3↓			ns
	Low-level data	3↑			3↓			3↓			3↓			
Input hold time, t_h		2↑			0↓			0↓			0↓			ns
Operating free-air temperature, T_A	Series 54S	−55		125	−55		125	−55		125	−55		125	°C
	Series 74S	0		70	0		70	0		70	0		70	

↑↓ The arrow indicates the edge of the clock pulse used for reference: ↑ for the rising edge, ↓ for the falling edge.

electrical characteristics over recommended operating free-air temperature range (unless otherwise noted)

PARAMETER	TEST CONDITIONS†	'S74 MIN	TYP‡	MAX	'S112 MIN	TYP‡	MAX	'S113 MIN	TYP‡	MAX	'S114 MIN	TYP‡	MAX	UNIT
V_{IH} High-level input voltage		2			2			2			2			V
V_{IL} Low-level input voltage				0.8			0.8			0.8			0.8	V
V_{IK} Input clamp voltage	V_{CC} = MIN, I_I = −18 mA			−1.2			−1.2			−1.2			−1.2	V
V_{OH} High-level output voltage (Series 54S)	V_{CC} = MIN, V_{IH} = 2 V, V_{IL} = 0.8 V, I_{OH} = −1 mA	2.5	3.4		2.5	3.4		2.5	3.4		2.5	3.4		V
V_{OH} High-level output voltage (Series 74S)		2.7	3.4		2.7	3.4		2.7	3.4		2.7	3.4		V
V_{OL} Low-level output voltage	V_{CC} = MIN, V_{IH} = 2 V, V_{IL} = 0.8 V, I_{OL} = 20 mA			0.5			0.5			0.5			0.5	V
I_I Input current at maximum input voltage	V_{CC} = MAX, V_I = 5.5 V			1			1			1			1	mA
I_{IH} High-level input current — J, K, or D	V_{CC} = MAX, V_I = 2.7 V			50			50			50			50	µA
I_{IH} High-level input current — Clear				150			100			100			200	
I_{IH} High-level input current — Preset				100			100			100			100	
I_{IH} High-level input current — Clock				100			100			100			200	
I_{IL} Low-level input current — J, K, or D	V_{CC} = MAX, V_I = 0.5 V			−2			−1.6			−1.6			−1.6	mA
I_{IL} Low-level input current — Clear ★				−6			−7			−7			−14	
I_{IL} Low-level input current — Preset ★				−4			−7			−7			−7	
I_{IL} Low-level input current — Clock				−4			−4			−4			−8	
I_{OS} Short-circuit output current ♦	V_{CC} = MAX	−40		−100	−40		−100	−40		−100	−40		−100	mA
I_{CC} Supply current (average per flip-flop)	V_{CC} = MAX, See Note 1		15	25		15	25		15	25		15	25	mA

† For conditions shown as MIN or MAX, use the appropriate value specified under recommended operating conditions.
‡ All typical values are at V_{CC} = 5 V, T_A = 25°C.
♦ Not more than one output should be shorted at a time, and duration of short-circuit should not exceed one second.
★ Clear is tested with preset high and preset is tested with clear high.

NOTE 1: With all outputs open, I_{CC} is measured with the Q and Q̄ outputs high in turn. At the time of measurement, the clock input is grounded.

TEXAS INSTRUMENTS
INCORPORATED
POST OFFICE BOX 5012 • DALLAS, TEXAS 75222

schematics of inputs and outputs

EQUIVALENT OF EACH INPUT

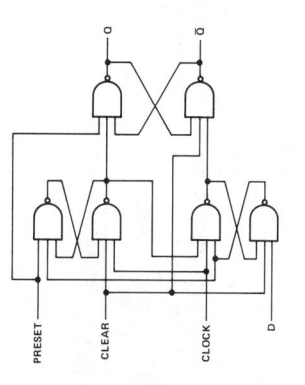

I_{IL} MAX	R_{eq} NOM
-1.6 mA	4 kΩ
-2 mA	2.8 kΩ
-4 mA	1.4 kΩ
-6 mA	940 Ω
-7 mA	900 Ω
-8 mA	700 Ω
-14 mA	450 Ω

TYPICAL OF ALL OUTPUTS

V_{CC} — OUTPUT — 50 Ω NOM

switching characteristics, V_{CC} = 5 V, T_A = 25°C

PARAMETER¶	FROM (INPUT)	TO (OUTPUT)	TEST CONDITIONS	'S74 MIN	'S74 TYP	'S74 MAX	'S112, 'S113, 'S114 MIN	'S112, 'S113, 'S114 TYP	'S112, 'S113, 'S114 MAX	UNIT
f_{max}				75	110		80	125		MHz
t_{PLH}	Preset or clear	Q or Q̄	C_L = 15 pF,		4	6		4	7	ns
t_{PHL}	Preset or clear (clock high)	Q̄ or Q	R_L = 280 Ω,		9	13.5		5	7	ns
t_{PLH}	Preset or clear (clock low)	Q or Q̄	See Note 2		5	8		5	7	
t_{PHL}	Clock	Q or Q̄			6	9		4	7	
					6	9		5	7	ns

¶ f_{max} ≡ maximum clock frequency
t_{PLH} ≡ propagation delay time, low-to-high-level output
t_{PHL} ≡ propagation delay time, high-to-low-level output
NOTE 2: Load circuit and voltage waveforms are shown on page 3-10.

functional block diagrams

'S74—DUAL D WITH CLEAR AND PRESET

'S112—DUAL J-K WITH CLEAR AND PRESET
'S113—DUAL J-K WITH PRESET
'S114—DUAL J-K WITH PRESET, COMMON CLEAR, AND COMMON CLOCK

TEXAS INSTRUMENTS
INCORPORATED
POST OFFICE BOX 5012 • DALLAS, TEXAS 75222

recommended operating conditions

PARAMETER		SN54279 / SN74279 MIN	NOM	MAX	SN54LS279 / SN74LS279 MIN	NOM	MAX	UNIT
Supply voltage, V_{CC}	54 Family	4.5	5	5.5	4.5	5	5.5	V
	74 Family	4.75	5	5.25	4.5	5	5.25	V
High-level output current, I_{OH}	54 Family			−800			−400	µA
	74 Family							
Low-level output current, I_{OL}	54 Family			16			4	mA
	74 Family			16			8	
Operating free-air temperature, T_A	54 Family	−55		125	−55		125	°C
	74 Family	0		70	0		70	

electrical characteristics over recommended free-air operating temperature range (unless otherwise noted)

PARAMETER	TEST CONDITIONS		SN54279 / SN74279 MIN	TYP‡	MAX	SN54LS279 / SN74LS279 MIN	TYP‡	MAX	UNIT
V_{IH} High-level input voltage			2			2			V
V_{IL} Low-level input voltage	54 Family				0.8			0.7	V
	74 Family				0.8			0.8	V
V_{IK} Input clamp voltage	V_{CC} = MIN, I_I = §				−1.5			−1.5	V
V_{OH} High-level output voltage	V_{CC} = MIN, V_{IH} = 2 V, I_{OH} = MAX	54 Family	2.4	3.4		2.5	3.4		V
		74 Family	2.4	3.4		2.7	3.4		
V_{OL} Low-level output voltage	V_{CC} = MIN, V_{IL} = V_{IL} max, V_{IH} = 2 V	54 Family, I_{OL} = MAX		0.2	0.4	0.25	0.35		V
		74 Family, I_{OL} = MAX		0.2	0.4	0.35		0.5	
		Series 74LS, I_{OL} = 4 mA				0.35		0.4	
I_I Input current at maximum input voltage	V_{CC} = MAX	V_I = 5.5 V			1				mA
		V_I = 7 V						0.1	
I_{IH} High-level input current	V_{CC} = MAX	V_I = 2.4 V			40				µA
		V_I = 2.7 V						20	
I_{IL} Low-level input current	V_{CC} = MAX, V_I = 0.4 V				−1.6			−0.4	mA
I_{OS} Short-circuit output current ◆	V_{CC} = MAX	54 Family	−18		−55	−20		−100	mA
		74 Family	−18		−57	−20		−100	mA
I_{CC} Supply current	V_{CC} = MAX, See note 1			18	30		3.8	7	mA

† For conditions shown as MIN or MAX, use the appropriate value specified under recommended operating conditions.

‡ All typical values are at V_{CC} = 5 V, T_A = 25°C.

§ I_I = −12 mA for SN54'/SN74' and −18 mA for SN54LS'/SN74LS'.

◆ Not more than one output should be shorted at a time, and for SN54LS'/SN74LS', duration of the output short circuit should not exceed one second.

NOTE 1: I_{CC} is measured with all R̄ inputs grounded, all S̄ inputs at 4.5 V, and all outputs open.

TEXAS INSTRUMENTS
INCORPORATED
POST OFFICE BOX 5012 • DALLAS, TEXAS 75222

switching characteristics, $V_{CC} = 5$ V, $T_A = 25°$ C

PARAMETER		TEST CONDITIONS	'279			'LS279			UNIT
			MIN	TYP	MAX	MIN	TYP	MAX	
t_{PLH}	Propagation delay time, low-to-high-level output from $\overline{S}$ input	$C_L = 15$ pF, See Notes 2 and 3		12	22		12	22	ns
t_{PHL}	Propagation delay time, high-to-low-level output from $\overline{S}$ input			9	15		13	21	
t_{PHL}	Propagation delay time, high-to-low-level output from $\overline{R}$ input			15	27		15	27	

NOTE 2: Load circuit and voltage waveforms are shown on pages 3-10 and 3-11.
NOTE 3: $R_L = 400 \, \Omega$ for '279, $R_L = 2 \, k\Omega$ for 'LS279.

schematics of inputs and outputs

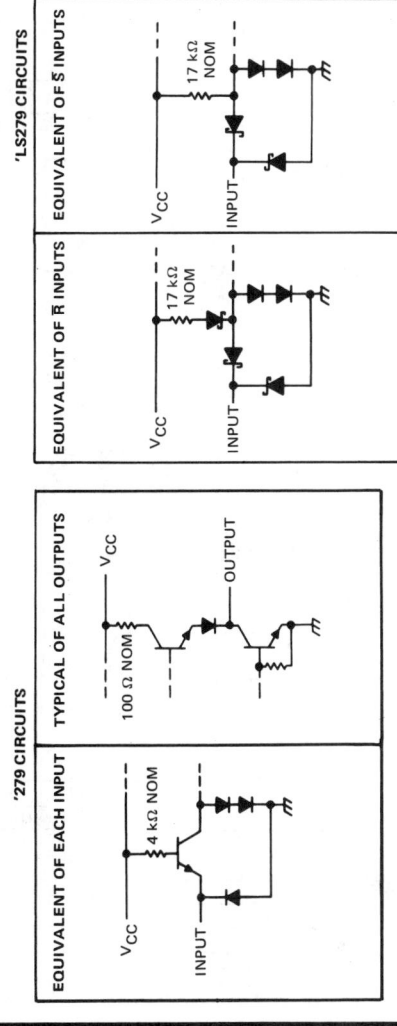

- Translates low-level input current to low-level output voltage
- Translates high-level input current to high-level output voltage
- Interfaces to PLA's or other logic elements that source current but do not sink current
- Operates from a single 5 V supply
- TTL compatible
- Low power dissipation . . .40 mW typical

SN54LS63 . . . J OR W PACKAGE
SN74LS63 . . . J OR N PACKAGE

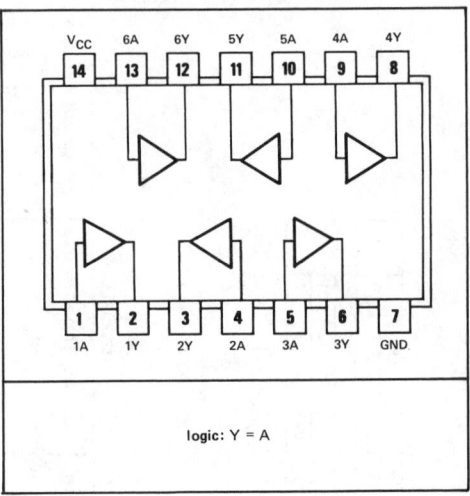

logic: Y = A

description

Each of these Schotty-clamped interface gates is able to discriminate between low-level ($\leqslant$ 50 μA) and high-level ($\geqslant$ 200 μA) input currents.

The outputs are fabricated with standard Low-Power Schottky design rules and are compatible with all TTL families.

schematic (each gate)

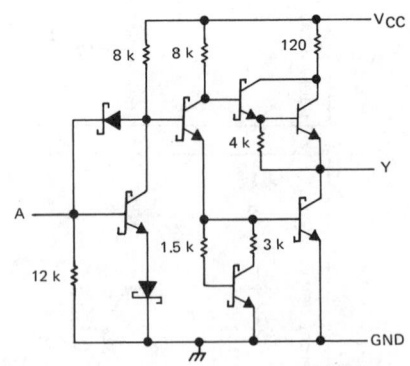

Resistor values shown are nominal and in ohms.

recommended operating conditions

	SN54LS63			SN74LS63			UNIT
	MIN	NOM	MAX	MIN	NOM	MAX	
Supply voltage, V_{CC}	4.5	5	5.5	4.75	5	5.25	V
High-level output current, I_{OH}			−400			−400	μA
Low-level output current, I_{OL}			4			8	mA
Input current, I_I			1			1	mA
Operating free-air temperature, T_A	−55		125	0		70	°C

TEXAS INSTRUMENTS
INCORPORATED
POST OFFICE BOX 5012 • DALLAS, TEXAS 75222

electrical characteristics over recommended operating free-air temperature range (unless otherwise noted)

PARAMETER		TEST CONDITIONS[†]			SN54LS63			SN74LS63			UNIT
					MIN	TYP[‡]	MAX	MIN	TYP[‡]	MAX	
V_I	Input voltage	$I_I = 50\,\mu A$,	$V_{CC} = MIN$		0.35	1.05	1.75	0.6	1.05	1.6	V
		$I_I = 200\,\mu A$,	$V_{CC} = MAX$		0.6	1.30	2	0.85	1.30	1.8	
V_{OH}	High-level output voltage	$V_{CC} = MAX$	$I_I = 200\,\mu A$	$I_{OH} = -400\,\mu A$,	3.5	3.4		3.2	3.4		V
V_{OL}	Low-level output voltage	$V_{CC} = MIN$,	$I_I = 50\,\mu A$	$I_{OL} = 4\,mA$		0.25	0.4		0.25	0.4	V
				$I_{OL} = 8\,mA$					0.35	0.5	
I_{OS}	Short-circuit output current[§]	$V_{CC} = MAX$	$I_I = 600\,\mu A$		−20		−100	−20		−100	mA
I_{CC}	Supply current	$V_{CC} = MAX$,	See Note 1			8	16		8	16	mA

[†]For conditions shown as MIN or MAX, use the appropriate value specified under recommended operating conditions.
[‡]All typical values are at $V_{CC} = 5$ V, $T_A = 25°C$.
[§]Not more than one output should be shorted at a time, and duration of output short circuit should not exceed one second.
NOTE 1: I_{CC} is measured with inputs and outputs open.

switching characteristics, $V_{CC} = 5$ V, $T_A = 25°C$

PARAMETER		TEST CONDITIONS	MIN	TYP	MAX	UNIT
t_{PLH}	Propagation delay time, low-to-high-level output	$C_L = 15$ pF,		27	45	ns
t_{PHL}	Propagation delay time, high-to-low-level output	$R_L = 2\,k\Omega$		15	25	ns

---

PARAMETER MEASUREMENT INFORMATION

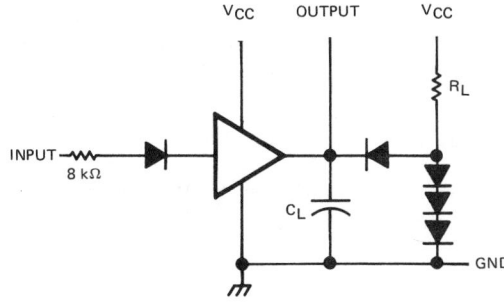

NOTES: a. C_L includes probe and jig capacitance
       b. All diodes are 1N916 or 1N3064

TEST CIRCUIT

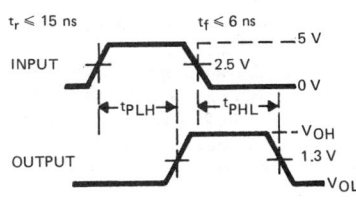

VOLTAGE WAVEFORMS

6

TEXAS INSTRUMENTS
INCORPORATED
POST OFFICE BOX 5012 • DALLAS, TEXAS 75222

- **Programmable Output Pulse Width**
  With R_{int} ... 35 ns Typ
  With R_{ext}/C_{ext} ... 40 ns to 28 Seconds

- **Internal Compensation for Virtual Temperature Independence**

- **Jitter-Free Operation up to 90% Duty Cycle**

- **Inhibit Capability**

SN54121 . . . J OR W PACKAGE
SN54L121 . . . J OR T PACKAGE
SN74121, SN74L121 . . . J OR N PACKAGE

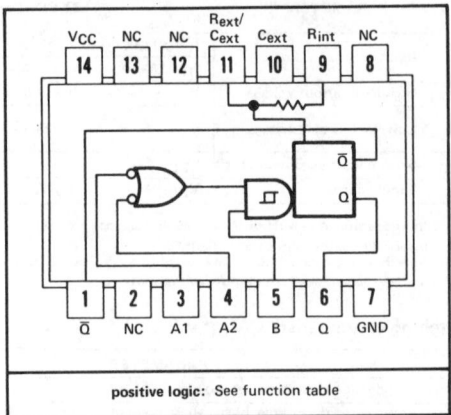

positive logic: See function table

NC—No internal connection

NOTES: 1. An external capacitor may be connected between C_{ext} (positive) and R_{ext}/C_{ext}.
2. To use the internal timing resistor, connect R_{int} to V_{CC}. For improved pulse width accuracy and repeatability, connect an external resistor between R_{ext}/C_{ext} and V_{CC} with R_{int} open-circuited.

FUNCTION TABLE

INPUTS			OUTPUTS	
A1	A2	B	Q	Q̄
L	X	H	L	H
X	L	H	L	H
X	X	L	L	H
H	H	X	L	H
H	↓	H	⎍	⊓̄
↓	H	H	⎍	⊓̄
↓	↓	H	⎍	⊓̄
L	X	↑	⎍	⊓̄
X	L	↑	⎍	⊓̄

For explanation of function table symbols, see page 3-8.

description

These multivibrators feature dual negative-transition-triggered inputs and a single positive-transition-triggered input which can be used as an inhibit input. Complementary output pulses are provided.

Pulse triggering occurs at a particular voltage level and is not directly related to the transition time of the input pulse. Schmitt-trigger input circuitry (TTL hysteresis) for the B input allows jitter-free triggering from inputs with transition rates as slow as 1 volt/second, providing the circuit with an excellent noise immunity of typically 1.2 volts. A high immunity to V_{CC} noise of typically 1.5 volts is also provided by internal latching circuitry.

Once fired, the outputs are independent of further transitions of the inputs and are a function only of the timing components. Input pulses may be of any duration relative to the output pulse. Output pulse length may be varied from 40 nanoseconds to 28 seconds by choosing appropriate timing components. With no external timing components (i.e., R_{int} connected to V_{CC}, C_{ext} and R_{ext}/C_{ext} open), an output pulse of typically 30 or 35 nanoseconds is achieved which may be used as a d-c triggered reset signal. Output rise and fall times are TTL compatible and independent of pulse length.

Pulse width stability is achieved through internal compensation and is virtually independent of V_{CC} and temperature. In most applications, pulse stability will only be limited by the accuracy of external timing components.

Jitter-free operation is maintained over the full temperature and V_{CC} ranges for more than six decades of timing capacitance (10 pF to 10 μF) and more than one decade of timing resistance (2 kΩ to 30 kΩ for the SN54121/SN54L121 and 2 kΩ to 40 kΩ for the SN74121/SN74L121). Throughout these ranges, pulse width is defined by the relationship $t_{w(out)} = C_{ext}R_T \ln 2 \approx 0.7 \, C_{ext}R_T$. In circuits where pulse cutoff is not critical, timing capacitance up to 1000 μF and timing resistance as low as 1.4 kΩ may be used. Also, the range of jitter-free output pulse widths is extended if V_{CC} is held to 5 volts and free-air temperature is 25°C. Duty cycles as high as 90% are achieved when using maximum recommended R_T. Higher duty cycles are available if a certain amount of pulse-width jitter is allowed.

6

107

TEXAS INSTRUMENTS
INCORPORATED
POST OFFICE BOX 5012 • DALLAS, TEXAS 75222

schematics of inputs and outputs

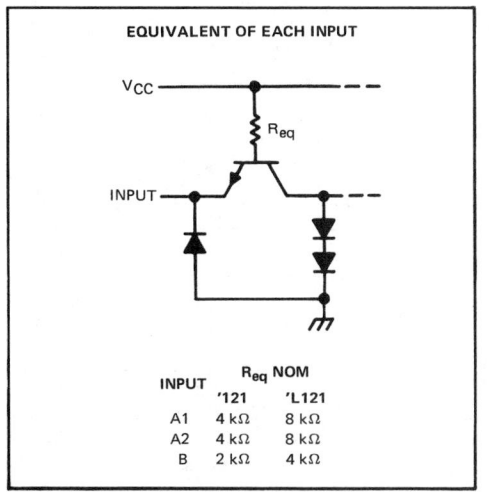

EQUIVALENT OF EACH INPUT

INPUT	R_{eq} NOM	
	'121	'L121
A1	4 kΩ	8 kΩ
A2	4 kΩ	8 kΩ
B	2 kΩ	4 kΩ

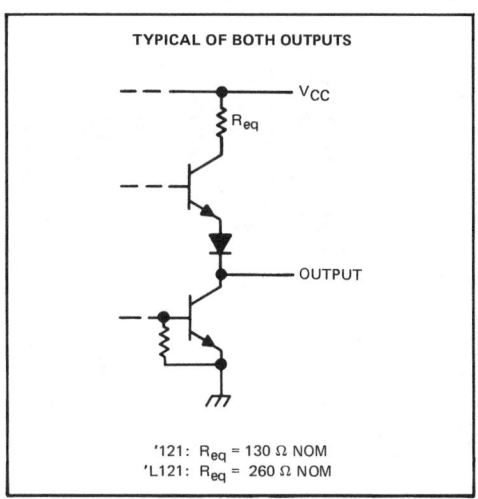

TYPICAL OF BOTH OUTPUTS

'121: R_{eq} = 130 Ω NOM
'L121: R_{eq} = 260 Ω NOM

recommended operating conditions

		54 FAMILY	SN54121			SN54L121			
		74 FAMILY	SN74121			SN74L121			UNIT
			MIN	NOM	MAX	MIN	NOM	MAX	
Supply voltage, V_{CC}		54 Family	4.5	5	5.5	4.5	5	5.5	V
		74 Family	4.75	5	5.25	4.75	5	5.25	
High-level output current, I_{OH}					−400			−200	μA
Low-level output current, I_{OL}					16			8	mA
Rate of rise or fall of input pulse, dv/dt	Schmitt input, B		1			1			V/s
	Logic inputs, A1, A2		1			1			V/μs
Input pulse width, $t_{w(in)}$			50			100			ns
External timing resistance, R_{ext}		54 Family	1.4		30	1.4		30	kΩ
		74 Family	1.4		40	1.4		40	
External timing capacitance, C_{ext}			0		1000	0		1000	μF
Duty cycle	R_T = 2 kΩ				67			67	%
	R_T = MAX R_{ext}				90			90	
Operating free-air temperature, T_A		54 Family	−55		125	−55		125	°C
		74 Family	0		70	0		70	

6

TEXAS INSTRUMENTS
INCORPORATED
POST OFFICE BOX 5012 • DALLAS, TEXAS 75222

electrical characteristics over recommended operating free-air temperature range (unless otherwise noted)

PARAMETER		TEST CONDITIONS†		SN54121 SN74121 MIN	SN54121 SN74121 TYP‡	SN54121 SN74121 MAX	SN54L121 SN74L121 MIN	SN54L121 SN74L121 TYP‡	SN54L121 SN74L121 MAX	UNIT
V_{T+}	Positive-going threshold voltage at A input	V_{CC} = MIN			1.4	2		1.4	2	V
V_{T-}	Negative-going threshold voltage at A input	V_{CC} = MIN		0.8	1.4		0.8	1.4		V
V_{T+}	Positive-going threshold voltage at B input	V_{CC} = MIN			1.55	2		1.55	2	V
V_{T-}	Negative-going threshold voltage at B input	V_{CC} = MIN		0.8	1.35		0.8	1.35		V
V_{IK}	Input clamp voltage	V_{CC} = MIN,	I_I = −12 mA			−1.5			−1.5	V
V_{OH}	High-level output voltage	V_{CC} = MIN,	I_{OH} = MAX	2.4	3.4		2.4	3.4		V
V_{OL}	Low-level output voltage	V_{CC} = MIN,	I_{OL} = MAX		0.2	0.4		0.2	0.4	V
I_I	Input current at maximum input voltage	V_{CC} = MAX,	V_I = 5.5 V			1			1	mA
I_{IH}	High-level input current	V_{CC} = MAX, V_I = 2.4 V	A1 or A2			40			20	µA
			B			80			40	
I_{IL}	Low-level input current	V_{CC} = MAX, V_I = 0.4 V	A1 or A2			−1.6			−0.8	mA
			B			−3.2			−1.6	
I_{OS}	Short-circuit output current♦	V_{CC} = MAX	54 Family	−20		−55	−10		−27	mA
			74 Family	−18		−55	−9		−27	
I_{CC}	Supply current	V_{CC} = MAX	Quiescent		13	25		7	12	mA
			Triggered		23	40		9	20	

†For conditions shown as MIN or MAX, use the appropriate value specified under recommended operating conditions.

‡All typical values are at V_{CC} = 5 V, T_A = 25°C.

♦Not more than one output should be shorted at a time.

switching characteristics, V_{CC} = 5 V, T_A = 25°C

PARAMETER		TEST CONDITIONS		'121 MIN	'121 TYP	'121 MAX	'L121 MIN	'L121 TYP	'L121 MAX	UNIT
t_{PLH}	Propagation delay time, low-to-high-level Q output from either A input				45	70			140	ns
t_{PLH}	Propagation delay time, low-to-high-level Q output from B input		C_{ext} = 80 pF, R_{int} to V_{CC}		35	55			110	ns
t_{PHL}	Propagation delay time, high-to-low-level $\overline{Q}$ output from either A input				50	80			160	ns
t_{PHL}	Propagation delay time, high-to-low-level $\overline{Q}$ output from B input	C_L = 15 pF, R_L = 400 Ω for '121, R_L = 800 Ω for 'L121, See Note 3			40	65			130	ns
$t_{w(out)}$	Pulse width obtained using internal timing resistor		C_{ext} = 80 pF, R_{int} to V_{CC}	70	110	150	70	225	260	ns
$t_{w(out)}$	Pulse width obtained with zero timing capacitance		C_{ext} = 0, R_{int} to V_{CC}		30	50		35	70	ns
$t_{w(out)}$	Pulse width obtained using external timing resistor		C_{ext} = 100 pF, R_T = 10 kΩ	600	700	800	600	700	850	ns
			C_{ext} = 1 µF, R_T = 10 kΩ	6	7	8	6	7	8	ms

NOTE 3: Load circuit and voltage waveforms are shown on pages 3-10 and 3-11.

6

TEXAS INSTRUMENTS
INCORPORATED
POST OFFICE BOX 5012 • DALLAS, TEXAS 75222

TYPICAL CHARACTERISTICS§

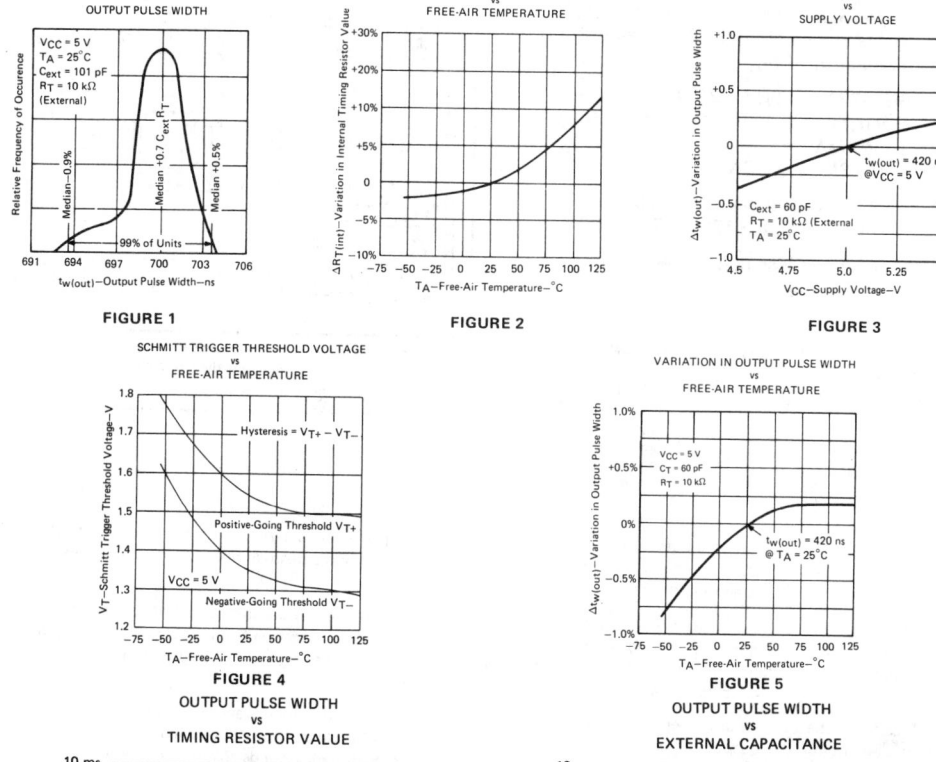

FIGURE 1

FIGURE 2

FIGURE 3

FIGURE 4

FIGURE 5

FIGURE 6

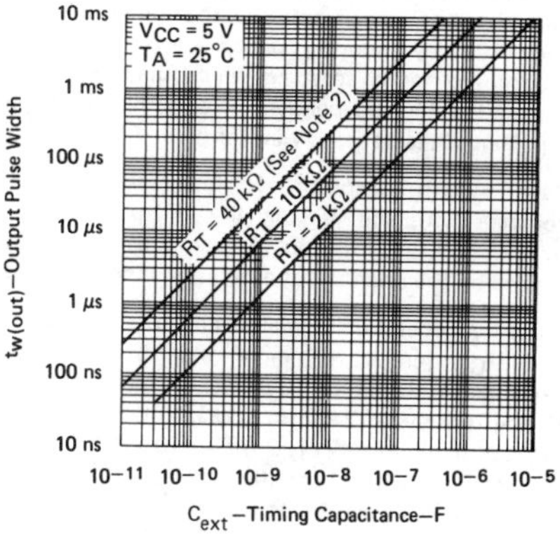

FIGURE 7

NOTE 4: These values of resistance exceed the maximum recommended for use over the full temperature range of the SN54L121.
§ Data for temperatures below 0°C and above 70°C are applicable for SN54121 and SN54L121.

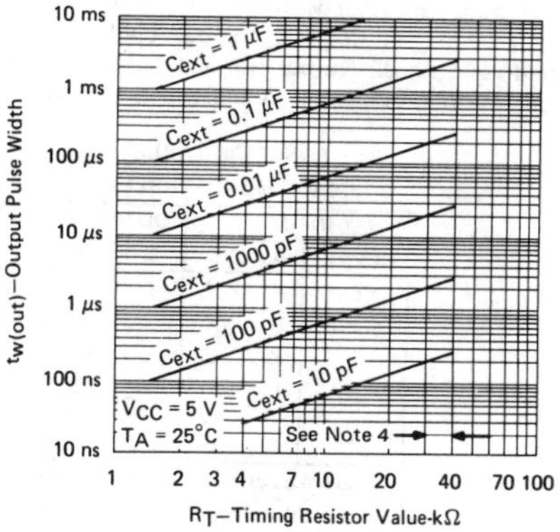

- SN54221, SN54LS221, SN74221 and SN74LS221 Are Dual Versions of Highly Stable SN54121, SN74121 One-Shots on a Monolithic Chip

- SN54221 and SN74221 Demonstrate Electrical and Switching Characteristics That Are Virtually Identical to the SN54121, SN74121 One-Shots

- Pin-Out Is Identical to the SN54123 SN74123, SN54LS123, SN74LS123

- Overriding Clear Terminates Output Pulse

SN54221, SN54LS221 . . . J OR W PACKAGE
SN74221, SN74LS221 . . . J OR N PACKAGE
(TOP VIEW)

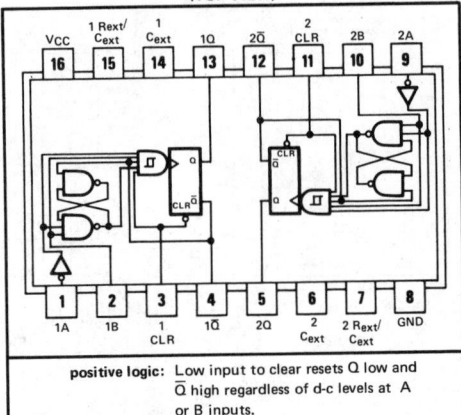

positive logic: Low input to clear resets Q low and Q̄ high regardless of d-c levels at A or B inputs.

TYPE	TYPICAL POWER DISSIPATION	MAXIMUM OUTPUT PULSE LENGTH
SN54221	130 mW	21 s
SN74221	130 mW	28 s
SN54LS221	23 mW	49 s
SN74LS221	23 mW	70 s

description

The '221 and 'LS221 are monolithic dual multivibrators with performance characteristics virtually identical to those of the '121. Each multivibrator features a negative-transition-triggered input and a positive-transition-triggered input either of which can be used as an inhibit input.

Pulse triggering occurs at a particular voltage level and is not directly related to the transition time of the input pulse. Schmitt-trigger input circuitry (TTL hysteresis) for B input allows jitter-free triggering from inputs with transition rates as slow as 1 volt/second, providing the circuit with excellent noise immunity of typically 1.2 volts. A high immunity to V_{CC} noise of typically 1.5 volts is also provided by internal latching circuitry.

Once fired, the outputs are independent of further transitions of the A and B inputs and are a function of the timing components, or the output pulses can be terminated by the overriding clear. Input pulses may be of any duration relative to the output pulse. Output pulse length may be varied from 35 nanoseconds to the maximums shown in the above table by choosing appropriate timing components. With R_{ext} = 2 kΩ and C_{ext} = 0, an output pulse of typically 30 nanoseconds is achieved which may be used as a d-c-triggered reset signal. Output rise and fall times are TTL compatible and independent of pulse length. Typical triggering and clearing sequences are illustrated as a part of the switching characteristics waveforms.

Pulse width stability is achieved through internal compensation and is virtually independent of V_{CC} and temperature. In most applications, pulse stability will only be limited by the accuracy of external timing components.

Jitter-free operation is maintained over the full temperature and V_{CC} ranges for more than six decades of timing capacitance (10 pF to 10 μF) and more than one decade of timing resistance (2 kΩ to 30 kΩ for the SN54221, 2 kΩ to 40 kΩ for the SN74221, 2 kΩ to 70 kΩ for the SN54LS221, and 2 kΩ to 100 kΩ for the SN74LS221). Throughout these ranges, pulse width is defined by the relationship: $t_{w(out)} = C_{ext}R_{ext} \ln 2 \approx 0.7\ C_{ext}R_{ext}$. In circuits where pulse cutoff is not critical, timing capacitance up to 1000 μF and timing resistance as low as 1.4 kΩ may be used. Also, the range of jitter-free output pulse widths is extended if V_{CC} is

FUNCTION TABLE
(EACH MONOSTABLE)

INPUTS			OUTPUTS	
CLEAR	A	B	Q	Q̄
L	X	X	L	H
X	H	X	L	H
X	X	L	L	H
H	L	↑	⎍	⎍
H	↓	H	⎍	⎍
↑	L	H	⎍	⎍

Also see description and switching characteristics

See explanation of function tables on page 3-8.

TEXAS INSTRUMENTS
INCORPORATED
POST OFFICE BOX 5012 • DALLAS, TEXAS 75222

description (continued)

held to 5 volts and free-air temperature is 25°C. Duty cycles as high as 90% are achieved when using maximum recommended R_T. Higher duty cycles are available if a certain amount of pulse-width jitter is allowed.

The variance in output pulse width from device to device is typically less than ±0.5% for given external timing components. An example of this distribution for the '221 is shown in Figure 2. Variations in output pulse width versus supply voltage and temperature for the '221 are shown in Figure 3 and 4, respectively.

Pin assignments for these devices are identical to those of the SN54123/SN74123 or SN54LS123/SN74LS123 so that the '221 or 'LS221 can be substituted for those products in systems not using the retrigger by merely changing the value of R_{ext} and/or C_{ext}.

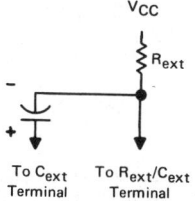

TIMING COMPONENT CONNECTIONS

schematics of inputs and outputs

'221

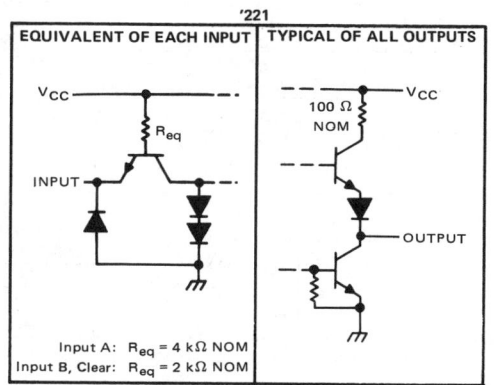

'LS221

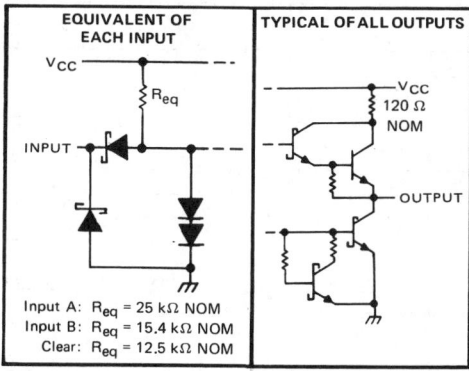

TEXAS INSTRUMENTS
INCORPORATED
POST OFFICE BOX 5012 • DALLAS, TEXAS 75222

recommended operating conditions

		SN54221 MIN	SN54221 NOM	SN54221 MAX	SN74221 MIN	SN74221 NOM	SN74221 MAX	UNIT
Supply voltage, V_{CC}		4.5	5	5.5	4.75	5	5.25	V
High-level output current, I_{OH}				−800			−800	μA
Low-level output current, I_{OL}				16			16	mA
Rate of rise or fall of input pulse, dv/dt	Schmitt input, B	1			1			V/s
	Logic input, A	1			1			V/μs
Input pulse width	A or B, $t_{W(in)}$	50			50			ns
	Clear, $t_{W(clear)}$	20			20			
Clear-inactive-state setup time, t_{su}		15			15			ns
External timing resistance, R_{ext}		1.4		30	1.4		40	kΩ
External timing capacitance, C_{ext}		0		1000	0		1000	μF
Output duty cycle	$R_{ext} = 2 k\Omega$			67			67	%
	$R_{ext} = MAX R_{ext}$			90			90	
Operating free-air temperature, T_A		−55		125	0		70	°C

electrical characteristics over recommended operating free-air temperature range (unless otherwise noted)

PARAMETER		TEST CONDITIONS[†]		MIN	TYP[‡]	MAX	UNIT
V_{T+}	Positive-going threshold voltage at A input	$V_{CC} = MIN$			1.4	2	V
V_{T-}	Negative-going threshold voltage at A input	$V_{CC} = MIN$		0.8	1.4		V
V_{T+}	Positive-going threshold voltage at B input	$V_{CC} = MIN$			1.55	2	V
V_{T-}	Negative-going threshold voltage at B input	$V_{CC} = MIN$		0.8	1.35		V
V_{IK}	Input clamp voltage	$V_{CC} = MIN$, $I_I = -12$ mA				−1.5	V
V_{OH}	High-level output voltage	$V_{CC} = MIN$, $I_{OH} = -800$ μA		2.4	3.4		V
V_{OL}	Low-level output voltage	$V_{CC} = MIN$, $I_{OL} = 16$ mA			0.2	0.4	V
I_I	Input current at maximum input voltage	$V_{CC} = MAX$, $V_I = 5.5$ V				1	mA
I_{IH}	High-level input current	$V_{CC} = MAX$, $V_I = 2.4$ V	Input A			40	μA
			Input B, Clear			80	
I_{IL}	Low-level input current	$V_{CC} = MAX$, $V_I = 0.4$ V	Input A			−1.6	mA
			Input B, Clear			−3.2	
I_{OS}	Short-circuit output current[§]	$V_{CC} = MAX$	SN54221	−20		−55	mA
			SN74221	−18		−55	
I_{CC}	Supply current	$V_{CC} = MAX$	Quiescent		26	50	mA
			Triggered		46	80	

[†]For conditions shown as MIN or MAX, use the appropriate value specified under recommended operating conditions.
[‡]All typical values are at $V_{CC} = 5$ V, $T_A = 25°C$.
[§]Not more than one output should be shorted at a time.

switching characteristics, $V_{CC} = 5$ V, $T_A = 25°C$

PARAMETER[¶]	FROM (INPUT)	TO (OUTPUT)	TEST CONDITIONS		MIN	TYP	MAX	UNIT
t_{PLH}	A	Q	$C_{ext} = 80$ pF, $R_{ext} = 2 k\Omega$			45	70	ns
	B	Q				35	55	
t_{PHL}	A	$\overline{Q}$	$C_{ext} = 80$ pF, $R_{ext} = 2 k\Omega$			50	80	ns
	B	$\overline{Q}$				40	65	
t_{PHL}	Clear	Q	$C_L = 15$ pF, $R_L = 400 \Omega$, See Figure 1 and Note 2				27	ns
t_{PLH}	Clear	$\overline{Q}$					40	ns
$t_{W(out)}$	A or B	Q or $\overline{Q}$	$C_{ext} = 80$ pF, $R_{ext} = 2 k\Omega$		70	110	150	ns
			$C_{ext} = 0$, $R_{ext} = 2 k\Omega$		20	30	50	
			$C_{ext} = 100$ pF, $R_{ext} = 10 k\Omega$		650	700	750	
			$C_{ext} = 1$ μF, $R_{ext} = 10 k\Omega$		6.5	7	7.5	ms

[¶]$t_{PLH} \equiv$ Propagation delay time, low-to-high-level output
$t_{PHL} \equiv$ Propagation delay time, high-to-low-level output
$t_{W(out)} \equiv$ Output pulse width
NOTE 2: Load circuit is shown on page 3-10.

TEXAS INSTRUMENTS
INCORPORATED
POST OFFICE BOX 5012 • DALLAS, TEXAS 75222

6

recommended operating conditions

		SN54LS221			SN74LS221			UNIT
		MIN	NOM	MAX	MIN	NOM	MAX	
Supply voltage, V_{CC}		4.5	5	5.5	4.75	5	5.25	V
High-level output current, I_{OH}				−400			−400	μA
Low-level output current, I_{OL}				4			8	mA
Rate of rise or fall of input pulse, dv/dt	Schmitt, B	1			1			V/s
	Logic input, A	1			1			V/μs
Input pulse width	A or B, $t_{w(in)}$	40			40			ns
	Clear, $t_{w(clear)}$	40			40			
Clear-inactive-state setup time, t_{su}		15			15			ns
External timing resistance, R_{ext}		1.4		70	1.4		100	kΩ
External timing capacitance, C_{ext}		0		1000	0		1000	μF
Output duty cycle	R_T = 2 kΩ			50			50	%
	R_T = MAX R_{ext}			90			90	
Operating free-air temperature, T_A		−55		125	0		70	°C

electrical characteristics over recommended operating free-air temperature range (unless otherwise noted)

PARAMETER		TEST CONDITIONS[†]		SN54LS221			SN74LS221			UNIT
				MIN	TYP[‡]	MAX	MIN	TYP[‡]	MAX	
V_{T+}	Positive-going threshold voltage at A input	V_{CC} = MIN			1.0	2		1.0	2	V
V_{T-}	Negative-going threshold voltage at A input	V_{CC} = MIN		0.7	1.0		0.8	1.0		V
V_{T+}	Positive=going threshold voltage at B input	V_{CC} = MIN			1.0	2		1.0	2	V
V_{T-}	Negative-going threshold voltage at B input	V_{CC} = MIN		0.7	0.9		0.8	0.9		V
V_{IK}	Input clamp voltage	V_{CC} = MIN, I_I = −18 mA				−1.5			−1.5	V
V_{OH}	High-level output voltage	V_{CC} = MIN, I_{OH} = −400 μA		2.5	3.4		2.7	3.4		V
V_{OL}	Low-level output voltage	V_{CC} = MIN	I_{OL} = 4 mA		0.25	0.4		0.25	0.4	V
			I_{OL} = 8 mA					0.35	0.5	
I_I	Input current at maximum input voltage	V_{CC} = MAX, V_I = 7 V				0.1			0.1	mA
I_{IH}	High-level input current	V_{CC} = MAX, V_I = 2.7 V				20			20	μA
I_{IL}	Low-level input current	Input A	V_{CC} = MAX, V_I = 0.4 V			−0.4			−0.4	mA
		Input B				−0.8			−0.8	
		Clear				−0.8			−0.8	
I_{OS}	Short-circuit output current[§]	V_{CC} = MAX		−20		−100	−20		−100	mA
I_{CC}	Supply current	V_{CC} = MAX	Quiescent		4.7	11		4.7	11	mA
			Triggered		19	27		19	27	

[†]For conditions shown as MIN or MAX, use the appropriate value specified under recommended operating conditions.
[‡]All typical values are at V_{CC} = 5 V, T_A = 25°C
[§]Not more than one output should be shorted at a time and duration of the short-circuit should not exceed one second.

6

switching characteristics, V_{CC} = 5 V, T_A = 25°C

PARAMETER¶	FROM (INPUT)	TO (OUTPUT)	TEST CONDITIONS		MIN	TYP	MAX	UNIT
t_{PLH}	A	Q	C_{ext} = 80 pF, R_{ext} = 2 kΩ			45	70	ns
	B	Q				35	55	
t_{PHL}	A	$\overline{Q}$				50	80	ns
	B	$\overline{Q}$				40	65	
t_{PHL}	Clear	Q	C_L = 15 pF, R_L = 2 kΩ, See Figure 1 and Note 3			35	55	ns
t_{PLH}	Clear	$\overline{Q}$				44	65	ns
$t_{w(out)}$	A or B	Q or $\overline{Q}$		C_{ext} = 80 pF, R_{ext} = 2 kΩ	70	120	150	
				C_{ext} = 0, R_{ext} = 2 kΩ	20	47	70	ns
				C_{ext} = 100 pF, R_{ext} = 10 kΩ	600	670	750	
				C_{ext} = 1 μF, R_{ext} = 10 kΩ	6	6.9	7.5	ms

¶t_{PLH} ≡ Propagation delay time, low-to-high-level output
t_{PHL} ≡ Propagation delay time, high-to-low-level output
$t_{w(out)}$ ≡ Output pulse width

NOTE 3: Load circuit is shown on page 3-11.

TEXAS INSTRUMENTS
INCORPORATED
POST OFFICE BOX 5012 • DALLAS, TEXAS 75222

PARAMETER MEASUREMENT INFORMATION

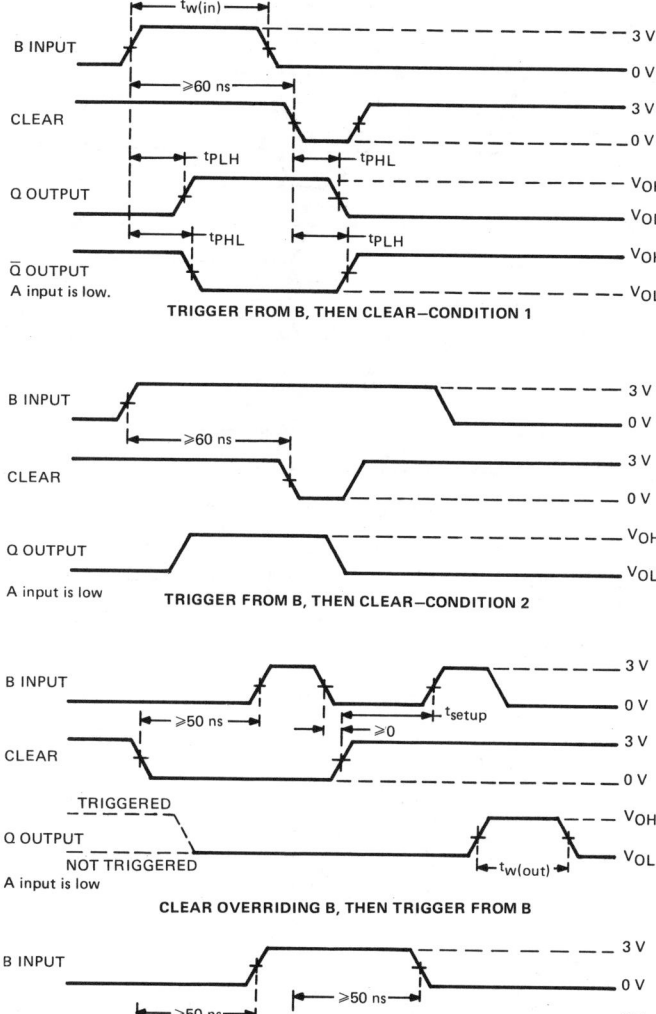

FIGURE 1—SWITCHING CHARACTERISTICS

PARAMETER MEASUREMENT INFORMATION

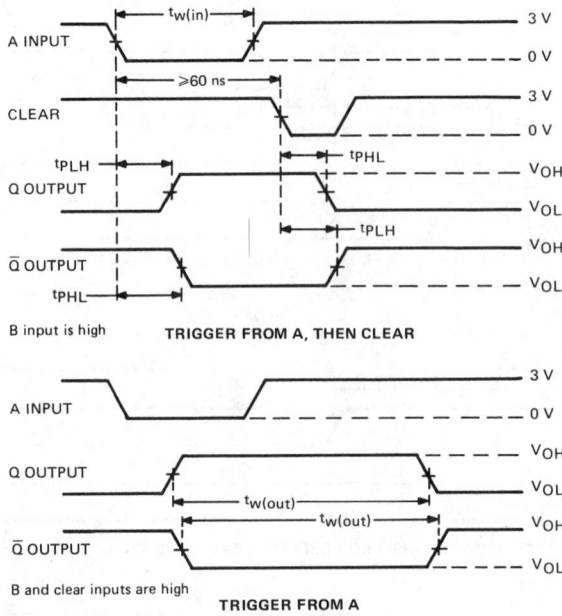

TRIGGER FROM A, THEN CLEAR

B input is high

TRIGGER FROM A

B and clear inputs are high

NOTES: A. Input pulses are supplied by generators having the following characteristics: PRR ≤ 1 MHz, Z$_{out}$ ≈ 50 Ω; for '221, t$_r$ ≤ 7 ns, t$_f$ ≤ 7 ns, for 'LS221, t$_r$ ≤ 15 ns, t$_f$ ≤ 6 ns.
   B. All measurements are made between the 1.5 V points of the indicated transitions for the '221 or between the 1.3 V points for the 'LS221.

FIGURE 1—SWITCHING CHARACTERISTICS (CONTINUED)

TEXAS INSTRUMENTS
INCORPORATED
POST OFFICE BOX 5012 • DALLAS, TEXAS 75222

TYPICAL CHARACTERISTICS ('221 ONLY)†

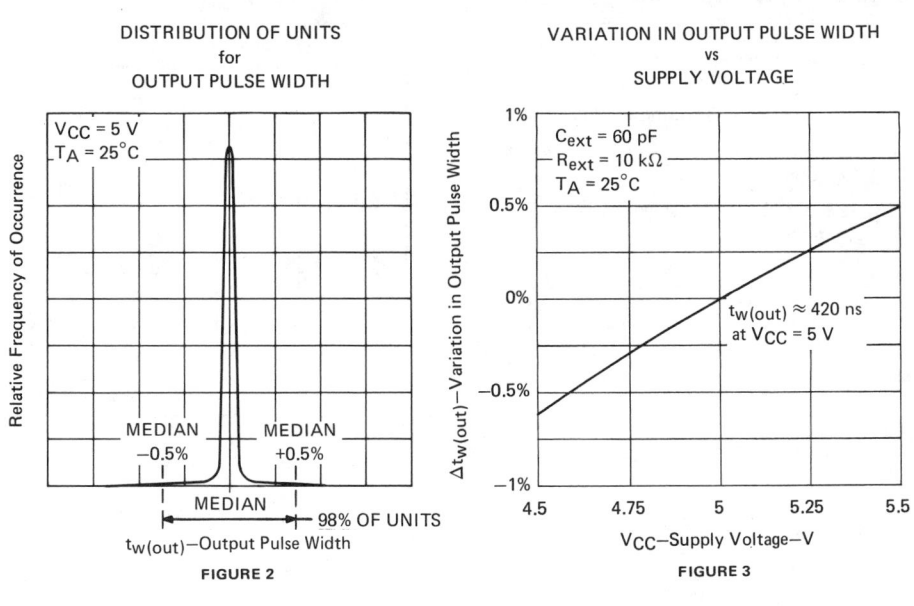

DISTRIBUTION OF UNITS
for
OUTPUT PULSE WIDTH

FIGURE 2

VARIATION IN OUTPUT PULSE WIDTH
vs
SUPPLY VOLTAGE

FIGURE 3

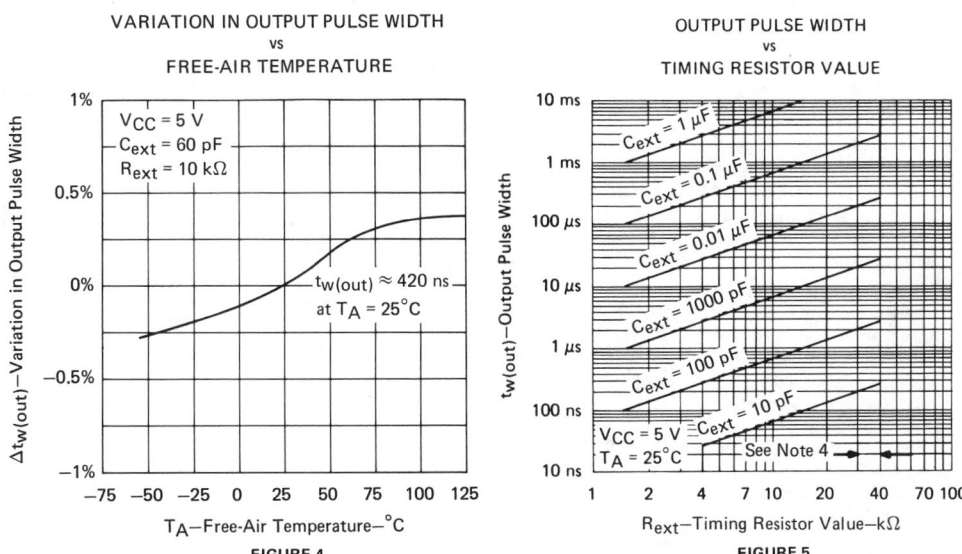

VARIATION IN OUTPUT PULSE WIDTH
vs
FREE-AIR TEMPERATURE

FIGURE 4

OUTPUT PULSE WIDTH
vs
TIMING RESISTOR VALUE

FIGURE 5

NOTE 4: These values of resistance exceed the maximum recommended for use over the full temperature range of the SN54221.

†Data for temperatures below 0°C and above 70°C, and for supply voltages below 4.75 V and above 5.25 V are applicable for the SN54221 only.

74

- D-C Triggered from Active-High or Active-Low Gated Logic Inputs
- Retriggerable for Very Long Output Pulses, Up to 100% Duty Cycle
- Overriding Clear Terminates Output Pulse
- Compensated for V_{CC} and Temperature Variations
- '122, 'L122, 'LS122 Have Internal Timing Resistors

SN54122, SN54LS122 . . . J OR W
SN54L122 . . . J OR T
SN74122, SN74L122, SN74LS122 . . . J OR N
(TOP VIEW) (SEE NOTES 1 THRU 4)

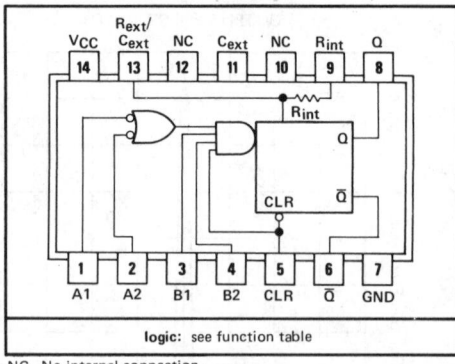

logic: see function table

NC—No internal connection.

'122, 'L122, 'LS122 FUNCTION TABLE

INPUTS				OUTPUTS	
CLEAR	A1	A2	B1	B2	Q	Q̄
L	X	X	X	X	L	H
X	H	H	X	X	L	H
X	X	X	L	X	L	H
X	X	X	X	L	L	H
H	L	X	↑	H	⊓	⊔
H	L	X	H	↑	⊓	⊔
H	X	L	↑	H	⊓	⊔
H	X	L	H	↑	⊓	⊔
H	H	↓	H	H	⊓	⊔
H	↓	↓	H	H	⊓	⊔
H	↓	H	H	H	⊓	⊔
↑	L	X	H	H	⊓	⊔
↑	X	L	H	H	⊓	⊔

'123, 'L123, 'LS123 FUNCTION TABLE

INPUTS		OUTPUTS	
CLEAR	A	B	Q	Q̄
L	X	X	L	H
X	H	X	L	H
X	X	L	L	H
H	L	↑	⊓	⊔
H	↓	H	⊓	⊔
↑	L	H	⊓	⊔

See explanation of function tables on page 3-8.

description

These d-c triggered multivibrators feature output pulse width control by three methods. The basic pulse time is programmed by selection of external resistance and capacitance values (see typical application data). The '122, 'L122, and 'LS122 have internal timing resistors that allow the circuits to be used with only an external capacitor, if so desired. Once triggered, the basic pulse width may be extended by retriggering the gated low-level-active (A) or high-level-active (B) inputs, or be reduced by use of the overriding clear. Figure 1 illustrates pulse control by retriggering and early clear.

The 'LS122 and 'LS123 are provided enough Schmitt hysteresis to ensure jitter-free triggering from the B input with transition rates as slow as 0.1 millivolt per nanosecond.

SN54123, SN54LS123 . . . J OR W
SN54L123 . . . J
SN74123, SN74L123, SN74LS123 . . . J OR N
(TOP VIEW) (SEE NOTES 1 THRU 4)

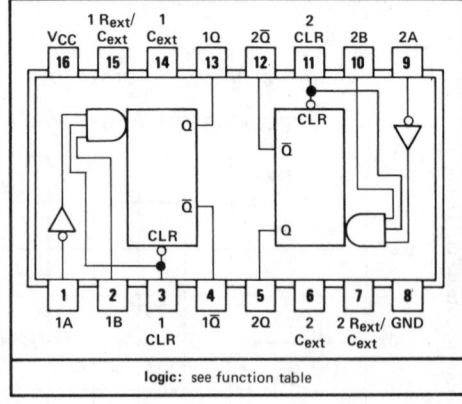

logic: see function table

NOTES: 1. An external timing capacitor may be connected between C_{ext} and R_{ext}/C_{ext} (positive).
2. To use the internal timing resistor of '122, 'L122 or 'LS122, connect R_{int} to V_{CC}.
3. For improved pulse width accuracy and repeatability, connect an external resistor between R_{ext}/C_{ext} and V_{CC} with R_{int} open-circuited.
4. To obtain variable pulse widths, connect an external variable resistance between R_{int} or R_{ext}/C_{ext} and V_{CC}.

1076

TEXAS INSTRUMENTS
INCORPORATED
POST OFFICE BOX 5012 • DALLAS, TEXAS 75222

TYPES SN54122, SN54123, SN54L122, SN54L123, SN54LS122, SN54LS123, SN74122, SN74123, SN74L122, SN74L123, SN74LS122, SN74LS123
RETRIGGERABLE MONOSTABLE MULTIVIBRATORS

description (continued)

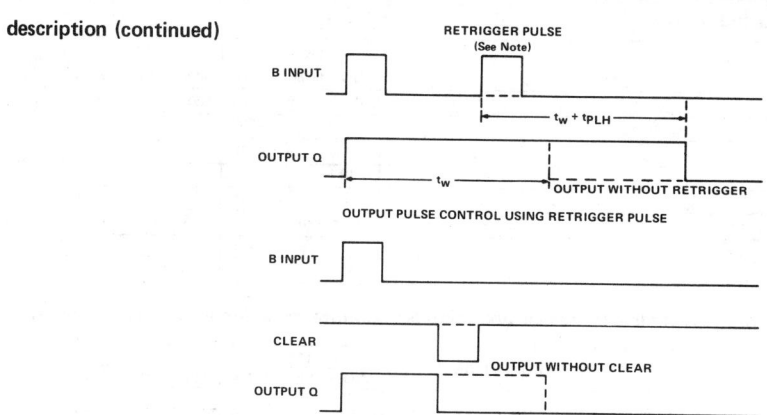

OUTPUT PULSE CONTROL USING RETRIGGER PULSE

OUTPUT PULSE CONTROL USING CLEAR INPUT

NOTE: Retrigger pulse must not start before 0.22 C_{ext} (in picofarads) nanoseconds after previous trigger pulse.

FIGURE 1—TYPICAL INPUT/OUTPUT PULSES

schematics of inputs and outputs

'122, '123, 'L122, 'L123 CIRCUITS

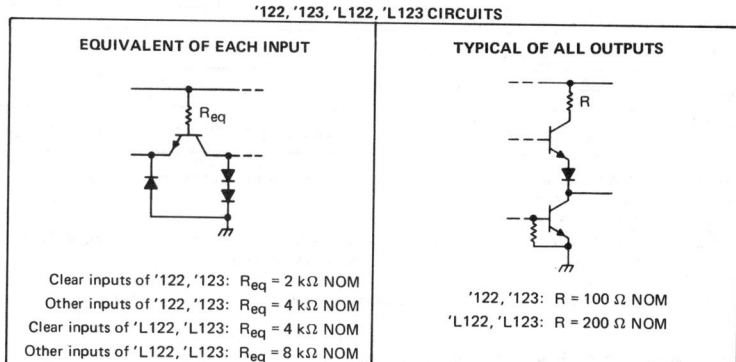

EQUIVALENT OF EACH INPUT

Clear inputs of '122, '123: R_{eq} = 2 kΩ NOM
Other inputs of '122, '123: R_{eq} = 4 kΩ NOM
Clear inputs of 'L122, 'L123: R_{eq} = 4 kΩ NOM
Other inputs of 'L122, 'L123: R_{eq} = 8 kΩ NOM

TYPICAL OF ALL OUTPUTS

'122, '123: R = 100 Ω NOM
'L122, 'L123: R = 200 Ω NOM

'LS122, 'LS123 CIRCUITS

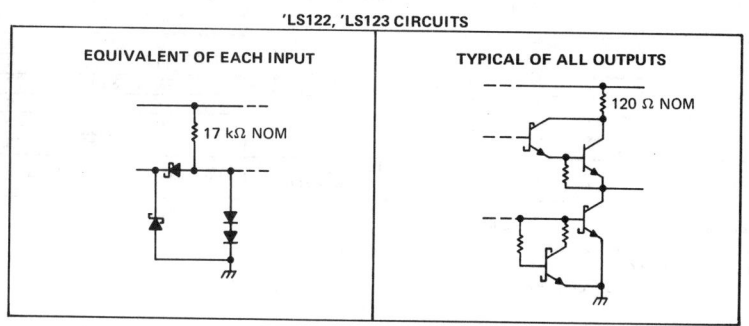

EQUIVALENT OF EACH INPUT

17 kΩ NOM

TYPICAL OF ALL OUTPUTS

120 Ω NOM

6

TYPES SN54122, SN54123, SN74122, SN74123
RETRIGGERABLE MONOSTABLE MULTIVIBRATORS

recommended operating conditions

	SN54' MIN	NOM	MAX	SN74' MIN	NOM	MAX	UNIT
Supply voltage, V_{CC}	4.5	5	5.5	4.75	5	5.25	V
High-level output current, I_{OH}			−800			−800	µA
Low-level output current, I_{OL}			16			16	mA
Pulse width, t_w	40			40			ns
External timing resistance, R_{ext}	5		25	5		50	kΩ
External capacitance, C_{ext}		No restriction			No restriction		
Wiring capacitance at R_{ext}/C_{ext} terminal			50			50	pF
Operating free-air temperature, T_A	−55		125	0		70	°C

electrical characteristics over recommended free-air operating temperature range (unless otherwise noted)

PARAMETER		TEST CONDITIONS[†]	'122 MIN	TYP[‡]	MAX	'123 MIN	TYP[‡]	MAX	UNIT
V_{IH}	High-level input voltage		2			2			V
V_{IL}	Low-level input voltage				0.8			0.8	V
V_{IK}	Input clamp voltage	V_{CC} = MIN, I_I = −12 mA			−1.5			−1.5	V
V_{OH}	High-level output voltage	V_{CC} = MIN, I_{OH} = −800 µA, See Note 1	2.4	3.4		2.4	3.4		V
V_{OL}	Low-level output voltage	V_{CC} = MIN, I_{OL} = 16 mA, See Note 1		0.2	0.4		0.2	0.4	V
I_I	Input current at maximum input voltage	V_{CC} = MAX, V_I = 5.5 V			1			1	mA
I_{IH}	High-level input current — Data inputs	V_{CC} = MAX, V_I = 2.4 V			40			40	µA
	Clear input				80			80	
I_{IL}	Low-level input current — Data inputs	V_{CC} = MAX, V_I = 0.4 V			−1.6			−1.6	mA
	Clear input				−3.2			−3.2	
I_{OS}	Short-circuit output current[♦]	V_{CC} = MAX, See Note 5	−10		−40	−10		−40	mA
I_{CC}	Supply current (quiescent or triggered)	V_{CC} = MAX, See Notes 6 and 7		23	28		46	66	mA

[†] For conditions shown as MIN or MAX, use the value specified under recommended operating conditions.
[‡] All typical values are at V_{CC} = 5 V, T_A = 25°C.
[♦] Not more than one output should be shorted at a time.
NOTES: 5. Ground C_{ext} to measure V_{OH} at Q, V_{OL} at $\overline{Q}$, or I_{OS} at Q. C_{ext} is open to measure V_{OH} at $\overline{Q}$, V_{OL} at Q, or I_{OS} at $\overline{Q}$.
   6. Quiescent I_{CC} is measured (after clearing) with 2.4 V applied to all clear and A inputs, B inputs grounded, all outputs open, C_{ext} = 0.02 µF, and R_{ext} = 25 kΩ. R_{int} of '122 is open.
   7. I_{CC} is measured in the triggered state with 2.4 V applied to all clear and B inputs, A inputs grounded, all outputs open, C_{ext} = 0.02 µF, and R_{ext} = 25 kΩ. R_{int} of '122 is open.

switching characteristics, V_{CC} = 5 V, T_A = 25°C, see note 8

PARAMETER[¶]	FROM (INPUT)	TO (OUTPUT)	TEST CONDITIONS	'122 MIN	TYP	MAX	'123 MIN	TYP	MAX	UNIT
t_{PLH}	A	Q			22	33		22	33	ns
	B				19	28		19	28	
t_{PHL}	A	$\overline{Q}$	C_{ext} = 0, R_{ext} = 5 kΩ,		30	40		30	40	ns
	B		C_L = 15 pF, R_L = 400 Ω		27	36		27	36	
t_{PHL}	Clear	Q			18	27		18	27	ns
t_{PLH}		$\overline{Q}$			30	40		30	40	
t_{wQ} (min)	A or B	Q			45	65		45	65	ns
t_{wQ}	A or B	Q	C_{ext} = 1000 pF, R_{ext} = 10 kΩ, C_L = 15 pF, R_L = 400 Ω	3.08	3.42	3.76	2.76	3.03	3.37	µs

[¶] t_{PLH} ≡ propagation delay time, low-to-high-level output
  t_{PHL} ≡ propagation delay time, high-to-low-level output
  t_{wQ} ≡ width of pulse at output Q
NOTE 8: Load circuit and voltage waveforms are shown on page 3-10.

6

TEXAS INSTRUMENTS
INCORPORATED
POST OFFICE BOX 5012 • DALLAS, TEXAS 75222

TYPES SN54L122, SN54L123, SN74L122, SN74L123
RETRIGGERABLE MONOSTABLE MULTIVIBRATORS

recommended operating conditions

	SN54L' MIN	SN54L' NOM	SN54L' MAX	SN74L' MIN	SN74L' NOM	SN74L' MAX	UNIT
Supply voltage, V_{CC}	4.5	5	5.5	4.75	5	5.25	V
High-level output current, I_{OH}			−400			−400	µA
Low-level output current, I_{OL}			8			8	mA
Pulse width, t_w	50			50			ns
External timing resistance, R_{ext}	5		25	5		50	kΩ
External capacitance, C_{ext}	No restriction			No restriction			
Wiring capacitance at R_{ext}/C_{ext} terminal			50			50	pF
Operating free-air temperature, T_A	−55		125	0		70	°C

electrical characteristics over recommended free-air operating temperature range (unless otherwise noted)

	PARAMETER	TEST CONDITIONS†		'L122 MIN	'L122 TYP‡	'L122 MAX	'L123 MIN	'L123 TYP‡	'L123 MAX	UNIT
V_{IH}	High-level input voltage			2			2			V
V_{IL}	Low-level input voltage					0.8			0.8	V
V_{IK}	Input clamp voltage	V_{CC} = MIN, I_I = −12 mA				−1.5			−1.5	V
V_{OH}	High-level output voltage	V_{CC} = MIN, I_{OH} = −400 µA, See Note 1		2.4	3.4		2.4	3.4		V
V_{OL}	Low-level output voltage	V_{CC} = MIN, I_{OL} = 8 mA, See Note 1			0.2	0.4		0.2	0.4	V
I_I	Input current at maximum input voltage	V_{CC} = MAX, V_I = 5.5 V				1			1	mA
I_{IH}	High-level input current	Data inputs	V_{CC} = MAX, V_I = 2.4 V			20			20	µA
		Clear input				40			40	
I_{IL}	Low-level input current	Data inputs	V_{CC} = MAX, V_I = 0.4 V			−0.8			−0.8	mA
		Clear input				−1.6			−1.6	
I_{OS}	Short-circuit output current♦	V_{CC} = MAX, See Note 9		−5		−20	−5		−20	mA
I_{CC}	Supply current (quiescent or triggered)	V_{CC} = MAX, See Notes 10 and 11			11	14		23	33	mA

†For conditions shown as MIN or MAX, use the value specified under recommended operating conditions.
‡All typical values are at V_{CC} = 5 V, T_A = 25°C.
♦Not more than one output should be shorted at a time.

NOTES: 9. Ground C_{ext} to measure V_{OH} at Q, V_{OL} at $\overline{Q}$, or I_{OS} at Q. C_{ext} is open to measure V_{OH} at $\overline{Q}$, V_{OL} at Q, or I_{OS} at $\overline{Q}$.
10. Quiescent I_{CC} is measured (after clearing) with 2.4 V applied to all clear and A inputs, B inputs grounded, all outputs open, C_{ext} = 0.02 µF, and R_{ext} = 25 kΩ. R_{int} of 'L122 is open.
11. I_{CC} is measured in the triggered state with 2.4 V applied to all clear and B inputs, A inputs grounded, all outputs open, C_{ext} = 0.02 µF, and R_{ext} = 25 kΩ. R_{int} of 'L122 is open.

6

switching characteristics, V_{CC} = 5 V, T_A = 25°C, see note 8

PARAMETER¶	FROM (INPUT)	TO (OUTPUT)	TEST CONDITIONS		'L122 MIN	'L122 TYP	'L122 MAX	'L123 MIN	'L123 TYP	'L123 MAX	UNIT
t_{PLH}	A	Q	C_{ext} = 0, C_L = 15 pF,	R_{ext} = 5 kΩ, R_L = 800 Ω		44	66		44	66	ns
	B					38	56		38	56	
t_{PHL}	A	$\overline{Q}$				60	80		60	80	ns
	B					54	72		54	72	
t_{PHL}	Clear	Q				36	54		36	54	ns
t_{PLH}		$\overline{Q}$				60	80		60	80	
t_{wQ} (min)	A or B	Q				90	135		90	135	ns
t_{wQ}	A or B	Q	C_{ext} = 400 pF, C_L = 15 pF,	R_{ext} = 10 kΩ R_L = 800 Ω	1.7	1.9	2.1	1.3		2.1	µs

¶ t_{PLH} ≡ propagation delay time, low-to-high-level output
t_{PHL} ≡ propagation delay time, high-to-low-level output
t_{wQ} ≡ width of pulse at output Q
NOTE 8: Load circuit and voltage waveforms are shown on page 3-10.

TEXAS INSTRUMENTS
INCORPORATED
POST OFFICE BOX 5012 • DALLAS, TEXAS 75222

TYPES SN54LS122, SN54LS123, SN74LS122, SN74LS123
RETRIGGERABLE MONOSTABLE MULTIVIBRATORS

recommended operating conditions

	SN54LS' MIN	NOM	MAX	SN74LS' MIN	NOM	MAX	UNIT
Supply voltage, V_{CC}	4.5	5	5.5	4.75	5	5.25	V
High-level output current, I_{OH}			−400			−400	µA
Low-level output current, I_{OL}			4			8	mA
Pulse width, t_w	40			40			ns
External timing resistance, R_{ext}	5		180	5		260	kΩ
External capacitance, C_{ext}	No restriction			No restriction			
Wiring capacitance at R_{ext}/C_{ext} terminal			50			50	pF
Operating free-air temperature, T_A	−55		125	0		70	°C

electrical characteristics over recommended operating free-air temperature range (unless otherwise noted)

PARAMETER		TEST CONDITIONS[†]		SN54LS' MIN	TYP[‡]	MAX	SN74LS' MIN	TYP[‡]	MAX	UNIT
V_{IH}	High-level input voltage			2			2			V
V_{IL}	Low-level input voltage					0.7			0.8	V
V_{IK}	Input clamp voltage	V_{CC} = MIN,	I_I = −18 mA			−1.5			−1.5	V
V_{OH}	High-level output voltage	V_{CC} = MIN, V_{IH} = 2 V, V_{IL} = V_{IL}max	I_{OH} = −400 µA	2.5	3.5		2.7	3.5		V
V_{OL}	Low-level output voltage	V_{CC} = MIN, V_{IH} = 2 V, V_{IL} = V_{IL}max	I_{OL} = 4 mA		0.25	0.4		0.25	0.4	V
			I_{OL} = 8 mA					0.35	0.5	
I_I	Input current at maximum input voltage	V_{CC} = MAX,	V_I = 7 V			0.1			0.1	mA
I_{IH}	High-level input current	V_{CC} = MAX,	V_I = 2.7 V			20			20	µA
I_{IL}	Low-level input current	V_{CC} = MAX,	V_I = 0.4 V			−0.4			−0.4	mA
I_{OS}	Short-circuit output current[♦]	V_{CC} = MAX		−20		−100	−20		−100	mA
I_{CC}	Supply current (quiescent or triggered)	V_{CC} = MAX, See Note 13	'LS122		6	11		6	11	mA
			'LS123		12	20		12	20	

[†] For conditions shown as MIN or MAX, use the appropriate value specified under recommended operating conditions.
[‡] All typical values are at V_{CC} = 5 V, T_A = 25°C.
[♦] Not more than one output should be shorted at a time and duration of the short-circuit should not exceed one second.
NOTES: 12. To measure V_{OH} at Q, V_{OL} at $\overline{Q}$, or I_{OS} at Q, ground R_{ext}/C_{ext}, apply 2 V to B and clear, and pulse A from 2 V to 0 V.
13. With all outputs open and 4.5 V applied to all data and clear inputs, I_{CC} is measured after a momentary ground, then 4.5 V, is applied to clock.

switching characteristics, V_{CC} = 5 V, T_A = 25°C, see note 14

PARAMETER[¶]	FROM (INPUT)	TO (OUTPUT)	TEST CONDITIONS		MIN	TYP	MAX	UNIT
t_{PLH}	A	Q				23	33	ns
	B					23	44	
t_{PHL}	A	$\overline{Q}$	C_{ext} = 0, C_L = 15 pF	R_{ext} = 5 kΩ, R_L = 2 kΩ		32	45	ns
	B					34	56	
t_{PHL}	Clear	Q				20	27	ns
t_{PLH}		$\overline{Q}$				28	45	
t_{wQ} (min)	A or B	Q				116	200	ns
t_{wQ}	A or B	Q	C_{ext} = 1000 pF, C_L = 15 pF,	R_{ext} = 10 kΩ, R_L = 2 kΩ	4	4.5	5	µs

[¶] t_{PLH} ≡ propagation delay time, low-to-high-level output
t_{PHL} ≡ propagation delay time, high-to-low-level output
t_{wQ} ≡ width of pulse at output Q
NOTE 14: Load circuit and voltage waveforms are shown on page 3-11.

6

TEXAS INSTRUMENTS
INCORPORATED
POST OFFICE BOX 5012 • DALLAS, TEXAS 75222

TYPICAL APPLICATION DATA FOR '122, '123, 'L122, 'L123

For pulse widths when $C_{ext} \leqslant 1000$ pF, See Figures 4 and 5.

The output pulse is primarily a function of the external capacitor and resistor. For $C_{ext} > 1000$ pF, the output pulse width (t_W) is defined as:

$$t_W = K \cdot R_T \cdot C_{ext} \left(1 + \frac{0.7}{R_T} \right)$$

where

K is 0.32 for '122, 0.28 for '123,
0.37 for 'L122, 0.33 for 'L123

R_T is in kΩ (internal or external timing resistance.

C_{ext} is in pF

t_W is in nanoseconds

To prevent reverse voltage across C_{ext}, it is recommended that the method shown in Figure 2 be employed when using electrolytic capacitors and in applications utilizing the clear function. In all applications using the diode, the pulse width is:

$$t_W = K_D \cdot R_T \cdot C_{ext} \left(1 + \frac{0.7}{R_T} \right)$$

K_D is 0.28 for '122, 0.25 for '123,
0.33 for 'L122, 0.29 for 'L123

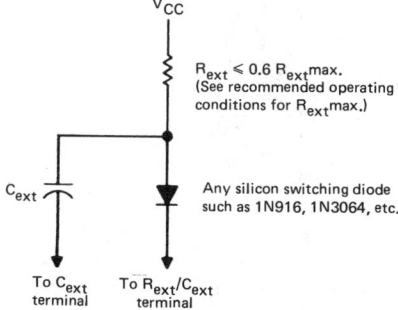

V_{CC}

$R_{ext} \leqslant 0.6 \ R_{ext}$max.
(See recommended operating conditions for R_{ext}max.)

C_{ext}

Any silicon switching diode such as 1N916, 1N3064, etc.

To C_{ext} terminal

To R_{ext}/C_{ext} terminal

TIMING COMPONENT CONNECTIONS WHEN
$C_{ext} > 1000$ pF AND CLEAR IS USED
FIGURE 2

Applications requiring more precise pulse widths (up to 28 seconds) and not requiring the clear feature can best be satisfied with the '121 or 'L121.

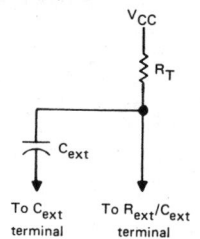

V_{CC}

R_T

C_{ext}

To C_{ext} terminal

To R_{ext}/C_{ext} terminal

TIMING COMPONENT CONNECTIONS
FIGURE 3

'122, '123
TYPICAL OUTPUT PULSE WIDTH
vs
EXTERNAL TIMING CAPACITANCE

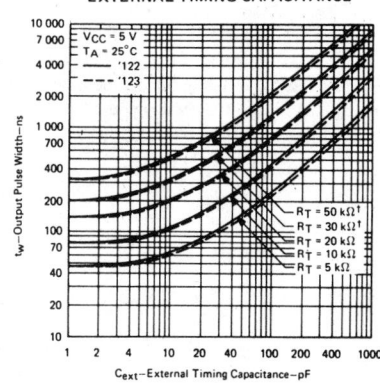

FIGURE 4

'L122
TYPICAL OUTPUT PULSE WIDTH
vs
EXTERNAL TIMING CAPACITANCE

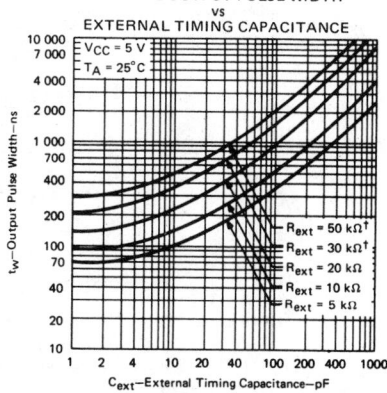

FIGURE 5
†These values of resistance exceed the maximum recommended for use over the full temperature range of the SN54' and SN54L' circuits.

6

TYPES SN54LS122, SN74LS122, SN54LS123, SN74LS123
RETRIGGERABLE MONOSTABLE MULTIVIBRATORS

TYPICAL APPLICATION DATA FOR 'LS122, 'LS123

The basic output pulse width is essentially determined by the values of external capacitance and timing resistance. For pulse widths when $C_{ext} \leqslant$ 1000 pF, see Figure 7.

When $C_{ext} > 1000$ pF, the output pulse width is defined as:

$$t_w = 0.45 \cdot R_T \cdot C_{ext}$$

where

R_T is in kΩ (internal or external timing resistance.)

C_{ext} is in pF

t_w is in nanoseconds

For best results, system ground should be applied to the C_{ext} terminal. The switching diode is not needed for electrolytic capacitance applications.

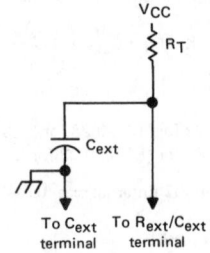

TIMING COMPONENT CONNECTIONS

FIGURE 6

'LS122, 'LS123
TYPICAL OUTPUT PULSE WIDTH
vs
EXTERNAL TIMING CAPACITANCE

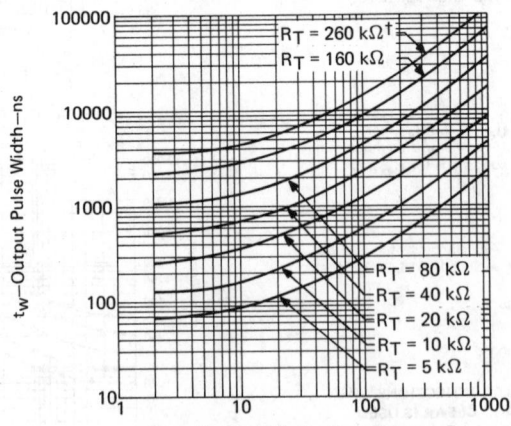

†This value of resistance exceeds the maximum recommended for use over the full temperature range of the SN54LS circuits.

FIGURE 7

TEXAS INSTRUMENTS
INCORPORATED
POST OFFICE BOX 5012 • DALLAS, TEXAS 75222

TYPES SN54LS240,SN54LS241,SN54LS244,SN54S240,SN54S241, SN74LS240,SN74LS241,SN74LS244,SN74S240,SN74S241
OCTAL BUFFERS AND LINE DRIVERS WITH 3-STATE OUTPUTS

	Typical I_{OL} (Sink Current)	Typical I_{OH} (Source Current)	Typical Propagation Delay Times		Typical Enable/ Disable Times	Typical Power Dissipation (Enabled)	
			Inverting	Noninverting		Inverting	Noninverting
SN54LS'	12 mA	−12 mA	10.5 ns	12 ns	18 ns	130 mW	135 mW
SN74LS'	24 mA	−15 mA	10.5 ns	12 ns	18 ns	130 mW	135 mW
SN54S'	48 mA	−12 mA	4.5 ns	6 ns	9 ns	450 mW	538 mW
SN74S'	64 mA	−15 mA	4.5 ns	6 ns	9 ns	450 mW	538 mW

- **3-State Outputs Drive Bus Lines or Buffer Memory Address Registers**
- **P-N-P Inputs Reduce D-C Loading**
- **Hysteresis at Inputs Improves Noise Margins**

description

These octal buffers and line drivers are designed specifically to improve both the performance and density of three-state memory address drivers, clock drivers, and bus-oriented receivers and transmitters. The designer has a choice of selected combinations of inverting and noninverting outputs, symmetrical $\overline{G}$ (active-low output control) inputs, and complementary G and $\overline{G}$ inputs. These devices feature high fan-out, improved fan-in, and 400-mV noise-margin. The SN74LS' and SN74S' can be used to drive terminated lines down to 133 ohms.

schematics of inputs and outputs
'LS240, 'LS241, 'LS244

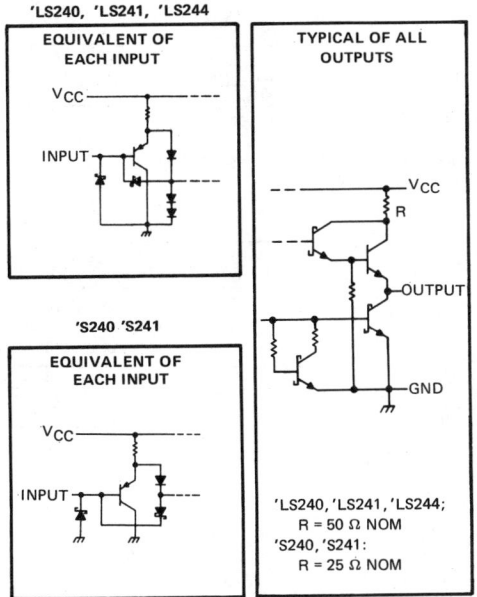

'S240 'S241

'LS240, 'LS241, 'LS244:
R = 50 Ω NOM
'S240, 'S241:
R = 25 Ω NOM

SN54LS240, SN54S240 . . . J
SN74LS240, SN74S240 . . . J OR N
(TOP VIEW)

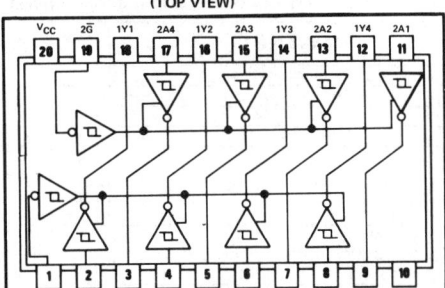

SN54LS241, SN54S241 . . . J
SN74LS241, SN74S241 . . . J OR N
(TOP VIEW)

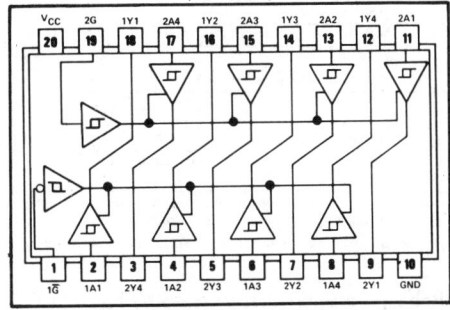

SN54LS244 . . . J
SN74LS244 . . . J OR N
(TOP VIEW)

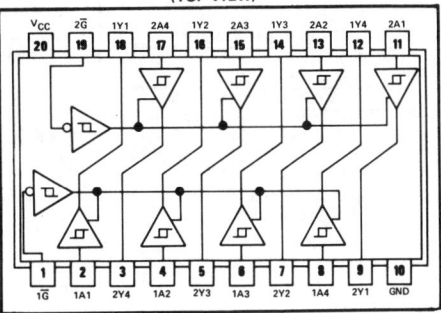

6

recommended operating conditions

PARAMETER	SN54LS'			SN74LS'			UNIT
	MIN	NOM	MAX	MIN	NOM	MAX	
Supply voltage, V_{CC} (see Note 1)	4.5	5	5.5	4.75	5	5.25	V
High-level output current, I_{OH}			−12			−15	mA
Low-level output current, I_{OL}			12			24	mA
Operating free-air temperature, T_A	−55		125	0		70	°C

NOTE 1: Voltage values are with respect to network ground terminal.

electrical characteristics over recommended operating free-air temperature range (unless otherwise noted)

PARAMETER		TEST CONDITIONS[†]		SN54LS'			SN74LS'			UNIT
				MIN	TYP[‡]	MAX	MIN	TYP[‡]	MAX	
V_{IH}	High-level input voltage			2			2			V
V_{IL}	Low-level input voltage					0.7			0.8	V
V_{IK}	Input clamp voltage	V_{CC} = MIN,	I_I = −18 mA			−1.5			−1.5	V
	Hysteresis $(V_{T+} − V_{T−})$	V_{CC} = MIN		0.2	0.4		0.2	0.4		V
V_{OH}	High-level output voltage	V_{CC} = MIN, V_{IH} = 2 V, V_{IL} = V_{IL} max, I_{OH} = −3 mA		2.4	3.4		2.4	3.4		V
		V_{CC} = MIN, V_{IH} = 2 V, V_{IL} = 0.5 V, I_{OH} = MAX		2			2			
V_{OL}	Low-level output voltage	V_{CC} = MIN, V_{IH} = 2 V, V_{IL} = V_{IL} max	I_{OL} = 12 mA			0.4			0.4	V
			I_{OL} = 24 mA						0.5	
I_{OZH}	Off-state output current, high-level voltage applied	V_{CC} = MAX, V_{IH} = 2 V,	V_O = 2.7 V			20			20	μA
I_{OZL}	Off-state output current, low-level voltage applied	V_{IL} = V_{IL} max	V_O = 0.4 V			−20			−20	
I_I	Input current at maximum input voltage	V_{CC} = MAX,	V_I = 7 V			0.1			0.1	mA
I_{IH}	High-level input current, any input	V_{CC} = MAX,	V_I = 2.7 V			20			20	μA
I_{IL}	Low-level input current	V_{CC} = MAX,	V_{IL} = 0.4 V			−0.2			−0.2	mA
I_{OS}	Short-circuit output current[♦]	V_{CC} = MAX		−40		−225	−40		−225	mA
I_{CC}	Supply current	Outputs high	V_{CC} = MAX	All	13	23		13	23	mA
		Outputs low		'LS240	26	44		26	44	
			Outputs open	'LS241, 'LS244	27	46		27	46	
		All outputs disabled		'LS240	29	50		29	50	
				'LS241, 'LS244	32	54		32	54	

[†]For conditions shown as MIN or MAX, use the appropriate value specified under recommended operating conditions.
[‡]All typical values are at V_{CC} = 5 V, T_A = 25°C.
[♦]Not more than one output should be shorted at a time, and duration of the short-circuit should not exceed one second.

switching characteristics, V_{CC} = 5 V, T_A = 25°C

PARAMETER		TEST CONDITIONS	'LS240			'LS241, 'LS244			UNIT
			MIN	TYP	MAX	MIN	TYP	MAX	
t_{PLH}	Propagation delay time, low-to-high-level output	C_L = 45 pF, R_L = 667 Ω, See Note 2		9	14		12	18	ns
t_{PHL}	Propagation delay time, high-to-low-level output			12	18		12	18	ns
t_{PZL}	Output enable time to low level			20	30		20	30	ns
t_{PZH}	Output enable time to high level			15	23		15	23	ns
t_{PLZ}	Output disable time from low level	C_L = 5 pF, R_L = 667 Ω, See Note 2		15	25		15	25	ns
t_{PHZ}	Output disable time from high level			10	18		10	18	ns

NOTE 2: Load circuit and voltage waveforms are shown on page 3-11.

TEXAS INSTRUMENTS
INCORPORATED
POST OFFICE BOX 5012 • DALLAS, TEXAS 75222

BUFFERS/LINE DRIVERS/LINE RECEIVERS WITH 3-STATE OUTPUTS

REVISED AUGUST 1977

recommended operating conditions

PARAMETER	SN54S' MIN	SN54S' NOM	SN54S' MAX	SN74S' MIN	SN74S' NOM	SN74S' MAX	UNIT
Supply voltage, V_{CC} (see Note 1)	4.5	5	5.5	4.75	5	5.25	V
High-level output current, I_{OH}			−12			−15	mA
Low-level output current, I_{OL}			48			64	mA
Operating free-air temperature, T_A (see Note 3)	−55		125	0		70	°C

NOTES: 1. Voltage values are with respect to network ground terminal.
3. An SN54S241J operating at free-air temperature above 116°C requires a heat sink that provides a thermal resistance from case to free-air, $R_{\theta CA}$, of not more than 40°C/W.

electrical characteristics over recommended operating free-air temperature range (unless otherwise noted)

	PARAMETER	TEST CONDITIONS[†]		'S240 MIN	'S240 TYP[‡]	'S240 MAX	'S241 MIN	'S241 TYP[‡]	'S241 MAX	UNIT
V_{IH}	High-level input voltage			2			2			V
V_{IL}	Low-level input voltage					0.8			0.8	V
V_{IK}	Input clamp voltage	V_{CC} = MIN,	I_I = −18 mA			−1.2			−1.2	V
	Hysteresis ($V_{T+} - V_{T-}$)	V_{CC} = MIN		0.2	0.4		0.2	0.4		V
V_{OH}	High-level output voltage	SN74S' — V_{CC} = MIN, V_{IH} = 2 V, V_{IL} = 0.8 V, I_{OH} = −1 mA		2.7			2.7			V
		SN54S' and SN74S' — V_{CC} = MIN, V_{IH} = 2 V, V_{IL} = 0.8 V, I_{OH} = −3 mA		2.4	3.4		2.4	3.4		
		SN54S' and SN74S' — V_{CC} = MIN, V_{IH} = 2 V, V_{IL} = 0.5 V, I_{OH} = MAX		2			2			
V_{OL}	Low-level output voltage	V_{CC} = MIN, V_{IH} = 2 V, V_{IL} = 0.8 V, I_{OL} = MAX				0.55			0.55	V
I_{OZH}	Off-state output current, high-level voltage applied	V_{CC} = MAX, V_{IH} = 2 V, V_{IL} = 0.8 V	V_O = 2.4 V			50			50	μA
I_{OZL}	Off-state output current, low-level voltage applied		V_O = 0.5 V			−50			−50	
I_I	Input current at maximum input voltage	V_{CC} = MAX,	V_I = 5.5 V			1			1	mA
I_{IH}	High-level input current, any input	V_{CC} = MAX,	V_I = 2.7 V			50			50	μA
I_{IL}	Low-level input current — Any A	V_{CC} = MAX,	V_I = 0.5 V			−400			−400	μA
	Low-level input current — Any G					−2			−2	mA
I_{OS}	Short-circuit output current[♦]	V_{CC} = MAX		−50		−225	−50		−225	mA
I_{CC}	Supply current — Outputs high	V_{CC} = MAX, Outputs open	SN54S'		80	123		95	147	mA
			SN74S'		80	135		95	160	
	Supply current — Outputs low		SN54S'		100	145		120	170	
			SN74S'		100	150		120	180	
	Outputs disabled		SN54S'		100	145		120	170	
			SN74S'		100	150		120	180	

[†]For conditions shown as MIN or MAX, use the appropriate value specified under recommended operating conditions.
[‡]All typical values are at V_{CC} = 5 V, T_A = 25°C.
[♦]Not more than one output should be shorted at a time, and duration of the short-circuit should not exceed one second.

switching characteristics, V_{CC} = 5 V, T_A = 25°C

	PARAMETER	TEST CONDITIONS	'S240 MIN	'S240 TYP	'S240 MAX	'S241 MIN	'S241 TYP	'S241 MAX	UNIT
t_{PLH}	Propagation delay time, low-to-high-level output	C_L = 50 pF, R_L = 90 Ω, See Note 4		4.5	7		6	9	ns
t_{PHL}	Propagation delay time, high-to-low-level output			4.5	7		6	9	ns
t_{PZL}	Output enable time to low level			10	15		10	15	ns
t_{PZH}	Output enable time to high level			6.5	10		8	12	ns
t_{PLZ}	Output disable time from low level	C_L = 5 pF, R_L = 90 Ω, See Note 4		10	15		10	15	ns
t_{PHZ}	Output disable time from high level			6	9		6	9	ns

NOTE 4: Load circuit and voltage waveforms are shown on page 3-10.

TEXAS INSTRUMENTS
INCORPORATED
POST OFFICE BOX 5012 • DALLAS, TEXAS 75222

TYPES SN54LS240, SN54LS241,
SN54LS244, SN54S240, SN54S241, SN74LS240,
SN74LS241, SN74LS244, SN74S240, SN74S241
OCTAL BUFFERS AND LINE DRIVERS WITH 3-STATE OUTPUTS

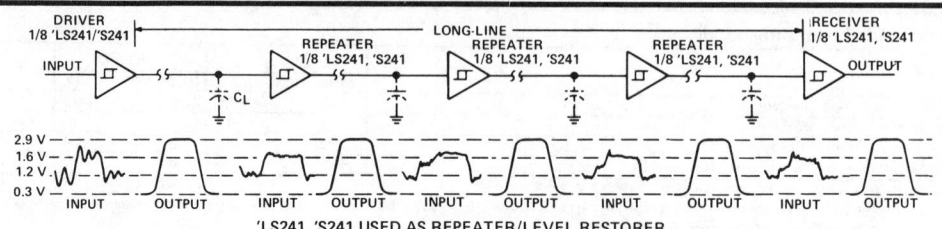

'LS241, 'S241 USED AS REPEATER/LEVEL RESTORER

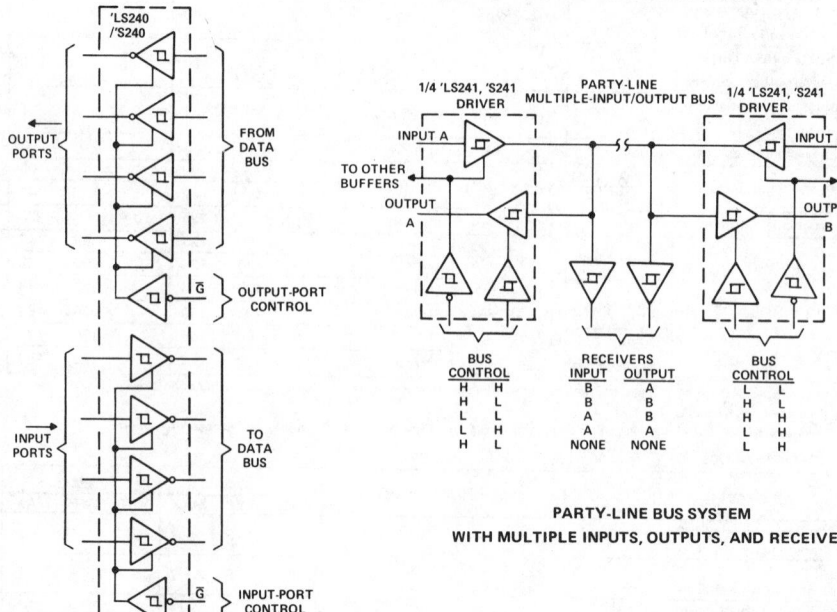

'LS241, 'S240 USED AS SYSTEM AND/OR MEMORY BUS DRIVER—4-BIT
ORGANIZATION CAN BE APPLIED TO HANDLE BINARY OR BCD

INDEPENDENT 4-BIT BUS DRIVERS/RECEIVERS
IN A SINGLE PACKAGE

BUS CONTROL	
H	H
H	L
L	L
L	H
H	L

RECEIVERS INPUT	OUTPUT
B	A
B	B
A	B
A	A
NONE	NONE

BUS CONTROL	
L	L
H	L
H	H
H	L
L	H

PARTY-LINE BUS SYSTEM
WITH MULTIPLE INPUTS, OUTPUTS, AND RECEIVERS

- **Two-Way Asynchronous Communication Between Data Buses**

- **P-N-P Inputs Reduce D-C Loading**

- **Hysteresis (Typically 400 mV) at Inputs Improves Noise Margin**

description

These four-data-line transceivers are designed for asynchromous two-way communications between data buses. The SN74LS' can be used to drive terminated lines down to 133 ohms.

FUNCTION TABLE (EACH TRANSCEIVER)

CONTROL INPUTS		'LS242 DATA PORT STATUS		'LS243 DATA PORT STATUS	
$\overline{GAB}$	GBA	A	B	A	B
H	H	$\overline{O}$	I	O	I
L	H	*	*	*	*
H	L	ISOLATED		ISOLATED	
L	L	I	$\overline{O}$	I	O

*Possibly destructive oscillation may occur if the transceivers are enabled in both directions at once.
I = Input, O = Output, $\overline{O}$ = Inverting Output.

schematics of inputs and outputs

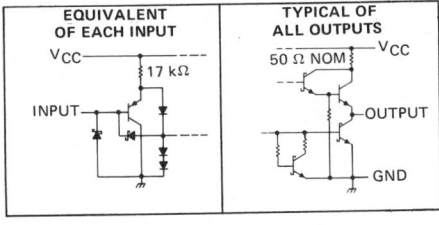

SN54LS242 . . . J OR W
SN74LS242 . . . J OR N
(TOP VIEW)

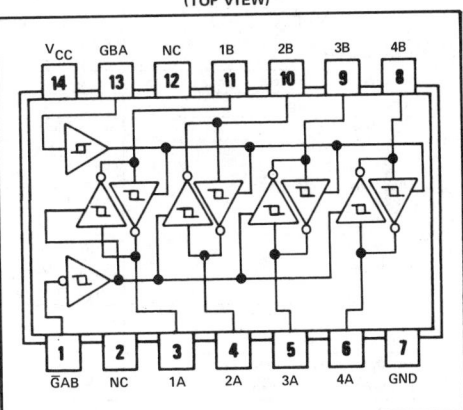

SN54LS243 . . . J OR W
SN74LS243 . . . J OR N
(TOP VIEW)

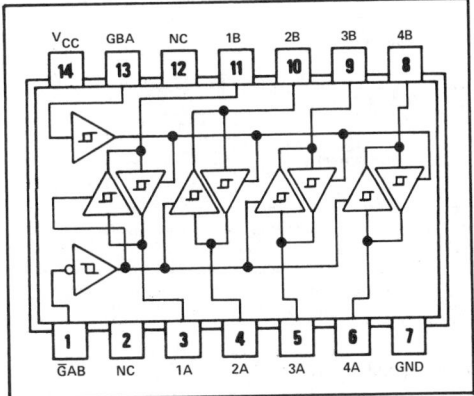

NC—No internal connection

recommended operating conditions

	SN54LS'			SN74LS'			UNIT
	MIN	NOM	MAX	MIN	NOM	MAX	
Supply voltage, V_{CC} (see Note 1)	4.5	5	5.5	4.75	5	5.25	V
High-level output current, I_{OH}			−12			−15	mA
Low-level output current, I_{OL}			12			24	mA
Operating free-air temperature, T_A	−55		125	0		70	°C

NOTE 1: Voltage values are with respect to network ground terminal.

electrical characteristics over recommended operating free-air temperature range (unless otherwise noted)

PARAMETER		TEST CONDITIONS†		SN54LS' MIN	SN54LS' TYP‡	SN54LS' MAX	SN74LS' MIN	SN74LS' TYP‡	SN74LS' MAX	UNIT
V_{IH}	High-level input voltage			2			2			V
V_{IL}	Low-level input voltage					0.7			0.8	V
V_{IK}	Input clamp voltage	V_{CC} = MIN,	$I_I = -18$ mA			−1.5			−1.5	V
	Hysteresis ($V_{T+} - V_{T-}$)	V_{CC} = MIN		0.2	0.4		0.2	0.4		V
V_{OH}	High-level output voltage	V_{CC} = MIN, V_{IH} = 2 V, $V_{IL} = V_{IL}$ max, $I_{OH} = -3$ mA		2.4	3.1		2.4	3.1		V
		V_{CC} = MIN, V_{IH} = 2 V, V_{IL} = 0.5 V, I_{OH} = MAX		2			2			
V_{OL}	Low-level output voltage	V_{CC} = MIN, V_{IH} = 2 V, $V_{IL} = V_{IL}$ max	I_{OL} = 12 mA		0.25	0.4		0.25	0.4	V
			I_{OL} = 24 mA					0.35	0.5	
I_{OZH}	Off-state output current, high-level voltage applied	V_{CC} = MAX, V_{IH} = 2 V,	V_O = 2.7 V			40			40	µA
I_{OZL}	Off-state output current, low-level voltage applied	$V_{IL} = V_{IL}$ max	V_O = 0.4 V			−200			−200	µA
I_I	Input current at maximum input voltage	A or B	V_{CC} = MAX,	V_I = 5.5 V			0.1			0.1	mA
		$\overline{GAB}$ or GBA		V_I = 7 V			0.1			0.1	
I_{IH}	High-level input current, any input	V_{CC} = MAX,	V_I = 2.7 V			20			20	µA
I_{IL}	Low-level input current	A inputs	V_{CC} = MAX, V_I = 0.4 V, $\overline{GAB}$ and GBA at V_{IL} max				−0.2			−0.2	mA
		B inputs	V_{CC} = MAX, V_I = 0.4 V, $\overline{GAB}$ and GBA at 2 V				−0.2			−0.2	
		$\overline{GAB}$ or GBA	V_{CC} = MAX, V_I = 0.4 V				−0.2			−0.2	
I_{OS}	Short-circuit output current♦	V_{CC} = MAX		−40		−225	−40		−225	mA
I_{CC}	Supply current	Outputs high	V_{CC} = MAX, Outputs open, See Note 2	'LS242, 'LS243		22	38		22	38	mA
		Outputs low		'LS242, 'LS243		29	50		29	50	
		All outputs disabled		'LS242		29	50		29	50	
				'LS243		32	54		32	54	

†For conditions shown as MIN or MAX, use the appropriate value specified under recommended operating conditions.
‡All typical values are at V_{CC} = 5 V, T_A = 25°C.
♦Not more than one output should be shorted at a time, and duration of the short-circuit should not exceed one second.
NOTE 2: I_{CC} is measured with transceivers enabled in one direction only, or with all transceivers disabled.

switching characteristics, V_{CC} = 5 V, T_A = 25°C

PARAMETER		TEST CONDITIONS	'LS242 MIN	'LS242 TYP	'LS242 MAX	'LS243 MIN	'LS243 TYP	'LS243 MAX	UNIT
t_{PLH}	Propagation delay time, low-to-high-level output	C_L = 45 pF, R_L = 667 Ω, See Note 3		9	14		12	18	ns
t_{PHL}	Propagation delay time, high-to-low-level output			12	18		12	18	ns
t_{PZL}	Output enable time to low level			20	30		20	30	ns
t_{PZH}	Output enable time to high level			15	23		15	23	ns
t_{PLZ}	Output disable time from low level	C_L = 5 pF, R_L = 667 Ω, See Note 3		15	25		15	25	ns
t_{PHZ}	Output disable time from high level			10	18		10	18	ns

NOTE 3: Load circuit and waveforms are shown on page 3-11.

TEXAS INSTRUMENTS
INCORPORATED
POST OFFICE BOX 5012 • DALLAS, TEXAS 75222

FOR SYMMETRICAL GENERATION OF COMPLEMENTARY TTL SIGNALS

- Switching Time Skew of the Complementary Outputs Is Typically 0.5 ns . . . Guaranteed to be No More than 3 ns at Rated Loading

- Full Fan-Out to 20 High-Level and 10 Low-Level 54/74 Loads

- Active Pull-Down Provides Square Transfer Characteristic

description

The SN54265 and SN74265 circuits feature complementary outputs from each logic element, which have virtually symmetrical switching time delays from the triggering input. They are designed specifically for use in applications such as:

- Symmetrical clock/$\overline{\text{clock}}$ generators

- Complementary input circuit for decoders and code converters

- Switch debouncing

- Differential line driver

Examples of these four functions are illustrated in the typical application data.

The SN54265 is characterized for operation over the full military temperature range of −55°C to 125°C; the SN74265 is characterized for operation from 0°C to 70°C.

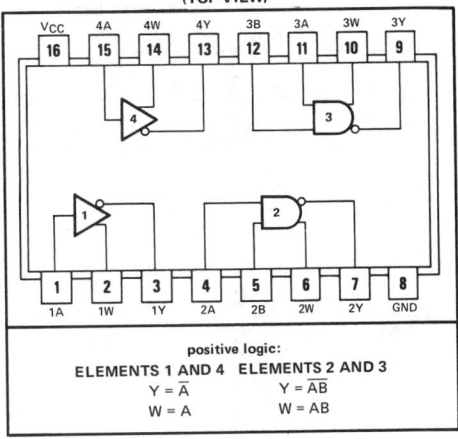

SN54265 . . . J OR W PACKAGE
SN74265 . . . J OR N PACKAGE
(TOP VIEW)

positive logic:

ELEMENTS 1 AND 4
Y = $\overline{A}$
W = A

ELEMENTS 2 AND 3
Y = $\overline{AB}$
W = AB

schematics of inputs and outputs

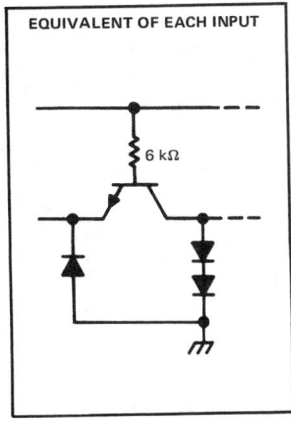

EQUIVALENT OF EACH INPUT

6 kΩ

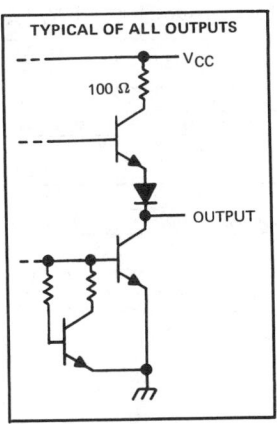

TYPICAL OF ALL OUTPUTS

V$_{CC}$

100 Ω

OUTPUT

recommended operating conditions

	SN54265			SN74265			UNIT
	MIN	NOM	MAX	MIN	NOM	MAX	
Supply voltage, V_{CC}	4.5	5	5.5	4.75	5	5.25	V
High-level output current, I_{OH}			−800			−800	μA
Low-level output current, I_{OL}			16			16	mA
Operating free-air temperature, T_A	−55		125	0		70	°C

electrical characteristics over recommended operating free-air temperature range (unless otherwise noted)

PARAMETER		TEST CONDITIONS[†]		MIN	TYP[‡]	MAX	UNIT
V_{IH}	High-level input voltage			2			V
V_{IL}	Low-level input voltage					0.8	V
V_{IK}	Input clamp voltage	V_{CC} = MIN,	I_I = −12 mA			−1.5	V
V_{OH}	High-level output voltage	V_{CC} = MIN,	I_{OH} = −800 μA	2.4	3.4		V
V_{OL}	Low-level output voltage	V_{CC} = MIN,	I_{OL} = 16 mA		0.2	0.4	V
I_I	Input current at maximum input voltage	V_{CC} = MAX,	V_I = 5.5 V			1	mA
I_{IH}	High-level input current	V_{CC} = MAX,	V_I = 2.4 V			40	μA
I_{IL}	Low-level input current	V_{CC} = MAX,	V_I = 0.4 V			−1.6	mA
I_{OS}	Short-circuit output current [§]	V_{CC} = MAX,	SN54265	−20		−57	mA
			SN74265	−18		−57	
I_{CC}	Supply current	V_{CC} = MAX,	See Note 3		25	34	mA

[†]For conditions shown as MIN or MAX, use the appropriate value specified under recommended operating conditions.
[‡]All typical values are at V_{CC} = 5 V, T_A = 25°C.
[§]Not more than one output should be shorted at a time.
NOTE 3: I_{CC} is measured with all outputs open and all inputs grounded.

switching characteristics, V_{CC} = 5 V, T_A = 25°C

PARAMETER[¶]	FROM (INPUT)	TO (OUTPUT)	TEST CONDITIONS	MIN	TYP	MAX	UNIT
$t_{PLH(W)}$	A or B	W			11.6	18	ns
$t_{PHL(Y)}$	(as applicable)	Y	R_L = 400 Ω,		11.3	18	
$t_{PHL(W)}$	A or B	W	C_L = 15 pF,		9.8	18	ns
$t_{PLH(Y)}$	(as applicable)	Y	See Note 4		10.2	18	
$t_{PLH(W)} - t_{PHL(Y)}$	A or B	W with			+0.3	±3	ns
$t_{PHL(W)} - t_{PLH(Y)}$	(as applicable)	respect to Y			−0.4	±3	

$t_{PLH} \equiv$ Propagation delay time, low-to-high-level output.
$t_{PHL} \equiv$ Propagation delay time, high-to-low-level output.
$t_{PXX(W)} - t_{PXX(Y)} \equiv$ Difference in indicated propagation delay times at the W and Y outputs, respectively.
NOTE 4: Load circuit and voltage waveforms are shown on page 3-10.

TEXAS INSTRUMENTS
INCORPORATED
POST OFFICE BOX 5012 • DALLAS, TEXAS 75222

TYPICAL CHARACTERISTICS†

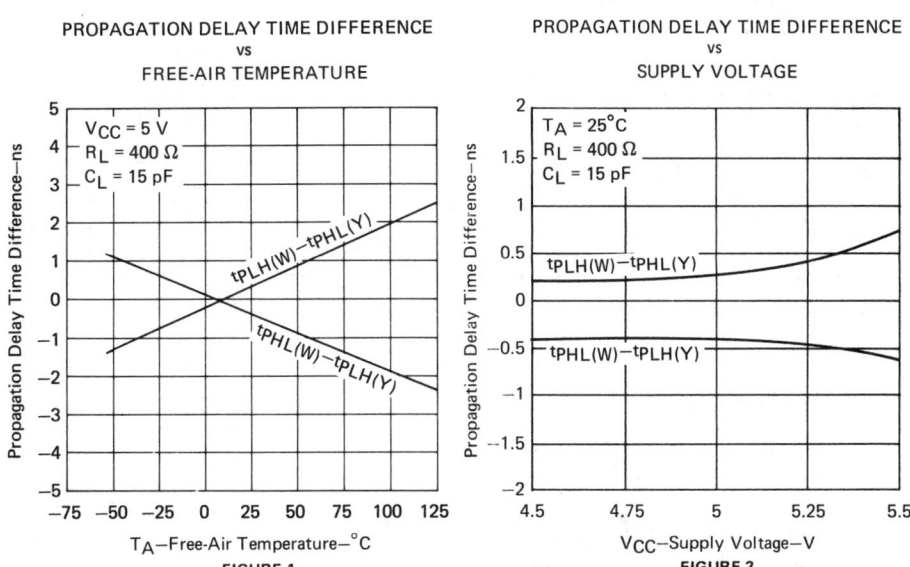

PROPAGATION DELAY TIME DIFFERENCE
vs
FREE-AIR TEMPERATURE

FIGURE 1

PROPAGATION DELAY TIME DIFFERENCE
vs
SUPPLY VOLTAGE

FIGURE 2

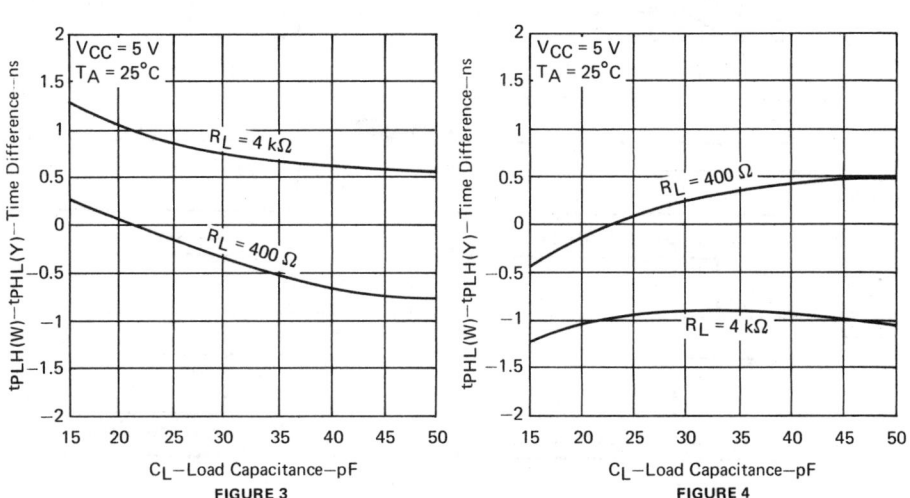

PROPAGATION DELAY TIME DIFFERENCE vs LOAD CAPACITANCE

FIGURE 3

FIGURE 4

†Data for temperatures below 0°C and above 70°C and for supply voltages below 4.75 V and above 5.25 V are applicable for SN54265 only.

TEXAS INSTRUMENTS
INCORPORATED
POST OFFICE BOX 5012 • DALLAS, TEXAS 75222

TYPES SN54265, SN74265
QUADRUPLE COMPLEMENTARY-OUTPUT ELEMENTS

TYPICAL APPLICATION DATA

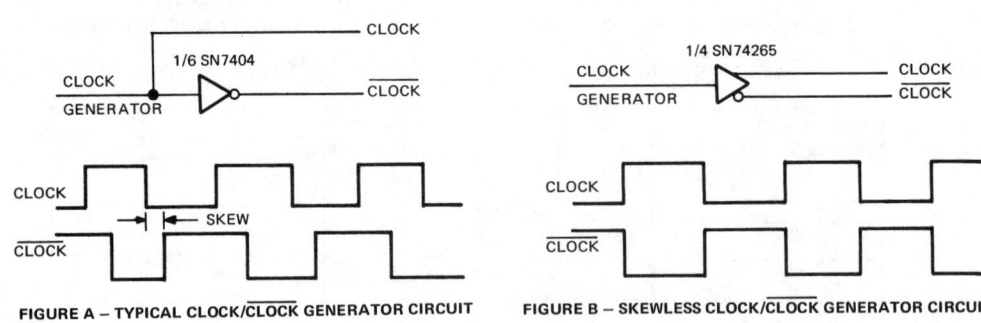

FIGURE A – TYPICAL CLOCK/$\overline{\text{CLOCK}}$ GENERATOR CIRCUIT

FIGURE B – SKEWLESS CLOCK/$\overline{\text{CLOCK}}$ GENERATOR CIRCUIT

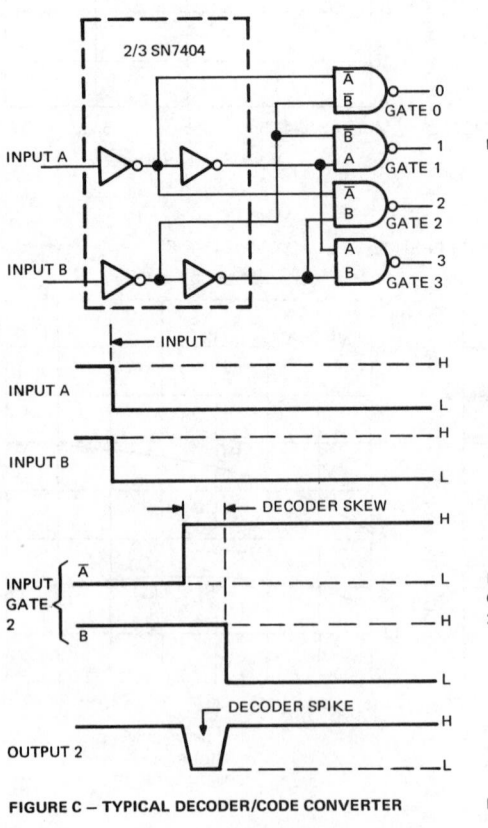

FIGURE C – TYPICAL DECODER/CODE CONVERTER

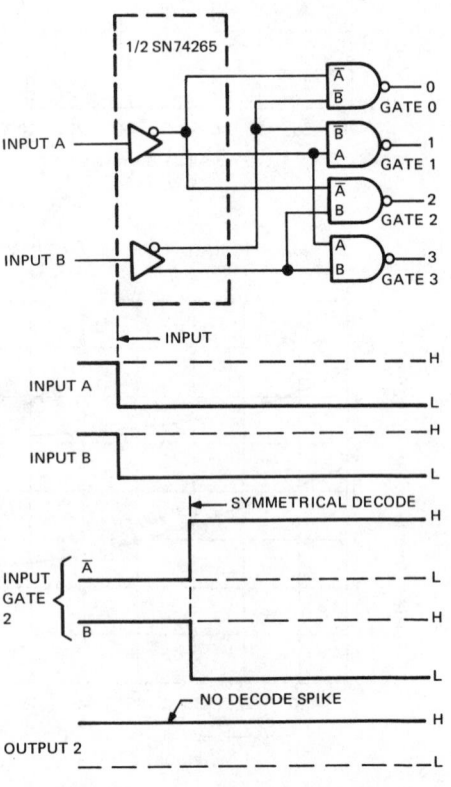

FIGURE D – SYMMETRICAL DECODER/CODE CONVERTER

TEXAS INSTRUMENTS
INCORPORATED
POST OFFICE BOX 5012 • DALLAS, TEXAS 75222

TYPICAL APPLICATION DATA

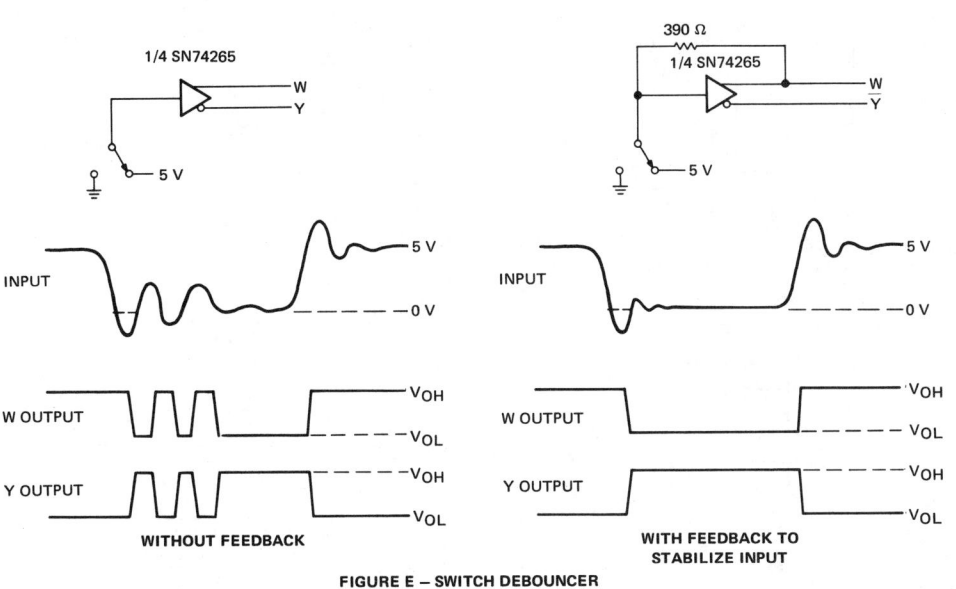

FIGURE E — SWITCH DEBOUNCER

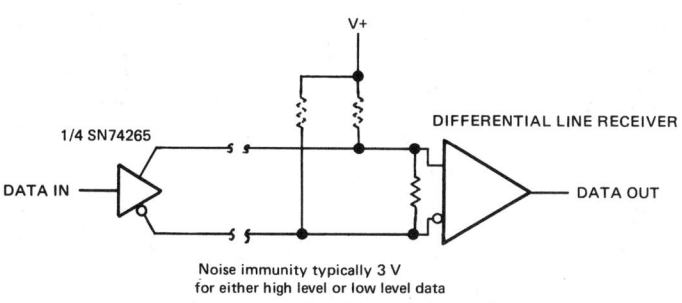

Noise immunity typically 3 V
for either high level or low level data

FIGURE F — DIFFERENTIAL LINE DRIVER

PARAMETER MEASUREMENT INFORMATION

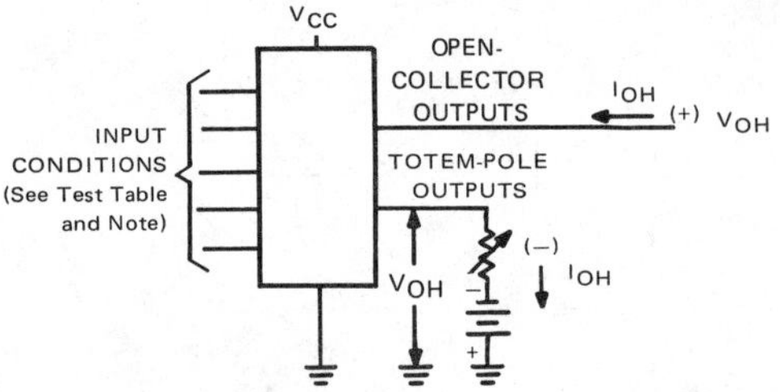

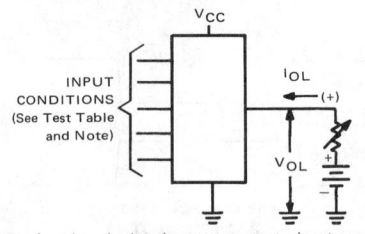

TEST TABLE	
FUNCTION	**INPUT CONDITIONS**
NAND	Input under test at V_{IL} max, all others at 4.5 V
AND	All inputs at V_{IH} min
NOR	All inputs at V_{IL} max
OR	Input under test at V_{IH} min, all others at GND
AND-OR-INVERT	Inputs under test (a set including one input of each AND gate) at V_{IL} max, all others at 4.5 V
AND-OR	All inputs of AND gate under test at V_{IH} min, all others at GND

NOTE: For functions having three-state outputs, input conditions are maintained which will cause the outputs to be enabled (low-impedance).

FIGURE 1—V_{IH}, V_{IL}, V_{OH}, I_{OH}

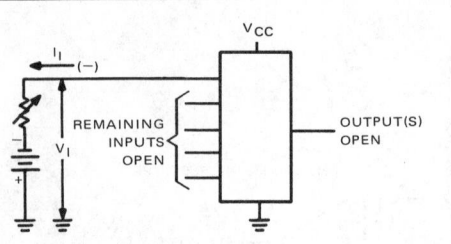

TEST TABLE	
FUNCTION	**INPUT CONDITIONS**
NAND	All inputs at V_{IH} min
AND	Input under test at V_{IL} max, all others at 4.5 V
NOR	Input under test at V_{IH} min, others at GND
OR	All inputs at V_{IL} max
AND-OR-INVERT	All inputs of AND gate under test at V_{IH} min, all others at GND
AND-OR	Inputs under test (a set including one input of each AND gate) at V_{IH} min, all others at 4.5 V

NOTE: For functions having three-state outputs, input conditions are maintained which will cause the outputs to be enabled (low-impedance).

FIGURE 2—V_{IH}, V_{IL}, V_{OL}

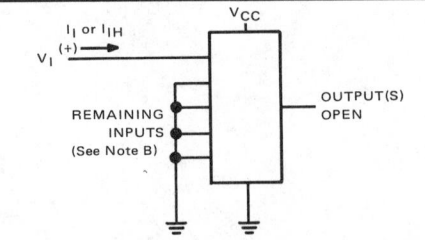

NOTE: Each input is tested separately.

FIGURE 3—V_I

NOTES: A. Each input is tested separately.
B. When testing AND-OR-INVERT or AND-OR gates, each AND gate is tested separately with inputs of AND gates not under test open when testing I_I and grounded when testing I_{IH}.

FIGURE 4—I_I, I_{IH}

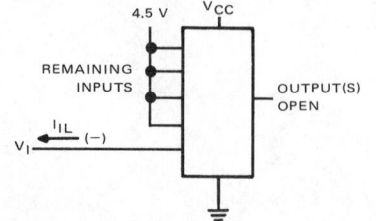

NOTES: A. Each input is tested separately.
B. When testing AND-OR-INVERT or AND-OR gates, each AND gate is tested separately with inputs of AND gates not under test open.

FIGURE 5—I_{IL}

TEXAS INSTRUMENTS
INCORPORATED
POST OFFICE BOX 5012 • DALLAS, TEXAS 75222

SERIES 54/74, 54H/74H, 54L/74L, 54LS/74LS, 54S/74S
TRANSISTOR-TRANSISTOR LOGIC

PARAMETER MEASUREMENT INFORMATION

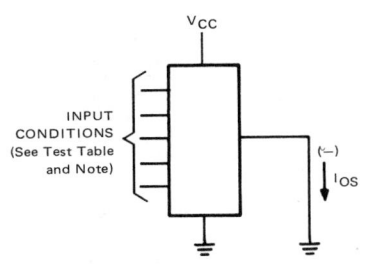

TEST TABLE

FUNCTION	INPUT CONDITIONS
NAND	All inputs at GND
AND	All inputs at 4.5 V
NOR	All inputs at GND
OR	All inputs at 4.5 V
AND-OR-INVERT	All inputs at GND
AND-OR	All inputs at 4.5 V

NOTE: For functions having three-state outputs, input conditions are maintained which will cause the outputs to be enabled (low-impedance).

FIGURE 6—I_{OS}

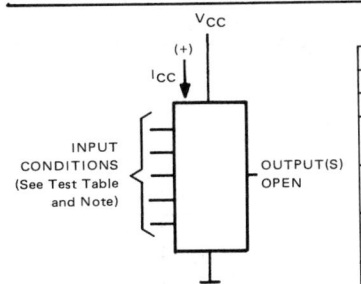

TEST TABLE

FUNCTION	INPUT CONDITIONS FOR I_{CCH}	INPUT CONDITIONS FOR I_{CCL}
NAND	All inputs at GND	All inputs at 4.5 V
AND	All inputs at 4.5 V	All inputs at GND
NOR	All inputs at GND	One input at 4.5 V, all others at GND
OR	One input at 4.5 V, all others at GND	All inputs at GND
AND-OR-INVERT	All inputs at GND	All inputs of one AND gate at 4.5 V, all others at GND
AND-OR	All inputs of one AND gate at 4.5 V, all others at GND	All inputs at GND

NOTE: I_{CC} is measured simultaneously for all functions in a package. The average-per-gate values are calculated from the appropriate one of the following equations:

$$I_{CC}, I_{CCH}, \text{ or } I_{CCL} \text{ (average per gate or flip-flop)} = \frac{\text{total } I_{CC}, I_{CCH}, \text{ or } I_{CCL}}{\text{(number of gates or flip-flops in package)}}$$

$$I_{CC} \text{ (average per gate, 50\% duty cycle)} = \frac{I_{CCH} + I_{CCL}}{2 \text{ (number of gates in package)}}$$

FIGURE 7—I_{CC}

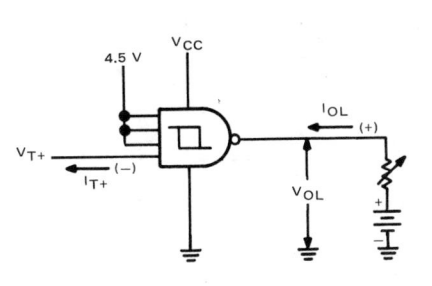

FIGURE 8—V_{T+}, I_{T+}, V_{OL} (FOR NAND SCHMITT TRIGGERS)

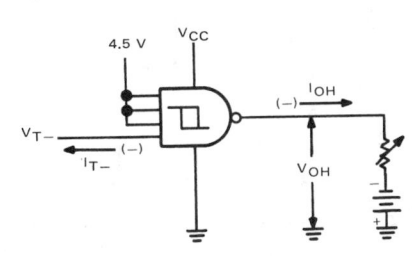

FIGURE 9—V_{T-}, I_{T-}, V_{OH} (FOR NAND SCHMITT TRIGGERS)

6

TEXAS INSTRUMENTS
INCORPORATED
POST OFFICE BOX 5012 • DALLAS, TEXAS 75222

SERIES 54/74, 54H/74H, 54L/74L, 54LS/74LS, 54S/74S
TRANSISTOR-TRANSISTOR LOGIC

PARAMETER MEASUREMENT INFORMATION

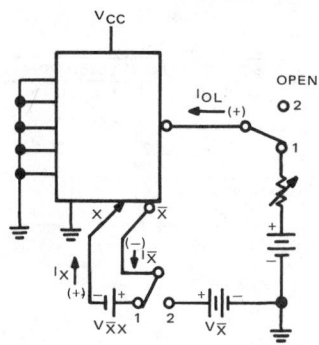

NOTES: A. Switches are in position 1 for SN54'/SN74', position 2 for SN54H'/SN74H'.

B. The $I_{\overline{X}}$ limit for SN54' and SN74' circuits may be verified by an alternate equivalent procedure. The $V_{\overline{X}X}$ source is replaced by a resistor (see table below) in parallel with a voltmeter between the X and $\overline{X}$ pins. If the measured voltage, $V_{\overline{X}X}$, is less than 0.4, the specified limit for $I_{\overline{X}}$ is met.

RESISTANCE VALUE TABLE

SN5423	114 Ω
SN5450, SN5453	138 Ω
SN7423	105 Ω
SN7450, SN7453	130 Ω

FIGURE 10—$I_{\overline{X}}$ (FOR EXPANDABLE GATES)

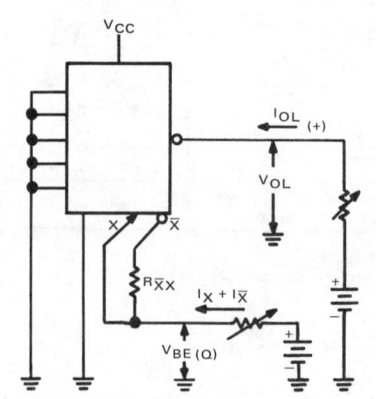

FIGURE 11—$V_{BE(Q)}$ (FOR EXPANDABLE GATES)

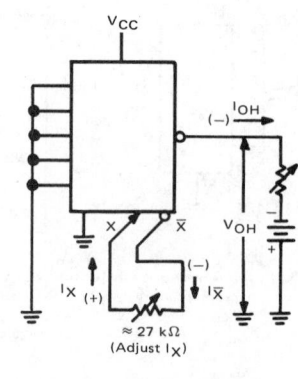

FIGURE 12—V_{OH} (FOR EXPANDABLE GATES)

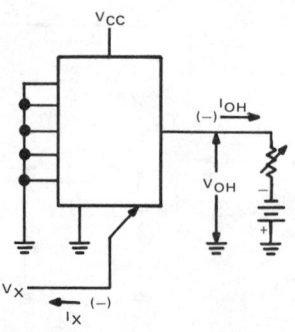

FIGURE 13—V_{OH} (FOR EXPANDABLE GATES)

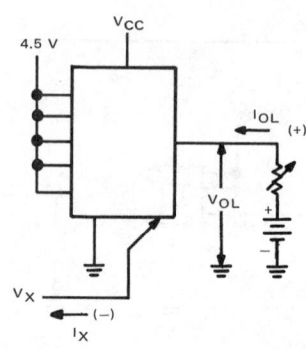

FIGURE 14—V_{OL} (FOR EXPANDABLE GATES)

TEXAS INSTRUMENTS
INCORPORATED
POST OFFICE BOX 5012 • DALLAS, TEXAS 75222

PARAMETER MEASUREMENT INFORMATION

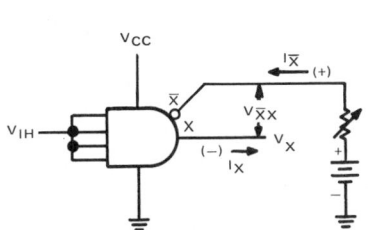

FIGURE 15—ON-STATE CHARACTERISTICS FOR EXPANDERS

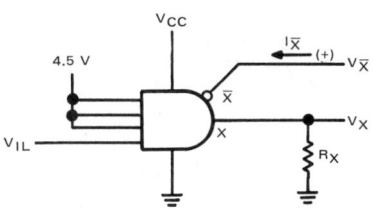

FIGURE 16—OFF-STATE CHARACTERISTICS FOR EXPANDERS

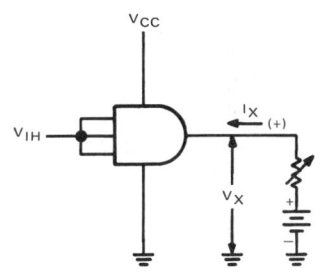

FIGURE 17—ON-STATE CHARACTERISTICS FOR EXPANDERS

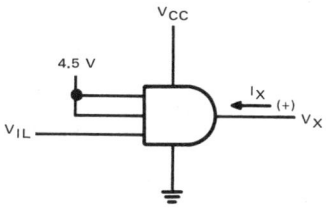

FIGURE 18—OFF-STATE CHARACTERISTICS FOR EXPANDERS

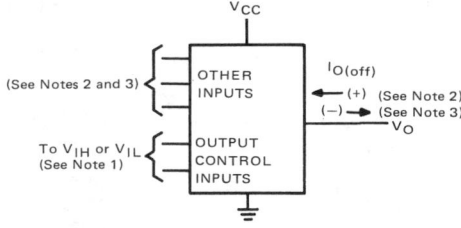

NOTES: 1. Input conditions are maintained which will ensure that the three-state output(s) is (are) disabled to the high-impedance state. See function table or logic for the particular device.
2. When testing for current into the output with a high-level output voltage, input conditions are applied that would cause the output to be low if it were enabled.
3. When testing for current out of the output with a low-level output voltage, input conditions are applied that would cause the output to be high if it were enabled.

FIGURE 19—$I_{O(off)}$ (THREE-STATE OUTPUTS)

TEXAS INSTRUMENTS
INCORPORATED
POST OFFICE BOX 5012 • DALLAS, TEXAS 75222

SERIES 54/74
TRANSISTOR-TRANSISTOR LOGIC

TYPICAL CHARACTERISTICS†§

OUTPUT VOLTAGE
vs
INPUT VOLTAGE

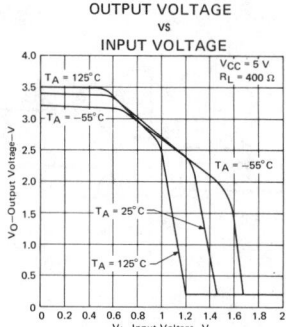

FIGURE A1

HIGH-LEVEL OUTPUT VOLTAGE
vs
HIGH-LEVEL OUTPUT CURRENT

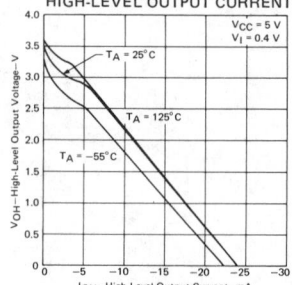

FIGURE A2

LOW-LEVEL OUTPUT VOLTAGE
vs
LOW-LEVEL OUTPUT CURRENT

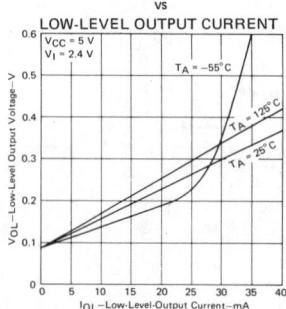

FIGURE A3

AVERAGE PROPAGATION DELAY TIME,
vs
FREE-AIR TEMPERATURE

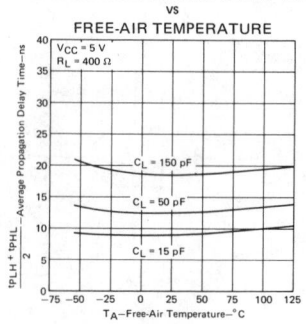

FIGURE A4

PROPAGATION DELAY TIME,
LOW-TO-HIGH LEVEL OUTPUT
vs
FREE-AIR TEMPERATURE

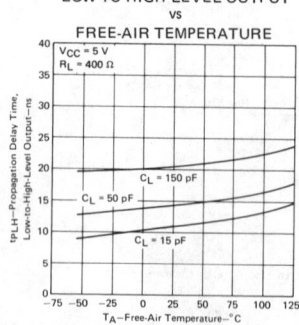

FIGURE A5

PROPAGATION DELAY TIME,
HIGH-TO-LOW-LEVEL OUTPUT
vs
FREE-AIR TEMPERATURE

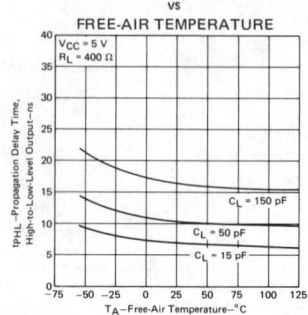

FIGURE A6

† Data for temperatures below $0°C$ and above $70°C$ are applicable for Series 54 circuits only.
§ Data as shown are applicable specifically for the NAND gates with totem-pole outputs.

TEXAS INSTRUMENTS
INCORPORATED
POST OFFICE BOX 5012 • DALLAS, TEXAS 75222

TYPICAL CHARACTERISTICS†§

PROPAGATION DELAY TIME,
LOW-TO-HIGH-LEVEL OUTPUT
vs
FREE-AIR TEMPERATURE

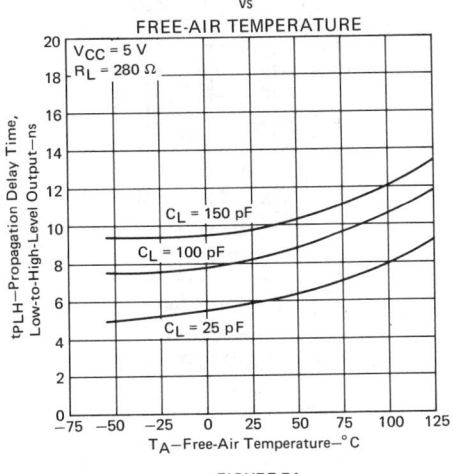

FIGURE B1

PROPAGATION DELAY TIME,
HIGH-TO-LOW-LEVEL OUTPUT
vs
FREE-AIR TEMPERATURE

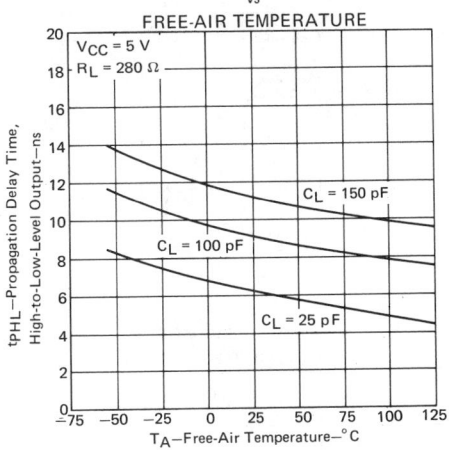

FIGURE B2

AVERAGE PROPAGATION DELAY TIME
vs
FREE-AIR TEMPERATURE

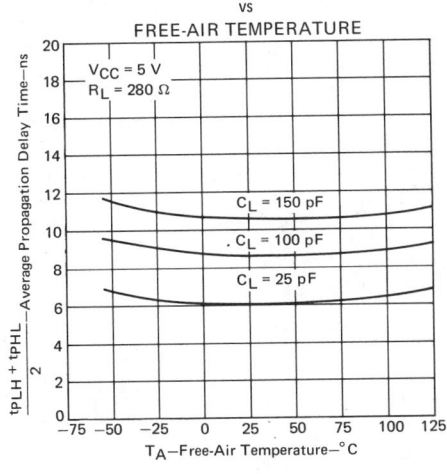

FIGURE B3

†Data for temperatures below 0°C and above 70°C are applicable for Series 54H circuits only.
§Data as shown are applicable specifically for the NAND gates with totem-pole outputs.

TEXAS INSTRUMENTS
INCORPORATED
POST OFFICE BOX 5012 • DALLAS, TEXAS 75222

SERIES 54L/74L
LOW-POWER TRANSISTOR-TRANSISTOR LOGIC

TYPICAL CHARACTERISTICS†§

OUTPUT VOLTAGE
vs
INPUT VOLTAGE

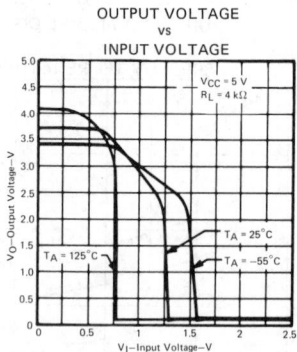

FIGURE C1

OUTPUT VOLTAGE
vs
HIGH-LEVEL OUTPUT CURRENT

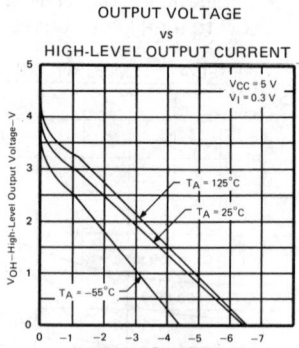

FIGURE C2

OUTPUT VOLTAGE
vs
LOW-LEVEL OUTPUT CURRENT

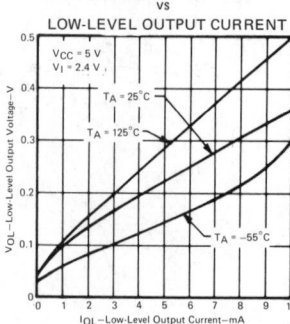

FIGURE C3

CLOCK INPUT CURRENT PER FLIP-FLOP
vs
INPUT VOLTAGE

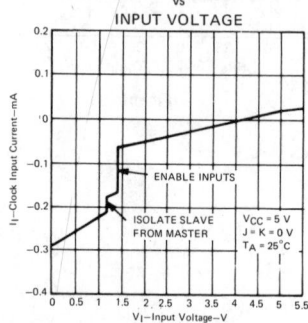

FIGURE C4

POWER DISSIPATION PER FLIP-FLOP
vs
FREQUENCY

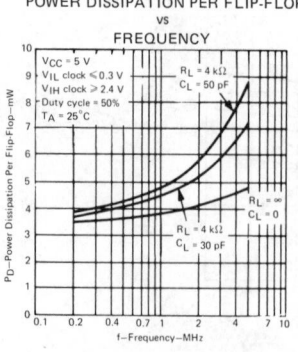

FIGURE C5

AVERAGE TOTAL D-C POWER DISSIPATION
PER FLIP-FLOP
vs
FREE-AIR TEMPERATURE

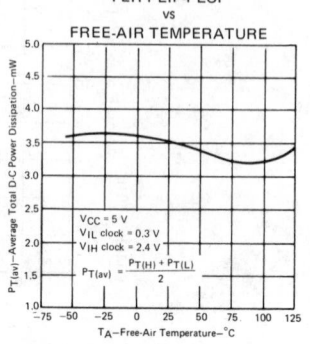

FIGURE C6

†Data for temperatures below 0°C and above 70°C are applicable for Series 54L circuits only.
§Unless otherwise noted, data as shown are applicable specifically for the NAND gates with totem-pole outputs.

TEXAS INSTRUMENTS
INCORPORATED
POST OFFICE BOX 5012 • DALLAS, TEXAS 75222

TYPICAL CHARACTERISTICS†§

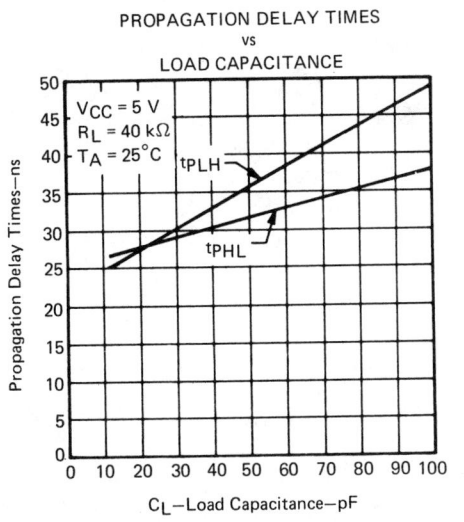

PROPAGATION DELAY TIMES
vs
LOAD CAPACITANCE

$V_{CC} = 5$ V
$R_L = 40$ kΩ
$T_A = 25°$C

tPLH
tPHL

Propagation Delay Times—ns

C_L—Load Capacitance—pF

FIGURE C7

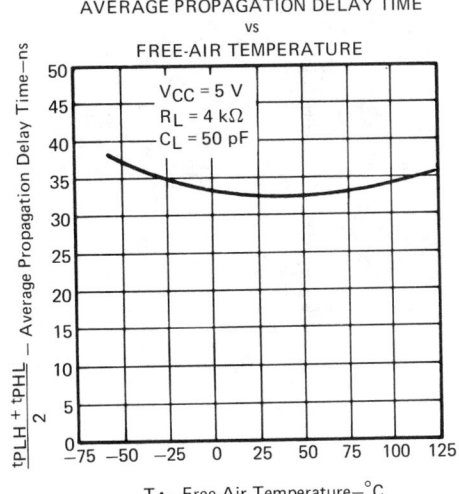

AVERAGE PROPAGATION DELAY TIME
vs
FREE-AIR TEMPERATURE

$V_{CC} = 5$ V
$R_L = 4$ kΩ
$C_L = 50$ pF

$\frac{t_{PLH} + t_{PHL}}{2}$ — Average Propagation Delay Time—ns

T_A—Free-Air Temperature—°C

FIGURE C8

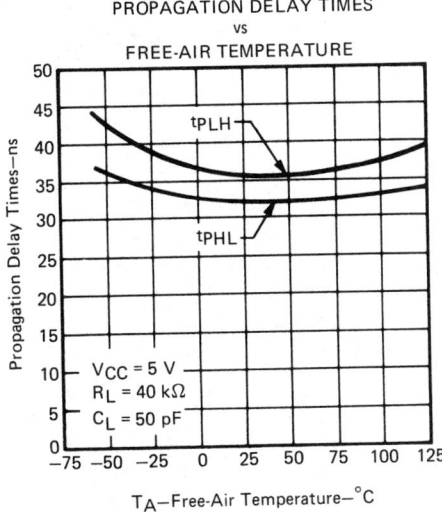

PROPAGATION DELAY TIMES
vs
FREE-AIR TEMPERATURE

tPLH
tPHL

$V_{CC} = 5$ V
$R_L = 40$ kΩ
$C_L = 50$ pF

Propagation Delay Times—ns

T_A—Free-Air Temperature—°C

FIGURE C9

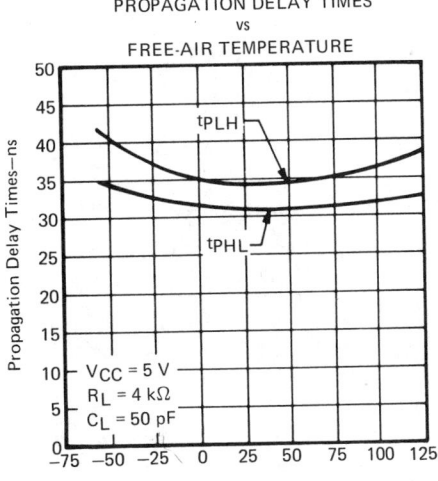

PROPAGATION DELAY TIMES
vs
FREE-AIR TEMPERATURE

tPLH
tPHL

$V_{CC} = 5$ V
$R_L = 4$ kΩ
$C_L = 50$ pF

Propagation Delay Times—ns

T_A—Free-Air Temperature—°C

FIGURE C10

†Data for temperatures below 0°C and above 70°C are applicable for Series 54L circuits only.
§Data as shown are applicable specifically for the NAND gates with totem-pole outputs.

TEXAS INSTRUMENTS
INCORPORATED
POST OFFICE BOX 5012 • DALLAS, TEXAS 75222

6

TYPICAL CHARACTERISTICS†§

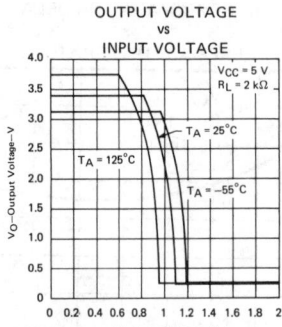

FIGURE D1

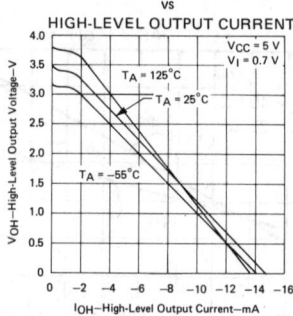

FIGURE D2

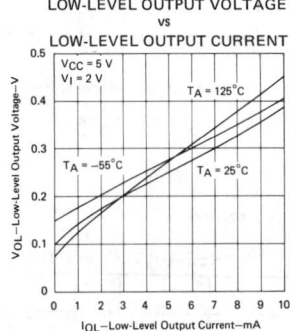

FIGURE D3

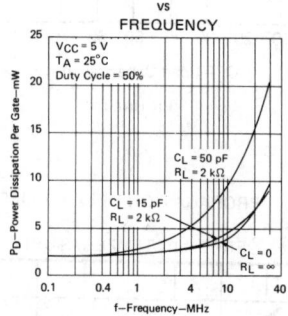

FIGURE D4

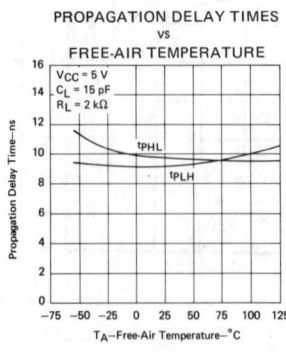

FIGURE D5

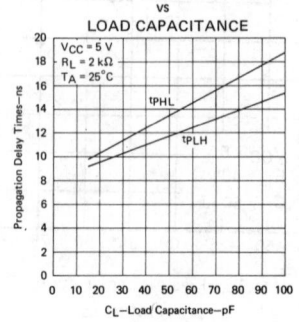

FIGURE D6

† Data for temperatures below 0°C and above 70°C are applicable for Series 54LS circuits only.
§ Data as shown are applicable specifically for the NAND gates with totem-pole outputs.

TEXAS INSTRUMENTS
INCORPORATED
POST OFFICE BOX 5012 • DALLAS, TEXAS 75222

TYPICAL CHARACTERISTICS†§

OUTPUT VOLTAGE
vs
INPUT VOLTAGE

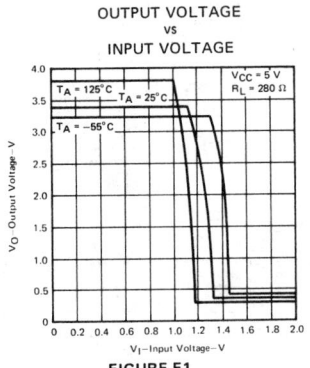

FIGURE E1

INPUT-CLAMPING-DIODE
FORWARD VOLTAGE
vs
FREE-AIR TEMPERATURE

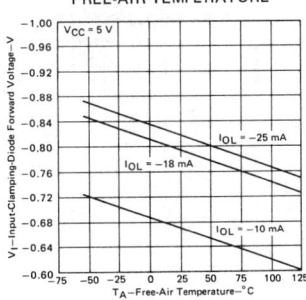

FIGURE E2

HIGH-LEVEL OUTPUT VOLTAGE
vs
HIGH-LEVEL OUTPUT CURRENT

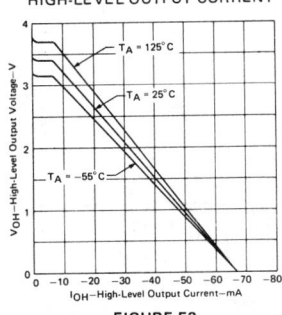

FIGURE E3

LOW-LEVEL OUTPUT VOLTAGE
vs
LOW-LEVEL OUTPUT CURRENT

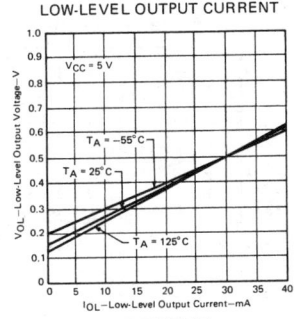

FIGURE E4

INPUT CURRENT
vs
INPUT VOLTAGE

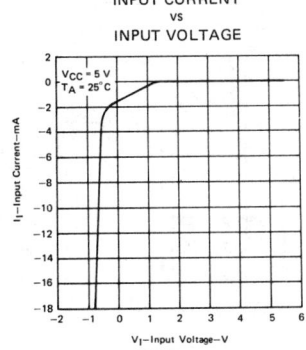

FIGURE E5

HIGH-LEVEL INPUT CURRENT
vs
FREE-AIR TEMPERATURE

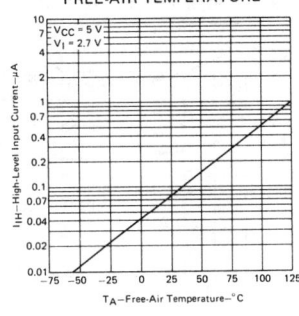

FIGURE E6

†Data for temperatures below 0°C and above 70°C are applicable for Series 54S circuits only.
§Data as shown are applicable specifically for the NAND gates with totem-pole outputs.

TEXAS INSTRUMENTS
INCORPORATED
POST OFFICE BOX 5012 • DALLAS, TEXAS 75222

6

SERIES 54S/74S
SCHOTTKY-CLAMPED TRANSISTOR-TRANSISTOR LOGIC

TYPICAL CHARACTERISTICS†§

PROPAGATION DELAY TIME,
LOW-TO-HIGH-LEVEL OUTPUT
vs
FREE-AIR TEMPERATURE

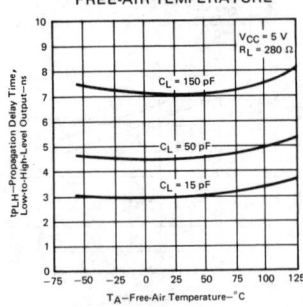

FIGURE E7

PROPAGATION DELAY TIME,
LOW-TO-HIGH-LEVEL OUTPUT
vs
SUPPLY VOLTAGE

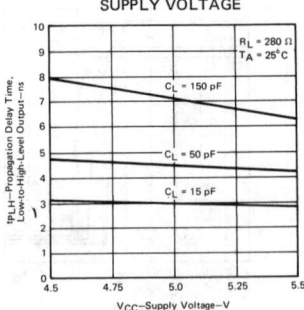

FIGURE E8

PROPAGATION DELAY TIME,
HIGH-TO-LOW-LEVEL OUTPUT
vs
FREE-AIR TEMPERATURE

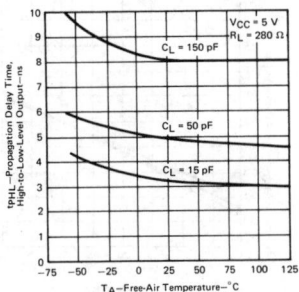

FIGURE E9

PROPAGATION DELAY TIME,
HIGH-TO-LOW-LEVEL OUTPUT
vs
SUPPLY VOLTAGE

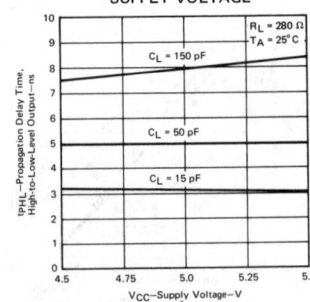

FIGURE E10

AVERAGE PROPAGATION DELAY TIME
vs
FREE-AIR TEMPERATURE

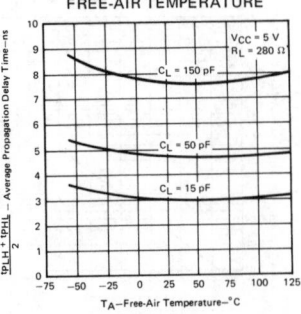

FIGURE E11

POWER DISSIPATION PER GATE
vs
FREQUENCY

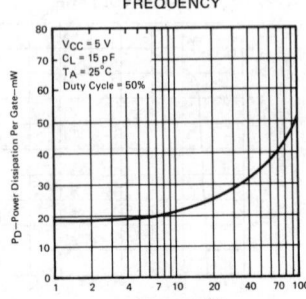

FIGURE E12

†Data for temperatures below 0°C and above 70°C are applicable for Series 54S circuits only.
§Data as shown are applicable specifically for the NAND gates with totem-pole outputs.

TEXAS INSTRUMENTS
INCORPORATED
POST OFFICE BOX 5012 • DALLAS, TEXAS 75222

12

TYPICAL CHARACTERISTICS FOR FLIP-FLOPS†

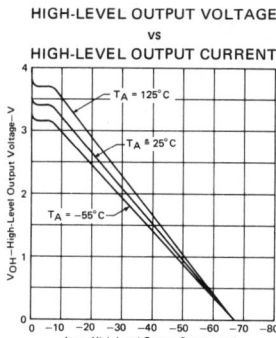

HIGH-LEVEL OUTPUT VOLTAGE
vs
HIGH-LEVEL OUTPUT CURRENT

FIGURE E13

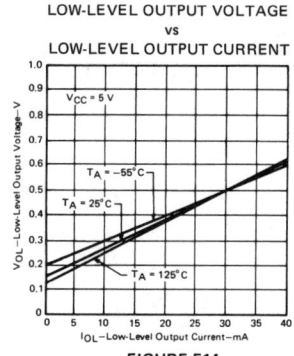

LOW-LEVEL OUTPUT VOLTAGE
vs
LOW-LEVEL OUTPUT CURRENT

FIGURE E14

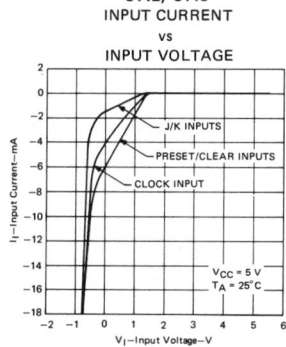

'S112, 'S113
INPUT CURRENT
vs
INPUT VOLTAGE

FIGURE E15

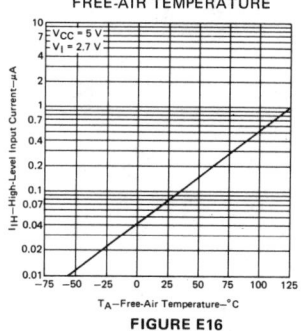

HIGH-LEVEL INPUT CURRENT
vs
FREE-AIR TEMPERATURE

FIGURE E16

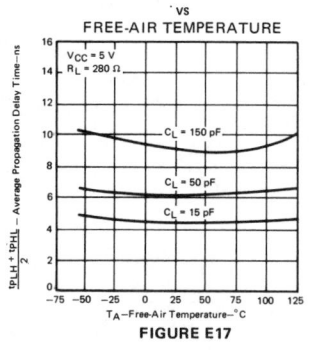

'S112, 'S113, 'S114
AVERAGE PROPAGATION DELAY TIME,
CLOCK TO OUTPUT
vs
FREE-AIR TEMPERATURE

FIGURE E17

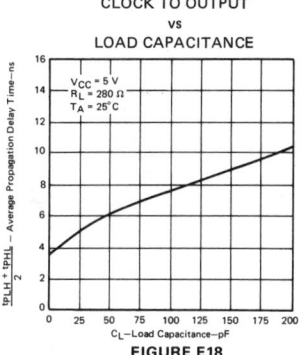

'S112, 'S113, 'S114
AVERAGE PROPAGATION DELAY TIME,
CLOCK TO OUTPUT
vs
LOAD CAPACITANCE

FIGURE E18

†Data for temperatures below 0°C and above 70°C are applicable for Series 54S circuits only.

54/74 Family
MSI/LSI Circuits

The following pages contain functional indexes and selection guides designed to simplify the choice of a particular function to fit a specific application. Essential characteristics of similar or like functions are grouped for comparative analysis, and the electrical specifications are referenced by page number. The following categories of functions are covered:

7

TEXAS INSTRUMENTS
INCORPORATED
POST OFFICE BOX 5012 • DALLAS, TEXAS 75222

ADDERS

DESCRIPTION	TYPICAL CARRY TIME	TYPICAL ADD TIME	TYP POWER DISSIPATION PER BIT	DEVICE TYPE AND PACKAGE −55°C to 125°C		0°C to 70°C		PAGE NO.
SINGLE 1-BIT GATED FULL ADDERS	10.5 ns	52 ns	105 mW	SN5480	J, W	SN7480	J, N	7-41
SINGLE 2-BIT FULL ADDERS	14.5 ns	25 ns	87 mW	SN5482	J, W	SN7482	J, N	7-49
SINGLE 4-BIT FULL ADDERS	10 ns	15 ns	24 mW	SN54LS83A	J, W	SN74LS83A	J, N	7-53
	10 ns	15 ns	24 mW	SN54LS283	J, W	SN74LS283	J, N	7-415
	11 ns	7 ns	124 mW	SN54S283	J	SN74S283	J, N	7-415
	10 ns	16 ns	76 mW	SN5483A	J, W	SN7483A	J, N	7-53
	10 ns	16 ns	76 mW	SN54283	J, W	SN74283	J, N	7-415
DUAL 1-BIT CARRY-SAVE FULL ADDERS	11 ns	11 ns	110 mW	SN54H183	J, W	SN74H183	J, N	7-287
	15 ns	15 ns	23 mW	SN54LS183	J, W	SN74LS183	J, N	7-287

ACCUMULATORS, ARITHMETIC LOGIC UNITS, LOOK-AHEAD CARRY GENERATORS

DESCRIPTION	TYPICAL CARRY TIME	TYPICAL ADD TIME	TYP TOTAL POWER DISSIPATION	DEVICE TYPE AND PACKAGE −55°C to 125°C		0°C to 70°C		PAGE NO.
4-BIT PARALLEL BINARY ACCUMULATORS	10 ns	20 ns	720 mW	SN54S281	J, W	SN74S281	J, N	7-410
4-BIT ARITHMETIC LOGIC UNITS/ FUNCTION GENERATORS	11 ns	20 ns	525 mW			SN74S381	N	7-484
	7 ns	11 ns	600 mW	SN54S181	J, W	SN74S181	J, N	7-271
	12.5 ns	24 ns	455 mW	SN54181	J, W	SN74181	J, N	7-271
	16 ns	24 ns	102 mW	SN54LS181	J, W	SN74LS181	J, N	7-271
LOOK-AHEAD CARRY GENERATORS	7 ns		260 mW	SN54S182	J, W	SN74S182	J, N	7-282
	13 ns		180 mW	SN54182	J, W	SN74182	J, N	

MULTIPLIERS

DESCRIPTION	DEVICE TYPE AND PACKAGE −55°C to 125°C		0°C to 70°C		PAGE NO.
2-BIT-BY-4-BIT PARALLEL BINARY MULTIPLIERS	SN54LS261	J, W	SN74LS261	J, N	7-380
4-BIT-BY-4-BIT PARALLEL BINARY MULTIPLIERS	SN54284, SN54285	J, W	SN74284, SN74285	J, N	7-420
	SN54S274	J	SN74S274	J, N	7-391
7-BIT-SLICE WALLACE TREES	SN54LS275	J	SN74LS275	J, N	7-391
	SN54S275	J	SN74S275	J, N	
25-MHz 6-BIT-BINARY RATE MULTIPLIERS	SN5497	J, W	SN7497	J, N	7-102
25-MHz DECADE RATE MULTIPLIERS	SN54167	J, W	SN74167	J, N	7-222

COMPARATORS

DESCRIPTION	TYPICAL COMPARE TIME	TYP TOTAL POWER DISSIPATION	DEVICE TYPE AND PACKAGE −55°C to 125°C		0°C to 70°C		PAGE NO.
4-BIT MAGNITUDE COMPARATORS	11.5 ns	365 mW	SN54S85	J, W	SN74S85	J, N	7-57
	21 ns	275 mW	SN5485	J, W	SN7485	J, N	
	23.5 ns	52 mW	SN54LS85	J, W	SN74LS85	J, N	
	82 ns	20 mW	SN54L85	J	SN74L85	J, N	

TEXAS INSTRUMENTS
INCORPORATED

POST OFFICE BOX 5012 • DALLAS, TEXAS 75222

PARITY GENERATORS/CHECKERS

DESCRIPTION	TYPICAL DELAY TIME	TYP TOTAL POWER DISSIPATION	DEVICE TYPE −55°C to 125°C		0°C to 70°C		PAGE NO.
9-BIT ODD/EVEN PARITY GENERATORS/CHECKERS	31 ns	80 mW	SN54LS280	J, W	SN74LS280	J, N	7-406
	13 ns	335 mW	SN54S280	J, W	SN74S280	J, N	
8-BIT ODD/EVEN PARITY GENERATORS/CHECKERS	35 ns	170 mW	SN54180	J, W	SN74180	J, N	7-269

OTHER ARITHMETIC OPERATORS

DESCRIPTION	TYPICAL DELAY TIME	TYP TOTAL POWER DISSIPATION	DEVICE TYPE AND PACKAGE −55°C to 125°C		0°C to 70°C		PAGE NO.
QUADRUPLE 2-INPUT EXCLUSIVE-OR GATES WITH TOTEM-POLE OUTPUTS	7 ns	250 mW	SN54S86	J, W	SN74S86	J, N	7-65
	10 ns	30 mW	SN54LS86	J, W	SN74LS86	J, N	7-65
	10 ns	30 mW	SN54LS386	J, W	SN74LS386	J, N	7-487
	14 ns	150 mW	SN5486	J, W	SN7486	J, N	7-65
	55 ns	15 mW	SN54L86	J, T	SN74L86	J, N	7-65
QUADRUPLE 2-INPUT EXCLUSIVE-OR GATES WITH OPEN-COLLECTOR OUTPUTS	18 ns	30 mW	SN54LS136	J, W	SN74LS136	J, N	7-131
	27 ns	150 mW	SN54136	J, W	SN74136	J, N	
QUADRUPLE 2-INPUT EXCLUSIVE-NOR GATES	18 ns	40 mW	SN54LS266	J, W	SN74LS266	J, N	7-386
QUADRUPLE EXCLUSIVE OR/NOR GATES	8 ns	325 mW	SN54S135	J, W	SN74S135	J, N	7-129
4-BIT TRUE/COMPLEMENT, ZERO/ONE ELEMENT	14 ns	270 mW	SN54H87	J, W	SN74H87	J, N	7-70

QUAD, HEX, AND OCTAL FLIP-FLOPS

DESCRIPTION	F-F PER PKG	FREQ	POWER PER FLIP-FLOP	SETUP ns	HOLD ns	DEVICE TYPE AND PACKAGE −55°C to 125°C		0°C to 70°C		PAGE NO.
D TYPE 3-STATE WITH ENABLE	8	50 MHz	26 mW	20↑	0↑	SN54LS364*	J	SN74LS364*	J, N	7-467
	8	50 MHz	17 mW	20↑	0↑	SN54LS374	J	SN74LS374	J, N	7-471
		100 MHz	56 mW	5↑	2↑	SN54S374	J	SN74S374	J, N	7-471
D TYPE WITH ENABLE	8	40 MHz	10.6 mW	20↑	5↑	SN54LS377	J	SN74LS377	J, N	7-481
	6	40 MHz	10.6 mW	20↑	5↑	SN54LS378	J, W	SN74LS378	J, N	7-481
	4	40 MHz	10.6 mW	20↑	5↑	SN54LS379	J	SN74LS379	J, N	7-481
D TYPE WITH CLEAR	8	40 MHz	39 mW	20↑	5↑	SN54273	J	SN74273	J, N,	7-388
		40 MHz	10.6 mW	20↑	5↑	SN54LS273	J	SN74LS273	J, N	
	6	35 MHz	38 mW	20↑	5↑	SN54174	J, W	SN74174	J, N	7-253
		40 MHz	10.6 mW	20↑	5↑	SN54LS174	J, W	SN74LS174	J, N	
		110 MHz	75 mW	5↑	3↑	SN54S174	J, W	SN74S174	J, N	
	4	35 MHz	38 mW	20↑	5↑	SN54175	J, W	SN74175	J, N	7-253
		40 MHz	10.6 mW	20↑	5↑	SN54LS175	J, W	SN74LS175	J, N	
		110 MHz	75 mW	5↑	3↑	SN54S175	J, W	SN74S175	J, N	
J-K TYPE WITH SEPARATE CLOCK	4	50 MHz	75 mW	3↓	10↓	SN54276	J	SN74276	J, N	7-401
J-K TYPE WITH COMMON CLOCK	4	45 MHz	65 mW	0↑	20↑	SN54376	J, W	SN74376	J, N	7-479

REGISTER FILES

DESCRIPTION	TYPICAL ADDRESS TIME	TYP READ ENABLE TIME	DATA INPUT RATE	TYP TOTAL POWER DISSIPATION	DEVICE TYPE AND PACKAGE −55°C to 125°C		0°C to 70°C		PAGE NO.
EIGHT WORDS OF TWO BITS	33 ns	15 ns	20 MHz	560 mW			SN74172	J, N	7-245
FOUR WORDS OF FOUR BITS	27 ns	15 ns	20 MHz	125 mW	SN54LS170	J, W	SN74LS170	J, N	7-237
	30 ns	15 ns	20 MHz	635 mW	SN54170	J, W	SN74170	J, N	
FOUR WORDS OF FOUR BITS (3-STATE OUTPUTS)	24 ns	19 ns	20 MHz	135 mW	SN54LS670	J, W	SN74LS670	J, N	7-526

*New product in development as of October 1976.

TEXAS INSTRUMENTS
INCORPORATED
POST OFFICE BOX 5012 • DALLAS, TEXAS 75222

SHIFT REGISTERS

DESCRIPTION	NO. OF BITS	SHIFT FREQ	SERIAL DATA INPUT	ASYNC CLEAR	MODES S-R‡	MODES S-L‡	MODES LOAD	MODES HOLD	TYP TOTAL POWER DISSIPATION	DEVICE TYPE −55°C to 125°C		DEVICE TYPE 0°C to 70°C		PAGE NO.
PARALLEL-IN, PARALLEL-OUT (BIDIRECTIONAL)	8	50 MHz	D	Low	X	X	X	X	750 mW	SN54S299	J, W	SN74S299	J, N	7-437
		35 MHz	D	Low	X	X	X	X	175 mW	SN54LS299*	J	SN74LS299*	J, N	7-437
		35 MHz	D	Sync L	X	X	X	X	175 mW	SN54LS323*	J	SN74LS323*	J, N	7-443
		25 MHz	D	Low	X	X	X	X	360 mW	SN54198	J, W	SN74198	J, N	7-338
	4	70 MHz	D	Low	X	X	X	X	450 mW	SN54S194	J, W	SN74S194	J, N	7-316
		25 MHz	D	Low	X	X	X	X	75 mW	SN54LS194A	J, W	SN74LS194A	J, N	
		25 MHz	D	Low	X	X	X	X	195 mW	SN54194	J, W	SN74194	J, N	
PARALLEL-IN, PARALLEL-OUT	8	25 MHz	J-K̄	Low	X		X	X	360 mW	SN54199	J, W	SN74199	J, N	7-338
	5	10 MHz	D	Low	X		X		60 mW	SN54LS96	J, W	SN74LS96	J, N	
		10 MHz	D	Low	X		X		240 mW	SN5496	J, W	SN7496	J, N	7-95
		5 MHz	D	Low	X		X		120 mW	SN54L96	J	SN74L96	J, N	
	4	70 MHz	J-K̄	Low	X		X		375 mW	SN54S195	J, W	SN74S195	J, N	7-324
		30 MHz	J-K̄	Low	X		X		195 mW	SN54195	J, W	SN74195	J, N	7-324
		30 MHz	D	Low	X		X		75 mW	SN54LS395A	J, W	SN74LS395A	J, N	7-496
		25 MHz	D	None	X		X		195 mW	SN5495A	J, W	SN7495A	J, N	7-89
		25 MHz	D	Low	X		X	X	230 mW	SN54179	J, W	SN74179	J, N	7-265
		25 MHz	D	None	X		X	X	230 mW	SN54178	J, W	SN74178	J, N	7-265
		30 MHz	J-K̄	Low	X		X		70 mW	SN54LS195A	J, W	SN74LS195A	J, N	7-324
		30 MHz	D	None	X		X		65 mW	SN54LS95B	J, W	SN74LS95B	J, N	7-89
		25 MHz	D	None	X		X		70 mW	SN54LS295B	J, W	SN74LS295B	J, N	7-429
		3 MHz	J-K̄	None	X		X		19 mW	SN54L99	J	SN74L99	J, N	7-109
		3 MHz	D	None	X		X		19 mW	SN54L95	J, T	SN74L95	J, N	7-89
SERIAL-IN, PARALLEL-OUT	8	25 MHz	Gated D	Low	X				80 mW	SN54LS164	J, W	SN74LS164	J, N	7-206
		25 MHz	Gated D	Low	X				167 mW	SN54164	J, W	SN74164	J, N	
		12 MHz	Gated D	Low	X				84 mW	SN54L164	J, T	SN74L164	J, N	
PARALLEL-IN, SERIAL-OUT	8	25 MHz	D	None	X		X	X	210 mW	SN54165	J, W	SN74165	J, N	7-212
		35 MHz	D	None	X		X	X	105 mW	SN54LS165	J, W	SN74LS165	J, N	7-212
		20 MHz	D	Low	X		X	X	360 mW	SN54166	J, W	SN74166	J, N	7-217
		35 MHz	D	Low	X		X	X	110 mW	SN54LS166	J, W	SN74LS166	J, N	7-217
	4	10 MHz	D	High	X		X		175 mW	SN5494	J, W	SN7494	J, N	7-86
SERIAL-IN, SERIAL-OUT	8	25 MHz	Gated D	None	X				60 mW	SN54LS91	J, W	SN74LS91	J, N	
		10 MHz	Gated D	None	X				175 mW	SN54S91A	J, W	SN7491A	J, N	7-81
		3 MHz	Gated D	None	X				17.5 mW	SN54L91	J, T	SN74L91	J, N	

‡S-R ≡ shift right, S-L ≡ shift left

OTHER REGISTERS

DESCRIPTION	FREQ	ASYNC CLEAR	TYP TOTAL POWER DISSIPATION	DEVICE TYPE −55°C to 125°C		DEVICE TYPE 0°C to 70°C		PAGE NO.
QUADRUPLE MULTIPLEXERS WITH STORAGE	30 MHz	None	36.5 mW	SN54LS398	J	SN74LS398	J, N	7-499
	30 MHz	None	36.5 mW	SN54LS399	J, W	SN74LS399	J, N	7-499
	25 MHz	None	65 mW	SN54LS298	J, W	SN74LS298	J, N	7-432
	25 MHz	None	195 mW	SN54298	J, W	SN74298	J, N	7-432
	3 MHz	None	25 mW	SN54L98	J	SN74L98	J, N	7-107
8-BIT UNIVERSAL SHIFT/STORAGE REGISTERS	35 MHz	Low	175 mW	SN54LS299*	J	SN74LS299*	J, N	7-437
	50 MHz	Low	750 mW	SN54S299	J, W	SN74S299	J, N	
QUADRUPLE BUS-BUFFER REGISTERS	25 MHz	High	250 mW	SN54173	J, W	SN74173	J, N	7-249
	50 MHz	High	85 mW	SN54LS173*	J, W	SN74LS173*	J, N	

*New product in development as of October 1976.

TEXAS INSTRUMENTS
INCORPORATED
POST OFFICE BOX 5012 • DALLAS, TEXAS 75222

LATCHES

DESCRIPTION	NO. OF BITS	CLEAR	OUTPUTS	TYPICAL DELAY TIME	TYP TOTAL POWER DISSIPATION	DEVICE TYPE AND PACKAGE −55°C to 125°C		DEVICE TYPE AND PACKAGE 0°C to 70°C		PAGE NO.
MULTI-MODE BUFFERED	8	Low	Q	11 ns	410 mW	SN54S412	J	SN74S412	J, N	7-502
ADDRESSABLE	8	Low	Q	12 ns	300 mW	SN54259	J, W	SN74259	J, N	7-376
		Low	Q	17 ns	110 mW	SN54LS259	J, W	SN74LS259	J, N	
TRANSPARENT	8	None	Q	17 ns	210 mW	SN54LS363*	J	SN74LS363*	J, N	7-467
		None	Q	19 ns	120 mW	SN54LS373	J	SN74LS373	J, N	7-471
		None	Q	7 ns	525 mW	SN54S373	J	SN74S373	J, N	7-471
DUAL 4-BIT WITH INDEPENDENT ENABLE	8	Low	Q	11 ns	250 mW	SN54116	J, W	SN74116	J, N	7-115
		None	Q	15 ns	320 mW	SN54100	J, W	SN74100	J, N	7-113
DUAL 2-BIT WITH INDEPENDENT ENABLE	4	None	Q, Q̄	15 ns	160 mW	SN5475	J, W	SN7475	J, N	7-35
		None	Q, Q̄	30 ns	80 mW	SN54L75	J	SN74L75	J, N	7-35
		None	Q, Q̄	11 ns	32 mW	SN54LS75	J, W	SN74LS75	J, N	7-35
		None	Q	15 ns	160 mW	SN5477	W			7-35
		None	Q	30 ns	80 mW	SN54L77	T			7-35
		None	Q	10 ns	35 mW	SN54LS77	W			7-35
		None	Q, Q̄	12 ns	32 mW	SN54LS375	J, W	SN74LS375	J, N	7-478
QUAD S̄-R̄ (SSI)	4	None	Q	12 ns	90 mW	SN54279	J, W	SN74279	J, N	6-60
		None	Q	12 ns	19 mW	SN54LS279	J, W	SN74LS279	J, N	

CLOCK GENERATOR CIRCUITS

DESCRIPTION		TYP TOTAL POWER DISSIPATION	DEVICE TYPE AND PACKAGE −55°C to 125°C		DEVICE TYPE AND PACKAGE 0°C to 70°C		PAGE NO.
CLOCK GENERATOR/DRIVERS	(FOR TMS 9900)	669 mW			SN74LS362	J, N	7-460
	(FOR TMS 8080A)	719 mW			SN74LS424	J, N	7-507
DUAL VOLTAGE-CONTROLLED OSCILLATOR WITH ENABLE		90 mW	SN54LS124	J, W	SN74LS124	J, N	7-123
		525 mW	SN54S124	J, W	SN74S124	J, N	7-123
		90 mW	SN54LS326	J, W	SN74LS326	J, N	7-445
DUAL VOLTAGE-CONTROLLED OSCILLATOR		150 mW	SN54LS325	J, W	SN74LS325	J, N	7-445
		150 mW	SN54LS327	J, W	SN74LS327	J, N	7-445
VOLTAGE-CONTROLLED OSCILLATOR WITH ENABLE		90 mW	SN54LS324	J, W	SN74LS324	J, N	7-445
DUAL 30-MHz PULSE SYNCHRONIZERS/DRIVERS		255 mW	SN54120	J, W	SN74120	J, N	7-118
QUAD COMPLIMENTARY GATES (CLOCK/CLOCK) [SSI]		125 mW	SN54265	J, W	SN74265	J, N	6-89

CODE CONVERTERS

DESCRIPTION	TYPICAL DELAY TIME PER PACKAGE LEVEL	TYPICAL TOTAL POWER DISSIPATION	DEVICE TYPE AND PACKAGE −55°C to 125°C		DEVICE TYPE AND PACKAGE 0°C to 70°C		PAGE NO.
6-LINE-BCD TO 6-LINE BINARY, OR 4-LINE TO 4-LINE BCD 9's/BCD 10's CONVERTERS	25 ns	280 mW	SN54184	J, W	SN74184	J, N	7-290
6-BIT-BINARY TO 6-BIT-BCD CONVERTERS	25 ns	280 mW	SN54185A	J, W	SN74185A	J, N	7-290

*New product in development as of October 1976.

TEXAS INSTRUMENTS
INCORPORATED
POST OFFICE BOX 5012 • DALLAS, TEXAS 75222

MSI/LSI FUNCTIONS
FUNCTIONAL INDEX/SELECTION GUIDE

PRIORITY ENCODERS/REGISTERS

DESCRIPTION	TYPICAL DELAY TIME	TYP TOTAL POWER DISSIPATION	DEVICE TYPE AND PACKAGE −55°C to 125°C		DEVICE TYPE AND PACKAGE 0°C to 70°C		PAGE NO.
FULL BCD PRIORITY ENCODERS	10 ns	225 mW	SN54147	J, W	SN74147	J, N	7-151
	15 ns	60 mW	SN54LS147	J, W	SN74LS147	J, N	
CASCADABLE OCTAL PRIORITY ENCODERS	12 ns	190 mW	SN54148	J, W	SN74148	J, N	7-151
	15 ns	60 mW	SN54LS148	J, W	SN74LS148	J, N	
CASCADABLE OCTAL PRIORITY ENCODERS WITH 3-STATE OUTPUTS	16 ns	63 mW	SN54LS348	J, W	SN74LS348	J, N	7-448
4-BIT CASCADABLE PRIORITY REGISTERS	35 ns	275 mW	SN54278	J, W	SN74278	J, N	7-403

DATA SELECTORS/MULTIPLEXERS

DESCRIPTION	TYPE OF OUTPUT	TYPICAL DELAY TIMES DATA TO INV OUTPUT	TYPICAL DELAY TIMES DATA TO NON-INV OUTPUT	TYPICAL DELAY TIMES FROM ENABLE	TYP TOTAL POWER DISSIPATION	DEVICE TYPE AND PACKAGE −55°C to 125°C		DEVICE TYPE AND PACKAGE 0°C to 70°C		PAGE NO.
16-LINE-TO-1-LINE	2-State	11 ns		18 ns	200 mW	SN54150	J, W	SN74150	J, N	7-157
DUAL 8-LINE-TO-1-LINE	3-State	10 ns		17 ns	220 mW			SN74351	N	7-451
8-LINE-TO-1-LINE	3-State	4.5 ns	8 ns	14 ns	275 mW	SN54S251	J, W	SN74S251	J, N	7-362
	3-State	17 ns	21 ns	21 ns	250 mW	SN54251	J, W	SN74251	J, N	7-362
	3-State	17 ns	21 ns	21 ns	35 mW	SN54LS251	J, W	SN74LS251	J, N	7-362
	2-State	4.5 ns	8 ns	9 ns	225 mW	SN54S151	J, W	SN74S151	J, N	7-157
	2-State	8 ns	16 ns	22 ns	145 mW	SN54151A	J, W	SN74151A	J, N	7-157
	2-State	8 ns			130 mW	SN54152A	W			7-157
	2-State	11 ns	18 ns	27 ns	30 mW	SN54LS151	J, W	SN74LS151	J, N	7-157
	2-State	11 ns		18 ns	28 mW	SN54LS152	W			7-157
DUAL 4-LINE-TO-1-LINE	3-State		12 ns	16 ns	35 mW	SN54LS253	J, W	SN74LS253	J, N	7-369
	2-State	15 ns		22 ns	31 mW	SN54LS352	J, W	SN74LS352	J, N	7-454
	3-State	12 ns		21 ns	43 mW	SN54LS353	J, W	SN74LS353	J, N	7-457
	2-State		6 ns	9.5 ns	225 mW	SN54S153	J, W	SN74S153	J, N	7-165
	2-State		14 ns	17 ns	180 mW	SN54153	J, W	SN74153	J, N	7-165
	2-State		14 ns	17 ns	31 mW	SN54LS153	J, W	SN74LS153	J, N	7-165
	2-State		27 ns	34 ns	90 mW	SN54L153	J	SN74L153	J, N	7-165
QUADRUPLE 2-LINE-TO-1-LINE WITH STORAGE	2-State		20 ns†		65 mW	SN54LS298	J, W	SN74LS298	J, N	7-432
	2-State		20 ns†		195 mW	SN54298	J, W	SN74298	J, N	7-432
	2-State		20 ns†		32 mW	SN54LS398	J	SN74LS398	J, N	7-499
	2-State	20 ns†	20 ns†		37 mW	SN54LS399	J, W	SN74LS399	J, N	7-499
	2-State		120 ns†		25 mW	SN54L98	J	SN74L98	J, N	7-107
QUADRUPLE 2-LINE-TO-1-LINE	3-State	4 ns		14 ns	280 mW	SN54S258	J, W	SN74S258	J, N	7-372
	3-State		5 ns	14 ns	320 mW	SN54S257	J, W	SN74S257	J, N	7-372
	2-State	4 ns		7 ns	195 mW	SN54S158	J, W	SN74S158	J, N	7-181
	2-State		5 ns	8 ns	250 mW	SN54S157	J, W	SN74S157	J, N	7-181
	3-State	12 ns		20 ns	60 mW	SN54LS258A*	J, W	SN74LS258A*	J, N	7-372
	3-State		12 ns	20 ns	60 mW	SN54LS257A*	J, W	SN74LS257A*	J, N	7-372
	2-State	7 ns		12 ns	24 mW	SN54LS158	J, W	SN74LS158	J, N	7-181
	2-State		9 ns	14 ns	49 mW	SN54LS157	J, W	SN74LS157	J, N	7-181
	2-State		9 ns	14 ns	150 mW	SN54157	J, W	SN74157	J, N	7-181
	2-State		18 ns	27 ns	75 mW	SN54L157	J	SN74L157	J, N	7-181

†From clock.
*New product in development as of October 1976.

TEXAS INSTRUMENTS
INCORPORATED
POST OFFICE BOX 5012 • DALLAS, TEXAS 75222

DECODERS/DEMULTIPLEXERS

DESCRIPTION	TYPE OF OUTPUT	TYPICAL SELECT TIME	TYPICAL ENABLE TIME	TYP TOTAL POWER DISSIPATION	DEVICE TYPE AND PACKAGE −55°C to 125°C		0°C to 70°C		PAGE NO.
4-LINE-TO-16-LINE	Totem-Pole	23 ns	19 ns	170 mW	SN54154	J, W	SN74154	J, N	7-171
	Totem-Pole	46 ns	38 ns	85 mW	SN54L154	J	SN74L154	J, N	7-171
	Open-Collector	24 ns	19 ns	170 mW	SN54159	J, W	SN74159	J, N	7-188
4-LINE-TO-10-LINE, BCD-TO-DECIMAL	Totem-Pole	17 ns		35 mW	SN54LS42	J, W	SN54LS42	J, N	
	Totem-Pole	17 ns		140 mW	SN5442A	J, W	SN7442A	J, N	7-15
	Totem-Pole	34 ns		70 mW	SN54L42	J	SN74L42	J, N	
4-LINE-TO-10-LINE, EXCESS-3-TO-DECIMAL	Totem-Pole	17 ns		140 mW	SN5443A	J, W	SN7443A	J, N	7-15
	Totem-Pole	34 ns		70 mW	SN54L43	J	SN74L43	J, N	
4-LINE-TO-10-LINE EXCESS-3-GRAY-TO-DECIMAL	Totem-Pole	17 ns		140 mW	SN5444A	J, W	SN7444A	J, N	7-15
	Totem-Pole	34 ns		70 mW	SN54L44	J	SN74L44	J, N	
3-LINE-TO-8-LINE	Totem-Pole	8 ns	7 ns	245 mW	SN54S138	J, W	SN74S138	J, N	7-134
	Totem-Pole	22 ns	21 ns	31 mW	SN54LS138	J, W	SN74LS138	J, N	7-134
DUAL 2-LINE-TO-4-LINE	Totem-Pole	7.5 ns	6 ns	300 mW	SN54S139	J, W	SN74S139	J, N	7-134
	Totem-Pole	22 ns	19 ns	34 mW	SN54LS139	J, W	SN74LS139	J, N	7-134
	Totem-Pole	18 ns	15 ns	30 mW	SN54LS155	J, W	SN74LS155	J, N	7-175
	Totem-Pole	21 ns	16 ns	125 mW	SN54155	J, W	SN74155	J, N	7-175
	Open-Collector	23 ns	18 ns	125 mW	SN54156	J, W	SN74156	J, N	7-175
	Open-Collector	33 ns	26 ns	31 mW	SN54LS156	J, W	SN74LS156	J, N	7-175

OPEN-COLLECTOR DISPLAY DECODERS/DRIVERS WITH COUNTERS/LATCHES

DESCRIPTION	OUTPUT SINK CURRENT	OFF-STATE OUTPUT VOLTAGE	TYP TOTAL POWER DISSIPATION	BLANKING	DEVICE TYPE AND PACKAGE −55°C to 125°C		0°C to 70°C		PAGE NO.
BCD COUNTER/ 4-BIT LATCH/ BCD-TO-DECIMAL DECODER/DRIVER	7 mA	55 V	340 mW				SN74142	J, N	7-140
BCD COUNTER/ 4-BIT LATCH/ BCD-TO-SEVEN-SEGMENT DECODER/ LED DRIVER	Constant Current 15 mA	7 V	280 mW	Ripple	SN54143	J, W	SN74143	J, N	7-143
BCD COUNTER/ 4-BIT LATCH/ BCD-TO-SEVEN-SEGMENT DECODER/ LAMP DRIVER	20 mA	15 V	280 mW	Ripple	SN54144	J, W			7-143
	25 mA	15 V	280 mW	Ripple			SN74144	J, N	

RESULTANT DISPLAYS USING '143, '144

0   1   2   3   4   5   6   7   8   9

OPEN-COLLECTOR DISPLAY DECODERS/DRIVERS

DESCRIPTION	OUTPUT SINK CURRENT	OFF-STATE OUTPUT VOLTAGE	TYP TOTAL POWER DISSIPATION	BLANKING	DEVICE TYPE AND PACKAGE −55°C to 125°C		0°C to 70°C		PAGE NO.
BCD-TO-DECIMAL DECODERS/DRIVERS	80 mA	30 V	215 mW	Invalid Codes	SN5445	J, W	SN7445	J, N	7-20
	80 mA	15 V	35 mW	Invalid Codes			SN74LS145	J, N	7-148
	12 mA	15 V	35 mW	Invalid Codes	SN54LS145	J, W			7-148
	80 mA	15 V	215 mW	Invlaid Codes	SN54145	J, W	SN74145	J, N	7-148
	7 mA	60 V	80 mW	Invalid Codes			SN74141	J, N	7-138
BCD-TO-SEVEN-SEGMENT DECODERS/DRIVERS	40 mA	30 V	320 mW	Ripple	SN5446A	J, W	SN7446A	J, N	7-22
	40 mA	30 V	320 mW	Ripple	SN54246	J, W	SN74246	J, N	7-22
	40 mA	15 V	320 mW	Ripple	SN5447A	J, W	SN7447A	J, N	7-22
	40 mA	15 V	320 mW	Ripple	SN54247	J, W	SN74247	J, N	7-351
	24 mA	15 V	35 mW	Ripple			SN74LS47	J, N	7-22
	24 mA	15 V	35 mW	Ripple			SN74LS247	J, N	7-351
	12 mA	15 V	35 mW	Ripple	SN54LS47	J, W			7-22
	12 mA	15 V	35 mW	Ripple	SN54LS247	J, W			7-351
	20 mA	30 V	133 mW	Ripple	SN54L46	J	SN74L46	J, N	7-22
	20 mA	15 V	133 mW	Ripple	SN54L47	J	SN74L47	J, N	7-22
	6.4 mA	5.5 V	265 mW	Ripple	SN5448	J, W	SN7448	J, N	7-22
	6.4 mA	5.5 V	265 mW	Ripple	SN54248	J, W	SN74248	J, N	7-351
	6 mA	5.5 V	125 mW	Ripple			SN74LS48	J, N	7-22
	6 mA	5.5 V	125 mW	Ripple			SN74LS248	J, N	7-351
	2 mA	5.5 V	125 mW	Ripple	SN54LS48	J, W			7-22
	2 mA	5.5 V	125 mW	Ripple	SN54LS248	J, W			7-351
	10 mA	5.5 V	165 mW	Direct	SN5449	W			7-22
	10 mA	5.5 V	265 mW	Direct	SN54249	J, W	SN74249	J, N	7-351
	8 mA	5.5 V	40 mW	Direct			SN74LS249	J, N	7-351
	8 mA	5.5 V	40 mW	Direct			SN74LS49	J, N	7-22
	4 mA	5.5 V	40 mW	Direct	SN54LS49	J, W			7-22
	4 mA	5.5 V	40 mW	Direct	SN54LS249	J, W			7-351

RESULTANT DISPLAYS USING '46A, '47A, '48, '49, 'L46, 'L47, 'LS47, 'LS48, 'LS49

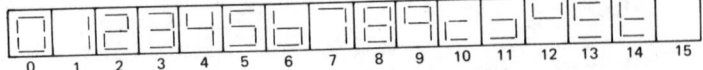

RESULTANT DISPLAYS USING '246, '247, '248, '249, 'LS247, 'LS248, 'LS249

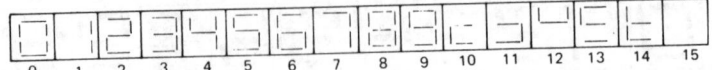

TEXAS INSTRUMENTS
INCORPORATED
POST OFFICE BOX 5012 • DALLAS, TEXAS 75222

BUS TRANSCEIVERS AND DRIVERS

DESCRIPTION	TYPICAL PROPAGATION DELAY TIMES	MAXIMUM SOURCE CURRENT	MAXIMUM SINK CURRENT	DEVICE TYPE AND PACKAGE				PAGE NO.
				−55°C to 125°C		0°C to 70°C		
CONTROLLER AND BUS DRIVER FOR 8080A SYSTEMS		−1 mA	10 mA			SN74S428	N	7-514
		−1 mA	10 mA			SN74S438	N	
OCTAL BUS TRANSCEIVERS	8 ns	−12 mA	12 mA	SN54LS245	J	SN74LS245	J, N	7-349
4-BIT BUS TRANSCEIVERS WITH STORAGE	10 ns	−6.5 mA	20 mA	SN54S226	J, W	SN74S226	J, N	7-345

ASYNCHRONOUS COUNTERS (RIPPLE CLOCK)—NEGATIVE-EDGE TRIGGERED

DESCRIPTION	COUNT FREQ	PARALLEL LOAD	CLEAR	TYP TOTAL POWER DISSIPATION	DEVICE TYPE AND PACKAGE				PAGE NO.
					−55°C to 125°C		0°C to 70°C		
DECADE	50 MHz	Yes	Low	240 mW	SN54196	J, W	SN74196	J, N	7-331
	100 MHz	Yes	Low	375 mW	SN54S196	J, W	SN74S196	J, N	7-331
	35 MHz	Yes	Low	150 mW	SN54176	J, W	SN74176	J, N	7-259
	32 MHz	Set-to-9	High	40 mW	SN54LS90	J, W	SN74LS90	J, N	7-72
	32 MHz	Set-to-9	High	40 mW	SN54LS290	J, W	SN74LS290	J, N	7-423
	32 MHz	Set-to-9	High	160 mW	SN5490A	J, W	SN7490A	J, N	7-72
	32 MHz	Set-to-9	High	160 mW	SN54290	J, W	SN74290	J, N	7-423
	30 MHz	Yes	Low	60 mW	SN54LS196	J, W	SN74LS196	J, N	7-331
	3 MHz	Set-to-9	High	20 mW	SN54L90	J, T	SN74L90	J, N	7-72
4-BIT BINARY	50 MHz	Yes	Low	240 mW	SN54197	J, W	SN74197	J, N	7-331
	100 MHz	Yes	Low	375 mW	SN54S197	J, W	SN74S197	J, N	7-331
	35 MHz	Yes	Low	150 mW	SN54177	J, W	SN74177	J, N	7-259
	32 MHz	None	High	39 mW	SN54LS93	J, W	SN74LS93	J, N	7-72
	32 MHz	None	High	39 mW	SN54LS293	J, W	SN74LS293	J, N	7-423
	32 MHz	None	High	160 mW	SN5493A	J, W	SN7493A	J, N	7-72
	32 MHz	None	High	160 mW	SN54293	J, W	SN74293	J, N	7-423
	30 MHz	Yes	Low	60 mW	SN54LS197	J, W	SN74LS197	J, N	7-331
	3 MHz	None	High	20 mW	SN54L93	J, T	SN74L93	J, N	7-72
DIVIDE-BY-12	32 MHz	None	High	39 mW	SN54LS92	J, W	SN74LS92	J, N	7-72
	32 MHz	None	High	160 mW	SN5492A	J, W	SN7492A	J, N	
DUAL DECADE	25 MHz	None	High	210 mW	SN54390	J, W	SN74390	J, N	7-489
	35 MHz	None	High	75 mW	SN54LS390	J, W	SN74LS390	J, N	7-489
	25 MHz	Set-to-9	High	225 mW	SN54490	J, W	SN74490	J, N	7-520
	35 MHz	Set-to-9	High	75 mW	SN54LS490	J, W	SN74LS490	J, N	7-520
DUAL 4-BIT BINARY	25 MHz	None	High	190 mW	SN54393	J, W	SN74393	J, N	7-489
	35 MHz	None	High	75 mW	SN54LS393	J, W	SN74LS393	J, N	7-489

7

SYNCHRONOUS COUNTERS—POSITIVE-EDGE TRIGGERED

DESCRIPTION	COUNT FREQ	PARALLEL LOAD	CLEAR	TYP TOTAL POWER DISSIPATION	DEVICE TYPE AND PACKAGE				PAGE NO.
					−55°C to 125°C		0°C to 70°C		
DECADE	40 MHz	Sync	Sync-L	475 mW	SN54S162	J, W	SN74S162	J, N	
	25 MHz	Sync	Sync-L	93 mW	SN54LS162A	J, W	SN74LS162A	J, N	
	25 MHz	Sync	Async-L	93 mW	SN54LS160A	J, W	SN74LS160A	J, N	7-190
	25 MHz	Sync	Sync-L	305 mW	SN54162	J, W	SN74162	J, N	
	25 MHz	Sync	Async-L	305 mW	SN54160	J, W	SN74160	J, N	
DECADE UP/DOWN	40 MHz	Sync	None	500 mW	SN54S168	J, W	SN74S168	J, N	7-226
	25 MHz	Sync	None	100 mW	SN54LS168A	J, W	SN74LS168A	J, N	7-226
	25 MHz	Async	Async-H	85 mW	SN54LS192	J, W	SN74LS192	J, N	7-306
	25 MHz	Async	Async-H	325 mW	SN54192	J, W	SN74192	J, N	7-306
	20 MHz	Async	None	100 mW	SN54LS190	J, W	SN74LS190	J, N	7-296
	20 MHz	Async	None	325 mW	SN54190	J, W	SN74190	J, N	7-296
	3 MHz	Async	Async-H	42 mW	SN54L192	J	SN74L192	J, N	7-306
DECADE RATE MULTIPLIER, $N_{10}\frac{1}{}$	25 MHz	Set-to-9	Async-H	270 mW	SN54167	J, W	SN74167	J, N	7-222
4-BIT BINARY	40 MHz	Sync	Sync-L	475 mW	SN54S163	J, W	SN74S163	J, N	
	25 MHz	Sync	Sync-L	93 mW	SN54LS163A	J, W	SN74LS163A	J, N	
	25 MHz	Sync	Async-L	93 mW	SN54LS161A	J, W	SN74LS161A	J, N	7-190
	25 MHz	Sync	Sync-L	305 mW	SN54163	J, W	SN74163	J, N	
	25 MHz	Sync	Async-L	305 mW	SN54161	J, W	SN74161	J, N	
4-BIT BINARY UP/DOWN	40 MHz	Sync	None	500 mW	SN54S169	J, N	SN74S169	J, N	7-226
	25 MHz	Sync	None	100 mW	SN54LS169A	J, W	SN74LS169A	J, N	7-226
	25 MHz	Async	Async-H	85 mW	SN54LS193	J, W	SN74LS193	J, N	7-306
	25 MHz	Async	Async-H	325 mW	SN54193	J, W	SN74193	J, N	7-306
	20 MHz	Async	None	90 mW	SN54LS191	J, W	SN74LS191	J, N	7-296
	20 MHz	Async	None	325 mW	SN54191	J, W	SN74191	J, N	7-296
	3 MHz	Async	Async-H	42 mW	SN54L193	J	SN74L193	J, N	7-306
6-BIT BINARY RATE MULTIPLIER, $N_2\frac{1}{}$	25 MHz		Async-H	345 mW	SN5497	J, W	SN7497	J, N	7-102

BIPOLAR BIT-SLICE PROCESSOR ELEMENTS[†]

DESCRIPTION	CASCADABLE TO N-BITS	TYPICAL μ-OPERATION TIME	TECHNOLOGY	DEVICE TYPE AND PACKAGE			
				−55°C to 125°C		0°C to 70°C	
4-BIT SLICE	Yes	100 ns	STTL	SN54S481	J	SN74S481	J, N
	Yes	230 ns	I^2L	SBP0400AM	J	SBP0400AC	J, N
	Yes	230 ns	I^2L	SBP0401AM	J	SBP0401AC	J, N

FIRST-IN FIRST-OUT MEMORIES (FIFO'S)[†]

DESCRIPTION	TYPE OF OUTPUT	DELAY TIME FROM CLOCK	TYP TOTAL POWER DISSIPATION	DEVICE TYPE AND PACKAGE			
				−55°C to 125°C		0°C to 70°C	
ASYNCHRONOUS 16 X 5	3-State	50 ns	400 mW			SN74S225	J

[†]See Bipolar Microcomputer Components Data Book, LCC4270.

TEXAS INSTRUMENTS
INCORPORATED
POST OFFICE BOX 5012 • DALLAS, TEXAS 75222

RANDOM-ACCESS READ-WRITE MEMORIES (RAM'S)

DESCRIPTION	ORGANI-ZATION	TYPE OF OUTPUT	TYPICAL ADDRESS TIME	TYPICAL ENABLE TIME	TYP POWER DISSIPATION PER BIT	DEVICE TYPE AND PACKAGE				PAGE NO.
						−55°C to 125°C		0°C to 70°C		
1024-BIT ARRAYS WITH POWER-DOWN	1024 X 1	3-State	65 ns	20 ns	0.2/0.07 mW	SN54LS215	JD	SN74LS215	JD, N	†
	1024 X 1	O-C	65 ns	20 ns	0.2/0.07 mW	SN54LS315	JD	SN74LS315	JD, N	†
1024-BIT ARRAYS	1024 X 1	3-State	65 ns	20 ns	0.2 mW	SN54LS214	JD	SN74LS214	JD, N	†
	1024 X 1	3-State	30 ns	15 ns	0.51 mW	SN54S214	JD	SN74S214	JD, N	†
	1024 X 1	O-C	65 ns	20 ns	0.2 mW	SN54LS314	JD	SN74LS314	JD, N	†
	1024 X 1	O-C	30 ns	15 ns	0.51 mW	SN54S314	JD	SN74S314	JD, N	†
	256 X 4	3-State	60 ns	20 ns	0.3 mW	SN54LS207	J	SN74LS207	J, N	†
	256 X 4	3-State	40 ns	15 ns	0.59 mW	SN54S207	J	SN74S207	J, N	†
	256 X 4	3-State	60 ns	20 ns	0.3 mW	SN54LS208	J	SN74LS208	J, N	†
	256 X 4	3-State	40 ns	15 ns	0.59 mW	SN54S208	J	SN74S208	J, N	†
256-BIT ARRAYS WITH POWER-DOWN	256 X 1	3-State	35 ns	15 ns	1.1/0.39 mW	SN54LS202	J, W	SN74LS202	J, N	†
	256 X 1	O-C	35 ns	15 ns	1.1/0.39 mW	SN54LS302	J, W	SN74LS302	J, N	†
256-BIT ARRAYS	256 X 1	3-State	35 ns	15 ns	1.1 mW	SN54LS200A	J, W	SN74LS200A	J, N	†
	256 X 1	3-State	25 ns	15 ns	1.9 mW	SN54S200A	J, W	SN74S200A	J, N	†
	256 X 1	3-State	42 ns	17 ns	1.9 mW	SN54S201	J, W	SN74S201	J, N	†
	256 X 1	O-C	35 ns	15 ns	1.1 mW	SN54LS300A	J, W	SN74LS300A	J, N	†
	256 X 1	O-C	25 ns	15 ns	1.9 mW	SN54S300A	J, W	SN74S300A	J, N	†
	256 X 1	O-C	42 ns	13 ns	1.9 mW	SN54S301	J, W	SN74S301	J, N	†
64-BIT ARRAYS	16 X 4	3-State	25 ns	12 ns	5.9 mW	SN54S189	J, W	SN74S189	J, N	†
	16 X 4	O-C	25 ns	12 ns	5.9 mW	SN54S289	J, W	SN74S289	J, N	†
	16 X 4	O-C	32 ns	30 ns	5.9 mW			SN7489	J, N	†
16-BIT ARRAYS	16 X 1	O-C	15 ns	15 ns	14 mW	SN5481A	J, W	SN7481A	J, N	†
	16 X 1	O-C	15 ns	15 ns	14 mW	SN5484A	J, W	SN7484A	J, N	†
16-BIT MULTIPLE-PORT REGISTER FILE	8 X 2	3-State	33 ns	15 ns	35 mW			SN74172	J, N	7-245
16-BIT REGISTER FILE	4 X 4	O-C	27 ns	15 ns	7.8 mW	SN54LS170	J, W	SN74LS170	J, N	7-237
	4 X 4	O-C	30 ns	15 ns	40 mW	SN54170	J, W	SN74170	J, N	7-237
	4 X 4	3-State	24 ns	19 ns	9.3 mW	SN54LS670	J, W	SN74LS670	J, N	7-526

READ-ONLY MEMORIES (ROM'S)†

DESCRIPTION	ORGANI-ZATION	TYPE OF OUTPUT	TYPICAL ADDRESS TIME	TYPICAL ENABLE TIME	TYP POWER DISSIPATION PER BIT	DEVICE TYPE AND PACKAGE			
						−55°C to 125°C		0°C to 70°C	
2048-BIT ARRAYS	512 X 4	O-C	45 ns	15 ns	0.26 mW	SN54S270	J	SN74S270	J, N
	256 X 8	O-C	45 ns	15 ns	0.26 mW	SN54S271	J	SN74S271	J, N
	512 X 4	3-State	45 ns	15 ns	0.26 mW	SN54S370	J	SN74S370	J, N
	256 X 8	3-State	45 ns	15 ns	0.26 mW	SN54S371	J	SN74S371	J, N
1024-BIT ARRAYS	256 X 4	O-C	40 ns	20 ns	0.46 mW	SN54187	J, W	SN74187	J, N
256-BIT ARRAYS	32 X 8	O-C	26 ns	22 ns	1.1 mW	SN5488A	J, W	SN7488A	J, N

†See Bipolar Microcomputer Components Data Book, LCC4270.

TEXAS INSTRUMENTS
INCORPORATED
POST OFFICE BOX 5012 • DALLAS, TEXAS 75222

PROGRAMMABLE READ-ONLY MEMORIES (PROM'S)[†]

DESCRIPTION	ORGANI-ZATION	TYPE OF OUTPUT	TYPICAL ADDRESS TIME	TYPICAL ENABLE TIME	TYP POWER DISSIPATION PER BIT	DEVICE TYPE AND PACKAGE			
						−55°C to 125°C		0°C to 70°C	
4096-BIT ARRAYS	512 X 8	3-State	55 ns	20 ns	0.14 mW	SN54S472	J	SN74S472	J, N
	512 X 8	O-C	55 ns	20 ns	0.14 mW	SN54S473	J	SN74S473	J, N
	512 X 8	3-State	55 ns	20 ns	0.14 mW	SN54S474	J, W	SN74S474	J, N
	512 X 8	O-C	55 ns	20 ns	0.14 mW	SN54S475	J, W	SN74S475	J, N
2048-BIT ARRAYS	256 X 8	O-C	50 ns	20 ns	0.24 mW	SN54S470	J	SN74S470	J, N
	256 X 8	3-State	50 ns	20 ns	0.27 mW	SN54S471	J	SN74S471	J, N
1024-BIT ARRAYS	256 X 4	3-State	40 ns	15 ns	0.49 mW	SN54S287	J, W	SN74S287	J, N
	256 X 4	O-C	40 ns	15 ns	0.49 mW	SN54S387	J, W	SN74S387	J, N
512-BIT ARRAYS	64 X 8	O-C	50 ns	47 ns	0.6 mW	SN54186	J, W	SN74186	J, N
256-BIT ARRAYS	32 X 8	O-C	29 ns	28 ns	1.3 mW	SN54188A	J, W	SN74188A	J, N
	32 X 8	O-C	25 ns	12 ns	1.56 mW	SN54S188	J, W	SN74S188	J, N
	32 X 8	3-State	25 ns	12 ns	1.56 mW	SN54S288	J, W	SN74S288	J, N

MICROPROCESSOR CONTROLLERS AND SUPPORT FUNCTIONS

DESCRIPTION	SYSTEM APPLICATION	TYP TOTAL POWER DISSIPATION	DEVICE TYPE AND PACKAGE				PAGE NO.
			−55°C to 125°C		0°C to 70°C		
SYSTEM CONTROLLERS	8080A	700 mW			SN74S428 (TIM8228)	N	7-514
	8080A	700 mW			SN74S438 (TIM8238)	N	7-514
	Universal	450 mW	SN54S482	J	SN74S482	J, N	†
REGISTERS	TMS 9900	110 mW	SN54LS259	J, W	SN74LS259 (TIM9906)	J, N	7-376
	MOS	210 mW	SN54LS363*	J	SN74LS363*	J, N	7-467
		210 mW	SN54LS364*	J	SN74LS364*	J, N	7-467
MULTI-MODE LATCHES	8080A	410 mW	SN54S412	J, W	SN74S412 (TIM8212)	J, N	7-502
TRANSCEIVERS AND BUS DRIVERS		625 mW	SN54S226*	J, W	SN74S226*	J, N	7-345
		207 mW	SN54LS245	J	SN74LS245	J, N	7-349
TRANSCEIVERS AND BUS DRIVERS (SSI)		98 mW	SN54LS240	J	SN74LS240	J, N	6-83
		450 mW	SN54S240	J	SN74S240	J, N	6-83
		100 mW	SN54LS241	J	SN74LS241	J, N	6-83
		538 mW	SN54S241	J	SN74S241	J, N	6-83
		128 mW	SN54LS242	J, W	SN74LS242	J, N	6-87
		128 mW	SN54LS243	J, W	SN74LS243	J, N	6-87
		100 mW	SN54LS244	J	SN74LS244	J, N	6-83
CLOCK ELEMENTS	TMS 9900	669 mW			SN74LS362 (TIM9904)	J, N	7-460
	8080A	719 mW			SN74LS424 (TIM8224)	J, N	7-507
LOGIC ELEMENTS	TMS 9900	190 mW	SN54148	J, W	SN74148 (TIM9907)	J, N	7-151
	TMS 9900	35 mW	SN54LS251	J, W	SN74LS251 (TIM9905)	J, N	7-362
	TMS 9900	63 mW	SN54LS348	J, W	SN74LS348 (TIM9908)	J, N	7-448

*New product in development as of October 1976.

[†]See Bipolar Microcomputer Components Data Book, LCC4270.

7

TEXAS INSTRUMENTS
INCORPORATED
POST OFFICE BOX 5012 • DALLAS, TEXAS 75222

TTL
MSI

TYPES SN5442A THRU SN5444A, SN54L42 THRU SN54L44, SN54LS42, SN7442A THRU SN7444A, SN74L42 THRU SN74L44, SN74LS42 4-LINE-TO-10-LINE DECODERS (1-OF-10)

BULLETIN NO. DL-S 7611861, MARCH 1974–REVISED OCTOBER 1976

'42A, 'L42, 'LS42 . . . BCD-TO-DECIMAL
'43A, 'L43 . . . EXCESS-3-TO-DECIMAL
'44A, 'L44 . . . EXCESS-3-GRAY-TO-DECIMAL

- All Outputs Are High for Invalid Input Conditions

- Also for Application as
  4-Line-to-16-Line Decoders
  3-Line-to-8-Line Decoders

- Diode-Clamped Inputs

TYPES	TYPICAL POWER DISSIPATION	TYPICAL PROPAGATION DELAYS
'42A, '43A, '44A	140 mW	17 ns
'L42, 'L43, 'L44	70 mW	49 ns
'LS42	35 mW	17 ns

SN5442A THRU SN5444A, SN54LS42 . . . J OR W PACKAGE
SN54L42 THRU SN54L44 . . . J PACKAGE
SN7442A THRU SN7444A,
SN74L42 THRU SN74L44, SN74LS42 . . . J OR N PACKAGE
(TOP VIEW)

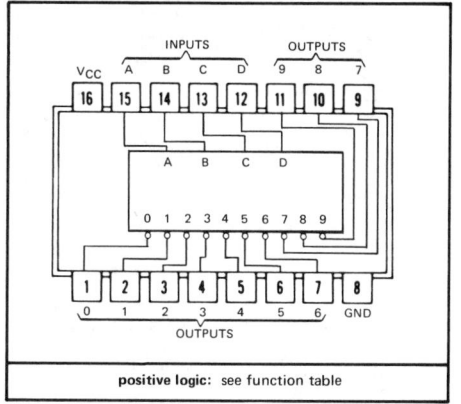

positive logic: see function table

description

These monolithic decimal decoders consist of eight inverters and ten four-input NAND gates. The inverters are connected in pairs to make BCD input data available for decoding by the NAND gates. Full decoding of valid input logic ensures that all outputs remain off for all invalid input conditions.

The '42A, 'L42, and 'LS42 BCD-to-decimal decoders, the '43A and 'L43 excess-3-to-decimal decoders, and the '44A and 'L44 excess-3-gray-to-decimal decoders feature inputs and outputs that are compatible for use with most TTL and other saturated low-level logic circuits. D-c noise margins are typically one volt.

Series 54, 54L, and 54LS circuits are characterized for operation over the full military temperature range of −55°C to 125°C; Series 74, 74L, and 74LS circuits are characterized for operation from 0°C to 70°C.

FUNCTION TABLE

NO.	'42A, 'L42, 'LS42 BCD INPUT				'43A, 'L43 EXCESS-3-INPUT				'44A, 'L44 EXCESS-3-GRAY INPUT				ALL TYPES DECIMAL OUTPUT									
	D	C	B	A	D	C	B	A	D	C	B	A	0	1	2	3	4	5	6	7	8	9
0	L	L	L	L	L	L	H	H	L	L	H	L	L	H	H	H	H	H	H	H	H	H
1	L	L	L	H	L	H	L	L	L	H	H	L	H	L	H	H	H	H	H	H	H	H
2	L	L	H	L	L	H	L	H	L	H	H	H	H	H	L	H	H	H	H	H	H	H
3	L	L	H	H	L	H	H	L	L	H	L	H	H	H	H	L	H	H	H	H	H	H
4	L	H	L	L	L	H	H	H	L	H	L	L	H	H	H	H	L	H	H	H	H	H
5	L	H	L	H	H	L	L	L	H	H	L	L	H	H	H	H	H	L	H	H	H	H
6	L	H	H	L	H	L	L	H	H	H	L	H	H	H	H	H	H	H	L	H	H	H
7	L	H	H	H	H	L	H	L	H	H	H	H	H	H	H	H	H	H	H	L	H	H
8	H	L	L	L	H	L	H	H	H	H	H	L	H	H	H	H	H	H	H	H	L	H
9	H	L	L	H	H	H	L	L	H	L	H	L	H	H	H	H	H	H	H	H	H	L
INVALID	H	L	H	L	H	H	L	H	H	L	L	H	H	H	H	H	H	H	H	H	H	H
	H	L	H	H	H	H	H	L	H	L	L	L	H	H	H	H	H	H	H	H	H	H
	H	H	L	L	H	H	H	H	H	L	H	H	H	H	H	H	H	H	H	H	H	H
	H	H	L	H	L	L	L	L	L	L	L	L	H	H	H	H	H	H	H	H	H	H
	H	H	H	L	L	L	L	H	L	L	L	H	H	H	H	H	H	H	H	H	H	H
	H	H	H	H	L	L	H	L	L	L	H	H	H	H	H	H	H	H	H	H	H	H

H = high level, L = low level

TEXAS INSTRUMENTS
INCORPORATED
POST OFFICE BOX 5012 • DALLAS, TEXAS 75222

7

TYPES SN5442A THRU SN5444A, SN54L42 THRU SN54L44, SN54LS42, SN7442A THRU SN7444A, SN74L42 THRU SN74L44, SN74LS42 4-LINE-TO-10-LINE DECODERS (1-OF-10)

REVISED OCTOBER 1976

functional block diagrams and schematics of inputs and outputs

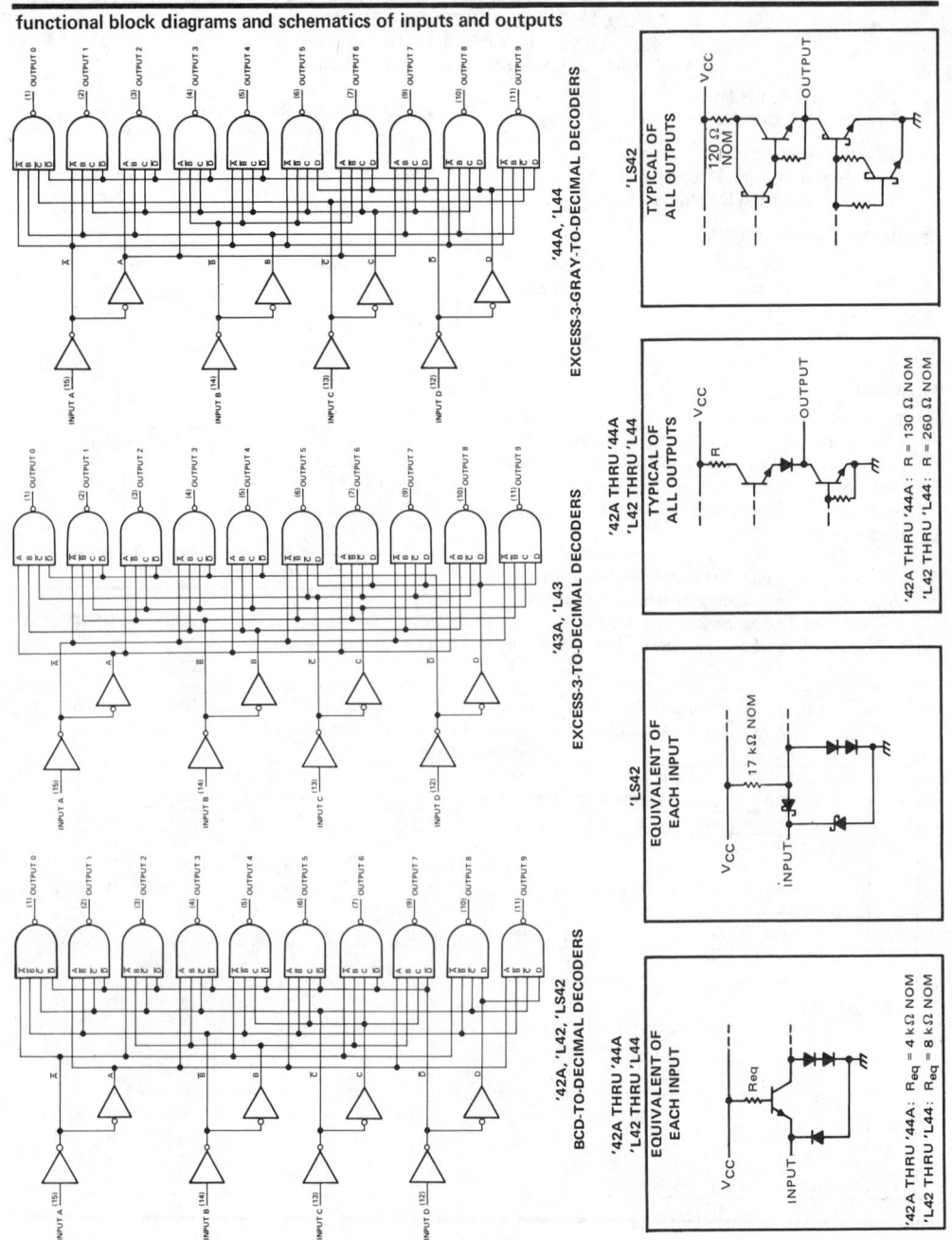

TEXAS INSTRUMENTS
INCORPORATED
POST OFFICE BOX 5012 • DALLAS, TEXAS 75222

TYPES SN5442A, SN5443A, SN5444A, SN7442A, SN7443A, SN7444A
4-LINE-TO-10-LINE DECODERS (1-OF-10)

absolute maximum ratings over operating free-air temperature range (unless otherwise noted)

Supply voltage, V_{CC} (see Note 1)	7 V
Input voltage	5.5 V
Operating free-air temperature range: SN54' Circuits	-55°C to 125°C
SN74' Circuits	0°C to 70°C
Storage temperature range	-65°C to 150°C

NOTE 1: Voltage values are with respect to network ground terminal.

recommended operating conditions

	SN5442A SN5443A SN5444A			SN7442A SN7443A SN7444A			UNIT
	MIN	NOM	MAX	MIN	NOM	MAX	
Supply voltage, V_{CC}	4.5	5	5.5	4.75	5	5.25	V
High-level output current, I_{OH}			-800			800	μA
Low-level output current, I_{OL}			16			16	mA
Operating free-air temperature, T_A	-55		125	0		70	$^{\circ}$C

electrical characteristics over recommended operating free-air temperature range (unless otherwise noted)

PARAMETER		TEST CONDITIONS[†]	SN5442A SN5443A SN5444A			SN7442A SN7443A SN7444A			UNIT
			MIN	TYP[‡]	MAX	MIN	TYP[‡]	MAX	
V_{IH}	High-level input voltage		2			2			V
V_{IL}	Low-level input voltage				0.8			0.8	V
V_{IK}	Input clamp voltage	V_{CC} = MIN, I_I = -12 mA			-1.5			-1.5	V
V_{OH}	High-level output voltage	V_{CC} = MIN, V_{IH} = 2 V, V_{IL} = 0.8 V, I_{OH} = -800 μA	2.4	3.4		2.4	3.4		V
V_{OL}	Low-level output voltage	V_{CC} = MIN, V_{IH} = 2 V, V_{IL} = 0.8 V, I_{OL} = 16 mA		0.2	0.4		0.2	0.4	V
I_I	Input current at maximum input voltage	V_{CC} = MAX, V_I = 5.5 V			1			1	mA
I_{IH}	High-level input current	V_{CC} = MAX, V_I = 2.4 V			40			40	μA
I_{IL}	Low level input current	V_{CC} = MAX, V_I = 0.4 V			-1.6			-1.6	mA
I_{OS}	Short-circuit output current[§]	V_{CC} = MAX	-20		-55	-18		-55	mA
I_{CC}	Supply current	V_{CC} = MAX, See Note 2		28	41		28	56	mA

[†]For conditions shown as MIN or MAX, use the appropriate values specified under recommended operating conditions.
[‡]All typical values are at V_{CC} = 5 V, T_A = 25°C.
[§]Not more than one output should be shorted at a time.
NOTE 2: I_{CC} is measured with all outputs open and all inputs grounded.

switching characteristics, V_{CC} = 5 V, T_A = 25°C

PARAMETER		TEST CONDITIONS	MIN	TYP	MAX	UNIT
t_{PHL}	Propagation delay time, high-to-low-level output from A, B, C, or D through 2 levels of logic			14	25	ns
t_{PHL}	Propagation delay time, high-to-low-level output from A, B, C, or D through 3 levels of logic	C_L = 15 pF, R_L = 400 Ω, See Note 3		17	30	ns
t_{PLH}	Propagation delay time, low-to-high-level output from A, B, C, and D through 2 levels of logic			10	25	ns
t_{PLH}	Propagation delay time, low-to-high-level output from A, B, C, and D through 3 levels of logic			17	30	ns

NOTE 3: Load circuits and waveforms are shown on page 3-10.

absolute maximum ratings over operating free-air temperature range (unless otherwise noted)

Supply voltage, V_{CC} (see Note 1) . . . . 7 V

Input voltage . . . . 5.5 V

Operating free-air temperature range: SN54L' Circuits . . . . −55°C to 125°C

SN74L' Circuits . . . . 0°C to 70°C

Storage temperature range . . . . −65°C to 150°C

NOTE 1: Voltage values are with respect to network ground terminal.

recommended operating conditions

	SN54L42 SN54L43 SN54L44			SN74L42 SN74L43 SN74L44			UNIT
	MIN	NOM	MAX	MIN	NOM	MAX	
Supply voltage, V_{CC}	4.5	5	5.5	4.75	5	5.25	V
High-level output current, I_{OH}			−400			−400	µA
Low-level output current, I_{OL}			8			8	mA
Operating free-air temperature, T_A	−55		125	0		70	°C

electrical characteristics over recommended operating free-air temperature range (unless otherwise noted)

	PARAMETER	TEST CONDITIONS[†]			MIN	TYP[‡]	MAX	UNIT
V_{IH}	High-level input voltage				2			V
V_{IL}	Low-level input voltage						0.8	V
V_{IK}	Input clamp voltage	V_{CC} = MIN,	I_I = −12 mA				−1.5	V
V_{OH}	High-level output voltage	V_{CC} = MIN, V_{IL} = 0.8 V,	V_{IH} = 2 V, I_{OH} = −400 µA		2.4	3.4		V
V_{OL}	Low-level output voltage	V_{CC} = MIN, V_{IL} = 0.8 V,	V_{IH} = 2 V, I_{OL} = 8 mA			0.2	0.4	V
I_I	Input current at maximum input voltage	V_{CC} = MAX,	V_I = 5.5 V				1	mA
I_{IH}	High-level input current	V_{CC} = MAX,	V_I = 2.4 V				20	µA
I_{IL}	Low-level input current	V_{CC} = MAX,	V_I = 0.4 V				−0.8	mA
I_{OS}	Short-circuit output current[§]	V_{CC} = MAX			−9		−28	mA
I_{CC}	Supply Current	V_{CC} = MAX, See Note 2		SN54L'		14	22	mA
				SN74L'		14	28	

[†]For conditions shown as MIN or MAX, use the appropriate values specified under recommended operating conditions.
[‡]All typical values are at V_{CC} = 5 V, T_A = 25°C.
[§]Not more than one output should be shorted at a time.
NOTE 2: I_{CC} is measured with all outputs open and inputs grounded.

switching characteristics, V_{CC} = 5 V, T_A = 25°C

	PARAMETER	TEST CONDITIONS	MIN	TYP	MAX	UNIT
t_{PHL}	Propagation delay time, high-to-low-level output from A, B, C, or D through 2 levels of logic		10	44	60	ns
t_{PHL}	Propagation delay time, high-to-low-level output from A, B, C, or D through 3 levels of logic	C_L = 15 pF, R_L = 800 Ω, See Note 3		46	70	ns
t_{PLH}	Propagation delay time, low-to-high-level output from A, B, C, and D through 2 levels of logic		10	34	50	ns
t_{PLH}	Propagation delay time, low-to-high-level output from A, B, C, and D through 3 levels of logic			52	70	ns

NOTE 3: Load circuit and voltage waveforms are shown on page 3-10.

7

TEXAS INSTRUMENTS
INCORPORATED
POST OFFICE BOX 5012 • DALLAS, TEXAS 75222

absolute maximum ratings over operating free-air temperature range (unless otherwise noted)

Supply voltage, V_{CC} (see Note 1) . . . . 7 V
Input voltage . . . . 7 V
Operating free-air temperature range: SN54LS42 . . . . −55°C to 125°C
                                SN74LS42 . . . . 0°C to 70°C
Storage temperature range . . . . −65°C to 150°C

NOTE 1: Voltage values are with respect to network ground terminal.

recommended operating conditions

	SN54LS42			SN74LS42			UNIT
	MIN	NOM	MAX	MIN	NOM	MAX	
Supply voltage, V_{CC}	4.5	5	5.5	4.75	5	5.25	V
High-level output current, I_{OH}			−400			−400	µA
Low-level output current, I_{OL}			4			8	mA
Operating free-air temperature, T_A	−55		125	0		70	°C

electrical characteristics over recommended operating free-air temperature range (unless otherwise noted)

PARAMETER		TEST CONDITIONS†		SN54LS42			SN74LS42			UNIT
				MIN	TYP‡	MAX	MIN	TYP‡	MAX	
V_{IH}	High-level input voltage			2			2			V
V_{IL}	Low-level input voltage					0.7			0.8	V
V_{IK}	Input clamp voltage	V_{CC} = MIN, I_I = −18 mA				−1.5			−1.5	V
V_{OH}	High-level output voltage	V_{CC} = MIN, V_{IH} = 2 V, V_{IL} = V_{IL} max, I_{OH} = −400 µA		2.5	3.5		2.7	3.5		V
V_{OL}	Low-level output voltage	V_{CC} = MIN, V_{IH} = 2 V, V_{IL} = V_{IL} max	I_{OL} = 4 mA		0.25	0.4		0.25	0.4	V
			I_{OL} = 8 mA					0.35	0.5	
I_I	Input current at maximum input voltage	V_{CC} = MAX, V_I = 7 V				0.1			0.1	mA
I_{IH}	High-level input current	V_{CC} = MAX, V_I = 2.7 V				20			20	µA
I_{IL}	Low-level input current	V_{CC} = MAX, V_I = 0.4 V				−0.4			−0.4	mA
I_{OS}	Short-circuit output current§	V_{CC} = MAX		−20		−100	−20		−100	mA
I_{CC}	Supply current	V_{CC} = MAX, See Note 2			7	13		7	13	mA

†For conditions shown as MIN or MAX, use the appropriate value specified under recommended operating conditions.
‡All typical values are at V_{CC} = 5 V, T_A = 25°C.
§Not more than one output should be shorted at a time, and duration of the short-circuit should not exceed one second.
NOTE 2. I_{CC} is measured with all outputs open and inputs grounded.

switching characteristics, V_{CC} = 5 V, T_A = 25°C

PARAMETER		TEST CONDITIONS	MIN	TYP	MAX	UNIT
t_{PHL}	Propagation delay time, high-to-low-level output from A, B, C, or D through 2 levels of logic			15	25	ns
t_{PHL}	Propagation delay time, high-to-low-level output from A, B, C, or D through 3 levels of logic	C_L = 15 pF, R_L = 2 kΩ, See Note 4		20	30	ns
t_{PLH}	Propagation delay time, low-to-high-level output from A, B, C, and D through 2 levels of logic			15	25	ns
t_{PLH}	Propagation delay time, low-to-high-level output from A, B, C, and D through 3 levels of logic			20	30	ns

NOTE 4: Load circuit and voltage waveforms are shown on page 3-11.

FOR USE AS LAMP, RELAY, OR MOS DRIVERS

featuring

- **Full Decoding of Input Logic**
- **80-mA Sink-Current Capability**
- **All Outputs Are Off for Invalid BCD Input Conditions**

logic

FUNCTION TABLE

NO.	INPUTS				OUTPUTS									
	D	C	B	A	0	1	2	3	4	5	6	7	8	9
0	L	L	L	L	L	H	H	H	H	H	H	H	H	H
1	L	L	L	H	H	L	H	H	H	H	H	H	H	H
2	L	L	H	L	H	H	L	H	H	H	H	H	H	H
3	L	L	H	H	H	H	H	L	H	H	H	H	H	H
4	L	H	L	L	H	H	H	H	L	H	H	H	H	H
5	L	H	L	H	H	H	H	H	H	L	H	H	H	H
6	L	H	H	L	H	H	H	H	H	H	L	H	H	H
7	L	H	H	H	H	H	H	H	H	H	H	L	H	H
8	H	L	L	L	H	H	H	H	H	H	H	H	L	H
9	H	L	L	H	H	H	H	H	H	H	H	H	H	L
INVALID	H	L	H	L	H	H	H	H	H	H	H	H	H	H
	H	L	H	H	H	H	H	H	H	H	H	H	H	H
	H	H	L	L	H	H	H	H	H	H	H	H	H	H
	H	H	L	H	H	H	H	H	H	H	H	H	H	H
	H	H	H	L	H	H	H	H	H	H	H	H	H	H
	H	H	H	H	H	H	H	H	H	H	H	H	H	H

H = high level (off), L = low level (on)

description

These monolithic BCD-to-decimal decoders/drivers consist of eight inverters and ten four-input NAND gates. The inverters are connected in pairs to make BCD input data available for decoding by the NAND gates. Full decoding of valid BCD input logic ensures that all outputs remain off for all invalid binary input conditions. These decoders feature TTL inputs and high-performance, n-p-n output transistors designed for use as indicator/relay drivers or as open-collector logic-circuit drivers. Each of the high-breakdown output transistors (30 volts) will sink up to 80 milliamperes of current. Each input is one normalized Series 54/74 load. Inputs and outputs are entirely compatible for use with TTL or DTL logic circuits, and the outputs are compatible for interfacing with most MOS integrated circuits. Power dissipation is typically 215 milliwatts.

SN5445 . . . J OR W PACKAGE
SN7445 . . . J OR N PACKAGE
(TOP VIEW)

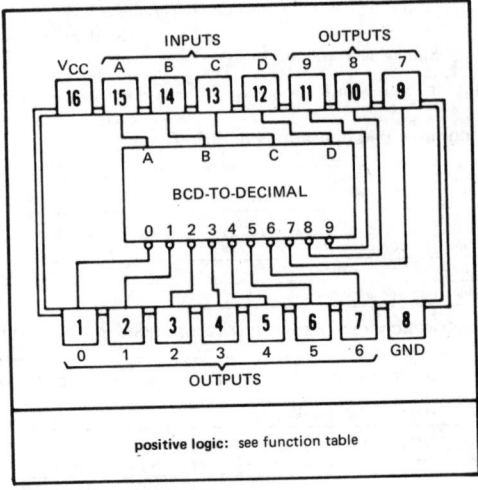

positive logic: see function table

functional block diagram

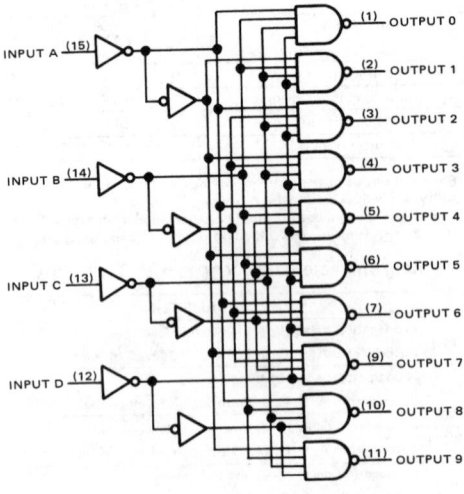

INPUT A (15)
INPUT B (14)
INPUT C (13)
INPUT D (12)

(1) OUTPUT 0
(2) OUTPUT 1
(3) OUTPUT 2
(4) OUTPUT 3
(5) OUTPUT 4
(6) OUTPUT 5
(7) OUTPUT 6
(9) OUTPUT 7
(10) OUTPUT 8
(11) OUTPUT 9

TEXAS INSTRUMENTS
INCORPORATED
POST OFFICE BOX 5012 • DALLAS, TEXAS 75222

absolute maximum ratings over operating free-air temperature range (unless otherwise noted)

Supply voltage, V_{CC} (see Note 1)	7 V
Input voltage	5.5 V
Maximum current into any output (off-state)	1 mA
Operating free-air temperature range: SN5445 Circuits	-55°C to 125°C
SN7445 Circuits	0°C to 70°C
Storage temperature range	-65°C to 150°C

NOTE 1: Voltage values are with respect to network ground terminal.

recommended operating conditions

	SN5445			SN7445			UNIT
	MIN	NOM	MAX	MIN	NOM	MAX	
Supply voltage, V_{CC}	4.5	5	5.5	4.75	5	5.25	V
Off-state output voltage			30			30	V
Operating free-air temperature, T_A	-55		125	0		70	$^{\circ}$C

electrical characteristics over recommended operating free-air temperature range (unless otherwise noted)

	PARAMETER	TEST CONDITIONS[†]		MIN	TYP[‡]	MAX	UNIT
V_{IH}	High-level input voltage			2			V
V_{IL}	Low-level input voltage					0.8	V
V_{IK}	Input clamp voltage	V_{CC} = MIN, I_I = -12 mA				-1.5	V
$V_{O(on)}$	On-state output voltage	V_{CC} = MIN, V_{IH} = 2 V, V_{IL} = 0.8 V	$I_{O(on)}$ = 80 mA		0.5	0.9	V
			$I_{O(on)}$ = 20 mA			0.4	
$I_{O(off)}$	Off-state output current	V_{CC} = MIN, V_{IH} = 2 V, V_{IL} = 0.8 V, $V_{O(off)}$ = 30 V				250	μA
I_I	Input current at maximum input voltage	V_{CC} = MAX, V_I = 5.5 V				1	mA
I_{IH}	High-level input current	V_{CC} = MAX, V_I = 2.4 V				40	μA
I_{IL}	Low-level input current	V_{CC} = MAX, V_I = 0.4 V				-1.6	mA
I_{CC}	Supply current	V_{CC} = MAX, See Note 2	SN5445		43	62	mA
			SN7445		43	70	

[†]For conditions shown as MIN or MAX, use the appropriate value specified under recommended operating conditions for the applicable type.
[‡]All typical values are at V_{CC} = 5 V, T_A = 25°C.
NOTE 2: I_{CC} is measured with all inputs grounded and outputs open.

switching characteristics, V_{CC} = 5 V, T_A = 25°C

	PARAMETER	TEST CONDITIONS	MIN	TYP	MAX	UNIT
t_{PLH}	Propagation delay time, low-to-high-level output	C_L = 15 pF, R_L = 100 Ω, See Note 3			50	ns
t_{PHL}	Propagation delay time, high-to-low-level output				50	ns

NOTE 3: Load circuit and waveforms are shown on page 3-10.

schematics of inputs and outputs

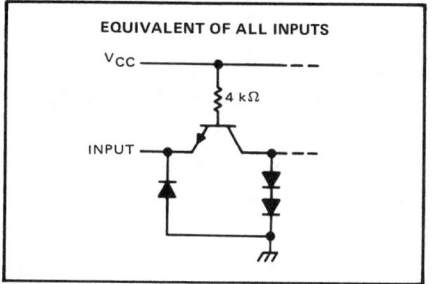

EQUIVALENT OF ALL INPUTS

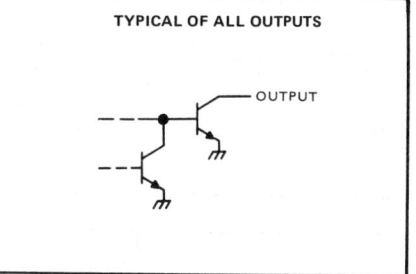

TYPICAL OF ALL OUTPUTS

'46A, '47A, 'L46, 'L47, 'LS47 feature	'48, 'LS48 feature	'49, 'LS49 feature
• **Open-Collector Outputs Drive Indicators Directly** • **Lamp-Test Provision** • **Leading/Trailing Zero Suppression**	• **Internal Pull-Ups Eliminate Need for External Resistors** • **Lamp-Test Provision** • **Leading/Trailing Zero Suppression**	• **Open-Collector Outputs** • **Blanking Input**

• **All Circuit Types Feature Lamp Intensity Modulation Capability**

TYPE	DRIVER OUTPUTS				TYPICAL POWER DISSIPATION	PACKAGES
	ACTIVE LEVEL	OUTPUT CONFIGURATION	SINK CURRENT	MAX VOLTAGE		
SN5446A	low	open-collector	40 mA	30 V	320 mW	J, W
SN5447A	low	open-collector	40 mA	15 V	320 mW	J, W
SN5448	high	2-kΩ pull-up	6.4 mA	5.5 V	265 mW	J, W
SN5449	high	open-collector	10 mA	5.5 V	165 mW	W
SN54L46	low	open-collector	20 mA	30 V	160 mW	J
SN54L47	low	open-collector	20 mA	15 V	160 mW	J
SN54LS47	low	open-collector	12 mA	15 V	35 mW	J, W
SN54LS48	high	2-kΩ pull-up	2 mA	5.5 V	125 mW	J, W
SN54LS49	high	open-collector	4 mA	5.5 V	40 mW	J, W
SN7446A	low	open-collector	40 mA	30 V	320 mW	J, N
SN7447A	low	open-collector	40 mA	15 V	320 mW	J, N
SN7448	high	2-kΩ pull-up	6.4 mA	5.5 V	265 mW	J, N
SN74L46	low	open-collector	20 mA	30 V	160 mW	J, N
SN74L47	low	open-collector	20 mA	15 V	160 mW	J, N
SN74LS47	low	open-collector	24 mA	15 V	35 mW	J, N
SN74LS48	high	2-kΩ pull-up	6 mA	5.5 V	125 mW	J, N
SN74LS49	high	open-collector	8 mA	5.5 V	40 mW	J, N

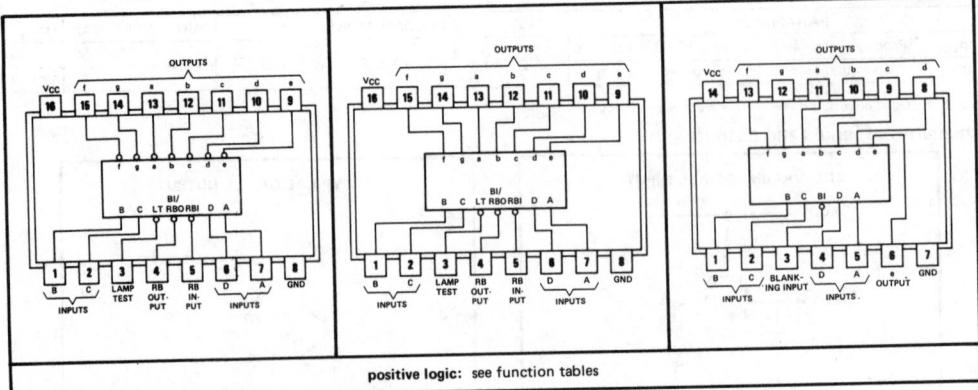

'46A, '47A, 'L46, 'L47, 'LS47 (TOP VIEW)   '48, 'LS48 (TOP VIEW)   '49, 'LS49 (TOP VIEW)

positive logic: see function tables

TEXAS INSTRUMENTS
INCORPORATED
POST OFFICE BOX 5012 • DALLAS, TEXAS 75222

description

The '46A, 'L46, '47A, 'L47, and 'LS47 feature active-low outputs designed for driving common-anode VLEDs or incandescent indicators directly, and the '48, '49, 'LS48, 'LS49 feature active-high outputs for driving lamp buffers or common-cathode VLEDs. All of the circuits except '49 and 'LS49 have full ripple-blanking input/output controls and a lamp test input. The '49 and 'LS49 circuits incorporate a direct blanking input. Segment identification and resultant displays are shown below. Display patterns for BCD input counts above 9 are unique symbols to authenticate input conditions.

The '46A, '47A, '48, 'L46, 'L47, 'LS47, and 'LS48 circuits incorporate automatic leading and/or trailing-edge zero-blanking control (RBI and RBO). Lamp test (LT) of these types may be performed at any time when the BI/RBO node is at a high level. All types (including the '49 and 'LS49) contain an overriding blanking input (BI) which can be used to control the lamp intensity by pulsing or to inhibit the outputs. Inputs and outputs are entirely compatible for use with TTL or DTL logic outputs.

The SN54246/SN74246 through '249 and the SN54LS247/SN74LS247 through 'LS249 compose the *6* and the *9* with tails and have been designed to offer the designer a choice between two indicator fonts. The SN54249/SN74249 and SN54LS249/SN74LS249 are 16-pin versions of the 14-pin SN5449 and 'LS49. Included in the '249 circuit and 'LS249 circuits are the full functional capability for lamp test and ripple blanking, which is not available in the '49 or 'LS49 circuit.

SEGMENT IDENTIFICATION

NUMERICAL DESIGNATIONS AND RESULTANT DISPLAYS

'46A, '47A, 'L46, 'L47, 'LS47 FUNCTION TABLE

DECIMAL OR FUNCTION	INPUTS						BI/RBO†	OUTPUTS							NOTE
	LT	RBI	D	C	B	A		a	b	c	d	e	f	g	
0	H	H	L	L	L	L	H	ON	ON	ON	ON	ON	ON	OFF	
1	H	X	L	L	L	H	H	OFF	ON	ON	OFF	OFF	OFF	OFF	
2	H	X	L	L	H	L	H	ON	ON	OFF	ON	ON	OFF	ON	
3	H	X	L	L	H	H	H	ON	ON	ON	ON	OFF	OFF	ON	
4	H	X	L	H	L	L	H	OFF	ON	ON	OFF	OFF	ON	ON	
5	H	X	L	H	L	H	H	ON	OFF	ON	ON	OFF	ON	ON	
6	H	X	L	H	H	L	H	OFF	OFF	ON	ON	ON	ON	ON	
7	H	X	L	H	H	H	H	ON	ON	ON	OFF	OFF	OFF	OFF	1
8	H	X	H	L	L	L	H	ON	ON	ON	ON	ON	ON	ON	
9	H	X	H	L	L	H	H	ON	ON	ON	OFF	OFF	ON	ON	
10	H	X	H	L	H	L	H	OFF	OFF	OFF	ON	ON	OFF	ON	
11	H	X	H	L	H	H	H	OFF	OFF	ON	ON	OFF	OFF	ON	
12	H	X	H	H	L	L	H	OFF	ON	OFF	OFF	OFF	ON	ON	
13	H	X	H	H	L	H	H	ON	OFF	OFF	ON	OFF	ON	ON	
14	H	X	H	H	H	L	H	OFF	OFF	OFF	ON	ON	ON	ON	
15	H	X	H	H	H	H	H	OFF	OFF	OFF	OFF	OFF	OFF	OFF	
BI	X	X	X	X	X	X	L	OFF	OFF	OFF	OFF	OFF	OFF	OFF	2
RBI	H	L	L	L	L	L	L	OFF	OFF	OFF	OFF	OFF	OFF	OFF	3
LT	L	X	X	X	X	X	H	ON	ON	ON	ON	ON	ON	ON	4

H = high level, L = low level, X = irrelevant

NOTES: 1. The blanking input (BI) must be open or held at a high logic level when output functions 0 through 15 are desired. The ripple-blanking input (RBI) must be open or high if blanking of a decimal zero is not desired.

2. When a low logic level is applied directly to the blanking input (BI), all segment outputs are off regardless of the level of any other input.

3. When ripple-blanking input (RBI) and inputs A, B, C, and D are at a low level with the lamp test input high, all segment outputs go off and the ripple-blanking output (RBO) goes to a low level (response condition).

4. When the blanking input/ripple blanking output (BI/RBO) is open or held high and a low is applied to the lamp-test input, all segment outputs are on.

†BI/RBO is wire-AND logic serving as blanking input (BI) and/or ripple-blanking output (RBO).

7

TYPES SN5446A, '47A, '48, '49, SN54L46, 'L47, SN54LS47, 'LS48, 'LS49, SN7446A, '47A, '48, SN74L46, 'L47, SN74LS47, 'LS48, 'LS49
BCD-TO-SEVEN-SEGMENT DECODERS/DRIVERS

'48, 'LS48
FUNCTION TABLE

DECIMAL OR FUNCTION	INPUTS						BI/RBO†	OUTPUTS							NOTE
	LT	RBI	D	C	B	A		a	b	c	d	e	f	g	
0	H	H	L	L	L	L	H	H	H	H	H	H	H	L	
1	H	X	L	L	L	H	H	L	H	H	L	L	L	L	
2	H	X	L	L	H	L	H	H	H	L	H	H	L	H	
3	H	X	L	L	H	H	H	H	H	H	H	L	L	H	
4	H	X	L	H	L	L	H	L	H	H	L	L	H	H	
5	H	X	L	H	L	H	H	H	L	H	H	L	H	H	
6	H	X	L	H	H	L	H	L	L	H	H	H	H	H	
7	H	X	L	H	H	H	H	H	H	H	L	L	L	L	
8	H	X	H	L	L	L	H	H	H	H	H	H	H	H	1
9	H	X	H	L	L	H	H	H	H	H	L	L	H	H	
10	H	X	H	L	H	L	H	L	L	L	H	H	L	H	
11	H	X	H	L	H	H	H	L	L	H	H	L	L	H	
12	H	X	H	H	L	L	H	L	H	L	L	L	H	H	
13	H	X	H	H	L	H	H	H	L	L	H	L	H	H	
14	H	X	H	H	H	L	H	L	L	L	H	H	H	H	
15	H	X	H	H	H	H	H	L	L	L	L	L	L	L	
BI	X	X	X	X	X	X	L	L	L	L	L	L	L	L	2
RBI	H	L	L	L	L	L	L	L	L	L	L	L	L	L	3
LT	L	X	X	X	X	X	H	H	H	H	H	H	H	H	4

H = high level, L = low level, X = irrelevant

NOTES: 1. The blanking input (BI) must be open or held at a high logic level when output functions 0 through 15 are desired. The ripple-blanking input (RBI) must be open or high, if blanking of a decimal zero is not desired.

2. When a low logic level is applied directly to the blanking input (BI), all segment outputs are low regardless of the level of any other input.

3. When ripple-blanking input (RBI) and inputs A, B, C, and D are at a low level with the lamp-test input high, all segment outputs go low and the ripple-blanking output (RBO) goes to a low level (response condition).

4. When the blanking input/ripple-blanking output (BI/RBO) is open or held high and a low is applied to the lamp-test input, all segment outputs are high.

†BI/RBO is wire-AND logic serving as blanking input (BI) and/or ripple-blanking output (RBO).

'49, 'LS49
FUNCTION TABLE

DECIMAL OR FUNCTION	INPUTS					OUTPUTS							NOTE
	D	C	B	A	BI	a	b	c	d	e	f	g	
0	L	L	L	L	H	H	H	H	H	H	H	L	
1	L	L	L	H	H	L	H	H	L	L	L	L	
2	L	L	H	L	H	H	H	L	H	H	L	H	
3	L	L	H	H	H	H	H	H	H	L	L	H	
4	L	H	L	L	H	L	H	H	L	L	H	H	
5	L	H	L	H	H	H	L	H	H	L	H	H	
6	L	H	H	L	H	L	L	H	H	H	H	H	
7	L	H	H	H	H	H	H	H	L	L	L	L	
8	H	L	L	L	H	H	H	H	H	H	H	H	1
9	H	L	L	H	H	H	H	H	L	L	H	H	
10	H	L	H	L	H	L	L	L	H	H	L	H	
11	H	L	H	H	H	L	L	H	H	L	L	H	
12	H	H	L	L	H	L	H	L	L	L	H	H	
13	H	H	L	H	H	H	L	L	H	L	H	H	
14	H	H	H	L	H	L	L	L	H	H	H	H	
15	H	H	H	H	H	L	L	L	L	L	L	L	
BI	X	X	X	X	L	L	L	L	L	L	L	L	2

H = high level, L = low level, X = irrelevant

NOTES: 1. The blanking input (BI) must be open or held at a high logic level when output functions 0 through 15 are desired.

2. When a low logic level is applied directly to the blanking input (BI), all segment outputs are low regardless of the level of any other input.

TEXAS INSTRUMENTS
INCORPORATED
POST OFFICE BOX 5012 • DALLAS, TEXAS 75222

TYPES SN5446A, '47A, '48, '49, SN54L46, 'L47, SN54LS47, 'LS48, 'LS49, SN7446A, '47A, '48, SN74L46, 'L47, SN74LS47, 'LS48, 'LS49
BCD-TO-SEVEN-SEGMENT DECODERS/DRIVERS

functional block diagrams

'46A, '47A, 'L46, 'L47, 'LS47

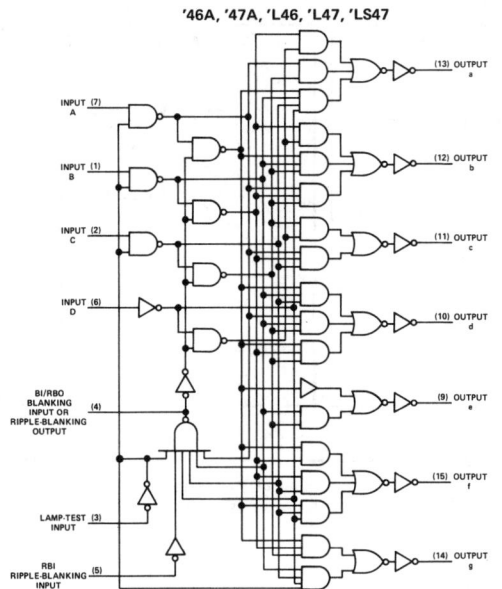

'48, 'LS48

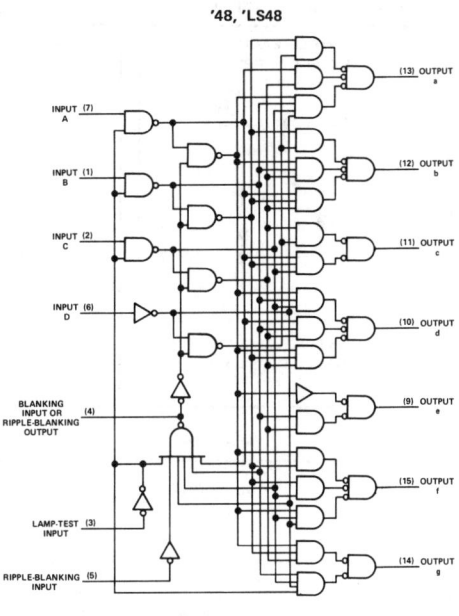

'49, 'LS49

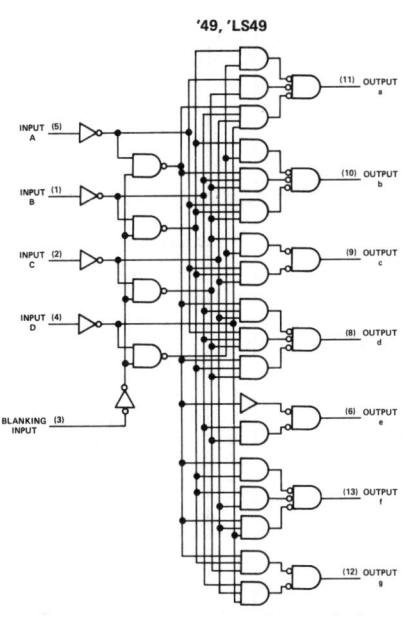

TYPES SN5446A, '47A, '48, '49, SN54L46, 'L47, SN7446A, '47A, '48, SN74L46, 'L47 BCD-TO-SEVEN-SEGMENT DECODERS/DRIVERS

schematics of inputs and outputs

'46A, '47A, '48, '49, 'L46, 'L47

'46A, '47A, '48

'L46, 'L47

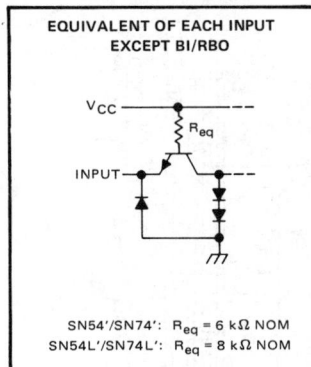

EQUIVALENT OF EACH INPUT EXCEPT BI/RBO

SN54'/SN74': R_{eq} = 6 kΩ NOM
SN54L'/SN74L': R_{eq} = 8 kΩ NOM

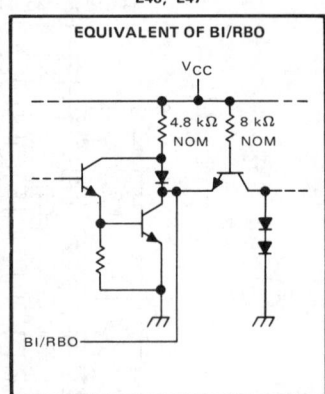

EQUIVALENT OF BI/RBO

'46A, '47A

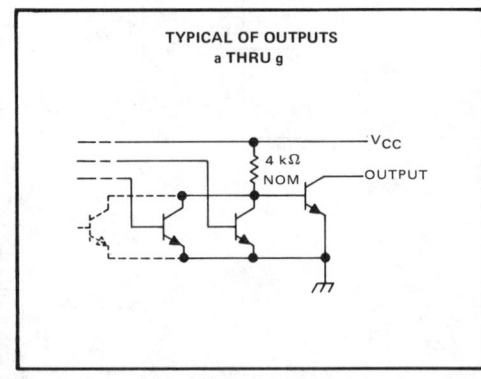

TYPICAL OF OUTPUTS
a THRU g

'L46, 'L47

TYPICAL OF OUTPUTS
a THRU g

'48

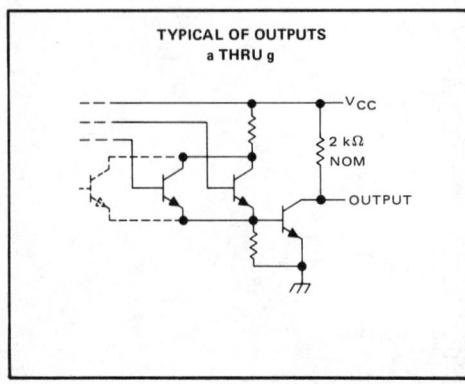

TYPICAL OF OUTPUTS
a THRU g

'49

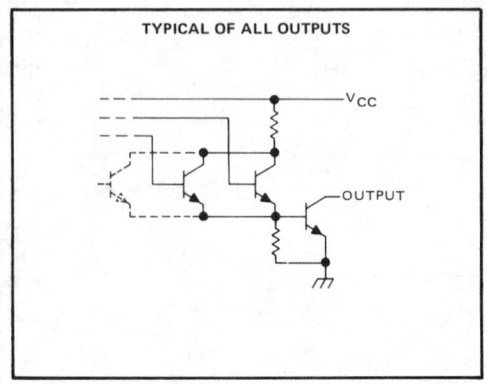

TYPICAL OF ALL OUTPUTS

TEXAS INSTRUMENTS
INCORPORATED
POST OFFICE BOX 5012 • DALLAS, TEXAS 75222

schematics of inputs and outputs

'LS47, 'LS48, 'LS49

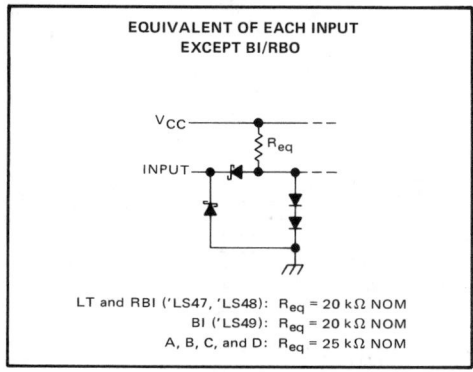

EQUIVALENT OF EACH INPUT
EXCEPT BI/RBO

LT and RBI ('LS47, 'LS48): R_{eq} = 20 kΩ NOM
BI ('LS49): R_{eq} = 20 kΩ NOM
A, B, C, and D: R_{eq} = 25 kΩ NOM

'LS47, 'LS48, 'LS49

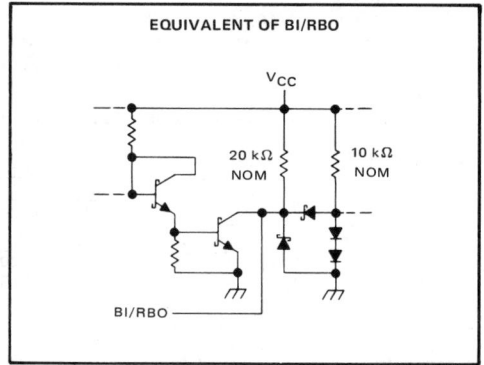

EQUIVALENT OF BI/RBO

'LS47

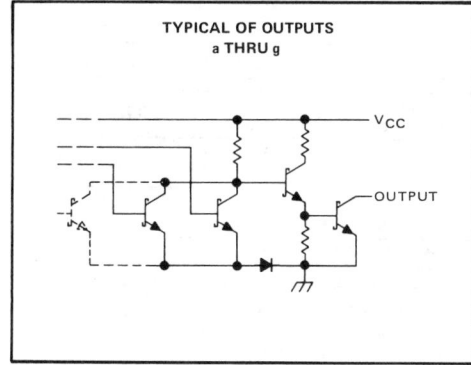

TYPICAL OF OUTPUTS
a THRU g

'LS48

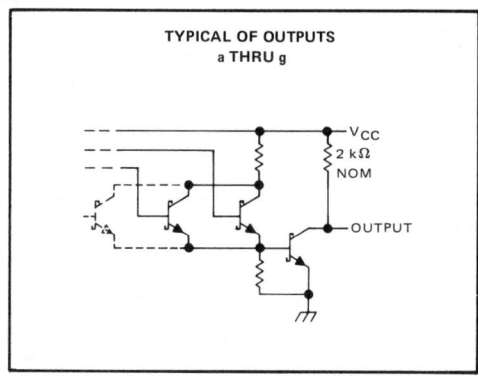

TYPICAL OF OUTPUTS
a THRU g

'LS49

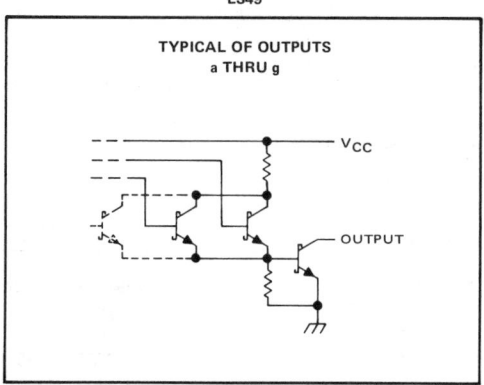

TYPICAL OF OUTPUTS
a THRU g

7

absolute maximum ratings over operating free-air temperature range (unless otherwise noted)

Supply voltage, V_{CC} (see Note 1) . . . . 7 V
Input voltage . . . . 5.5 V
Current forced into any output in the off state . . . . 1 mA
Operating free-air temperature range: SN5446A, SN5447A . . . . $-55°C$ to $125°C$
SN7446A, SN7447A . . . . $0°C$ to $70°C$
Storage temperature range . . . . $-65°C$ to $150°C$

NOTE 1: Voltage values are with respect to network ground terminal.

recommended operating conditions

		SN5446A			SN5447A			SN7446A			SN7447A			UNIT
		MIN	NOM	MAX	MIN	NOM	MAX	MIN	NOM	MAX	MIN	NOM	MAX	
Supply voltage, V_{CC}		4.5	5	5.5	4.5	5	5.5	4.75	5	5.25	4.75	5	5.25	V
Off-state output voltage, $V_{O(off)}$	a thru g			30			15			30			15	V
On-state output current, $I_{O(on)}$	a thru g			40			40			40			40	mA
High-level output current, I_{OH}	BI/RBO			-200			-200			-200			-200	μA
Low-level output current, I_{OL}	BI/RBO			8			8			8			8	mA
Operating free-air temperature, T_A		-55		125	-55		125	0		70	0		70	$°C$

electrical characteristics over recommended operating free-air temperature range (unless otherwise noted)

	PARAMETER		TEST CONDITIONS[†]		MIN	TYP[‡]	MAX	UNIT
V_{IH}	High-level input voltage				2			V
V_{IL}	Low-level input voltage						0.8	V
V_{IK}	Input clamp voltage		V_{CC} = MIN, $I_I = -12$ mA				-1.5	V
V_{OH}	High-level output voltage	BI/RBO	V_{CC} = MIN, V_{IH} = 2 V, V_{IL} = 0.8 V, $I_{OH} = -200$ μA		2.4	3.7		V
V_{OL}	Low-level output voltage	BI/RBO	V_{CC} = MIN, V_{IH} = 2 V, V_{IL} = 0.8 V, I_{OL} = 8 mA			0.27	0.4	V
$I_{O(off)}$	Off-state output current	a thru g	V_{CC} = MAX, V_{IH} = 2 V, V_{IL} = 0.8 V, $V_{O(off)}$ = MAX				250	μA
$V_{O(on)}$	On-state output voltage	a thru g	V_{CC} = MAX, V_{IH} = 2 V, V_{IL} = 0.8 V, $I_{O(on)}$ = 40 mA			0.3	0.4	V
I_I	Input current at maximum input voltage	Any input except BI/RBO	V_{CC} = MAX, V_I = 5.5 V				1	mA
I_{IH}	High-level input current	Any input except BI/RBO	V_{CC} = MAX, V_I = 2.4 V				40	μA
I_{IL}	Low-level input current	Any input except BI/RBO	V_{CC} = MAX, V_I = 0.4 V				-1.6	mA
		BI/RBO					-4	
I_{OS}	Short-circuit output current	BI/RBO	V_{CC} = MAX				-4	mA
I_{CC}	Supply current		V_{CC} = MAX, See Note 2	SN54'		64	85	mA
				SN74'		64	103	

[†]For conditions shown as MIN or MAX, use the appropriate value specified under recommended operating conditions.
[‡]All typical values are at V_{CC} = 5 V, T_A = 25°C.
NOTE 2: I_{CC} is measured with all outputs open and all inputs at 4.5 V.

switching characteristics, V_{CC} = 5 V, T_A = 25°C

	PARAMETER	TEST CONDITIONS	MIN	TYP	MAX	UNIT
t_{off}	Turn-off time from A input	C_L = 15 pF, R_L = 120 Ω, See Note 3			100	ns
t_{on}	Turn-on time from A input				100	
t_{off}	Turn-off time from RBI input				100	ns
t_{on}	Turn-on time from RBI input				100	

NOTE 3: Load circuit and voltage waveforms are shown on page 3-10; t_{off} corresponds to t_{PLH} and t_{on} corresponds to t_{PHL}.

7

TEXAS INSTRUMENTS
INCORPORATED
POST OFFICE BOX 5012 • DALLAS, TEXAS 75222

TYPES SN54L46, SN54L47, SN74L46, SN74L47
BCD-TO-SEVEN-SEGMENT DECODERS/DRIVERS

absolute maximum ratings over operating free-air temperature range (unless otherwise noted)

Supply voltage, V_{CC} (see Note 1) . . . . 7 V
Input voltage . . . . 5.5 V
Peak output current ($t_w \leqslant 1$ ms, duty cycle $\leqslant 10\%$) . . . . 200 mA
Current forced into any output in the off state . . . . 1 mA
Operating free-air temperature range: SN54L46, SN54L47 . . . . $-55°C$ to $125°C$
                           SN74L46, SN74L47 . . . . $0°C$ to $70°C$
Storage temperature range . . . . $-65°C$ to $150°C$

NOTE 1: Voltage values are with respect to network ground terminal.

recommended operating conditions

		SN54L46			SN54L47			SN74L46			SN74L47			UNIT
		MIN	NOM	MAX	MIN	NOM	MAX	MIN	NOM	MAX	MIN	NOM	MAX	
Supply voltage, V_{CC}		4.5	5	5.5	4.5	5	5.5	4.75	5	5.25	4.75	5	5.25	V
Off-state output voltage, $V_{O(off)}$	a thru g			30			15			30			15	V
On-state output current, $I_{O(on)}$	a thru g			20			20			20			20	mA
High-level output current, I_{OH}	BI/RBO			-100			-100			-100			-100	μA
Low-level output current, I_{OL}	BI/RBO			4			4			4			4	mA
Operating free-air temperature, T_A		-55		125	-55		125	0		70	0		70	$°C$

electrical characteristics over recommended operating free-air temperature range (unless otherwise noted)

PARAMETER		TEST CONDITIONS[†]		MIN	TYP[‡]	MAX	UNIT
V_{IH}	High-level input voltage			2			V
V_{IL}	Low-level input voltage					0.8	V
V_{IK}	Input clamp voltage	Any input except BI/RBO	V_{CC} = MIN, $I_I = -12$ mA			-1.5	V
V_{OH}	High-level output voltage	BI/RBO	V_{CC} = MIN, $V_{IH} = 2$ V, $V_{IL} = 0.8$ V, $I_{OH} = -100$ μA	2.4	3.4		V
V_{OL}	Low-level output voltage	BI/RBO	V_{CC} = MIN, $V_{IH} = 2$ V, $V_{IL} = 0.8$ V, $I_{OL} = 4$ mA		0.2	0.4	V
$I_{O(off)}$	Off-state output current	a thru g	V_{CC} = MAX, $V_{IH} = 2$ V, $V_{IL} = 0.8$ V, $V_{O(off)}$ = MAX			250	μA
$V_{O(on)}$	On-state output voltage	a thru g	V_{CC} = MAX, $V_{IH} = 2$ V, $V_{IL} = 0.8$ V, $I_{O(on)} = 20$ mA		0.3	0.4	V
I_I	Input current at maximum input voltage	Any input except BI/RBO	V_{CC} = MAX, $V_I = 5.5$ V			1	mA
I_{IH}	High-level input current	Any input except BI/RBO	V_{CC} = MAX, $V_I = 2.4$ V			20	μA
I_{IL}	Low-level input current	Any input except BI/RBO	V_{CC} = MAX, $V_I = 0.4$ V			-0.8	mA
		BI/RBO				-2	
I_{OS}	Short-circuit output current	BI/RBO	V_{CC} = MAX			-2	mA
I_{CC}	Supply current		V_{CC} = MAX, See Note 2	SN54L'		32	43	mA
				SN74L'		32	52	

[†]For conditions shown as MIN or MAX, use the appropriate value specified under recommended operating conditions.
[‡]All typical values are at $V_{CC} = 5$ V, $T_A = 25°C$.
NOTE 2: I_{CC} is measured with all outputs open and all inputs at 4.5 V.

switching characteristics, $V_{CC} = 5$ V, $T_A = 25°C$

PARAMETER		TEST CONDITIONS	MIN	TYP	MAX	UNIT
t_{off}	Turn-off time from A input	$C_L = 15$ pF, $R_L = 280$ Ω, See Note 3			200	ns
t_{on}	Turn-on time from A input				200	
t_{off}	Turn-off time from RBI input				200	ns
t_{on}	Turn-on time from RBI input				200	

NOTE 3: Load circuit and voltage waveforms are shown on page 3-10; t_{off} corresponds to t_{PLH} and t_{on} corresponds to t_{PHL}.

7

76

TEXAS INSTRUMENTS
INCORPORATED
POST OFFICE BOX 5012 • DALLAS, TEXAS 75222

absolute maximum ratings over operating free-air temperature range (unless otherwise noted)

Supply voltage, V_{CC} (see Note 1) . . . . 7 V
Input voltage . . . . 7 V
Peak output current ($t_W \leqslant 1$ ms, duty cycle $\leqslant 10\%$) . . . . 200 mA
Current forced into any output in the off state . . . . 1 mA
Operating free-air temperature range: SN54LS47 . . . . -55°C to 125°C
    SN74LS47 . . . . 0°C to 70°C
Storage temperature range . . . . -65°C to 150°C

NOTE 1: Voltage values are with respect to network ground terminal.

recommended operating conditions

		SN54LS47			SN74LS47			UNIT
		MIN	NOM	MAX	MIN	NOM	MAX	
Supply voltage, V_{CC}		4.5	5	5.5	4.75	5	5.25	V
Off-state output voltage, $V_{O(off)}$	a thru g			15			15	V
On-state output current, $I_{O(on)}$	a thru g			12			24	mA
High-level output current, I_{OH}	BI/RBO			-50			-50	μA
Low-level output current, I_{OL}	BI/RBO			1.6			3.2	mA
Operating free-air temperature, T_A		-55		125	0		70	$^\circ$C

electrical characteristics over recommended operating free-air temperature range (unless otherwise noted)

PARAMETER			TEST CONDITIONS[†]		SN54LS47			SN74LS47			UNIT
					MIN	TYP[‡]	MAX	MIN	TYP[‡]	MAX	
V_{IH}	High-level input voltage				2			2			V
V_{IL}	Low-level input voltage						0.7			0.8	V
V_{IK}	Input clamp voltage		V_{CC} = MIN,	I_I = -18 mA			-1.5			-1.5	V
V_{OH}	High-level output voltage	BI/RBO	V_{CC} = MIN, V_{IL} = V_{IL} max,	V_{IH} = 2 V, I_{OH} = -50 μA	2.4	4.2		2.4	4.2		V
V_{OL}	Low-level output voltage	BI/RBO	V_{CC} = MIN, V_{IH} = 2 V, V_{IL} = V_{IL} max	I_{OL} = 1.6 mA		0.25	0.4		0.25	0.4	V
				I_{OL} = 3.2 mA					0.35	0.5	
$I_{O(off)}$	Off-state output current	a thru g	V_{CC} = MAX, V_{IH} = 2 V, V_{IL} = V_{IL} max, $V_{O(off)}$ = 15 V				250			250	μA
$V_{O(on)}$	On-state output voltage	a thru g	V_{CC} = MAX, V_{IH} = 2 V, V_{IL} = V_{IL} max	$I_{O(on)}$ = 12 mA	0.25		0.4	0.25		0.4	V
				$I_{O(on)}$ = 24 mA					0.35	0.5	
I_I	Input current at maximum input voltage		V_{CC} = MAX,	V_I = 7 V			0.1			0.1	mA
I_{IH}	High-level input current		V_{CC} = MAX,	V_I = 2.7 V			20			20	μA
I_{IL}	Low-level input current	Any input except BI/RBO	V_{CC} = MAX,	V_I = 0.4 V			-0.4			-0.4	mA
		BI/RBO					-1.2			-1.2	
I_{OS}	Short-circuit output current	BI/RBO	V_{CC} = MAX		-0.3		-2	-0.3		-2	mA
I_{CC}	Supply current		V_{CC} = MAX,	See Note 2		7	13		7	13	mA

[†]For conditions shown as MIN or MAX, use the appropriate value specified under recommended operating conditions.
[‡]All typical values are at V_{CC} = 5 V, T_A = 25°C.
NOTE 2: I_{CC} is measured with all outputs open and all inputs at 4.5 V.

switching characteristics, V_{CC} = 5 V, T_A = 25°C

	PARAMETER	TEST CONDITIONS	MIN	TYP	MAX	UNIT
t_{off}	Turn-off time from A input				100	ns
t_{on}	Turn-on time from A input	C_L = 15 pF, R_L = 665 Ω, See Note 4			100	
t_{off}	Turn-off time from RBI input				100	ns
t_{on}	Turn-on time from RBI input				100	

NOTE 4: Load circuit and voltage waveforms are shown on page 3-11; t_{off} corresponds to t_{PLH} and t_{on} corresponds to t_{PHL}.

7

TEXAS INSTRUMENTS
INCORPORATED
POST OFFICE BOX 5012 • DALLAS, TEXAS 75222

absolute maximum ratings over operating free-air temperature range (unless otherwise noted)

Supply voltage, V_{CC} (see Note 1)	7 V
Input voltage	5.5 V
Operating free-air temperature range: SN5448	−55°C to 125°C
SN7448	0°C to 70°C
Storage temperature range	−65°C to 150°C

NOTE 1: Voltage values are with respect to network ground terminal.

recommended operating conditions

		SN5448			SN7448			UNIT
		MIN	NOM	MAX	MIN	NOM	MAX	
Supply voltage, V_{CC}		4.5	5	5.5	4.75	5	5.25	V
High-level output current, I_{OH}	a thru g			−400			−400	μA
	BI/RBO			−200			−200	
Low-level output current, I_{OL}	a thru g			6.4			6.4	mA
	BI/RBO			8			8	
Operating free-air temperature, T_A		−55		125	0		70	°C

electrical characteristics over recommended operating free-air temperature range (unless otherwise noted)

PARAMETER		TEST CONDITIONS[†]		MIN	TYP[‡]	MAX	UNIT
V_{IH}	High-level input voltage			2			V
V_{IL}	Low-level input voltage					0.8	V
V_{IK}	Input clamp voltage	V_{CC} = MIN, I_I = −12 mA				−1.5	V
V_{OH}	High-level output voltage	a thru g	V_{CC} = MIN, V_{IH} = 2 V,	2.4	4.2		V
		BI/RBO	V_{IL} = 0.8 V, I_{OH} = MAX	2.4	3.7		
I_O	Output current	a thru g	V_{CC} = MIN, V_O = 0.85 V, Input conditions as for V_{OH}	−1.3	−2		mA
V_{OL}	Low-level output voltage		V_{CC} = MIN, V_{IH} = 2 V, V_{IL} = 0.8 V, I_{OL} = MAX		0.27	0.4	V
I_I	Input current at maximum input voltage	Any input except BI/RBO	V_{CC} = MAX, V_I = 5.5 V			1	mA
I_{IH}	High-level input current	Any input except BI/RBO	V_{CC} = MAX, V_I = 2.4 V			40	μA
I_{IL}	Low-level input current	Any input except BI/RBO	V_{CC} = MAX, V_I = 0.4 V			−1.6	mA
		BI/RBO				−4	
I_{OS}	Short-circuit output current	BI/RBO	V_{CC} = MAX			−4	mA
I_{CC}	Supply current		V_{CC} = MIN, See Note 2	SN5448		53	76	mA
				SN7448		53	90	

[†]For conditions shown as MIN or MAX, use the appropriate value specified under recommended operating conditions.
[‡]All typical values are at V_{CC} = 5 V, T_A = 25°C.
NOTE 2: I_{CC} is measured with all outputs open and all inputs at 4.5 V.

switching characteristics, V_{CC} = 5 V, T_A = 25°C

PARAMETER		TEST CONDITIONS	MIN	TYP	MAX	UNIT
t_{PHL}	Propagation delay time, high-to-low-level output from A input				100	ns
t_{PLH}	Propagation delay time, low-to-high-level output from A input	C_L = 15 pF, R_L = 1 kΩ, See Note 5			100	
t_{PHL}	Propagation delay time, high-to-low-level output from RBI input				100	ns
t_{PLH}	Propagation delay time, low-to-high-level output from RBI input				100	

NOTE 5: Load circuit and voltage waveforms are shown on page 3-10.

TYPES SN54LS48, SN74LS48
BCD-TO-SEVEN-SEGMENT DECODERS/DRIVERS

REVISED OCTOBER 1976

absolute maximum ratings over operating free-air temperature range (unless otherwise noted)

Supply voltage, V_{CC} (see Note 1) . . . . 7 V
Input voltage . . . . 7 V
Operating free-air temperature range: SN54LS48 . . . . −55°C to 125°C
                              SN74LS48 . . . . 0°C to 70°C
Storage temperature range . . . . −65°C to 150°C

NOTE 1: Voltage values are with respect to network ground terminal.

recommended operating conditions

		SN54LS48			SN74LS48			UNIT
		MIN	NOM	MAX	MIN	NOM	MAX	
Supply voltage, V_{CC}		4.5	5	5.5	4.75	5	5.25	V
High-level output current, I_{OH}	a thru g			−100			−100	μA
	BI/RBO			−50			−50	
Low-level output current, I_{OL}	a thru g			2			6	mA
	BI/RBO			1.6			3.2	
Operating free-air temperature, T_A		−55		125	0		70	°C

electrical characteristics over recommended operating free-air temperature range (unless otherwise noted)

	PARAMETER	TEST CONDITIONS†			SN54LS48			SN74LS48			UNIT
					MIN	TYP‡	MAX	MIN	TYP‡	MAX	
V_{IH}	High-level input voltage				2			2			V
V_{IL}	Low-level input voltage						0.7			0.8	V
V_{IK}	Input clamp voltage	V_{CC} = MIN,	I_I = −18 mA				−1.5			−1.5	V
V_{OH}	High-level output voltage	a thru g and BI/RBO	V_{CC} = MIN, V_{IH} = 2 V, $V_{IL} = V_{IL}$ max, I_{OH} = MAX		2.4	4.2		2.4	4.2		V
I_O	Output current	a thru g	V_{CC} = MIN, V_O = 0.85 V, Input conditions as for V_{OH}		−1.3	−2		−1.3	−2		mA
V_{OL}	Low-level output voltage	a thru g	V_{CC} = MIN, V_{IH} = 2 V, $V_{IL} = V_{IL}$ max	I_{OL} = 2 mA	0.25	0.4		0.25	0.4		V
				I_{OL} = 6 mA				0.35	0.5		
		BI/RBO	V_{CC} = MIN, V_{IH} = 2 V, $V_{IL} = V_{IL}$ max	I_{OL} = 1.6 mA	0.25	0.4		0.25	0.4		V
				I_{OL} = 3.2 mA				0.35	0.5		
I_I	Input current at maximum input voltage	Any input except BI/BRO	V_{CC} = MAX, V_I = 7 V				0.1			0.1	mA
I_{IH}	High-level input current	Any input except BI/RBO	V_{CC} = MAX, V_I = 2.7 V				20			20	μA
I_{IL}	Low-level input current	Any input except BI/RBO	V_{CC} = MAX, V_I = 0.4 V				−0.4			−0.4	mA
		BI/RBO					−1.2			−1.2	
I_{OS}	Short-circuit output current	BI/RBO	V_{CC} = MAX		−0.3		−2	−0.3		−2	mA
I_{CC}	Supply current		V_{CC} = MAX,	See Note 2		25	38		25	38	mA

†For conditions shown as MIN or MAX, use the appropriate value specified under recommended operating conditions.
‡All typical values are at V_{CC} = 5 V, T_A 25°C.
NOTE 2: I_{CC} is measured with all outputs open and all inputs at 4.5 V.

switching characteristics, V_{CC} = 5 V, T_A = 25°C

PARAMETER		TEST CONDITIONS	MIN	TYP	MAX	UNIT
t_{PHL}	Propagation delay time, high-to-low-level output from A input	C_L = 15 pF, R_L = 4 kΩ, See Note 6			100	ns
t_{PLH}	Propagation delay time, low-to-high-level output from A input				100	
t_{PHL}	Propagation delay time, high-to-low-level output from RBI input	C_L = 15 pF, R_L = 6 kΩ, See Note 6			100	ns
t_{PLH}	Propagation delay time, low-to-high-level output from RBI input				100	

NOTE 6: Load circuit and voltage waveforms are shown on page 3-11.

TEXAS INSTRUMENTS
INCORPORATED
POST OFFICE BOX 5012 • DALLAS, TEXAS 75222

absolute maximum ratings over operating free-air temperature range (unless otherwise noted)

Supply voltage, V_{CC} (see Note 1) . . . . 7 V
Input voltage . . . . 5.5 V
Current forced into any output in the off state . . . . 1 mA
Operating free-air temperature range . . . . $-55°C$ to $125°C$
Storage temperature range . . . . $-65°C$ to $150°C$

NOTE 1: Voltage values are with respect to network ground terminal.

recommended operating conditions

	SN5449			UNIT
	MIN	NOM	MAX	
Supply voltage, V_{CC}	4.5	5	5.5	V
High-level output voltage, V_{OH}			5.5	V
Low-level output current, I_{OL}			10	mA
Operating free-air temperature, T_A	-55		125	$°C$

electrical characteristics over recommended operating free-air temperature range (unless otherwise noted)

	PARAMETER	TEST CONDITIONS†	SN5449			UNIT
			MIN	TYP‡	MAX	
V_{IH}	High-level input voltage		2			V
V_{IL}	Low-level input voltage				0.6	V
V_{IK}	Input clamp voltage	V_{CC} = MIN, I_I = -10 mA			-1.5	V
I_{OH}	High-level output current	V_{CC} = MIN, V_{IH} = 2 V, V_{IL} = 0.8 V, V_{OH} = 5.5 V			250	μA
V_{OL}	Low-level output voltage	V_{CC} = MIN, V_{IH} = 2 V, V_{IL} = 0.8 V, I_{OL} = 10 mA		0.27	0.4	V
I_I	Input current at maximum input voltage	V_{CC} = MAX, V_I = 5.5 V			1	mA
I_{IH}	High-level input current	V_{CC} = MAX, V_I = 2.4 V			40	μA
I_{IL}	Low-level input current	V_{CC} = MAX, V_I = 0.4 V			-1.6	mA
I_{CC}	Supply current	V_{CC} = MAX, See Note 2		33	47	mA

†For conditions shown as MIN or MAX, use the appropriate value specified under recommended operating conditions.
‡All typical values are at V_{CC} = 5 V, T_A = $25°C$.
NOTE 2: I_{CC} is measured with all outputs open and all inputs at 4.5 V.

switching characteristics, V_{CC} = 5 V, T_A = $25°C$

	PARAMETER	TEST CONDITIONS	MIN	TYP	MAX	UNIT
t_{PHL}	Propagation delay time, high-to-low-level output from A input	C_L = 15 pF, R_L = 667 Ω, See Note 5			100	ns
t_{PLH}	Propagation delay time, low-to-high-level output from A input				100	
t_{PHL}	Propagation delay time, high-to-low-level output from RBI input				100	ns
t_{PLH}	Propagation delay time, low-to-high-level output from RBI input				100	

NOTE 5: Load circuit and voltage waveforms are shown on page 3-10.

7

TEXAS INSTRUMENTS
INCORPORATED
POST OFFICE BOX 5012 • DALLAS, TEXAS 75222

TYPES SN54LS49, SN74LS49
BCD-TO-SEVEN-SEGMENT DECODERS/DRIVERS

REVISED OCTOBER 1976

absolute maximum ratings over operating free-air temperature range (unless otherwise noted)

Supply voltage, V_{CC} (see Note 1) . . . . 7 V
Input voltage . . . . 7 V
Current forced into any output in the off state . . . . 1 mA
Operating free-air temperature range: SN54LS49 . . . . −55°C to 125°C
                                   SN74LS49 . . . . 0°C to 70°C
Storage temperature range . . . . −65°C to 150°C

NOTE 1: Voltage values are with respect to network ground terminal.

recommended operating conditions

	SN54LS49			SN74LS49			UNIT
	MIN	NOM	MAX	MIN	NOM	MAX	
Supply voltage, V_{CC}	4.5	5	5.5	4.75	5	5.25	V
High-level output voltage, V_{OH}			5.5			5.5	V
Low-level output current, I_{OL}			4			8	mA
Operating free-air temperature, T_A	−55		125	0		70	°C

electrical characteristics over recommended operating free-air temperature range (unless otherwise noted)

PARAMETER		TEST CONDITIONS[†]		SN54LS49			SN74LS49			UNIT
				MIN	TYP[‡]	MAX	MIN	TYP[‡]	MAX	
V_{IH}	High-level input voltage			2			2			V
V_{IL}	Low-level input voltage					0.7			0.8	V
V_{IK}	Input clamp voltage	V_{CC} = MIN,	I_I = −18 mA			−1.5			−1.5	V
I_{OH}	High-level output current	V_{CC} = MIN, V_{IH} = 2 V, V_{IL} = V_{IL} max, V_{OH} = 5.5 V				250			250	μA
V_{OL}	Low-level output voltage	V_{CC} = MIN, V_{IH} = 2 V, V_{IL} = V_{IL} max	I_{OL} = 4 mA	0.25		0.4	0.25		0.4	V
			I_{OL} = 8 mA				0.35		0.5	
I_I	Input current at maximum input voltage	V_{CC} = MAX,	V_I = 7 V			0.1			0.1	mA
I_{IH}	High-level input current	V_{CC} = MAX,	V_I = 2.7 V			20			20	μA
I_{IL}	Low-level input current	V_{CC} = MAX,	V_I = 0.4 V			−0.4			−0.4	mA
I_{CC}	Supply current	V_{CC} = MAX,	See Note 2		8	15		8	15	mA

[†]For conditions shown as MIN or MAX, use the appropriate value specified under recommended operating conditions.
[‡]All typical values are at V_{CC} = 5 V, T_A = 25°C.
NOTE 2: I_{CC} is measured with all outputs open and all inputs at 4.5 V.

switching characteristics, V_{CC} = 5 V, T_A = 25°C

PARAMETER		TEST CONDITIONS	MIN	TYP	MAX	UNIT
t_{PHL}	Propagation delay time, high-to-low-level output from A input	C_L = 15 pF, R_L = 2 kΩ, See Note 6			100	ns
t_{PLH}	Propagation delay time, low-to-high-level output from A input				100	
t_{PHL}	Propagation delay time, high-to-low-level output from RBI input	C_L = 15 pF, R_L = 6 kΩ, See Note 6			100	ns
t_{PLH}	Propagation delay time, low-to-high-level output from RBI input				100	

NOTE 6: Load circuit and voltage waveforms are shown on page 3-11.

7

TEXAS INSTRUMENTS
INCORPORATED
POST OFFICE BOX 5012 • DALLAS, TEXAS 75222

TTL
MSI

TYPES SN5475, SN5477, SN54L75, SN54L77, SN54LS75, SN54LS77, SN7475, SN74L75, SN74L77, SN74LS75
4-BIT BISTABLE LATCHES
BULLETIN NO. DL-S 7611851, MARCH 1974—REVISED OCTOBER 1976

logic

FUNCTION TABLE
(Each Latch)

INPUTS		OUTPUTS	
D	G	Q	$\bar{Q}$
L	H	L	H
H	H	H	L
X	L	Q_0	$\bar{Q}_0$

H = high level, L = low level, X = irrelevant
Q_0 = the level of Q before the high-to-low transition of G

description

These latches are ideally suited for use as temporary storage for binary information between processing units and input/output or indicator units. Information present at a data (D) input is transferred to the Q output when the enable (G) is high and the Q output will follow the data input as long as the enable remains high. When the enable goes low, the information (that was present at the data input at the time the transition occurred) is retained at the Q output until the enable is permitted to go high.

The '75, 'L75, and 'LS75 feature complementary Q and $\bar{Q}$ outputs from a 4-bit latch, and are available in various 16-pin packages. For higher component density applications, the '77, 'L77, and 'LS77 4-bit latches are available in 14-pin flat packages.

These circuits are completely compatible with all popular TTL or DTL families. All inputs are diode-clamped to minimize transmission-line effects and simplify system design. Series 54, 54L, and 54LS devices are characterized for operation over the full military temperature range of $-55°C$ to $125°C$; Series 74, 74L, and 74LS devices are characterized for operation from $0°C$ to $70°C$.

SN5475, SN54LS75 . . . J OR W PACKAGE
SN54L75 . . . J PACKAGE
SN7475, SN74L75, SN74LS75 . . . J OR N PACKAGE
(TOP VIEW)

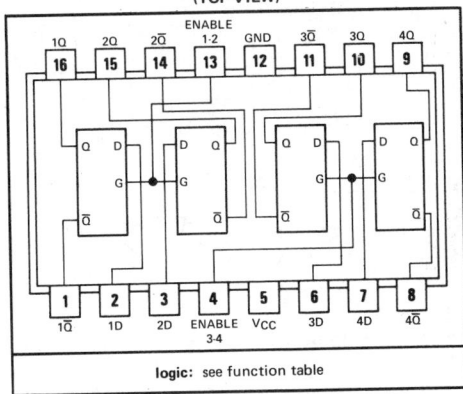

logic: see function table

SN5477, SN54L77 . . . W PACKAGE
SN54L77, SN74L77 . . . T PACKAGE

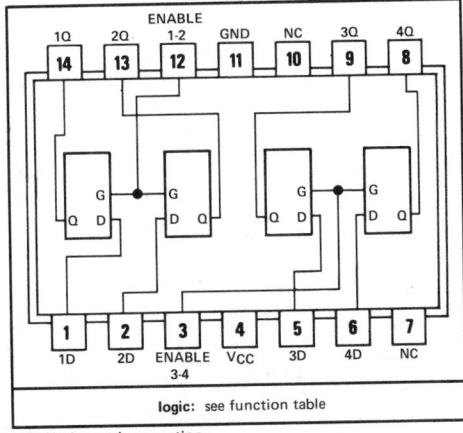

logic: see function table

NC—No internal connection

absolute maximum ratings over operating free-air temperature range (unless otherwise noted)

Supply voltage, V_{CC} (see Note 1)	7 V
Input voltage: '75, 'L75, '77, 'L77	5.5 V
'LS75, 'LS77	7 V
Interemitter voltage (see Note 2)	5.5 V
Operating free-air temperature range: SN54', SN54L', SN54LS' Circuits	$-55°C$ to $125°C$
SN74', SN74L', SN74LS' Circuits	$0°C$ to $70°C$
Storage temperature range	$-65°C$ to $150°C$

NOTES: 1. Voltage values, except interemitter voltage, are with respect to network ground terminal.
2. This is the voltage between two emitters of a multiple-emitter input transistor and is not applicable to the 'LS75 and 'LS77.

7

TYPES SN5475, SN5477, SN54L75, SN54L77, SN54LS75, SN54LS77, SN7475, SN74L75, SN74L77, SN74LS75
4-BIT BISTABLE LATCHES

REVISED OCTOBER 1976

functional block diagrams (each latch)

'75, '77, 'L75, 'L77

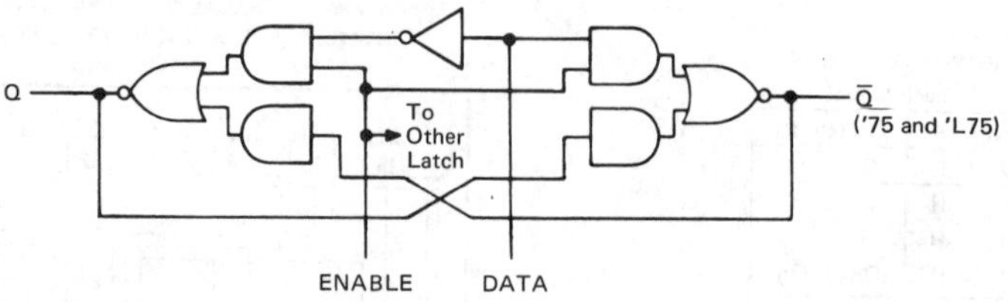

Q — — Q̄ ('75 and 'L75)

To Other Latch

ENABLE   DATA

'LS75

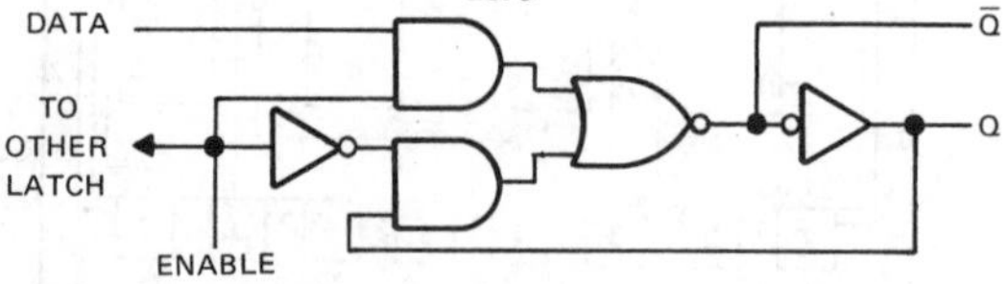

DATA — Q̄
TO OTHER LATCH
ENABLE — Q

'LS77

DATA — Q
TO OTHER LATCH
ENABLE

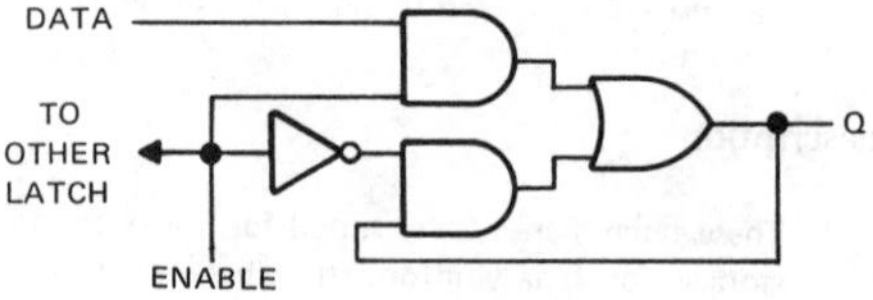

schematics of inputs and outputs

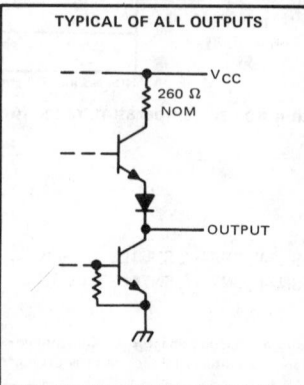

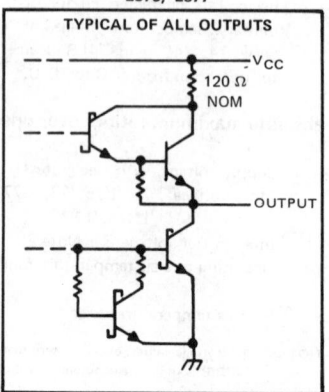

'75, '77	**'L75, 'L77**	**'LS75, 'LS77**
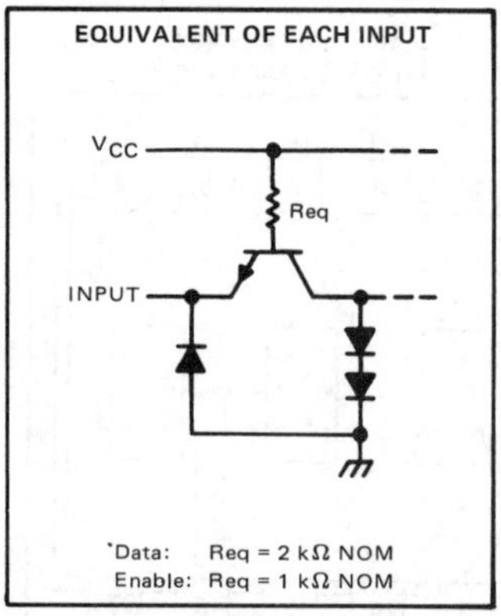 EQUIVALENT OF EACH INPUT	EQUIVALENT OF EACH INPUT	EQUIVALENT OF EACH INPUT
V_CC Req INPUT ⏚	V_CC Req INPUT ⏚	V_CC Req INPUT ⏚
*Data: Req = 2 kΩ NOM Enable: Req = 1 kΩ NOM	Data: Req = 4 kΩ NOM Enable: Req = 2 kΩ NOM	Data: Req = 17 kΩ Enable: Req = 4.2 kΩ

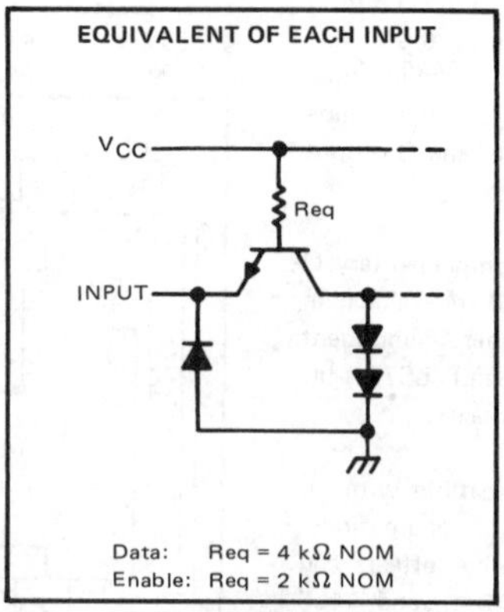

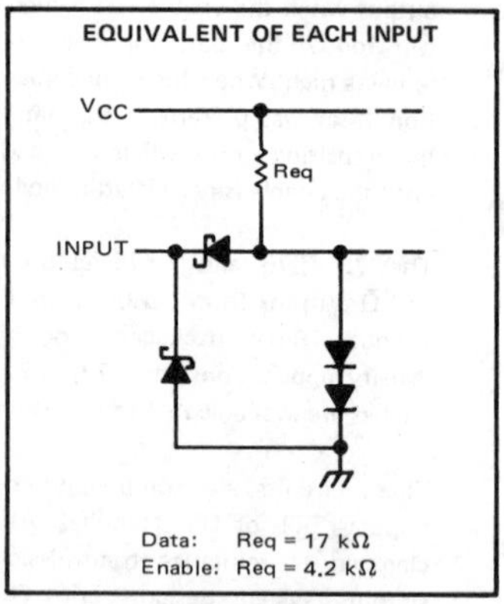

'75, '77	**'L75, 'L77**	**'LS75, 'LS77**
TYPICAL OF ALL OUTPUTS	TYPICAL OF ALL OUTPUTS	TYPICAL OF ALL OUTPUTS
130 Ω NOM V_CC OUTPUT ⏚	260 Ω NOM V_CC OUTPUT ⏚	120 Ω NOM V_CC OUTPUT ⏚

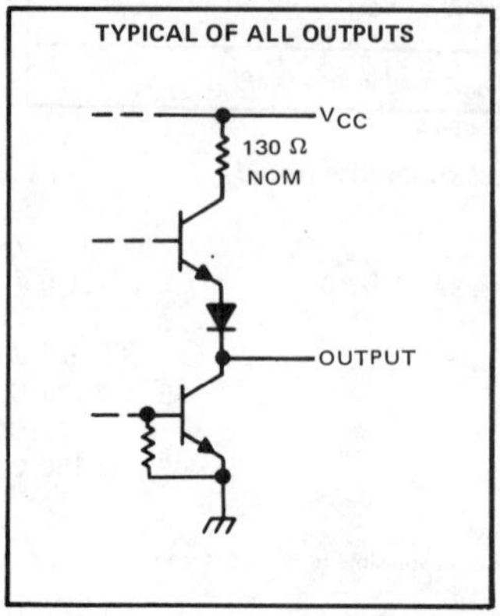

TEXAS INSTRUMENTS
INCORPORATED
POST OFFICE BOX 5012 • DALLAS, TEXAS 75222

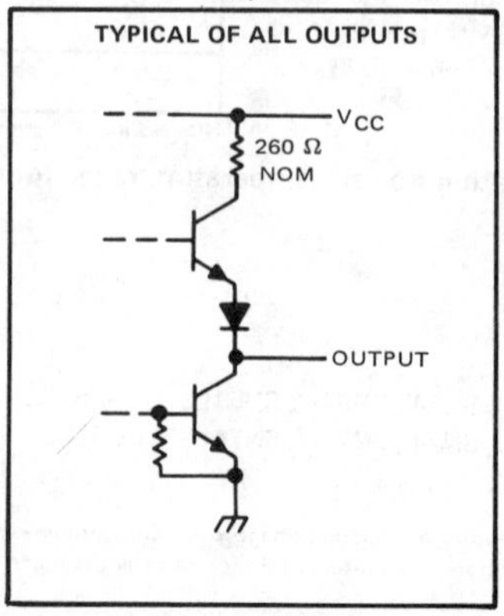

TYPES SN5475, SN5477, SN7475
4-BIT BISTABLE LATCHES

recommended operating conditions

	SN5475, SN5477			SN7475			UNIT
	MIN	NOM	MAX	MIN	NOM	MAX	
Supply voltage, V_{CC}	4.5	5	5.5	4.75	5	5.25	V
High-level output current, I_{OH}			−400			−400	μA
Low-level output current, I_{OL}			16			16	mA
Width of enabling pulse, t_W	20			20			ns
Setup time, t_{su}	20			20			ns
Hold time, t_h	5			5			ns
Operating free-air temperature, T_A	−55		125	0		70	°C

electrical characteristics over recommended operating free-air temperature range (unless otherwise noted)

PARAMETER		TEST CONDITIONS[†]		MIN	TYP[‡]	MAX	UNIT
V_{IH}	High-level input voltage			2			V
V_{IL}	Low-level input voltage					0.8	V
V_{IK}	Input clamp voltage	V_{CC} = MIN,	I_I = −12 mA			−1.5	V
V_{OH}	High-level output voltage	V_{CC} = MIN, V_{IH} = 2 V, V_{IL} = 0.8 V,	I_{OH} = −400 μA	2.4	3.4		V
V_{OL}	Low-level output voltage	V_{CC} = MIN, V_{IH} = 2 V, V_{IL} = 0.8 V,	I_{OL} = 16 mA		0.2	0.4	V
I_I	Input current at maximum input voltage	V_{CC} = MAX,	V_I = 5.5 V			1	mA
I_{IH}	High-level input current	D input	V_{CC} = MAX, V_I = 2.4 V			80	μA
		G input				160	
I_{IL}	Low-level input current	D input	V_{CC} = MAX, V_I = 0.4 V			−3.2	mA
		G input				−6.4	
I_{OS}	Short-circuit output current[§]		V_{CC} = MAX SN54'	−20		−57	mA
			SN74'	−18		−57	
I_{CC}	Supply current		V_{CC} = MAX, See Note 3 SN54'		32	46	mA
			SN74'		32	53	

[†]For conditions shown as MIN or MAX, use the appropriate value specified under recommended operating conditions.
[‡]All typical values are at V_{CC} = 5 V, T_A = 25°C.
[§]Not more than one output should be shorted at a time.
NOTE 3: I_{CC} is tested with all inputs grounded and all outputs open.

switching characteristics, V_{CC} = 5 V, T_A = 25°C

PARAMETER[◊]	FROM (INPUT)	TO (OUTPUT)	TEST CONDITIONS	MIN	TYP	MAX	UNIT
t_{PLH}	D	Q			16	30	ns
t_{PHL}					14	25	
t_{PLH}[¶]	D	$\overline{Q}$	C_L = 15 pF, R_L = 400 Ω, See Figure 1		24	40	ns
t_{PHL}[¶]					7	15	
t_{PLH}	G	Q			16	30	ns
t_{PHL}					7	15	
t_{PLH}[¶]	G	$\overline{Q}$			16	30	ns
t_{PHL}[¶]					7	15	

[◊]t_{PLH} ≡ propagation delay time, low-to-high-level output
t_{PHL} ≡ propagation delay time, high-to-low-level output
[¶] These parameters are not applicable for the SN5477.

7

recommended operating conditions

	SN54L75, SN54L77			SN74L75, SN74L77			UNIT
	MIN	NOM	MAX	MIN	NOM	MAX	
Supply voltage, V_{CC}	4.5	5	5.5	4.75	5	5.25	V
High-level output current, I_{OH}			−200			−200	µA
Low-level output current, I_{OL}			8			8	mA
Width of enabling pulse, t_w	100			100			ns
Setup time, t_{su}	40			40			ns
Hold time, t_h	10			10			ns
Operating free-air temperature, T_A	−55		125	0		70	°C

electrical characteristics over recommended operating free-air temperature range (unless otherwise noted)

PARAMETER		TEST CONDITIONS[†]		MIN	TYP[‡]	MAX	UNIT
V_{IH}	High-level input voltage			2			V
V_{IL}	Low-level input voltage					0.8	V
V_{IK}	Input clamp voltage	V_{CC} = MIN,	I_I = −12 mA			−1.5	V
V_{OH}	High-level output voltage	V_{CC} = MIN, V_{IL} = 0.8 V,	V_{IH} = 2 V, I_{OH} = −200 µA	2.4	3.4		V
V_{OL}	Low-level output voltage	V_{CC} = MIN, V_{IL} = 0.8 V,	V_{IH} = 2 V, I_{OL} = 8 mA		0.2	0.4	V
I_I	Input current at maximum input voltage	V_{CC} = MAX,	V_I = 5.5 V			1	mA
I_{IH}	High-level input current	D input	V_{CC} = MAX,	V_I = 2.4 V			40	µA
		G input					80	
I_{IL}	Low-level input current	D input	V_{CC} = MAX,	V_I = 0.4 V			−1.6	mA
		G input					−3.2	
I_{OS}	Short-circuit output current[§]	V_{CC} = MAX	SN54L'	−10		−29	mA
			SN74L'	−9		−29	
I_{CC}	Supply current	V_{CC} = MAX, See Note 3	SN54L'		16	23	mA
			SN74L'		16	27	

[†]For conditions shown as MIN or MAX, use the appropriate value specified under recommended operating conditions.
[‡]All typical values are at V_{CC} = 5 V, T_A = 25°C.
[§]Nor more than one output should be shorted at a time.
NOTE 3: I_{CC} is tested with all inputs grounded and all outputs open.

switching characteristics, V_{CC} = 5 V, T_A = 25°C

PARAMETER[◊]	FROM (INPUT)	TO (OUTPUT)	TEST CONDITIONS	MIN	TYP	MAX	UNIT
t_{PLH}	D	Q			32	60	ns
t_{PHL}					28	50	
t_{PLH}[¶]	D	$\overline{Q}$	C_L = 15 pF,		48	80	ns
t_{PHL}[¶]			R_L = 800 Ω,		14	30	
t_{PLH}	G	Q	See Figure 1		32	60	ns
t_{PHL}					14	30	
t_{PLH}[¶]	G	$\overline{Q}$			32	60	ns
t_{PHL}[¶]					14	30	

[◊]t_{PLH} ≡ propagation delay time, low-to-high-level output
t_{PHL} ≡ propagation delay time, high-to-low-level output
[¶] These parameters are not applicable for the SN54L77 and SN74L77.

TEXAS INSTRUMENTS
INCORPORATED
POST OFFICE BOX 5012 • DALLAS, TEXAS 75222

recommended operating conditions

	SN54LS75 SN54LS77			SN74LS75			UNIT
	MIN	NOM	MAX	MIN	NOM	MAX	
Supply voltage, V_{CC}	4.5	5	5.5	4.75	5	5.25	V
High-level output current, I_{OH}			−400			−400	μA
Low-level output current, I_{OL}			4			8	mA
Width of enabling pulse, t_w	20			20			ns
Setup time, t_{su}	20			20			ns
Hold time, t_h	0			0			ns
Operating free-air temperature, T_A	−55		125	0		70	°C

electrical characteristics over recommended operating free-air temperature range (unless otherwise noted)

PARAMETER		TEST CONDITIONS†		SN54LS75 SN54LS77			SN74LS75			UNIT
				MIN	TYP‡	MAX	MIN	TYP‡	MAX	
V_{IH}	High-level input voltage			2			2			V
V_{IL}	Low-level input voltage					0.7			0.8	V
V_{IK}	Input clamp voltage	V_{CC} = MIN,	I_I = −18 mA			−1.5			−1.5	V
V_{OH}	High-level output voltage	V_{CC} = MIN, V_{IH} = 2 V, $V_{IL} = V_{IL}$ max, I_{OH} = −400 μA		2.5	3.5		2.7	3.5		V
V_{OL}	Low-level output voltage	V_{CC} = MIN, V_{IH} = 2 V, $V_{IL} = V_{IL}$ max	I_{OL} = 4 mA		0.25	0.4		0.25	0.4	V
			I_{OL} = 8 mA					0.35	0.5	
I_I	Input current at maximum input voltage	V_{CC} = MAX, V_I = 7 V	D input			0.1			0.1	mA
			G input			0.4			0.4	
I_{IH}	High-level input current	V_{CC} = MAX, V_I = 2.7 V	D input			20			20	μA
			G input			80			80	
I_{IL}	Low-level input current	V_{CC} = MAX, V_I = 0.4 V	D input			−0.4			−0.4	mA
			G input			−1.6			−1.6	
I_{OS}	Short-circuit output current§	V_{CC} = MAX		−20		−100	−20		−100	mA
I_{CC}	Supply current	V_{CC} = MAX, See Note 2	'LS75		6.3	12		6.3	12	mA
			'LS77		6.9	13				

†For conditions shown as MIN or MAX, use the appropriate value specified under recommended operating conditions.
‡All typical values are at V_{CC} = 5 V, T_A = 25°C.
§Not more than one output should be shorted at a time, and duration of the short-circuit should not exceed one second
NOTE 2: I_{CC} is tested with all inputs grounded and all outputs open.

switching characteristics, V_{CC} = 5 V, T_A = 25°C

PARAMETER◊	FROM (INPUT)	TO (OUTPUT)	TEST CONDITIONS	'LS75			'LS77			UNIT
				MIN	TYP	MAX	MIN	TYP	MAX	
t_{PLH}	D	Q			15	27		11	19	ns
t_{PHL}					9	17		9	17	
t_{PLH}	D	$\overline{Q}$	C_L = 15 pF, R_L = 2 kΩ, See Figure 1		12	20				ns
t_{PHL}					7	15				
t_{PLH}	G	Q			15	27		10	18	ns
t_{PHL}					14	25		10	18	
t_{PLH}	G	$\overline{Q}$			16	30				ns
t_{PHL}					7	15				

◊$t_{PLH} \equiv$ propagation delay time, low-to-high-level output
$t_{PHL} \equiv$ propagation delay time, high-to-low-level output

7

TYPES SN5475, SN5477, SN54L75, SN54L77, SN54LS75, SN54LS77, SN7475, SN74L75, SN74L77, SN74LS75
4-BIT BISTABLE LATCHES

PARAMETER MEASUREMENT INFORMATION

switching characteristics

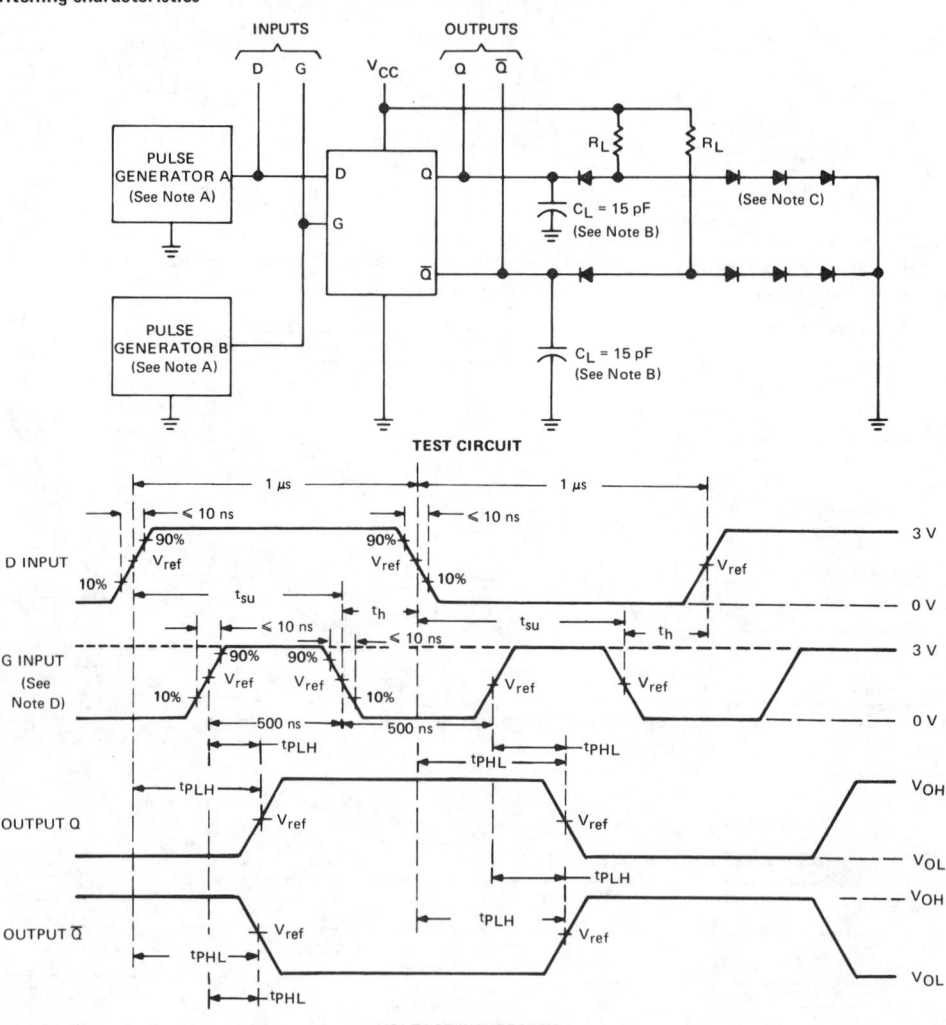

TEST CIRCUIT

VOLTAGE WAVEFORMS

NOTES: A. The pulse generators have the following characteristics: $Z_{out} \approx 50\ \Omega$; for pulse generator A, PRR ≤ 500 kHz; for pulse generator B, PRR ≤ 1 MHz. Positions of D and G input pulses are varied with respect to each other to verify setup times.
B. C_L includes probe and jig capacitance.
C. All diodes are 1N3064.
D. When measuring propagation delay times from the D input, the corresponding G input must be held high.
E. For '75, '77, 'L75, and 'L77, V_{ref} = 1.5 V; for 'LS75 and 'LS77, V_{ref} = 1.3 V.
†Complementary $\overline{Q}$ outputs are on the '75, 'L75, and 'LS75 only.

FIGURE 1

TEXAS INSTRUMENTS
INCORPORATED
POST OFFICE BOX 5012 • DALLAS, TEXAS 75222

TTL
MSI

logic

FUNCTION TABLE
(See Notes 1, 2, and 3)

INPUTS			OUTPUTS		
C_n	B	A	$\overline{C}_{n+1}$	$\overline{\Sigma}$	Σ
L	L	L	H	H	L
L	L	H	H	L	H
L	H	L	H	L	H
L	H	H	L	H	L
H	L	L	H	L	H
H	L	H	L	H	L
H	H	L	L	H	L
H	H	H	L	L	H

H = high level, L = low level

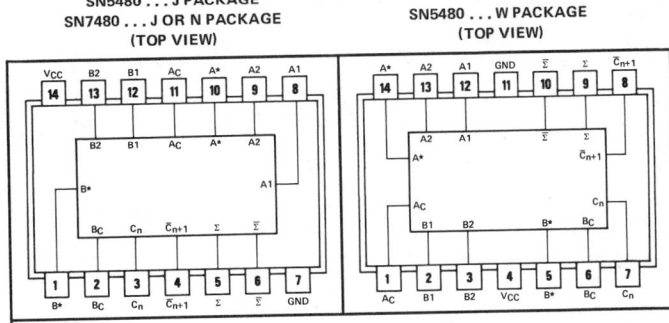

SN5480 . . . J PACKAGE
SN7480 . . . J OR N PACKAGE
(TOP VIEW)

SN5480 . . . W PACKAGE
(TOP VIEW)

positive logic: see function table

NOTES: 1. $A = \overline{A}_C + \overline{A}\star + A1 \cdot A2$, $B = \overline{B}_C + \overline{B}\star + B1 \cdot B2$.
     2. When A★ is used as an input, A1 or A2 must be low. When B★ is used as an input, B1 or B2 must be low.
     3. When A1 and A2 or B1 and B2 are used as inputs, A★ or B★, respectively, must be open or used to perform dot-AND logic.

description

These single-bit, high-speed, binary full adders with gated complementary inputs, complementary sum (Σ and $\overline{\Sigma}$) outputs and inverted carry output are designed for medium- and high-speed, multiple-bit, parallel-add/serial-carry applications. These circuits (see schematic) utilize diode-transistor logic (DTL) for the gated inputs, and high-speed, high-fan-out transistor-transistor logic (TTL) for the sum and carry outputs and are entirely compatible with both DTL and TTL logic families. The implementation of a single-inversion, high-speed, Darlington-connected serial-carry circuit minimizes the necessity for extensive "look-ahead" and carry-cascading circuits.

absolute maximum ratings over operating free-air temperature range (unless otherwise noted)

Supply voltage, V_{CC} (see Note 4) . . . . 7 V
Input voltage (see Note 5) . . . . 5.5 V
Operating free-air temperature range: SN5480 Circuits . . . . −55°C to 125°C
                                 SN7480 Circuits . . . . 0° to 70°C
Storage temperature range . . . . −65°C to 150°C

NOTES: 4. Voltage values are with respect to network ground terminal.
     5. Input signals must be zero or positive with respect to network ground terminal.

recommended operating conditions

		SN5480			SN7480			UNIT
		MIN	NOM	MAX	MIN	NOM	MAX	
Supply voltage, V_{CC}		4.5	5	5.5	4.75	5	5.25	V
High-level output current, I_{OH}	Σ or $\overline{\Sigma}$			−400			−400	μA
	$\overline{C}_{n+1}$			−200			−200	
	A★ or B★			−120			−120	
Low-level output current, I_{OL}	Σ or $\overline{\Sigma}$			16			16	mA
	$\overline{C}_{n+1}$			8			8	
	A★ or B★			4.8			4.8	
Operating free-air temperature, T_A		−55		125	0		70	°C

electrical characteristics over recommended operating free-air temperature range (unless otherwise noted)

PARAMETER		TEST CONDITIONS[†]		SN5480 MIN	SN5480 TYP[‡]	SN5480 MAX	SN7480 MIN	SN7480 TYP[‡]	SN7480 MAX	UNIT
V_{IH} High-level input voltage				2			2			V
V_{IL} Low-level input voltage						0.8			0.8	V
V_{OH} High-level output voltage	Σ or $\bar{\Sigma}$	V_{CC} = MAX,	I_{OH} = −400 µA	2.4	3.5		2.4	3.5		V
	$\bar{C}_{n+1}$	V_{IH} = 2 V,	I_{OH} = −200 µA							
	A★ or B★	V_{IL} = 0.8 V	I_{OH} = −120 µA							
V_{OL} Low-level output voltage	Σ or $\bar{\Sigma}$	V_{CC} = MAX,	I_{OL} = 16 mA		0.22	0.4		0.22	0.4	V
	$\bar{C}_{n+1}$	V_{IH} = 2 V,	I_{OL} = 8 mA							
	A★ or B★	V_{IL} = 0.8 V	I_{OL} = 4.8 mA							
I_I Input current at maximum input voltage		V_{CC} = MAX, V_I = 5.5 V				1			1	mA
I_{IH} High-level input current	$A_1, A_2, B_1, B_2,$ $A_C,$ or B_C	V_{CC} = MAX, V_I = 2.4 V				15			15	µA
	A★ or B★					−1.1			−1.1	
	C_n					200			200	
I_{IL} Low-level input current	$A_1, A_2, B_1, B_2,$ $A_C,$ or B_C	V_{CC} = MAX, V_I = 0.4 V				−1.6			−1.6	mA
	A★ or B★					−2.6			−2.6	
	C_n					−8			−8	
I_{OS} Short-circuit output-current[§]	Σ or $\bar{\Sigma}$	V_{CC} = MAX		−20		−57	−18		−57	mA
	$\bar{C}_{n+1}$			−20		−70	−18		−70	
	A★ or B★			−0.9		−2.9	−0.9		−2.9	
I_{CC} Supply current		V_{CC} = MAX, See Note 6			21	31		21	35	mA

[†]For conditions shown as MIN or MAX, use the appropriate value specified under recommended operating conditions for the applicable type.
[‡]All typical values are at V_{CC} = 5 V, T_A = 25°C.
[§]Not more than one output should be shorted at a time.
NOTE 6: I_{CC} is measured with all inputs and outputs open.

switching characteristics, V_{CC} = 5 V, T_A = 25°C

PARAMETER[¶]	FROM INPUT	TO OUTPUT	TEST CONDITIONS	MIN	TYP	MAX	UNIT
t_{PLH}	C_n	$\bar{C}_{n+1}$	C_L = 15 pF, R_L = 780 Ω, See Note 7		13	17	ns
t_{PHL}					8	12	
t_{PLH}	B_C	$\bar{C}_{n+1}$			18	25	
t_{PHL}					38	55	
t_{PLH}	A_C	Σ	C_L = 15 pF, R_L = 400 Ω, See Note 7		52	70	ns
t_{PHL}					62	80	
t_{PLH}	B_C	$\bar{\Sigma}$			38	55	
t_{PHL}					56	75	
t_{PLH}	A1	A★	C_L = 15 pF, See Note 7		48	65	ns
t_{PHL}					17	25	
t_{PLH}	B1	B★			48	65	
t_{PHL}					17	25	

[¶]t_{PLH} ≡ propagation delay time, low-to-high-level output
t_{PHL} ≡ propagation delay time, high-to-low-level output

NOTE 7: The load for testing outputs A★ and B★ consists only of capacitance C_L to ground. The load circuit for the other outputs and voltage waveforms are shown on page 3-10.

TEXAS INSTRUMENTS
INCORPORATED
POST OFFICE BOX 5012 ★ DALLAS, TEXAS 75222

functional block diagram

(DUAL-IN-LINE) [FLAT PACKAGE]

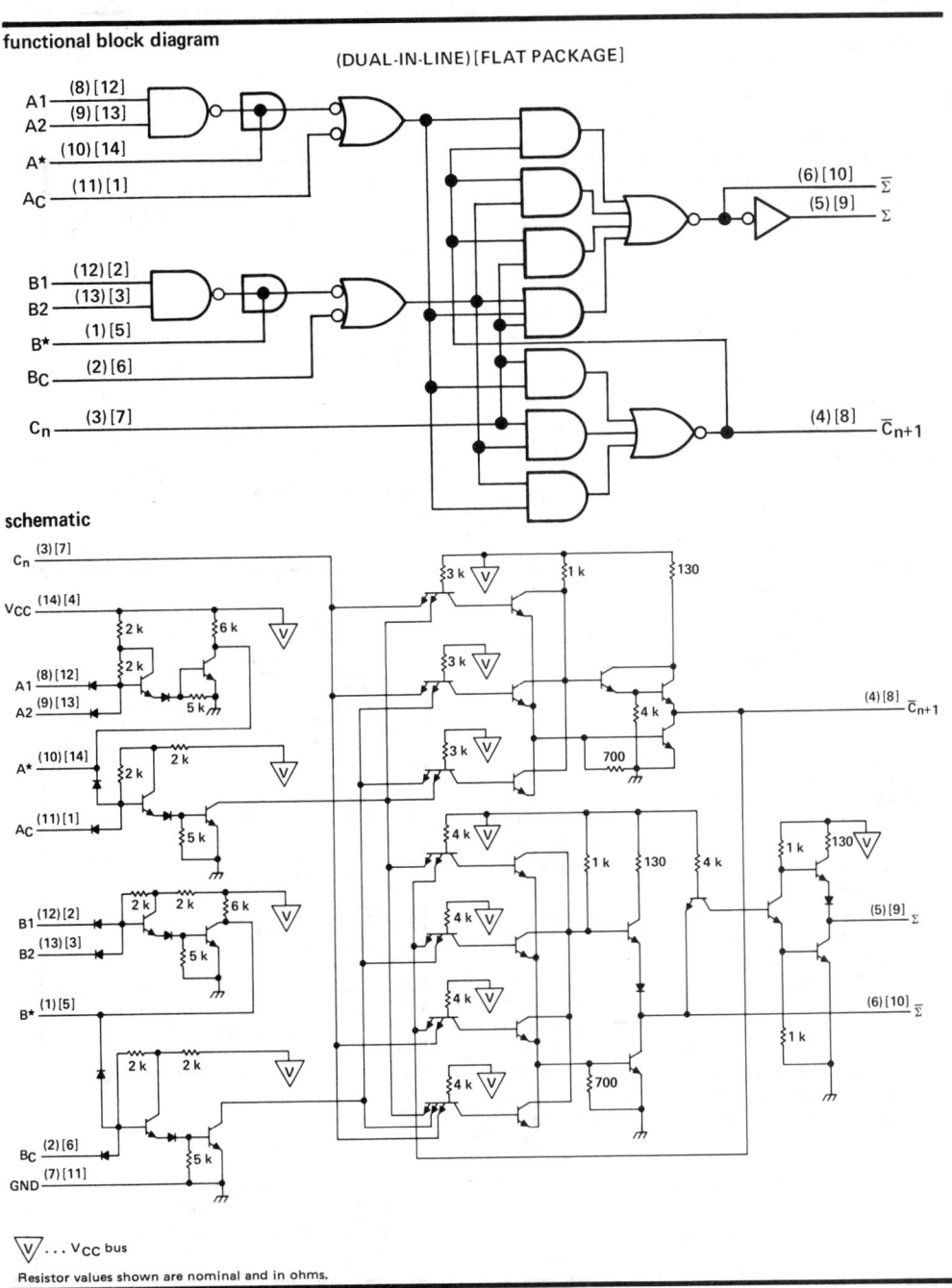

schematic

$\overline{V}$ ... V_{CC} bus

Resistor values shown are nominal and in ohms.

TEXAS INSTRUMENTS
INCORPORATED
POST OFFICE BOX 5012 • DALLAS, TEXAS 75222

description

Each of these 16-bit active-element memories is a high-speed, monolithic, transistor-transistor-logic (TTL) array of 16 flip-flops and two write amplifiers interconnected to form a scratch-pad memory with direct-address and nondestructive read-out. These devices are interchangeable with and replace SN5481, SN7481, SN5484, and SN7484, but feature diode-clamped inputs, improved switching speeds, and lower supply current requirements.

The flip-flops are arranged in a four-by-four matrix with each flip-flop representing one bit of 16 words. Four X-address lines and four Y-address lines permit the address of one bit at a time. Each flip-flop, composed of two cross-coupled three-emitter transistors, is used to store one bit. To determine if a logic 1 or logic 0 has been stored, it is necessary to know which one of the two flip-flop transistors is conducting. One emitter of each of these transistors serves as the sensing output. All 16 of the logic 1 sensing outputs are connected to the sense 1 (S_1) amplifier input and all 16 of the logic 0 sensing outputs are connected to the sense 0 (S_0) amplifier input. The two remaining emitters of each transistor are used to complete the matrix connections necessary for the X- and Y-address lines. Address line inputs are normally held low and currents from all conducting flip-flop transistors flow out of these address lines.

To address a flip-flop both the X- and Y-address lines associated with that flip-flop are taken to a high level. Due to the matrix nature of the circuit, at least one address line of all flip-flops except the one being addressed will continue to remain at a low level and no change will occur in those flip-flops. But, in the addressed flip-flop, the current in the conducting transistor diverts from the address lines to the appropriate sense line and then to one of the sense amplifiers. Thus, either the sense 1 amplifier or the sense 0 amplifier is activated. When this occurs, the output of the activated sense amplifier drops from a high logic level to a low logic level. The memory is nondestructive as the states of the flip-flops are not disturbed during sensing. The memory is volatile and information will be lost if the supply voltage is removed.

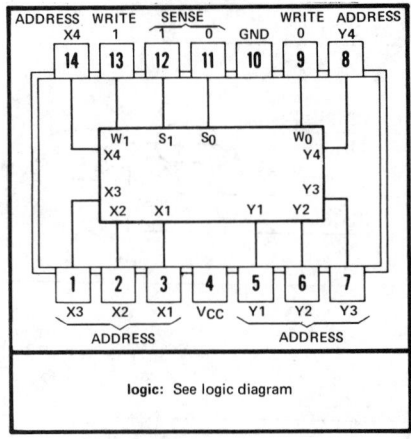

SN5481A . . . J OR W PACKAGE
SN7481A . . . J OR N PACKAGE
(TOP VIEW)

logic: See logic diagram

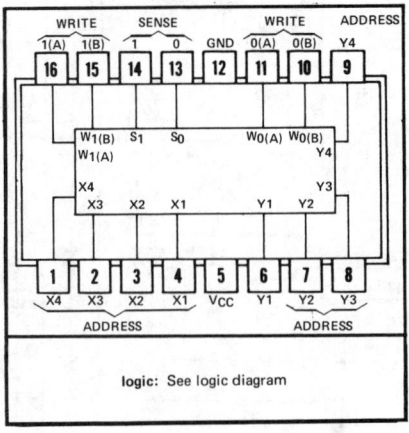

SN5484A . . . J OR W PACKAGE
SN7484A . . . J OR N PACKAGE
(TOP VIEW)

logic: See logic diagram

To store new information in a flip-flop, it is necessary to address it and apply a high-level voltage to the appropriate write amplifier. (The SN5484A and SN7484A have gated write-amplifier inputs). The output of the write amplifier responds by dropping to a low logic level. Since all Sense 0 lines are connected to the output of the write 0 amplifier and all sense 1 lines are connected to the output of the write 1 amplifier, a low level at the output of a write amplifier

7

TEXAS INSTRUMENTS
INCORPORATED
POST OFFICE BOX 5012 • DALLAS, TEXAS 75222

description (continued)

will cause the emitters of all flip-flop transistors connected to that amplifier to go low. In all the flip-flops except the one being addressed, this low voltage has no effect since at least one other emitter on each of the flip-flop transistors is held low by the address lines. Two possibilities exist with the flip-flop that is addressed. The flip-flop may already be in the desired state, in which case no change occurs. If the flip-flop must be changed from one state to the other, the low voltage applied to the emitter of the transistor which is not conducting turns that transistor on causing the other transistor to turn off.

Since the connection between the output of the write amplifier and the sense line is common to the input of the sense amplifier, the memory cannot be used to provide information on the state of a bit while the write amplifiers are activated.

A number of active-element memories may be paralleled to form the desired matrix size (number of words) and to form the desired word length (number of bits). All inputs and outputs are compatible with most DTL and TTL circuits. Average power dissipation is typically 225 milliwatts, and the open-collector outputs may be wire-AND connected to similar outputs. Internal circuitry of the write and sense amplifiers are operated within their linear range to improve speed. Sensing propagation delay times are typically 12 nanoseconds when operated at full fan-out and 30 picofarads of circuit capacitance. The SN5481A and SN5484A circuits are designed for operation over the full military temperature range of -55°C to 125°C; the SN7481A circuits are designed for operation from 0°C to 70°C.

logic diagram

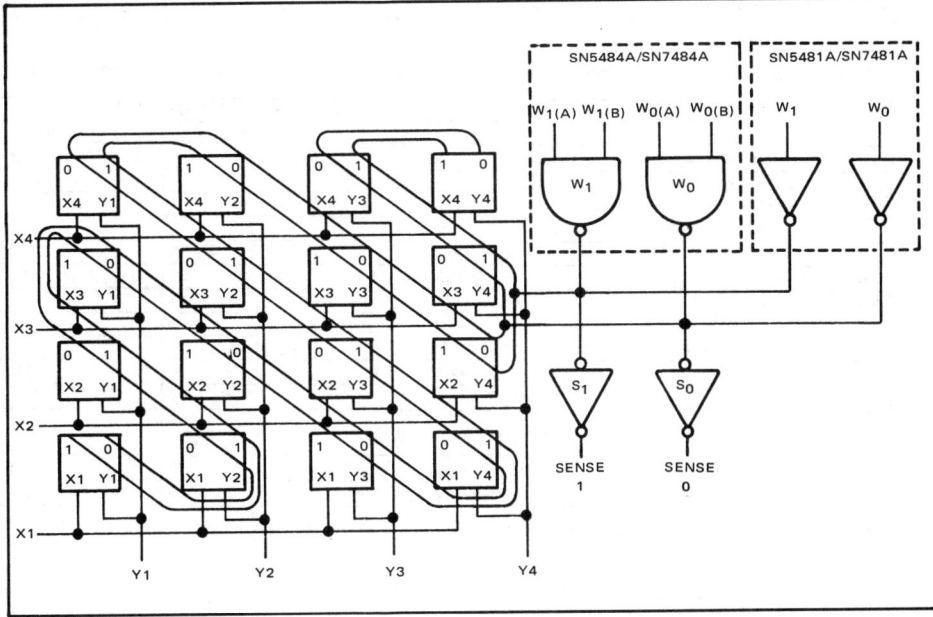

TEXAS INSTRUMENTS
INCORPORATED
POST OFFICE BOX 5012 • DALLAS, TEXAS 75222

absolute maximum ratings over operating free-air temperature range (unless otherwise noted)

Supply voltage, V_{CC} (see Note 1) . . . . 7 V
Input voltage . . . . 5.5 V
Interemitter voltage (see Note 2) . . . . 5.5 V
High-level output voltage . . . . 5.5 V
Operating free-air temperature range: SN5481A, SN5484A Circuits . . . . -55°C to 125°C
SN7481A, SN7484A Circuits . . . . 0°C to 70°C
Storage temperature range . . . . -65°C to 150°C

NOTES: 1. Voltage values, except interemitter voltage, are with respect to network ground terminal.
2. This is the voltage between two emitters of a multiple-emitter transistor. For this circuit, this rating applies to any X input in conjunction with any Y input.

recommended operating conditions

	SN5481A, SN5484A			SN7481A, SN7484A			UNIT
	MIN	NOM	MAX	MIN	NOM	MAX	
Supply voltage, V_{CC}	4.5	5	5.5	4.75	5	5.25	V
High-level output voltage, V_{OH}			5.5			5.5	V
Low-level output current, I_{OL}			20			40	mA
Width of write pulse, $t_{w(write)}$ (see Figure 1)	20			20			ns
Address input setup time, t_{su} (see Figure 1)	0			0			ns
Operating free-air temperature, T_A	-55		125	0		70	$^{\circ}$C

electrical characteristics over recommended operating free-air temperature range (unless otherwise noted)

PARAMETER		TEST CONDITIONS[†]	SN5481A, SN5484A			SN7481A, SN7484A			UNIT
			MIN	TYP[‡]	MAX	MIN	TYP[‡]	MAX	
V_{IH}	High-level voltage at any input		2			2			V
V_{IL}	Low-level voltage	to prevent writing			0.8			0.8	V
	at address inputs	to prevent sensing			1			1	
V_{IL}	Low-level voltage at write inputs				0.8			1	V
V_{IK}	Input clamp voltage	V_{CC} = MIN, I_I = -12 mA			-1.5			-1.5	V
I_{OH}	High-level output current	V_{CC} = MIN, V_{OH} = 5.5 V			250			250	μA
V_{OL}	Low-level output voltage	V_{CC} = MIN, I_{OL} = MAX			0.4			0.4	V
I_I	Input current at	Write	V_{CC} = MAX, V_I = 5.5 V			1			1	mA
	maximum input voltage	Address				3			3	
I_{IH}	High-level input current	Write	V_{CC} = MAX, V_I = 2.4 V			40			40	μA
		Address	V_{CC} = MAX, V_I = 4.5 V			400			400	
I_{IL}	Low-level input current	Write	V_{CC} MAX, V_I = 0.4 V			-1.6			-1.6	mA
		Address				-11			-11	
I_{CC}	Supply current		V_{CC} = MAX, All inputs at 0 V			70			65	mA
			V_{CC} = 5 V, All inputs at 0 V	45	60		45	60	

[†] For conditions shown as MIN or MAX, use the appropriate value specified under recommended operating conditions.
[‡] All typical values are at V_{CC} = 5 V, T_A = 25°C.

TEXAS INSTRUMENTS
INCORPORATED
POST OFFICE BOX 5012 • DALLAS, TEXAS 75222

switching characteristics, $V_{CC} = 5$ V, $I_{OL} = MAX^\dagger$, $T_A = 25°C$, see figure 1

PARAMETER§	LOCATION ADDRESSED	TEST CONDITIONS	SN5481A, SN5484A			SN7481A, SN7484A			UNIT
			MIN	TYP	MAX	MIN	TYP	MAX	
t_{SR}	X1 – Y1	$C_L = 30$ pF		13			13		ns
		$C_L = 200$ pF		18	30		18	30	
t_{PHL}	X1 – Y1	$C_L = 30$ pF		11	19		12	20	ns
		$C_L = 200$ pF		17	26		18	27	
t_{PLH}		$C_L = 30$ pF		13	20		12	19	
		$C_L = 200$ pF		27	40		18	27	
t_{PHL}	X1 thru X4 and Y1	$C_L = 30$ pF		10	18		11	19	ns
		$C_L = 200$ pF		16	25		17	26	
t_{PLH}		$C_L = 30$ pF		13	20		13	20	
		$C_L = 200$ pF		27	40		19	28	

†For conditions shown as MIN or MAX, use the appropriate value specified under recommended operating conditions for the applicable device type.

§t_{SR} ≡ Sense recovery time after writing

t_{PHL} ≡ Propagation delay time, high-to-low-level output

t_{PLH} ≡ Propagation delay time, low-to-high-level output

schematic

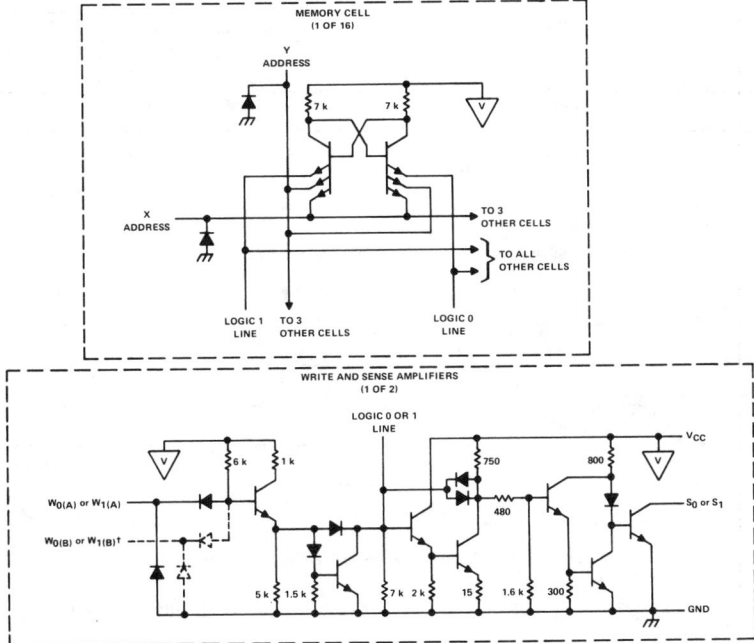

$^\dagger W_{0(B)}$ and $W_{1(B)}$ inputs (indicated with dashed lines) are applicable for the SN5484A, SN7484A only.

▽ . . . V_{CC} bus

Resistor values shown are nominal and in ohms.

TEXAS INSTRUMENTS
INCORPORATED

POST OFFICE BOX 5012 • DALLAS, TEXAS 75222

TYPES SN5481A, SN5484A, SN7481A, SN7484A
16-BIT RANDOM-ACCESS MEMORIES

PARAMETER MEASUREMENT INFORMATION

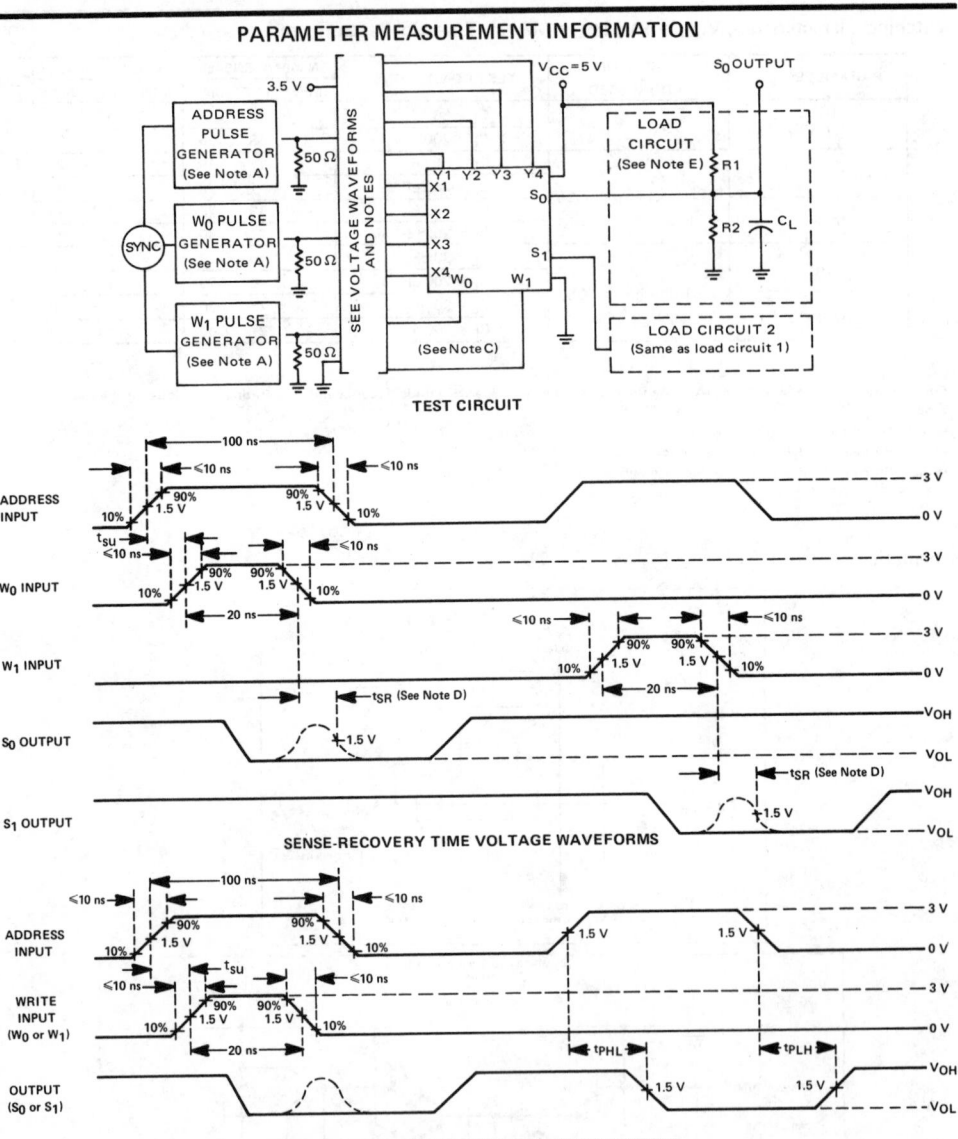

TEST CIRCUIT

SENSE-RECOVERY TIME VOLTAGE WAVEFORMS

PROPAGATION DELAY TIME VOLTAGE WAVEFORMS

NOTES: A. The pulse generators have the following characteristics: for the address pulse generator, PRR = 2 MHz; for the W_0 and W_1 pulse generators, PRR = 1 MHz.
- B. C_L includes probe and jig capacitance.
- C. For the SN5484A and SN7484A, unused W_0 and W_1 inputs are at 3.5 V.
- D. $t_{SR} \equiv$ sense-recovery time
- E. For the SN5481A and SN5484A: R1 = 240 Ω and R2 = 560 Ω. For the SN7481A and SN7484A: R1 = 120 Ω and R2 = 330 Ω.

FIGURE 1—SWITCHING CHARACTERISTICS

TEXAS INSTRUMENTS
INCORPORATED
POST OFFICE BOX 5012 • DALLAS, TEXAS 75222

For applications in:

- Digital Computer Systems
- Data-Handling Systems
- Control Systems

logic

SN5482 . . . J OR W PACKAGE
SN7482 . . . J OR N PACKAGE
(TOP VIEW)

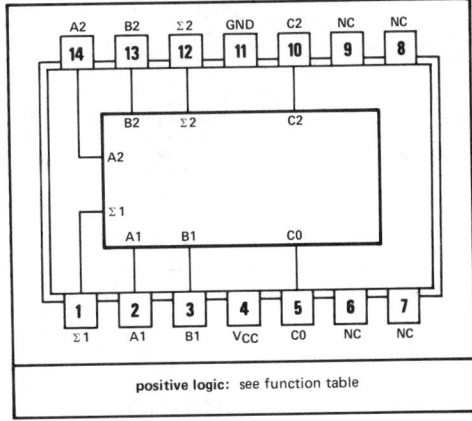

positive logic: see function table

NC—No internal connection

FUNCTION TABLE

INPUTS				OUTPUTS					
				WHEN C0 = L			WHEN C0 = H		
A1	B1	A2	B2	Σ1	Σ2	C2	Σ1	Σ2	C2
L	L	L	L	L	L	L	H	L	L
H	L	L	L	H	L	L	L	H	L
L	H	L	L	H	L	L	L	H	L
H	H	L	L	L	H	L	H	H	L
L	L	H	L	L	H	L	H	H	L
H	L	H	L	H	H	L	L	L	H
L	H	H	L	H	H	L	L	L	H
H	H	H	L	L	L	H	H	L	H
L	L	L	H	L	H	L	H	H	L
H	L	L	H	H	H	L	L	L	H
L	H	L	H	H	H	L	L	L	H
H	H	L	H	L	L	H	H	L	H
L	L	H	H	L	L	H	H	L	H
H	L	H	H	H	L	H	L	H	H
L	H	H	H	H	L	H	L	H	H
H	H	H	H	L	H	H	H	H	H

H = high level, L = low level

description

These full adders perform the addition of two 2-bit binary numbers. The sum (Σ) outputs are provided for each bit and the resultant carry (C2) is obtained from the second bit. Designed for medium-to-high-speed, multiple-bit, parallel-add/serial-carry applications, these circuits utilize high-speed, high-fan-out transistor-transistor logic (TTL) and are compatible with both DTL and TTL logic families. The implementation of a single-inversion, high-speed, Darlington-connected serial-carry circuit within each bit minimizes the necessity for extensive "look-ahead" and carry-cascading circuits.

functional block diagram

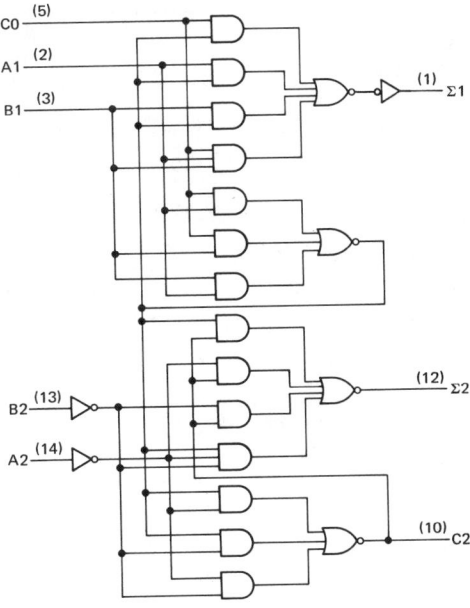

TEXAS INSTRUMENTS
INCORPORATED
POST OFFICE BOX 5012 • DALLAS, TEXAS 75222

TYPES SN5482, SN7482
2-BIT BINARY FULL ADDERS

absolute maximum ratings over operating free-air temperature range (unless otherwise noted)

Supply voltage, V_{CC} (see Note 1)	7 V
Input voltage (see Note 2)	5.5 V
Operating free-air temperature range: SN5482 Circuits	$-55°C$ to $125°C$
SN7482 Circuits	$0°C$ to $70°C$
Storage temperature range	$-65°C$ to $150°C$

NOTES: 1. Voltage values are with respect to network ground terminal.
2. Input signals must be zero or positive with respect to network ground terminal.

recommended operating conditions

		SN5482			SN7482			UNIT
		MIN	NOM	MAX	MIN	NOM	MAX	
Supply voltage, V_{CC}		4.5	5	5.5	4.75	5	5.25	V
High-level output current, I_{OH}	Σ1 or Σ2			−400			−400	μA
	C2			−200			−200	
Low-level output current, I_{OL}	Σ1 or Σ2			16			16	mA
	C2			8			8	
Operating free-air temperature, T_A		−55		125	0		70	°C

electrical characteristics over recommended operating free-air temperature range (unless otherwise noted)

PARAMETER		TEST CONDITIONS[†]			SN5482			SN7482			UNIT
					MIN	TYP[‡]	MAX	MIN	TYP[‡]	MAX	
V_{IH}	High-level input voltage				2			2			V
V_{IL}	Low-level input voltage						0.8			0.8	V
V_{OH}	High-level output voltage	Σ1 or Σ2	V_{CC} = MIN, V_{IH} = 2 V, V_{IL} = 0.4 V	I_{OH} = −400 μA	2.4	3.4		2.4	3.4		V
		C2		I_{OH} = −200 μA							
V_{OL}	Low-level output voltage	Σ1 or Σ2	V_{CC} = MIN, V_{IH} = 2 V, V_{IL} = 0.4 V	I_{OL} = 16 mA		0.2	0.4		0.2	0.4	V
		C2		I_{OL} = 8 mA							
I_I	Input current at maximum input voltage		V_{CC} = MAX, V_I = 5.5 V				1			1	mA
I_{IH}	High-level input current	A1, B1, or C0	V_{CC} = MAX, V_I = 2.4 V				160			160	μA
		A2 or B2					40			40	
I_{IL}	Low-level input current	A1, B1, or C0	V_{CC} = MAX, V_I = 0.4 V				−6.4			−6.4	mA
		A2 or B2					−1.6			−1.6	
I_{OS}	Short-circuit output current [§]	Σ1 or Σ2	V_{CC} = MAX		−20		−55	−18		−55	mA
		C2			−20		−70	−18		−70	
I_{CC}	Supply current		V_{CC} = MAX, See Note 3			35	50		35	58	mA

[†]For conditions shown as MIN or MAX, use the appropriate value specified under recommended operating conditions for the applicable type.
[‡]All typical values are at V_{CC} = 5 V, T_A = 25°C.
[§]Not more than one output should be shorted at a time.
NOTE 3: I_{CC} is measured with outputs open, B1 and B2 grounded, and 4.5 V applied to A1, A2, and C0.

7

TEXAS INSTRUMENTS
INCORPORATED
POST OFFICE BOX 5012 • DALLAS, TEXAS 75222

switching characteristics, V_{CC} = 5 V, T_A = 25°C (see note 4)

PARAMETER¶	FROM (INPUT)	TO (OUTPUT)	TEST CONDITIONS	MIN	TYP	MAX	UNIT
t_{PLH}	C0	Σ1				34	ns
t_{PHL}						40	
t_{PLH}	B2	Σ2	C_L = 15 pF, R_L = 400 Ω			40	ns
t_{PHL}						35	
t_{PLH}	C0	Σ2				38	ns
t_{PHL}						42	
t_{PLH}	C0	C2	C_L = 15 pF, R_L = 780 Ω		12	19	ns
t_{PHL}					17	27	

¶t_{PLH} ≡ propagation delay time, low-to-high-level output
t_{PHL} ≡ propagation delay time, high-to-low-level output
NOTE 4: Load circuit and voltage waveforms are shown on page 3-10.

schematics of inputs and outputs

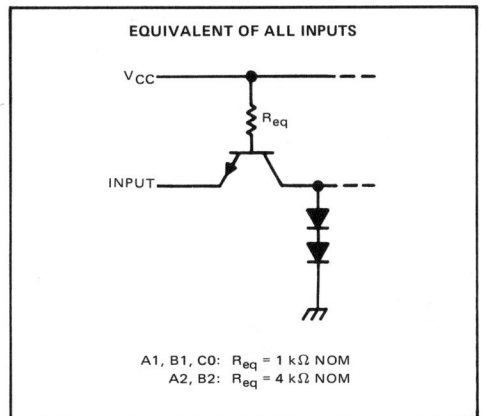

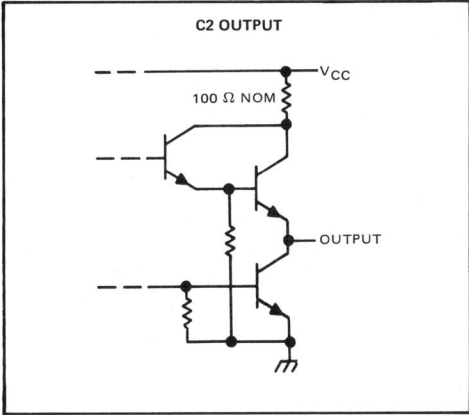

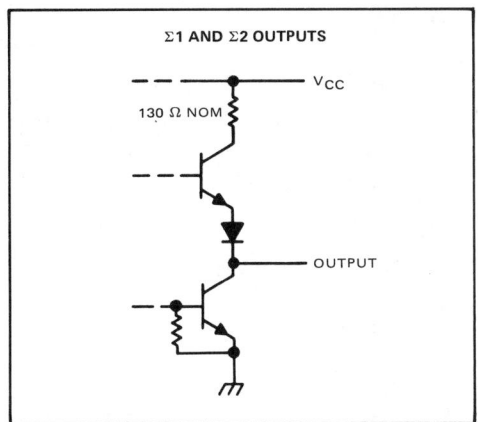

TYPES SN5483A, SN54LS83A, SN7483A, SN74LS83A
4-BIT BINARY FULL ADDERS WITH FAST CARRY

BULLETIN NO. DL-S 7611853, MARCH 1974—REVISED OCTOBER 1976

- Full-Carry Look-Ahead across the Four Bits
- Systems Achieve Partial Look-Ahead Performance with the Economy of Ripple Carry
- SN54283/SN74283 and SN54LS283/SN74LS283 Are Recommended For New Designs as They Feature Supply Voltage and Ground on Corner Pins to Simplify Board Layout

| TYPE | TYPICAL ADD TIMES | | TYPICAL POWER DISSIPATION PER 4-BIT ADDER |
	TWO 8-BIT WORDS	TWO 16-BIT WORDS	
'83A	23 ns	43 ns	310 mW
'LS83A	25 ns	45 ns	95 mW

description

These improved full adders perform the addition of two 4-bit binary numbers. The sum (Σ) outputs are provided for each bit and the resultant carry (C4) is obtained from the fourth bit. These adders feature full internal look ahead across all four bits generating the carry term in ten nanoseconds typically. This provides the system designer with partial look-ahead performance at the economy and reduced package count of a ripple-carry implementation.

The adder logic, including the carry, is implemented in its true form meaning that the end-around carry can be accomplished without the need for logic or level inversion.

Designed for medium-speed applications, the circuits utilize transistor-transistor logic that is compatible with most other TTL families and other saturated low-level logic families.

Series 54 and 54LS circuits are characterized for operation over the full military temperature range of −55°C to 125°C, and Series 74 and 74LS circuits are characterized for operation from 0°C to 70°C.

SN5483A, SN54LS83A . . . J OR W PACKAGE
SN7483A, SN74LS83A . . . J OR N PACKAGE
(TOP VIEW)

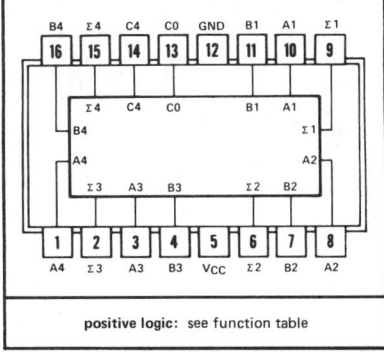

positive logic: see function table

FUNCTION TABLE

INPUT				OUTPUT					
				WHEN C0 = L			WHEN C0 = H		
						WHEN C2 = L			WHEN C2 = H
A1 / A3	B1 / B3	A2 / A4	B2 / B4	Σ1 / Σ3	Σ2 / Σ4	C2 / C4	Σ1 / Σ3	Σ2 / Σ4	C2 / C4
L	L	L	L	L	L	L	H	L	L
H	L	L	L	H	L	L	L	H	L
L	H	L	L	H	L	L	L	H	L
H	H	L	L	L	H	L	H	H	L
L	L	H	L	L	H	L	H	H	L
H	L	H	L	H	H	L	L	L	H
L	H	H	L	H	H	L	L	L	H
H	H	H	L	L	L	H	H	L	H
L	L	L	H	L	H	L	H	H	L
H	L	L	H	H	H	L	L	L	H
L	H	L	H	H	H	L	L	L	H
H	H	L	H	L	L	H	H	L	H
L	L	H	H	L	L	H	H	L	H
H	L	H	H	H	L	H	L	H	H
L	H	H	H	H	L	H	L	H	H
H	H	H	H	L	H	H	H	H	H

H = high level, L = low level

NOTE: Input conditions at A1, B1, A2, B2, and C0 are used to determine outputs Σ1 and Σ2 and the value of the internal carry C2. The values at C2, A3, B3, A4, and B4 are then used to determine outputs Σ3, Σ4, and C4.

absolute maximum ratings over operating free-air temperature range (unless otherwise noted)

Supply voltage, V_CC (see Note 1)	7 V
Input voltage: '83A	5.5 V
'LS83A	7 V
Interemitter voltage (see Note 2)	5.5 V
Operating free-air temperature range: SN5483A, SN54LS83A	−55°C to 125°C
SN7483A, SN74LS83A	0°C to 70°C
Storage temperature range	−65°C to 150°C

NOTES: 1. Voltage values, except interemitter voltage, are with respect to network ground terminal.
2. This is the voltage between two emitters of a multiple-emitter transistor. This rating applies for the '83A only between the following pairs: A1 and B1, A2 and B2, A3 and B3, A4 and B4.

TEXAS INSTRUMENTS
INCORPORATED
POST OFFICE BOX 5012 • DALLAS, TEXAS 75222

TYPES SN5483A, SN54LS83A, SN7483A, SN74LS83A
4-BIT BINARY FULL ADDERS WITH FAST CARRY

REVISED OCTOBER 1976

functional block diagram

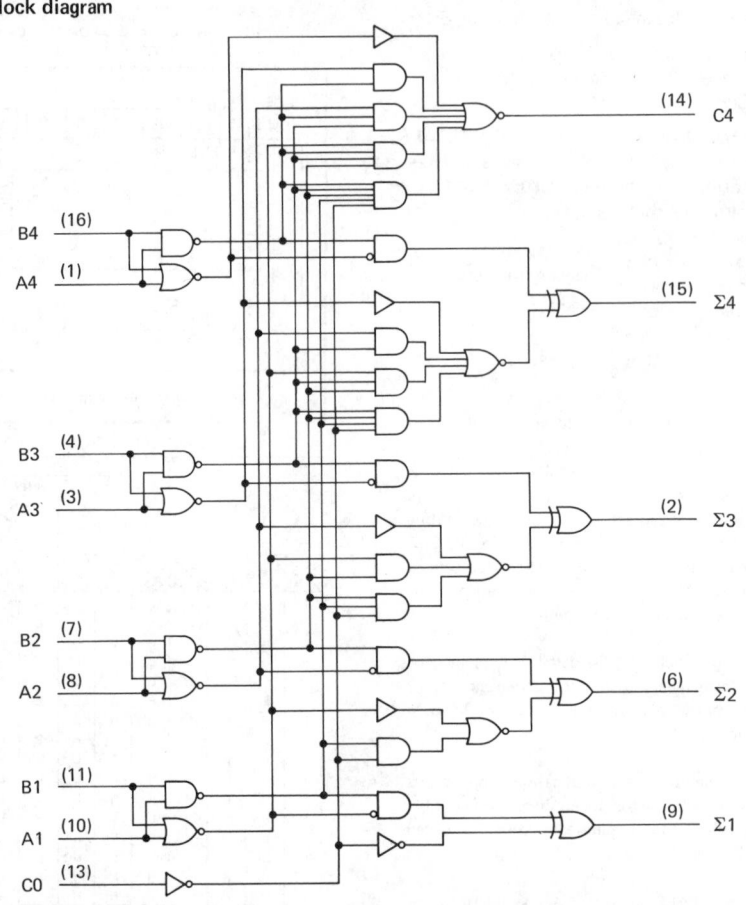

schematics of inputs and outputs

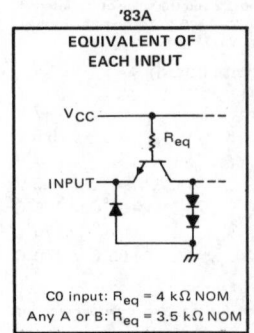

'83A

EQUIVALENT OF
EACH INPUT

C0 input: R_{eq} = 4 kΩ NOM
Any A or B: R_{eq} = 3.5 kΩ NOM

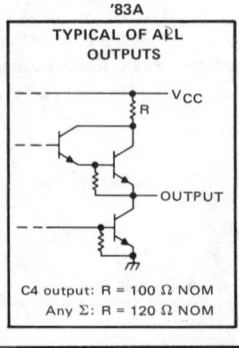

'83A

TYPICAL OF ALL
OUTPUTS

C4 output: R = 100 Ω NOM
Any Σ: R = 120 Ω NOM

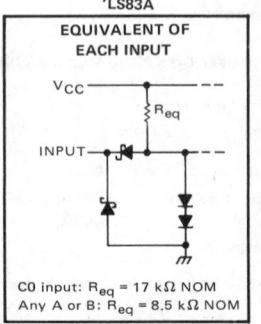

'LS83A

EQUIVALENT OF
EACH INPUT

C0 input: R_{eq} = 17 kΩ NOM
Any A or B: R_{eq} = 8.5 kΩ NOM

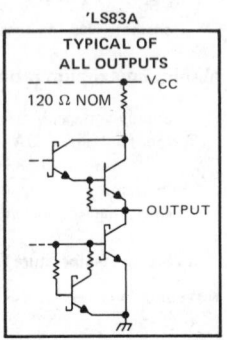

'LS83A

TYPICAL OF
ALL OUTPUTS

120 Ω NOM

TEXAS INSTRUMENTS
INCORPORATED
POST OFFICE BOX 5012 • DALLAS, TEXAS 75222

recommended operating conditions

		SN5483A MIN	SN5483A NOM	SN5483A MAX	SN7483A MIN	SN7483A NOM	SN7483A MAX	UNIT
Supply Voltage, V_{CC}		4.5	5	5.5	4.75	5	5.25	V
High-level output current, I_{OH}	Any output except C4			−800			−800	μA
	Output C4			−400			−400	
Low-level output current, I_{OL}	Any output except C4			16			16	mA
	Output C4			8			8	
Operating free-air temperature, T_A		−55		125	0		70	°C

electrical characteristics over recommended operating free-air temperature range (unless otherwise noted)

PARAMETER		TEST CONDITIONS[†]	SN5483A MIN	SN5483A TYP[‡]	SN5483A MAX	SN7483A MIN	SN7483A TYP[‡]	SN7483A MAX	UNIT
V_{IH} High-level input voltage			2			2			V
V_{IL} Low-level input voltage					0.8			0.8	V
V_{IK} Input clamp voltage		V_{CC} = MIN, I_I = −12 mA			−1.5			−1.5	V
V_{OH} High-level output voltage		V_{CC} = MIN, V_{IH} = 2 V, V_{IL} = 0.8 V, I_{OH} = MAX	2.4	3.4		2.4	3.4		V
V_{OL} Low-level output voltage		V_{CC} = MIN, V_{IH} = 2 V, V_{IL} = 0.8 V, I_{OL} = MAX		0.2	0.4		0.2	0.4	V
I_I Input current at maximum input voltage		V_{CC} = MAX, V_I = 5.5 V			1			1	mA
I_{IH} High-level input current		V_{CC} = MAX, V_I = 2.4 V			40			40	μA
I_{IL} Low-level input current		V_{CC} = MAX, V_I = 0.4 V			−1.6			−1.6	mA
I_{OS} Short-circuit output current[§]	Any output except C4	V_{CC} = MAX	−20		−55	−18		−55	mA
	Output C4		−20		−70	−18		−70	
I_{CC} Supply current		V_{CC} = MAX, All B low, other inputs at 4.5 V		56			56		mA
	Outputs open	All inputs at 4.5 V		66	99		66	110	

[†]For conditions shown as MIN or MAX, use the appropriate value specified under recommended operating conditions.
[‡]All typical values are at V_{CC} = 5 V, T_A = 25°C.
[§]Only one output should be shorted at a time.

switching characteristics, V_{CC} = 5 V, T_A = 25°C

PARAMETER[¶]	FROM (INPUT)	TO (OUTPUT)	TEST CONDITIONS	MIN	TYP	MAX	UNIT
t_{PLH}	C0	Any Σ	C_L = 15 pF, R_L = 400 Ω, See Note 3		14	21	ns
t_{PHL}					12	21	
t_{PLH}	A_i or B_i	$Σ_i$			16	24	ns
t_{PHL}					16	24	
t_{PLH}	C0	C4	C_L = 15 pF, R_L = 780 Ω, See Note 3		9	14	ns
t_{PHL}					11	16	
t_{PLH}	A_i or B_i	C4			9	14	ns
t_{PHL}					11	16	

[¶] t_{PLH} ≡ Propagation delay time, low-to-high-level output
t_{PHL} ≡ Propagation delay time, high-to-low-level output
NOTE 3: Load circuit and voltage waveforms are shown on page 3-10.

7

TEXAS INSTRUMENTS
INCORPORATED
POST OFFICE BOX 5012 • DALLAS, TEXAS 75222

recommended operating conditions

	SN54LS83A			SN74LS83A			UNIT
	MIN	NOM	MAX	MIN	NOM	MAX	
Supply voltage, V_{CC}	4.5	5	5.5	4.75	5	5.25	V
High-level output current, I_{OH}			−400			−400	µA
Low-level output current, I_{OL}			4			8	mA
Operating free-air temperature, T_A	−55		125	0		70	°C

electrical characteristics over recommended operating free-air temperature range (unless otherwise noted)

PARAMETER		TEST CONDITIONS[†]		SN54LS83A			SN74LS83A			UNIT
				MIN	TYP[‡]	MAX	MIN	TYP[‡]	MAX	
V_{IH} High-level input voltage				2			2			V
V_{IL} Low-level input voltage						0.7			0.8	V
V_{IK} Input clamp voltage		V_{CC} = MIN, I_I = −18 mA				−1.5			−1.5	V
V_{OH} High-level output voltage		V_{CC} = MIN, V_{IH} = 2 V, V_{IL} = V_{IL} max, I_{OH} = −400 µA		2.5	3.4		2.7	3.4		V
V_{OL} Low-level output voltage		V_{CC} = MIN, V_{IH} = 2 V, V_{IL} = V_{IL} max	I_{OL} = 4 mA	0.25	0.4		0.25	0.4	V
			I_{OL} = 8 mA					0.35	0.5	
I_I Input current at maximum input voltage	Any A or B	V_{CC} = MAX, V_I = 7 V				0.2			0.2	mA
	C0					0.1			0.1	
I_{IH} High-level input current	Any A or B	V_{CC} = MAX, V_I = 2.7 V				40			40	µA
	C0					20			20	
I_{IL} Low-level input current	Any A or B	V_{CC} = MAX, V_I = 0.4 V				−0.8			−0.8	mA
	C0					−0.4			−0.4	
I_{OS} Short-circuit output current[§]		V_{CC} = MAX		−20		−100	−20		−100	mA
I_{CC} Supply current		V_{CC} = MAX, Outputs open	All inputs grounded		22	39		22	39	mA
			All B low, other inputs at 4.5 V		19	34		19	34	
			All inputs at 4.5 V		19	34		19	34	

[†] For conditions shown as MIN or MAX, use the appropriate value specified under recommended operating conditions.
[‡] All typical values are at V_{CC} = 5 V, T_A = 25°C.
[§] Only one output should be shorted at a time, and duration of the short-circuit should not exceed one second.

switching characteristics, V_{CC} = 5 V, T_A = 25°C

PARAMETER[¶]	FROM (INPUT)	TO (OUTPUT)	TEST CONDITIONS	MIN	TYP	MAX	UNIT
t_{PLH}	C0	Any Σ			16	24	ns
t_{PHL}					15	24	
t_{PLH}	A_i or B_i	Σ_i	C_L = 15 pF, R_L = 2 kΩ, See Note 4		15	24	ns
t_{PHL}					15	24	
t_{PLH}	C0	C4			11	17	ns
t_{PHL}					15	22	
t_{PLH}	A_i or B_i	C4			11	17	ns
t_{PHL}					12	17	

[¶] t_{PLH} ≡ Propagation delay time, low-to-high-level output
t_{PHL} ≡ Propagation delay time, high-to-low-level output
Note 4: Load circuit and voltage waveforms are shown on page 3-11.

7

TEXAS INSTRUMENTS
INCORPORATED
POST OFFICE BOX 5012 • DALLAS, TEXAS 75222

TYPES SN5485, SN54L85, SN54LS85, SN54S85, SN7485, SN74L85, SN74LS85, SN74S85
4-BIT MAGNITUDE COMPARATORS
BULLETIN NO. DL-S 7611810, MARCH 1974—REVISED OCTOBER 1976

SN5485, SN54LS85, SN54S85 . . . J OR W PACKAGE
SN7485, SN74LS85, SN74S85 . . . J OR N PACKAGE
(TOP VIEW)

SN54L85 . . . J PACKAGE
SN74L85 . . . J OR N PACKAGE
(TOP VIEW)

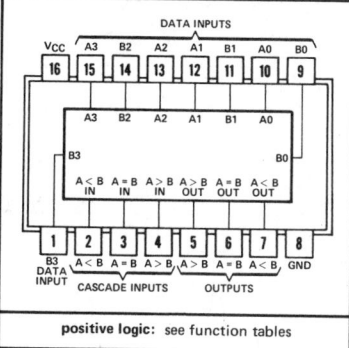
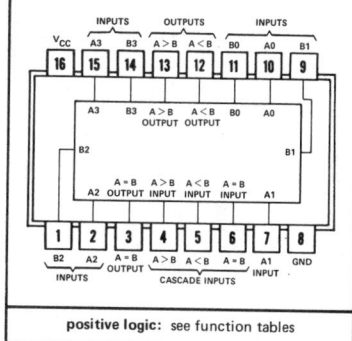

TYPE	TYPICAL POWER DISSI- PATION	TYPICAL DELAY (4-BIT WORDS)
'85	275 mW	23 ns
'L85	20 mW	90 ns
'LS85	52 mW	24 ns
'S85	365 mW	11 ns

positive logic: see function tables

positive logic: see function tables

description

These four-bit magnitude comparators perform comparison of straight binary and straight BCD (8-4-2-1) codes. Three fully decoded decisions about two 4-bit words (A, B) are made and are externally available at three outputs. These devices are fully expandable to any number of bits without external gates. Words of greater length may be compared by connecting comparators in cascade. The A > B, A < B, and A = B outputs of a stage handling less-significant bits are connected to the corresponding A > B, A < B, and A = B inputs of the next stage handling more-significant bits. The stage handling the least-significant bits must have a high-level voltage applied to the A = B input and in addition for the 'L85, low-level voltages applied to the A > B and A < B inputs. The cascading paths of the '85, 'LS85, and 'S85 are implemented with only a two-gate-level delay to reduce overall comparison times for long words. An alternate method of cascading which further reduces the comparison time is shown in the typical application data.

FUNCTION TABLES

COMPARING INPUTS				CASCADING INPUTS			OUTPUTS		
A3, B3	A2, B2	A1, B1	A0, B0	A > B	A < B	A = B	A > B	A < B	A = B
A3 > B3	X	X	X	X	X	X	H	L	L
A3 < B3	X	X	X	X	X	X	L	H	L
A3 = B3	A2 > B2	X	X	X	X	X	H	L	L
A3 = B3	A2 < B2	X	X	X	X	X	L	H	L
A3 = B2	A2 = B2	A1 > B1	X	X	X	X	H	L	L
A3 = B3	A2 = B2	A1 < B1	X	X	X	X	L	H	L
A3 = B3	A2 = B2	A1 = B1	A0 > B0	X	X	X	H	L	L
A3 = B3	A2 = B2	A1 = B1	A0 < B0	X	X	X	L	H	L
A3 = B3	A2 = B2	A1 = B1	A0 = B0	H	L	L	H	L	L
A3 = B3	A2 = B2	A1 = B1	A0 = B0	L	H	L	L	H	L
A3 = B3	A2 = B2	A1 = B1	A0 = B0	L	L	H	L	L	H

'85, 'LS85, 'S85

A3 = B3	A2 = B2	A1 = B1	A0 = B0	X	X	H	L	L	H
A3 = B3	A2 = B2	A1 = B1	A0 = B0	H	H	L	L	L	L
A3 = B3	A2 = B2	A1 = B1	A0 = B0	L	L	L	H	H	L

'L85

A3 = B3	A2 = B2	A1 = B1	A0 = B0	L	H	H	L	H	H
A3 = B3	A2 = B2	A1 = B1	A0 = B0	H	L	H	H	L	H
A3 = B3	A2 = B2	A1 = B1	A0 = B0	H	H	H	H	H	H
A3 = B3	A2 = B2	A1 = B1	A0 = B0	H	H	L	H	H	L
A3 = B3	A2 = B2	A1 = B1	A0 = B0	L	L	L	L	L	L

H = high level, L = low level, X = irrelevant

TEXAS INSTRUMENTS
INCORPORATED
POST OFFICE BOX 5012 • DALLAS, TEXAS 75222

TYPES SN5485, SN54L85, SN54LS85, SN54S85, SN7485, SN74L85, SN74LS85, SN74S85
4-BIT MAGNITUDE COMPARATORS

functional block diagrams

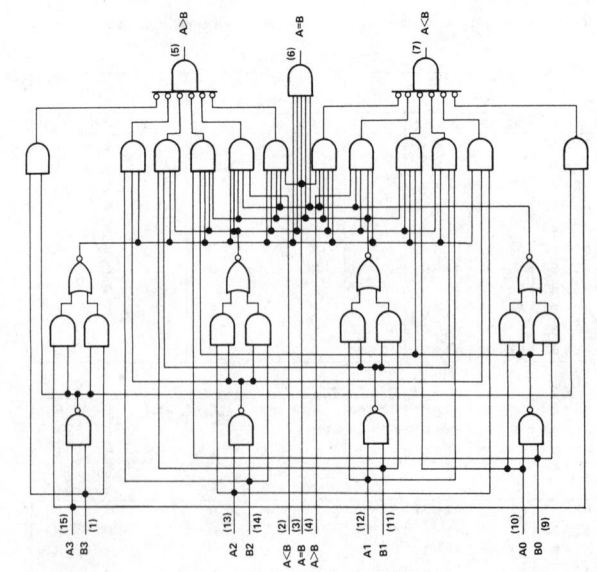

TEXAS INSTRUMENTS
INCORPORATED
POST OFFICE BOX 5012 • DALLAS, TEXAS 75222

schematics of inputs and outputs

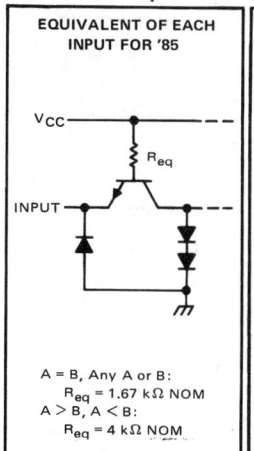

EQUIVALENT OF EACH INPUT FOR '85

A = B, Any A or B:
R_{eq} = 1.67 kΩ NOM
A > B, A < B:
R_{eq} = 4 kΩ NOM

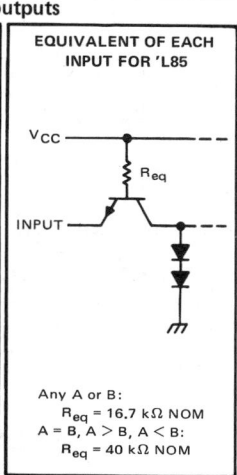

EQUIVALENT OF EACH INPUT FOR 'L85

Any A or B:
R_{eq} = 16.7 kΩ NOM
A = B, A > B, A < B:
R_{eq} = 40 kΩ NOM

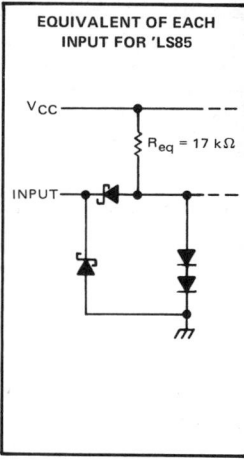

EQUIVALENT OF EACH INPUT FOR 'LS85

R_{eq} = 17 kΩ

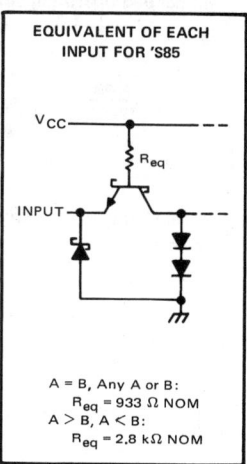

EQUIVALENT OF EACH INPUT FOR 'S85

A = B, Any A or B:
R_{eq} = 933 Ω NOM
A > B, A < B:
R_{eq} = 2.8 kΩ NOM

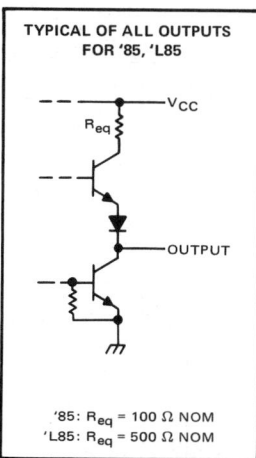

TYPICAL OF ALL OUTPUTS FOR '85, 'L85

'85: R_{eq} = 100 Ω NOM
'L85: R_{eq} = 500 Ω NOM

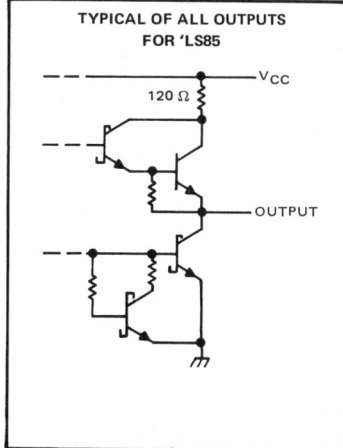

TYPICAL OF ALL OUTPUTS FOR 'LS85

120 Ω

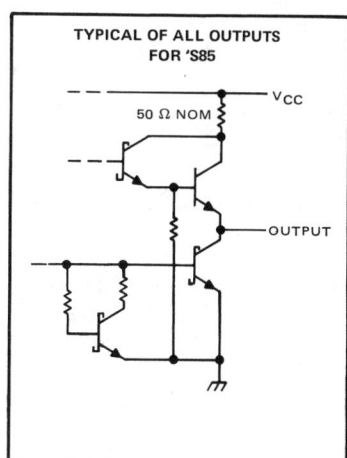

TYPICAL OF ALL OUTPUTS FOR 'S85

50 Ω NOM

absolute maximum ratings over operating free-air temperature range (unless otherwise noted)

	SN54' SN54S'	SN54L'	SN54LS'	SN74' SN74S'	SN74L'	SN74LS'	UNIT
Supply voltage, V_{CC} (see Note 1)	7	8	7	7	8	7	V
Input voltage (see Note 2)	5.5	5.5	7	5.5	5.5	7	V
Interemitter voltage (see Note 3)	5.5			5.5			V
Operating free-air temperature range	−55 to 125			0 to 70			°C
Storage temperature range	−65 to 150			−65 to 150			°C

NOTES: 1. Voltage values, except interemitter voltage, are with respect to network ground terminal.
2. Input voltages for 'L85 must be zero or positive with respect to network ground terminal.
3. This is the voltage between two emitters of a multiple-emitter input transistor. This rating applies to each A input in conjunction with its respective B input of the '85 and 'S85.

7

recommended operating conditions

	SN5485 MIN	SN5485 NOM	SN5485 MAX	SN7485 MIN	SN7485 NOM	SN7485 MAX	UNIT
Supply voltage, V_{CC}	4.5	5	5.5	4.75	5	5.25	V
High-level output current, I_{OH}			−400			−400	μA
Low-level output current, I_{OL}			16			16	mA
Operating free-air temperature, T_A	−55		125	0		70	°C

electrical characteristics over recommended operating free-air temperature range (unless otherwise noted)

	PARAMETER		TEST CONDITIONS†		MIN	TYP‡	MAX	UNIT
V_{IH}	High-level input voltage				2			V
V_{IL}	Low-level input voltage						0.8	V
V_{IK}	Input clamp voltage		V_{CC} = MIN,	I_I = −12 mA			−1.5	V
V_{OH}	High-level output voltage		V_{CC} = MIN, V_{IL} = 0.8 V,	V_{IH} = 2 V, I_{OH} = −400 μA	2.4	3.4		V
V_{OL}	Low-level output voltage		V_{CC} = MIN, V_{IL} = 0.8 V,	V_{IH} = 2 V, I_{OL} = 16 mA		0.2	0.4	V
I_I	Input current at maximum input voltage		V_{CC} = MAX,	V_I = 5.5 V			1	mA
I_{IH}	High-level input current	A < B, A > B inputs	V_{CC} = MAX,	V_I = 2.4 V			40	μA
		all other inputs					120	
I_{IL}	Low-level input current	A < B, A > B inputs	V_{CC} = MAX,	V_I = 0.4 V			−1.6	mA
		all other inputs					−4.8	
I_{OS}	Short-circuit output current§		V_{CC} = MAX, V_O = 0 SN5485		−20		−55	mA
			SN7485		−18		−55	
I_{CC}	Supply current		V_{CC} = MAX,	See Note 4		55	88	mA

†For conditions shown as MIN or MAX, use the appropriate value specified under recommended operating conditions.
‡All typical values are at V_{CC} = 5 V, T_A = 25°C.
§Not more than one output should be shorted at a time.
NOTE 4: I_{CC} is measured with outputs open, A = B grounded, and all other inputs at 4.5 V.

switching characteristics, V_{CC} = 5 V, T_A = 25°C

PARAMETER¶	FROM INPUT	TO OUTPUT	NUMBER OF GATE LEVELS	TEST CONDITIONS	MIN	TYP	MAX	UNIT
t_{PLH}	Any A or B data input	A < B, A > B	1			7		ns
			2			12		
			3			17	26	
		A = B	4			23	35	
t_{PHL}	Any A or B data input	A < B, A > B	1	C_L = 15 pF, R_L = 400 Ω, See Note 5		11		ns
			2			15		
			3			20	30	
		A = B	4			20	30	
t_{PLH}	A < B or A = B	A > B	1			7	11	ns
t_{PHL}	A < B or A = B	A > B	1			11	17	ns
t_{PLH}	A = B	A = B	2			13	20	ns
t_{PHL}	A = B	A = B	2			11	17	ns
t_{PLH}	A > B or A = B	A < B	1			7	11	ns
t_{PHL}	A > B or A = B	A < B	1			11	17	ns

¶ t_{PLH} ≡ propagation delay time, low-to-high-level output
t_{PHL} ≡ propagation delay time, high-to-low-level output.
NOTE 5: Load circuit and voltage waveforms are shown on page 3-10.

TEXAS INSTRUMENTS
INCORPORATED
POST OFFICE BOX 5012 • DALLAS, TEXAS 75222

recommended operating conditions

	SN54L85			SN74L85			UNIT
	MIN	NOM	MAX	MIN	NOM	MAX	
Supply voltage, V_{CC}	4.5	5	5.5	4.75	5	5.25	V
High-level output current, I_{OH}			−100			−200	µA
Low-level output current, I_{OL}			2			3.6	mA
Operating free-air temperature, T_A	−55		125	0		70	°C

electrical characteristics over recommended operating free-air temperature range (unless otherwise noted)

	PARAMETER		TEST CONDITIONS[†]		MIN	TYP[‡]	MAX	UNIT
V_{IH}	High-level input voltage				2			V
V_{IL}	Low-level input voltage						0.7	V
V_{OH}	High-level output voltage		V_{CC} = MIN, V_{IH} = 2 V,	SN54L85	2.4	3.3		V
			V_{IL} = 0.7 V, I_{OH} = MAX	SN74L85	2.4	3.2		
V_{OL}	Low-level output voltage		V_{CC} = MIN, V_{IH} = 2 V,	SN54L85		0.15	0.3	V
			V_{IL} = 0.7 V, I_{OL} = MAX	SN74L85		0.2	0.4	
I_I	Input current at	A < B, A > B, or A = B	V_{CC} = MAX, V_I = 5.5 V				100	µA
	maximum input voltage	A or B inputs					300	
I_{IH}	High-level input current	A < B, A < B, or A = B	V_{CC} = MAX, V_I = 2.4 V				10	µA
		A or B inputs					30	
I_{IL}	Low-level input current	A < B, A > B, or A = B	V_{CC} = MAX, V_I = 0.3 V				−0.18	mA
		A or B inputs					−0.54	
I_{OS}	Short-circuit output current[§]		V_{CC} = MAX		−3		−15	mA
I_{CC}	Supply current		V_{CC} = MAX, See Note 6	Condition A		4.0	7.7	mA
				Condition B		3.2	7.2	

[†]for conditions shown as MIN or MAX, use the appropriate value specified under recommended operating conditions.
[‡]All typical values are at V_{CC} = 5 V, T_A = 25°C.
[§]Not more than one output should be shorted at a time.
NOTE 6: With all outputs open, I_{CC} is measured for Condition A with all inputs at 4.5 V, and for Condition B with all inputs grounded.

switching characteristics, V_{CC} = 5 V, T_A = 25°C

PARAMETER[¶]	FROM (INPUT)	TO (OUTPUT)	TEST CONDITIONS	MIN	TYP	MAX	UNIT
t_{PLH}	Any A or B	Any	C_L = 50 pF, R_L = 4 kΩ, See Note 7		90	150	ns
t_{PHL}					75	150	
t_{PLH}	A > B, A < B, or A = B	Any			75	150	ns
t_{PHL}					55	100	

[¶] $t_{PLH} \equiv$ propagation delay time, low-to-high-level output
$t_{PHL} \equiv$ propagation delay time, high-to-low-level output
NOTE 7: Load circuit and voltage waveforms are shown on page 3-11.

7

74

TEXAS INSTRUMENTS
INCORPORATED
POST OFFICE BOX 5012 • DALLAS, TEXAS 75222

recommended operating conditions

	SN54LS85			SN74LS85			UNIT
	MIN	NOM	MAX	MIN	NOM	MAX	
Supply voltage, V_{CC}	4.5	5	5.5	4.75	5	5.25	V
High-level output current, I_{OH}			−400			−400	μA
Low-level output current, I_{OL}			4			8	mA
Operating free-air temperature, T_A	−55		125	0		70	°C

electrical characteristics over recommended operating free-air temperature range (unless otherwise noted)

PARAMETER			TEST CONDITIONS[†]		SN54LS85			SN74LS85			UNIT
					MIN	TYP[‡]	MAX	MIN	TYP[‡]	MAX	
V_{IH}	High-level input voltage				2			2			V
V_{IL}	Low-level input voltage						0.7			0.8	V
V_{IK}	Input clamp voltage		V_{CC} = MIN,	I_I = −18 mA			−1.5			−1.5	V
V_{OH}	High-level output voltage		V_{CC} = MIN, V_{IL} = V_{IL} max,	V_{IH} = 2 V, I_{OH} = −400 μA	2.5	3.4		2.7	3.4		V
V_{OL}	Low-level output voltage		V_{CC} = MIN, V_{IH} = 2 V, V_{IL} = V_{IL} max	I_{OL} = 4 mA		0.25	0.4		0.25	0.4	V
				I_{OL} = 8 mA					0.35	0.5	
I_I	Input current at maximum input voltage	A < B, A > B inputs	V_{CC} = MAX,	V_I = 7 V			0.1			0.1	mA
		all other inputs					0.3			0.3	
I_{IH}	High-level input current	A < B, A > B inputs	V_{CC} = MAX,	V_I = 2.7 V			20			20	μA
		all other inputs					60			60	
I_{IL}	Low-level input current	A < B, A > B inputs	V_{CC} = MAX,	V_I = 0.4 V			−0.4			−0.4	mA
		all other inputs					−1.2			−1.2	
I_{OS}	Short-circuit output current[§]		V_{CC} = MAX		−20		−100	−20		−100	mA
I_{CC}	Supply current		V_{CC} = MAX,	See Note 4		10.4	20		10.4	20	mA

[†]For conditions shown as MIN or MAX, use the appropriate value specified under recommended operating conditions.
[‡]All typical values are at V_{CC} = 5 V, T_A = 25°C.
[§]Not more than one output should be shorted at a time, and duration of the short-circuit should not exceed one second.
NOTE 4: I_{CC} is measured with outputs open, A = B grounded, and all other inputs at 4.5 V.

switching characteristics, V_{CC} = 5 V, T_A = 25°C

PARAMETER[¶]	FROM INPUT	TO OUTPUT	NUMBER OF GATE LEVELS	TEST CONDITIONS	MIN	TYP	MAX	UNIT
t_{PLH}	Any A or B data input	A < B, A > B	1			14		ns
			2			19		
			3			24	36	
		A = B	4			27	45	
t_{PHL}	Any A or B data input	A < B, A > B	1			11		ns
			2			15		
			3	C_L = 15 pF, R_L = 2 kΩ, See Note 7		20	30	
		A = B	4			23	45	
t_{PLH}	A < B or A = B	A > B	1			14	22	ns
t_{PHL}	A < B or A = B	A > B	1			11	17	ns
t_{PLH}	A = B	A = B	2			13	20	ns
t_{PHL}	A = B	A = B	2			13	26	ns
t_{PLH}	A > B or A = B	A < B	1			14	22	ns
t_{PHL}	A > B or A = B	A < B	1			11	17	ns

[¶]t_{PLH} ≡ propagation delay time, low-to-high-level output
t_{PHL} ≡ propagation delay time, high-to-low-level output
NOTE 7: Load circuit and voltage waveforms are shown on page 3-11.

7

TEXAS INSTRUMENTS
INCORPORATED
POST OFFICE BOX 5012 • DALLAS, TEXAS 75222

recommended operating conditions

	SN54S85			SN74S85			UNIT
	MIN	NOM	MAX	MIN	NOM	MAX	
Supply voltage, V_{CC}	4.5	5	5.5	4.75	5	5.25	V
High-level output current, I_{OH}			−1			−1	mA
Low-level output current, I_{OL}			20			20	mA
Operating free-air temperature, T_A	−55		125	0		70	°C

electrical characteristics over recommended operating free-air temperature range (unless otherwise noted)

PARAMETER		TEST CONDITIONS[†]		MIN	TYP[‡]	MAX	UNIT
V_{IH}	High-level input voltage			2			V
V_{IL}	Low-level input voltage					0.8	V
V_{IK}	Input clamp voltage	V_{CC} = MIN, I_I = −18 mA				−1.2	V
V_{OH}	High-level output voltage	V_{CC} = MIN, V_{IH} = 2 V, V_{IL} = 0.8 V, I_{OH} = −1 mA	SN54S85	2.5	3.4		V
			SN74S85	2.7	3.4		
V_{OL}	Low-level output voltage	V_{CC} = MIN, V_{IH} = 2 V, V_{IL} = 0.8 V, I_{OL} = 20 mA				0.5	V
I_I	Input current at maximum input voltage	V_{CC} = MAX, V_I = 5.5 V				1	mA
I_{IH}	High-level input current	A < B, A > B inputs	V_{CC} = MAX, V_I = 2.7 V			50	μA
		all other inputs				150	
I_{IL}	Low-level input current	A < B, A > B inputs	V_{CC} = MAX, V_I = 0.5 V			−2	mA
		all other inputs				−6	
I_{OS}	Short-circuit output current[§]	V_{CC} = MAX		−40		−100	mA
I_{CC}	Supply current	V_{CC} = MAX, See Note 4			73	115	mA
		V_{CC} = MAX, T_A = 125°C, See Note 4	SN54S85W			110	

[†] For conditions shown as MIN or MAX, use the appropriate value specified under recommended operating conditions.
[‡] All typical values are at V_{CC} = 5 V, T_A = 25°C.
[§] Not more than one output should be shorted at a time, and duration of the short-circuit should not exceed one second.
NOTE 4: I_{CC} is measured with outputs open, A = B grounded, and all other inputs at 4.5 V.

switching characteristics, V_{CC} = 5 V, T_A = 25°C

PARAMETER[¶]	FROM INPUT	TO OUTPUT	NUMBER OF GATE LEVELS	TEST CONDITIONS	MIN	TYP	MAX	UNIT
t_{PLH}	Any A or B data input	A < B, A > B	1			5		ns
			2			7.5		
			3			10.5	16	
		A = B	4			12	18	
t_{PHL}	Any A or B data input	A < B, A > B	1	C_L = 15 pF, R_L = 280 Ω, See Note 5		5.5		ns
			2			7		
			3			11	16.5	
		A = B	4			11	16.5	
t_{PLH}	A < B or A = B	A > B	1			5	7.5	ns
t_{PHL}	A < B or A = B	A > B	1			5.5	8.5	ns
t_{PLH}	A = B	A = B	2			7	10.5	ns
t_{PHL}	A = B	A = B	2			5	7.5	ns
t_{PLH}	A > B or A = B	A < B	1			5	7.5	ns
t_{PHL}	A > B or A = B	A < B	1			5.5	8.5	ns

[¶] t_{PLH} ≡ propagation delay time, low-to-high-level output
t_{PHL} ≡ propagation delay time, high-to-low-level output

NOTE 5: Load circuit and voltage waveforms are shown on page 3-10.

7

TEXAS INSTRUMENTS
INCORPORATED
POST OFFICE BOX 5012 • DALLAS, TEXAS 75222

TYPES SN5485, SN54L85, SN54LS85, SN54S85, SN7485, SN74L85, SN74LS85, SN74S85
4-BIT MAGNITUDE COMPARATORS

TYPICAL APPLICATION DATA

COMPARISON OF TWO N-BIT WORDS

This application demonstrates how these magnitude comparators can be cascaded to compare longer words. The example illustrated shows the comparison of two 24-bit words; however, the design is expandable to n-bits. As an example, one comparator can be used with five of the 24-bit comparators illustrated to expand the word length to 120-bits. Typical comparison times for various word lengths using the '85, 'L85, 'LS85, or 'S85 are:

WORD LENGTH	NUMBER OF PKGS	'85	'L85	'LS85	'S85
1-4 bits	1	23 ns	90 ns	24 ns	11 ns
5-24 bits	2-6	46 ns	180 ns	48 ns	22 ns
25-120 bits	8-31	69 ns	270 ns	72 ns	33 ns

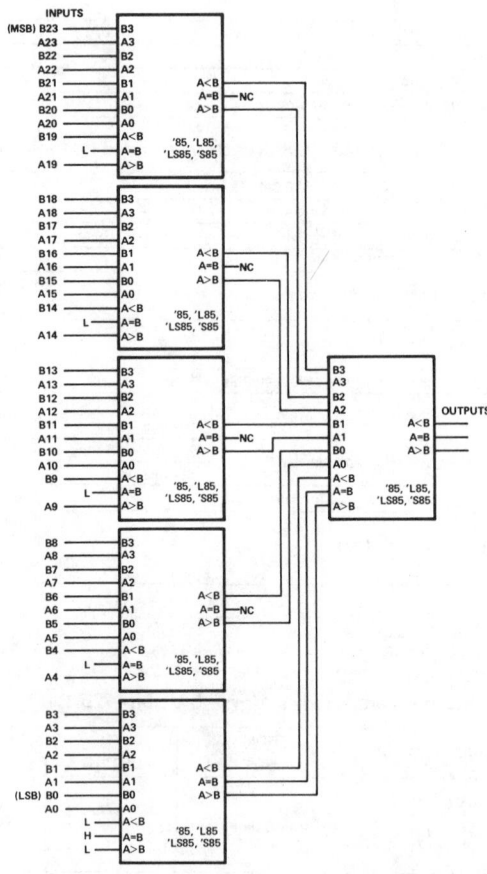

COMPARISON OF TWO 24-BIT WORDS

TEXAS INSTRUMENTS
INCORPORATED
POST OFFICE BOX 5012 • DALLAS, TEXAS 75222

TYPES SN5486, SN54L86, SN54LS86, SN54S86, SN7486, SN74L86, SN74LS86, SN74S86
QUADRUPLE 2-INPUT EXCLUSIVE-OR GATES

BULLETIN NO. DL-S 7611825, DECEMBER 1972—REVISED OCTOBER 1976

schematics of inputs and outputs

'86

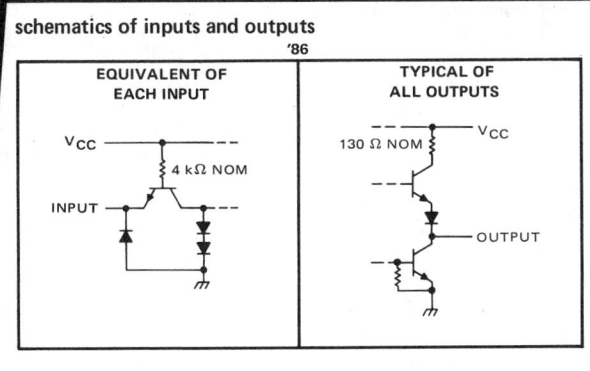

**SN54', SN54LS', SN54S' . . . J OR W PACKAGE
SN74', SN74LS', SN74S' . . . J OR N PACKAGE
(TOP VIEW)**

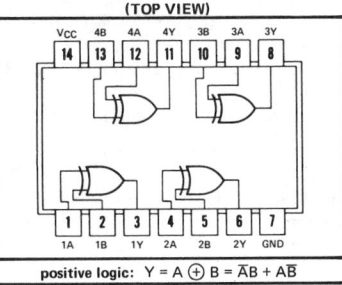

positive logic: $Y = A \oplus B = \overline{A}B + A\overline{B}$

'L86

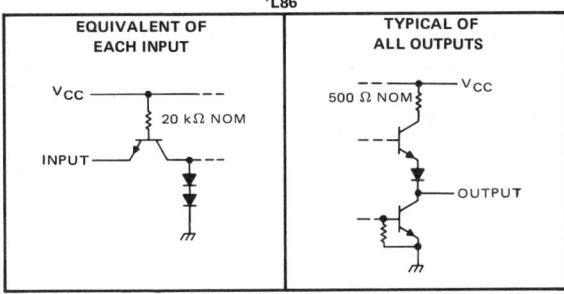

**SN54L86 . . . J PACKAGE
SN74L86 . . . J OR N PACKAGE
(TOP VIEW)**

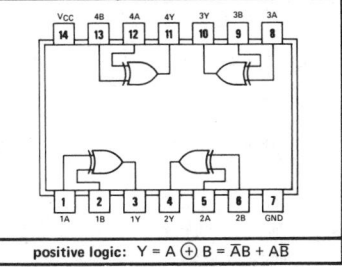

positive logic: $Y = A \oplus B = \overline{A}B + A\overline{B}$

SN54L86 . . . T PACKAGE (TOP VIEW)

'LS86

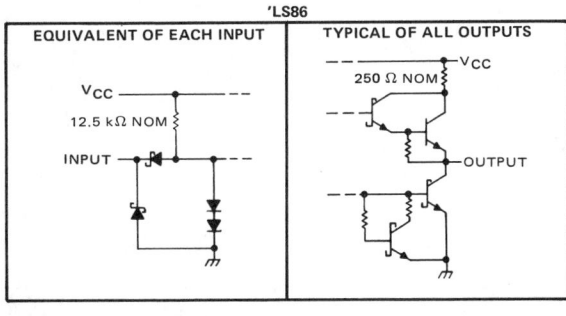

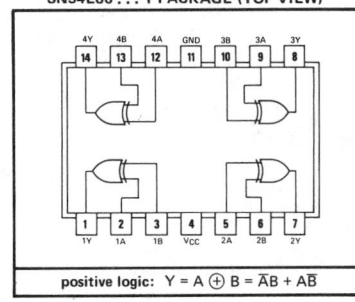

positive logic: $Y = A \oplus B = \overline{A}B + A\overline{B}$

FUNCTION TABLE

INPUTS		OUTPUT
A	B	Y
L	L	L
L	H	H
H	L	H
H	H	L

H = high level, L = low level

'S86

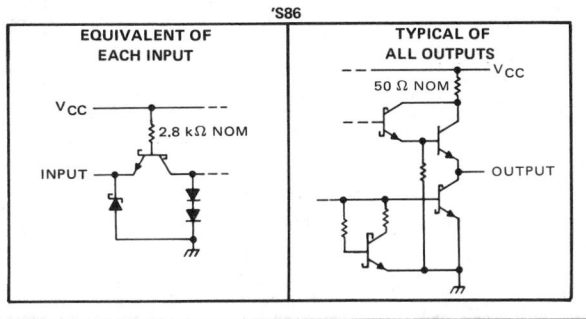

TYPE	TYPICAL AVERAGE PROPAGATION DELAY TIME	TYPICAL TOTAL POWER DISSIPATION
'86	14 ns	150 mW
'L86	55 ns	15 mW
'LS86	10 ns	30.5 mW
'S86	7 ns	250 mW

TYPES SN5486, SN7486
QUADRUPLE 2-INPUT EXCLUSIVE-OR GATES

absolute maximum ratings over operating free-air temperature range (unless otherwise noted)

Supply voltage, V_{CC} (see Note 1)	7 V
Input voltage	5.5 V
Operating free-air temperature range: SN5486	$-55°C$ to $125°C$
SN7486	$0°C$ to $70°C$
Storage temperature range	$-65°C$ to $150°C$

NOTE 1: Voltage values are with respect to network ground terminal.

recommended operating conditions

	SN5486			SN7486			UNIT
	MIN	NOM	MAX	MIN	NOM	MAX	
Supply voltage, V_{CC}	4.5	5	5.5	4.75	5	5.25	V
High-level output current, I_{OH}			-800			-800	μA
Low-level output current, I_{OL}			16			16	mA
Operating free-air temperature, T_A	-55		125	0		70	°C

electrical characteristics over recommended operating free-air temperature range (unless otherwise noted)

PARAMETER		TEST CONDITIONS[†]	SN5486			SN7486			UNIT
			MIN	TYP[‡]	MAX	MIN	TYP[‡]	MAX	
V_{IH}	High-level input voltage		2			2			V
V_{IL}	Low-level input voltage				0.8			0.8	V
V_{IK}	Input clamp voltage	V_{CC} = MIN, I_I = -8 mA			-1.5			-1.5	V
V_{OH}	High-level output voltage	V_{CC} = MIN, V_{IH} = 2 V, V_{IL} = 0.8 V, I_{OH} = -800μA	2.4	3.4		2.4	3.4		V
V_{OL}	Low-level output voltage	V_{CC} = MIN, V_{IH} = 2 V V_{IL} = 0.8 V, I_{OL} = 16 mA		0.2	0.4		0.2	0.4	V
I_I	Input current at maximum input voltage	V_{CC} = MAX, V_I = 5.5 V			1			1	mA
I_{IH}	High-level input current	V_{CC} = MAX, V_I = 2.4 V			40			40	μA
I_{IL}	Low-level input current	V_{CC} = MAX, V_I = 0.4 V			-1.6			-1.6	mA
I_{OS}	Short-circuit output current§	V_{CC} = MAX	-20		-55	-18		-55	mA
I_{CC}	Supply current	V_{CC} = MAX, See Note 2		30	43		30	50	mA

†For conditions shown as MIN or MAX, use the appropriate value specified under recommended operating conditions for the applicable type.
‡All typical values are at V_{CC} = 5 V, T_A = 25°C.
§Not more than one output should be shorted at a time.
NOTE 2: I_{CC} is measured with the inputs grounded and the outputs open.

switching characteristics, V_{CC} = 5 V, T_A = 25°C

PARAMETER¶	FROM (INPUT)	TEST CONDITIONS		MIN	TYP	MAX	UNIT
t_{PLH}	A or B	Other input low	C_L = 15 pF, R_L = 400 Ω, See Note 3		15	23	ns
t_{PHL}					11	17	
t_{PLH}	A or B	Other input high			18	30	ns
t_{PHL}					13	22	

¶t_{PLH} ≡ propagation delay time, low-to-high-level output
t_{PHL} ≡ propagation delay time, high-to-low-level output
NOTE 3: Load circuit and voltage waveforms are shown on page 3-10.

7

TEXAS INSTRUMENTS
INCORPORATED
POST OFFICE BOX 5012 • DALLAS, TEXAS 75222

absolute maximum ratings over operating free-air temperature range (unless otherwise noted)

Supply voltage, V_{CC} (see Note 1) . . . . 7 V

Input voltage (see Note 4) . . . . 5.5 V

Operating free-air temperature range: SN54L86 . . . . $-55°C$ to $125°C$

                                  SN74L86 . . . . $0°C$ to $70°C$

Storage temperature range . . . . $-65°C$ to $150°C$

NOTES: 1. Voltage values are with respect to network ground terminal.
          4. Input voltages must be zero or positive with respect to network ground terminal.

recommended operating conditions

	SN54L86			SN74L86			UNIT
	MIN	NOM	MAX	MIN	NOM	MAX	
Supply voltage, V_{CC}	4.5	5	5.5	4.75	5	5.25	V
High-level output current, I_{OH}			-100			-200	μA
Low-level output current, I_{OL}			2			3.6	mA
Operating free-air temperature, T_A	-55		125	0		70	$°C$

electrical characteristics over recommended operating free-air temperature range (unless otherwise noted)

PARAMETER		TEST CONDITIONS[†]	SN54L86			SN74L86			UNIT
			MIN	TYP[‡]	MAX	MIN	TYP[‡]	MAX	
V_{IH}	High-level input voltage		2			2			V
V_{IL}	Low-level input voltage				0.7			0.7	V
V_{OH}	High-level output voltage	V_{CC} = MIN, V_{IH} = 2 V, V_{IL} = 0.7 V, I_{OH} = MAX	2.4	3.3		2.4	3.2		V
V_{OL}	Low-level output voltage	V_{CC} = MIN, V_{IH} = 2 V, V_{IL} = 0.7 V, I_{OL} = MAX		0.15	0.3		0.2	0.4	V
I_I	Input current at maximum input voltage	V_{CC} = MAX, V_I = 5.5 V			200			200	μA
I_{IH}	High-level input current	V_{CC} = MAX, V_I = 2.4 V			20			20	μA
I_{IL}	Low-level input current	V_{CC} = MAX, V_I = 0.3 V			-0.36			-0.36	mA
I_{OS}	Short-circuit output current	V_{CC} = MAX	-3		-15	-3		-15	mA
I_{CCH}	Supply current, all outputs high	V_{CC} = MAX, See Note 5		2.2	4.4		2.2	4.4	mA
I_{CCL}	Supply current, all outputs low	V_{CC} = MAX, See Note 6		3.8	6.68		3.8	6.68	mA

[†] For conditions shown as MIN or MAX, use the appropriate value specified under recommended operating conditions.
[‡] All typical values are at V_{CC} = 5 V, T_A = 25°C.
NOTES: 5. I_{CCH} is measured with all outputs open, one input of each gate at 4.5 V, and the other inputs grounded.
          6. I_{CCL} is measured with all outputs open and all inputs at 4.5 V.

switching characteristics, V_{CC} = 5 V, T_A = 25°C

PARAMETER[¶]	FROM (INPUT)	TEST CONDITIONS		MIN	TYP	MAX	UNIT
t_{PLH}	A or B	Other input low	C_L = 50 pF, R_L = 4 kΩ, See Note 7		75	150	ns
t_{PHL}					60	150	
t_{PLH}	A or B	Other input high			50	90	ns
t_{PHL}					35	60	

[¶] t_{PLH} ≡ propagation delay time, low-to-high-level output
  t_{PHL} ≡ propagation delay time, high-to-low-level output
NOTE 7: Load circuit and voltage waveforms are shown on page 3-11.

7

TEXAS INSTRUMENTS
INCORPORATED
POST OFFICE BOX 5012 • DALLAS, TEXAS 75222

TYPES SN54LS86, SN74LS86
QUADRUPLE 2-INPUT EXCLUSIVE-OR GATES

REVISED OCTOBER 1976

absolute maximum ratings over operating free-air temperature range (unless otherwise noted)

Supply voltage, V_{CC} (see Note 1) . . . . 7 V
Input voltage . . . . 7 V
Operating free-air temperature range: SN54LS86 . . . . −55°C to 125°C
SN74LS86 . . . . 0°C to 70°C
Storage temperature range . . . . −65°C to 150°C

NOTE 1: Voltage values are with respect to network ground terminal.

recommended operating conditions

	SN54LS86			SN74LS86			UNIT
	MIN	NOM	MAX	MIN	NOM	MAX	
Supply voltage, V_{CC}	4.5	5	5.5	4.75	5	5.25	V
High-level output current, I_{OH}			−400			−400	μA
Low-level output current, I_{OL}			4			8	mA
Operating free-air temperature, T_A	−55		125	0		70	°C

electrical characteristics over recommended operating free-air temperature range (unless otherwise noted)

PARAMETER		TEST CONDITIONS[†]	SN54LS86			SN74LS86			UNIT
			MIN	TYP[‡]	MAX	MIN	TYP[‡]	MAX	
V_{IH}	High-level input voltage		2			2			V
V_{IL}	Low-level input voltage				0.7			0.8	V
V_{IK}	Input clamp voltage	V_{CC} = MIN, I_I = −18 mA			−1.5			−1.5	V
V_{OH}	High-level output voltage	V_{CC} = MIN, V_{IH} = 2 V, $V_{IL} = V_{IL}$ max, I_{OH} = −400 μA	2.5	3.4		2.7	3.4		V
V_{OL}	Low-level output voltage	V_{CC} = MIN, V_{IH} = 2 V, $V_{IL} = V_{IL}$ max, I_{OL} = 4 mA		0.25	0.4		0.25	0.4	V
		I_{OL} = 8 mA					0.35	0.5	
I_I	Input current at maximum input voltage	V_{CC} = MAX, V_I = 7 V			0.2			0.2	mA
I_{IH}	High-level input current	V_{CC} = MAX, V_I = 2.7 V			40			40	μA
I_{IL}	Low-level input current	V_{CC} = MAX, V_I = 0.4 V			−0.8			−0.8	mA
I_{OS}	Short-circuit output current[§]	V_{CC} = MAX	−6		−40	−5		−42	mA
I_{CC}	Supply current	V_{CC} = MAX, See Note 2		6.1	10		6.1	10	mA

[†]For conditions shown as MIN or MAX, use the appropriate value specified under recommended operating conditions for the applicable type.
[‡]All typical values are at V_{CC} = 5 V, T_A = 25°C.
[§]Not more than one output should be shorted at a time.
NOTE 2: I_{CC} is measured with the inputs grounded and the outputs open.

switching characteristics, V_{CC} = 5 V, T_A = 25°C

PARAMETER[¶]	FROM (INPUT)	TEST CONDITIONS		MIN	TYP	MAX	UNIT
t_{PLH}	A or B	Other input low	C_L = 15 pF, R_L = 2 kΩ, See Note 7		12	23	ns
t_{PHL}					10	17	
t_{PLH}	A or B	Other input high			20	30	ns
t_{PHL}					13	22	

[¶]t_{PLH} ≡ propagation delay time, low-to-high-level output
t_{PHL} ≡ propagation delay time, high-to-low-level output
NOTE 7: Load circuit and voltage waveforms are shown on page 3-11.

7

TEXAS INSTRUMENTS
INCORPORATED
POST OFFICE BOX 5012 • DALLAS, TEXAS 75222

absolute maximum ratings over operating free-air temperature range (unless otherwise noted)

Supply voltage, V_{CC} (see Note 1)	7 V
Input voltage	5.5 V
Operating free-air temperature range: SN54S86	−55°C to 125°C
SN74S86	0°C to 70°C
Storage temperature range	−65°C to 150°C

NOTE 1: Voltage values are with respect to network ground terminal.

recommended operating conditions

	SN54S86			SN74S86			UNIT
	MIN	NOM	MAX	MIN	NOM	MAX	
Supply voltage, V_{CC}	4.5	5	5.5	4.75	5	5.25	V
High-level output current, I_{OH}			−1			−1	mA
Low-level output current, I_{OL}			20			20	mA
Operating free-air temperature, T_A	−55		125	0		70	°C

electrical characteristics over recommended operating free-air temperature range (unless otherwise noted)

PARAMETER		TEST CONDITIONS[†]	SN54S86			SN74S86			UNIT
			MIN	TYP[‡]	MAX	MIN	TYP[‡]	MAX	
V_{IH}	High-level input voltage		2			2			V
V_{IL}	Low-level input voltage				0.8			0.8	V
V_{IK}	Input clamp voltage	V_{CC} = MIN, I_I = −18 mA			−1.2			−1.2	V
V_{OH}	High-level output voltage	V_{CC} = MIN, V_{IH} = 2 V, V_{IL} = 0.8 V, I_{OH} = −1 mA	2.5	3.4		2.7	3.4		V
V_{OL}	Low-level output voltage	V_{CC} = MIN, V_{IH} = 2 V V_{IL} = 0.8 V, I_{OL} = 20 mA			0.5			0.5	V
I_I	Input current at maximum input voltage	V_{CC} = MAX, V_I = 5.5 V			1			1	mA
I_{IH}	High-level input current	V_{CC} = MAX, V_I = 2.7 V			50			50	μA
I_{IL}	Low-level input current	V_{CC} = MAX, V_I = 0.5 V			−2			−2	mA
I_{OS}	Short-circuit output current[§]	V_{CC} = MAX	−40		−100	−40		−100	mA
I_{CC}	Supply current	V_{CC} = MAX, See Note 2		50	75		50	75	mA

[†]For conditions shown as MIN or MAX, use the appropriate value specified under recommended operating conditions for the applicable type.
[‡]All typical values are at V_{CC} = 5 V, T_A = 25°C.
[§]Not more than one output should be shorted at a time, and duration of the short-circuit should not exceed one second.
NOTE 2: I_{CC} is measured with the inputs grounded and the outputs open.

switching characteristics, V_{CC} = 5 V, T_A = 25°C

PARAMETER[¶]	FROM (INPUT)	TEST CONDITIONS		MIN	TYP	MAX	UNIT
t_{PLH}	A or B	Other input low	C_L = 15 pF, R_L = 280 Ω, See Note 3		7	10.5	ns
t_{PHL}					6.5	10	
t_{PLH}	A or B	Other input high			7	10.5	ns
t_{PHL}					6.5	10	

[¶]t_{PLH} ≡ propagation delay time, low-to-high-level output
t_{PHL} ≡ propagation delay time, high-to-low-level output
NOTE 3: Load circuit and voltage waveforms are shown on page 3-10.

7

description

Operation of these monolithic 4-bit true/complement elements is controlled by the B and C inputs. With the B input low, the 4-bit binary input (A) is transferred to the output (Y) in either complementary form (with C low) or true form (with C high). When the B input is high, the output will be at the complementary level of the C input regardless of the levels of the data inputs.

These circuits are fully compatible for use with other TTL or DTL circuits. Input clamping diodes are provided to minimize transmission line effects and thereby simplify system design. Each input represents only one normalized series 54H/74H load, and full fan-out to 10 series 54H/74H loads is available from each of the outputs in the low-level condition.

Power dissipation is 270 mW typically with an average propagation delay of 14 ns from data inputs to output.

The SN54H87 is characterized for operation over the full military temperature range of -55°C to 125°C, and the SN74H87 is characterized for operation from 0°C to 70°C.

SN54H87 . . . J OR W PACKAGE
SN74H87 . . . J OR N PACKAGE
(TOP VIEW)

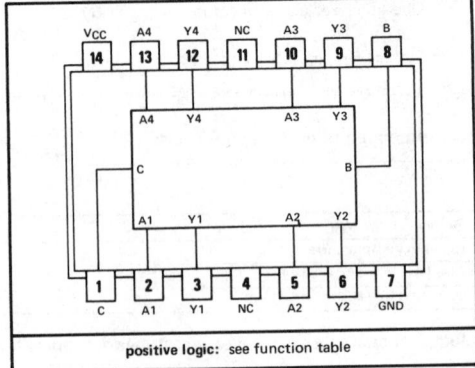

positive logic: see function table

NC—No internal connection

FUNCTION TABLE

CONTROL INPUTS		OUTPUTS			
B	C	Y1	Y2	Y3	Y4
L	L	$\overline{A1}$	$\overline{A2}$	$\overline{A3}$	$\overline{A4}$
L	H	A1	A2	A3	A4
H	L	H	H	H	H
H	H	L	L	L	L

H = high level, L = low level
A1, A2, A3, A4 = the level of the respective A input.

absolute maximum ratings over operating free-air temperature range (unless otherwise noted)

Supply voltage, V_{CC} (see Note 1) . . . . 7 V
Input voltage . . . . 5.5 V
Operating free-air temperature range: SN54H87 Circuits . . . . -55°C to 125°C
SN74H87 Circuits . . . . 0°C to 70°C
Storage temperature range . . . . -65°C to 150°C

NOTE 1: Voltage values are with respect to network ground terminal.

recommended operating conditions

	SN54H87			SN74H87			UNIT
	MIN	NOM	MAX	MIN	NOM	MAX	
Supply voltage, V_{CC}	4.5	5	5.5	4.75	5	5.25	V
High-level output current, I_{OH}			-1			-1	mA
Low-level output current, I_{OL}			20			20	mA
Operating free-air temperature, T_A	-55		125	0		70	$^\circ$C

electrical characteristics over recommended operating free-air temperature range (unless otherwise noted)

PARAMETER		TEST CONDITIONS†		MIN	TYP‡	MAX	UNIT
V_{IH}	High-level input voltage			2			V
V_{IL}	Low-level input voltage					0.8	V
V_{IK}	Input clamp voltage	V_{CC} = MIN,	I_I = −8 mA			−1.5	V
V_{OH}	High-level output voltage	V_{CC} = MIN, V_{IH} = 2 V, V_{IL} = 0.8 V, I_{OH} = −1 mA		2.4	3.5		V
V_{OL}	Low-level output voltage	V_{CC} = MIN, V_{IH} = 2 V, V_{IL} = 0.8 V, I_{OL} = 20 mA			0.2	0.4	V
I_I	Input current at maximum input voltage	V_{CC} = MAX, V_I = 5.5 V				1	mA
I_{IH}	High-level input current	V_{CC} = MAX, V_I = 2.4 V				50	μA
I_{IL}	Low-level input current	V_{CC} = MAX, V_I = 0.4 V				−2	mA
I_{OS}	Short-circuit output current§	V_{CC} = MAX		−40		−100	mA
I_{CC}	Supply current	V_{CC} = MAX, See Note 2	SN54H87		54	78	mA
			SN74H87		54	89	

†For conditions shown as MIN or MAX, use the appropriate value specified under recommended operating conditions for the applicable type.
‡All typical values are at V_{CC} = 5 V, T_A = 25°C.
§Not more than one output should be shorted at a time and duration of the short-circuit should not exceed 1 second.
NOTE 2: I_{CC} is measured for the following conditions:
      a. All A inputs are at 4.5 V, B and C inputs are grounded, and all outputs are open.
      b. B and C inputs are at 4.5 V, all A inputs are grounded, and all outputs are open.

switching characteristics, V_{CC} = 5 V, T_A = 25°C

PARAMETER		TEST CONDITIONS	MIN	TYP	MAX	MAX
t_{PLH}	Propagation delay time, low-to-high-level output from any A input	C_L = 25 pF, R_L = 280 Ω, See Note 3		14	20	ns
t_{PHL}	Propagation delay time, high-to-low-level output from any A input			13	19	ns
t_{PLH}	Propagation delay time, low-to-high-level output from B or C inputs			17	25	ns
t_{PHL}	Propagation delay time, high-to-low-level output from B or C inputs			17	25	ns

NOTE 3: Load circuit and voltage waveforms are shown on page 3-10.

functional block diagram and schematics of inputs and outputs

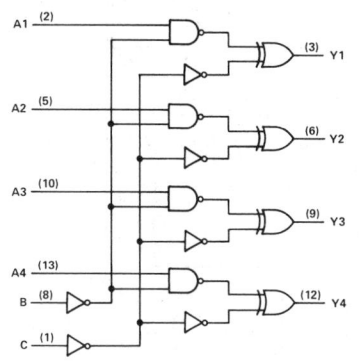

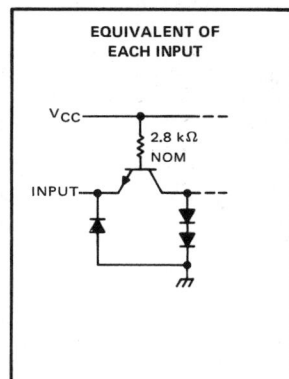

EQUIVALENT OF EACH INPUT

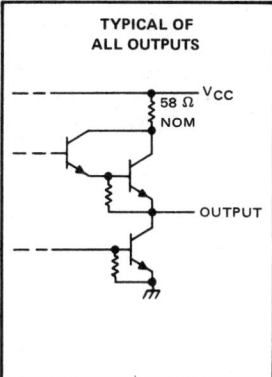

TYPICAL OF ALL OUTPUTS

TTL MSI

TYPES SN5490A, SN5492A, SN5493A, SN54L90, SN54L93, SN54LS90, SN54LS92, SN54LS93, SN7490A, SN7492A, SN7493A, SN74L90, SN74L93, SN74LS90, SN74LS92, SN74LS93
DECADE, DIVIDE-BY-TWELVE, AND BINARY COUNTERS
BULLETIN NO. DL-S 7611807, MARCH 1974—REVISED OCTOBER 1976

'90A, 'L90, 'LS90 . . . DECADE COUNTERS

'92A, 'LS92 . . . DIVIDE-BY-TWELVE COUNTERS

'93A, 'L93, 'LS93 . . . 4-BIT BINARY COUNTERS

TYPES	TYPICAL POWER DISSIPATION
'90A	145 mW
'L90	20 mW
'LS90	45 mW
'92A, '93A	130 mW
'LS92, 'LS93	45 mW
'L93	16 mW

description

Each of these monolithic counters contains four master-slave flip-flops and additional gating to provide a divide-by-two counter and a three-stage binary counter for which the count cycle length is divide-by-five for the '90A, 'L90, and 'LS90, divide-by-six for the '92A and 'LS92, and divide-by-eight for the '93A, 'L93, and 'LS93.

All of these counters have a gated zero reset and the '90A, 'L90, and 'LS90 also have gated set-to-nine inputs for use in BCD nine's complement applications.

To use their maximum count length (decade, divide-by-twelve, or four-bit binary) of these counters, the B input is connected to the Q_A output. The input count pulses are applied to input A and the outputs are as described in the appropriate function table. A symmetrical divide-by-ten count can be obtained from the '90A, 'L90, or 'LS90 counters by connecting the Q_D output to the A input and applying the input count to the B input which gives a divide-by-ten square wave at output Q_A.

SN54', SN54LS' . . . J OR W PACKAGE
SN54L' . . . J OR T PACKAGE
SN54', SN74L', SN74LS' . . . J OR N PACKAGE

'90A, 'L90, 'LS90 (TOP VIEW)

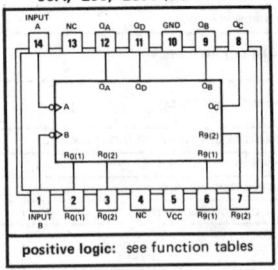

positive logic: see function tables

'92A, 'LS92, (TOP VIEW)

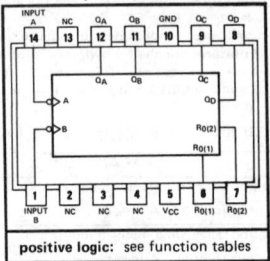

positive logic: see function tables

'93A, 'LS93 (TOP VIEW)

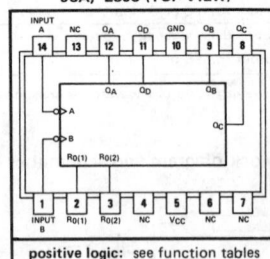

positive logic: see function tables

'L93 (TOP VIEW)

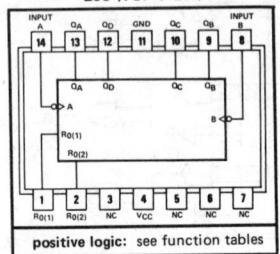

positive logic: see function tables

NC—No internal connection

TEXAS INSTRUMENTS
INCORPORATED
POST OFFICE BOX 5012 • DALLAS, TEXAS 75222

10

'90A, 'L90, 'LS90
BCD COUNT SEQUENCE
(See Note A)

COUNT	OUTPUT			
	Q_D	Q_C	Q_B	Q_A
0	L	L	L	L
1	L	L	L	H
2	L	L	H	L
3	L	L	H	H
4	L	H	L	L
5	L	H	L	H
6	L	H	H	L
7	L	H	H	H
8	H	L	L	L
9	H	L	L	H

'90A, 'L90, 'LS90
BI-QUINARY (5-2)
(See Note B)

COUNT	OUTPUT			
	Q_A	Q_D	Q_C	Q_B
0	L	L	L	L
1	L	L	L	H
2	L	L	H	L
3	L	L	H	H
4	L	H	L	L
5	H	L	L	L
6	H	L	L	H
7	H	L	H	L
8	H	L	H	H
9	H	H	L	L

'92A, 'LS92
COUNT SEQUENCE
(See Note C)

COUNT	OUTPUT			
	Q_D	Q_C	Q_B	Q_A
0	L	L	L	L
1	L	L	L	H
2	L	L	H	L
3	L	L	H	H
4	L	H	L	L
5	L	H	L	H
6	H	L	L	L
7	H	L	L	H
8	H	L	H	L
9	H	L	H	H
10	H	H	L	L
11	H	H	L	H

'93A, 'L93, 'LS93
COUNT SEQUENCE
(See Note C)

COUNT	OUTPUT			
	Q_D	Q_C	Q_B	Q_A
0	L	L	L	L
1	L	L	L	H
2	L	L	H	L
3	L	L	H	H
4	L	H	L	L
5	L	H	L	H
6	L	H	H	L
7	L	H	H	H
8	H	L	L	L
9	H	L	L	H
10	H	L	H	L
11	H	L	H	H
12	H	H	L	L
13	H	H	L	H
14	H	H	H	L
15	H	H	H	H

'90A, 'L90, 'LS90
RESET/COUNT FUNCTION TABLE

RESET INPUTS				OUTPUT			
$R_{0(1)}$	$R_{0(2)}$	$R_{9(1)}$	$R_{9(2)}$	Q_D	Q_C	Q_B	Q_A
H	H	L	X	L	L	L	L
H	H	X	L	L	L	L	L
X	X	H	H	H	L	L	H
X	L	X	L	COUNT			
L	X	L	X	COUNT			
L	X	X	L	COUNT			
X	L	L	X	COUNT			

'92A, 'LS92, '93A, 'L93, 'LS93
RESET/COUNT FUNCTION TABLE

RESET INPUTS		OUTPUT			
$R_{0(1)}$	$R_{0(2)}$	Q_D	Q_C	Q_B	Q_A
H	H	L	L	L	L
L	X	COUNT			
X	L	COUNT			

NOTES: A. Output Q_A is connected to input B for BCD count.
   B. Output Q_D is connected to input A for bi-quinary count.
   C. Output Q_A is connected to input B.
   D. H = high level, L = low level, X = irrelevant

functional block diagrams

'90A, 'L90, 'LS90

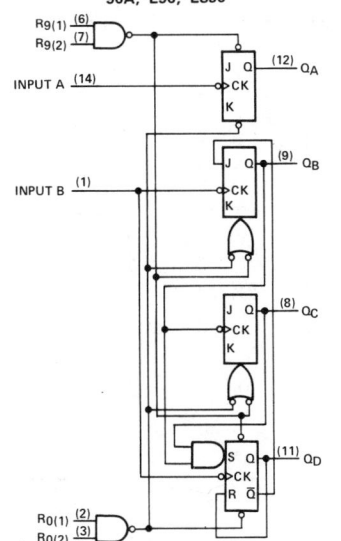

'92A, 'LS92   **'93A, 'L93, 'LS93**

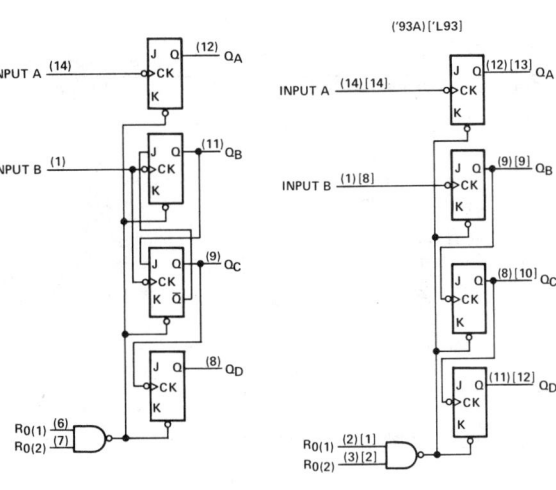

The J and K inputs shown without connection are for reference only and are functionally at a high level.

TEXAS INSTRUMENTS
INCORPORATED
POST OFFICE BOX 5012 • DALLAS, TEXAS 75222

7

TYPES SN5490A, '92A, '93A, SN54L90, 'L93, SN54LS90, 'LS92, 'LS93, SN7490A, '92A, '93A, SN74L90, 'L93, SN74LS90, 'LS92, 'LS93
DECADE, DIVIDE-BY-TWELVE, AND BINARY COUNTERS
REVISED AUGUST 1977

schematics of inputs and outputs

'90A, '92A, '93A

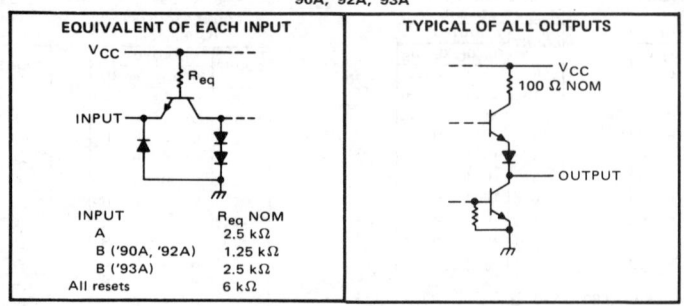

INPUT	R_{eq} NOM
A	2.5 kΩ
B ('90A, '92A)	1.25 kΩ
B ('93A)	2.5 kΩ
All resets	6 kΩ

'L90, 'L93

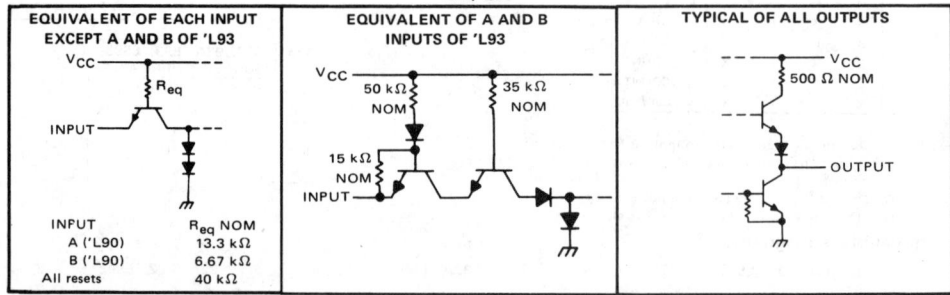

INPUT	R_{eq} NOM
A ('L90)	13.3 kΩ
B ('L90)	6.67 kΩ
All resets	40 kΩ

'LS90, 'LS92, 'LS93

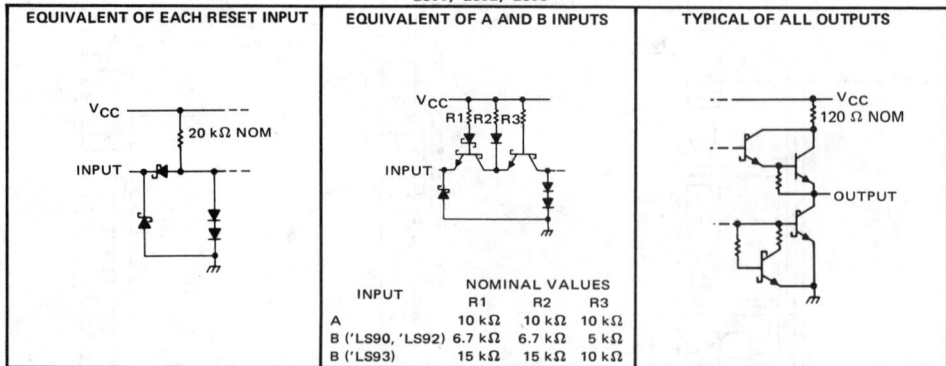

INPUT	NOMINAL VALUES		
	R1	R2	R3
A	10 kΩ	10 kΩ	10 kΩ
B ('LS90, 'LS92)	6.7 kΩ	6.7 kΩ	5 kΩ
B ('LS93)	15 kΩ	15 kΩ	10 kΩ

TEXAS INSTRUMENTS
INCORPORATED
POST OFFICE BOX 5012 • DALLAS, TEXAS 75222

absolute maximum ratings over operating free-air temperature range (unless otherwise noted)

Supply voltage, V_{CC} (see Note 1) . . . . 7 V
Input voltage . . . . 5.5 V
Interemitter voltage (see Note 2) . . . . 5.5 V
Operating free-air temperature range: SN5490A, SN5492A, SN5493A . . . . −55°C to 125°C
SN7490A, SN7492A, SN7493A . . . . 0°C to 70°C
Storage temperature range . . . . −65°C to 150°C

NOTES: 1. Voltage values, except interemitter voltage, are with respect to network ground terminal.
2. This is the voltage between two emitters of a multiple-emitter transistor. For these circuits, this rating applies between the two R_0 inputs, and for the '90A circuit, it also applies between the two R_9 inputs.

recommended operating conditions

		SN5490A, SN5492A SN5493A			SN7490A, SN7492A SN7493A			UNIT
		MIN	NOM	MAX	MIN	NOM	MAX	
Supply voltage, V_{CC}		4.5	5	5.5	4.75	5	5.25	V
High-level output current, I_{OH}				−800			−800	μA
Low-level output current, I_{OL}				16			16	mA
Count frequency, f_{count} (see Figure 1)	A input	0		32	0		32	MHz
	B input	0		16	0		16	
Pulse width, t_w	A input	15			15			ns
	B input	30			30			
	Reset inputs	15			15			
Reset inactive-state setup time, t_{su}		25			25			ns
Operating free-air temperature, T_A		−55		125	0		70	°C

electrical characteristics over recommended operating free-air temperature range (unless otherwise noted)

PARAMETER		TEST CONDITIONS[†]		'90A			'92A			'93A			UNIT
				MIN	TYP[‡]	MAX	MIN	TYP[‡]	MAX	MIN	TYP[‡]	MAX	
V_{IH}	High-level input voltage			2			2			2			V
V_{IL}	Low-level input voltage					0.8			0.8			0.8	V
V_{IK}	Input clamp voltage	V_{CC} = MIN, I_I = −12 mA				−1.5			−1.5			−1.5	V
V_{OH}	High-level output voltage	V_{CC} = MIN, V_{IH} = 2 V, V_{IL} = 0.8 V, I_{OH} = −800 μA		2.4	3.4		2.4	3.4		2.4	3.4		V
V_{OL}	Low-level output voltage	V_{CC} = MIN, V_{IH} = 2 V, V_{IL} = 0.8 V, I_{OL} = 16 mA[¶]			0.2	0.4		0.2	0.4		0.2	0.4	V
I_I	Input current at maximum input voltage	V_{CC} = MAX, V_I = 5.5 V				1			1			1	mA
I_{IH}	High-level input current	Any reset	V_{CC} = MAX, V_I = 2.4 V			40			40			40	μA
		A input				80			80			80	
		B input				120			120			80	
I_{IL}	Low-level input current	Any reset	V_{CC} = MAX, V_I = 0.4 V			−1.6			−1.6			−1.6	mA
		A input				−3.2			−3.2			−3.2	
		B input				−4.8			−4.8			−3.2	
I_{OS}	Short-circuit output current[§]	V_{CC} = MAX	SN54'	−20		−57	−20		−57	−20		−57	mA
			SN74'	−18		−57	−18		−57	−18		−57	
I_{CC}	Supply current	V_{CC} = MAX, See Note 3			29	42		26	39		26	39	mA

[†]For conditions shown as MIN or MAX, use the appropriate value specified under recommended operating conditions.
[‡]All typical values are at V_{CC} = 5 V, T_A = 25°C.
[§]Not more than one output should be shorted at a time.
[¶]Q_A outputs are tested at I_{OL} = 16 mA plus the limit value for I_{IL} for the B input. This permits driving the B input while maintaining full fan-out capability.
NOTE 3: I_{CC} is measured with all outputs open, both R_0 inputs grounded following momentary connection to 4.5 V, and all other inputs grounded.

7

TEXAS INSTRUMENTS
INCORPORATED
POST OFFICE BOX 5012 • DALLAS, TEXAS 75222

TYPES SN5490A, SN5492A, SN5493A, SN7490A, SN7492A, SN7493A
DECADE, DIVIDE-BY-TWELVE, AND BINARY COUNTERS
REVISED OCTOBER 1976

switching characteristics, V_{CC} = 5 V, T_A = 25°C

PARAMETER¶	FROM (INPUT)	TO (OUTPUT)	TEST CONDITIONS	'90A MIN	'90A TYP	'90A MAX	'92A MIN	'92A TYP	'92A MAX	'93A MIN	'93A TYP	'93A MAX	UNIT
f_{max}	A	Q_A		32	42		32	42		32	42		MHz
	B	Q_B		16			16			16			
t_{PLH}	A	Q_A			10	16		10	16		10	16	ns
t_{PHL}					12	18		12	18		12	18	
t_{PLH}	A	Q_D			32	48		32	48		46	70	ns
t_{PHL}					34	50		34	50		46	70	
t_{PLH}	B	Q_B	C_L = 15 pF,		10	16		10	16		10	16	ns
t_{PHL}			R_L = 400 Ω,		14	21		14	21		14	21	
t_{PLH}	B	Q_C	See Figure 1		21	32		10	16		21	32	ns
t_{PHL}					23	35		14	21		23	35	
t_{PLH}	B	Q_D			21	32		21	32		34	51	ns
t_{PHL}					23	35		23	35		34	51	
t_{PHL}	Set-to-0	Any			26	40		26	40		26	40	ns
t_{PLH}	Set-to-9	Q_A, Q_D			20	30							ns
t_{PHL}		Q_B, Q_C			26	40							

¶ f_{max} ≡ maximum count frequency
t_{PLH} ≡ propagation delay time, low-to-high-level output
t_{PHL} ≡ propagation delay time, high-to-low-level output

7

TEXAS INSTRUMENTS
INCORPORATED
POST OFFICE BOX 5012 • DALLAS, TEXAS 75222

absolute maximum ratings over operating free-air temperature range (unless otherwise noted)

Supply voltage, V_{CC} (see Note 4) . . . . 8 V
Input voltage (see Note 5) . . . . 5.5 V
Operating free-air temperature range: SN54L90, SN54L93 . . . . −55°C to 125°C
SN74L90, SN74L93 . . . . 0°C to 70°C
Storage temperature range . . . . −65°C to 150°C

NOTES: 4. Voltage values are with respect to network ground terminal.
5. Input voltages must be zero or positive with respect to network ground terminal.

recommended operating conditions

	SN54L90, SN54L93			SN74L90, SN74L93			UNIT
	MIN	NOM	MAX	MIN	NOM	MAX	
Supply voltage, V_{CC}	4.5	5	5.5	4.75	5	5.25	V
Count frequency, f_{count}	0		3	0		3	MHz
High-level output current, I_{OH}			−100			−200	μA
Low-level output current, I_{OL}			2			3.6	mA
Width of input count pulse, $t_{w(count)}$	200			200			ns
Width of reset pulse, $t_{w(reset)}$	200			200			ns
Operating free-air temperature, T_A	−55		125	0		70	°C

electrical characteristics over recommended operating free-air temperature range (unless otherwise noted)

PARAMETER		TEST CONDITIONS[†]		'L90			'L93			UNIT
				MIN	TYP[‡]	MAX	MIN	TYP[‡]	MAX	
V_{IH}	High-level input voltage			2			2			V
V_{IL}	Low-level input voltage					0.7			0.7	V
V_{OH}	High-level output voltage	SN54L'	V_{CC} = MIN, V_{IH} = 2 V,	2.4	3.3		2.4	3.3		V
		SN74L'	V_{IL} = 0.7 V, I_{OH} = MAX	2.4	3.2		2.4	3.2		
V_{OL}	Low-level output voltage	SN54L'	V_{CC} = MIN, V_{IH} = 2 V,		0.15	0.3		0.15	0.3	V
		SN74L'	V_{IL} = 0.7 V, I_{OL} = MAX[¶]		0.2	0.4		0.2	0.4	
I_I	Input current at maximum input voltage	Any reset input	V_{CC} = MAX, V_I = 5.5 V			100			100	μA
		A input				300			200	
		B input				600			200	
I_{IH}	High-level input current	Any reset input	V_{CC} = MAX, V_I = 2.4 V			10			10	μA
		A input				30			20	
		B input				60			20	
I_{IL}	Low-level input current	Any reset input	V_{CC} = MAX, V_I = 0.3 V			−0.18			−0.18	mA
		A input				−0.54			−0.36	
		B input				−1.08			−0.36	
I_{OS}	Short-circuit output current[§]		V_{CC} = MAX	−3		−15	−3		−15	mA
I_{CC}	Supply current		V_{CC} = MAX, See Note 3		4	7.2		3.2	6.6	mA

[†] For conditions shown as MIN or MAX, use the appropriate value specified under recommended operating conditions.
[‡] All typical values are at V_{CC} = 5 V, T_A = 25°C.
[§] Not more than one output should be shorted at a time.
[¶] Q_A outputs are tested at I_{OL} = MAX plus the limit value for I_{IL} for the B input. This permits driving the B input while maintaining full fan-out capability.
NOTE 3: I_{CC} is measured with all outputs open, both R_0 inputs grounded following momentary connection to 4.5 V, and all other inputs grounded.

switching characteristics, V_{CC} = 5 V, T_A = 25°C

PARAMETER		TEST CONDITIONS		'L90			'L93			UNIT
				MIN	TYP	MAX	MIN	TYP	MAX	
f_{max}	Maximum count frequency			3	6		3	6		MHz
t_{PLH}	Propagation delay time, low-to-high-level Q_D output from input A	C_L = 50 pF,	R_L = 4 kΩ,		230	340		280	450	ns
t_{PHL}	Propagation delay time, high-to-low-level Q_D output from input A	See Figure 1			230	340		280	450	ns

TEXAS INSTRUMENTS
INCORPORATED
POST OFFICE BOX 5012 • DALLAS, TEXAS 75222

absolute maximum ratings over operating free-air temperature range (unless otherwise noted)

Supply voltage, V_{CC} (see Note 4) . . . . 7 V
Input voltage: R inputs . . . . 7 V
              A and B inputs . . . . 5.5 V
Operating free-air temperature range: SN54LS' Circuits . . . . −55°C to 125°C
                             SN74LS' Circuits . . . . 0°C to 70°C
Storage temperature range . . . . −65°C to 150°C

NOTE 4: Voltage values are with respect to network ground terminal.

recommended operating conditions

			SN54LS90 SN54LS92 SN54LS93			SN74LS90 SN74LS92 SN74LS93			UNIT
			MIN	NOM	MAX	MIN	NOM	MAX	
Supply voltage, V_{CC}			4.5	5	5.5	4.75	5	5.25	V
High-level output current, I_{OH}					−400			−400	μA
Low-level output current, I_{OL}					4			8	mA
Count frequency, f_{count} (see Figure 1)		A input	0		32	0		32	MHz
		B input	0		16	0		16	
Pulse width, t_w		A input	15			15			ns
		B input	30			30			
		Reset inputs	15			15			
Reset inactive-state setup time, t_{su}			25			25			ns
Operating free-air temperature, T_A			−55		125	0		70	°C

electrical characteristics over recommended operating free-air temperature range (unless otherwise noted)

PARAMETER		TEST CONDITIONS[†]		SN54LS90 SN54LS92			SN74LS90 SN74LS92			UNIT
				MIN	TYP[‡]	MAX	MIN	TYP[‡]	MAX	
V_{IH}	High-level input voltage			2			2			V
V_{IL}	Low-level input voltage					0.7			0.8	V
V_{IK}	Input clamp voltage	V_{CC} = MIN, I_I = −18 mA				−1.5			−1.5	V
V_{OH}	High-level output voltage	V_{CC} = MIN, V_{IH} = 2 V, V_{IL} = V_{IL}max, I_{OH} = −400 μA		2.5	3.4		2.7	3.4		V
V_{OL}	Low-level output voltage	V_{CC} = MIN, V_{IH} = 2 V, V_{IL} = V_{IL} max,	I_{OL} = 4 mA[¶]		0.25	0.4		0.25	0.4	V
			I_{OL} = 8 mA[¶]					0.35	0.5	
I_I	Input current at maximum input voltage	Any reset	V_{CC} = MAX, V_I = 7 V			0.1			0.1	mA
		A input	V_{CC} = MAX, V_I = 5.5 V			0.2			0.2	
		B input				0.4			0.4	
I_{IH}	High-level input current	Any reset	V_{CC} = MAX, V_I = 2.7 V			20			20	μA
		A input				40			40	
		B input				80			80	
I_{IL}	Low-level input current	Any reset	V_{CC} = MAX, V_I = 0.4 V			−0.4			−0.4	mA
		A input				−2.4			−2.4	
		B input				−3.2			−3.2	
I_{OS}	Short-circuit output current[§]	V_{CC} = MAX		−20		−100	−20		−100	mA
I_{CC}	Supply current	V_{CC} = MAX, See Note 3	'LS90		9	15		9	15	mA
			'LS92		9	15		9	15	

[†]For conditions shown as MIN or MAX, use the appropriate value specified under recommended operating conditions.

[‡]All typical values are at V_{CC} = 5 V, T_A = 25°C.

[§]Not more than one output should be shorted at a time, and duration of the short-circuit should not exceed one second.

[¶]Q_A outputs are tested at specified I_{OL} plus the limit value of I_{IL} for the B input. This permits driving the B input while maintaining full fan-out capability.

NOTE 3: I_{CC} is measured with all outputs open, both R_O inputs grounded following momentary connection to 4.5 V, and all other inputs grounded.

TEXAS INSTRUMENTS
INCORPORATED
POST OFFICE BOX 5012 • DALLAS, TEXAS 75222

electrical characteristics over recommended operating free-air temperature range (unless otherwise noted)

	PARAMETER	TEST CONDITIONS[†]		SN54LS93 MIN	TYP[‡]	MAX	SN74LS93 MIN	TYP[‡]	MAX	UNIT
V_{IH}	High-level input voltage			2			2			V
V_{IL}	Low-level input voltage					0.7			0.8	V
V_{IK}	Input clamp voltage	V_{CC} = MIN,	I_I = −18 mA			−1.5			−1.5	V
V_{OH}	High-level output voltage	V_{CC} = MIN, V_{IH} = 2 V, V_{IL} = V_{IL} max, I_{OH} = −400 µA		2.5	3.4		2.7	3.4		V
V_{OL}	Low-level output voltage	V_{CC} = MIN, V_{IH} = 2 V, V_{IL} = V_{IL} max	I_{OL} = 4 mA¶		0.25	0.4		0.25	0.4	V
			I_{OL} = 8 mA¶					0.35	0.5	
I_I	Input current at maximum input voltage	Any reset V_{CC} = MAX, V_I = 7 V				0.1			0.1	mA
		A or B input V_{CC} = MAX, V_I = 5.5 V				0.2			0.2	
I_{IH}	High-level input current	Any reset V_{CC} = MAX, V_I = 2.7 V				20			20	µA
		A or B input				40			80	
I_{IL}	Low-level input current	Any reset V_{CC} = MAX, V_I = 0.4 V				−0.4			−0.4	mA
		A input				−2.4			−2.4	
		B input				−1.6			−1.6	
I_{OS}	Short-circuit output current§	V_{CC} = MAX		−20		−100	−20		−100	mA
I_{CC}	Supply current	V_{CC} = MAX, See Note 3			9	15		9	15	mA

†For conditions shown as MIN or MAX, use the appropriate value specified under recommended operating conditions.
‡All typical values are at V_{CC} = 5 V, T_A = 25°C.
§Not more than one output should be shorted at a time, and duration of the short-circuit should not exceed one second.
¶Q_A outputs are tested at specified I_{OL} plus the limit value for I_{IL} for the B input. This permits driving the B input while maintaining full fan-out capability.
NOTE 3: I_{CC} is measured with all outputs open, both R_0 inputs grounded following momentary connection to 4.5 V, and all other inputs grounded.

switching characteristics, V_{CC} = 5 V, T_A = 25°C

PARAMETER¶	FROM (INPUT)	TO (OUTPUT)	TEST CONDITIONS	'LS90 MIN	TYP	MAX	'LS92 MIN	TYP	MAX	'LS93 MIN	TYP	MAX	UNIT
f_{max}	A	Q_A		32	42		32	42		32	42		MHz
	B	Q_B		16			16			16			
t_{PLH}	A	Q_A			10	16		10	16		10	16	ns
t_{PHL}					12	18		12	18		12	18	
t_{PLH}	A	Q_D			32	48		32	48		46	70	ns
t_{PHL}					34	50		34	50		46	70	
t_{PLH}	B	Q_B	C_L = 15 pF, R_L = 2 kΩ See Figure 1		10	16		10	16		10	16	ns
t_{PHL}					14	21		14	21		14	21	
t_{PLH}	B	Q_C			21	32		10	16		21	32	ns
t_{PHL}					23	35		14	21		23	35	
t_{PLH}	B	Q_D			21	32		21	32		34	51	ns
t_{PHL}					23	35		23	35		34	51	
t_{PHL}	Set-to-0	Any			26	40		26	40		26	40	ns
t_{PLH}	Set-to-9	Q_A, Q_D			20	30							ns
t_{PHL}		Q_B, Q_C			26	40							

¶f_{max} ≡ maximum count frequency
t_{PLH} ≡ propagation delay time, low-to-high-level output
t_{PHL} ≡ propagation delay time, high-to-low-level output

TEXAS INSTRUMENTS
INCORPORATED
POST OFFICE BOX 5012 • DALLAS, TEXAS 75222

TYPES SN5490A, SN5492A, SN5493A, SN54L90, SN54L93, SN54LS90, SN54LS92, SN54LS93, SN7490A, SN7492A, SN7493A, SN74L90, SN74L93, SN74LS90, SN74LS92, SN74LS93 DECADE, DIVIDE-BY-TWELVE, AND BINARY COUNTERS

PARAMETER MEASUREMENT INFORMATION

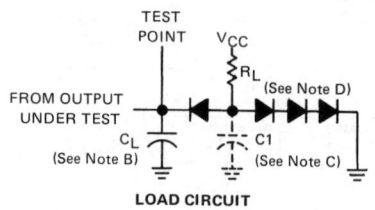

LOAD CIRCUIT

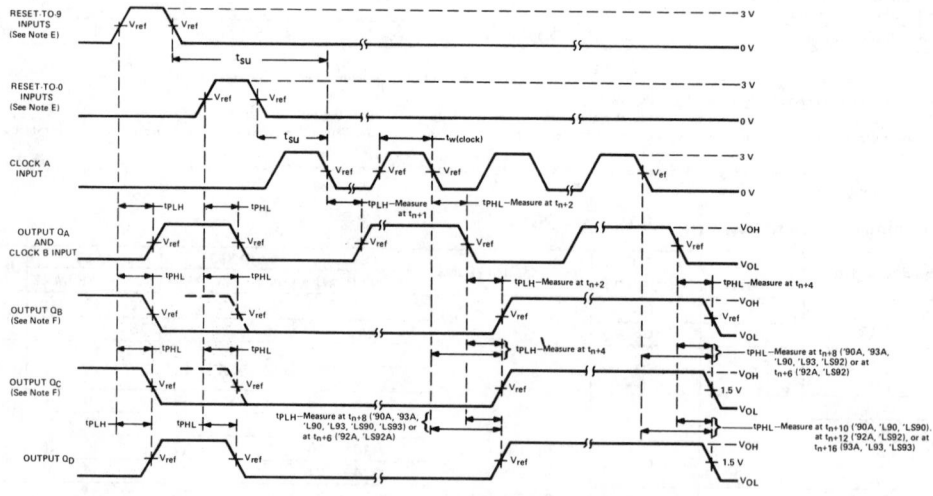

VOLTAGE WAVEFORMS

NOTES: A. Input pulses are supplied by a generator having the following characteristics:
for '90A, '92A, '93A, $t_r \leqslant 5$ ns, $t_f \leqslant 5$ ns, PRR = 1 MHz, duty cycle = 50%, $Z_{out} \approx 50$ ohms;
for 'L90, 'L93, $t_r \leqslant 15$ ns, $t_f \leqslant 15$ ns, PRR = 500 kHz, duty cycle = 50%, $Z_{out} \approx 50$ ohms;
for 'LS90, 'LS92, 'LS93, $t_r \leqslant 15$ ns, $t_f \leqslant 5$ ns, PRR = 1 MHz, duty cycle = 50%, $Z_{out} \approx 50$ ohms.
   B. C_L includes probe and jig capacitance.
   C. C1 (30 pF) is applicable for testing 'L90 and 'L93.
   D. All diodes are 1N916 or 1N3064.
   E. Each reset input is tested separately with the other reset at 4.5 V.
   F. Reference waveforms are shown with dashed lines.
   G. For '90A, '92A, and '93A; V_{ref} = 1.5 V. For 'L90, 'L93, 'LS90, 'LS92, and 'LS93; V_{ref} = 1.3 V.

FIGURE 1

TEXAS INSTRUMENTS
INCORPORATED
POST OFFICE BOX 5012 • DALLAS, TEXAS 75222

7

MSI TTL SHIFT REGISTERS
for applications in

- **Digital Computer Systems**
- **Data-Handling Systems**
- **Control Systems**

SN5491A, SN54LS91 . . . J PACKAGE
SN54L91, SN7491A, SN74L91, SN74LS91 . . . J OR N PACKAGE
DUAL-IN-LINE PACKAGE (TOP VIEW)

SN5491A, SN54LS91 . . . W PACKAGE
SN54L91, SN74L91 . . . T PACKAGE
FLAT PACKAGE (TOP VIEW)

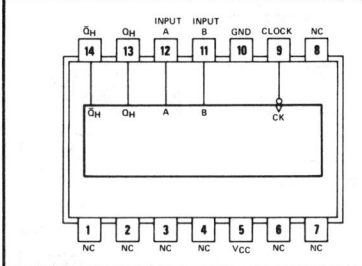

positive logic: see function table

FUNCTION TABLE

INPUTS AT t_n		OUTPUTS AT t_{n+8}	
A	B	Q_H	$\bar{Q}_H$
H	H	H	L
L	X	L	H
X	L	L	H

H = high, L = low,
X = irrelevant
t_n = Reference bit time, clock low
t_{n+8} = Bit time after 8 low-to-high clock transitions.
NC—No internal connection

TYPE	TYPICAL MAXIMUM CLOCK FREQUENCY	TYPICAL POWER DISSIPATION
'91A	18 MHz	175 mW
'L91	6.5 MHz	17.5 mW
'LS91	18 MHz	60 mW

description

These monolithic serial-in, serial-out, 8-bit shift registers utilize transistor-transistor logic (TTL) circuits and are composed of eight R-S master-slave flip-flops, input gating, and a clock driver. Single-rail data and input control are gated through inputs A and B and an internal inverter to form the complementary inputs to the first bit of the shift register. Drive for the internal common clock line is provided by an inverting clock driver. This clock pulse inverter/driver causes these circuits to shift information one bit on the positive edge of an input clock pulse.

schematics of inputs and outputs

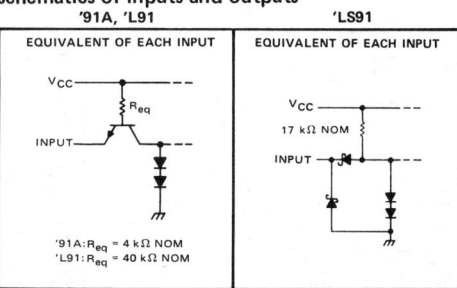

'91A, 'L91 — EQUIVALENT OF EACH INPUT
'LS91 — EQUIVALENT OF EACH INPUT

'91A: R_{eq} = 4 kΩ NOM
'L91: R_{eq} = 40 kΩ NOM

17 kΩ NOM

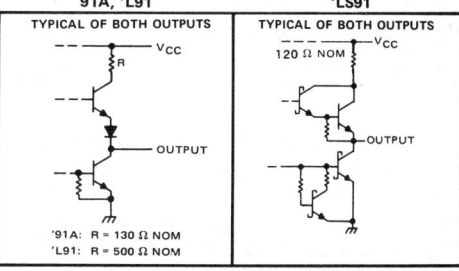

'91A, 'L91 — TYPICAL OF BOTH OUTPUTS
'LS91 — TYPICAL OF BOTH OUTPUTS

120 Ω NOM

'91A: R = 130 Ω NOM
'L91: R = 500 Ω NOM

functional block diagram

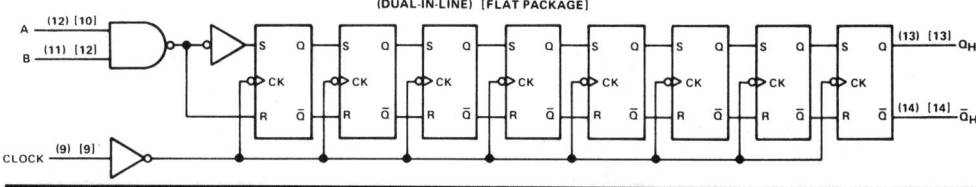

(DUAL-IN-LINE) [FLAT PACKAGE]

TEXAS INSTRUMENTS
INCORPORATED
POST OFFICE BOX 5012 • DALLAS, TEXAS 75222

absolute maximum ratings over operating free-air temperature range (unless otherwise noted)

Supply voltage, V_{CC} (see Note 1)	7 V
Input voltage (see Note 2)	5.5 V
Operating free-air temperature range: SN5491A	−55°C to 125°C
SN7491A	0°C to 70°C
Storage temperature range	−65°C to 150°C

NOTES: 1. Voltage values are with respect to network ground terminal.
2. Input signals must be zero or positive with respect to network ground terminal.

recommended operating conditions

	SN5491A			SN7491A			UNIT
	MIN	NOM	MAX	MIN	NOM	MAX	
Supply voltage, V_{CC}	4.5	5	5.5	4.75	5	5.25	V
High-level output current, I_{OH}			−400			−400	μA
Low-level output current, I_{OL}			16			16	mA
Width of clock input pulse, t_w	25			25			ns
Setup time, t_{su} (see Figure 1)	25			25			ns
Hold time, t_h (see Figure 1)	0			0			ns
Operating free-air temperature, T_A	−55		125	0		70	°C

electrical characteristics over recommended operating free-air temperature range (unless otherwise noted)

PARAMETER		TEST CONDITIONS[†]	SN5491A			SN7491A			UNIT
			MIN	NOM	MAX	MIN	NOM	MAX	
V_{IH}	High-level input voltage		2			2			V
V_{IL}	Low-level input voltage				0.8			0.8	V
V_{OH}	High-level output voltage	V_{CC} = MIN, V_{IH} = 2 V, V_{IL} = 0.8 V, I_{OH} = −400 μA	2.4	3.5		2.4	3.5		V
V_{OL}	Low-level output voltage	V_{CC} = MIN, V_{IH} = 2 V, V_{IL} = 0.8 V, I_{OL} = 16 mA		0.2	0.4		0.2	0.4	V
I_I	Input current at maximum input voltage	V_{CC} = MAX, V_I = 5.5 V			1			1	mA
I_{IH}	High-level input current	V_{CC} = MAX, V_I = 2.4 V			40			40	μA
I_{IL}	Low-level input current	V_{CC} = MAX, V_I = 0.4 V			−1.6			−1.6	mA
I_{OS}	Short-circuit output current§	V_{CC} = MAX	−20		−57	−18		−57	mA
I_{CC}	Supply current	V_{CC} = MAX, See Note 3		35	50		35	58	mA

[†]For conditions shown as MIN or MAX, use the appropriate value specified under recommended operating conditions.
‡All typical values are at V_{CC} = 5 V, T_A = 25°C.
§Not more than one output should be shorted at a time.
NOTE 3: I_{CC} is measured after the eighth clock pulse with the output open and A and B inputs grounded.

switching characteristics, V_{CC} = 5 V, T_A = 25°C

PARAMETER		TEST CONDITIONS	MIN	TYP	MAX	UNIT
f_{max}	Maximum clock frequency	C_L = 15 pF, R_L = 400 Ω, See Figure 1	10	18		MHz
t_{PLH}	Propagation delay time, low-to-high-level output			24	40	ns
t_{PHL}	Propagation delay time, high-to-low-level output			27	40	ns

7

TEXAS INSTRUMENTS
INCORPORATED

POST OFFICE BOX 5012 • DALLAS, TEXAS 75222

absolute maximum ratings over operating free-air temperature range (unless otherwise noted)

Supply voltage, V_{CC} (see Note 1)	8 V
Input voltage (see Note 2)	5.5 V
Operating free-air temperature range: SN54L91	-55°C to 125°C
SN74L91	0°C to 70°C
Storage temperature range	-65°C to 150°C

NOTES: 1. Voltage values are with respect to network ground terminal.
2. Input signals must be zero or positive with respect to network ground terminal.

recommended operating conditions

		SN54L91			SN74L91			UNIT
		MIN	NOM	MAX	MIN	NOM	MAX	
Supply voltage, V_{CC}		4.5	5	5.5	4.75	5	5.25	V
High-level output current, I_{OH}				−100			−200	μA
Low-level output current, I_{OL}				2			3.6	mA
Width of clock input pulse, $t_{w(clock)}$	High logic level	100			100			ns
	Low logic level	150			150			ns
Setup time, t_{su} (see Figure 1)		120			120			ns
Hold time, t_h (see Figure 1)		0			0			ns
Operating free-air temperature, T_A		−55		125	0		70	°C

electrical characteristics over recommended operating free-air temperature range (unless otherwise noted)

PARAMETER		TEST CONDITIONS†		SN54L91			SN74L91			UNIT
				MIN	TYP‡	MAX	MIN	TYP‡	MAX	
V_{IH}	High-level input voltage			2			2			V
V_{IL}	Low-level input voltage					0.7			0.7	V
V_{OH}	High-level output voltage	V_{CC} = MIN,	V_{IH} = 2 V,	2.4	3.3		2.4	3.2		V
		V_{IL} = 0.7 V,	I_{OH} = MAX							
V_{OL}	Low-level output voltage	V_{CC} = MIN,	V_{IH} = 2 V		0.15	0.3		0.2	0.4	V
		V_{IL} = 0.7 V,	I_{OL} = MAX							
I_I	Input current at maximum input voltage	V_{CC} = MAX,	V_I = 5.5 V			100			100	μA
I_{IH}	High-level input current	V_{CC} = MAX,	V_I = 2.4 V			10			10	μA
I_{IL}	Low-level input current	V_{CC} = MAX,	V_I = 0.3 V			−0.18			−0.18	mA
I_{OS}	Short-circuit output current	V_{CC} = MAX		−3		−15	−3		−15	mA
I_{CC}	Supply current	V_{CC} = MAX,	See Note 3		3.5	6.6		3.5	6.6	mA

†For conditions shown as MIN or MAX, use the appropriate value specified under recommended operating conditions.
‡All typical values are at V_{CC} = 5 V, T_A = 25°C.
NOTE 3: I_{CC} is measured after the eighth clock pulse with the outputs open and A and B inputs grounded.

switching characteristics, V_{CC} = 5 V, T_A = 25°C

PARAMETER		TEST CONDITIONS	MIN	TYP	MAX	UNIT
f_{max}	Maximum clock frequency		3	6.5		MHz
t_{PLH}	Propagation delay time, low-to-high-level output	C_L = 50 pF, R_L = 4 kΩ, See Figure 1		55	100	ns
t_{PHL}	Propagation delay time, high-to-low-level output			100	150	ns

7

TYPES SN54LS91, SN74LS91
8-BIT SHIFT REGISTERS

REVISED OCTOBER 1976

absolute maximum ratings over operating free-air temperature range (unless otherwise noted)

Supply voltage, V_{CC} (see Note 1) . . . . 7 V
Input voltage . . . . 7 V
Operating free-air temperature range: SN54LS91 . . . . −55°C to 125°C
                                  SN74LS91 . . . . 0°C to 70°C
Storage temperature range . . . . −65°C to 150°C

NOTES: 1. Voltage values are with respect to network ground terminal.

recommended operating conditions

	SN54LS91			SN74LS91			UNIT
	MIN	NOM	MAX	MIN	NOM	MAX	
Supply voltage, V_{CC}	4.5	5	5.5	4.75	5	5.25	V
High-level output current, I_{OH}			−400			−400	µA
Low-level output current, I_{OL}			4			8	mA
Width of clock input pulse, t_w	25			25			ns
Setup time, t_{su} (see Figure 1)	25			25			ns
Hold time, t_h (see Figure 1)	0			0			ns
Operating free-air temperature, T_A	−55		125	0		70	°C

electrical characteristics over recommended operating free-air temperature range (unless otherwise noted)

PARAMETER		TEST CONDITIONS[†]		SN54LS91			SN74LS91			UNIT
				MIN	TYP[‡]	MAX	MIN	TYP[‡]	MAX	
V_{IH}	High-level input voltage			2			2			V
V_{IL}	Low-level input voltage					0.7			0.8	V
V_{IK}	Input clamp voltage	V_{CC} = MIN,	I_I = −18 mA			−1.5			−1.5	V
V_{OH}	High-level output voltage	V_{CC} = MIN, V_{IH} = 2 V, V_{IL} = V_{IL} max, I_{OH} = −400 µA		2.5	3.5		2.7	3.5		V
V_{OL}	Low-level output voltage	V_{CC} = MIN, V_{IH} = 2 V, V_{IL} = V_{IL} max	I_{OL} = 4 mA		0.25	0.4		0.25	0.4	V
			I_{OL} = 8 mA					0.35	0.5	
I_I	Input current at maximum input voltage	V_{CC} = MAX,	V_I = 7 V			0.1			0.1	mA
I_{IH}	High-level input current	V_{CC} = MAX,	V_I = 2.7 V			20			20	µA
I_{IL}	Low-level input current	V_{CC} = MAX,	V_I = 0.4 V			−0.4			−0.4	mA
I_{OS}	Short-circuit output current [§]	V_{CC} = MAX		−20		−100	−20		−100	mA
I_{CC}	Supply current	V_{CC} = MAX,	See Note 3		12	20		12	20	mA

[†] For conditions shown as MIN or MAX, use the appropriate value specified under recommended operating conditions.
[‡] All typical values are at V_{CC} = 5 V, T_A = 25°C.
[§] Not more than one output should be shorted at a time, and duration of the short-circuit should not exceed one second.
NOTE 3: I_{CC} is measured after the eighth clock pulse with the output open and A and B inputs grounded.

switching characteristics, V_{CC} = 5 V, T_A = 25°C

PARAMETER		TEST CONDITIONS	MIN	TYP	MAX	UNIT
f_{max}	Maximum clock frequency	C_L = 15 pF,	10	18		MHz
t_{PLH}	Propagation delay time, low-to-high-level output	R_L = 2 kΩ,		24	40	ns
t_{PHL}	Propagation delay time, high-to-low-level output	See Figure 1		27	40	ns

TEXAS INSTRUMENTS
INCORPORATED
POST OFFICE BOX 5012 • DALLAS, TEXAS 75222

7

PARAMETER MEASUREMENT INFORMATION

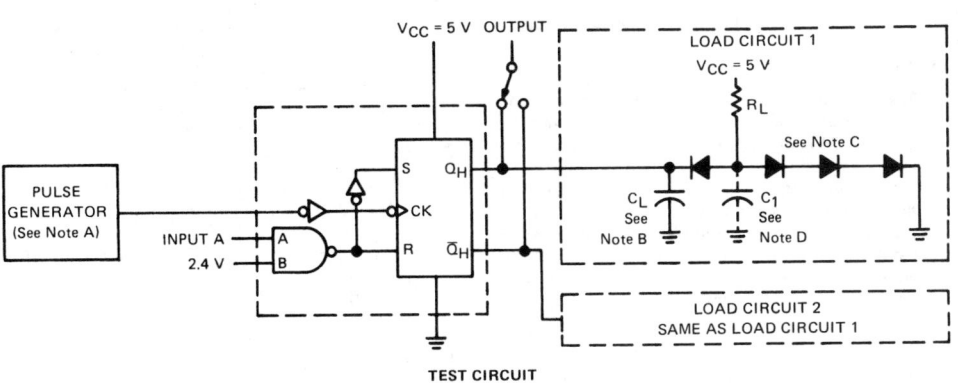

TEST CIRCUIT

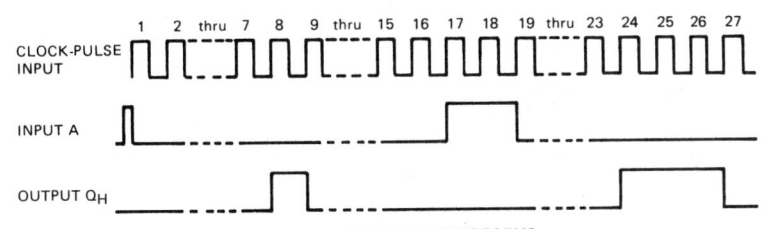

TYPICAL INPUT/OUTPUT WAVEFORMS

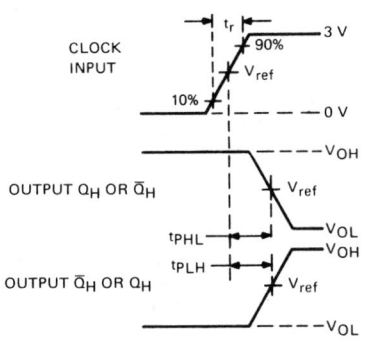

PROPAGATION DELAY TIMES VOLTAGE WAVEFORMS

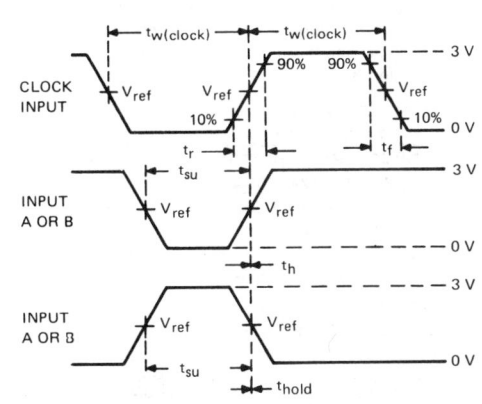

SWITCHING TIMES VOLTAGE WAVEFORMS

NOTES: A. The generator has the following characteristics: $t_{w(clock)}$ = 500 ns, PRR ≤ 1 MHz, Z_{out} ≈ 50 Ω. For SN5491A/SN7491A, t_r ≤ 10 ns and t_f ≤ 10 ns; for SN54L91/SN74L91, t_r ≤ 15 ns and t_f ≤ 15 ns; and for SN54LS91/SN74LS91, t_r = 15 ns, and t_f = 6 ns.
   B. C_L includes probe and jig capacitance.
   C. All diodes are 1N3064 or 1N916.
   D. C_1 = 30 pF and is used for SN54L91/SN74L91 only.
   E. For SN5491A/SN7491A, V_{ref} = 1.5 V; for SN54L91/SN74L91 and SN54LS91/SN74LS91, V_{ref} = 1.3 V.

FIGURE 1—SWITCHING TIMES

TEXAS INSTRUMENTS
INCORPORATED
POST OFFICE BOX 5012 • DALLAS, TEXAS 75222

TTL MSI PARALLEL-IN SERIAL-OUT REGISTERS
for application as

- **Dual-Source, Parallel-To-Serial Converter**
- **Serial-In Serial-Out Register**

description

These monolithic shift registers which utilize transistor-transistor logic (TTL) circuits in the familiar Series 54/74 configuration, are composed of four R-S master-slave flip-flops, four AND-OR-INVERT gates, and four inverter-drivers. Internal interconnections of these functions provide a versatile register which performs right-shift operations as a serial-in, serial-out register or as a dual-source, parallel-to-serial converter. A number of these registers may be connected in series to form an n-bit register.

All flip-flops are simultaneously set to a low output level by applying a high-level voltage to the clear input while the internal presets are inactive (high). See the preset function table below. Clearing is independent of the level of the clock input.

The register may be parallel loaded by using the clear input in conjunction with the preset inputs. After clearing all stages to low output levels, data to be loaded is applied to either the P1 or P2 inputs of each register stage (A, B, C, and D) with the corresponding preset enable input, PE1 or PE2, high. Presetting, like clearing, is independent of the level of the clock input.

SN5494 . . . J OR W PACKAGE
SN7494 . . . J OR N PACKAGE
(TOP VIEW)

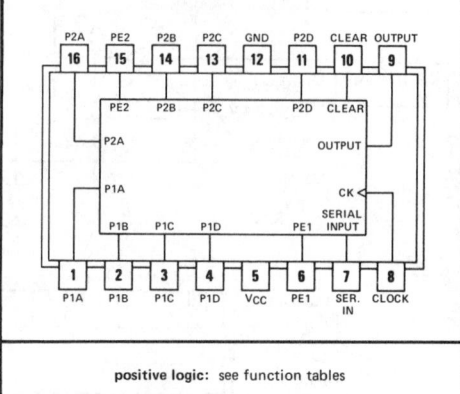

positive logic: see function tables

Transfer of information to the outputs occurs on the positive-going edge of the clock pulse. The proper information must be setup at the R-S inputs of each flip-flop prior to the rising edge of the clock input waveform. The serial input provides this information for the first flip-flop, while the outputs of the subsequent flip-flops provide information for the remaining R-S inputs. The clear input must be at a low level and the internal presets must be inactive (high) when clocking occurs.

PRESET FUNCTION TABLE
(BIT A, TYPICAL OF ALL)

PRESET INPUTS				INTERNAL
PE1	P1A	PE2	P2A	PRESET A
L	X	L	X	H (inactive)
L	X	X	L	H (inactive)
X	L	L	X	H (inactive)
X	L	X	L	H (inactive)
H	H	X	X	L (active)
X	X	H	H	L (active)

REGISTER FUNCTION TABLE

INTERNAL PRESETS				INPUTS			INTERNAL OUTPUTS			OUTPUT
A	B	C	D	CLEAR	CLOCK	SERIAL	Q_A	Q_B	Q_C	Q_D
H	H	H	H	H	X	X	L	L	L	L
L	L	L	L	L	X	X	H	H	H	H
H	H	H	H	L	L	X	Q_{A0}	Q_{B0}	Q_{C0}	Q_{D0}
L	H	L	H	L	L	X	H	Q_{B0}	H	Q_{D0}
H	H	H	H	L	↑	H	H	Q_{An}	Q_{Bn}	Q_{Cn}
H	H	H	H	L	↑	L	L	Q_{An}	Q_{Bn}	Q_{Cn}

H = high level (steady state), L = low level (steady state), X = irrelevant, ↑ = transition from low to high level
Q_{A0}, Q_{B0}, Q_{C0}, Q_{D0} = the level of Q_A, Q_B, Q_C, or Q_D, respectively, before the indicated steady-state input conditions were established.
Q_{An}, Q_{Bn}, Q_{Cn} = the level of Q_A, Q_B, or Q_C, respectively, before the most-recent ↑ transition of the clock.

absolute maximum ratings over operating free-air temperature range (unless otherwise noted)

Supply voltage, V_{CC} (see Note 1) . . . . 7 V
Input voltage (see Note 2) . . . . 5.5 V
Operating free-air temperature range: SN5494 Circuits . . . . −55°C to 125°C
                                  SN7494 Circuits . . . . 0°C to 70°C
Storage temperature range . . . . −65°C to 150°C

NOTES: 1. Voltage values are with respect to network ground terminal.
        2. Input voltage must be zero or positive with respect to network ground terminal.

TEXAS INSTRUMENTS
INCORPORATED
POST OFFICE BOX 5012 • DALLAS, TEXAS 75222

functional block diagram

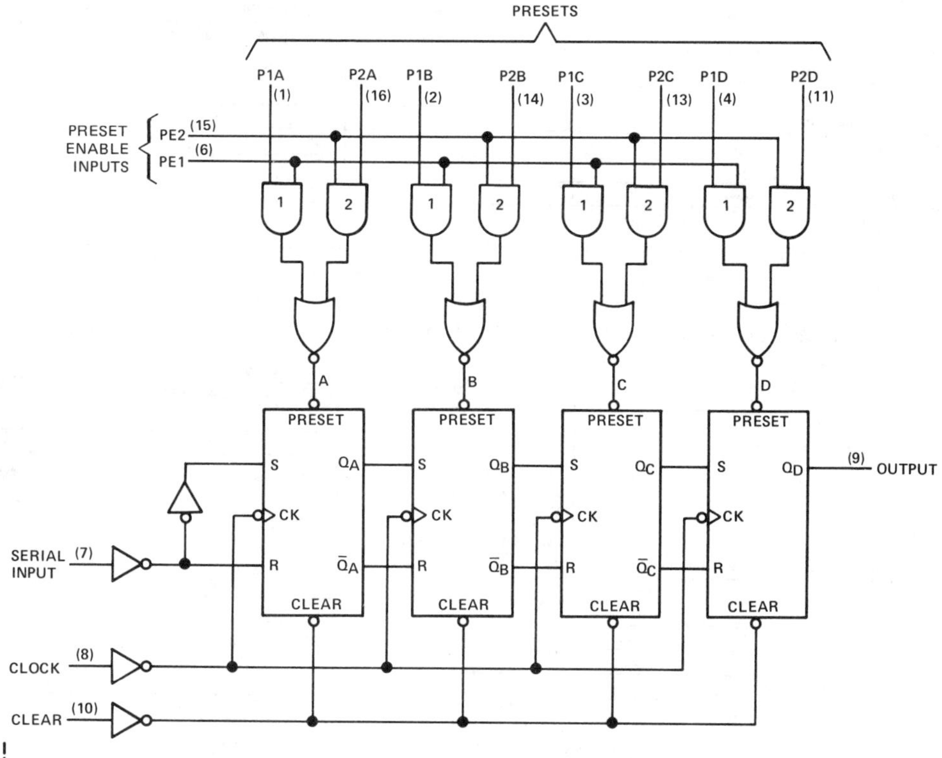

PRESETS

| P1A (1) | P2A (16) | P1B (2) | P2B (14) | P1C (3) | P2C (13) | P1D (4) | P2D (11) |

PRESET ENABLE INPUTS { PE2 (15) PE1 (6)

A   B   C   D

PRESET   PRESET   PRESET   PRESET

S Q_A S Q_B S Q_C S Q_D (9) OUTPUT

CK   CK   CK   CK

SERIAL INPUT (7)

R $\bar{Q}_A$ R $\bar{Q}_B$ R $\bar{Q}_C$ R

CLEAR   CLEAR   CLEAR   CLEAR

CLOCK (8)

CLEAR (10)

... dynamic input activated by transition from a high level to a low level

schematics of inputs and output

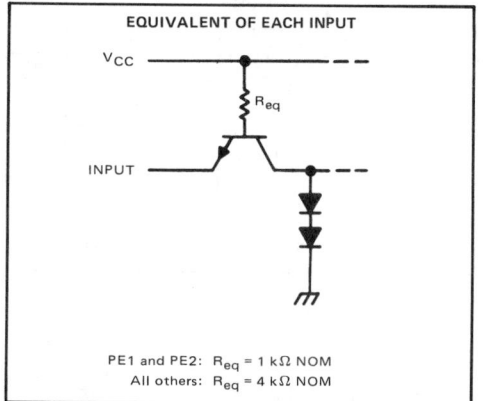

EQUIVALENT OF EACH INPUT

V_{CC}

R_{eq}

INPUT

PE1 and PE2: R_{eq} = 1 kΩ NOM
All others: R_{eq} = 4 kΩ NOM

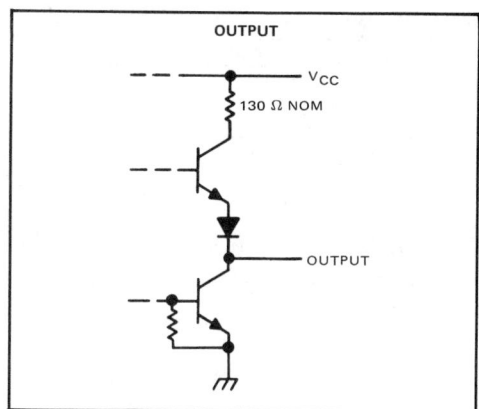

OUTPUT

V_{CC}

130 Ω NOM

OUTPUT

recommended operating conditions

		SN5494			SN7494			UNIT
		MIN	NOM	MAX	MIN	NOM	MAX	
Supply voltage, V_{CC}		4.5	5	5.5	4.75	5	5.25	V
High-level output current, I_{OH}				−400			−400	μA
Low-level output current, I_{OL}				16			16	mA
Width of clock pulse, $t_{w(clock)}$		35			35			ns
Width of clear pulse, $t_{w(clear)}$		30			30			ns
Width of preset pulse, $t_{w(preset)}$		30			30			ns
Setup time, t_{su}	High-level data	35			35			ns
	Low-level data	25			25			
Hold time, t_h		0			0			ns
Operating free-air temperature, T_A		−55		125	0		70	°C

electrical characteristics over recommended operating free-air temperature range (unless otherwise noted)

	PARAMETER	TEST CONDITIONS†		SN5494			SN7494			UNIT
				MIN	TYP‡	MAX	MIN	TYP‡	MAX	
V_{IH}	High-level input voltage			2			2			V
V_{IL}	Low-level input voltage					0.8			0.8	V
V_{OH}	High-level output voltage	V_{CC} = MIN, V_{IH} = 2 V, V_{IL} = 0.8 V, I_{OH} = −400 μA		2.4	3.5		2.4	3.5		V
V_{OL}	Low-level output voltage	V_{CC} = MIN, V_{IH} = 2 V, V_{IL} = 0.8 V, I_{OL} = 16 mA			0.2	0.4		0.2	0.4	V
I_I	Input current at maximum input voltage	V_{CC} = MAX, V_I = 5.5 V				1			1	mA
I_{IH}	High-level input current	Presets 1 and 2	V_{CC} = MAX, V_I = 2.4 V			160			160	μA
		Other inputs				40			40	
I_{IL}	Low-level input current	Presets 1 and 2	V_{CC} = MAX, V_I = 0.4 V			−6.4			−6.4	mA
		Other inputs				−1.6			−1.6	
I_{OS}	Short-circuit output current§	V_{CC} = MAX		−20		−57	−18		−57	mA
I_{CC}	Supply current	V_{CC} = MAX, See Note 3			35	50		35	58	mA

†For conditions shown as MIN or MAX, use the appropriate value specified under recommended operating conditions.
‡All typical values are at V_{CC} = 5 V, T_A = 25°C.
§Not more than one output should be shorted at a time.
NOTE 3: I_{CC} is measured with the outputs open, clear grounded following momentary application of 4.5 V, both preset-enable inputs grounded, and all other inputs at 4.5 V.

switching characteristics, V_{CC} = 5 V, T_A = 25°C

	PARAMETER	TEST CONDITIONS	MIN	TYP	MAX	UNIT
f_{max}	Maximum clock frequency		10			MHz
t_{PLH}	Propagation delay time, low-to-high-level output from clock			25	40	ns
t_{PHL}	Propgaation delay time, high-to-low-level output from clock	C_L = 15 pF, R_L = 400 Ω, See Note 4		25	40	ns
t_{PLH}	Propagation delay time, low-to-high-level output from preset				35	ns
t_{PHL}	Propagation delay time, high-to-low-level output from clear				40	ns

NOTE 4: Load circuit and voltage waveforms are shown on page 3-10.

7

TYPES SN5495A, SN54L95, SN54LS95B, SN7495A, SN74L95, SN74LS95B
4-BIT PARALLEL-ACCESS SHIFT REGISTERS

BULLETIN NO. DL-S 7611872, MARCH 1974—REVISED OCTOBER 1976

TYPE	TYPICAL MAXIMUM CLOCK FREQUENCY	TYPICAL POWER DISSIPATION
'95A	36 MHz	195 mW
'L95	5 MHz	19 mW
'LS95B	36 MHz	65 mW

description

These 4-bit registers feature parallel and serial inputs, parallel outputs, mode control, and two clock inputs. The registers have three modes of operation:

Parallel (broadside) load
Shift right (the direction Q_A toward Q_D)
Shift left (the direction Q_D toward Q_A)

Parallel loading is accomplished by applying the four bits of data and taking the mode control input high. The data is loaded into the associated flip-flops and appears at the outputs after the high-to-low transition of the clock-2 input. During loading, the entry of serial data is inhibited.

Shift right is accomplished on the high-to-low transition of clock 1 when the mode control is low; shift left is accomplished on the high-to-low transition of clock 2 when the mode control is high by connecting the output of each flip-flop to the parallel input of the previous flip-flop (Q_D to input C, etc.) and serial data is entered at input D. The clock input may be applied commonly to clock 1 and clock 2 if both modes can be clocked from the same source. Changes at the mode control input should normally be made while both clock inputs are low; however, conditions described in the last three lines of the function table will also ensure that register contents are protected.

SN5495A, SN54LS95B . . . J OR W PACKAGE
SN7495A, SN74LS95B . . . J OR N PACKAGE
(TOP VIEW)

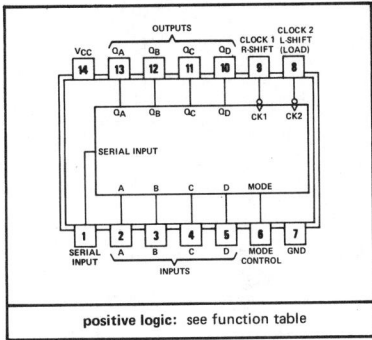

positive logic: see function table

SN54L95 . . . J OR T PACKAGE
SN74L95 . . . J OR N PACKAGE
(TOP VIEW)

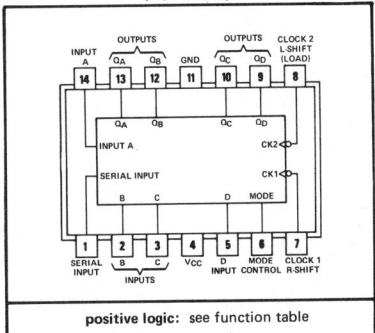

positive logic: see function table

FUNCTION TABLE

INPUTS								OUTPUTS			
MODE CONTROL	CLOCKS		SERIAL	PARALLEL				Q_A	Q_B	Q_C	Q_D
	2 (L)	1 (R)		A	B	C	D				
H	H	X	X	X	X	X	X	Q_{A0}	Q_{B0}	Q_{C0}	Q_{D0}
H	↓	X	X	a	b	c	d	a	b	c	d
H	↓	X	X	Q_B†	Q_C†	Q_D†	d	Q_{Bn}	Q_{Cn}	Q_{Dn}	d
L	L	H	X	X	X	X	X	Q_{A0}	Q_{B0}	Q_{C0}	Q_{D0}
L	X	↓	H	X	X	X	X	H	Q_{An}	Q_{Bn}	Q_{Cn}
L	X	↓	L	X	X	X	X	L	Q_{An}	Q_{Bn}	Q_{Cn}
↑	L	L	X	X	X	X	X	Q_{A0}	Q_{B0}	Q_{C0}	Q_{D0}
↓	L	L	X	X	X	X	X	Q_{A0}	Q_{B0}	Q_{C0}	Q_{D0}
↓	L	H	X	X	X	X	X	Q_{A0}	Q_{B0}	Q_{C0}	Q_{D0}
↑	H	L	X	X	X	X	X	Q_{A0}	Q_{B0}	Q_{C0}	Q_{D0}
↑	H	H	X	X	X	X	X	Q_{A0}	Q_{B0}	Q_{C0}	Q_{D0}

†Shifting left requires external connection of Q_B to A, Q_C to B, and Q_D to C. Serial data is entered at input D.
H = high level (steady state), L = low level (steady state), X = irrelevant (any input, including transitions)
↓ = transition from high to low level, ↑ = transition from low to high level
a, b, c, d = the level of steady-state input at inputs A, B, C, or D, respectively.
Q_{A0}, Q_{B0}, Q_{C0}, Q_{D0} = the level of Q_A, Q_B, Q_C, or Q_D, respectively, before the indicated steady-state input conditions were established.
Q_{An}, Q_{Bn}, Q_{Cn}, Q_{Dn} = the level of Q_A, Q_B, Q_C, or Q_D, respectively, before the most-recent ↓ transition of the clock.

TEXAS INSTRUMENTS
INCORPORATED
POST OFFICE BOX 5012 • DALLAS, TEXAS 75222

TYPES SN5495A, SN54L95, SN54LS95B, SN7495A, SN74L95, SN74LS95B
4-BIT PARALLEL-ACCESS SHIFT REGISTERS

REVISED OCTOBER 1976

functional block diagram

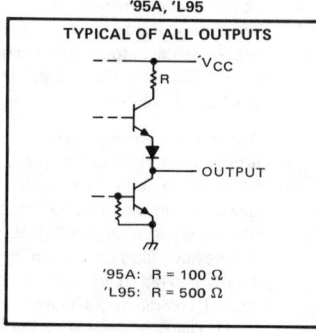

schematics of inputs and outputs

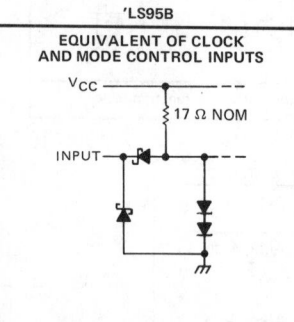

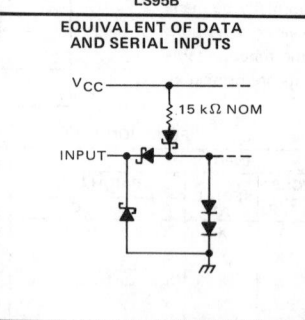

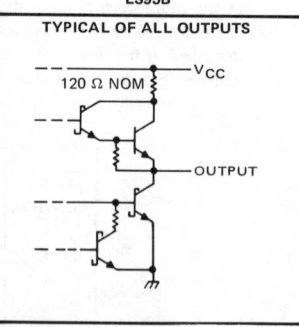

absolute maximum ratings over operating free-air temperature range (unless otherwise noted)

	SN54'	SN54L'	SN54LS'	SN74'	SN74L'	SN74LS'	UNIT
Supply voltage, V_CC (see Note 1)	7	8	7	7	8	7	V
Input voltage (see Note 2)	5.5	5.5	7	5.5	5.5	7	V
Interemitter voltage (see Note 3)	5.5	5.5		5.5	5.5		V
Operating free-air temperature range	−55 to 125			0 to 70			°C
Storage temperature range	−65 to 150			−65 to 150			°C

NOTES: 1. Voltage values, except interemitter voltage, are with respect to network ground terminal.
2. For the 'L95, input voltages must be zero or positive with respect to network ground terminal.
3. This is the voltage between two emitters of a multiple-emitter input transistor. This rating applies between the clock-2 input and the mode control input of the '95A and 'L95.

TEXAS INSTRUMENTS
INCORPORATED
POST OFFICE BOX 5012 • DALLAS, TEXAS 75222

recommended operating conditions

	SN5495A MIN	SN5495A NOM	SN5495A MAX	SN7495A MIN	SN7495A NOM	SN7495A MAX	UNIT
Supply voltage, V_{CC}	4.5	5	5.5	4.75	5	5.25	V
High-level output current, I_{OH}			−800			−800	µA
Low-level output current, I_{OL}			16			16	mA
Clock frequency, f_{clock}	0		25	0		25	MHz
Width of clock pulse, $t_{w(clock)}$ (see Figure 1)	20			20			ns
Setup time, high-level or low-level data, t_{su} (see Figure 1)	15			15			ns
Hold time, high-level or low-level data, t_h (see Figure 1)	0			0			ns
Time to enable clock 1, $t_{enable\ 1}$ (see Figure 2)	15			15			ns
Time to enable clock 2, $t_{enable\ 2}$ (see Figure 2)	15			15			ns
Time to inhibit clock 1, $t_{inhibit\ 1}$ (see Figure 2)	5			5			ns
Time to inhibit clock 2, $t_{inhibit\ 2}$ (see Figure 2)	5			5			ns
Operating free-air temperature, T_A	−55		125	0		70	°C

electrical characteristics over recommended operating free-air temperature range (unless otherwise noted)

PARAMETER		TEST CONDITIONS[†]	SN5495A MIN	SN5495A TYP[‡]	SN5495A MAX	SN7495A MIN	SN7495A TYP[‡]	SN7495A MAX	UNIT
V_{IH}	High-level input voltage		2			2			V
V_{IL}	Low-level input voltage				0.8			0.8	V
V_{IK}	Input clamp voltage	V_{CC} = MIN, I_I = −12 mA			−1.5			−1.5	V
V_{OH}	High-level output voltage	V_{CC} = MIN, V_{IH} = 2 V, V_{IL} = 0.8 V, I_{OH} = −800 µA	2.4	3.4		2.4	3.4		V
V_{OL}	Low-level output voltage	V_{CC} = MIN, V_{IH} = 2 V, V_{IL} = 0.8 V, I_{OL} = 16 mA		0.2	0.4		0.2	0.4	V
I_I	Input current at maximum input voltage	V_{CC} = MAX, V_I = 5.5 V			1			1	mA
I_{IH}	High-level input current — Serial, A, B, C, D, Clock 1 or 2	V_{CC} = MAX, V_I = 2.4 V			40			40	µA
	High-level input current — Mode control				80			80	
I_{IL}	Low-level input current — Serial, A, B, C, D, Clock 1 or 2	V_{CC} = MAX, V_I = 0.4 V			−1.6			−1.6	mA
	Low-level input current — Mode control				−3.2			−3.2	
I_{OS}	Short-circuit output current§	V_{CC} = MAX	−18		−57	−18		−57	mA
I_{CC}	Supply current	V_{CC} = MAX, See Note 4		39	63		39	63	mA

[†]For conditions shown as MIN or MAX, use the appropriate value specified under recommended operating conditions.
[‡]All typical values are at V_{CC} = 5 V, T_A = 25°C.
§Not more than one output should be shorted at a time.
NOTE 4: I_{CC} is measured with all outputs and serial input open; A, B, C, and D inputs grounded; mode control at 4.5 V; and a momentary 3 V, then ground, applied to both clock inputs.

switching characteristics, V_{CC} = 5 V, T_A = 25°C

PARAMETER		TEST CONDITIONS	MIN	TYP	MAX	UNIT
f_{max}	Maximum clock frequency	C_L = 15 pF, R_L = 400 Ω, See Figure 1	25	36		MHz
t_{PLH}	Propagation delay time, low-to-high-level output from clock			18	27	ns
t_{PHL}	Propagation delay time, high-to-low-level output from clock			21	32	ns

7

TYPES SN54L95, SN74L95
4-BIT PARALLEL-ACCESS SHIFT REGISTERS

recommended operating conditions

	SN54L95			SN74L95			UNIT
	MIN	NOM	MAX	MIN	NOM	MAX	
Supply voltage, V_{CC}	4.5	5	5.5	4.75	5	5.25	V
High-level output current, I_{OH}			−100			−200	μA
Low-level output current, I_{OL}			2			3.6	mA
Clock frequency, f_{clock}	0		3	0		3	MHz
Width of clock pulse, $t_{w(clock)}$ (see Figure 1)	200			200			ns
Setup time, high-level data, t_{su} (see Figure 1)	100			100			ns
Setup time, low-level data, t_{su} (see Figure 1)	120			120			ns
Hold time, high-level or low-level data, t_h (see Figure 1)	0			0			ns
Time to enable clock 1, $t_{enable\ 1}$ (see Figure 2)	225			225			ns
Time to enable clock 2, $t_{enable\ 2}$ (see Figure 2)	200			200			ns
Time to inhibit clock 1, $t_{inhibit\ 1}$ (see Figure 2)	100			100			ns
Time to inhibit clock 2, $t_{inhibit\ 2}$ (see Figure 2)	0			0			ns
Operating free-air temperature, T_A	−55		125	0		70	°C

electrical characteristics over recommended operating free-air temperature range (unless otherwise noted)

PARAMETER		TEST CONDITIONS[†]	SN54L95			SN74L95			UNIT
			MIN	TYP[‡]	MAX	MIN	TYP[‡]	MAX	
V_{IH} High-level input voltage			2			2			V
V_{IL} Low-level input voltage					0.7			0.7	V
V_{OH} High-level output voltage		V_{CC} = MIN, V_{IH} = 2 V, V_{IL} = 0.7 V, I_{OH} = MAX	2.4	3.3		2.4	3.2		V
V_{OL} Low-level output voltage		V_{CC} = MIN, V_{IH} = 2 V, V_{IL} = 0.7 V, I_{OL} = MAX		0.15	0.3		0.2	0.4	V
I_I Input current at maximum input voltage	Serial, A, B, C, D, Clock 1 or 2	V_{CC} = MAX, V_I = 5.5 V			100			100	μA
	Mode control				200			200	
I_{IH} High-level input current	Serial, A, B, C, D, Clock 1 or 2	V_{CC} = MAX, V_I = 2.4 V			10			10	μA
	Mode control				20			20	
I_{IL} Low-level input current	Serial, A, B, C, D, clock 1 or 2	V_{CC} = MAX, V_I = 0.3 V			−0.18			−0.18	mA
	Mode control				−0.36			−0.36	
I_{OS} Short-circuit output current §		V_{CC} = MAX	−3		−15	−3		−15	mA
I_{CC} Supply current		V_{CC} = MAX, See Note 4		3.8	9		3.8	9	mA

[†]For conditions shown as MIN or MAX, use the appropriate value specified under recommended operating conditions.
[‡]All typical values are at V_{CC} = 5 V, T_A = 25°C.
§Not more than one output should be shorted at a time.
NOTE 4: I_{CC} is measured with all outputs and serial input open; A, B, C, and D inputs grounded; mode control at 4.5 V; and a momentary 3 V, then ground, applied to both clock inputs.

switching characteristics, V_{CC} = 5 V, T_A = 25°C

PARAMETER	TEST CONDITIONS	MIN	TYP	MAX	UNIT
f_{max} Maximum clock frequency	C_L = 50 pF, R_L = 4 kΩ, See Figure 1	3	5		MHz
t_{PLH} Propagation delay time, low-to-high-level output from clock			115	200	ns
t_{PHL} Propagation delay time, high-to-low-level output from clock			125	200	ns

7

TEXAS INSTRUMENTS
INCORPORATED
POST OFFICE BOX 5012 • DALLAS, TEXAS 75222

recommended operating conditions

	SN54LS95B			SN74LS95B			UNIT
	MIN	NOM	MAX	MIN	NOM	MAX	
Supply voltage, V_{CC}	4.5	5	5.5	4.75	5	5.25	V
High-level output current, I_{OH}			−400			−400	μA
Low-level output current, I_{OL}			4			8	mA
Clock frequency, f_{clock}	0		25	0		25	MHz
Width of clock pulse, $t_{w(clock)}$ (see Figure 1)	25			25			ns
Setup time, high-level or low-level data, t_{su} (see Figure 1)	20			20			ns
Hold time, high-level or low-level data, t_h (see Figure 1)	20			10			ns
Time to enable clock 1, $t_{enable\ 1}$ (see Figure 2)	20			20			ns
Time to enable clock 2, $t_{enable\ 2}$ (see Figure 2)	20			20			ns
Time to inhibit clock 1, $t_{inhibit\ 1}$ (see Figure 2)	20			20			ns
Time to inhibit clock 2, $t_{inhibit\ 2}$ (see Figure 2)	20			20			ns
Operating free-air temperature, T_A	−55		125	0		70	°C

electrical characteristics over recommended operating free-air temperature range (unless otherwise noted)

PARAMETER		TEST CONDITIONS[†]		SN54LS95B			SN74LS95B			UNIT
				MIN	TYP[‡]	MAX	MIN	TYP[‡]	MAX	
V_{IH}	High-level input voltage			2			2			V
V_{IL}	Low-level input voltage					0.7			0.8	V
V_{IK}	Input clamp voltage	V_{CC} = MIN,	I_I' = −18 mA			−1.5			−1.5	V
V_{OH}	High-level output voltage	V_{CC} = MIN, V_{IH} = 2 V, V_{IL} = V_{IL} max, I_{OH} = −400 μA		2.5	3.4		2.7	3.4		V
V_{OL}	Low-level output voltage	V_{CC} = MIN, V_{IH} = 2 V, V_{IL} = V_{IL} max	I_{OL} = 4 mA		0.25	0.4		0.25	0.4	V
			I_{OL} = 8 mA					0.35	0.5	
I_I	Input current at maximum input voltage	V_{CC} = MAX,	V_I = 7 V			0.1			0.1	mA
I_{IH}	High-level input current	V_{CC} = MAX,	V_I = 2.7 V			20			20	μA
I_{IL}	Low-level input current	V_{CC} = MAX,	V_I = 0.4 V			−0.4			−0.4	mA
I_{OS}	Short-circuit output current[§]	V_{CC} = MAX		−20		−100	−20		−100	mA
I_{CC}	Supply current	V_{CC} = MAX,	See Note 4		13	21		13	21	mA

[†]For conditions shown as MIN or MAX, use the appropriate value specified under recommended operating conditions.
[‡]All typical values are at V_{CC} = 5 V, T_A = 25°C.
[§]Not more than one output should be shorted at a time, and duration of the short-circuit should not exceed one second.
NOTE 4: I_{CC} is measured with all outputs and serial input open; A, B, C, and D inputs grounded; mode control at 4.5 V; and a momentary 3 V, then ground, applied to both clock inputs.

switching characteristics, V_{CC} = 5 V, T_A = 25°C

PARAMETER		TEST CONDITIONS	MIN	TYP	MAX	UNIT
f_{max}	Maximum clock frequency	C_L = 15 pF, R_L = 2 kΩ, See Figure 1	25	36		MHz
t_{PLH}	Propagation delay time, low-to-high-level output from clock			18	27	ns
t_{PHL}	Propagation delay time, high-to-low-level output from clock			21	32	ns

7

TEXAS INSTRUMENTS
INCORPORATED
POST OFFICE BOX 5012 • DALLAS, TEXAS 75222

TYPES SN5495A, SN54L95, SN54LS95B, SN7495A, SN74L95, SN74LS95B
4-BIT PARALLEL-ACCESS SHIFT REGISTERS

PARAMETER MEASUREMENT INFORMATION

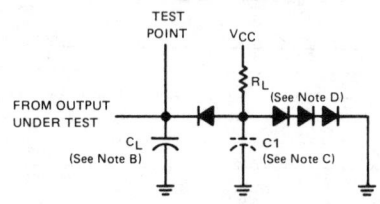

LOAD CIRCUIT

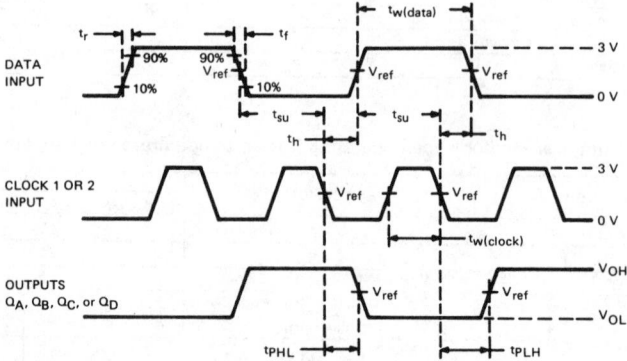

NOTES: A. Input pulses are supplied by a generator having the following characteristics: $t_r \leqslant$ 10 ns, $t_f \leqslant$ 10 ns, and $Z_{out} \approx$ 50 Ω. For the data pulse generator, PRR = 500 kHz; for the clock pulse generator, PRR = 1 MHz. When testing f_{max}, vary PRR. For '95A, $t_{w(data)} \geqslant$ 20 ns; $t_{w(clock)} \geqslant$ 15 ns. For 'L95, $t_{w(data)} \geqslant$ 150 ns; $t_{w(clock)} \geqslant$ 200 ns. For 'LS95B, $t_{w(data)} \geqslant$ 20 ns, $t_{w(clock)} \geqslant$ 15 ns.
   B. C_L includes probe and jig capacitance.
   C. C1 (30 pF) is applicable for testing 'L95.
   D. All diodes are 1N916 or 1N3064.
   E. For '95A, V_{ref} = 1.5 V; for 'L95 and 'LS95B, V_{ref} = 1.3 V.

VOLTAGE WAVEFORMS
FIGURE 1—SWITCHING TIMES

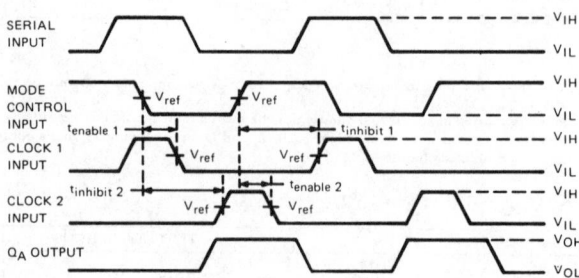

NOTES: A. Input A is at a low level.
   B. For '95A, V_{ref} = 1.5 V; for 'L95 and 'LS95B, V_{ref} = 1.3 V.

VOLTAGE WAVEFORMS
FIGURE 2—CLOCK ENABLE/INHIBIT TIMES

TEXAS INSTRUMENTS
INCORPORATED
POST OFFICE BOX 5012 • DALLAS, TEXAS 75222

TTL
MSI

TYPES SN5496, SN54L96, SN54LS96,
SN7496, SN74L96, SN74LS96
5-BIT SHIFT REGISTERS
BULLETIN NO. DL-S 7611821, MARCH 1974—REVISED OCTOBER 1976

- N-Bit Serial-To-Parallel Converter
- N-Bit Parallel-To-Serial Converter
- N-Bit Storage Register

TYPE	TYPICAL PROPAGATION DELAY TIME	TYPICAL POWER DISSIPATION
'96	25 ns	240 mW
'L96	50 ns	120 mW
'LS96	25 ns	60 mW

SN5496, SN54LS96 . . . J OR W PACKAGE
SN54L96 . . . J PACKAGE
SN7496, SN74L96, SN74LS96 . . . J OR N PACKAGE
(TOP VIEW)

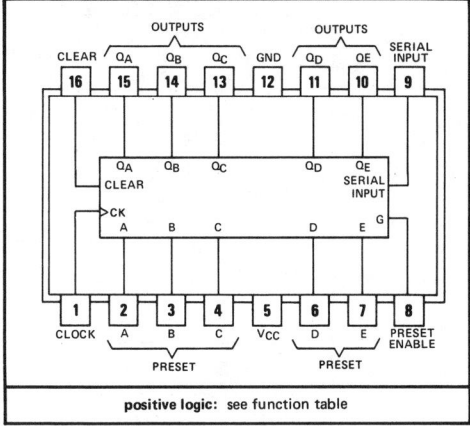

positive logic: see function table

description

These shift registers consist of five R-S master-slave flip-flops connected to perform parallel-to-serial or serial-to-parallel conversion of binary data. Since both inputs and outputs for all flip-flops are accessible, parallel-in/parallel-out or serial-in/serial-out operation may be performed.

All flip-flops are simultaneously set to a low output level by applying a low-level voltage to the clear input while the preset is inactive (low). Clearing is independent of the level of the clock input.

The register may be parallel loaded by using the clear input in conjunction with the preset inputs. After clearing all stages to low output levels, data to be loaded is applied to the individual preset inputs (A, B, C, D, and E) and a high-level load pulse is applied to the preset enable input. Presetting like clearing is independent of the level of the clock input.

Transfer of information to the outputs occurs on the positive-going edge of the clock pulse. The proper information must be set up at the R-S inputs of each flip-flop prior to the rising edge of the clock input waveform. The serial input provides this information to the first flip-flop, while the outputs of the subsequent flip-flops provide information for the remaining R-S inputs. The clear input must be high and the preset or preset enable inputs must be low when clocking occurs.

FUNCTION TABLE

INPUTS									OUTPUTS				
CLEAR	PRESET ENABLE	A	B	C	D	E	CLOCK	SERIAL	Q_A	Q_B	Q_C	Q_D	Q_E
L	L	X	X	X	X	X	X	X	L	L	L	L	L
L	X	L	L	L	L	L	X	X	L	L	L	L	L
H	H	H	H	H	H	H	X	X	H	H	H	H	H
H	H	L	L	L	L	L	L	X	Q_{A0}	Q_{B0}	Q_{C0}	Q_{D0}	Q_{E0}
H	H	H	L	H	L	H	L	X	H	Q_{B0}	H	Q_{D0}	H
H	L	X	X	X	X	X	L	X	Q_{A0}	Q_{B0}	Q_{C0}	Q_{D0}	Q_{E0}
H	L	X	X	X	X	X	↑	H	H	Q_{An}	Q_{Bn}	Q_{Cn}	Q_{Dn}
H	L	X	X	X	X	X	↑	L	L	Q_{An}	Q_{Bn}	Q_{Cn}	Q_{Dn}

H = high level (steady state), L = low level (steady state)
X = irrelevant (any input, including transitions)
↑ = transition from low to high level
Q_{A0}, Q_{B0}, etc = the level of Q_A, Q_B, etc, respectively before the indicated steady-state input conditions were established.
Q_{An}, Q_{Bn}, etc = the level of Q_A, Q_B, etc, respectively before the most-recent ↑ transition of the clock.

TEXAS INSTRUMENTS
INCORPORATED
POST OFFICE BOX 5012 • DALLAS, TEXAS 75222

typical clear, shift, preset, and shift sequences

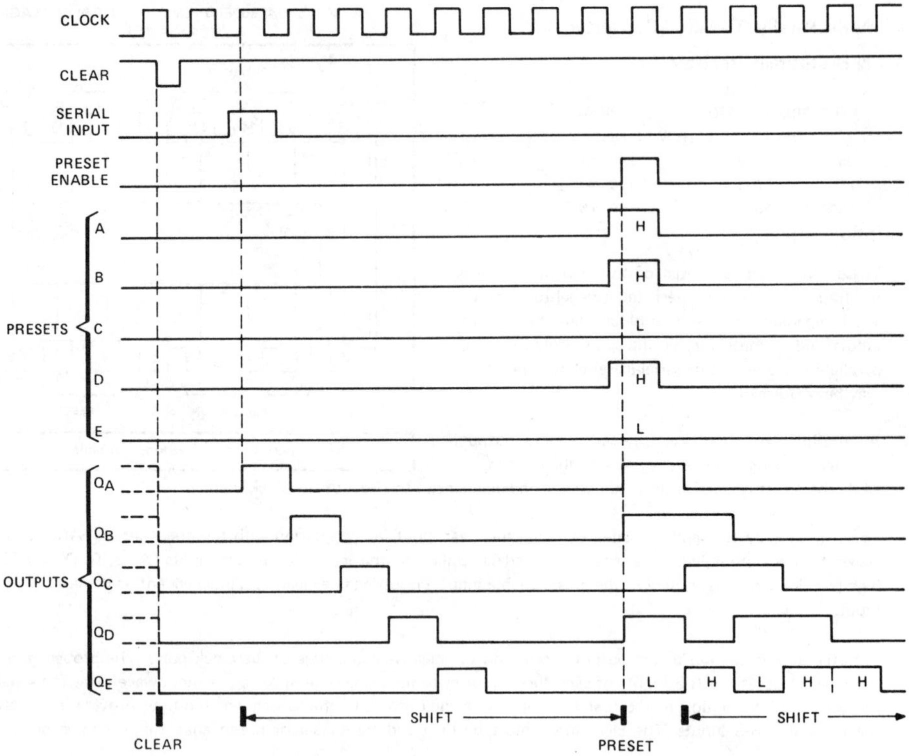

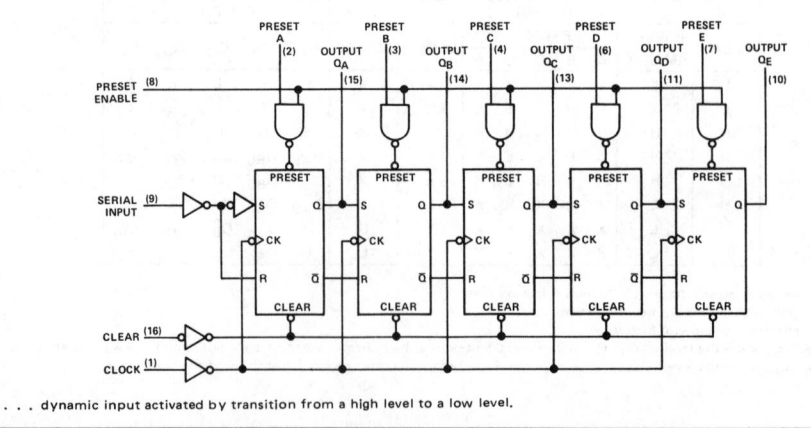

functional block diagram

⟶ . . . dynamic input activated by transition from a high level to a low level.

TEXAS INSTRUMENTS
INCORPORATED
POST OFFICE BOX 5012 • DALLAS, TEXAS 75222

schematics of inputs and outputs

'96

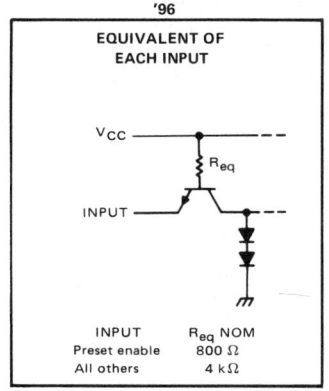

'96

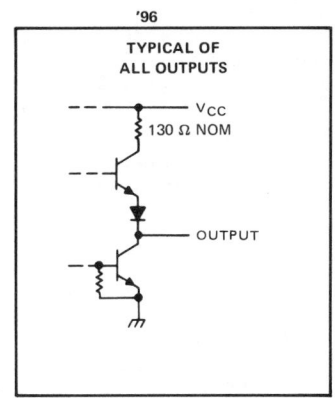

'L96

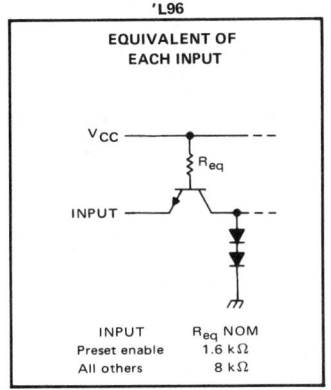

'L96

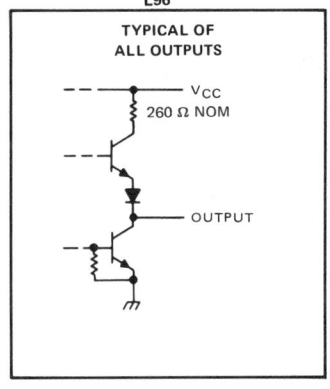

'LS96

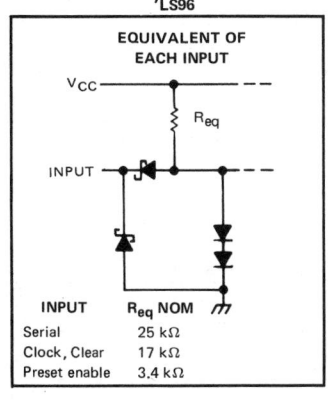

'LS96

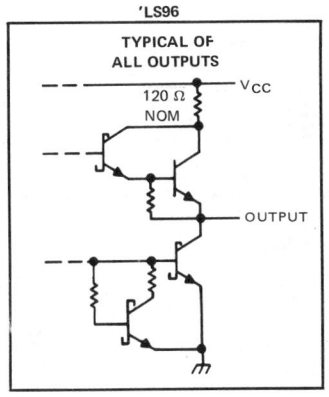

7

absolute maximum ratings over operating free-air temperature range (unless otherwise noted)

Supply voltage, V_{CC} (see Note 1) . . . . 7 V
Input voltage (see Note 2) . . . . 5.5 V
Operating free-air temperature range: SN5496 . . . . −55°C to 125°C
                              SN7496 . . . . 0°C to 70°C
Storage temperature range . . . . −65°C to 150°C

NOTES: 1. Voltage values are with respect to network ground terminal.
         2. Input voltages must be zero or positive with respect to network ground terminal.

recommended operating conditions

	SN5496			SN7496			UNIT
	MIN	NOM	MAX	MIN	NOM	MAX	
Supply voltage, V_{CC}	4.5	5	5.5	4.75	5	5.25	V
High-level output current, I_{OH}			−400			−400	μA
Low-level output current, I_{OL}			16			16	mA
Clock frequency, f_{clock}	0		10	0		10	MHz
Width of clock input pulse, $t_{w(clock)}$	35			35			ns
Width of preset and clear input pulse, t_w	30			30			ns
Serial input setup time, t_{su} (see Figure 1)	30			30			ns
Serial input hold time, t_h (see Figure 1)	0			0			ns
Operating free-air temperature, T_A	−55		125	0		70	°C

electrical characteristics over recommended operating free-air temperature range (unless otherwise noted)

PARAMETER		TEST CONDITIONS†	SN5496			SN7496			UNIT
			MIN	TYP‡	MAX	MIN	TYP‡	MAX	
V_{IH}	High-level input voltage		2			2			V
V_{IL}	Low-level input voltage				0.8			0.8	V
V_{OH}	High-level output voltage	V_{CC} = MIN, V_{IH} = 2 V, V_{IL} = 0.8 V, I_{OH} = −400 μA	2.4	3.4		2.4	3.4		V
V_{OL}	Low-level output voltage	V_{CC} = MIN, V_{IH} = 2 V, V_{IL} = 0.8 V, I_{OL} = 16 mA		0.2	0.4		0.2	0.4	V
I_I	Input current at maximum input voltage	V_{CC} = MAX, V_I = 5.5 V			1			1	mA
I_{IH}	High-level input current — any input except preset enable	V_{CC} = MAX, V_I = 2.4 V			40			40	μA
	High-level input current — preset enable				200			200	
I_{IL}	Low-level input current — any input except preset enable	V_{CC} = MAX, V_I = 0.4 V			−1.6			−1.6	mA
	Low-level input current — preset enable				−8			−8	
I_{OS}	Short-circuit output current§	V_{CC} = MAX	−20		−57	−18		−57	mA
I_{CC}	Supply current	V_{CC} = MAX, See Note 3		48	68		48	79	mA

†For conditions shown at MIN or MAX, use the appropriate value specified under recommended operating conditions.
‡All typical values are at V_{CC} = 5 V, T_A = 25°C.
§Not more than one output should be shorted at a time.
NOTE 3: I_{CC} is measured with the clear input grounded and all other inputs and outputs open.

switching characteristics, V_{CC} = 5 V, T_A = 25°C

PARAMETER		TEST CONDITIONS	MIN	TYP	MAX	UNIT
t_{PLH}	Propagation delay time, low-to-high-level output from clock	C_L = 15 pF, R_L = 400 Ω, See Figure 1		25	40	ns
t_{PHL}	Propagation delay time, high-to-low-level output from clock			25	40	ns
t_{PLH}	Propagation delay time, low-to-high-level output from preset or preset enable			28	35	ns
t_{PHL}	Propagation delay time, high-to-low-level output from clear				55	ns

TEXAS INSTRUMENTS
INCORPORATED
POST OFFICE BOX 5012 • DALLAS, TEXAS 75222

absolute maximum ratings over operating free-air temperature range (unless otherwise noted)

Supply voltage, V_{CC} (see Note 1) . . . . 7 V
Input voltage (see Note 2) . . . . 5.5 V
Operating free-air temperature range: SN54L96 . . . . -55°C to 125°C
SN74L96 . . . . 0°C to 70°C
Storage temperature range . . . . -65°C to 150°C

NOTES: 1. Voltage values are with respect to network ground terminal.
2. Input voltage must be zero or positive with respect to network ground terminal.

recommended operating conditions

	SN54L96			SN74L96			UNIT
	MIN	NOM	MAX	MIN	NOM	MAX	
Supply voltage, V_{CC}	4.5	5	5.5	4.75	5	5.25	V
High-level output current, I_{OH}			-200			-200	μA
Low-level output current, I_{OL}			8			8	mA
Clock frequency, f_{clock}	0		5	0		5	MHz
Width of clock, preset, or clear input pulse, t_w	100			100			ns
Serial input setup time, t_{su} (see Figure 1)	100			100			ns
Serial input hold time, t_h (see Figure 1)	0			0			ns
Operating free-air temperature, T_A	-55		125	0		70	$^{\circ}$C

electrical characteristics over recommended operating free-air temperature range (unless otherwise noted)

PARAMETER		TEST CONDITIONS[†]	SN54L96			SN74L96			UNIT
			MIN	TYP[‡]	MAX	MIN	TYP[‡]	MAX	
V_{IH}	High-level input voltage		2			2			V
V_{IL}	Low-level input voltage				0.8			0.8	V
V_{OH}	High-level output voltage	V_{CC} = MIN, V_{IH} = 2 V, V_{IL} = 0.8 V, I_{OH} = $-200\,\mu$A	2.4	3.2		2.4	3.2		V
V_{OL}	Low-level output voltage	V_{CC} = MIN, V_{IH} = 2 V, V_{IL} = 0.8 V, I_{OL} = 8 mA		0.2	0.4		0.2	0.4	V
I_I	Input current at maximum input voltage	V_{CC} = MAX, V_I = 5.5 V			1			1	mA
I_{IH}	High-level input current — any input except preset enable	V_{CC} = MAX, V_I = 2.4 V			20			20	μA
	High-level input current — preset enable				100			100	
I_{IL}	Low-level input current — any input except preset enable	V_{CC} = MAX, V_I = 0.4 V			-0.8			-0.8	mA
	Low-level input current — preset enable				-4			-4	
I_{OS}	Short-circuit output current§	V_{CC} = MAX	-10		-29	-9		-29	mA
I_{CC}	Supply current	V_{CC} = MAX, See Note 3		24	34		24	40	mA

[†]For conditions shown at MIN or MAX, use the appropriate value specified under recommended operating conditions.
[‡]All typical values are at V_{CC} = 5 V, T_A = 25°C.
§Not more than one output should be shorted at a time.
NOTE 3: I_{CC} is measured with the clear input grounded and all other inputs and outputs open.

switching characteristics, V_{CC} = 5 V, T_A = 25°C

PARAMETER		TEST CONDITIONS	MIN	TYP	MAX	UNIT
t_{PLH}	Propagation delay time, low-to-high-level output from clock	C_L = 15 pF, R_L = 800 Ω, See Figure 1		50	80	ns
t_{PHL}	Propagation delay time, high-to-low-level output from clock			50	80	ns
t_{PLH}	Propagation delay time, low-to-high-level output from preset or preset enable			56	70	ns
t_{PHL}	Propagation delay time, high-to-low-level output from clear				110	ns

TYPES SN54LS96, SN74LS96
5-BIT SHIFT REGISTERS

REVISED AUGUST 1977

absolute maximum ratings over operating free-air temperature range (unless otherwise noted)

Supply voltage, V_{CC} (see Note 1)	7 V
Input voltage	7 V
Operating free-air temperature range: SN54LS96	-55°C to 125°C
SN74LS96	0°C to 70°C
Storage temperature range	-65°C to 150°C

NOTE 1: Voltage values are with respect to network ground terminal.

recommended operating conditions

	SN54LS96			SN74LS96			UNIT
	MIN	NOM	MAX	MIN	NOM	MAX	
Supply voltage, V_{CC}	4.5	5	5.5	4.75	5	5.25	V
High-level output current, I_{OH}			−400			−400	μA
Low-level output current, I_{OL}			4			8	mA
Clock frequency, f_{clock}	0		25	0		25	MHz
Width of clock input pulse, $t_{w(clock)}$	20			20			ns
Width of preset and clear input pulse, t_w	30			30			ns
Serial input setup time, t_{setup} (see Figure 1)	30			30			ns
Serial input hold time, t_{hold} (see Figure 1)	0			0			ns
Operating free-air temperature, T_A	−55		125	0		70	$^\circ$C

electrical characteristics over recommended operating free-air temperature range (unless otherwise noted)

PARAMETER		TEST CONDITIONS[†]		SN54LS96			SN74LS96			UNIT
				MIN	TYP[‡]	MAX	MIN	TYP[‡]	MAX	
V_{IH}	High-level input voltage			2			2			V
V_{IL}	Low-level input voltage					0.7			0.8	V
V_{IK}	Input clamp voltage	V_{CC} = MIN, I_I = −18 mA				−1.5			−1.5	V
V_{OH}	High-level output voltage	V_{CC} = MIN, V_{IH} = 2 V, V_{IL} = V_{IL} max, I_{OH} = −400 μA		2.5	3.5		2.7	3.5		V
V_{OL}	Low-level output voltage	V_{CC} = MIN, V_{IH} = 2 V, V_{IL} = V_{IL} max	I_{OL} = 4 mA		0.25	0.4		0.25	0.4	V
			I_{OL} = 8 mA					0.35	0.5	
I_I	Input current at maximum input voltage	Preset enable	V_{CC} = MAX, V_I = 7 V			0.5			0.5	mA
		All others				0.1			0.1	
I_{IH}	High-level input current	Preset enable	V_{CC} = MAX, V_I = 2.7 V			100			100	μA
		All others				20			20	
I_{IL}	Low-level input current	Preset enable	V_{CC} = MAX, V_I = 0.4 V			−2			−2	mA
		All others				−0.4			−0.4	
I_{OS}	Short-circuit output current[§]	V_{CC} = MAX		−20		−100	−20		−100	mA
I_{CC}	Supply current	V_{CC} = MAX, See Note 3			12	20		12	20	mA

[†] For conditions shown at MIN or MAX, use the appropriate value specified under recommended operating conditions.
[‡] All typical values are at V_{CC} = 5 V, T_A = 25°C.
[§] Not more than one output should be shorted at a time, and duration of the short-circuit should not exceed one second.
NOTE 3: I_{CC} is measured with the clear input grounded and all other inputs and outputs open.

switching characteristics, V_{CC} = 5 V, T_A = 25°C

PARAMETER		TEST CONDITIONS	MIN	TYP	MAX	UNIT
t_{PLH}	Propagation delay time, low-to-high-level output from clock	C_L = 15 pF, R_L = 2 kΩ, See Figure 1		25	40	ns
t_{PHL}	Propagation delay time, high-to-low-level output from clock			25	40	ns
t_{PLH}	Propagation delay time, low-to-high-level output from preset or preset enable			28	35	ns
t_{PHL}	Propagation delay time, high-to-low-level output from clear				55	ns

7

TEXAS INSTRUMENTS
INCORPORATED
POST OFFICE BOX 5012 • DALLAS, TEXAS 75222

PARAMETER MEASUREMENT INFORMATION

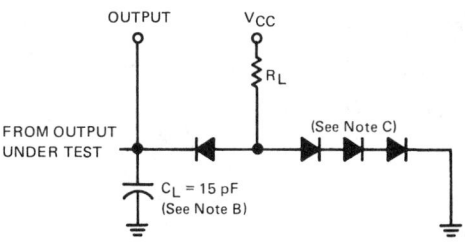

LOAD CIRCUIT

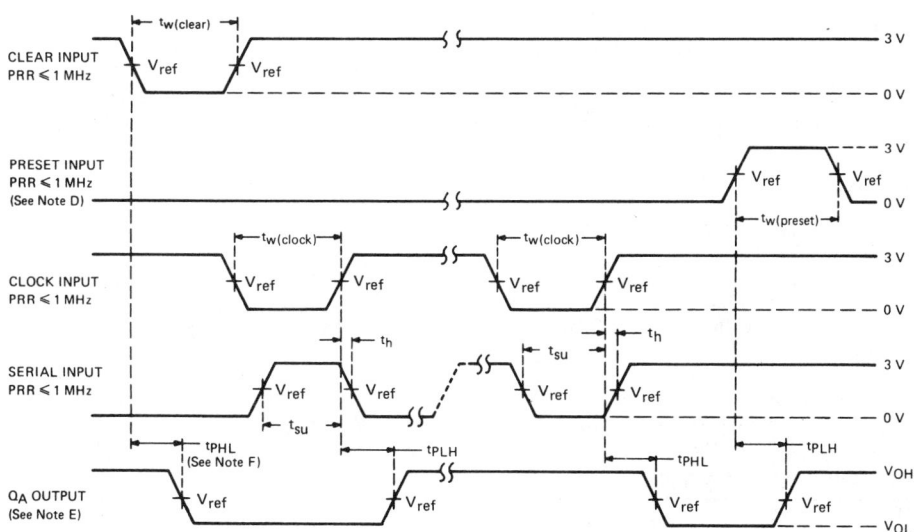

VOLTAGE WAVEFORMS

NOTES: A. Input pulses are supplied by pulse generators having the following characteristics: duty cycle ≤ 50%, $Z_{out} \approx 50 \ \Omega$; for '96 and
'L96, $t_r \leqslant 10$ ns, $t_f \leqslant 10$ ns, and for 'LS96 $t_r = 15$ ns, $t_f = 6$ ns.
B. C_L includes probe and jig capacitance.
C. All diodes are 1N3064 or 1N916.
D. Preset may be tested by applying a high-level voltage to the individual preset inputs and pulsing the preset enable or by applying a
high-level voltage to the preset enable and pulsing the individual preset inputs.
E. Q_A output is illustrated. Relationship of serial input to other Q outputs is illustrated in the typical shift sequence.
F. Outputs are set to the high level prior to the measurement of t_{PHL} from the clear input.
G. For '96 and 'L96, V_{ref} = 1.5 V; for 'LS96 V_{ref} = 1.3 V.

FIGURE 1—SWITCHING TIMES

- Perform Fixed-Rate or Variable-Rate Frequency Division

- For Applications in Arithmetic, Radar, Digital-to-Analog (D/A), Analog-to-Digital (A/D), and other Conversion Operations

- Typical Maximum Clock Frequency . . . 32 Megahertz

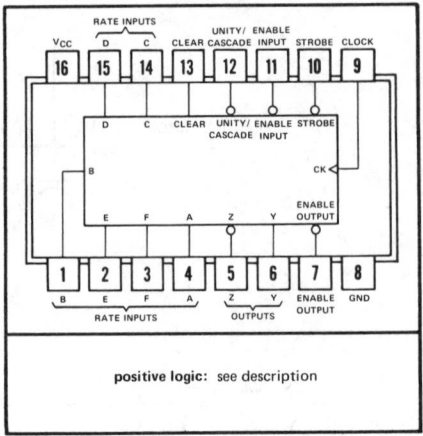

SN5497 . . . J OR W PACKAGE
SN7497 . . . J OR N PACKAGE
(TOP VIEW)

positive logic: see description

description

These monolithic, fully synchronous, programmable counters utilize Series 54/74 TTL circuitry to achieve 32-megahertz typical maximum operating frequencies. These six-bit serial binary counters feature buffered clock, clear, and enable inputs to control the operation of the counter, and a strobe input to enable or inhibit the rate input/decoding AND-OR-INVERT gates. The outputs have additional gating for cascading and transferring unity-count rates.

The counter is enabled when the clear, strobe, and enable inputs are low. With the counter enabled, the output frequency is equal to the input frequency multiplied by the rate input M and divided by 64, ie.:

$$f_{out} = \frac{M \cdot f_{in}}{64}$$

where: $M = F \cdot 2^5 + E \cdot 2^4 + D \cdot 2^3 + C \cdot 2^2 + B \cdot 2^1 + A \cdot 2^0$

When the rate input is binary 0 (all rate inputs low), Z remains high. In order to cascade devices to perform 12-bit rate multiplication, the enable output is connected to the enable and strobe inputs of the next stage, the Z output of each stage is connected to the unity/cascade input of the other stage, and the sub-multiple frequency is taken from the Y output.

The unity/cascade input, when connected to the clock input, may be utilized to pass the clock frequency (inverted) to the Y output when the rate input/decoding gates are inhibited by the strobe. The unity/cascade input may also be used as a control for the Y output.

schematics of inputs and outputs

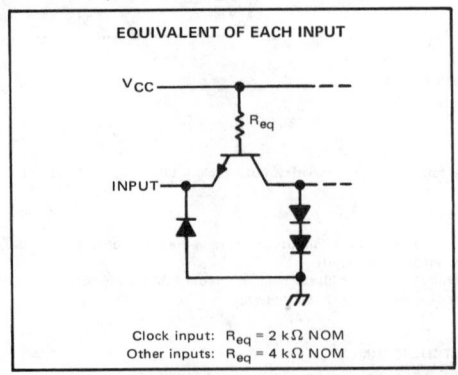

EQUIVALENT OF EACH INPUT

Clock input: R_{eq} = 2 kΩ NOM
Other inputs: R_{eq} = 4 kΩ NOM

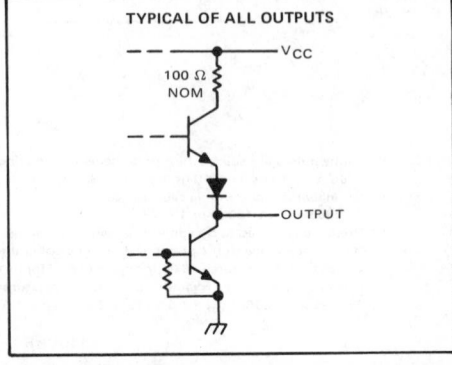

TYPICAL OF ALL OUTPUTS

TEXAS INSTRUMENTS
INCORPORATED
POST OFFICE BOX 5012 • DALLAS, TEXAS 75222

description (continued)

STATE AND/OR RATE FUNCTION TABLE (See Note A)

INPUTS											OUTPUTS			
			BINARY RATE						NUMBER OF	UNITY/	LOGIC LEVEL OR NUMBER OF PULSES			
CLEAR	ENABLE	STROBE	F	E	D	C	B	A	CLOCK PULSES	CASCADE	Y	Z	ENABLE	NOTES
H	X	H	X	X	X	X	X	X	X	H	L	H	H	B
L	L	L	L	L	L	L	L	L	64	H	L	H	1	C
L	L	L	L	L	L	L	L	H	64	H	1	1	1	C
L	L	L	L	L	L	L	H	L	64	H	2	2	1	C
L	L	L	L	L	L	H	L	L	64	H	4	4	1	C
L	L	L	L	L	H	L	L	L	64	H	8	8	1	C
L	L	L	L	H	L	L	L	L	64	H	16	16	1	C
L	L	L	H	L	L	L	L	L	64	H	32	32	1	C
L	L	L	H	H	H	H	H	H	64	H	63	63	1	C
L	L	L	H	H	H	H	H	H	64	L	H	63	1	D
L	L	L	H	L	H	L	L	L	64	H	40	40	1	E

NOTES: A. H = high level, L = low level, X = irrelevant. All remaining entries are numeric counts.

B. This is a simplified illustration of the clear function. The states of clock and strobe can affect the logic level of Y and Z. A low unity/cascade will cause output Y to remain high.

C. Each rate illustrated assumes a constant value at rate inputs; however, these illustrations in no way prohibit variable-rate inputs.

D. Unity/cascade is used to inhibit output Y.

E. $f_{out} = \dfrac{M \cdot f_{in}}{64} = \dfrac{(8+32) f_{in}}{64} = \dfrac{40 f_{in}}{64} = 0.625\, f_{in}$

functional block diagram

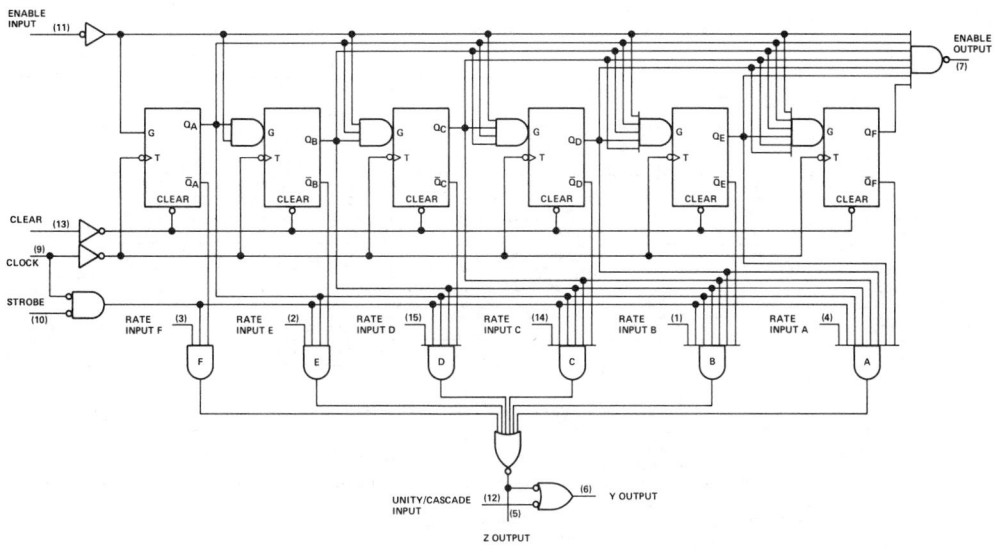

TEXAS INSTRUMENTS
INCORPORATED
POST OFFICE BOX 5012 • DALLAS, TEXAS 75222

TYPES SN5497, SN7497
SYNCHRONOUS 6-BIT BINARY RATE MULTIPLIERS

absolute maximum ratings over operating free-air temperature range (unless otherwise noted)

Supply voltage, V_{CC} (see Note 1)	7 V
Input voltage	5.5 V
Operating free-air temperature range: SN5497 (see Note 2)	-55°C to 125°C
SN7497	0°C to 70°C
Storage temperature range	-65°C to 150°C

recommended operating conditions

	SN5497			SN7494			UNIT
	MIN	NOM	MAX	MIN	NOM	MAX	
Supply voltage, V_{CC}	4.5	5	5.5	4.75	5	5.25	V
High-level output current, I_{OH}			−400			−400	μA
Low-level output current, I_{OL}			16			16	mA
Clock frequency, f_{clock}	0		25	0		25	MHz
Width of clock pulse, $t_{w(clock)}$	20			20			ns
Width of clear pulse, $t_{w(clear)}$	15			15			ns
Enable setup time, t_{su}: (See Figure 1)							ns
Before positive-going transition of clock pulse	25			25			
Before negative-going transition of previous clock pulse	0		$t_{w(clock)}$−10	0		$t_{w(clock)}$−10	
Enable hold time, t_h: (See Figure 1)							ns
After positive-going transition of clock pulse	0		$t_{w(clock)}$−10	0		$t_{w(clock)}$−10	
After negative-going transition of previous clock pulse	20		t_{cp}−10	20		t_{cp}−10	
Operating free-air temperature, T_A (See Note 2)	−55		125	0		70	$^{\circ}$C

electrical characteristics over recommended operating free-air temperature range (unless otherwise noted)

	PARAMETER		TEST CONDITIONS[†]		MIN	TYP[‡]	MAX	UNIT
V_{IH}	High-level input voltage				2			V
V_{IL}	Low-level input voltage						0.8	V
V_{IK}	Input clamp voltage		V_{CC} = MIN,	I_I = −12 mA			−1.5	V
V_{OH}	High-level output voltage		V_{CC} = MIN, V_{IH} = 2 V, V_{IL} = 0.8 V, I_{OH} = −400 μA		2.4	3.4		V
V_{OL}	Low-level output voltage		V_{CC} = MIN, V_{IH} = 2 V, V_{IL} = 0.8 V, I_{OL} = 16 mA			0.2	0.4	V
I_I	Input current at maximum input voltage		V_{CC} = MAX, V_I = 5.5 V				1	mA
I_{IH}	High-level input current	clock input	V_{CC} = MAX, V_I = 2.4 V				80	μA
		other inputs					40	
I_{IL}	Low-level input current	clock input	V_{CC} = MAX, V_I = 0.4 V				−3.2	mA
		other inputs					−1.6	
I_{OS}	Short circuit output current[§]		V_{CC} = MAX			−18	−55	mA
I_{CCH}	Supply current, outputs high		V_{CC} = MAX, See Note 3			58		mA
I_{CCL}	Supply current, outputs low		V_{CC} = MAX, See Note 4			80	120	mA

[†]For test conditions shown as MIN or MAX, use the appropriate value specified under recommended operating conditions.
[‡]All typical values are at V_{CC} = 5 V, T_A = 25°C.
[§]Not more than one output should be shorted at a time.
NOTES: 1. Voltage values are with respet to network ground terminal.
       2. An SN5497 in the W package operating at free-air temperatures above 118°C requires a heat sink that provides a thermal resistance from case to free-air, $R_{\theta CA}$, of not more than 55°C/W.
       3. I_{CCH} is measured with outputs open and all inputs grounded.
       4. I_{CCL} is measured with outputs open and all inputs at 4.5 V.

TEXAS INSTRUMENTS
INCORPORATED
POST OFFICE BOX 5012 • DALLAS, TEXAS 75222

switching characteristics, V_{CC} = 5 V, T_A = 25°C, N = 10

PARAMETERS¶	FROM INPUT	TO OUTPUT	TEST CONDITIONS	MIN	TYP	MAX	UNIT
f_{max}				25	32		MHz
t_{PLH}	Enable	Enable			13	20	ns
t_{PHL}					14	21	
t_{PLH}	Strobe	Z			12	18	ns
t_{PHL}					15	23	
t_{PLH}	Clock	Y			26	39	ns
t_{PHL}					20	30	
t_{PLH}	Clock	Z			12	18	ns
t_{PHL}			C_L = 15 pF,		17	26	
t_{PLH}	Rate	Z	R_L = 400 Ω,		6	10	ns
t_{PHL}			See Figure 1		9	14	
t_{PLH}	Unity/Cascade	Y			9	14	ns
t_{PHL}					6	10	
t_{PLH}	Strobe	Y			19	30	ns
t_{PHL}					22	33	
t_{PLH}	Clock	Enable			19	30	ns
t_{PHL}					22	33	
t_{PLH}	Clear	Y			24	36	ns
t_{PHL}		Z			15	23	
t_{PLH}	Any Rate Input	Y			15	23	ns
t_{PHL}					15	23	

¶f_{max} ≡ maximum clock frequency.

t_{PLH} ≡ propagation delay time, low-to-high-level output.

t_{PHL} ≡ propagation delay time, high-to-low-level output.

TYPICAL APPLICATION DATA

This application demonstrates how the '97 can be cascaded to perform 18-bit rate multiplication. This scheme is expandable to n-bits by extending the pattern illustrated.

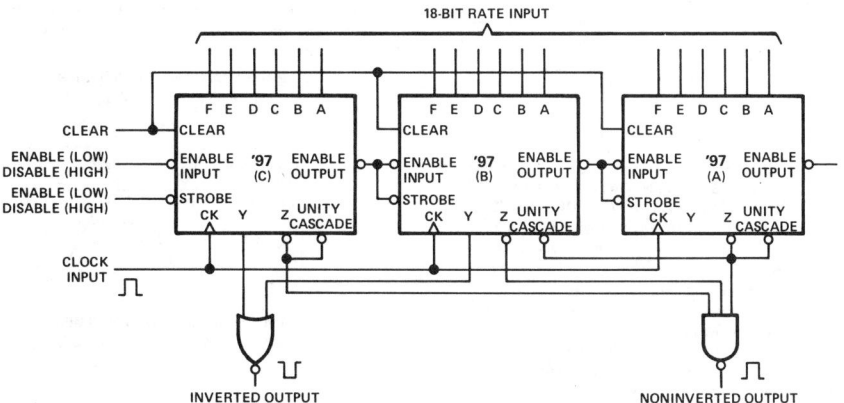

As illustrated, two of the 6-bit multipliers can be cascaded by connecting the Z output of unit A to the unity cascade input of unit B, in which case, a two-input NOR gate is used to cascade the remaining multipliers. Alternatively, all three Y outputs can be cascaded with a 3-input NOR gate. The three unused unity cascade inputs can be conveniently terminated by connecting each to its Z output.

PARAMETER MEASUREMENT INFORMATION

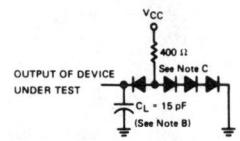

All three outputs are loaded during testing
LOAD CIRCUIT

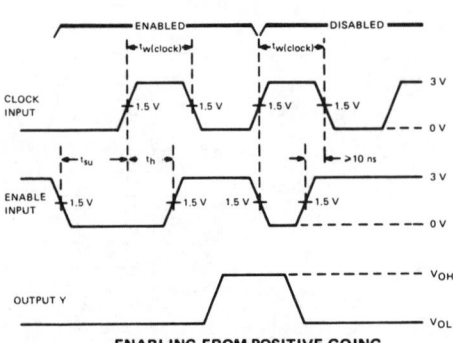

**ENABLING FROM POSITIVE-GOING
TRANSITION OF CLOCK PULSE**

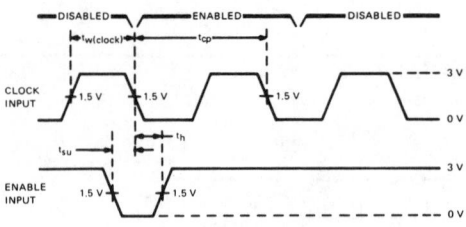

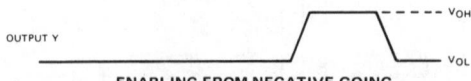

**ENABLING FROM NEGATIVE-GOING
TRANSITION OF PREVIOUS CLOCK PULSE**

1. Unity/Cascade and pin 2 (rate input) are high, other inputs are low. Clear the counter and apply clock and enable pulse as illustrated.
2. Setup and hold times are illustrated for enabling a single clock pulse (count). Continued application of the enable function will enable subsequent clock pulse (counts) until disabling occurs (enable goes high). The total number of counts will be determined by the total number of positive-going clock transition enabled.

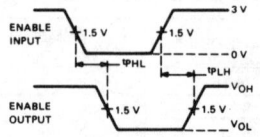

Flip-flops are at the maximum count. Other inputs are low.

**PROPAGATION DELAY TIMES,
ENABLE INPUT TO ENABLE OUTPUT**

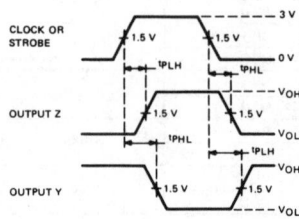

Unity/cascade and rate inputs are high, other inputs are low, and flip-flops are at any count other than maximum.

**PROPAGATION DELAY TIMES, CLOCK TO Z AND Y,
AND STROBE INPUT TO Z AND Y**

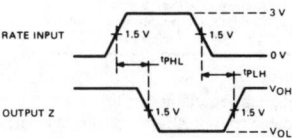

Flip-flops are at a count so that all other inputs to the gate under test are high and all other inputs, including other rate inputs, are low.

**PROPAGATION DELAY TIMES,
RATE INPUT TO Z**

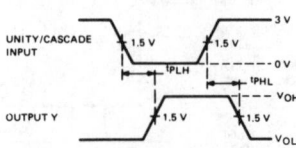

Output Z is high.

**PROPAGATION DELAY TIMES,
UNITY/CASCADE INPUT TO Y**

NOTES: A. The input pulse generator has the following characteristics: $t_{w(clock)}$ = 20 ns, $t_{TLH} \leqslant$ 10 ns, $t_{THL} \leqslant$ 10 ns, PRR = 1 MHz, $Z_{out} \approx$ 50 Ω.
      B. C_L includes probe and jig capacitance.
      C. All diodes are 1N3064.

FIGURE 1—SWITCHING TIMES

TEXAS INSTRUMENTS
INCORPORATED
POST OFFICE BOX 5012 • DALLAS, TEXAS 75222

description

These monolithic data selectors/storage registers are composed of four S-R master-slave flip-flops, four AND-OR-INVERT gates, one buffer, and six inverter/drivers.

When the word select input is low, word 1 (A1, B1, C1, D1) is applied to the flip-flops. A high input to word select will cause the selection of word 2 (A2, B2, C2, D2). The selected word is shifted to the output terminals on the negative-going edge of the clock pulse.

Typical power dissipation is 25 mW. The SN54L98 is characterized for operation over the full military temperature range of −55°C to 125°C; the SN74L98 is characterized for operation from 0°C to 70°C.

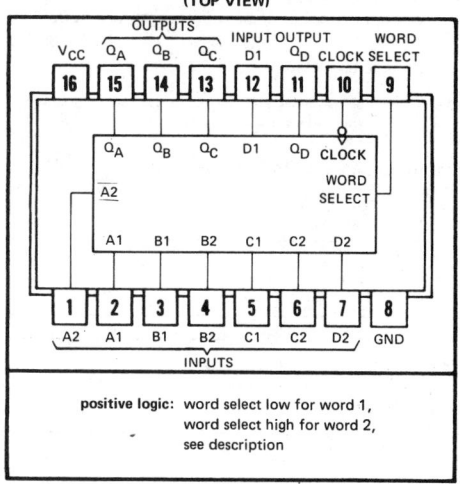

SN54L98 . . . J PACKAGE
SN74L98 . . . J OR N PACKAGE
(TOP VIEW)

positive logic: word select low for word 1,
word select high for word 2,
see description

functional block diagram and schematics of inputs and outputs

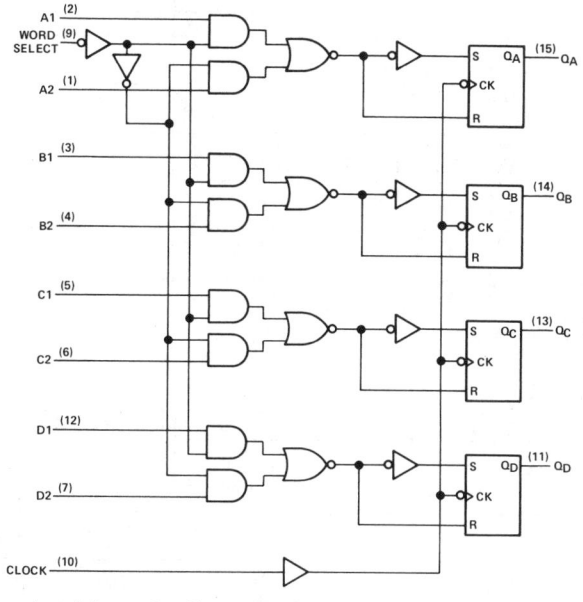

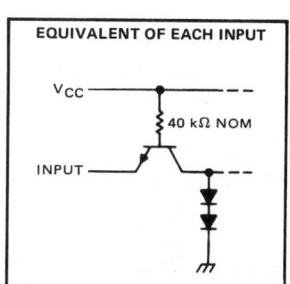

EQUIVALENT OF EACH INPUT

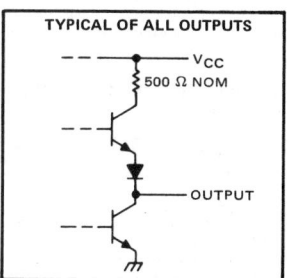

TYPICAL OF ALL OUTPUTS

⊸◁ . . . dynamic input activated by transition from a high level to a low level.

absolute maximum ratings over operating free-air temperature range (unless otherwise noted)

Supply voltage, V_{CC} (see Note 1)	8 V
Input voltage (see Note 2)	5.5 V
Operating free-air temperature range: SN54L98	-55°C to 125°C
SN74L98	0°C to 70°C
Storage temperature range	-65°C to 150°C

NOTES: 1. Voltage values are with respect to network ground terminal.
2. Input voltages must be zero or positive with respect to network ground terminal.

recommended operating conditions

		SN54L98			SN74L98			UNIT
		MIN	NOM	MAX	MIN	NOM	MAX	
Supply voltage, V_{CC}		4.5	5	5.5	4.75	5	5.25	V
High-level output current, I_{OH}				−100			−200	μA
Low-level output current, I_{OL}				2			3.6	mA
Width of clock pulse, $t_{w(clock)}$		200			200			ns
Setup time for high-level data, $t_{su(H)}$	at A, B, C, or D	100			100			ns
	at word select	150			150			
Setup time for low-level data, $t_{su(L)}$	at A, B, C, or D	120			120			ns
	at word select	100			100			
Operating free-air temperature, T_A		−55		125	0		70	°C

electrical characteristics over recommended operating free-air temperature range (unless otherwise noted)

PARAMETER		TEST CONDITIONS†		SN54L98			SN74L98			UNIT
				MIN	TYP‡	MAX	MIN	TYP‡	MAX	
V_{IH}	High-level input voltage			2			2			V
V_{IL}	Low-level input voltage					0.7			0.7	V
V_{OH}	High-level output voltage	V_{CC} = MIN, V_{IH} = 2 V, V_{IL} = 0.7 V, I_{OH} = MAX		2.4	3.3		2.4	3.2		V
V_{OL}	Low-level output voltage	V_{CC} = MIN, V_{IH} = 2 V V_{IL} = 0.7 V, I_{OL} = MAX			0.15	0.3		0.2	0.4	V
I_I	Input current at maximum input voltage	V_{CC} = MAX, V_I = 5.5 V				100			100	μA
I_{IH}	High-level input current	V_{CC} = MAX, V_I = 2.4 V				10			10	μA
I_{IL}	Low-level input current	V_{CC} = MAX, V_I = 0.3 V				−0.18			−0.18	mA
I_{OS}	Short-circuit output current§	V_{CC} = MAX		−3		−15	−3		−15	mA
I_{CC}	Supply current	V_{CC} = MAX, See Note 3			5	9		5	9	mA

†For conditions shown as MIN or MAX, use the appropriate value specified under recommended operating conditions.
‡All typical values are at V_{CC} = 5 V, T_A = 25°C.
§Not more than one output should be shorted at a time.
NOTE 3: I_{CC} is measured with all inputs grounded and all outputs open.

switching characteristics, V_{CC} = 5 V, T_A = 25°C

PARAMETER		TEST CONDITIONS	MIN	TYP	MAX	UNIT
f_{max}	Maximum clock frequency	C_L = 50 pF, R_L = 4 kΩ, See Note 4	3	5		MHz
t_{PLH}	Propagation delay time, low-to-high-level output from clock input			115	200	ns
t_{PHL}	Propagation delay time, high-to-low-level output from clock input			125	200	ns

NOTE 4: Load circuit and voltage waveforms are shown on page 3-11.

PRINTED IN U.S.A.   1076

TEXAS INSTRUMENTS
INCORPORATED
POST OFFICE BOX 5012 • DALLAS, TEXAS 75222

TEXAS INSTRUMENTS RESERVES THE RIGHT TO MAKE CHANGES AT ANY TIME
IN ORDER TO IMPROVE DESIGN AND TO SUPPLY THE BEST PRODUCT POSSIBLE.

- N-Bit Serial-to-Parallel Converter
- N-Bit Parallel-to-Serial Converter
- N-Bit Storage Register
- J-$\bar{\text{K}}$ Serial Input

description

These 4-bit registers feature parallel inputs, parallel outputs, J-$\bar{\text{K}}$ serial inputs, mode control, and two clock inputs. The registers have three modes of operation:

Parallel (Broadside) load
Shift right (the direction Q_A toward Q_D)
Shift left (the direction Q_D toward Q_A)

Parallel loading is accomplished by applying the four bits of data and taking the mode control input high. The data is loaded into the associated flip-flop and appears at the outputs after the high-to-low transition of the clock-2 input. During loading, the entry of serial data is inhibited.

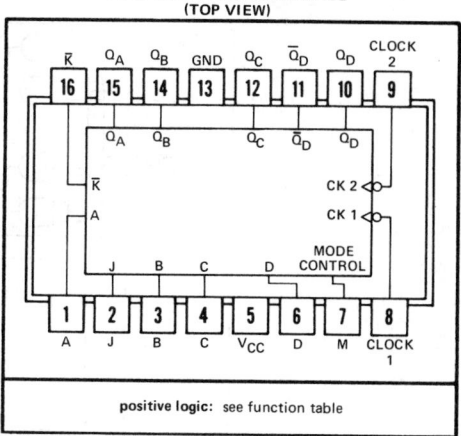

SN54L99 . . . J PACKAGE
SN74L99 . . . J OR N PACKAGE
(TOP VIEW)

positive logic: see function table

Shift right is accomplished on a high-to-low transition of clock 1 when the mode control is low. Serial data for the right-shift mode is entered at the J-$\bar{\text{K}}$ inputs. These inputs permit the first stage to perform as a J-$\bar{\text{K}}$, a D-type, or T-type flip-flop as shown in the function table. Shift left is accomplished on the high-to-low transition of clock 2 when the mode control is high by connecting the output of each flip-flop to the parallel input of the previous flip-flop (Q_D to input C, etc.). Serial data for this mode is entered at the D input. The clock input may be applied commonly to clock 1 and clock 2 if both modes can be clocked from the same source. Changes at the mode control input should normally be made while both clock inputs are low; however, conditions described in the last three lines of the function table will also ensure that register contents are protected.

FUNCTION TABLE

INPUTS								OUTPUTS				
MODE	CLOCKS		SERIAL		PARALLEL							
CONTROL	2 (L)	1 (R)	J	$\bar{\text{K}}$	A	B	C	D	Q_A	Q_B	Q_C	Q_D	$\bar{Q}_D$
H	H	X	X	X	X	X	X	X	Q_{A0}	Q_{B0}	Q_{C0}	Q_{D0}	$\bar{Q}_{D0}$
H	↓	X	X	X	a	b	c	d	a	b	c	d	$\bar{d}$
H	↓	X	X	X	Q_B†	Q_C†	Q_D†	d	Q_{Bn}	Q_{Cn}	Q_{Dn}	d	$\bar{d}$
L	L	H	X	X	X	X	X	X	Q_{A0}	Q_{B0}	Q_{C0}	Q_{D0}	$\bar{Q}_{D0}$
L	X	↓	L	H	X	X	X	X	Q_{A0}	Q_{A0}	Q_{Bn}	Q_{Cn}	$\bar{Q}_{Cn}$
L	X	↓	L	L	X	X	X	X	L	Q_{An}	Q_{Bn}	Q_{Cn}	$\bar{Q}_{Cn}$
L	X	↓	H	H	X	X	X	X	H	Q_{An}	Q_{Bn}	Q_{Cn}	$\bar{Q}_{Cn}$
L	X	↓	H	L	X	X	X	X	$\bar{Q}_{An}$	Q_{An}	Q_{Bn}	Q_{Cn}	$\bar{Q}_{Cn}$
↑	L	L	X	X	X	X	X	X	Q_{A0}	Q_{B0}	Q_{C0}	Q_{D0}	$\bar{Q}_{D0}$
↓	L	L	X	X	X	X	X	X	Q_{A0}	Q_{B0}	Q_{C0}	Q_{D0}	$\bar{Q}_{D0}$
↓	L	H	X	X	X	X	X	X	Q_{A0}	Q_{B0}	Q_{C0}	Q_{D0}	$\bar{Q}_{D0}$
↑	H	L	X	X	X	X	X	X	Q_{A0}	Q_{B0}	Q_{C0}	Q_{D0}	$\bar{Q}_{D0}$
↑	H	H	X	X	X	X	X	X	Q_{A0}	Q_{B0}	Q_{C0}	Q_{D0}	$\bar{Q}_{D0}$

†Shifting left requires external connection of Q_B to A, Q_C to B, and Q_D to C. Serial data is entered at input D.

H = high level (steady state), L = low level (steady state)
X = irrelevant (any input, including transitions)
↓ = transition from high to low level, ↑ = transition from low to high level.
a, b, c, d = the level of steady-state input at inputs A, B, C, or D, respectively.
Q_{A0}, Q_{B0}, Q_{C0}, Q_{D0} = the level of Q_A, Q_B, Q_C, or Q_D, respectively, before the indicated steady-state input conditions were established.
Q_{An}, Q_{Bn}, Q_{Cn}, Q_{Dn} = the level of Q_A, Q_B, Q_C, or Q_D, respectively, before the most-recent ↓ transition of the clock.

7

TEXAS INSTRUMENTS
INCORPORATED
POST OFFICE BOX 5012 • DALLAS, TEXAS 75222

TYPES SN54L99, SN74L99
4-BIT RIGHT-SHIFT LEFT-SHIFT REGISTERS

functional block diagram

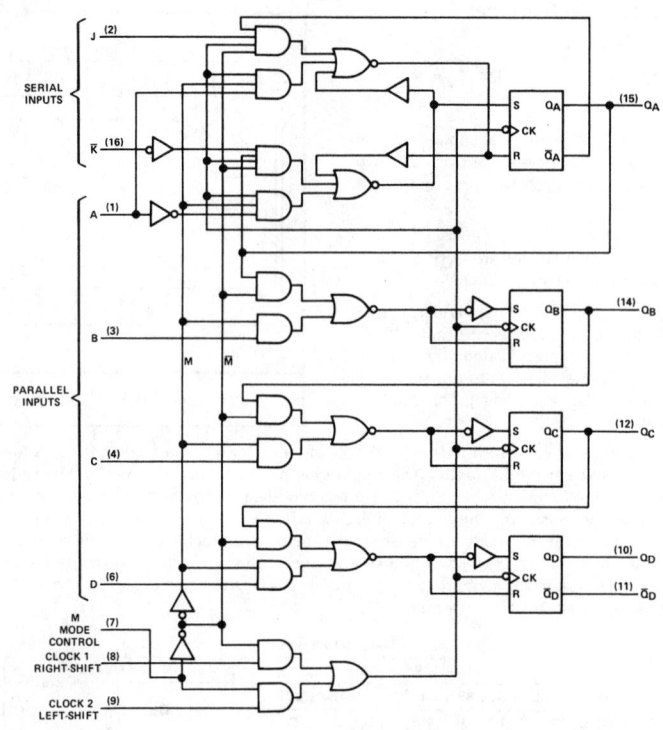

⎓ . . . dynamic input activated by transition from a high level to a low level.

schematics of inputs and outputs

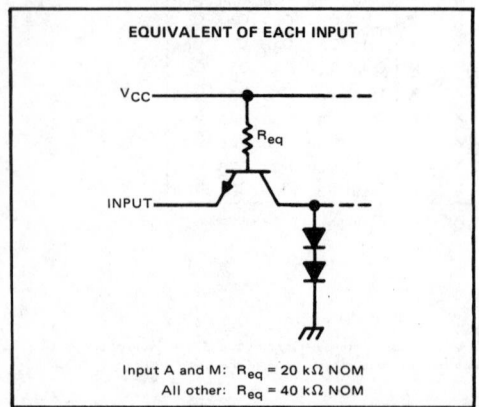

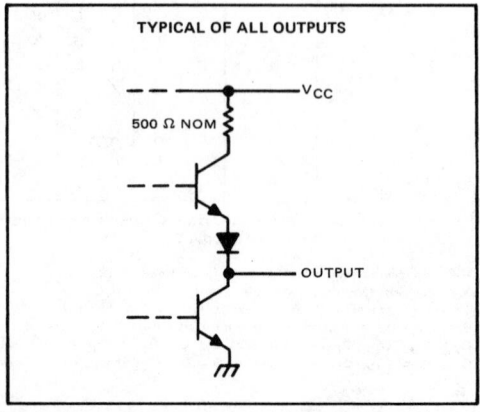

TEXAS INSTRUMENTS
INCORPORATED
POST OFFICE BOX 5012 • DALLAS, TEXAS 75222

absolute maximum ratings over operating free-air temperature range (unless otherwise noted)

Supply voltage, V_{CC} (see Note 1) . . . . 8 V
Input voltage (see Note 2) . . . . 5.5 V
Operating free-air temperature range: SN54L99 Circuits . . . . −55°C to 125°C
                               SN74L99 Circuits . . . . 0°C to 70°C
Storage temperature range . . . . −65°C to 150°C

NOTES: 1. Voltage values are with respect to network ground terminal.
           2. Input voltages must be zero or positive with respect to network ground terminal.

recommended operating conditions

	SN54L99			SN74L99			UNIT
	MIN	NOM	MAX	MIN	NOM	MAX	
Supply voltage, V_{CC}	4.5	5	5.5	4.75	5	5.25	V
High-level output current, I_{OH}			−100			−200	μA
Low-level output current, I_{OL}			2			3.6	mA
Width of clock pulse, $t_{w(clock)}$	200			200			ns
Setup time for high-level data at J, $\overline{K}$, A, B, C, or D inputs, $t_{su(H)}$	100			100			ns
Setup time for low-level data at J, $\overline{K}$, A, B, C, or D inputs, $t_{su(L)}$	120			120			ns
Hold time at J, $\overline{K}$, A, B, C, or D inputs, t_h	0			0			ns
Time to enable clock 1, $t_{enable\ 1}$ (see Figure 1)	225			225			ns
Time to enable clock 2, $t_{enable\ 2}$ (see Figure 1)	200			200			ns
Time to inhibit clock 1, $t_{inhibit\ 1}$ (see Figure 1)	100			100			ns
Time to inhibit clock 2, $t_{inhibit\ 2}$ (see Figure 1)	0			0			ns
Operating free-air temperature, T_A	−55		125	0		70	°C

electrical characteristics over recommended operating free-air temperature range (unless otherwise noted)

PARAMETER			TEST CONDITIONS[†]		SN54L99			SN74L99			UNIT
					MIN	TYP[‡]	MAX	MIN	TYP[‡]	MAX	
V_{IH}	High-level input voltage				2			2			V
V_{IL}	Low-level input voltage						0.7			0.7	V
V_{OH}	High-level output voltage		V_{CC} = MIN,	V_{IH} = 2 V,	2.4	3.3		2.4	3.2		V
			V_{IL} = 0.7 V,	I_{OH} = MAX							
V_{OL}	Low-level output voltage		V_{CC} = MIN,	V_{IH} = 2 V		0.15	0.3		0.2	0.4	V
			V_{IL} = 0.7 V,	I_{OL} = MAX							
I_I	Input current at	J, $\overline{K}$, B, C, or D	V_{CC} = MAX,	V_I = 5.5 V			100			100	μA
	maximum input voltage	M or A					200			200	
I_{IH}	High-level	J, $\overline{K}$, B, C, or D	V_{CC} = MAX,	V_I = 2.4 V			10			10	μA
	input current	M or A					20			20	
I_{IL}	Low-level	J, $\overline{K}$, B, C, or D	V_{CC} = MAX,	V_I = 0.3 V			−0.18			−0.18	mA
	input current	M or A					−0.36			−0.36	
I_{OS}	Short-circuit output current§		V_{CC} = MAX		−3		−15	−3		−15	mA
I_{CC}	Supply current		V_{CC} = MAX,	See Note 3		3.8	9		3.8	9	mA

[†]For conditions shown as MIN or MAX, use the appropriate value specified under recommended operating conditions for the applicable type.
[‡]All typical values are at V_{CC} = 5 V, T_A = 25°C.
§Not more than one output should be shorted at a time.
NOTE 3: With all outputs and J and $\overline{K}$ inputs open, mode control at 4.5 V, inputs A through D grounded, I_{CC} is measured after a momentary 3 V, then ground, is applied to both clock inputs.

switching characteristics, V_{CC} = 5 V, T_A = 25°C

PARAMETER		TEST CONDITIONS	MIN	TYP	MAX	UNIT
f_{max}	Maximum clock frequency	C_L = 50 pF, R_L = 4 kΩ, See Figure 2	3	5		MHz
t_{PLH}	Propagation delay time, low-to-high-level output from either clock			115	200	ns
t_{PHL}	Propagation delay time, high-to-low-level output from either clock			125	200	ns

7

TEXAS INSTRUMENTS
INCORPORATED
POST OFFICE BOX 5012 • DALLAS, TEXAS 75222

TYPES SN54L99, SN74L99
4-BIT RIGHT-SHIFT LEFT-SHIFT REGISTERS

PARAMETER MEASUREMENT INFORMATION

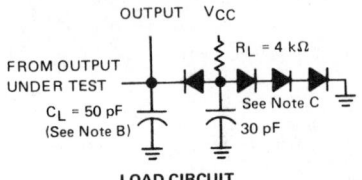

LOAD CIRCUIT

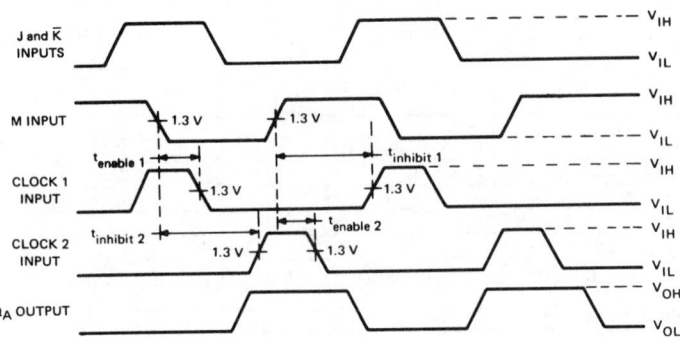

NOTE: A input is at the low level.

VOLTAGE WAVEFORMS
FIGURE 1—CLOCK ENABLE/INHIBIT TIMES

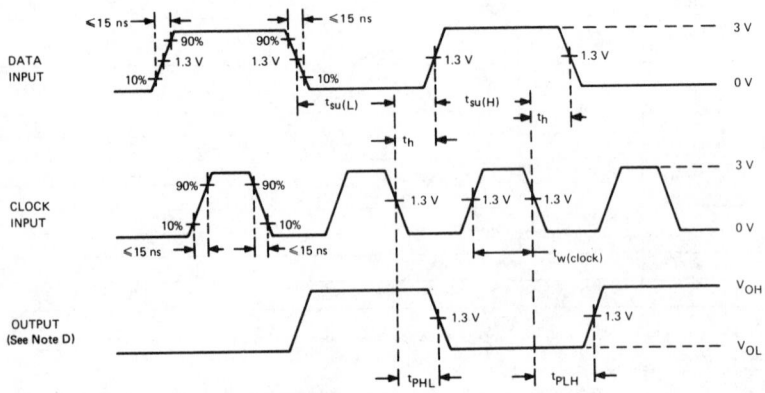

VOLTAGE WAVEFORMS
FIGURE 2—SWITCHING TIMES

NOTES: A. The input waveforms are supplied by pulse generators having the following characteristics: $Z_{out} \approx 50\ \Omega$. For data pulse generator: $t_w \geqslant 150$ ns, PRR $\leqslant 500$ kHz, $t_{setup(L)} = 120$ ns, and $t_{setup(H)} = 100$ ns. For clock pulse generator: $t_w \geqslant 200$ ns and PRR $\leqslant 1$ MHz. When testing f_{max}, vary PRR.
       B. C_L includes probe and jig capacitance.
       C. All diodes are 1N916.
       D. When data input is applied to J and $\overline{K}$ inputs, the output waveform applies only to output Q_A.

TEXAS INSTRUMENTS
INCORPORATED
POST OFFICE BOX 5012 • DALLAS, TEXAS 75222

logic

FUNCTION TABLE
(Each Latch)

INPUTS		OUTPUTS	
D	G	Q	$\bar{Q}$
L	H	L	H
H	H	H	L
X	L	Q_0	$\bar{Q}_0$

H = high level, X = irrelevant
Q_0 = the level of Q before the
high-to-low transition of G

SN54100 . . . J OR W PACKAGE
SN54100 . . . J OR N PACKAGE
(TOP VIEW)

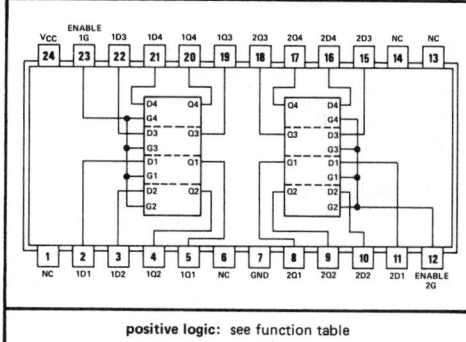

positive logic: see function table

NC—No internal connection

description

These latches are ideally suited for use as temporary storage for binary information between processing units and input/output or indicator units. Information present at a data (D) input is transferred to the Q output when the enable (G) is high and the Q output will follow the data input as long as the enable remains high. When the enable goes low, the information (that was setup at the data input at the time the transition occurred) is retained at the Q output until the enable is permitted to go high.

These circuits are completely compatible with all popular TTL or DTL families. All inputs are diode-clamped to minimize transmission-line effects and simplify system design. Typical power dissipation is 40 milliwatts per latch. The SN54100 is characterized for operation over the full military temperature range of −55° to 125°C; the SN74100 is characterized for operation from 0°C to 70°C.

functional block diagram (each latch)

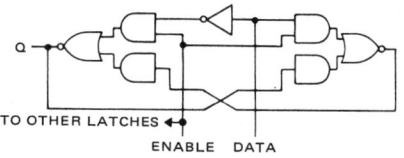

schematic (each latch)

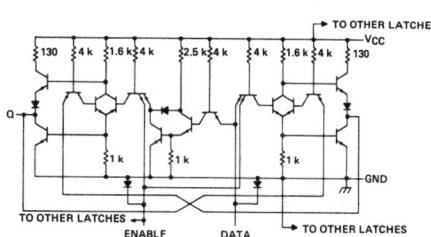

Resistor values shown are nominal and in ohms.

absolute maximum ratings over operating free-air temperature range (unless otherwise noted)

Supply voltage, V_{CC} (see Note 1) . . . . 7 V
Input voltage . . . . 5.5 V
Intermitter voltage (see Note 2) . . . . 5.5 V
Operating free-air temperature range: SN54100 . . . . −55°C to 125°C
SN74100 . . . . 0°C to 70°C
Storage temperature range . . . . −65°C to 150°C

NOTES: 1. Voltage values, except interemitter voltage, are with respect to network ground terminal.
2. This is the voltage between two emitters of a multiple-emitter input transistor. For this circuit, this rating applies between the enable and D inputs of any latch.

7

TYPES SN54100, SN74100
8-BIT BISTABLE LATCHES

REVISED OCTOBER 1976

recommended operating conditions

	SN54100			SN74100			UNIT
	MIN	NOM	MAX	MIN	NOM	MAX	
Supply voltage, V_{CC}	4.5	5	5.5	4.75	5	5.25	V
High-level output current, I_{OH}			−400			−400	μA
Low-level output current, I_{OL}			16			16	mA
Width of enabling pulse, t_w	20			20			ns
Setup time, t_{su}	20			20			ns
Hold time, t_h	5			5			ns
Operating free-air temperature, T_A	−55		125	0		70	°C

electrical characteristics over recommended operating free-air temperature range (unless otherwise noted)

PARAMETER		TEST CONDITIONS[†]		MIN	TYP[‡]	MAX	UNIT
V_{IH}	High-level input voltage			2			V
V_{IL}	Low-level input voltage					0.8	V
V_{IK}	Input clamp voltage	V_{CC} = MIN,	I_I = −12 mA			−1.5	V
V_{OH}	High-level output voltage	V_{CC} = MIN, V_{IH} = 2 V, V_{IL} = 0.8 V,	I_{OH} = −400 μA	2.4	3.4		V
V_{OL}	Low-level output voltage	V_{CC} = MIN, V_{IH} = 2 V, V_{IL} = 0.8 V,	I_{OL} = 16 mA		0.2	0.4	V
I_I	Input current at maximum input voltage	V_{CC} = MAX,	V_I = 5.5 V			1	mA
I_{IH}	High-level input current	D input	V_{CC} = MAX, V_I = 2.4 V			80	μA
		G input				320	
I_{IL}	Low-level input current	D input	V_{CC} = MAX, V_I = 0.4 V			−3.2	mA
		G input				−12.8	
I_{OS}	Short-circuit output current[§]	V_{CC} = MAX	SN54100	−20		−57	mA
			SN74100	−18		−57	
I_{CC}	Supply current	V_{CC} = MAX, See Note 3	SN54100		64	92	mA
			SN74100		64	106	

[†]For conditions shown as MIN or MAX, use the appropriate value specified under recommended operating conditions.
[‡]All typical values are at V_{CC} = 5 V, T_A = 25°C.
[§]Not more than one output should be shorted at a time.
NOTE 3: I_{CC} is tested with all inputs grounded and all outputs open.

switching characteristics, V_{CC} = 5 V, T_A = 25°C

PARAMETER[¶]	FROM (INPUT)	TO (OUTPUT)	TEST CONDITIONS	MIN	TYP	MAX	UNIT
t_{PLH}	D	Q	C_L = 15 pF, R_L = 400 Ω, See Note 4		16	30	ns
t_{PHL}					14	25	
t_{PLH}	G	Q			16	30	ns
t_{PHL}					7	15	

[¶]t_{PLH} ≡ propagation delay time, low-to-high-level output
t_{PHL} ≡ propagation delay time, high-to-low-level output
NOTE 4: Test circuit and voltage waveforms are the same as those shown for the '75, '77, 'L75, and 'L77 on page 7-40.

7

TEXAS INSTRUMENTS
INCORPORATED
POST OFFICE BOX 5012 • DALLAS, TEXAS 75222

1076

TYPES SN54116, SN74116
DUAL 4-BIT LATCHES WITH CLEAR

BULLETIN NO. DL-S 7211849, DECEMBER 1972

- Two Independent 4-Bit Latches in a Single Package
- Separate Clear Inputs Provide One-Step Clearing Operation
- Dual Gated Enable Inputs Simplify Cascading and Register Implementations
- Compatible for Use with TTL and DTL Circuits
- Input Clamping Diodes Simplify System Design

SN54116...J OR W PACKAGE
SN74116...J OR N PACKAGE
(TOP VIEW)

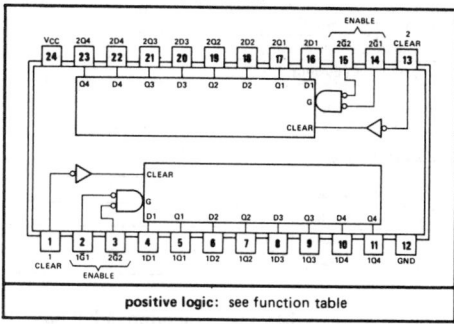

positive logic: see function table

description

These monolithic TTL circuits utilize D-type bistables to implement two independent four-bit latches in a single package. Each four-bit latch has an independent asynchronous clear input and a gated two-input enable circuit. When both enable inputs are low, the output levels will follow the data input levels. When either or both of the enable inputs are taken high, the outputs remain at the last levels setup at the inputs prior to the low-to-high-level transition at the enable input(s). After this, the data inputs are locked out.

The clear input is overriding and when taken low will reset all four outputs low regardless of the levels of the enable inputs.

The SN54116 is characterized for operation over the full military temperature range of −55°C to 125°C; the SN74116 is characterized for operation from 0°C to 70°C.

functional block diagram (each 4-bit latch)

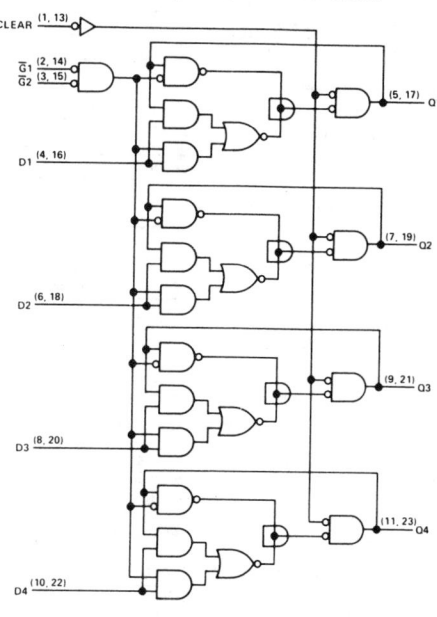

FUNCTION TABLE
(EACH LATCH)

INPUTS				OUTPUT
CLEAR	ENABLE		DATA	Q
	$\overline{G1}$	$\overline{G2}$		
H	L	L	L	L
H	L	L	H	H
H	X	H	X	Q_0
H	H	X	X	Q_0
L	X	X	X	L

H = high level, L = low level, X = irrelevant
Q_0 = the level of Q before these input conditions were established.

absolute maximum ratings over operating free-air temperature range (unless otherwise noted)

Supply voltage, V_{CC} (see Note 1) . . . . 7 V
Input voltage . . . . 5.5 V
Operating free-air temperature range: SN54116 Circuits . . . . −55°C to 125°C
SN74116 Circuits . . . . 0°C to 70°C
Storage temperature range . . . . −65°C to 150°C

NOTE 1: Voltage values are with respect to network ground terminal.

TEXAS INSTRUMENTS
INCORPORATED
POST OFFICE BOX 5012 • DALLAS, TEXAS 75222

recommended operating conditions

		SN54116 MIN	SN54116 NOM	SN54116 MAX	SN74116 MIN	SN74116 NOM	SN74116 MAX	UNIT
Supply voltage, V_{CC}		4.5	5	5.5	4.75	5	5.25	V
High-level output current, I_{OH}				−800			−800	µA
Low-level output current, I_{OL}				16			16	mA
Input pulse width, t_w	Enable	18			18			ns
	Clear	18			18			
Data setup time, t_{su}	High logic level	8			8			ns
	Low logic level	14			14			
Clear inactive-state setup time, t_{su}		8			8			ns
Data release time, high-level data, $t_{release}$				2			2	ns
Data hold time, low-level data, t_h		8			8			
Operating free-air temperature, T_A		−55		125	0		70	°C

electrical characteristics over recommended operating free-air temperature range (unless otherwise noted)

PARAMETER		TEST CONDITIONS[†]		MIN	TYP[‡]	MAX	UNIT
V_{IH}	High-level input voltage			2			V
V_{IL}	Low-level input voltage					0.8	V
V_{IK}	Input clamp voltage	V_{CC} = MIN, I_I = −12 mA				−1.5	V
V_{OH}	High-level output voltage	V_{CC} = MIN, V_{IH} = 2 V, V_{IL} = 0.8 V, I_{OH} = −800 µA		2.4	3.4		V
V_{OL}	Low-level output voltage	V_{CC} = MIN, V_{IH} = 2 V, V_{IL} = 0.8 V, I_{OL} = 16 mA			0.2	0.4	V
I_I	Input current at maximum input voltage	V_{CC} = MAX, V_I = 5.5 V				1	mA
I_{IH}	High-level input current	$\overline{G}1, \overline{G}2$, or clear	V_{CC} = MAX, V_I = 2.4 V			40	µA
		Any D				60	
I_{IL}	Low-level input current	$\overline{G}1, \overline{G}2$, or clear	V_{CC} = MAX, V_I = 0.4 V			−1.6	mA
		Any D, initial peak				−2.4	
		Any D, steady-state				−1.6	
I_{OS}	Short-circuit output current[§]	SN54116	V_{CC} = MAX	−20		−57	mA
		SN74116		−18		−57	
I_{CC}	Supply current	Condition A	V_{CC} = MAX, See Note 2		60	100	mA
		Condition B			40	70	

[†]For conditions shown as MIN or MAX, use the appropriate value specified under recommended operating conditions for the applicable device type.

[‡]All typical values are at V_{CC} = 5 V, T_A = 25°C.

[§]Not more than one output should be shorted at a time.

NOTE 2: With outputs open, I_{CC} is measured for the following conditions:
    A. All inputs grounded.
    B. All $\overline{G}$ inputs are grounded and all other inputs are at 4.5 V.

switching characteristics, V_{CC} = 5 V, T_A = 25°C

PARAMETER[¶]	FROM (INPUT)	TO (OUTPUT)	TEST CONDITIONS	MIN	TYP	MAX	UNIT
t_{PLH}	Enable	Any Q	C_L = 15 pF, R_L = 400 Ω, See Figure 1		19	30	ns
t_{PHL}					15	22	
t_{PLH}	Data	Q			10	15	ns
t_{PHL}					12	18	
t_{PHL}	Clear	Any Q			15	22	ns

[¶] t_{PLH} ≡ propagation delay time, low-to-high-level output
   t_{PHL} ≡ propagation delay time, high-to-low-level output

7

10

TEXAS INSTRUMENTS
INCORPORATED
POST OFFICE BOX 5012 • DALLAS, TEXAS 75222

schematics of inputs and outputs

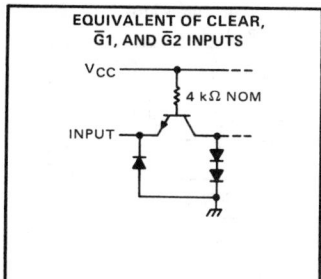

EQUIVALENT OF CLEAR, G̅1, AND G̅2 INPUTS

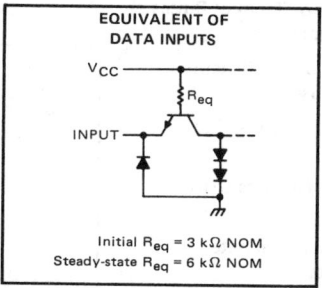

EQUIVALENT OF DATA INPUTS

Initial R_{eq} = 3 kΩ NOM
Steady-state R_{eq} = 6 kΩ NOM

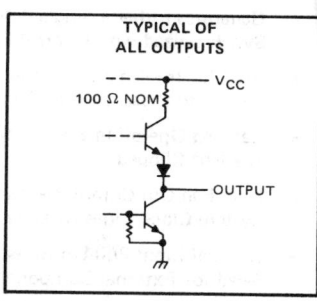

TYPICAL OF ALL OUTPUTS

PARAMETER MEASUREMENT INFORMATION

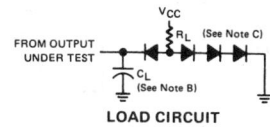

LOAD CIRCUIT

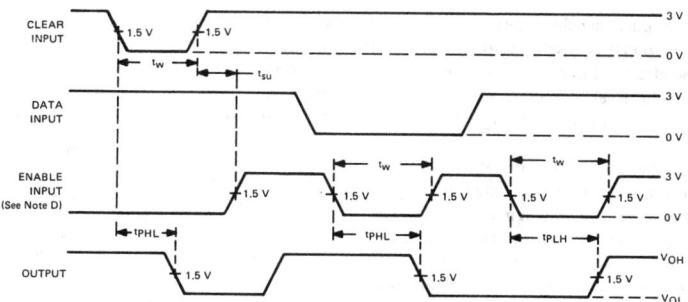

SWITCHING TIMES FROM CLEAR AND ENABLE INPUTS

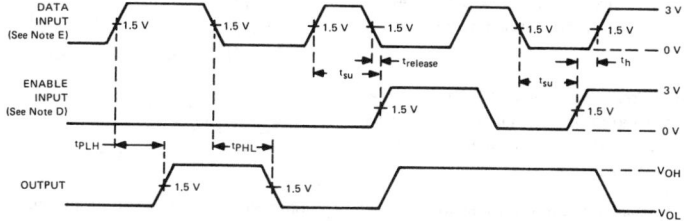

SWITCHING TIMES FROM DATA INPUTS

NOTES: A. Input pulses are supplied by generators having the following characteristics: t_r ≤ 10 ns, t_f ≤ 10 ns, PRR = 1 MHz, duty cycle ≤ 50%, Z_{out} ≈ 50 Ω.
      B. C_L includes probe and jig capacitance.
      C. All diodes are 1N3064.
      D. The other enable input is low.
      E. Clear input is high.

FIGURE 1

7

TEXAS INSTRUMENTS
INCORPORATED
POST OFFICE BOX 5012 • DALLAS, TEXAS 75222

- Generates Either a Single Pulse or Train of Pulses Synchronized with Control Functions

- Ideal for Implementing Sync-Control Circuits Similar to those Used in Oscilloscopes

- Latched Operation Ensures that Output Pulses Are Not Clipped

- High-Fan-Out Complementary Outputs Drive System Clock Lines Directly

- Internal Input Pull-Up Resistors Eliminate Need for External Components

- Diode-Clamped Inputs Simplify System Design

- Typical Propagation Delays:

    9 Nanoseconds through One Level
    16 Nanoseconds through Two Levels

SN54120 . . . J OR W PACKAGE
SN74120 . . . J OR N PACKAGE
(TOP VIEW)

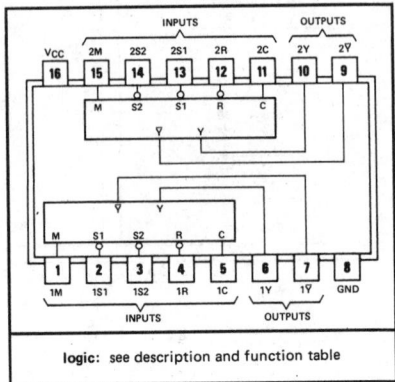

logic: see description and function table

description

These monolithic pulse synchronizers are designed to synchronize an asynchronous or manual signal with a system clock. Reliable response is ensured as the input signals are latched up; therefore duration of logic input is not critical and the adverse effects of contact-bounce of a manual input are eliminated. The ability to pass output pulses is started and stopped by the levels or pulses applied to the latch inputs S1, S2, or R in accordance with the function table. High-speed circuitry is utilized throughout the clock paths to minimize skew with respect to the system clock.

After initiation, the mode control (M) input determines whether a series of pulses or only one pulse is passed. In the absence of a stop command, the clock driver will continue to pass clock pulses as long as the mode control input is low (see Figures 2 through 4). If the mode control input is high only a single clock pulse will be passed (see Figure 5).

When the mode control is set to pass a series of pulses, the last pulse out is determined by two general rules:

a. When pulses are terminated by the S or R inputs, conditions meeting the setup times (specified under recommended operating conditions) will dominate.

b. Low-to-high-level transitions at the mode control input should be avoided during the 20-nanosecond period immediately following the negative transition of the input clock pulse as transitions during this time period may or may not allow the next pulse to pass (see Figures 4 and 5). When pulses are terminated by the mode control input, a positive transition at the mode control input meeting the high-level setup time, t_{su} (H), (specified under recommended operating conditions) will pass that positive clock pulse then inhibit remaining clock pulses. The clock input (C) is latch-controlled ensuring that once initiated the output pulse will not be terminated until the full pulse has been passed.

FUNCTION TABLE

INPUTS			FUNCTION
R	S1	S2	
X	L	X	Pass Output Pulses
X	X	L	Pass Output Pulses
L	H	H	Inhibit Output Pulses
H	↓	H	Start Output Pulses
H	H	↓	Start Output Pulses
↓	H	H	Stop Output Pulses
H	H	H	Continue[†]

H = high level (steady state)
L = low level (steady state)
↓ = transition from H to L
X = irrelevant
[†]Operation initiated by last ↓ transition continues.

TEXAS INSTRUMENTS
INCORPORATED
POST OFFICE BOX 5012 • DALLAS, TEXAS 75222

description (continued)

This clock driver circuit is entirely compatible for use with either digital logic circuits or mechanical switches for input controls since all inputs, except the clock, have internal pull-up resistors. This eliminates the requirement to supply an external resistor to prevent the input from floating when the control switch is open. The internal resistor also means that these inputs may be left disconnected if unused.

Typical propagation delay time is 9 nanoseconds to the $\overline{Y}$ output and 16 nanoseconds to the Y output from the clock input. The outputs will drive 60 Series 54/74 loads at a high logic level and 30 loads at a low logic level. Typical power dissipation is 127 milliwatts per driver. The SN54120 is characterized for operation from $-55°C$ to $125°C$; the SN74120 is characterized for operation from $0°C$ to $70°C$.

functional block diagram (each driver)

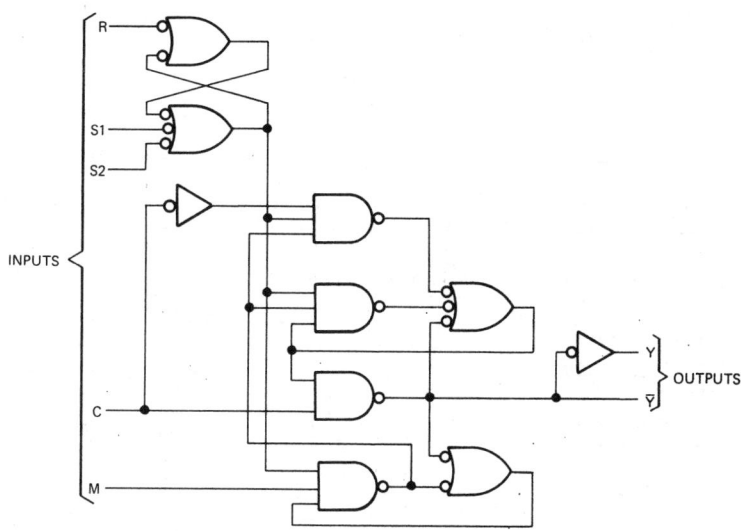

schematics of inputs and outputs

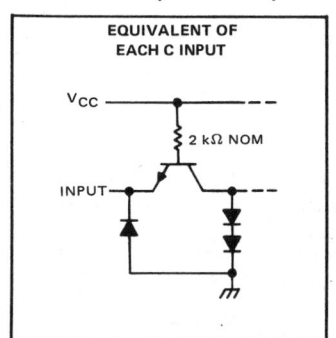

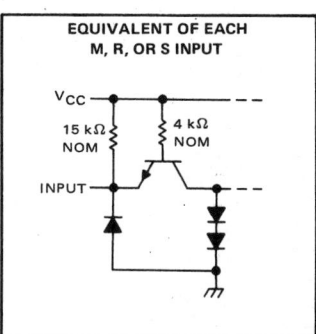

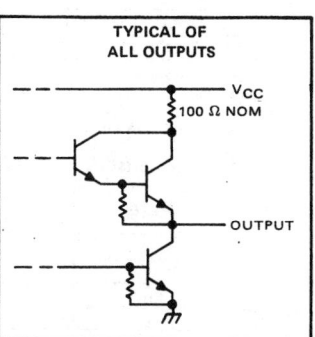

TYPES SN54120, SN74120
DUAL PULSE SYNCHRONIZERS/DRIVERS

absolute maximum ratings over operating free-air temperature range (unless otherwise noted)

Supply voltage, V_{CC} (see Note 1) . . . . 7 V
Input voltage . . . . 5.5 V
Interemitter voltage (see Note 2) . . . . 5.5 V
Operating free-air temperature range: SN54120 Circuits . . . . −55°C to 125°C
                                  SN74120 Circuits . . . . 0°C to 70°C
Storage temperature range . . . . −65°C to 150°C

NOTES: 1. Voltage values, except interemitter voltage, are with respect to network ground terminal.
          2. This is the voltage between two emitters of a multiple-emitter transistor. For this circuit, this rating applies between the S1 and S2 inputs.

recommended operating conditions

			SN54120			SN74120			UNIT
			MIN	NOM	MAX	MIN	NOM	MAX	
Supply voltage, V_{CC}			4.5	5	5.5	4.75	5	5.25	V
High-level output current, I_{OH}					−2.4			−2.4	mA
Low-level output current, I_{OL}					48			48	mA
Setup time (see Figures 2 thru 5)	Any input except mode control, t_{su}(H or L)		12			12			ns
	Mode control	t_{su}(H)	0			0			
		t_{su}(L)	12			12			
Hold time (see Figures 3 and 5)	Any input except mode control, t_h(H or L)		3			3			ns
	Mode control, t_h(H or L)		20			20			
Operating free-air temperature, T_A			−55		125	0		70	°C

electrical characteristics over recommended operating free-air temperature range (unless otherwise noted)

PARAMETER		TEST CONDITIONS[†]	MIN	TYP[‡]	MAX	UNIT
V_{IH}	High-level input voltage		2			V
V_{IL}	Low-level input voltage				0.8	V
V_{IK}	Input clamp voltage	V_{CC} = MIN, I_I = −12 mA			−1.5	V
V_{OH}	High-level output voltage	V_{CC} = MIN, V_{IH} = 2 V, V_{IL} = 0.8 V, I_{OH} = −2.4 mA	2.4	3.4		V
V_{OL}	Low-level output voltage	V_{CC} = MIN, V_{IH} = 2 V, V_{IL} = 0.8 V, I_{OL} = 48 mA		0.2	0.4	V
I_I	Input current at maximum input voltage	V_{CC} = MAX, V_I = 5.5 V			1	mA
I_{IH}	High-level input current	Clock input	V_{CC} = MAX, V_I = 2.4 V			80	μA
		Other inputs		−0.12	−0.2	−0.36	mA
I_{IL}	Low-level input current	Clock input	V_{CC} = MAX, V_I = 0.4 V			−3.2	mA
		Other inputs				−2.1	
I_{OS}	Short-circuit output current[§]	V_{CC} = MAX	−35		−90	mA
I_{CC}	Supply current	V_{CC} = MAX, See Note 3		51	90	mA

[†]For conditions shown as MIN or MAX, use the appropriate value specified under recommended operating conditions.
[‡]All typical values are at V_{CC} = 5 V, T_A = 25°C.
[§]Not more than one output should be shorted at a time.
NOTE 3: I_{CC} is measured with ground applied to all inputs except R which is at 4.5 V and all outputs open.

switching characteristics, V_{CC} = 5 V, T_A = 25°C

PARAMETER[¶]	FROM (INPUT)	TO (OUTPUT)	TEST CONDITIONS	MIN	TYP	MAX	UNIT
t_{PLH}	C	Y	C_L = 45 pF, R_L = 133 Ω, See Figure 1		14	22	ns
t_{PHL}					17	25	
t_{PLH}	C	$\overline{Y}$			10	16	ns
t_{PHL}					8	13	

[¶] t_{PLH} ≡ Propagation delay time, low-to-high-level output
    t_{PHL} ≡ Propagation delay time, high-to-low-level output

7

TEXAS INSTRUMENTS
INCORPORATED
POST OFFICE BOX 5012 • DALLAS, TEXAS 75222

PARAMETER MEASUREMENT INFORMATION

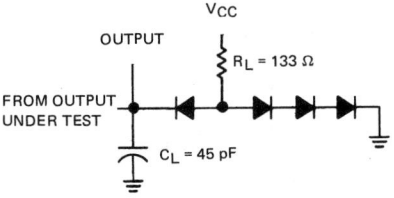

NOTES: A. The clock input pulse in figures 2 through 5 is supplied by a generator having the following characteristics: $t_{w(clock)} \geqslant 15$ ns, PRR $\leqslant 1$ MHz, and $Z_{out} \approx 50 \, \Omega$.
B. C_L includes probe and jig capacitance.
C. All diodes are 1N3064.

FIGURE 1—LOAD CIRCUIT FOR SWITCHING TESTS

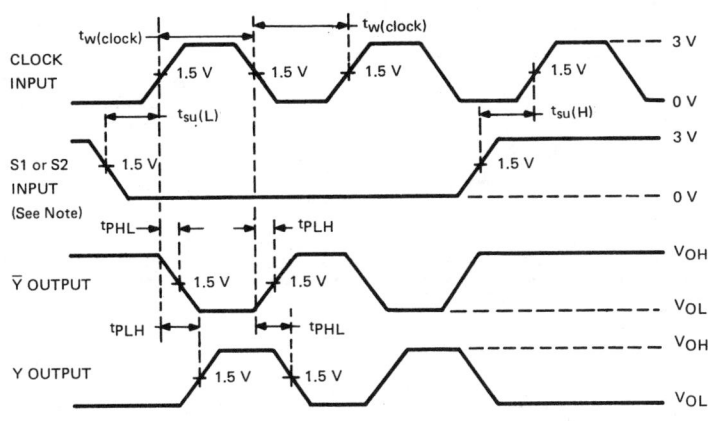

NOTE: Mode control and R inputs are low unused S input is high.

FIGURE 2—INITIATING AND TERMINATING PULSE TRAIN FROM S INPUTS

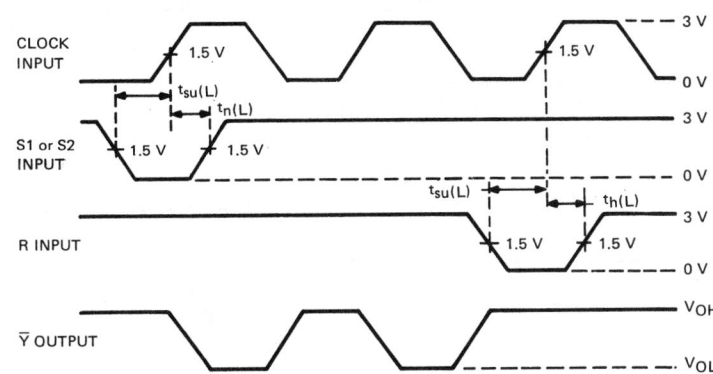

NOTE: Mode control input is low and unused S input is high.

FIGURE 3—INITIATING PULSE TRAIN FROM S AND TERMINATING WITH R INPUTS

TYPES SN54120, SN74120
DUAL PULSE SYNCHRONIZERS/DRIVERS

PARAMETER MEASUREMENT INFORMATION

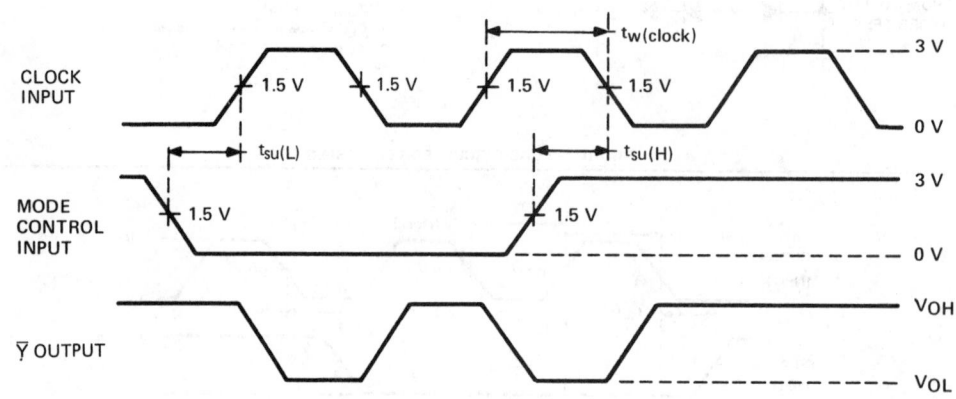

NOTE: At least one of the S inputs is low.

FIGURE 4—INITIATING AND TERMINATING PULSE TRAIN WITH MODE CONTROL INPUT

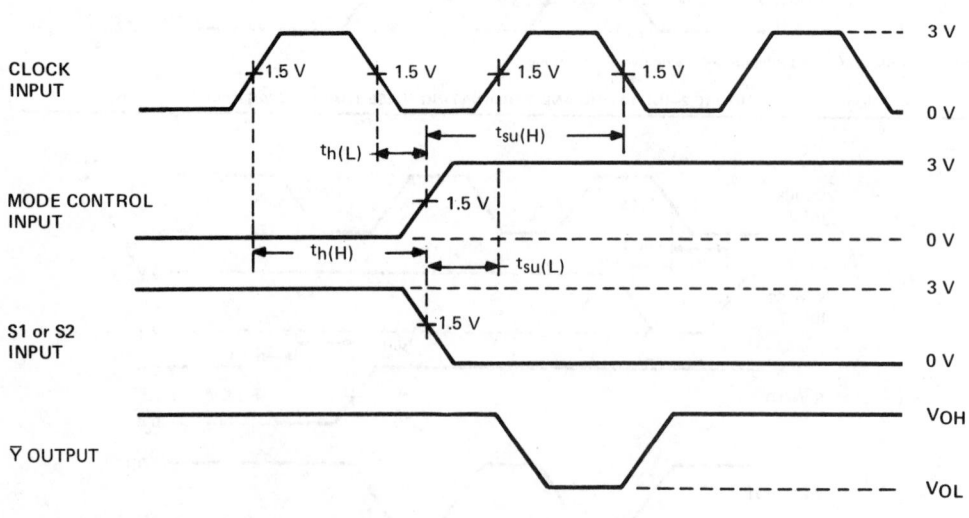

NOTE: Input R is low and the unused S input is high.

FIGURE 5—ENABLING SINGLE PULSE

TEXAS INSTRUMENTS
INCORPORATED
POST OFFICE BOX 5012 • DALLAS, TEXAS 75222

TYPES SN54LS124, SN54S124, SN74LS124, SN74S124
DUAL VOLTAGE-CONTROLLED OSCILLATORS

BULLETIN NO. DL-S 7612025, MARCH 1974–REVISED OCTOBER 1976

- Two Independent VCO's in a 16-Pin Package
- Output Frequency Set by Single External Component:
  Crystal for High-Stability Fixed-Frequency Operation
  Capacitor for Fixed- or Variable-Frequency Operation
- Separate Supply Voltage Pins for Isolation of Frequency Control Inputs and Oscillators from Output Circuitry
- Highly Stable Operation over Specified Temperature and/or Supply Voltage Ranges

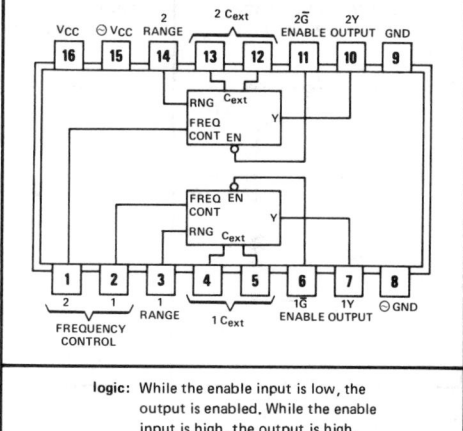

SN54LS124, SN54S124 . . . J OR W PACKAGE
SN74LS124, SN74S124 . . . J OR N PACKAGE
(TOP VIEW)

logic: While the enable input is low, the output is enabled. While the enable input is high, the output is high.

TYPE	GUARANTEED FREQUENCY SPECTRUM	TYPICAL f_{max}	TYPICAL POWER DISSIPATION
'LS124	1 Hz to 20 MHz	30 MHz	150 mW
'S124	1 Hz to 60 MHz	85 MHz	525 mW

description

The 'LS124 and 'S124 feature two independent voltage-controlled oscillators (VCO) in a single monolithic chip. The output frequency of each VCO is established by a single external component, either a capacitor or a crystal, in combination with two voltage-sensitive inputs, one for frequency range and one for frequency control. These inputs can be used to vary the output frequency as shown under typical characteristics for the 'S124. The concept also applies for the 'LS124. These highly stable oscillators can be set to operate at any frequency typically between 0.12 Hz and 30 MHz ('LS124) or 0.12 hertz and 85 megahertz ('S124). Under the conditions used in Figure 3, the output frequency can be approximated as follows:

$$f_O = \frac{1 \times 10^{-4}}{C_{ext}} \text{ for 'LS124,} \quad f_O = \frac{5 \times 10^{-4}}{C_{ext}} \text{ for 'S124}$$

where: f_O = output frequency in hertz

C_{ext} = external capacitance in farads.

These devices can operate from a single 5-volt supply. However, one set of supply-voltage and ground pins (V_{CC} and GND) is provided for the enable, synchronization-gating, and output sections, and a separate set ($\ominus V_{CC}$ and $\ominus$ GND) is provided for the oscillator and associated frequency-control circuits so that effective isolation can be accomplished in the system.

The enable input of these devices starts or stops the output pulses when it is low or high, respectively. The internal oscillator of the 'LS124 runs continuously even while the output is disabled, whereas the internal oscillator of the 'S124 is itself started and stopped by the enable input. The enable input is one standard load in each series. The enable input and the buffered output operate at standard Schottky-clamped TTL levels.

The pulse synchronization-gating section ensures that the first output pulse is neither clipped nor extended. Duty cycle of the square-wave output is fixed at approximately 50 percent.

The SN54LS124 and SN54S124 are characterized for operation over the full military temperature range of -55°C to 125°C; the SN74LS124 and SN74S124 are characterized for operation from 0°C to 70°C.

7

TEXAS INSTRUMENTS
INCORPORATED
POST OFFICE BOX 5012 • DALLAS, TEXAS 75222

schematics of inputs and outputs

'LS124

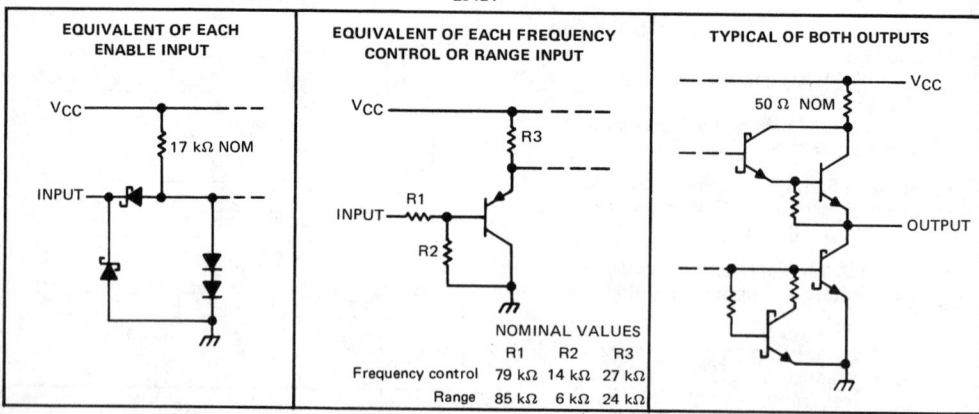

'S124

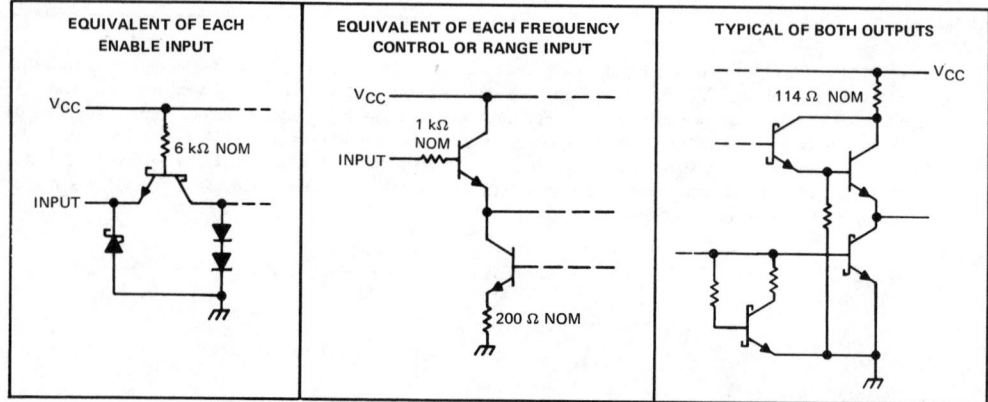

absolute maximum ratings over operating free-air temperature range (unless otherwise noted)

Supply voltage, V_{CC} (see Notes 1 and 2) . . . . 7 V
Input voltage: 'LS124 Enable input . . . . 7 V
             'LS124 Frequency control or range input . . . . V_{CC}
             'S124 . . . . 5.5 V
Operating free-air temperature range: SN54LS124, SN54S124 . . . . $-55°C$ to $125°C$
                       SN74LS124, SN74S124 . . . . $0°C$ to $70°C$
Storage temperature range . . . . $-65°C$ to $150°C$

NOTES: 1. Voltage values are with respect to the appropriate ground terminal.
      2. Throughout this data sheet, the symbol V_{CC} is used for the voltage applied to both the V_{CC} and $\bigodot V_{CC}$ terminals, unless otherwise noted.

TEXAS INSTRUMENTS
INCORPORATED
POST OFFICE BOX 5012 • DALLAS, TEXAS 75222

recommended operating conditions

	SN54LS124			SN74LS124			UNIT
	MIN	NOM	MAX	MIN	NOM	MAX	
Supply voltage, V_{CC}	4.5	5	5.5	4.75	5	5.25	V
Input voltage at frequency control or range input, $V_{I(freq)}$ or $V_{I(rng)}$	0		5	0		5	V
High-level output current, I_{OH}			−1.2			−1.2	mA
Low-level output current, I_{OL}			12			24	mA
Output frequency (enabled), f_o	1			1			Hz
			20			20	MHz
Operating free-air temperature, T_A	−55		125	0		70	°C

electrical characteristics over recommended operating free-air temperature range (unless otherwise noted)

PARAMETER			TEST CONDITIONS[†]		SN54LS124			SN74LS124			UNIT
					MIN	TYP[‡]	MAX	MIN	TYP[‡]	MAX	
V_{IH}	High-level input voltage at enable				2			2			V
V_{IL}	Low-level input voltage at enable						0.7			0.8	V
V_{IK}	Input clamp voltage at enable		V_{CC} = MIN, I_I = −18 mA				−1.5			−1.5	V
V_{OH}	High-level output voltage		V_{CC} = MIN, V_{IH} = 2 V, I_{OH} = −1.2 mA		2.5	3.4		2.7	3.4		V
V_{OL}	Low-level output voltage		V_{CC} = MIN, ⊘V_{CC} open, V_{IL} = V_{IL}max	I_{OL} = 12 mA		0.25	0.4		0.25	0.4	V
				I_{OL} = 24 mA					0.35	0.5	
I_I	Input current	Freq control or range	V_{CC} = MAX	V_I = 5 V	50		250	50		250	μA
				V_I = 1 V	10		50	10		50	
I_I	Input current at maximum input voltage	Enable	V_{CC} = MAX, V_I = 7 V				0.1			0.1	mA
I_{IH}	High-level input current	Enable	V_{CC} = MAX, V_I = 2.7 V				20			20	μA
I_{IL}	Low-level input current	Enable	V_{CC} = MAX, V_I = 0.4 V				−0.4			−0.4	mA
I_{OS}	Short-circuit output current[§]		V_{CC} = MAX		−40		−225	−40		−225	mA
I_{CC}	Supply current, total into pins 15 and 16		V_{CC} = MAX, See Note 2			30	50		30	50	mA

[†]For conditions shown as MIN or MAX, use the appropriate value specified under recommended operating conditions.
[‡]All typical values are at V_{CC} = 5 V, T_A = 25°C.
[§]Not more than one output should be shorted at a time and duration of the short-circuit should not exceed one second.
NOTE 2: I_{CC} is measured with the outputs disabled and open.

switching characteristics, V_{CC} = 5 V (unless otherwise noted), R_L = 667 Ω, C_L = 45 pF, T_A = 25°C

PARAMETER		TEST CONDITIONS		MIN	TYP	MAX	UNIT
f_o	Output frequency (capacitor controlled)	C_{ext} = 2 pF	$V_{I(freq)}$ = 4 V, $V_{I(rng)}$ = 1 V	20	30		MHz
			$V_{I(freq)}$ = 1 V, $V_{I(rng)}$ = 5 V	11	20		
f_o	Output frequency (crystal controlled)	⊘V_{CC} = 3 V, $V_{I(freq)}$ = $V_{I(rng)}$ = 0 V		10	20		MHz
	Output duty cycle	C_{ext} = 8.3 pF to 500 μF			50%		
t_{PHL}	Propagation delay time, high-to-low-level output from enable	$f_o ⩾$ 1 Hz			30+*		ns

*The delay will typically be 30 ns plus up to one period of one cycle (i.e. 30 ns to 30 ns + $\dfrac{1 \times 10^9}{f_{o(Hz)}}$ ns) depending upon the timing of the enable pulse with respect to the signal generated by the internal oscillator.

7

TYPES SN54S124, SN74S124
DUAL VOLTAGE-CONTROLLED OSCILLATORS

recommended operating conditions

		SN54S124			SN74S124			UNIT
		MIN	NOM	MAX	MIN	NOM	MAX	
Supply voltage, V_{CC} (see Note 1)		4.5	5	5.5	4.75	5	5.25	V
Input voltage at frequency control or range input, $V_{I(freq)}$ or $V_{I(rng)}$		1		5	1		5	V
High-level output current, I_{OH}				−1			−1	mA
Low-level output current, I_{OL}				20			20	mA
Output frequency (enabled), f_o		1			1			Hz
				60			60	MHz
Operating free-air temperature, T_A		−55		125	0		70	°C

NOTE 1: Throughout this data sheet, the symbol V_{CC} is used for the voltage applied to both pins 15 and 16.

electrical characteristics over recommended operating free-air temperature range (unless otherwise noted)

PARAMETER		TEST CONDITIONS[†]		MIN	TYP[‡]	MAX	UNIT
V_{IH} High-level input voltage at enable				2			V
V_{IL} Low-level input voltage at enable						0.8	V
V_{IK} Input clamp voltage at enable		V_{CC} = MIN, I_I = −18 mA				−1.2	V
V_{OH} High-level output voltage		V_{CC} = MIN, V_{IH} = 2 V,	SN54S'	2.5	3.4		V
		I_{OH} = −1 mA	SN74S'	2.7	3.4		
V_{OL} Low-level output voltage		V_{CC} = MIN, V_{IL} = 0.8 V, I_{OL} = 20 mA				0.5	V
I_I Input current	Freq control or range	V_{CC} = MAX	V_I = 5 V			10	50	μA
			V_I = 1 V		1	15	
I_I Input current at maximum input voltage	Enable	V_{CC} = MAX, V_I = 5.5 V				1	mA
I_{IH} High-level input current	Enable	V_{CC} = MAX, V_I = 2.7 V				50	μA
I_{IL} Low-level input current	Enable	V_{CC} = MAX, V_I = 0.5 V				−2	mA
I_{OS} Short-circuit output current[§]		V_{CC} = MAX		−40		−100	mA
I_{CC} Supply current, total into pins 15 and 16		V_{CC} = MAX, See Note 2			105	150	mA
		V_{CC} = MAX, T_A = 125°C, See Note 2	W package only			110	

[†]For conditions shown as MIN or MAX, use the appropriate value specified under recommended operating conditions.
[‡]All typical values are at V_{CC} = 5 V, T_A = 25°C.
[§]Not more than one output should be shorted at a time and duration of the short-circuit should not exceed one second.
NOTE 2: I_{CC} is measured with the outputs disabled and open.

switching characteristics, V_{CC} = 5 V, R_L = 280 Ω, C_L = 15 pF, T_A = 25°C

PARAMETER		TEST CONDITIONS		MIN	TYP	MAX	UNIT
f_o Output frequency		C_{ext} = 2 pF	$V_{I(freq)}$ = 4 V, $V_{I(rng)}$ = 1 V	60	85		MHz
			$V_{I(freq)}$ = 1 V, $V_{I(rng)}$ = 5 V	25	40		
Output duty cycle		C_{ext} = 8.3 pF to 500 μF			50%		
t_{PHL} Propagation delay time, high-to-low-level output from enable		f_o = 1 Hz to 20 MHz			$\dfrac{1.4}{f_{o}(Hz)}$		s
		f_o > 20 MHz			70		ns

TEXAS INSTRUMENTS
INCORPORATED
POST OFFICE BOX 5012 • DALLAS, TEXAS 75222

TYPICAL APPLICATION DATA

free-running oscillator

Free-running oscillators can be implemented for most systems by setting the output frequency of the VCO with either a capacitor or a crystal. If excitation is provided with a capacitor the frequency control and/or range inputs can be used to vary the output frequency.

When the 'S124 is excited with a crystal, low-frequency response ($\leqslant$ 1 MHz) can be improved if a relatively small capacitor (5 to 15 pF) is paralleled with the crystal. When operated at the fundamental frequency of a crystal, the frequency control input should be high ($\approx$ 5 V) and the range input should be low (grounded) for maximum stability over temperature and supply voltage variations.

When the 'LS124 is excited with a crystal, a small capacitor (2 to 10 pF) should be placed in series with the crystal and the $\ominus$ V_{CC} supply should be lowered to approximately 3 V. A series-resonant, fundamental-mode crystal with series resistance less than 200 ohms should be used. The frequency control and range inputs should be grounded. The maximum recommended frequency for crystal-excited operation is 10 MHz.

phase-locked loops

A basic crystal-controlled phase-locked loop is illustrated in Figure 1. This application can be used for implementation of:

    a. A highly stable fixed-frequency clock generator.
    b. A highly stable fixed- or variable-frequency synthesizer.
    c. A highly efficient "slave-clock" system for synchronizing off-card, remote, or data-interfacing clock systems

With fixed division rates for both M and N, the output frequency (f_0) will be stable at $f_0 = \frac{N}{M} f_1$. Obviously, either M or N, or both, could be programmable counters in which case the output frequency (f_0) will be a variable frequency dependent on the instantaneous value of $\frac{N}{M} f_1$.

The crystal-controlled VCO can be operated up to 60 MHz with an accuracy that is dependent on the crystal. At the higher frequencies, response of the phase comparator can become a limiting factor and one of the following approaches may be necessary to extend the operating frequency range.

    a. Frequencies $\frac{f_1}{M}$ and $\frac{f}{N}$ can be divided equally by the same constant (K) also shown in Figure 1. The constant can be any value greater than unity (K > 1), and should be selected to yield frequency ranges that can be handled adequately by the phase-comparator and filter. The output frequency (f_0) retains the same relationship as previously explained because now:

$$f_0 = \frac{KN}{KM} f_1 = \frac{N}{M} f_1$$

    b. In another method, the comparison of $\frac{f_1}{M}$ and $\frac{f}{N}$ can be performed with either an SN54LS85/SN74LS85 or SN54S85/SN74S85. The resultant A > B and A < B outputs from the 'LS85 or 'S85 permit the detector to be simplified to a charge-pump circuit. See Figure 2.

TEXAS INSTRUMENTS
INCORPORATED
POST OFFICE BOX 5012 • DALLAS, TEXAS 75222

TYPICAL APPLICATION DATA

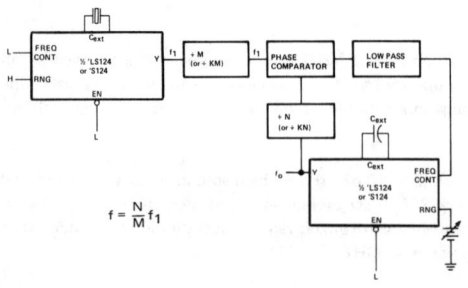

$$f = \frac{N}{M} f_1$$

FIGURE 1—PHASE-LOCKED LOOP

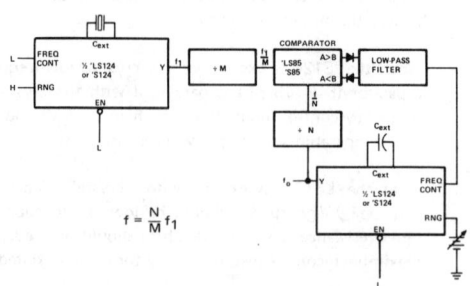

$$f = \frac{N}{M} f_1$$

FIGURE 2—HIGH-FREQUENCY PHASE-LOCKED LOOP

TYPICAL CHARACTERISTICS ('S124 only)

BASE OUTPUT FREQUENCY
vs
EXTERNAL CAPACITANCE

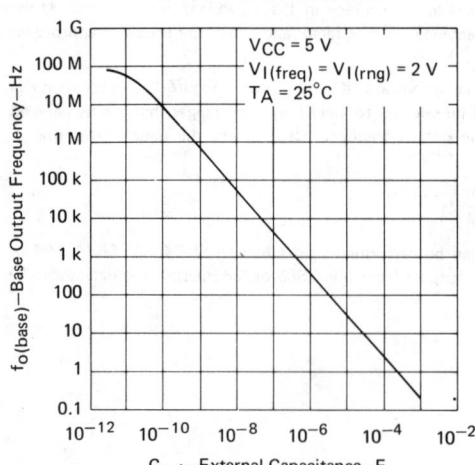

$V_{CC} = 5\ V$
$V_{I(freq)} = V_{I(rng)} = 2\ V$
$T_A = 25^{\circ}C$

$f_{o(base)}$—Base Output Frequency—Hz

C_{ext}—External Capacitance—F

FIGURE 3

NORMALIZED OUTPUT FREQUENCY
vs
INPUT VOLTAGE

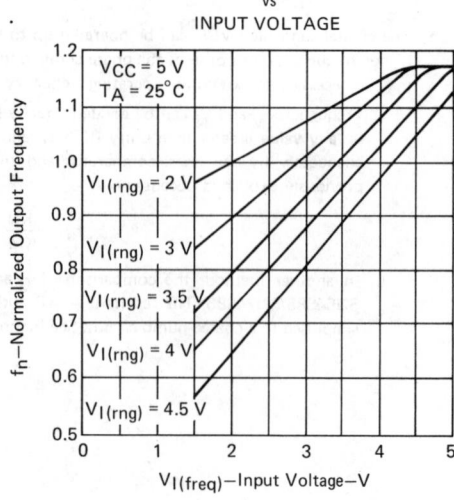

$V_{CC} = 5\ V$
$T_A = 25^{\circ}C$

$V_{I(rng)} = 2\ V$
$V_{I(rng)} = 3\ V$
$V_{I(rng)} = 3.5\ V$
$V_{I(rng)} = 4\ V$
$V_{I(rng)} = 4.5\ V$

f_n—Normalized Output Frequency

$V_{I(freq)}$—Input Voltage—V

FIGURE 4

NOTE: $f_o = f_n \times f_{o(base)}$.

TEXAS INSTRUMENTS
INCORPORATED
POST OFFICE BOX 5012 • DALLAS, TEXAS 75222

- Fully Compatible with Most TTL and TTL MSI Circuits

- Fully Schottky Clamping Reduces Delay Times . . . 8 ns Typical

- Can Operate as Exclusive-OR Gate (C Input Low) or as Exclusive-NOR Gate (C Input High)

SN54S135 . . . J OR W PACKAGE
SN74S135 . . . J OR N PACKAGE
(TOP VIEW)

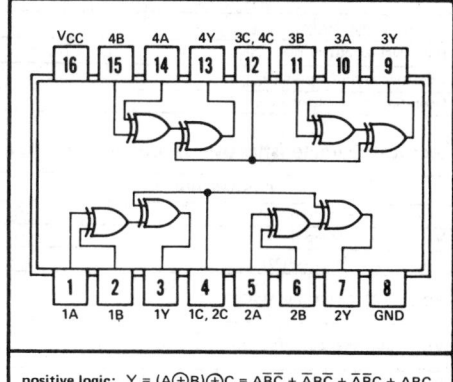

FUNCTION TABLE

INPUTS			OUTPUT
A	**B**	**C**	**Y**
L	L	L	L
L	H	L	H
H	L	L	H
H	H	L	L
L	L	H	H
L	H	H	L
H	L	H	L
H	H	H	H

H = high level, L = low level

positive logic: $Y = (A \oplus B) \oplus C = A\overline{B}\overline{C} + \overline{A}B\overline{C} + \overline{A}\overline{B}C + ABC$

schematics of inputs and outputs

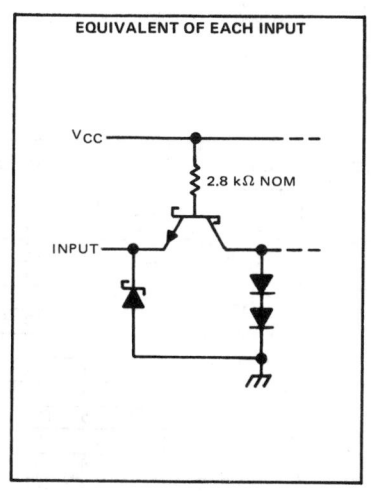

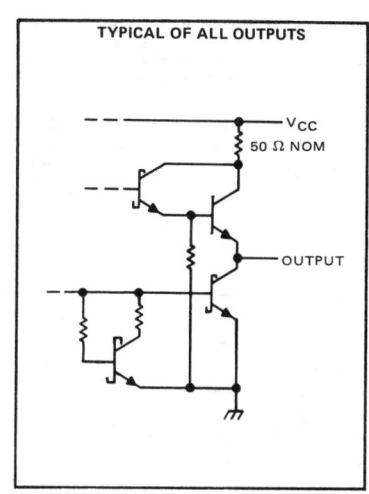

absolute maximum ratings over operating free-air temperature range (unless otherwise noted)

Supply voltage, V_{CC} (see Note 1) . . . . 7 V
Input voltage . . . . 5.5 V
Operating free-air temperature range: SN54S135 . . . . −55°C to 125°C
                                SN74S135 . . . . 0°C to 70°C
Storage temperature range . . . . −65°C to 150°C

NOTE 1: Voltage values are with respect to network ground terminal.

TEXAS INSTRUMENTS
INCORPORATED
POST OFFICE BOX 5012 • DALLAS, TEXAS 75222

recommended operating conditions

	SN54S135			SN74S135			UNIT
	MIN	NOM	MAX	MIN	NOM	MAX	
Supply voltage, V_{CC}	4.5	5	5.5	4.75	5	5.25	V
High-level output current, I_{OH}			−1			−1	mA
Low-level output current, I_{OL}			20			20	mA
Operating free-air temperature, T_A	−55		125	0		70	°C

electrical characteristics over recommended operating free-air temperature range (unless otherwise noted)

PARAMETER		TEST CONDITIONS[†]		MIN	TYP[‡]	MAX	UNIT
V_{IH}	High-level input voltage			2			V
V_{IL}	Low-level input voltage					0.8	V
V_{IK}	Input clamp voltage	V_{CC} = MIN, I_I = −18 mA				−1.2	V
V_{OH}	High-level output voltage	V_{CC} = MIN, V_{IH} = 2 V,	SN54S'	2.5	3.4		V
		V_{IL} = 0.8 V, I_{OH} = −1 mA	SN74S'	2.7	3.4		
V_{OL}	Low-level output voltage	V_{CC} = MIN, V_{IH} = 2 V, V_{IL} = 0.8 V, I_{OL} = 20 mA				0.5	V
I_I	Input current at maximum input voltage	V_{CC} = MAX, V_I = 5.5 V				1	mA
I_{IH}	High-level input current	V_{CC} = MAX, V_I = 2.7 V				50	µA
I_{IL}	Low-level input current	V_{CC} = MAX, V_I = 0.5 V				−2	mA
I_{OS}	Short-circuit output current[§]	V_{CC} = MAX		−40		−100	mA
I_{CC}	Supply current	V_{CC} = MAX, See Note 2			65	99	mA

[†]For conditions shown as MIN or MAX, use the appropriate value specified under recommended operating conditions for the applicable type.
[‡]All typical values are at V_{CC} = 5 V, T_A = 25°C.
[§]Not more than one output should be shorted at a time and duration of the short circuit should not exceed one second.
NOTE 2: I_{CC} is measured with the inputs grounded and the outputs open.

switching characteristics, V_{CC} = 5 V, T_A = 25°C

PARAMETER[¶]	FROM (INPUT)	TEST CONDITIONS		MIN	TYP	MAX	UNIT
t_{PLH}	A or B	B or A = L, C = L			8.5	13	ns
t_{PHL}					11	15	
t_{PLH}	A or B	B or A = H, C = L			8	12	ns
t_{PHL}					9	13.5	
t_{PLH}	A or B	B or A = L, C = H	C_L = 15 pF, R_L = 280 Ω, See Note 3		10	15	ns
t_{PHL}					6.5	10	
t_{PLH}	A or B	B or A = H, C = H			8.5	12	ns
t_{PHL}					7	11	
t_{PLH}	C	A = B			8	12	ns
t_{PHL}					9.5	14.5	
t_{PLH}	C	A ≠ B			7.5	11.5	ns
t_{PHL}					8	12	

[¶]t_{PLH} ≡ propagation delay time, low-to-high-level output
t_{PHL} ≡ propagation delay time, high-to-low-level output
NOTE 3: Load circuit and voltage waveforms are shown on page 3-10.

TEXAS INSTRUMENTS
INCORPORATED
POST OFFICE BOX 5012 • DALLAS, TEXAS 75222

TYPES SN54136, SN54LS136, SN74136, SN74LS136
QUADRUPLE 2-INPUT EXCLUSIVE-OR GATES
WITH OPEN-COLLECTOR OUTPUTS

BULLETIN NO. DL-S 7611827, DECEMBER 1972—REVISED OCTOBER 1976

SN54136, SN54LS136 . . . J OR W PACKAGE
SN74136, SN74LS136 . . . J OR N PACKAGE
(TOP VIEW)

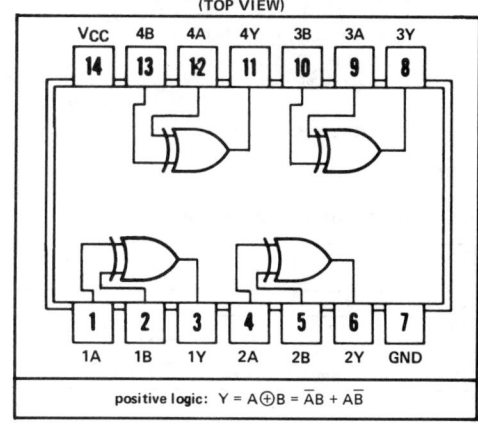

FUNCTION TABLE

INPUTS		OUTPUT
A	B	Y
L	L	L
L	H	H
H	L	H
H	H	L

H = high level, L = low level

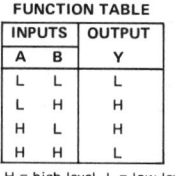

positive logic: $Y = A \oplus B = \overline{A}B + A\overline{B}$

schematics of inputs and outputs

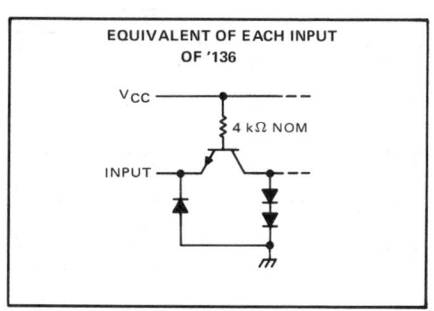

EQUIVALENT OF EACH INPUT
OF '136

V_{CC}

4 kΩ NOM

INPUT

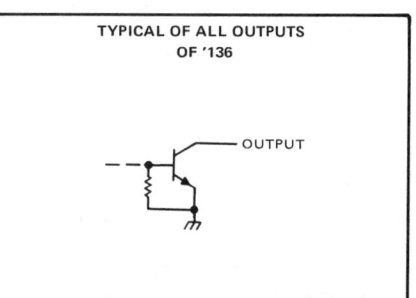

TYPICAL OF ALL OUTPUTS
OF '136

OUTPUT

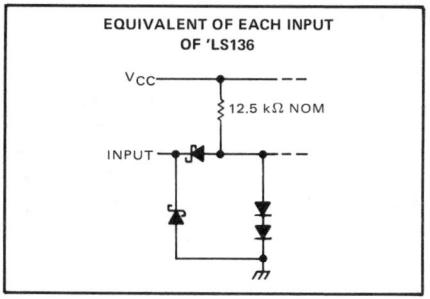

EQUIVALENT OF EACH INPUT
OF 'LS136

V_{CC}

12.5 kΩ NOM

INPUT

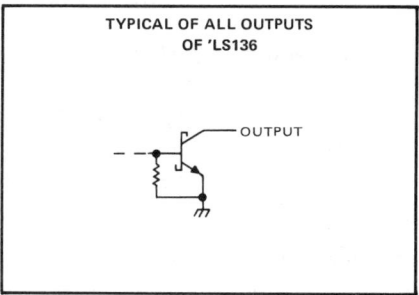

TYPICAL OF ALL OUTPUTS
OF 'LS136

OUTPUT

7

TEXAS INSTRUMENTS
INCORPORATED
POST OFFICE BOX 5012 • DALLAS, TEXAS 75222

absolute maximum ratings over operating free-air temperature range (unless otherwise noted)

Supply voltage, V_{CC} (see Note 1) . . . . 7 V
Input voltage . . . . 5.5 V
Operating free-air temperature range: SN54136 . . . . −55°C to 125°C
SN74136 . . . . 0°C to 70°C
Storage temperature range . . . . −65°C to 150°C

NOTE 1: Voltage values are with respect to network ground terminal.

recommended operating conditions

	SN54136			SN74136			UNIT
	MIN	NOM	MAX	MIN	NOM	MAX	
Supply voltage, V_{CC}	4.5	5	5.5	4.75	5	5.25	V
High-level output voltage, V_{OH}			5.5			5.5	V
Low-level output current, I_{OL}			16			16	mA
Operating free-air temperature, T_A	−55		125	0		70	°C

electrical characteristics over recommended operating free-air temperature range (unless otherwise noted)

PARAMETER		TEST CONDITIONS†		MIN	TYP‡	MAX	UNIT
V_{IH}	High-level input voltage			2			V
V_{IL}	Low-level input voltage					0.8	V
V_{IK}	Input clamp voltage	V_{CC} = MIN,	I_I = −8 mA			−1.5	V
I_{OH}	High-level output current	V_{CC} = MIN, V_{IL} = 0.8 V,	V_{IH} = 2 V, V_{OH} = 5.5 V			250	µA
V_{OL}	Low-level output voltage	V_{CC} = MIN, V_{IL} = 0.8 V,	V_{IH} = 2 V, I_{OL} = 16 mA		0.2	0.4	V
I_I	Input current at maximum input voltage	V_{CC} = MAX,	V_I = 5.5 V			1	mA
I_{IH}	High-level input current	V_{CC} = MAX,	V_I = 2.4 V			40	µA
I_{IL}	Low-level input current	V_{CC} = MAX,	V_I = 0.4 V			−1.6	mA
I_{CC}	Supply current, high-level output	V_{CC} = MAX, See Note 2	SN54136		30	43	mA
			SN74136		30	50	

†For conditions shown as MIN or MAX, use the appropriate value specified under recommended operating conditions for the applicable device type.
‡All typical values are at V_{CC} = 5 V, T_A = 25°C.
NOTE 2: I_{CC} is measured with one input of each gate at 4.5 V, the other inputs grounded, and the outputs open.

switching characteristics, V_{CC} = 5 V, T_A = 25°C

PARAMETER¶	FROM (INPUT)	TEST CONDITIONS		MIN	TYP	MAX	UNIT
t_{PLH}	A or B	Other input low	C_L = 15 pF, R_L = 400 Ω, See Note 3		12	18	ns
t_{PHL}					39	50	
t_{PLH}	A or B	Other input high			14	22	ns
t_{PHL}					42	55	

¶ t_{PLH} ≡ propagation delay time, low-to-high-level output
t_{PHL} ≡ propagation delay time, high-to-low-level output
NOTE 3: Load circuit and voltage waveforms are shown on page 3-10.

absolute maximum ratings over operating free-air temperature range (unless otherwise noted)

Supply voltage, V_{CC} (see Note 1) . . . . 7 V
Input voltage . . . . 7 V
Operating free-air temperature range: SN54LS136 . . . . −55°C to 125°C
SN74LS136 . . . . 0°C to 70°C
Storage temperature range . . . . −65°C to 150°C

NOTE 1: Voltage values are with respect to network ground terminal.

recommended operating conditions

	SN54LS136			SN74LS136			UNIT
	MIN	NOM	MAX	MIN	NOM	MAX	
Supply voltage, V_{CC}	4.5	5	5.5	4.75	5	5.25	V
High-level output voltage, V_{OH}			5.5			5.5	V
Low-level output current, I_{OL}			4			8	mA
Operating free-air temperature, T_A	−55		125	0		70	°C

electrical characteristics over recommended operating free-air temperature range (unless otherwise noted)

PARAMETER		TEST CONDITIONS†		SN54LS136			SN74LS136			UNIT
				MIN	TYP‡	MAX	MIN	TYP‡	MAX	
V_{IH}	High-level input voltage			2			2			V
V_{IL}	Low-level input voltage					0.7			0.8	V
V_{IK}	Input clamp voltage	V_{CC} = MIN,	I_I = −18 mA			−1.5			−1.5	V
I_{OH}	High-level output current	V_{CC} = MIN, V_{IH} = 2 V, V_{IL} = V_{IL} max, V_{OH} = 5.5 V				100			100	μA
V_{OL}	Low-level output voltage	V_{CC} = MIN, V_{IH} = 2 V, V_{IL} = V_{IL} max	I_{OL} = 4 mA	0.25	0.4		0.25	0.4		V
			I_{OL} = 8 mA					0.35	0.5	
I_I	Input current at maximum input voltage	V_{CC} = MAX,	V_I = 7 V			0.2			0.2	mA
I_{IH}	High-level input current	V_{CC} = MAX,	V_I = 2.7 V			40			40	μA
I_{IL}	Low-level input current	V_{CC} = MAX,	V_I = 0.4 V			−0.8			−0.8	mA
I_{CC}	Supply current	V_{CC} = MAX,	See Note 2		6.1	10		6.1	10	mA

†For conditions shown as MIN or MAX, use the appropriate value specified under recommended operating conditions for the applicable type.
‡All typical values are at V_{CC} = 5 V, T_A = 25°C.
NOTE 2: I_{CC} is measured with one input of each gate at 4.5 V, the other inputs grounded, and the outputs open.

switching characteristics, V_{CC} = 5 V, T_A = 25°C

PARAMETER¶	FROM (INPUT)	TEST CONDITIONS		MIN	TYP	MAX	UNIT
t_{PLH}	A or B	Other input low	C_L = 15 pF, R_L = 2 kΩ, See Note 4		18	30	ns
t_{PHL}					18	30	
t_{PLH}	A or B	Other input high			18	30	ns
t_{PHL}					18	30	

¶t_{PLH} ≡ propagation delay time, low-to-high-level output
t_{PHL} ≡ propagation delay time, high-to-low-level output
NOTE 4: Load circuit and voltage waveforms are shown on page 3-11.

7

6

- Designed Specifically for High-Speed:
  Memory Decoders
  Data Transmission Systems

- 'S138 and 'LS138 3-to-8-Line Decoders
  Incorporate 3 Enable Inputs to Simplify
  Cascading and/or Data Reception

- 'S139 and 'LS139 Contain Two Fully
  Independent 2-to-4-Line Decoders/
  Demultiplexers

- Schottky Clamped for High Performance

TYPE	TYPICAL PROPAGATION DELAY (3 LEVELS OF LOGIC)	TYPICAL POWER DISSIPATION
'LS138	22 ns	32 mW
'S138	8 ns	245 mW
'LS139	22 ns	34 mW
'S139	7.5 ns	300 mW

SN54LS138, SN54S138 . . . J OR W PACKAGE
SN74LS138, SN74S138 . . . J OR N PACKAGE
(TOP VIEW)

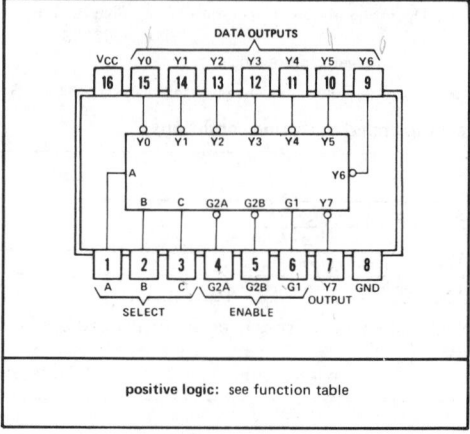

positive logic: see function table

description

These Schottky-clamped TTL MSI circuits are designed to be used in high-performance memory-decoding or data-routing applications requiring very short propagation delay times. In high-performance memory systems these decoders can be used to minimize the effects of system decoding. When employed with high-speed memories utilizing a fast-enable circuit the delay times of these decoders and the enable time of the memory are usually less than the typical access time of the memory. This means that the effective system delay introduced by the Schottky-clamped system decoder is negligible.

The 'LS138 and 'S138 decode one-of-eight lines dependent on the conditions at the three binary select inputs and the three enable inputs. Two active-low and one active-high enable inputs reduce the need for external gates or inverters when expanding. A 24-line decoder can be implemented without external inverters and a 32-line decoder requires only one inverter. An enable input can be used as a data input for demultiplexing applications.

SN54LS139, SN54S139 . . . J OR W PACKAGE
SN74LS139, SN74S139 . . . J OR N PACKAGE
(TOP VIEW)

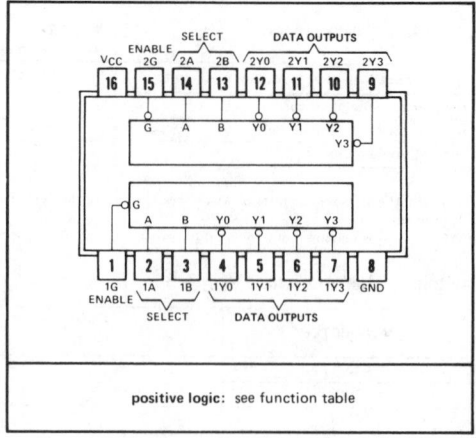

positive logic: see function table

The 'LS139 and 'S139 comprise two individual two-line-to-four-line decoders in a single package. The active-low enable input can be used as a data line in demultiplexing applications.

All of these decoders/demultiplexers feature fully buffered inputs each of which represents only one normalized Series 54LS/74LS load ('LS138, 'LS139) or one normalized Series 54S/74S load ('S138, 'S139) to its driving circuit. All inputs are clamped with high-performance Schottky diodes to suppress line-ringing and simplify system design. Series 54LS and 54S devices are characterized for operation over the full military temperature range of −55°C to 125°C; Series 74LS and 74S devices are characterized for 0°C to 70°C industrial systems.

TEXAS INSTRUMENTS
INCORPORATED
POST OFFICE BOX 5012 • DALLAS, TEXAS 75222

functional block diagrams and logic

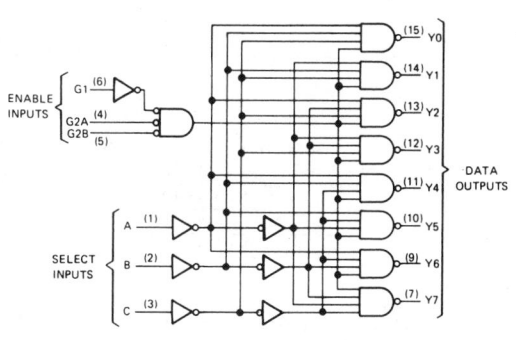

'LS138, 'S138

'LS138, 'S138 FUNCTION TABLE

INPUTS					OUTPUTS							
ENABLE		SELECT										
G1	G2*	C	B	A	Y0	Y1	Y2	Y3	Y4	Y5	Y6	Y7
X	H	X	X	X	H	H	H	H	H	H	H	H
L	X	X	X	X	H	H	H	H	H	H	H	H
H	L	L	L	L	L	H	H	H	H	H	H	H
H	L	L	L	H	H	L	H	H	H	H	H	H
H	L	L	H	L	H	H	L	H	H	H	H	H
H	L	L	H	H	H	H	H	L	H	H	H	H
H	L	H	L	L	H	H	H	H	L	H	H	H
H	L	H	L	H	H	H	H	H	H	L	H	H
H	L	H	H	L	H	H	H	H	H	H	L	H
H	L	H	H	H	H	H	H	H	H	H	H	L

*G2 = G2A + G2B

H = high level, L = low level, X = irrelevant

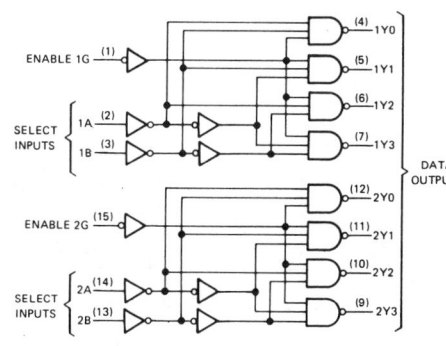

'LS139, 'S139

'LS139, 'S139 (EACH DECODER/DEMULTIPLEXER) FUNCTION TABLE

INPUTS			OUTPUTS			
ENABLE	SELECT					
G	B	A	Y0	Y1	Y2	Y3
H	X	X	H	H	H	H
L	L	L	L	H	H	H
L	L	H	H	L	H	H
L	H	L	H	H	L	H
L	H	H	H	H	H	L

H = high level, L = low level, X = irrelevant

schematics of inputs and outputs

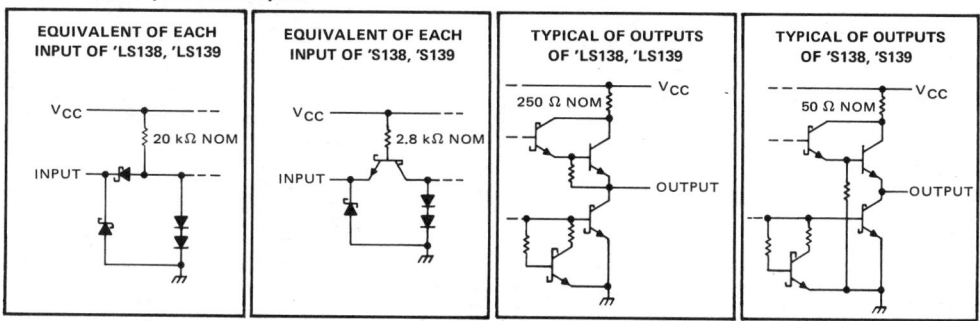

EQUIVALENT OF EACH INPUT OF 'LS138, 'LS139	EQUIVALENT OF EACH INPUT OF 'S138, 'S139	TYPICAL OF OUTPUTS OF 'LS138, 'LS139	TYPICAL OF OUTPUTS OF 'S138, 'S139

TYPES SN54LS138, SN54LS139, SN74LS138, SN74LS139, DECODERS/DEMULTIPLEXERS

REVISED OCTOBER 1976

absolute maximum ratings over operating free-air temperature range (unless otherwise noted)

Supply voltage, V_{CC} (see Note 1) . . . . 7 V
Input voltage . . . . 7 V
Operating free-air temperature range: SN54LS138, SN54LS139 Circuits . . . . −55°C to 125°C
                      SN74LS138, SN74LS139 Circuits . . . . 0°C to 70°C
Storage temperature range . . . . −65°C to 150°C

NOTE 1: Voltage values are with respect to network ground terminal.

recommended operating conditions

	SN54LS138 SN54LS139			SN74LS138 SN74LS139			UNIT
	MIN	NOM	MAX	MIN	NOM	MAX	
Supply voltage, V_{CC}	4.5	5	5.5	4.75	5	5.25	V
High-level output current, I_{OH}			−400			−400	µA
Low-level output current, I_{OL}			4			8	mA
Operating free-air temperature, T_A	−55		125	0		70	°C

electrical characteristics over recommended operating free-air temperature range (unless otherwise noted)

PARAMETER	TEST CONDITIONS†		SN54LS138 SN54LS139			SN74LS138 SN74LS139			UNIT
			MIN	TYP‡	MAX	MIN	TYP‡	MAX	
V_{IH} High-level input voltage			2			2			V
V_{IL} Low-level input voltage					0.7			0.8	V
V_{IK} Input clamp voltage	V_{CC} = MIN,	I_I = −18 mA			−1.5			−1.5	V
V_{OH} High-level output voltage	V_{CC} = MIN, V_{IH} = 2 V, $V_{IL} = V_{IL\ max}$, I_{OH} = −400 µA		2.5	3.4		2.7	3.4		V
V_{OL} Low-level output voltage	V_{CC} = MIN, V_{IH} = 2 V, $V_{IL} = V_{IL\ max}$	I_{OL} = 4 mA		0.25	0.4		0.25	0.4	V
		I_{OL} = 8 mA					0.35	0.5	
I_I Input current at maximum input voltage	V_{CC} = MAX,	V_I = 7 V			0.1			0.1	mA
I_{IH} High-level input current	V_{CC} = MAX,	V_I = 2.7 V			20			20	µA
I_{IL} Low-level input current	V_{CC} = MAX,	V_I = 0.4 V			−0.4			−0.4	mA
I_{OS} Short-circuit output current§	V_{CC} = MAX		−6		−40	−5		−42	mA
I_{CC} Supply current	V_{CC} = MAX, Outputs enabled and open	'LS138		6.3	10		6.3	10	mA
		'LS139		6.8	11		6.8	11	

†For conditions shown as MIN or MAX, use the appropriate value specified under recommended operating conditions for the applicable device type.
‡All typical values are at V_{CC} = 5 V, T_A = 25°C.
§Not more than one output should be shorted at a time.

switching characteristics, V_{CC} = 5 V, T_A = 25°C

PARAMETER¶	FROM (INPUT)	TO (OUTPUT)	LEVELS OF DELAY	TEST CONDITIONS	SN54LS138 SN74LS138			SN54LS139 SN74LS139			UNIT
					MIN	TYP	MAX	MIN	TYP	MAX	
t_{PLH}	Binary Select	Any	2			13	20		13	20	ns
t_{PHL}						27	41		22	33	ns
t_{PLH}			3	C_L = 15 pF, R_L = 2 kΩ, See Note 2		18	27		18	29	ns
t_{PHL}						26	39		25	38	ns
t_{PLH}	Enable	Any	2			12	18		16	24	ns
t_{PHL}						21	32		21	32	ns
t_{PLH}			3			17	26				ns
t_{PHL}						25	38				ns

¶t_{PLH} ≡ propagation delay time, low-to-high-level output; t_{PHL} ≡ propagation delay time, high-to-low-level output.
NOTE 2: Load circuits and waveforms are shown on page 3-11.

7

TEXAS INSTRUMENTS
INCORPORATED
POST OFFICE BOX 5012 • DALLAS, TEXAS 75222

absolute maximum ratings over operating free-air temperature range (unless otherwise noted)

Supply voltage, V_{CC} (see Note 1)	7 V
Input voltage	5.5 V
Operating free-air temperature range: SN54S138, SN54S139 Circuits	$-55°C$ to $125°C$
SN74S138, SN74S139 Circuits	$0°C$ to $70°C$
Storage temperature range	$-65°C$ to $150°C$

NOTE 1: Voltage values are with respect to network ground terminal.

recommended operating conditions

	SN54S138 SN74S139			SN74S138 SN74S139			UNIT
	MIN	NOM	MAX	MIN	NOM	MAX	
Supply voltage, V_{CC}	4.5	5	5.5	4.75	5	5.25	V
High-level output current, I_{OH}			-1			-1	mA
Low-level output current, I_{OL}			20			20	mA
Operating free-air temperature, T_A	-55		125	0		70	°C

electrical characteristics over recommended operating free-air temperature range (unless otherwise noted)

PARAMETER	TEST CONDITIONS[†]		SN54S138 SN74S138			SN54S139 SN74S139			UNIT
			MIN	TYP[‡]	MAX	MIN	TYP[‡]	MAX	
V_{IH} High-level input voltage			2			2			V
V_{IL} Low-level input voltage					0.8			0.8	V
V_{IK} Input clamp voltage	V_{CC} = MIN, $I_I = -18$ mA				-1.2			-1.2	V
V_{OH} High-level output voltage	V_{CC} = MIN, V_{IH} = 2 V,	SN54S'	2.5	3.4		2.5	3.4		V
	V_{IL} = 0.8 V, $I_{OH} = -1$ mA	SN74S'	2.7	3.4		2.7	3.4		
V_{OL} Low-level output voltage	V_{CC} = MIN, V_{IH} = 2 V, V_{IL} = 0.8 V, I_{OL} = 20 mA				0.5			0.5	V
I_I Input current at maximum input voltage	V_{CC} = MAX, V_I = 5.5 V				1			1	mA
I_{IH} High-level input current	V_{CC} = MAX, V_I = 2.7 V				50			50	μA
I_{IL} Low-level input current	V_{CC} = MAX, V_I = 0.5 V				-2			-2	mA
I_{OS} Short-circuit output current[§]	V_{CC} = MAX		-40		-100	-40		-100	mA
I_{CC} Supply current	V_{CC} = MAX, Outputs enabled and open			49	74		60	90	mA

[†]For conditions shown as MIN or MAX, use the appropriate value specified under recommended operating conditions for the applicable device type.
[‡]All typical values are at V_{CC} = 5 V, $T_A = 25°C$.
[§]Not more than one output should be shorted at a time, and duration of the short-circuit test should not exceed one second.

switching characteristics, V_{CC} = 5 V, $T_A = 25°C$

PARAMETER[¶]	FROM (INPUT)	TO (OUTPUT)	LEVELS OF DELAY	TEST CONDITIONS	SN54S138, SN74S138			SN54S139 SN74S139			UNIT
					MIN	TYP	MAX	MIN	TYP	MAX	
t_{PLH}	Binary select	Any	2			4.5	7		5	7.5	ns
t_{PHL}						7	10.5		6.5	10	
t_{PLH}			3	C_L = 15 pF,		7.5	12		7	12	ns
t_{PHL}				R_L = 280 Ω,		8	12		8	12	
t_{PLH}	Enable	Any	2	See Note 3		5	8		5	8	ns
t_{PHL}						7	11		6.5	10	
t_{PLH}			3			7	11				ns
t_{PHL}						7	11				

[¶] $t_{PLH} \equiv$ propagation delay time, low-to-high-level output
$t_{PHL} \equiv$ propagation delay time, high-to-low-level output
NOTE 3: Load circuits and waveforms are shown on page 3-10.

TEXAS INSTRUMENTS
INCORPORATED
POST OFFICE BOX 5012 • DALLAS, TEXAS 75222

7

- Drives gas-filled cold-cathode indicator tubes directly
- Fully decoded inputs ensure all outputs are off for invalid codes
- Input clamping diodes minimize transmission-line effects

FUNCTION TABLE

INPUT				OUTPUT
D	C	B	A	ON†
L	L	L	L	0
L	L	L	H	1
L	L	H	L	2
L	L	H	H	3
L	H	L	L	4
L	H	L	H	5
L	H	H	L	6
L	H	H	H	7
H	L	L	L	8
H	L	L	H	9
H	L	H	L	NONE
H	L	H	H	NONE
H	H	L	L	NONE
H	H	L	H	NONE
H	H	H	L	NONE
H	H	H	H	NONE

H = high level, L = low level
†All other outputs are off

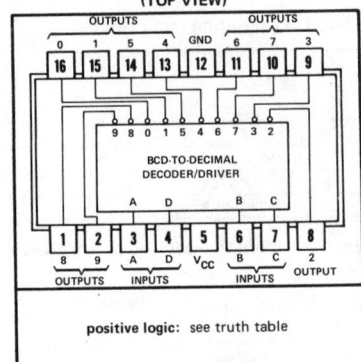

J OR N PACKAGE
(TOP VIEW)

positive logic: see truth table

description

The SN74141 is a second-generation BCD-to-decimal decoder designed specifically to drive cold-cathode indicator tubes. This decoder demonstrates an improved capability to minimize switching transients in order to maintain a stable display.

Full decoding is provided for all possible input states. For binary inputs 10 through 15, all the outputs are off. Therefore the SN74141, combined with a minimum of external circuitry, can use these invalid codes in blanking leading- and/or trailing-edge zeros in a display. The ten high-performance, n-p-n output transistors have a maximum reverse current of 50 microamperes at 55 volts.

Low-forward-impedance diodes are also provided for each input to clamp negative-voltage transitions in order to minimize transmission-line effects. Power dissipation is typically 80 milliwatts. The SN74141 is characterized for operation over the temperature range of 0°C to 70°C.

functional block diagram

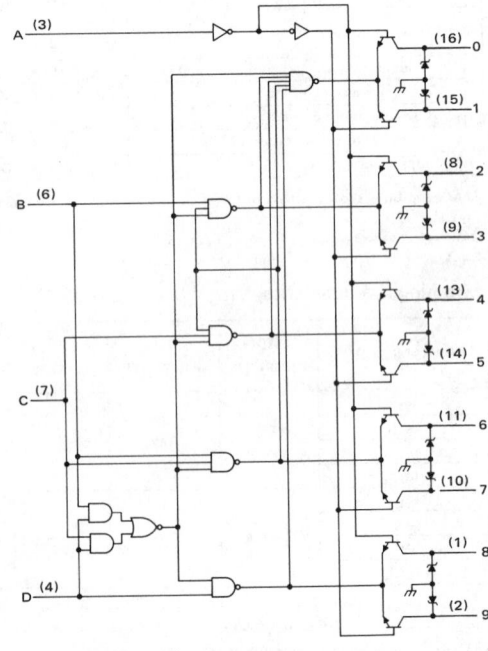

TEXAS INSTRUMENTS
INCORPORATED
POST OFFICE BOX 5012 • DALLAS, TEXAS 75222

absolute maximum ratings over operating free-air temperature range (unless otherwise noted)

Supply voltage, V_{CC} (see Note 1) . . . . 7 V
Input voltage . . . . 5.5 V
Current into any output (off-state) . . . . 2 mA
Operating free-air temperature range . . . . 0°C to 70°C
Storage temperature range . . . . −65°C to 150°C

NOTE 1: Voltage values are with respect to network ground terminal.

recommended operating conditions

	MIN	NOM	MAX	UNIT
Supply voltage, V_{CC}	4.75	5	5.25	V
Off-state output voltage			60	V
Operating free-air temperature, T_A	0		70	°C

electrical characteristics over recommended operating free-air temperature range (unless otherwise noted)

PARAMETER		TEST CONDITIONS[†]	MIN	TYP[‡]	MAX	UNIT
V_{IH}	High-level input voltage		2			V
V_{IL}	Low-level input voltage				0.8	V
V_{IK}	Input clamp voltage	V_{CC} = MIN, I_I = −5 mA			−1.5	V
$V_{O(on)}$	On-state output voltage	V_{CC} = MIN, I_O = 7 mA			2.5	V
$V_{O(off)}$	Off-state output voltage for input counts 0 thru 9	V_{CC} = MAX, I_O = 0.5 mA	60			V
$I_{O(off)}$	Off-state reverse current	V_{CC} = MAX, V_O = 55 V			50	µA
$I_{O(off)}$	Off-state reverse current for input counts 10 thru 15	V_{CC} = MAX, T_A = 55°C V_O = 30 V T_A = 70°C			5 15	µA
I_I	Input current at maximum input voltage	V_{CC} = MAX, V_I = 5.5 V			1	mA
I_{IH}	High-level input current	A input	V_{CC} = MAX, V_I = 2.4 V			40	µA
		B, C, or D input				80	
I_{IL}	Low-level input current	A input	V_{CC} = MAX, V_I = 0.4 V			−1.6	mA
		B, C, or D input				−3.2	
I_{CC}	Supply current		V_{CC} = MAX, See Note 2		16	25	mA

[†]For conditions shown as MIN or MAX, use the appropriate value specified under recommended operating conditions.
[‡]This typical value is at V_{CC} = 5 V, T_A = 25°C.
NOTE 2: I_{CC} is measured with all inputs grounded and outputs open.

schematics of inputs and outputs

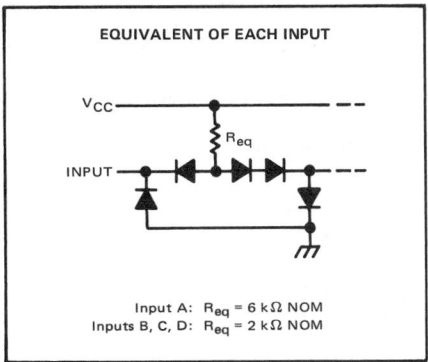

EQUIVALENT OF EACH INPUT

V_{CC}

R_{eq}

INPUT

Input A: R_{eq} = 6 kΩ NOM
Inputs B, C, D: R_{eq} = 2 kΩ NOM

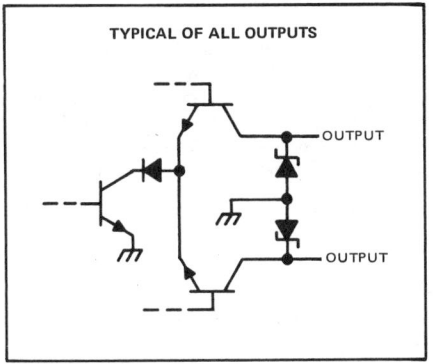

TYPICAL OF ALL OUTPUTS

OUTPUT

OUTPUT

FUNCTION TABLE

INPUTS			OUTPUTS	
COUNT PULSE (CLOCK)	CLEAR	LATCH STROBE	ON[†]	$\overline{Q}_D$
X	L	L	0	H
1	H	L	1	H
2	H	L	2	H
3	H	L	3	H
4	H	L	4	H
5	H	L	5	H
6	H	L	6	H
7	H	L	7	H
8	H	L	8	L
9	H	L	9	L
10	H	L	0	H
11	H	H	0	H

[†]All other outputs are off.

H = high level, L = low level, X = irrelevant

JORN
DUAL-IN-LINE PACKAGE (TOP VIEW)

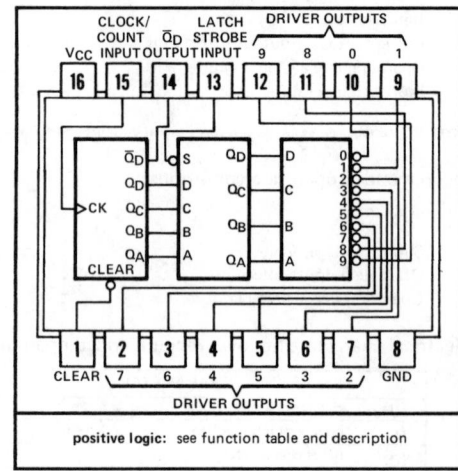

positive logic: see function table and description

description

The SN74142 contains a divide-by-ten (BCD) counter, a four-bit latch, and a decoder/*Nixie*[‡] tube driver on a monolithic chip and is packaged in popular 16-pin packages. This single MSI function can replace the equivalent of three separately packaged MSI circuits to reduce printed-circuit board area and the number of system interconnections, resulting in reduced costs and improved reliability.

Four master-slave flip-flops are fully decoded to provide a divide-by-ten counter. A direct clear input will, when taken low, reset and hold the counter at zero (all Q outputs low, $\overline{Q}_D$ output high). While the clear input is inactive (high), each positive-going transition of the clock will increment the counter. The $\overline{Q}_D$ output is made available externally for cascading to n-bit counters.

The Q outputs of the counter are routed to the data inputs of the four-bit latch. While the latch strobe input is low, the internal latch outputs will follow the respective Q outputs of the counter. When the latch strobe input is taken high, the latch stores the data which has been setup by the counter outputs prior to the low-to-high level transition of the latch strobe input. The $\overline{Q}_D$ output from the counter is not stored by the latch since it is intended for clocking the next counter stage. This means that the system counter can continuously acquire new data. Since all outputs of the latch and Q outputs of the counter drive low-capacitance on-chip loads, the circuitry is considerably simplified with respect to the number of components required. This results in a highly efficient function which typically reduces power requirements 15% when compared to systems using the three separate packages.

The SN74142 counter/latch/driver features fully buffered inputs to reduce drive requirements to one normalized Series 74 load per input, and diode-clamping of all inputs to minimize transmission line effects. The counter will accept input clock frequencies up to 20 MHz and is entirely compatible for use with all popular TTL and DTL logic circuits. The high-performance n-p-n driver outputs are identical to the SN74141 and have a maximum off-state reverse current of 50 microamperes at 55 volts.

[‡]*Nixie* is a registered trademark of the Burroughs Corporation.

TEXAS INSTRUMENTS
INCORPORATED
POST OFFICE BOX 5012 • DALLAS, TEXAS 75222

absolute maximum ratings over operating free-air temperature range (unless otherwise noted)

Supply voltage, V_{CC} (see Note 1)	7 V
Input voltage	5.5 V
Off-state current into outputs 0 thru 9	1 mA
Operating free-air temperature range	$0°C$ to $70°C$
Storage temperature range	$-65°C$ to $150°C$

NOTE 1: All voltage values are with respect to the network ground terminal.

recommended operating conditions

		MIN	NOM	MAX	UNIT
Supply voltage, V_{CC}		4.75	5	5.25	V
High-level output current from $\bar{Q}_D$, I_{OH}				-400	μA
Low-level output current from $\bar{Q}_D$, I_{OL}				8	mA
Input clock frequency, f_{clock}		0		20	MHz
Clock pulse width, $t_{w(clock)}$ (see Figure 1)	High logic level	15			ns
	Low logic level	35			
Clear pulse width, $t_{w(clear)}$ (see Figure 1)		25			ns
Strobe pulse width, $t_{w(strobe)}$ (see Figure 1)		20			ns
Clear inactive-state setup time, t_{su} (see Figure 1)		25			ns
Strobe time, t_{strobe} (see Figure 1)		45		$t_{w(clock)}$ +10	ns
Operating free-air temperature, T_A		0		70	$°C$

electrical characteristics over recommended operating free-air temperature range (unless otherwise noted)

	PARAMETER	TEST CONDITIONS[†]	MIN	TYP[‡]	MAX	UNIT
V_{IH}	High-level input voltage		2			V
V_{IL}	Low-level input voltage				0.8	V
V_{IK}	Input clamp voltage	V_{CC} = MIN, $I_I = -12$ mA			-1.5	V
V_{OH}	High-level $\bar{Q}_D$ output voltage	V_{CC} = MIN, $I_{OH} = -400\,\mu$A	2.4	3.4		V
V_{OL}	Low-level $\bar{Q}_D$ output voltage	V_{CC} = MIN, $I_{OL} = 8$ mA		0.2	0.4	V
$V_{O(on)}$	On-state voltage, outputs 0 thru 9	V_{CC} = MIN, $I_O = 7$ mA			2.5	V
$V_{O(off)}$	Off-state voltage, outputs 0 thru 9	V_{CC} = MAX, $I_O = 0.5$ mA	60			V
$I_{O(off)}$	Off-state current, outputs 0 thru 9	V_{CC} = MAX, $V_O = 55$ V			50	μA
I_I	Input current at maximum input voltage	V_{CC} = MAX, $V_I = 5.5$ V			1	mA
I_{IH}	High-level input current	V_{CC} = MAX, $V_I = 2.4$ V			40	μA
I_{IL}	Low-level input current	V_{CC} = MAX, $V_I = 0.4$ V			-1.6	mA
I_{OS}	Short-circuit $\bar{Q}_D$ output current	V_{CC} = MAX	-18		-55	mA
I_{CC}	Supply current	V_{CC} = MAX, All outputs open		68	102	mA

[†]For conditions shown as MIN or MAX, use the appropriate value specified under recommended operating conditions.
[‡]All typical values are at V_{CC} = 5 V, $T_A = 25°C$.

switching characteristics, V_{CC} = 5 V, $T_A = 25°C$

	PARAMETER	TEST CONDITIONS	MIN	TYP	MAX	UNIT
t_{PLH}	Propagation delay time, low-to-high-level $\bar{Q}_D$ output from clock	$C_L = 15$ pF, $R_L = 800\,\Omega$, See Figure 1		35	55	ns
t_{PHL}	Propagation delay time, high-to-low-level $\bar{Q}_D$ output from clock			30	45	
t_{PLH}	Propagation delay time, low-to-high-level $\bar{Q}_D$ output from clear			30	45	ns

7

TYPE SN74142
BCD COUNTER/4-BIT LATCH/BCD DECODER/DRIVER

schematics of inputs and outputs

EQUIVALENT OF EACH INPUT	OUTPUT Q̄	TYPICAL OF OUTPUTS 0 THRU 9
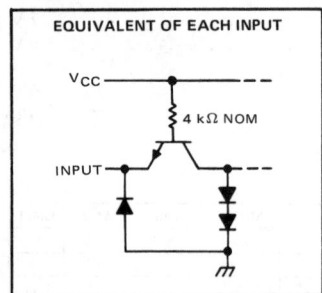	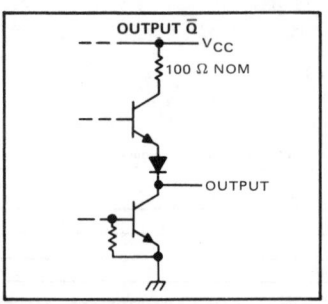	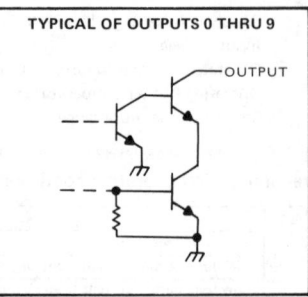

PARAMETER MEASUREMENT INFORMATION

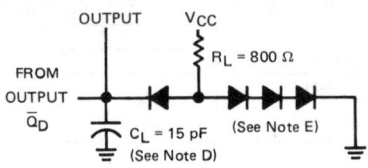

LOAD CIRCUIT

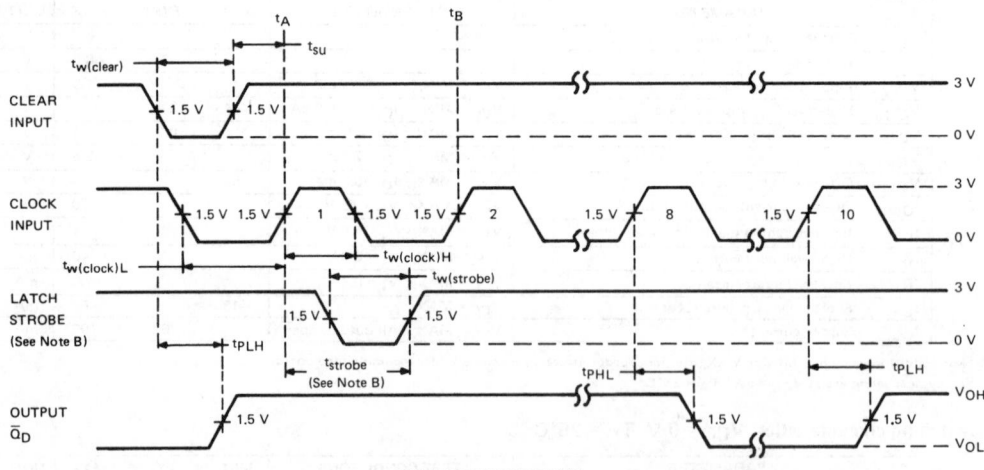

VOLTAGE WAVEFORMS

NOTES: A. This typical abbreviated sequence illustrates clearing from count 8 or 9 and counting through ten clock pulses. Clock pulses 3 through 7 and 9 are omitted for brevity.

B. Strobe input can go low at any time; however, the positive transition to store data from any given clock transition (t_A) must occur a minimum of 45 ns after t_A and prior to 10 ns after the next positive-going clock transition (t_B + 10 ns).

C. Input pulses are supplied by generators having the following characteristics: $t_r \leqslant 7$ ns, $t_f \leqslant 7$ ns, PRR = 1 MHz, and $Z_{out} \approx 50\ \Omega$.

D. C_L includes probe and jig capacitance.

E. All diodes are 1N3064.

FIGURE 1

TEXAS INSTRUMENTS
INCORPORATED

POST OFFICE BOX 5012 • DALLAS, TEXAS 75222

TYPES SN54143, SN54144, SN74143, SN74144
4-BIT COUNTER/LATCH, SEVEN-SEGMENT LED/LAMP DRIVERS

BULLETIN NO. DL-S 7211538, NOVEMBER 1971—REVISED DECEMBER 1972

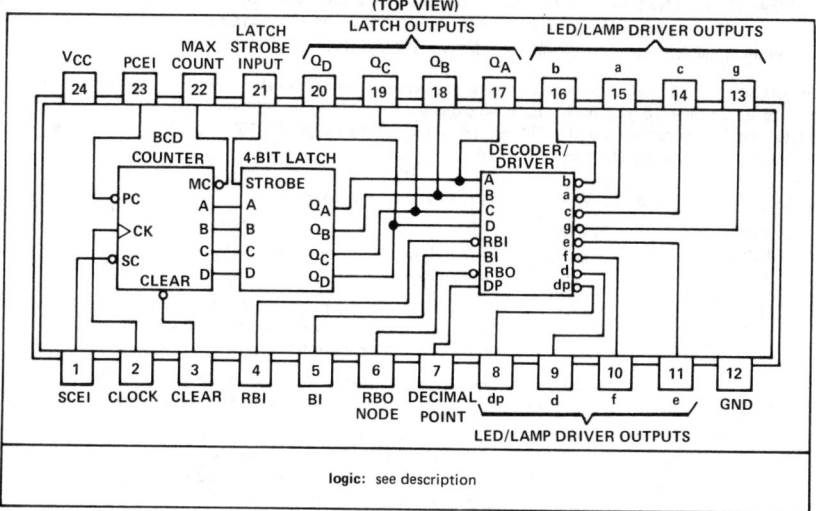

SN54143, SN54144 . . . J OR W PACKAGE
SN74143, SN74144 . . . J OR N PACKAGE
(TOP VIEW)

logic: see description

- **Choice of Driver Outputs:**

  SN54143 and SN74143 have 15-mA Constant-Current Outputs for Driving Common-Anode LED's such as TIL302 or TIL303 without Series Resistors

  SN54144 and SN74144 Drive High-Current Lamps, Numitrons†, or LED's from Saturated Open-Collector Outputs

- **Universal Logic Capabilities**

  Ripple Blanking of Extraneous Zeros
  Latch Outputs Can Drive Logic Processors Simultaneously
  Decimal Point Driver Is Included

- **Synchronous BCD Counter Capability Includes:**

  Cascadable to N-Bits
  Look-Ahead-Enable Techniques Minimize Speed Degradation When Cascaded for Large-Word Display
  Direct Clear Input

description

These TTL MSI circuits contain the equivalent of 86 gates on a single chip. Logic inputs and outputs are completely TTL/DTL compatible. The buffered inputs are implemented with relatively large resistors in series with the bases of the input transistors to lower drive-current requirements to one-half of that required for a standard Series 54/74 TTL input. The serial-count-enable, actually two internal emitters, is rated as one standard series 54/74 load. The logic outputs, except RBO, have active pull-ups.

The SN54143 and SN74143 driver outputs are designed specifically to maintain a relatively constant on-level sink current of approximately 15 milliamperes from outputs "a" through "g" and seven milliamperes from output "dp" over a voltage range from one to five volts. Any number of LED's in series may be driven as long as the output voltage rating is not exceeded.

†Trademark of RCA

TEXAS INSTRUMENTS
INCORPORATED
POST OFFICE BOX 5012 • DALLAS, TEXAS 75222

TYPES SN54143, SN54144, SN74143, SN74144
4-BIT COUNTER/LATCH, SEVEN-SEGMENT LED/LAMP DRIVERS

description (continued)

The SN54144 and SN74144 drivers have high-sink-current saturated outputs for driving indicators having voltage ratings up to 15 volts or requiring up to 25 milliamperes drive. The SN54144 sinks 20 milliamperes and the SN74144 sinks 25 milliamperes at an on-level voltage of 0.6 volts across their respective operating temperature ranges.

All inputs are diode-clamped to minimize transmission-line effects, thereby simplifying system design. Maximum clock frequency is typically 18 megahertz and power dissipation is typically 280 milliwatts. The SN54143 and SN54144 are characterized for operation over the full military temperature range of -55°C to 125°C; the SN74143 and SN74144 are characterized for operation from 0°C to 70°C.

Functions of the inputs and outputs of these devices are as follows:

FUNCTION	PIN NO.	DESCRIPTION
CLEAR INPUT	3	When low, resets and holds counter at 0. Must be high for normal counting.
CLOCK INPUT	2	Each positive-going transition will increment the counter provided that the circuit is in the normal counting mode (serial and parallel count enable inputs low, clear input high).
PARALLEL COUNT ENABLE INPUT (PCEI)	23	Must be low for normal counting mode. When high, counter will be inhibited. Logic level must not be changed when the clock is low.
SERIAL COUNT ENABLE INPUT (SCEI)	1	Must be low for normal counting mode, also must be low to enable maximum count output to go low. When high, counter will be inhibited and maximum count output will be driven high. Logic level must not be changed when the clock is low.
MAXIMUM COUNT OUTPUT	22	Will go low when the counter is at 9 and serial count enable input is low. Will return high when the counter changes to 0 and will remain high during counts 1 through 8. Will remain high (inhibited) as long as serial count enable input is high.
LATCH STROBE INPUT	21	When low, data in latches follow the data in the counter. When high, the data in the latches are held constant, and the counter may be operated independently.
LATCH OUTPUTS (Q_A, Q_B, Q_C, Q_D)	17, 18, 19, 20	The BCD data that drives the decoder can be stored in the 4-bit latch and is available at these outputs for driving other logic and/or processors. The binary weights of the outputs are: $Q_A = 1$, $Q_B = 2$, $Q_C = 4$, $Q_D = 8$.
DECIMAL POINT INPUT	7	Must be high to display decimal point. The decimal point is not displayed when this input is low or when the display is blanked.
BLANKING INPUT (BI)	5	When high, will blank (turn off) the entire display and force RBO low. Must be low for normal display. May be pulsed to implement intensity control of the display.
RIPPLE-BLANKING INPUT (RBI)	4	When the data in the latches is BCD 0, a low input will blank the entire display and force the RBO low. This input has no effect if the data in the latches is other than 0.
RIPPLE-BLANKING OUTPUT (RBO)	6	Supplies ripple blanking information for the ripple blanking input of the next decade. Provides a low if BI is high, or if RBI is low and the data in the latches is BCD 0; otherwise, this output is high. This pin has a resistive pull-up circuit suitable for performing a wire-AND function with any open-collector output. Whenever this pin is low the entire display will be blanked; therefore, this pin may be used as an active-low blanking input.
LED/LAMP DRIVER OUTPUTS (a, b, c, d, e, f, g, dp)	15, 16, 14, 9 11, 10, 13, 8	Outputs for driving seven-segment LED's or lamps and their decimal points. See segment identification and resultant displays on following page.

7

TEXAS INSTRUMENTS
INCORPORATED
POST OFFICE BOX 5012 • DALLAS, TEXAS 75222

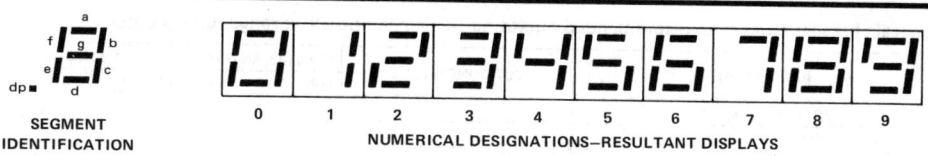

SEGMENT IDENTIFICATION

NUMERICAL DESIGNATIONS—RESULTANT DISPLAYS

schematics of inputs and outputs

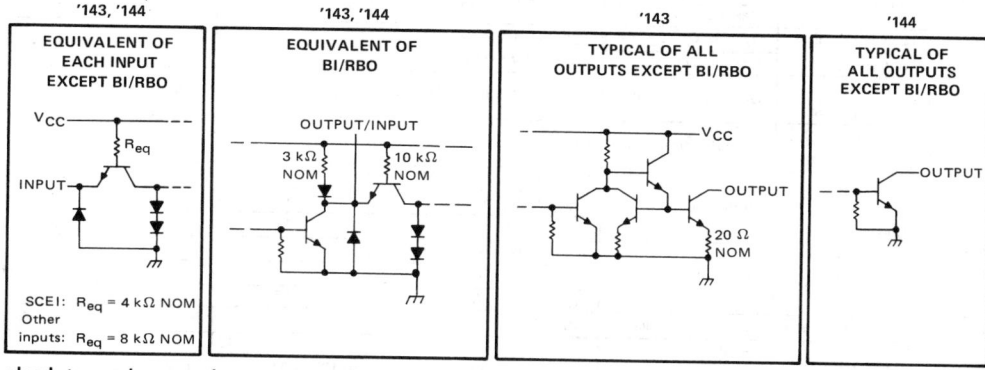

'143, '144	'143, '144	'143	'144
EQUIVALENT OF EACH INPUT EXCEPT BI/RBO	EQUIVALENT OF BI/RBO	TYPICAL OF ALL OUTPUTS EXCEPT BI/RBO	TYPICAL OF ALL OUTPUTS EXCEPT BI/RBO

absolute maximum ratings over operating free-air temperature range (unless otherwise noted)

Supply voltage, V_{CC} (see Note 1) . . . . 7 V
Input voltage . . . . 5.5 V
Off-state voltage at outputs "a" thru "g" and "dp", '144 . . . . 15 V
Off-state current at outputs "a" thru "g" and "dp", '143 . . . . 250 µA
Continuous total power dissipation at (or below) 70°C free-air temperature (see Note 2) . . . . 1.4 W
Operating free-air temperature range: SN54' Circuits . . . . −55°C to 125°C
SN74' Circuits . . . . 0°C to 70°C
Storage temperature range . . . . −65°C to 150°C

NOTES: 1. Voltage values are with respect to network ground terminal.
2. For the SN54143 and SN54144 in the N and W packages, this rating applies at (or below) 80°C free-air temperature. For operation above this temperature, derate linearly at the rate of 11.7 mW/°C for the W package and 14.7 mW/°C for the N package. No derating is required for these devices in the J package.

recommended operating conditions

		SN54143, SN54144			SN74143, SN74144			UNIT
		MIN	NOM	MAX	MIN	NOM	MAX	
Supply voltage, V_{CC}		4.5	5	5.5	4.75	5	5.25	V
On-state voltage at outputs a thru g and dp ('143 only)		1		5	1		5	V
High-level output current, I_{OH}	Q_A, Q_B, Q_C, Q_D			−240			−240	µA
	Maximum count			−560			−560	
	RBO			−120			−120	
Low-level output current, I_{OL}	Q_A, Q_B, Q_C, Q_D, RBO			4.8			4.8	mA
	Maximum count			11.2			11.2	
Clock pulse width, $t_{w(clock)}$	High logic level	25			25			ns
	Low logic level	55			55			
Clear pulse width, $t_{w(clear)}$		25			25			ns
Setup time, t_{su}	Serial and parallel carry	30↑			30↑			ns
	Clear inactive state	60↑			60↑			
Operating free-air temperature, T_A		−55		125	0		70	°C

↑The arrow indicates that the rising edge of the clock pulse is used for reference.

TEXAS INSTRUMENTS
INCORPORATED
POST OFFICE BOX 5012 • DALLAS, TEXAS 75222

electrical characteristics over recommended operating free-air temperature range (unless otherwise noted)

PARAMETER		TEST CONDITIONS†	SN54143, SN74143 MIN	TYP‡	MAX	SN54144, SN74144 MIN	TYP‡	MAX	UNIT
V_{IH}	High-level input voltage		2			2			V
V_{IL}	Low-level input voltage				0.8			0.8	V
V_{IK}	Input clamp voltage	V_{CC} = MIN, I_I = −12 mA			−1.5			−1.5	V
V_{OH}	High-level output voltage	RBO	V_{CC} = MIN, V_{IH} = 2 V, V_{IL} = 0.8 V, I_{OH} = MAX	2.4			2.4			V
		Q_A, Q_B, Q_C, Q_D								
		Maximum count								
V_{OL}	Low-level output voltage	Q_A, Q_B, Q_C, Q_D, RBO	V_{CC} = MIN, V_{IH} = 2 V, V_{IL} = 0.8 V, I_{OL} = MAX			0.4			0.4	V
		Maximum count								
$V_{O(off)}$	Off-state output voltage	Outputs a thru g, dp	V_{CC} = MAX, I_{OH} = 250 μA	7			15			V
$V_{O(on)}$	On-State output voltage	Outputs a thru g, dp	V_{CC} = MIN, See Note 3						0.6	V
$I_{O(on)}$	On-state output current	Outputs a thru g	V_{CC} = MIN, V_O = 1 V	9	15					mA
			V_{CC} = 5 V, V_O = 2 V		15					
			V_{CC} = MAX, V_O = 5 V		15	22				
		Output dp	V_{CC} = MIN, V_O = 1 V	4.5	7					
			V_{CC} = 5 V, V_O = 2 V		7					
			V_{CC} = MAX, V_O = 5 V		7	12				
I_I	Input current at maximum input voltage		V_{CC} = MAX, V_I = 5.5 V			1			1	mA
I_{IH}	High-level input current	Serial carry	V_{CC} = MAX, V_I = 2.4 V			40			40	μA
		RBO node		−0.12	−0.5		−0.12	−0.5		mA
		Other inputs				20			20	μA
I_{IL}	Low-level input current	Serial carry	V_{CC} = MAX, V_I = 0.4 V, See Note 4			−1.6			−1.6	mA
		RBO node			−1.5	−2.4		−1.5	−2.4	
		Other inputs				−0.8			−0.8	
I_{OS}	Short-circuit output current	Q_A, Q_B, Q_C, Q_D	V_{CC} = MAX	−9		−27.5	−9		−27.5	mA
		Maximum count		−15		−55	−15		−55	
I_{CC}	Supply current		V_{CC} = MAX, See Note 5		56	93		56	93	mA

†For conditions shown as MIN or MAX, use the appropriate value specified under recommended operating conditions for the applicable type.
‡All typical values are at V_{CC} = 5 V, T_A = 25°C.
NOTES: 3. For SN54144, I_{OL} = 20 mA; for SN74144, I_{OL} = 25 mA.
4. I_{IL} at RBO node is tested with BI grounded and RBI at 4.5 V.
5. I_{CC} is measured after the following conditions are established:
    a) Strobe = RBI = DP = 4.5 V
    b) Parallel count enable = serial count enable = BI = GND
    c) Clear (⎍) then clock until all outputs are on (⌁)
    d) For '143, outputs "a" through "g" and "dp" = 2.5 V, all other outputs open. For '144, all outputs are open.

switching characteristics, V_{CC} = 5 V, T_A = 25°C

PARAMETER §	FROM (INPUT)	TO (OUTPUT)	TEST CONDITIONS	MIN	TYP	MAX	UNIT
f_{max}				12	18		MHz
t_{PLH}	Serial look-ahead	Maximum count	C_L = 15 pF, R_L = 560 Ω, See Note 6		12	20	ns
t_{PHL}					23	35	
t_{PLH}	Clock	Maximum count			26	40	ns
t_{PHL}					29	45	
t_{PLH}	Clock	Q_A, Q_B, Q_C, Q_D	C_L = 15 pF, R_L = 1.2 kΩ, See Note 6		28	45	ns
t_{PHL}					38	60	
t_{PHL}	Clear	Q_A, Q_B, Q_C, Q_D			57	90	ns

§ f_{max} ≡ Maximum clock frequency, t_{PLH} ≡ Propagation delay time, low-to-high-level output,
t_{PHL} ≡ Propagation delay time, high-to-low-level output
NOTE 6: Load circuit and voltage waveforms are shown on page 3-10.

TEXAS INSTRUMENTS
INCORPORATED
POST OFFICE BOX 5012 • DALLAS, TEXAS 75222

functional block diagram

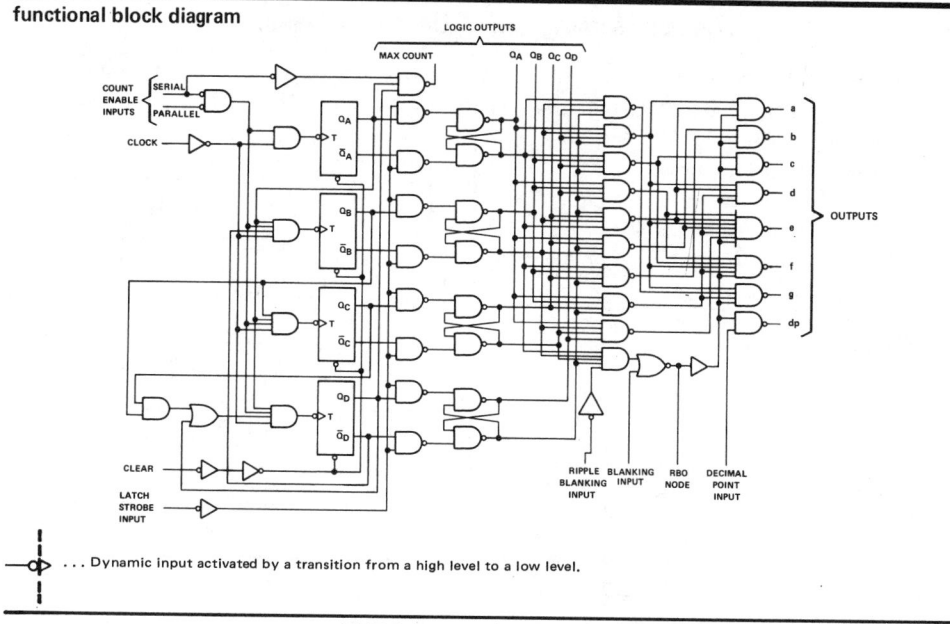

... Dynamic input activated by a transition from a high level to a low level.

TYPICAL APPLICATION DATA

This application demonstrates how the drivers may be cascaded for N-bit display applications. It features:

Synchronous, look-ahead counting

Ripple blanking of leading zeros; blanking of trailing zeros (not illustrated) can also be implemented

Overriding blanking for total suppression or intensity modulation of display

Direct parallel clear

Latch strobe permits counter to acquire next display while viewing current display

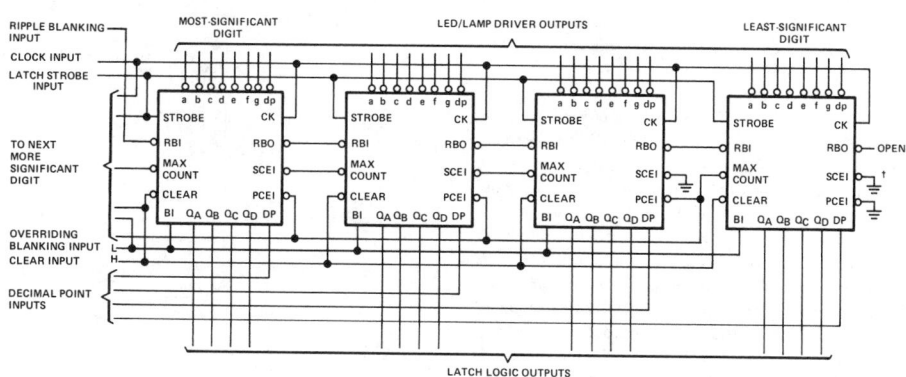

†The serial count-enable input of the least-significant digit is normally grounded; however, it may be used as a count-enable control for the entire counter (high to disable, low to count) provided the logic level on this pin is not changed while the clock line is low or false counting may result.

FOR USE AS LAMP, RELAY, OR MOS DRIVERS

- Full Decoding of Input Logic
- SN54145, SN74145, and SN74LS145 Have 80-mA Sink-Current Capability
- All Outputs Are Off for Invalid BCD Input Conditions
- Low Power Dissipation of 'LS145 . . . 35 mW Typical

logic

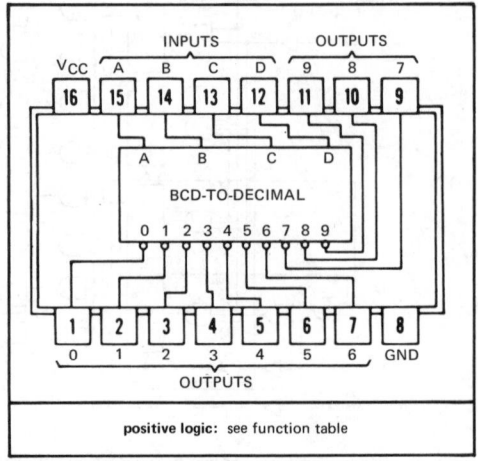

SN54145, SN54LS145 . . . J OR W PACKAGE
SN74145, SN74LS145 . . . J OR N PACKAGE
(TOP VIEW)

positive logic: see function table

FUNCTION TABLE

NO.	INPUTS				OUTPUTS									
	D	C	B	A	0	1	2	3	4	5	6	7	8	9
0	L	L	L	L	L	H	H	H	H	H	H	H	H	H
1	L	L	L	H	H	L	H	H	H	H	H	H	H	H
2	L	L	H	L	H	H	L	H	H	H	H	H	H	H
3	L	L	H	H	H	H	H	L	H	H	H	H	H	H
4	L	H	L	L	H	H	H	H	L	H	H	H	H	H
5	L	H	L	H	H	H	H	H	H	L	H	H	H	H
6	L	H	H	L	H	H	H	H	H	H	L	H	H	H
7	L	H	H	H	H	H	H	H	H	H	H	L	H	H
8	H	L	L	L	H	H	H	H	H	H	H	H	L	H
9	H	L	L	H	H	H	H	H	H	H	H	H	H	L
INVALID	H	L	H	L	H	H	H	H	H	H	H	H	H	H
INVALID	H	L	H	H	H	H	H	H	H	H	H	H	H	H
INVALID	H	H	L	L	H	H	H	H	H	H	H	H	H	H
INVALID	H	H	L	H	H	H	H	H	H	H	H	H	H	H
INVALID	H	H	H	L	H	H	H	H	H	H	H	H	H	H
INVALID	H	H	H	H	H	H	H	H	H	H	H	H	H	H

H = high level (off), L = low level (on)

description

These monilithic BCD-to-decimal decoder/drivers consist of eight inverters and ten four-input NAND gates. The inverters are connected in pairs to make BCD input data available for decoding by the NAND gates. Full decoding of valid BCD input logic ensures that all outputs remain off for all invalid binary input conditions. These decoders feature high-performance, n-p-n output transistors designed for use as indicator/relay drivers or as open-collector logic-circuit drivers. Each of the high-breakdown output transistors (15 volts) of the SN54145, SN74145, or SN74LS145 will sink up to 80 milliamperes of current. Each input is one Series 54/74 or Series 54LS/74LS standard load, respectively. Inputs and outputs are entirely compatible for use with TTL or DTL logic circuits, and the outputs are compatible for interfacing with most MOS integrated circuits. Power dissipation is typically 215 milliwatts for the '145 and 35 milliwatts for the 'LS145.

functional block diagram

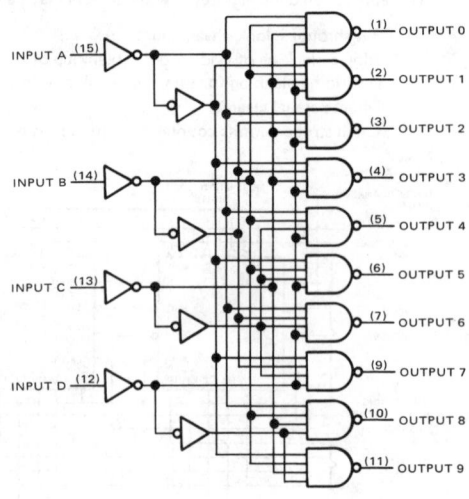

TEXAS INSTRUMENTS
INCORPORATED
POST OFFICE BOX 5012 • DALLAS, TEXAS 75222

absolute maximum ratings over operating free-air temperature range (unless otherwise noted)

Supply voltage, V_{CC} (see Note 1)	7 V
Input voltage	5.5 V
Maximum current into any output (off-state)	1 mA
Operating free-air temperature range: SN54145	-55°C to 125°C
SN74145	0°C to 70°C
Storage temperature range	-65°C to 150°C

NOTE 1: Voltage values are with respect to network ground terminal.

recommended operating conditions

	SN54145			SN74145			UNIT
	MIN	NOM	MAX	MIN	NOM	MAX	
Supply voltage, V_{CC}	4.5	5	5.5	4.75	5	5.25	V
Off-state output voltage, $V_{O(off)}$			15			15	V
Operating free-air temperature, T_A	-55		125	0		70	$^{\circ}$C

electrical characteristics over recommended operating free-air temperature range (unless otherwise noted)

PARAMETER		TEST CONDITIONS†		MIN	TYP‡	MAX	UNIT
V_{IH}	High-level input voltage			2			V
V_{IL}	Low-level input voltage					0.8	V
V_{IK}	Input clamp voltage	V_{CC} = MIN, I_I = -12 mA				-1.5	V
$I_{O(off)}$	Off-state output current	V_{CC} = MIN, V_{IH} = 2 V, V_{IL} = 0.8 V, $V_{O(off)}$ = 15 V				250	µA
$V_{O(on)}$	On-state output voltage	V_{CC} = MIN, V_{IH} = 2 V, V_{IL} = 0.8 V	$I_{O(on)}$ = 80 mA		0.5	0.9	V
			$I_{O(on)}$ = 20 mA			0.4	
I_I	Input current at maximum input voltage	V_{CC} = MAX, V_I = 5.5 V				1	mA
I_{IH}	High-level input current	V_{CC} = MAX, V_I = 2.4 V				40	µA
I_{IL}	Low-level input current	V_{CC} = MAX, V_I = 0.4 V				-1.6	mA
I_{CC}	Supply current	V_{CC} = MAX, See Note 2	SN54145		43	62	mA
			SN74145		43	70	

†For conditions shown as MIN or MAX, use the appropriate value specified under recommended operating conditions.
‡All typical values are at V_{CC} = 5 V, T_A = 25°C.
NOTE 2: I_{CC} is measured with all inputs grounded and outputs open.

switching characteristics, V_{CC} = 5 V, T_A = 25°C

PARAMETER		TEST CONDITIONS		MIN	MAX	UNIT
t_{PLH}	Propagation delay time, low-to-high-level output	C_L = 15 pF, R_L = 100 Ω, See Note 3			50	ns
t_{PHL}	Propagation delay time, high-to-low-level output				50	ns

NOTE 3: Load circuit and waveforms are shown on page 3-10.

schematics of inputs and outputs

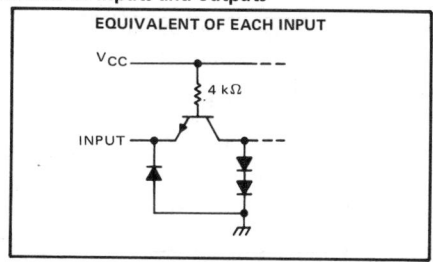

EQUIVALENT OF EACH INPUT

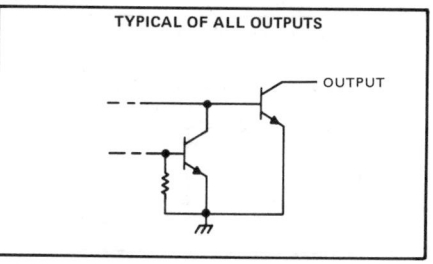

TYPICAL OF ALL OUTPUTS

TYPES SN54LS145, SN74LS145
BCD-TO-DECIMAL DECODERS/DRIVERS

REVISED OCTOBER 1976

absolute maximum ratings over operating free-air temperature range (unless otherwise noted)

Supply voltage, V_{CC} (see Note 1) . . . . 7 V
Input voltage . . . . 7 V
Operating free-air temperature range: SN54LS145 . . . . -55°C to 125°C
                               SN74LS145 . . . . 0°C to 70°C
Storage temperature range . . . . -65°C to 150°C

NOTE 1: Voltage values are with respect to network ground terminal.

recommended operating conditions

	SN54LS145			SN74LS145			UNIT
	MIN	NOM	MAX	MIN	NOM	MAX	
Supply voltage, V_{CC}	4.5	5	5.5	4.75	5	5.25	V
Off-state output voltage, $V_{O(off)}$			15			15	V
Operating free-air temperature, T_A	-55		125	0		70	$^{\circ}$C

electrical characteristics over recommended operating free-air temperature range (unless otherwise noted)

PARAMETER		TEST CONDITIONS[†]		SN54LS145			SN74LS145			UNIT
				MIN	TYP[‡]	MAX	MIN	TYP[‡]	MAX	
V_{IH}	High-level input voltage			2			2			V
V_{IL}	Low-level input voltage					0.7			0.8	V
V_{IK}	Input clamp voltage	V_{CC} = MIN,	I_I = -18 mA			-1.5			-1.5	V
$I_{O(off)}$	Off-state output current	V_{CC} = MIN, V_{IL} = V_{IL} max,	V_{IH} = 2 V, V_{OH} = 15 V			250			250	μA
$V_{O(on)}$	On-state output voltage	V_{CC} = MIN,	I_{OL} = 12 mA	0.25		0.4	0.25		0.4	V
		V_{IH} = 2 V,	I_{OL} = 24 mA					0.35	0.5	
		V_{IL} = V_{IL} max	I_{OL} = 80 mA					2.3	3	
I_I	Input current at maximum input voltage	V_{CC} = MAX,	V_I = 7 V			0.1			0.1	mA
I_{IH}	High-level input current	V_{CC} = MAX,	V_I = 2.7 V			20			20	μA
I_{IL}	Low-level input current	V_{CC} = MAX,	V_I = 0.4 V			-0.4			-0.4	mA
I_{CC}	Supply current	V_{CC} = MAX,	See Note 2		7	13		7	13	mA

[†]For conditions shown as MIN or MAX, use the appropriate value specified under recommended operating conditions.
[‡]All typical values are at V_{CC} = 5 V, T_A = 25°C.
NOTE 2: I_{CC} is measured with all inputs grounded and outputs open.

switching characteristics, V_{CC} = 5 V, T_A = 25°C

PARAMETER		TEST CONDITIONS	MIN	MAX	UNIT
t_{PLH}	Propagation delay time, low-to-high-level output	C_L = 45 pF, R_L = 665 Ω, See Note 4		50	ns
t_{PHL}	Propagation delay time, high-to-low-level output			50	ns

NOTE 4: Load circuit and waveforms are shown on page 3-11.

schematic of inputs and outputs

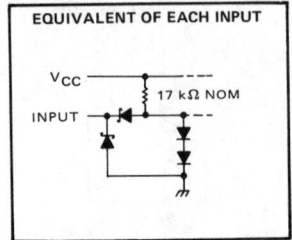

EQUIVALENT OF EACH INPUT

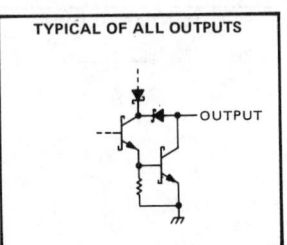

TYPICAL OF ALL OUTPUTS

7

TEXAS INSTRUMENTS
INCORPORATED
POST OFFICE BOX 5012 • DALLAS, TEXAS 75222

TTL MSI

TYPES SN54147, SN54148, SN54LS147, SN54LS148, SN74147, SN74148 (TIM9907), SN74LS147, SN74LS148
10-LINE-TO-4-LINE AND 8-LINE-TO-3-LINE PRIORITY ENCODERS

BULLETIN NO. DL-S 7711727, OCTOBER 1976—REVISED AUGUST 1977

'147, 'LS147

- Encodes 10-Line Decimal to 4-Line BCD

- Applications Include:

  Keyboard Encoding
  Range Selection

'148, 'LS148

- Encodes 8 Data Lines to 3-Line Binary (Octal)

- Applications Include:

  N-Bit Encoding
  Code Converters and Generators

TYPE	TYPICAL DATA DELAY	TYPICAL POWER DISSIPATION
'147	10 ns	225 mW
'148	10 ns	190 mW
'LS147	15 ns	60 mW
'LS148	15 ns	60 mW

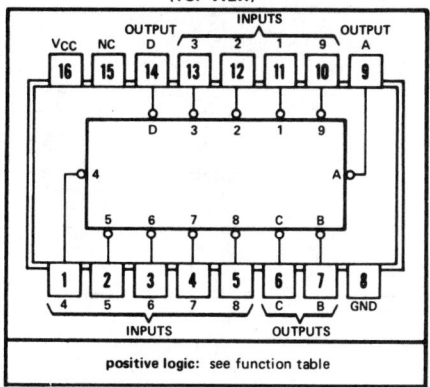

SN54147, SN54LS147 . . . J OR W PACKAGE
SN74147, SN74LS147 . . . J OR N PACKAGE
(TOP VIEW)

positive logic: see function table

NC—No internal connection

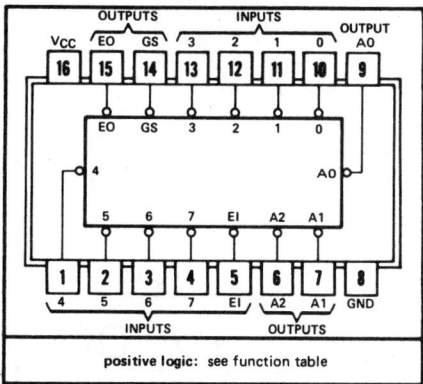

SN54148, SN54LS148 . . . J OR W PACKAGE
SN74148, SN74LS148 . . . J OR N PACKAGE
(TOP VIEW)

positive logic: see function table

description

These TTL encoders feature priority decoding of the inputs to ensure that only the highest-order data line is encoded. The '147 and 'LS147 encode nine data lines to four-line (8-4-2-1) BCD. The implied decimal zero condition requires no input condition as zero is encoded when all nine data lines are at a high logic level. The '148 and 'LS148 encode eight data lines to three-line (4-2-1) binary (octal). Cascading circuitry (enable input EI and enable output EO) has been provided to allow octal expansion without the need for external circuitry. For all types, data inputs and outputs are active at the low logic level. All inputs are buffered to represent one normalized Series 54/74 or 54LS/74LS load, respectively.

7

'147, 'LS147 FUNCTION TABLE

INPUTS									OUTPUTS			
1	2	3	4	5	6	7	8	9	D	C	B	A
H	H	H	H	H	H	H	H	H	H	H	H	H
X	X	X	X	X	X	X	X	L	L	H	H	L
X	X	X	X	X	X	X	L	H	L	H	H	H
X	X	X	X	X	X	L	H	H	H	L	L	L
X	X	X	X	X	L	H	H	H	H	L	L	H
X	X	X	X	L	H	H	H	H	H	L	H	L
X	X	X	L	H	H	H	H	H	H	L	H	H
X	X	L	H	H	H	H	H	H	H	H	L	L
X	L	H	H	H	H	H	H	H	H	H	L	H
L	H	H	H	H	H	H	H	H	H	H	H	L

'148, 'LS148 FUNCTION TABLE

INPUTS									OUTPUTS				
EI	0	1	2	3	4	5	6	7	A2	A1	A0	GS	EO
H	X	X	X	X	X	X	X	X	H	H	H	H	H
L	H	H	H	H	H	H	H	H	H	H	H	H	L
L	X	X	X	X	X	X	X	L	L	L	L	L	H
L	X	X	X	X	X	X	L	H	L	L	H	L	H
L	X	X	X	X	X	L	H	H	L	H	L	L	H
L	X	X	X	X	L	H	H	H	L	H	H	L	H
L	X	X	X	L	H	H	H	H	H	L	L	L	H
L	X	X	L	H	H	H	H	H	H	L	H	L	H
L	X	L	H	H	H	H	H	H	H	H	L	L	H
L	L	H	H	H	H	H	H	H	H	H	H	L	H

H = high logic level, L = low logic level, X = irrelevant

TEXAS INSTRUMENTS
INCORPORATED
POST OFFICE BOX 5012 • DALLAS, TEXAS 75222

TYPES SN54147, SN54148, SN54LS147, SN54LS148, SN74147, SN74148 (TIM9907), SN74LS147, SN74LS148
10-LINE-TO-4-LINE AND 8-LINE-TO-3-LINE PRIORITY ENCODERS

functional block diagrams

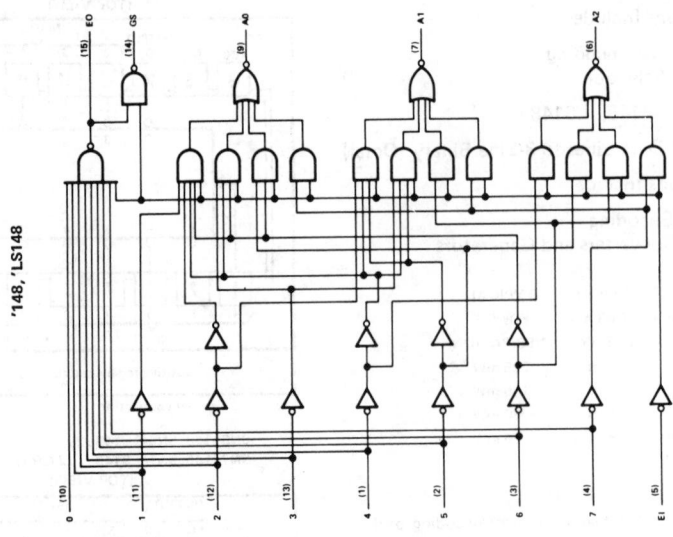

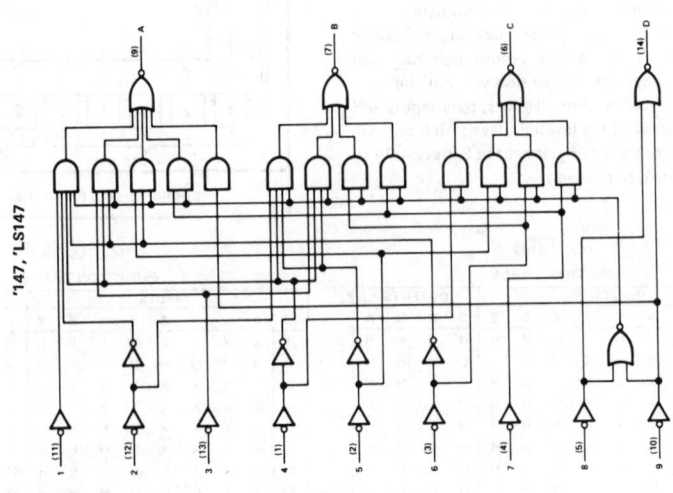

TEXAS INSTRUMENTS
INCORPORATED
POST OFFICE BOX 5012 • DALLAS, TEXAS 75222

schematics of inputs and outputs

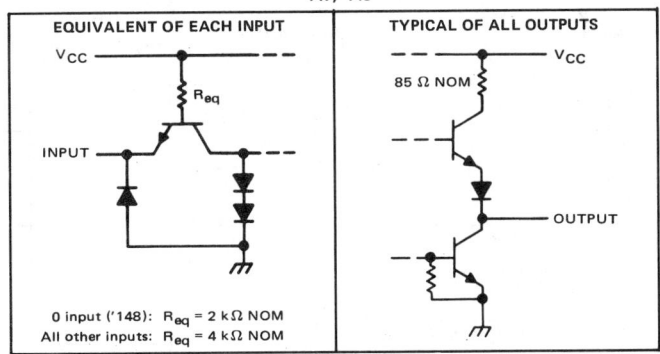

'147, '148

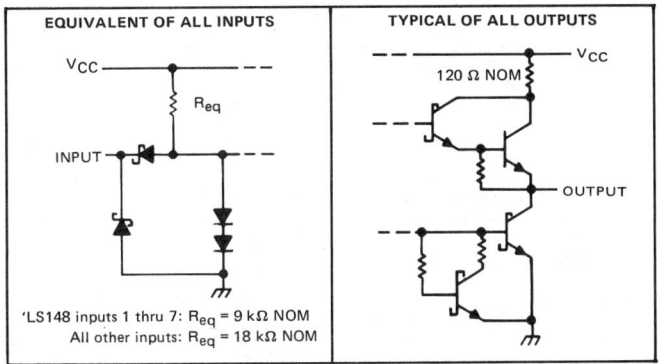

'LS147, 'LS148

absolute maximum ratings over operating free-air temperature range (unless otherwise noted)

Supply voltage, V_{CC} (see Note 1) . . . . 7 V
Input voltage: '147, '148 . . . . 5.5 V
         'LS147, 'LS148 . . . . 7 V
Interemitter voltage: '148 only (see Note 2) . . . . 5.5 V
Operating free-air temperature range: SN54', SN54LS Circuits . . . . −55°C to 125°C
                        SN74', SN74LS Circuits . . . . 0°C to 70°C
Storage temperature range . . . . −65°C to 150°C

NOTES: 1. Voltage values, except intermitter voltage, are with respect to network ground terminal.
        2. This is the voltage between two emitters of a multiple-emitter transistor. For '148 circuits, this rating applies between any two of
          the eight data lines, 0 through 7.

recommended operating conditions

	SN54'			SN74'			SN54LS'			SN74LS'			UNIT
	MIN	NOM	MAX	MIN	NOM	MAX	MIN	NOM	MAX	MIN	NOM	MAX	
Supply voltage, V_{CC}	4.5	5	5.5	4.75	5	5.25	4.5	5	5.5	4.75	5	5.25	V
High-level output current, I_{OH}			−800			−800			−400			−400	µA
Low-level output current, I_{OL}			16			16			4			8	mA
Operating free-air temperature, T_A	−55		125	0		70	−55		125	0		70	°C

electrical characteristics over recommended operating free-air temperature range (unless otherwise noted)

PARAMETER		TEST CONDITIONS†	'147 MIN	'147 TYP‡	'147 MAX	'148 MIN	'148 TYP‡	'148 MAX	UNIT
V_{IH}	High-level input voltage		2			2			V
V_{IL}	Low-level input voltage				0.8			0.8	V
V_{IK}	Input clamp voltage	V_{CC} = MIN, I_I = −12 mA			−1.5			−1.5	V
V_{OH}	High-level output voltage	V_{CC} = MIN, V_{IH} = 2 V, V_{IL} = 0.8 V, I_{OH} = −800 µA	2.4	3.3		2.4	3.3		V
V_{OL}	Low-level output voltage	V_{CC} = MIN, V_{IH} = 2 V, V_{IL} = 0.8 V, I_{OL} = 16 mA		0.2	0.4		0.2	0.4	V
I_I	Input current at maximum input voltage	V_{CC} = MAX, V_I = 5.5 V			1			1	mA
I_{IH}	High-level input current — 0 input	V_{CC} = MAX, V_I = 2.4 V						40	µA
I_{IH}	High-level input current — Any input except 0	V_{CC} = MAX, V_I = 2.4 V			40			80	µA
I_{IL}	Low-level input current — 0 input	V_{CC} = MAX, V_I = 0.4 V						−1.6	mA
I_{IL}	Low-level input current — Any input except 0	V_{CC} = MAX, V_I = 0.4 V			−1.6			−3.2	mA
I_{OS}	Short-circuit output current§	V_{CC} = MAX	−35		−85	−35		−85	mA
I_{CC}	Supply current — Condition 1	V_{CC} = MAX, See Note 3		50	70		40	60	mA
I_{CC}	Supply current — Condition 2	V_{CC} = MAX, See Note 3		42	62		35	55	mA

NOTE 3: For '147, I_{CC} (condition 1) is measured with input 7 grounded, other inputs and outputs open; I_{CC} (condition 2) is measured with all inputs and outputs open. For '148, I_{CC} (condition 1) is measured with inputs 7 and EI grounded, other inputs and outputs open; I_{CC} (condition 2) is measured with all inputs and outputs open.

† For conditions shown as MIN or MAX, use the appropriate value specified under recommended operating conditions.
‡ All typical values are at V_{CC} = 5 V, T_A = 25°C.
§ Not more than one output should be shorted at a time.

SN54147, SN74147 switching characteristics, V_{CC} = 5 V, T_A = 25°C

PARAMETER¶	FROM (INPUT)	TO (OUTPUT)	WAVEFORM	TEST CONDITIONS	MIN	TYP	MAX	UNIT
t_{PLH}	Any	Any	In-phase output	C_L = 15 pF, R_L = 400 Ω, See Note 4		9	14	ns
t_{PHL}	Any	Any	In-phase output			7	11	ns
t_{PLH}	Any	Any	Out-of-phase output			13	19	ns
t_{PHL}	Any	Any	Out-of-phase output			12	19	ns

SN54148, SN74148 switching characteristics, V_{CC} = 5 V, T_A = 25°C

PARAMETER¶	FROM (INPUT)	TO (OUTPUT)	WAVEFORM	TEST CONDITIONS	MIN	TYP	MAX	UNIT
t_{PLH}	0 thru 7	A0, A1, or A2	In-phase output			10	15	ns
t_{PHL}	0 thru 7	A0, A1, or A2	In-phase output			9	14	ns
t_{PLH}	0 thru 7	A0, A1, or A2	Out-of-phase output			13	19	ns
t_{PHL}	0 thru 7	A0, A1, or A2	Out-of-phase output			12	19	ns
t_{PLH}	0 thru 7	EO	Out-of-phase output	C_L = 15 pF, R_L = 400 Ω, See Note 4		6	10	ns
t_{PHL}	0 thru 7	EO	Out-of-phase output			14	25	ns
t_{PLH}	0 thru 7	GS	In-phase output			18	30	ns
t_{PHL}	0 thru 7	GS	In-phase output			14	25	ns
t_{PLH}	EI	A0, A1, or A2	In-phase output			10	15	ns
t_{PHL}	EI	A0, A1, or A2	In-phase output			10	15	ns
t_{PLH}	EI	GS	In-phase output			8	12	ns
t_{PHL}	EI	GS	In-phase output			10	15	ns
t_{PLH}	EI	EO	In-phase output			10	15	ns
t_{PHL}	EI	EO	In-phase output			17	30	ns

¶ t_{PLH} ≡ propagation delay time, low-to-high-level output
t_{PHL} ≡ propagation delay time, high-to-low-level output
NOTE 4: Load circuits and waveforms are shown on page 3-10.

7

TEXAS INSTRUMENTS
INCORPORATED
POST OFFICE BOX 5012 • DALLAS, TEXAS 75222

electrical characteristics over recommended operating free-air temperature range (unless otherwise noted)

PARAMETER		TEST CONDITIONS†		SN54LS' MIN	TYP‡	MAX	SN74LS' MIN	TYP‡	MAX	UNIT
V_{IH} High-level input voltage				2			2			V
V_{IL} Low-level input voltage						0.7			0.8	V
V_{IK} Input clamp voltage		V_{CC} = MIN, I_I = −18 mA				−1.5			−1.5	V
V_{OH} High-level output voltage		V_{CC} = MIN, V_{IH} = 2 V, V_{IL} = 0.8 V, I_{OH} = −400 µA		2.5	3.4		2.7	3.4		V
V_{OL} Low-level output voltage		V_{CC} = MIN, V_{IH} = 2 V, V_{IL} = V_{IL}max	I_{OL} = 4 mA		0.25	0.4		0.25	0.4	V
			I_{OL} = 8 mA					0.35	0.5	
I_I Input current at maximum input voltage	'LS148 inputs 1 thru 7	V_{CC} = MAX, V_I = 7 V				0.2			0.2	mA
	All other inputs					0.1			0.1	
I_{IH} High-level input current	'LS148 inputs 1 thru 7	V_{CC} = MAX, V_I = 2.7 V				40			40	µA
	All other inputs					20			20	
I_{IL} Low-level input current	'LS148 inputs 1 thru 7	V_{CC} = MAX, V_I = 0.4 V				−0.8			−0.8	mA
	All other inputs					−0.4			−0.4	
I_{OS} Short-circuit output current§		V_{CC} = MAX		−20		−100	−20		−100	mA
I_{CC} Supply current		V_{CC} = MAX, See Note 5	Condition 1		12	20		12	20	mA
			Condition 2		10	17		10	17	mA

NOTE 5: For 'LS147, I_{CC} (condition 1) is measured with input 7 grounded, other inputs and outputs open; I_{CC} (condition 2) is measured with all inputs and outputs open. For 'LS148, I_{CC} (condition 1) is measured with inputs 7 and EI grounded, other inputs and outputs open, I_{CC} (condition 2) is measured with all inputs and outputs open.
†For conditions shown as MIN or MAX, use the appropriate value specified under recommended operating conditions.
‡All typical values are at V_{CC} = 5 V, T_A = 25°C.
§Not more than one output should be shorted at a time.

SN54LS147, SN74LS147 switching characteristics, V_{CC} = 5 V, T_A = 25°C

PARAMETER¶	FROM (INPUT)	TO (OUTPUT)	WAVEFORM	TEST CONDITIONS	MIN'	TYP	MAX	UNIT
t_{PLH}	Any	Any	In-phase output	C_L = 15 pF, R_L = 2 kΩ, See Note 4		12	18	ns
t_{PHL}						12	18	
t_{PLH}	Any	Any	Out-of-phase output			21	33	ns
t_{PHL}						15	23	

SN54LS148, SN74LS148 switching characteristics, V_{CC} = 5 V, T_A = 25°C

PARAMETER¶	FROM (INPUT)	TO (OUTPUT)	WAVEFORM	TEST CONDITIONS	MIN	TYP	MAX	UNIT
t_{PLH}	0 thru 7	A0, A1, or A2	In-phase output			14	18	ns
t_{PHL}						15	25	
t_{PLH}	0 thru 7	A0, A1, or A2	Out-of-phase output			20	36	ns
t_{PHL}						16	29	
t_{PLH}	0 thru 7	EO	Out-of-phase output			7	18	ns
t_{PHL}						25	40	
t_{PLH}	0 thru 7	GS	In-phase output	C_L = 15 pF, R_L = 2 kΩ, See Note 6		35	55	ns
t_{PHL}						9	21	
t_{PLH}	EI	A0, A1, or A2	In-phase output			16	25	ns
t_{PHL}						12	25	
t_{PLH}	EI	GS	In-phase output			12	17	ns
t_{PHL}						14	36	
t_{PLH}	EI	EO	In-phase output			12	21	ns
t_{PHL}						23	35	

¶t_{PLH} ≡ propagation delay time, low-to-high-level output
t_{PHL} ≡ propagation delay time, high-to-low-level output
NOTE 6: Load circuits and waveforms are shown on page 3-11.

7

TYPICAL APPLICATION DATA

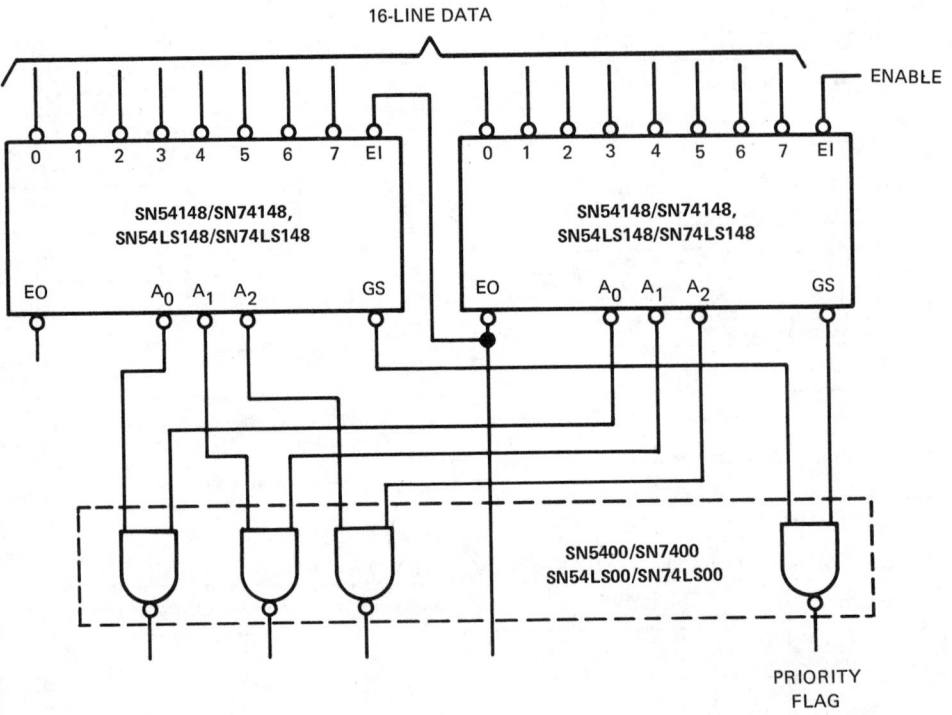

Full 4-bit binary 16-line-to-4-line encoding can be implemented as shown above. The enable input must be low to enable the function. Decoding with 2-input NAND gates produces true (active-high) data for the 4-line binary outputs. If active-low data is required, the SN5408/SN7408 or SN54LS08/SN74LS08 AND gate may be used, respectively.

7

TEXAS INSTRUMENTS
INCORPORATED
POST OFFICE BOX 5012 • DALLAS, TEXAS 75222

TYPES SN54150, SN54151A, SN54152A, SN54LS151, SN54LS152, SN54S151, SN74150, SN74151A, SN74LS151, SN74S151
DATA SELECTORS/MULTIPLEXERS

BULLETIN NO. DL-S 7611819, DECEMBER 1972—REVISED OCTOBER 1976

- '150 Selects One-of-Sixteen Data Sources
- Others Select One-of-Eight Data Sources
- Performs Parallel-to-Serial Conversion
- Permits Multiplexing from N Lines to One Line
- Also For Use as Boolean Function Generator
- Input-Clamping Diodes Simplify System Design
- Fully Compatible with Most TTL and DTL Circuits

TYPE	TYPICAL AVERAGE PROPAGATION DELAY TIME DATA INPUT TO W OUTPUT	TYPICAL POWER DISSIPATION
'150	11 ns	200 mW
'151A	8 ns	145 mW
'152A	8 ns	130 mW
'LS151	11 ns[†]	30 mW
'LS152	11 ns[†]	28 mW
'S151	4.5 ns	225 mW

[†]Tentative data

description

These monolithic data selectors/multiplexers contain full on-chip binary decoding to select the desired data source. The '150 selects one-of-sixteen data sources; the '151A, '152A, 'LS151, 'LS152, and 'S151 select one-of-eight data sources. The '150, '151A, 'LS151, and 'S151 have a strobe input which must be at a low logic level to enable these devices. A high level at the strobe forces the W output high, and the Y output (as applicable) low.

The '151A, 'LS151, and 'S151 feature complementary W and Y outputs whereas the '150, '152A, and 'LS152 have an inverted (W) output only.

The '151A and '152A incorporate address buffers which have symmetrical propagation delay times through the complementary paths. This reduces the possibility of transients occurring at the output(s) due to changes made at the select inputs, even when the '151A outputs are enabled (i.e., strobe low).

SN54150 . . . J OR W PACKAGE
SN74150 . . . J OR N PACKAGE
(TOP VIEW)

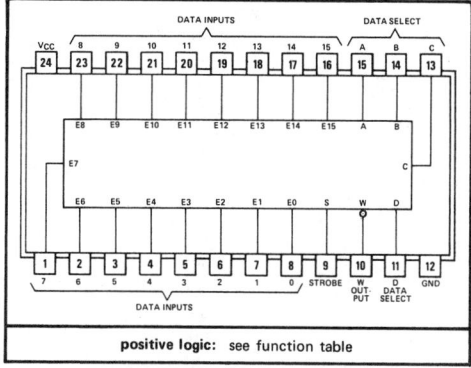

positive logic: see function table

SN54151A, SN54LS151, SN54S151 . . . J OR W PACKAGE
SN74151A SN74LS151, SN74S151 . . . J OR N PACKAGE
(TOP VIEW)

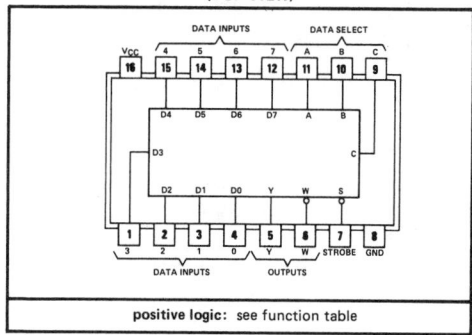

positive logic: see function table

SN54152A, SN54LS152 . . . W PACKAGE
(TOP VIEW)

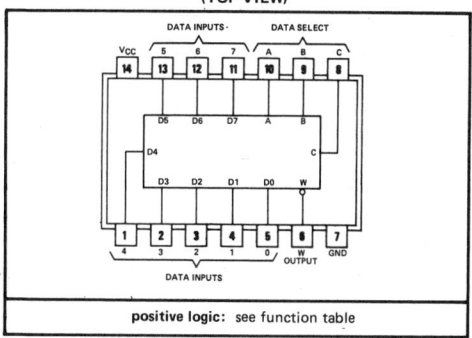

positive logic: see function table

7

TEXAS INSTRUMENTS
INCORPORATED
POST OFFICE BOX 5012 • DALLAS, TEXAS 75222

logic

'150
FUNCTION TABLE

INPUTS				OUTPUT
SELECT			STROBE	W
D	C	B	A	S	
X	X	X	X	H	H
L	L	L	L	L	$\overline{E0}$
L	L	L	H	L	$\overline{E1}$
L	L	H	L	L	$\overline{E2}$
L	L	H	H	L	$\overline{E3}$
L	H	L	L	L	$\overline{E4}$
L	H	L	H	L	$\overline{E5}$
L	H	H	L	L	$\overline{E6}$
L	H	H	H	L	$\overline{E7}$
H	L	L	L	L	$\overline{E8}$
H	L	L	H	L	$\overline{E9}$
H	L	H	L	L	$\overline{E10}$
H	L	H	H	L	$\overline{E11}$
H	H	L	L	L	$\overline{E12}$
H	H	L	H	L	$\overline{E13}$
H	H	H	L	L	$\overline{E14}$
H	H	H	H	L	$\overline{E15}$

'151A, 'LS151, 'S151
FUNCTION TABLE

INPUTS				OUTPUTS	
SELECT			STROBE	Y	W
C	B	A	S		
X	X	X	H	L	H
L	L	L	L	D0	$\overline{D0}$
L	L	H	L	D1	$\overline{D1}$
L	H	L	L	D2	$\overline{D2}$
L	H	H	L	D3	$\overline{D3}$
H	L	L	L	D4	$\overline{D4}$
H	L	H	L	D5	$\overline{D5}$
H	H	L	L	D6	$\overline{D6}$
H	H	H	L	D7	$\overline{D7}$

H = high level, L = low level, X = irrelevant
E0, E1 . . . E15 = the complement of the level of the respective E input
D0, D1 . . . D7 = the level of the D respective input

'152A, 'LS152
FUNCTION TABLE

SELECT INPUTS			OUTPUT
C	B	A	W
L	L	L	$\overline{D0}$
L	L	H	$\overline{D1}$
L	H	L	$\overline{D2}$
L	H	H	$\overline{D3}$
H	L	L	$\overline{D4}$
H	L	H	$\overline{D5}$
H	H	L	$\overline{D6}$
H	H	H	$\overline{D7}$

functional block diagrams

'150

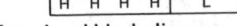
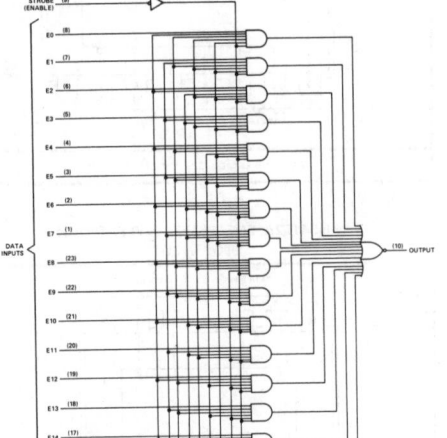

'151A, 'LS151, 'S151

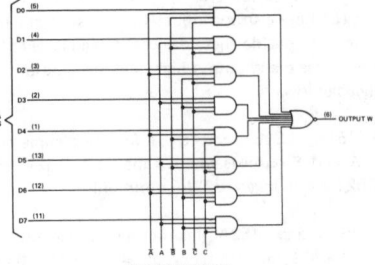

'152A, 'LS152

ADDRESS BUFFERS FOR '151A, '152A
ADDRESS BUFFERS FOR 'LS151, 'S151, 'LS152

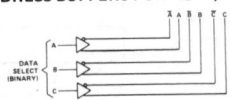

TEXAS INSTRUMENTS
INCORPORATED
POST OFFICE BOX 5012 • DALLAS, TEXAS 75222

107

absolute maximum ratings over operating free-air temperature range (unless otherwise noted)

Supply voltage, V_{CC} (see Note 1) . . . . 7 V
Input voltage (see Note 2) . . . . 5.5 V
Operating free-air temperature range: SN54' Circuits . . . . $-55°$C to $125°$C
SN74' Circuits . . . . $0°$C to $70°$C
Storage temperature range: . . . . $-65°$C to $150°$C

NOTES: 1. Voltage values are with respect to network ground terminal.
2. For the '150, input voltages must be zero or positive with respect to network ground terminal.

recommended operating conditions

	SN54'			SN74'			UNIT
	MIN	NOM	MAX	MIN	NOM	MAX	
Supply voltage, V_{CC}	4.5	5	5.5	4.75	5	5.25	V
High-level output current, I_{OH}			−800			−800	μA
Low-level output current, I_{OL}			16			16	mA
Operating free-air temperature, T_A	−55		125	0		70	°C

electrical characteristics over recommended operating free-air temperature range (unless otherwise noted)

PARAMETER		TEST CONDITIONS†		'150			'151A, '152A			UNIT
				MIN	TYP‡	MAX	MIN	TYP‡	MAX	
V_{IH}	High-level input voltage			2			2			V
V_{IL}	Low-level input voltage					0.8			0.8	V
V_{IK}	Input clamp voltage	V_{CC} = MIN,	I_I = −8 mA						−1.5	V
V_{OH}	High-level output voltage	V_{CC} = MIN, V_{IH} = 2 V, V_{IL} = 0.8 V, I_{OH} = −800 μA		2.4	3.4		2.4	3.4		V
V_{OL}	Low-level output voltage	V_{CC} = MIN, V_{IH} = 2 V, V_{IL} = 0.8 V, I_{OL} = 16 mA			0.2	0.4		0.2	0.4	V
I_I	Input current at maximum input voltage	V_{CC} = MAX, V_I = 5.5 V				1			1	mA
I_{IH}	High-level input current	V_{CC} = MAX, V_I = 2.4 V				40			40	μA
I_{IL}	Low-level input current	V_{CC} = MAX, V_I = 0.4 V				−1.6			−1.6	mA
I_{OS}	Short-circuit output current§	V_{CC} = MAX	SN54'	−20		−55	−20		−55	mA
			SN74'	−18		−55	−18		−55	
I_{CC}	Supply current	V_{CC} = MAX, See Note 3	'150		40	68				mA
			'151A					29	48	
			'152A					26	43	

†For conditions shown as MIN or MAX, use the appropriate value specified under recommended operating conditions for the applicable device type.
‡All typical values at V_{CC} = 5 V, T_A = 25°C.
§Not more than one output of the '151A should be shorted at a time.
NOTE 3: I_{CC} is measured with the strobe and data select inputs at 4.5 V, all other inputs and outputs open.

7

TEXAS INSTRUMENTS
INCORPORATED
POST OFFICE BOX 5012 • DALLAS, TEXAS 75222

switching characteristics, $V_{CC} = 5$ V, $T_A = 25°C$

PARAMETER¶	FROM (INPUT)	TO (OUTPUT)	TEST CONDITIONS	'150			'151A, '152A			UNIT
				MIN	TYP	MAX	MIN	TYP	MAX	
t_{PLH}	A, B, or C	Y						25	38	ns
t_{PHL}	(4 levels)							25	38	
t_{PLH}	A, B, C, or D	W			23	35		17	26	ns
t_{PHL}	(3 levels)				22	33		19	30	
t_{PLH}	Strobe	Y	$C_L = 15$ pF,					21	33	ns
t_{PHL}			$R_L = 400$ Ω,					22	33	
t_{PLH}	Strobe	W	See Note 4		15.5	24		14	21	ns
t_{PHL}					21	30		15	23	
t_{PLH}	D0 thru D7	Y						13	20	ns
t_{PHL}								18	27	
t_{PLH}	E0 thru E15, or	W			13	20		8	14	ns
t_{PHL}	D0 thru D7				8.5	14		8	14	

¶$t_{PLH} \equiv$ propagation delay time, low-to-high-level output
$t_{PHL} \equiv$ propagation delay time, high-to-low-level output
NOTE 4: Load circuit and voltage waveforms are shown on page 3-10.

schematics of inputs and outputs

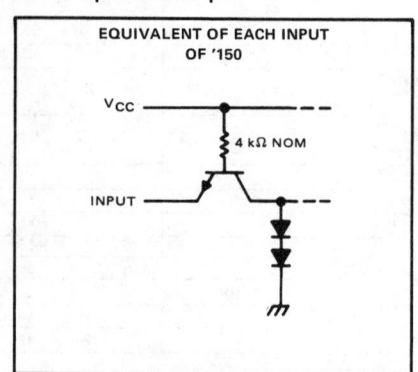

EQUIVALENT OF EACH INPUT OF '150

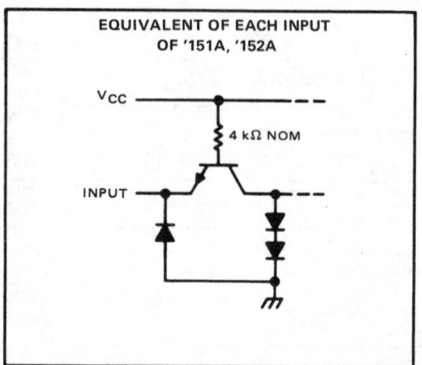

EQUIVALENT OF EACH INPUT OF '151A, '152A

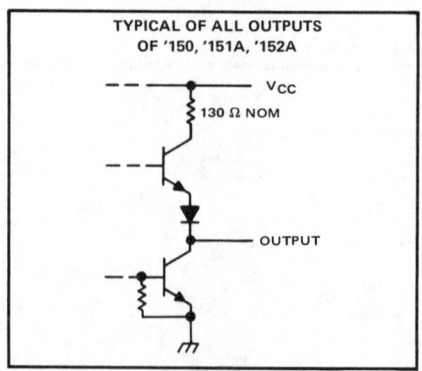

TYPICAL OF ALL OUTPUTS OF '150, '151A, '152A

TEXAS INSTRUMENTS
INCORPORATED
POST OFFICE BOX 5012 • DALLAS, TEXAS 75222

TYPES SN54LS151, SN54LS152, SN74LS151
DATA SELECTORS/MULTIPLEXERS

absolute maximum ratings over operating free-air temperature range (unless otherwise noted)

Supply voltage, V_{CC} (see Note 1) . . . . 7 V
Input voltage . . . . 7 V
Operating free-air temperature range: SN54LS' Circuits . . . . $-55°C$ to $125°C$
SN74LS' Circuits . . . . $0°C$ to $70°C$
Storage temperature range . . . . $-65°C$ to $150°C$

NOTE 1: Voltage values are with respect to network ground terminal.

recommended operating conditions

	SN54LS'			SN74LS'			UNIT
	MIN	NOM	MAX	MIN	NOM	MAX	
Supply voltage, V_{CC}	4.5	5	5.5	4.75	5	5.25	V
High-level output current, I_{OH}			−400			−400	μA
Low-level output current, I_{OL}			4			8	mA
Operating free-air temperature, T_A	−55		125	0		70	$°C$

electrical characteristics over recommended operating free-air temperature range (unless otherwise noted)

PARAMETER		TEST CONDITIONS[†]		SN54LS'			SN74LS'			UNIT
				MIN	TYP[‡]	MAX	MIN	TYP[‡]	MAX	
V_{IH}	High-level input voltage			2			2			V
V_{IL}	Low-level input voltage					0.7			0.8	V
V_{IK}	Input clamp voltage	V_{CC} = MIN, I_I = −18 mA				−1.5			−1.5	V
V_{OH}	High-level output voltage	V_{CC} = MIN, V_{IH} = 2 V, $V_{IL} = V_{IL}$ max, I_{OH} = −400 μA		2.5	3.4		2.7	3.4		V
V_{OL}	Low-level output voltage	V_{CC} = MIN, V_{IH} = 2 V, $V_{IL} = V_{IL}$ max	I_{OL} = 4 mA		0.25	0.4		0.25	0.4	V
			I_{OL} = 8 mA					0.35	0.5	
I_I	Input current at maximum input voltage	V_{CC} = MAX, V_I = 7 V				0.1			0.1	mA
I_{IH}	High-level input current	V_{CC} = MAX, V_I = 2.7 V				20			20	μA
I_{IL}	Low-level input current	V_{CC} = MAX, V_I = 0.4 V				−0.4			−0.4	mA
I_{OS}	Short-circuit output current[§]	V_{CC} = MAX		−20		−100	−20		−100	mA
I_{CC}	Supply current	V_{CC} = MAX, Outputs open, All inputs at 4.5 V	'LS151		6.0	10		6.0	10	mA
			'LS152		5.6	9				

[†]For conditions shown as MIN or MAX, use the appropriate value specified under recommended operating conditions for the applicable device type.
[‡]All typical values are at V_{CC} = 5 V, T_A = $25°C$.
[§]Not more than one output should be shorted at a time and duration of short-circuit should not exceed one second.

7

switching characteristics, V_{CC} = 5 V, T_A = 25°C

PARAMETER¶	FROM (INPUT)	TO (OUTPUT)	TEST CONDITIONS	SN54LS', SN74LS'			UNIT
				MIN	TYP	MAX	
tPLH	A, B, or C	Y			27	43	ns
tPHL	(4 levels)				18	30	
tPLH	A, B, or C	W			14	23	ns
tPHL	(3 levels)				20	32	
tPLH	Strobe	Y	C_L = 15 pF,		26	42	ns
tPHL			R_L = 2 kΩ,		20	32	
tPLH	Strobe	W	See Note 5		15	24	ns
tPHL					18	30	
tPLH	Any D	Y			20	32	ns
tPHL					16	26	
tPLH	Any D	W			13	21	ns
tPHL					12	20	

¶ t_{PLH} ≡ Propagation delay time, low-to-high-level output
  t_{PHL} ≡ Propagation delay time, high-to-low-level output
NOTE 5: See load circuits and waveforms on page 3-11.

schematics of inputs and outputs

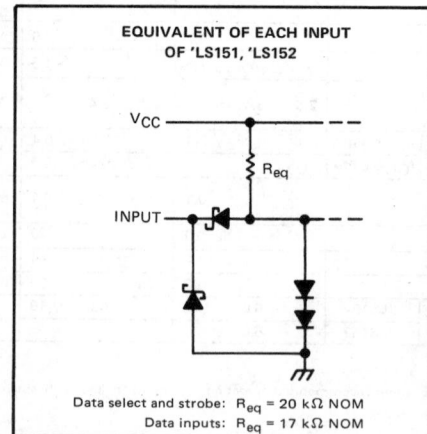

EQUIVALENT OF EACH INPUT
OF 'LS151, 'LS152

V_{CC}

R_{eq}

INPUT

Data select and strobe: R_{eq} = 20 kΩ NOM
Data inputs: R_{eq} = 17 kΩ NOM

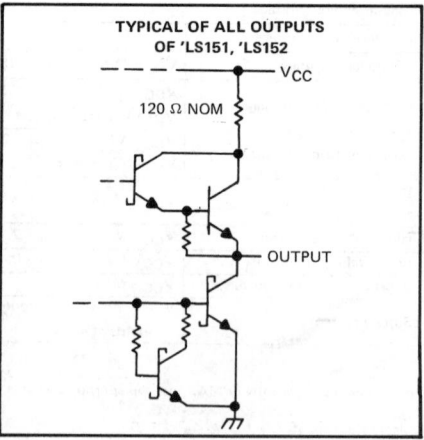

TYPICAL OF ALL OUTPUTS
OF 'LS151, 'LS152

V_{CC}

120 Ω NOM

OUTPUT

7

TEXAS INSTRUMENTS
INCORPORATED
POST OFFICE BOX 5012 • DALLAS, TEXAS 75222

absolute maximum ratings over operating free-air temperature range (unless otherwise noted)

Supply voltage, V_{CC} (see Note 1)	7 V
Input voltage	5.5 V
Operating free-air temperature range: SN54S151 Circuits	$-55^{\circ}C$ to $125^{\circ}C$
SN74S151 Circuits	$0^{\circ}C$ to $70^{\circ}C$
Storage temperature range	$-65^{\circ}C$ to $150^{\circ}C$

NOTE 1: Voltage values are with respect to network ground terminal.

recommended operating conditions

	SN54S151			SN74S151			UNIT
	MIN	NOM	MAX	MIN	NOM	MAX	
Supply voltage, V_{CC}	4.5	5	5.5	4.75	5	5.25	V
High-level output current, I_{OH}			-1			-1	mA
Low-level output current, I_{OL}			20			20	mA
Operating free-air temperature, T_A	-55		125	0		70	$^{\circ}C$

electrical characteristics over recommended operating free-air temperature range (unless otherwise noted)

PARAMETER		TEST CONDITIONS[†]		MIN	TYP[‡]	MAX	UNIT
V_{IH}	High-level input voltage			2			V
V_{IL}	Low-level input voltage					0.8	V
V_{IK}	Input clamp voltage	V_{CC} = MIN, I_I = -18 mA				-1.2	V
V_{OH}	High-level output voltage	V_{CC} = MIN, V_{IH} = 2 V, V_{IL} = 0.8 V, I_{OH} = -1 mA	SN54S'	2.5	3.4		V
			SN74S'	2.7	3.4		
V_{OL}	Low-level output voltage	V_{CC} = MIN, V_{IH} = 2 V, V_{IL} = 0.8 V, I_{OL} = 20 mA				0.5	V
I_I	Input current at maximum input voltage	V_{CC} = MAX, V_I = 5.5 V				1	mA
I_{IH}	High-level input current	V_{CC} = MAX, V_I = 2.7 V				50	μA
I_{IL}	Low-level input current	V_{CC} = MAX, V_I = 0.5 V				-2	mA
I_{OS}	Short-circuit output current[§]	V_{CC} = MAX		-40		-100	mA
I_{CC}	Supply current	V_{CC} = MAX, All inputs at 4.5 V, All outputs open			45	70	mA

[†]For conditions shown as MIN or MAX, use the appropriate value specified under recommended operating conditions for the applicable device type.
[‡]All typical values are at V_{CC} = 5 V, $T_A = 25^{\circ}C$.
[§]Not more than one output should be shorted at a time, and duration of the short-circuit should not exceed one second.

7

TYPES SN54S151, SN74S151
DATA SELECTORS/MULTIPLEXERS

switching characteristics, V_{CC} = 5 V, T_A = 25°C

PARAMETER¶	FROM (INPUT)	TO (OUTPUT)	TEST CONDITIONS	SN54S151, SN74S151			UNIT
				MIN	TYP	MAX	
t_{PLH}	A, B, or C	Y			12	18	ns
t_{PHL}	(4 levels)				12	18	
t_{PLH}	A, B, or C	W			10	15	ns
t_{PHL}	(3 levels)				9	13.5	
t_{PLH}	Any D	Y	C_L = 15 pF,		8	12	ns
t_{PHL}			R_L = 280 Ω,		8	12	
t_{PLH}	Any D	W	See Note 4		4.5	7	ns
t_{PHL}					4.5	7	
t_{PLH}	Strobe	Y			11	16.5	ns
t_{PHL}					12	18	
t_{PLH}	Strobe	W			9	13	ns
t_{PHL}					8.5	12	

¶ t_{PLH} ≡ Propagation delay time, low-to-high-level output
t_{PHL} ≡ Propagation delay time, high-to-low-level output
NOTE 4: See load circuits and waveforms on page 3-10.

schematics of inputs and outputs

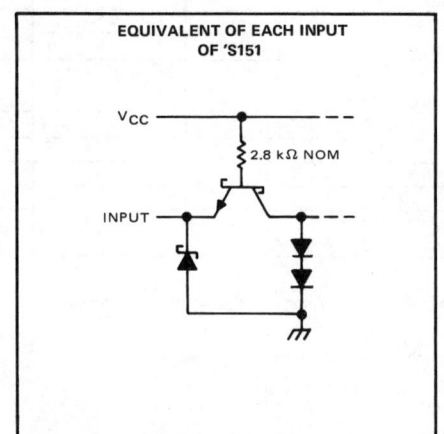

EQUIVALENT OF EACH INPUT
OF 'S151

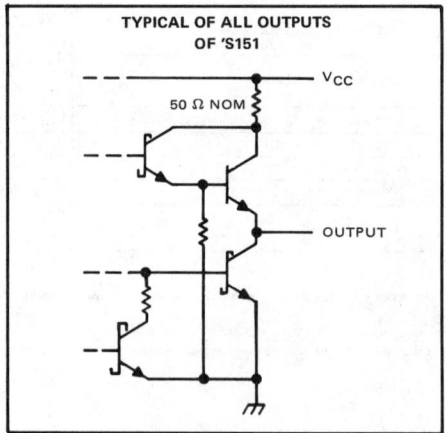

TYPICAL OF ALL OUTPUTS
OF 'S151

TEXAS INSTRUMENTS
INCORPORATED
POST OFFICE BOX 5012 • DALLAS, TEXAS 75222

TYPES SN54153, SN54L153, SN54LS153, SN54S153, SN74153, SN74L153, SN74LS153, SN74S153
DUAL 4-LINE-TO-1-LINE DATA SELECTORS/MULTIPLEXERS
BULLETIN NO. DL-S 7611852, DECEMBER 1972 — REVISED OCTOBER 1976

SN54153, SN54LS153, SN54S153 . . . J OR W PACKAGE
SN54L153 . . . J PACKAGE
SN74153, SN74L153, SN74LS153, SN74S153 . . . J OR N PACKAGE
(TOP VIEW)

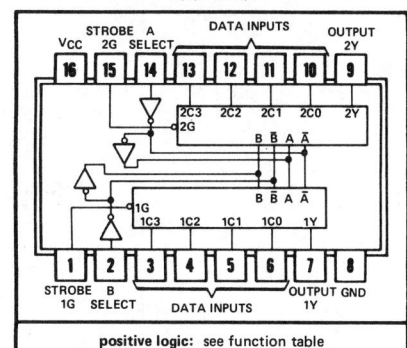

positive logic: see function table

- Permits Multiplexing from N lines to 1 line
- Performs Parallel-to-Serial Conversion
- Strobe (Enable) Line Provided for Cascading (N lines to n lines)
- High-Fan-Out, Low-Impedance, Totem-Pole Outputs
- Fully Compatible with most TTL and DTL Circuits

TYPE	TYPICAL AVERAGE PROPAGATION DELAY TIMES			TYPICAL POWER DISSIPATION
	FROM DATA	FROM STROBE	FROM SELECT	
'153	14 ns	17 ns	22 ns	180 mW
'L153	27 ns	34 ns	44 ns	90 mW
'LS153	14 ns	19 ns	22 ns	31 mW
'S153	6 ns	9.5 ns	12 ns	225 mW

description

Each of these monolithic, data selectors/multiplexers contains inverters and drivers to supply fully complementary, on-chip, binary decoding data selection to the AND-OR-invert gates. Separate strobe inputs are provided for each of the two four-line sections.

FUNCTION TABLE

SELECT INPUTS		DATA INPUTS				STROBE	OUTPUT
B	A	C0	C1	C2	C3	G	Y
X	X	X	X	X	X	H	L
L	L	L	X	X	X	L	L
L	L	H	X	X	X	L	H
L	H	X	L	X	X	L	L
L	H	X	H	X	X	L	H
H	L	X	X	L	X	L	L
H	L	X	X	H	X	L	H
H	H	X	X	X	L	L	L
H	H	X	X	X	H	L	H

Select inputs A and B are common to both sections.
H = high level, L = low level, X = irrelevant

absolute maximum ratings over operating free-air temperature range (unless otherwise noted)

Supply voltage, V_{CC} (see Note 1) . . . . 7 V
Input voltage: '153, 'L153, 'S153 . . . . 5.5 V
             'LS153 . . . . 7 V
Operating free-air temperature range: SN54', SN54L', SN54LS', SN54S' Circuits . . . . −55°C to 125°C
                      SN74', SN74L', SN74LS', SN74S' Circuits . . . . 0°C to 70°C
Storage temperature range . . . . −65°C to 150°C

NOTE 1: Voltage values are with respect to network ground terminal.

TEXAS INSTRUMENTS
INCORPORATED
POST OFFICE BOX 5012 • DALLAS, TEXAS 75222

TYPES SN54153, SN54L153, SN54LS153, SN54S153, SN74153, SN74L153, SN74LS153, SN74S153
DUAL 4-LINE-TO-1-LINE DATA SELECTORS/MULTIPLEXERS

REVISED OCTOBER 1976

functional block diagram

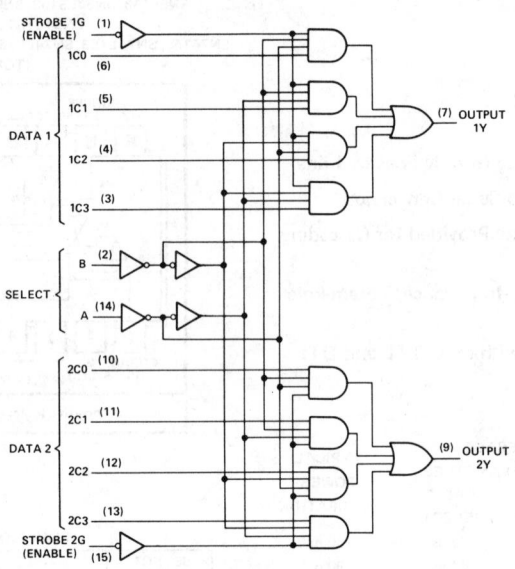

schematics of inputs and outputs

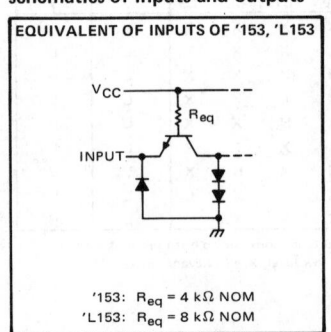

EQUIVALENT OF INPUTS OF '153, 'L153

'153: R_{eq} = 4 kΩ NOM
'L153: R_{eq} = 8 kΩ NOM

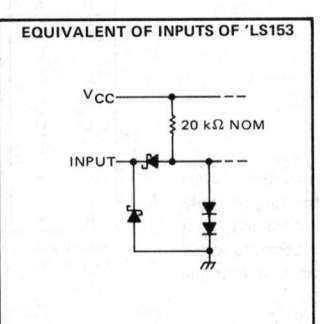

EQUIVALENT OF INPUTS OF 'LS153

20 kΩ NOM

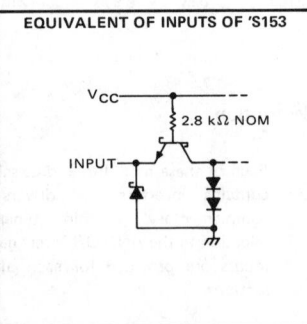

EQUIVALENT OF INPUTS OF 'S153

2.8 kΩ NOM

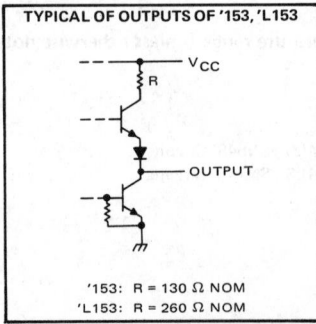

TYPICAL OF OUTPUTS OF '153, 'L153

'153: R = 130 Ω NOM
'L153: R = 260 Ω NOM

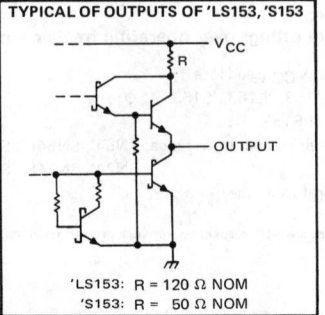

TYPICAL OF OUTPUTS OF 'LS153, 'S153

'LS153: R = 120 Ω NOM
'S153: R = 50 Ω NOM

TEXAS INSTRUMENTS
INCORPORATED
POST OFFICE BOX 5012 • DALLAS, TEXAS 75222

10

recommended operating conditions

	SN54153			SN74153			UNIT
	MIN	NOM	MAX	MIN	NOM	MAX	
Supply voltage, V_{CC}	4.5	5	5.5	4.75	5	5.25	V
High-level output current, I_{OH}			−800			−800	μA
Low-level output current, I_{OL}			16			16	mA
Operating free-air temperature, T_A	−55		125	0		70	°C

electrical characteristics over recommended operating free-air temperature range (unless otherwise noted)

PARAMETER		TEST CONDITIONS[†]	SN54153			SN74153			UNIT
			MIN	TYP[‡]	MAX	MIN	TYP[‡]	MAX	
V_{IH}	High-level input voltage		2			2			V
V_{IL}	Low-level input voltage				0.8			0.8	V
V_{IK}	Input clamp voltage	V_{CC} = MIN, I_I = −12 mA			−1.5			−1.5	V
V_{OH}	High-level output voltage	V_{CC} = MIN, V_{IH} = 2 V, V_{IL} = 0.8 V, I_{OH} = −800 μA	2.4	3.4		2.4	3.4		V
V_{OL}	Low-level output voltage	V_{CC} = MIN, V_{IH} = 2 V, V_{IL} = 0.8 V, I_{OL} = 16 mA		0.2	0.4		0.2	0.4	V
I_I	Input current at maximum input voltage	V_{CC} = MAX, V_I = 5.5 V			1			1	mA
I_{IH}	High-level input current	V_{CC} = MAX, V_I = 2.4 V			40			40	μA
I_{IL}	Low-level input current	V_{CC} = MAX, V_I = 0.4 V			−1.6			−1.6	mA
I_{OS}	Short-circuit output current[§]	V_{CC} = MAX	−20		−55	−18		−57	mA
I_{CCL}	Supply current, output low	V_{CC} = MAX, See Note 2		36	52		36	60	mA

[†]For conditions shown as MIN or MAX, use the appropriate value specified under recommended operating conditions.
[‡]All typical values are at V_{CC} = 5 V, T_A = 25°C.
[§]Not more than one output should be shorted at a time.
NOTE 2: I_{CCL} is measured with the outputs open and all inputs grounded.

switching characteristics, V_{CC} = 5 V, T_A = 25°C

PARAMETER[¶]	FROM (INPUT)	TO (OUTPUT)	TEST CONDITIONS	MIN	TYP	MAX	UNIT
t_{PLH}	Data	Y			12	18	ns
t_{PHL}	Data	Y			15	23	ns
t_{PLH}	Select	Y	C_L = 30 pF, R_L = 400 Ω,		22	34	ns
t_{PHL}	Select	Y	See Note 3		22	34	ns
t_{PLH}	Strobe	Y			19	30	ns
t_{PHL}	Strobe	Y			15	23	ns

[¶]t_{PLH} ≡ propagation delay time, low-to-high-level output
t_{PHL} ≡ propagation delay time, high-to-low-level output
NOTE 3: Load circuit and voltage waveforms are shown on page 3-10.

recommended operating conditions

	SN54L153			SN74L153			UNIT
	MIN	NOM	MAX	MIN	NOM	MAX	
Supply voltage, V_{CC}	4.5	5	5.5	4.75	5	5.25	V
High-level output current, I_{OH}			−400			−400	μA
Low-level output current, I_{OL}			8			8	mA
Operating free-air temperature, T_A	−55		125	0		70	°C

electrical characteristics over recommended operating free-air temperature range (unless otherwise noted)

PARAMETER		TEST CONDITIONS[†]	SN54L153			SN74L153			UNIT
			MIN	TYP[‡]	MAX	MIN	TYP[‡]	MAX	
V_{IH}	High-level input voltage		2			2			V
V_{IL}	Low-level input voltage				0.8			0.8	V
V_{IK}	Input clamp voltage	V_{CC} = MIN, I_I = −12 mA			−1.5			−1.5	V
V_{OH}	High-level output voltage	V_{CC} = MIN, V_{IH} = 2 V, V_{IL} = 0.8 V, I_{OH} = −400 μA	2.4	3.4		2.4	3.4		V
V_{OL}	Low-level output voltage	V_{CC} = MIN, V_{IH} = 2 V, V_{IL} = 0.8 V, I_{OL} = 8 mA		0.2	0.4		0.2	0.4	V
I_I	Input current at maximum input voltage	V_{CC} = MAX, V_I = 5.5 V			1			1	mA
I_{IH}	High-level input current	V_{CC} = MAX, V_I = 2.4 V			20			20	μA
I_{IL}	Low-level input current	V_{CC} = MAX, V_I = 0.4 V			−0.8			−0.8	mA
I_{OS}	Short-circuit output current[§]	V_{CC} = MAX	−10		−28	−9		−30	mA
I_{CCL}	Supply current, output low	V_{CC} = MAX, See Note 2		18	26		18	30	mA

[†] For conditions shown as MIN or MAX, use the appropriate value specified under recommended operating conditions.

[‡] All typical values are at V_{CC} = 5 V, T_A = 25°C.
[§] Not more than one output should be shorted at a time.
NOTE 2: I_{CCL} is measured with the outputs open and all inputs grounded.

switching characteristics, V_{CC} = 5 V, T_A = 25°C

PARAMETER[¶]	FROM INPUT	TO OUTPUT	TEST CONDITIONS	MIN	TYP	MAX	UNIT
t_{PLH}	Data	Y			24	36	ns
t_{PHL}	Data	Y			30	46	ns
t_{PLH}	Select	Y	C_L = 30 pF, R_L = 400 Ω,		44	68	ns
t_{PHL}	Select	Y	See Note 3		44	68	ns
t_{PLH}	Strobe	Y			38	60	ns
t_{PHL}	Strobe	Y			30 ·	46	ns

[¶] t_{PLH} ≡ propagation delay time, low-to-high-level output
  t_{PHL} ≡ propagation delay time, high-to-low-level output
NOTE 3: Load circuit and voltage waveforms are shown on page 3-10.

1076

TEXAS INSTRUMENTS
INCORPORATED
POST OFFICE BOX 5012 • DALLAS, TEXAS 75222

recommended operating conditions

	SN54LS153 MIN	NOM	MAX	SN74LS153 MIN	NOM	MAX	UNIT
Supply voltage, V_{CC}	4.5	5	5.5	4.75	5	5.25	V
High-level output current, I_{OH}			−400			−400	μA
Low-level output current, I_{OL}			4			8	mA
Operating free-air temperature, T_A	−55		125	0		70	°C

electrical characteristics over recommended operating free-air temperature range (unless otherwise noted)

PARAMETER		TEST CONDITIONS[†]		SN54LS153 MIN	TYP[‡]	MAX	SN74LS153 MIN	TYP[‡]	MAX	UNIT
V_{IH}	High-level input voltage			2			2			V
V_{IL}	Low-level input voltage					0.7			0.8	V
V_{IK}	Input clamp voltage	V_{CC} = MIN,	I_I = −18 mA			−1.5			−1.5	V
V_{OH}	High-level output voltage	V_{CC} = MIN, V_{IH} = 2 V, V_{IL} = V_{IL} max, I_{OH} = −400 μA		2.5	3.4		2.7	3.4		V
V_{OL}	Low-level output voltage	V_{CC} = MIN, V_{IH} = 2 V, V_{IL} = V_{IL} max	I_{OL} = 4 mA		0.25	0.4		0.25	0.4	V
			I_{OL} = 8 mA					0.35	0.5	
I_I	Input current at maximum input voltage	V_{CC} = MAX,	V_I = 7 V			0.1			0.1	mA
I_{IH}	High-level input current	V_{CC} = MAX,	V_I = 2.7 V			20			20	μA
I_{IL}	Low-level input current	V_{CC} = MAX,	V_I = 0.4 V			−0.4			−0.4	mA
I_{OS}	Short-circuit output current[§]	V_{CC} = MAX		−20		−100	−20		−100	mA
I_{CCL}	Supply current, output low	V_{CC} = MAX,	See Note 2		6.2	10		6.2	10	mA

[†]For conditions shown as MIN or MAX, use the appropriate value specified under recommended operating conditions.

[‡]All typical values are at V_{CC} = 5 V, T_A = 25°C.
[§]Not more than one output should be shorted at a time and duration of short-circuit should not exceed one second.
NOTE 2: I_{CCL} is measured with the outputs open and all inputs grounded.

switching characteristics, V_{CC} = 5 V, T_A = 25°C

PARAMETER[¶]	FROM (INPUT)	TO (OUTPUT)	TEST CONDITIONS	MIN	TYP	MAX	UNIT
t_{PLH}	Data	Y			10	15	ns
t_{PHL}	Data	Y			17	26	ns
t_{PLH}	Select	Y	C_L = 15 pF,		19	29	ns
t_{PHL}	Select	Y	R_L = 2 kΩ,		25	38	ns
t_{PLH}	Strobe	Y	See Note 4		16	24	ns
t_{PHL}	Strobe	Y			21	32	ns

[¶]t_{PLH} ≡ propagation delay time, low-to-high-level output
t_{PHL} ≡ propagation delay time, high-to-low-level output
NOTE 4: Load circuits and voltage waveforms are shown on page 3-11.

7

recommended operating conditions

	SN54S153			SN74S153			UNIT
	MIN	NOM	MAX	MIN	NOM	MAX	
Supply voltage, V_{CC}	4.5	5	5.5	4.75	5	5.25	V
High-level output current, I_{OH}			−1			−1	mA
Low-level output current, I_{OL}			20			20	mA
Operating free-air temperature, T_A	−55		125	0		70	°C

electrical characteristics over recommended operating free-air temperature range (unless otherwise noted)

	PARAMETER	TEST CONDITIONS†		MIN	TYP‡	MAX	UNIT
V_{IH}	High-level input voltage			2			V
V_{IL}	Low-level input voltage					0.8	V
V_{IK}	Input clamp voltage	$V_{CC} = MIN$, $I_I = -18\ mA$				−1.2	V
V_{OH}	High-level output voltage	$V_{CC} = MIN$, $V_{IH} = 2\ V$,	Series 54S	2.5	3.4		V
		$V_{IL} = 0.8\ V$, $I_{OH} = -1\ mA$	Series 74S	2.7	3.4		
V_{OL}	Low-level output voltage	$V_{CC} = MIN$, $V_{IH} = 2\ V$, $V_{IL} = 0.8\ V$, $I_{OL} = 20\ mA$				0.5	V
I_I	Input current at maximum input voltage	$V_{CC} = MAX$, $V_I = 5.5\ V$				1	mA
I_{IH}	High-level input current	$V_{CC} = MAX$, $V_I = 2.7\ V$				50	μA
I_{IL}	Low-level input current	$V_{CC} = MAX$, $V_I = 0.5\ V$				−2	mA
I_{OS}	Short-circuit output current§	$V_{CC} = MAX$		−40		−100	mA
I_{CCL}	Supply current, low-level output	$V_{CC} = MAX$, See Note 2			45	70	mA

†For conditions shown as MIN or MAX, use the appropriate value specified under recommended operating conditions.
‡All typical values are at $V_{CC} = 5\ V$, $T_A = 25°C$.
§Not more than one output should be shorted at a time and duration of short-circuit should not exceed one second.
NOTE 2: I_{CCL} is measured with the outputs open and all inputs grounded.

switching characteristics, $V_{CC} = 5\ V$, $T_A = 25°C$

PARAMETER¶	FROM (INPUT)	TO (OUTPUT)	TEST CONDITIONS	MIN	TYP	MAX	UNIT
t_{PLH}	Data	Y			6	9	ns
t_{PHL}	Data	Y			6	9	ns
t_{PLH}	Select	Y	$C_L = 15\ pF$, $R_L = 280\ \Omega$,		11.5	18	ns
t_{PHL}	Select	Y	See Note 3		12	18	ns
t_{PLH}	Strobe	Y			10	15	ns
t_{PHL}	Strobe	Y			9	13.5	ns

¶$t_{PLH} \equiv$ propagation delay time, low-to-high-level output
$t_{PHL} \equiv$ propagation delay time, high-to-low-level output
NOTE 3: Load circuit and voltage waveforms are shown on page 3-10.

TEXAS INSTRUMENTS
INCORPORATED
POST OFFICE BOX 5012 • DALLAS, TEXAS 75222

- '154 is Ideal for High-Performance Memory Decoding
- 'L154 is Designed for Power-Critical Applications
- Decodes 4 Binary-Coded Inputs into One of 16 Mutually Exclusive Outputs
- Performs the Demultiplexing Function by Distributing Data From One Input Line to Any One of 16 Outputs
- Input Clamping Diodes Simplify System Design
- High Fan-Out, Low-Impedance, Totem-Pole Outputs
- Fully Compatible with Most TTL, DTL, and MSI Circuits

SN54154 . . . J OR W PACKAGE
SN54L154 . . . J PACKAGE
SN74154, SN74L154 . . . J OR N PACKAGE
(TOP VIEW)

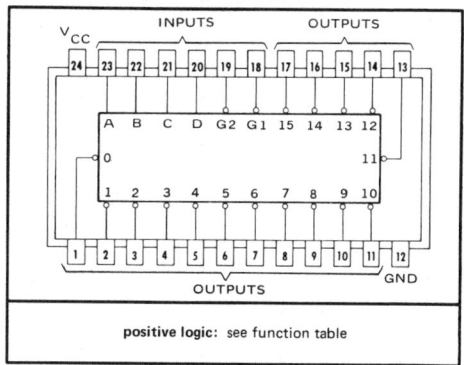

positive logic: see function table

TYPE	TYPICAL AVERAGE PROPAGATION DELAY		TYPICAL POWER DISSIPATION
	3 LEVELS OF LOGIC	STROBE	
'154	23 ns	19 ns	170 mW
'L154	46 ns	38 ns	85 mW

7

description

Each of these monolithic, 4-line-to-16-line decoders utilizes TTL circuitry to decode four binary-coded inputs into one of sixteen mutually exclusive outputs when both the strobe inputs, G1 and G2, are low. The demultiplexing function is performed by using the 4 input lines to address the output line, passing data from one of the strobe inputs with the other strobe input low. When either strobe input is high, all outputs are high. These demultiplexers are ideally suited for implementing high-performance memory decoders. For ultra-high-speed systems, SN54S138/SN74S138 and SN54S139/SN74S139 are recommended.

These circuits are fully compatible for use with most other TTL and DTL circuits. All inputs are buffered and input clamping diodes are provided to minimize transmission-line effects and thereby simplify system design.

Series 54 and 54L devices are characterized for operation over the full military temperature range of −55°C to 125°C; Series 74 and 74L devices are characterized for operation from 0°C to 70°C.

TEXAS INSTRUMENTS
INCORPORATED
POST OFFICE BOX 5012 • DALLAS, TEXAS 75222

TYPES SN54154, SN54L154, SN74154, SN74L154
4-LINE-TO-16-LINE DECODERS/DEMULTIPLEXERS

logic

FUNCTION TABLE

INPUTS						OUTPUTS															
G1	G2	D	C	B	A	0	1	2	3	4	5	6	7	8	9	10	11	12	13	14	15
L	L	L	L	L	L	L	H	H	H	H	H	H	H	H	H	H	H	H	H	H	H
L	L	L	L	L	H	H	L	H	H	H	H	H	H	H	H	H	H	H	H	H	H
L	L	L	L	H	L	H	H	L	H	H	H	H	H	H	H	H	H	H	H	H	H
L	L	L	L	H	H	H	H	H	L	H	H	H	H	H	H	H	H	H	H	H	H
L	L	L	H	L	L	H	H	H	H	L	H	H	H	H	H	H	H	H	H	H	H
L	L	L	H	L	H	H	H	H	H	H	L	H	H	H	H	H	H	H	H	H	H
L	L	L	H	H	L	H	H	H	H	H	H	L	H	H	H	H	H	H	H	H	H
L	L	L	H	H	H	H	H	H	H	H	H	H	L	H	H	H	H	H	H	H	H
L	L	H	L	L	L	H	H	H	H	H	H	H	H	L	H	H	H	H	H	H	H
L	L	H	L	L	H	H	H	H	H	H	H	H	H	H	L	H	H	H	H	H	H
L	L	H	L	H	L	H	H	H	H	H	H	H	H	H	H	L	H	H	H	H	H
L	L	H	L	H	H	H	H	H	H	H	H	H	H	H	H	H	L	H	H	H	H
L	L	H	H	L	L	H	H	H	H	H	H	H	H	H	H	H	H	L	H	H	H
L	L	H	H	L	H	H	H	H	H	H	H	H	H	H	H	H	H	H	L	H	H
L	L	H	H	H	L	H	H	H	H	H	H	H	H	H	H	H	H	H	H	L	H
L	L	H	H	H	H	H	H	H	H	H	H	H	H	H	H	H	H	H	H	H	L
L	H	X	X	X	X	H	H	H	H	H	H	H	H	H	H	H	H	H	H	H	H
H	L	X	X	X	X	H	H	H	H	H	H	H	H	H	H	H	H	H	H	H	H
H	H	X	X	X	X	H	H	H	H	H	H	H	H	H	H	H	H	H	H	H	H

H = high level, L = low level, X = irrelevant

functional block diagram and schematics of inputs and outputs

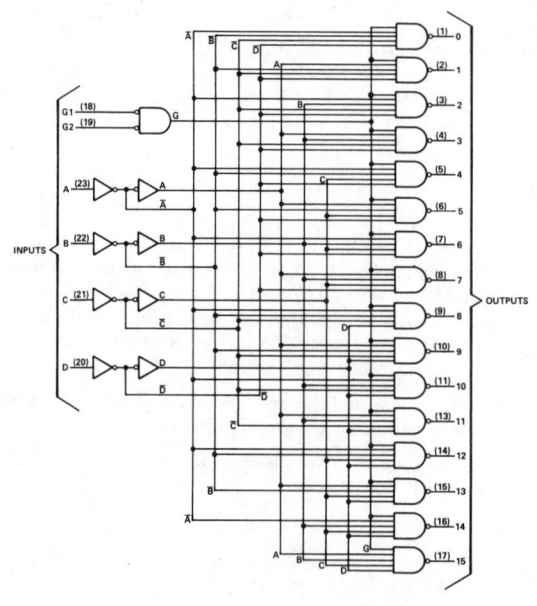

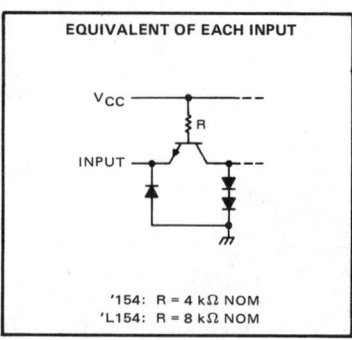

EQUIVALENT OF EACH INPUT

'154: R = 4 kΩ NOM
'L154: R = 8 kΩ NOM

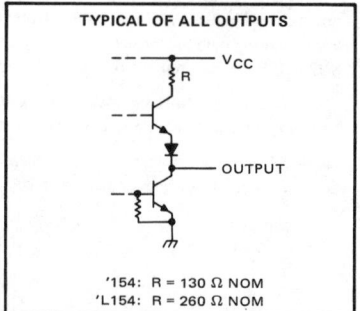

TYPICAL OF ALL OUTPUTS

'154: R = 130 Ω NOM
'L154: R = 260 Ω NOM

7

TEXAS INSTRUMENTS
INCORPORATED
POST OFFICE BOX 5012 • DALLAS, TEXAS 75222

absolute maximum ratings over operating free-air temperature range (unless otherwise noted)

Supply voltage, V_{CC} (see Note 1) . . . . 7 V
Input voltage . . . . 5.5 V
Operating free-air temperature range: SN54154 Circuits . . . . −55°C to 125°C
SN74154 Circuits . . . . 0°C to 70°C
Storage temperature range . . . . −65°C to 150°C

NOTE 1: Voltage values are with respect to network ground terminal.

recommended operating conditions

	SN54154			SN74154			UNIT
	MIN	NOM	MAX	MIN	NOM	MAX	
Supply voltage, V_{CC}	4.5	5	5.5	4.75	5	5.25	V
High-level output current, I_{OH}			−800			−800	μA
Low-level output current, I_{OL}			16			16	mA
Operating free-air temperature, T_A	−55		125	0		70	°C

electrical characteristics over recommended operating free-air temperature range (unless otherwise noted)

PARAMETER		TEST CONDITIONS†	SN54154			SN74154			UNIT
			MIN	TYP	MAX	MIN	TYP‡	MAX	
V_{IH}	High-level input voltage		2			2			V
V_{IL}	Low-level input voltage				0.8			0.8	V
V_{IK}	Input clamp voltage	V_{CC} = MIN, I_I = −12 mA			−1.5			−1.5	V
V_{OH}	High-level output voltage	V_{CC} = MIN, V_{IH} = 2 V, V_{IL} = 0.8 V, I_{OH} = −800 μA	2.4	3.4		2.4	3.4		V
V_{OL}	Low-level output voltage	V_{CC} = MIN, V_{IH} = 2 V, V_{IL} = 0.8 V, I_{OL} = 16 mA		0.2	0.4		0.2	0.4	V
I_I	Input current at maximum input voltage	V_{CC} = MAX, V_I = 5.5 V			1			1	mA
I_{IH}	High-level input current	V_{CC} = MAX, V_I = 2.4 V			40			40	μA
I_{IL}	Low-level input current	V_{CC} = MAX, V_I = 0.4 V			−1.6			−1.6	mA
I_{OS}	Short-circuit output current§	V_{CC} = MAX	−20		−55	−18		−57	mA
I_{CC}	Supply current	V_{CC} = MAX, See Note 2		34	49		34	56	mA

†For conditions shown as MIN or MAX, use the appropriate value specified under recommended operating conditions for the applicable type.
‡All typical values are at V_{CC} = 5 V, T_A = 25°C.
§Not more than one output should be shorted at a time.
NOTE 2: I_{CC} is measured with all inputs grounded and all outputs open.

switching characteristics, V_{CC} = 5 V, T_A = 25°C

PARAMETER		TEST CONDITIONS	MIN	TYP	MAX	UNIT
t_{PLH}	Propagation delay time, low-to-high-level output, from A, B, C, or D inputs through 3 levels of logic	C_L = 15 pF, R_L = 400 Ω, See Note 3		24	36	ns
t_{PHL}	Propagation delay time, high-to-low-level output, from A, B, C, or D inputs through 3 levels of logic			22	33	ns
t_{PLH}	Propagation delay time, low-to-high-level output, from either strobe input			20	30	ns
t_{PHL}	Propagation delay time, high-to-low-level output, from either strobe input			18	27	ns

NOTE 3: Load circuit and voltage waveforms are shown on page 3-10.

7

absolute maximum ratings over operating free-air temperature range (unless otherwise noted)

Supply voltage, V_{CC} (see Note 1)	7 V
Input voltage	5.5 V
Operating free-air temperature range: SN54L154 Circuits	−55°C to 125°C
SN74L154 Circuits	0°C to 70°C
Storage temperature range	−65°C to 150°C

NOTE 1: Voltage values are with respect to network ground terminal.

recommended operating conditions

	SN54L154 MIN	NOM	MAX	SN74L154 MIN	NOM	MAX	UNIT
Supply voltage, V_{CC}	4.5	5	5.5	4.75	5	5.25	V
High-level output current, I_{OH}			−400			−400	µA
Low-level output current, I_{OL}			8			8	mA
Operating free-air temperature, T_A	−55		125	0		70	°C

electrical characteristics over recommended operating free-air temperature range (unless otherwise noted)

PARAMETER		TEST CONDITIONS[†]	MIN	TYP[‡]	MAX	UNIT
V_{IH}	High-level input voltage		2			V
V_{IL}	Low-level input voltage				0.8	V
V_{IK}	Input clamp voltage	V_{CC} = MIN, I_I = −12 mA			−1.5	V
V_{OH}	High-level output voltage	V_{CC} = MIN, V_{IH} = 2 V, V_{IL} = 0.8 V, I_{OH} = −400 µA	2.4	3.4		V
V_{OL}	Low-level output voltage	V_{CC} = MIN, V_{IH} = 2 V, V_{IL} = 0.8 V, I_{OL} = 8 mA		0.2	0.4	V
I_I	Input current at maximum input voltage	V_{CC} = MAX, V_I = 5.5 V			1	mA
I_{IH}	High-level input current	V_{CC} = MAX, V_I = 2.4 V			20	µA
I_{IL}	Low-level input current	V_{CC} = MAX, V_I = 0.4 V			−0.8	mA
I_{OS}	Short-circuit output current§	V_{CC} = MAX	−9		−29	mA
I_{CC}	Supply current	V_{CC} = MAX, SN54L154 See Note 2		17	25	mA
		SN74L154		17	28	

†For conditions shown as MIN or MAX, use the appropriate value specified under recommended operating conditions for the applicable type.
‡All typical values are at V_{CC} = 5 V, T_A = 25°C.
§ Not more than one output should be shorted at a time.
NOTE 2: I_{CC} is measured with all inputs grounded and all outputs open.

switching characteristics, V_{CC} = 5 V, T_A = 25°C

PARAMETER		TEST CONDITIONS	MIN	TYP	MAX	UNIT
t_{PLH}	Propagation delay time, low-to-high-level output, from A, B, C, or D inputs through 3 levels of logic			48	72	ns
t_{PHL}	Propagation delay time, high-to-low-level output, from A, B, C, or D inputs through 3 levels of logic	C_L = 15 pF, R_L = 800 Ω, See Note 3		44	66	ns
t_{PLH}	Propagation delay time, low-to-high-level output, from either strobe input			40	60	ns
t_{PHL}	Propagation delay time, high-to-low-level output, from either strobe input			36	54	ns

NOTE 3: Load circuit and voltage waveforms are shown on page 3-10.

TYPES SN54155, SN54156, SN54LS155, SN54LS156, SN74155, SN74156, SN74LS155, SN74LS156
DUAL 2-LINE-TO-4-LINE DECODERS/DEMULTIPLEXERS

BULLETIN NO. DL-S 7711850, MARCH 1974—REVISED AUGUST 1977

- **Applications:**
  Dual 2-to-4-Line Decoder
  Dual 1-to-4-Line Demultiplexer
  3-to-8-Line Decoder
  1-to-8-Line Demultiplexer

- **Individual Strobes Simplify Cascading for Decoding or Demultiplexing Larger Words**

- **Input Clamping Diodes Simplify System Design**

- **Choice of Outputs:**
  Totem Pole ('155, 'LS155)
  Open-Collector ('156, 'LS156)

SN54155, SN54156, SN54LS155, SN54LS156 . . . J OR W PACKAGE
SN74155, SN74156, SN74LS155, SN74LS156 . . . J OR N PACKAGE
(TOP VIEW)

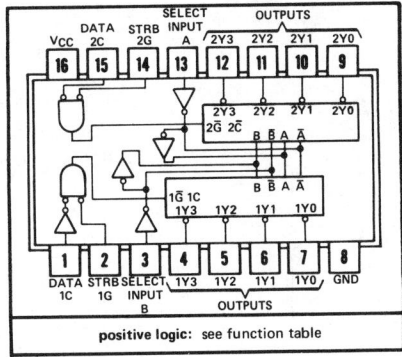

positive logic: see function table

TYPES	TYPICAL AVERAGE PROPAGATION DELAY 3 GATE LEVELS	TYPICAL POWER DISSIPATION
'155, '156	21 ns	125 mW
'LS155	18 ns	31 mW
'LS156	32 ns	31 mW

description

These monolithic transistor-transistor-logic (TTL) circuits feature dual 1-line-to-4-line demultiplexers with individual strobes and common binary-address inputs in a single 16-pin package. When both sections are enabled by the strobes, the common binary-address inputs sequentially select and route associated input data to the appropriate output of each section. The individual strobes permit activating or inhibiting each of the 4-bit sections as desired. Data applied to input 1C is inverted at its outputs and data applied at 2C is not inverted through its outputs. The inverter following the 1C data input permits use as a 3-to-8-line decoder or 1-to-8-line demultiplexer without external gating. Input clamping diodes are provided on all of these circuits to minimize transmission-line effects and simplify system design.

Series 54 and 54LS are characterized for operation over the full military temperature range of -55°C to 125°C; Series 74 and 74LS are characterized for operation from 0°C to 70°C.

schematics of inputs and outputs

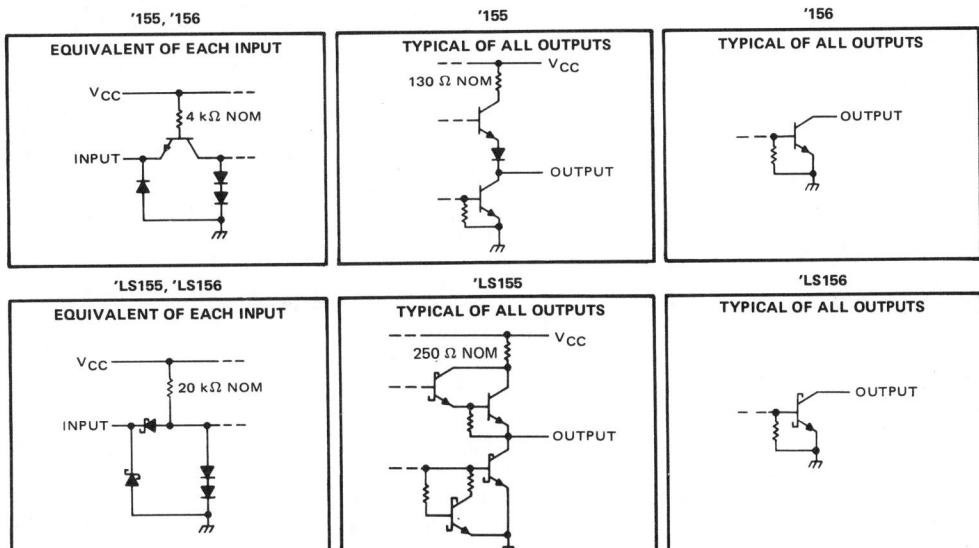

TEXAS INSTRUMENTS
INCORPORATED
POST OFFICE BOX 5012 • DALLAS, TEXAS 75222

TYPES SN54155, SN54156, SN54LS155, SN54LS156, SN74155, SN74156, SN74LS155, SN74LS156
DUAL 2-LINE-TO-4-LINE DECODERS/DEMULTIPLEXERS

functional block diagram and logic

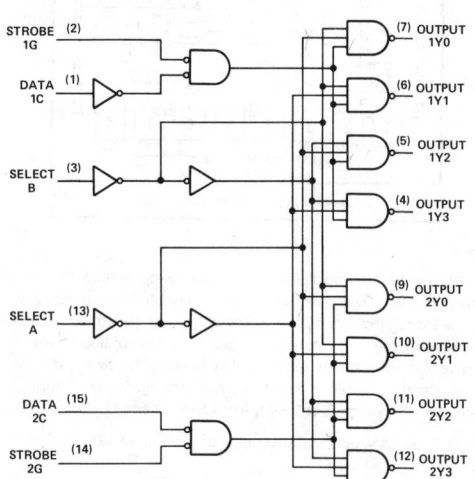

FUNCTION TABLES
2-LINE-TO-4-LINE DECODER
OR 1-LINE-TO-4-LINE DEMULTIPLEXER

INPUTS				OUTPUTS			
SELECT		STROBE	DATA	1Y0	1Y1	1Y2	1Y3
B	A	1G	1C				
X	X	H	X	H	H	H	H
L	L	L	H	L	H	H	H
L	H	L	H	H	L	H	H
H	L	L	H	H	H	L	H
H	H	L	H	H	H	H	L
X	X	X	L	H	H	H	H

INPUTS				OUTPUTS			
SELECT		STROBE	DATA	2Y0	2Y1	2Y2	2Y3
B	A	2G	2C				
X	X	H	X	H	H	H	H
L	L	L	L	L	H	H	H
L	H	L	L	H	L	H	H
H	L	L	L	H	H	L	H
H	H	L	L	H	H	H	L
X	X	X	H	H	H	H	H

FUNCTION TABLE
3-LINE-TO-8-LINE DECODER
OR 1-LINE-TO-8-LINE DEMULTIPLEXER

INPUTS				OUTPUTS							
SELECT			STROBE OR DATA	(0)	(1)	(2)	(3)	(4)	(5)	(6)	(7)
C†	B	A	G‡	2Y0	2Y1	2Y2	2Y3	1Y0	1Y1	1Y2	1Y3
X	X	X	H	H	H	H	H	H	H	H	H
L	L	L	L	L	H	H	H	H	H	H	H
L	L	H	L	H	L	H	H	H	H	H	H
L	H	L	L	H	H	L	H	H	H	H	H
L	H	H	L	H	H	H	L	H	H	H	H
H	L	L	L	H	H	H	H	L	H	H	H
H	L	H	L	H	H	H	H	H	L	H	H
H	H	L	L	H	H	H	H	H	H	L	H
H	H	H	L	H	H	H	H	H	H	H	L

†C = inputs 1C and 2C connected together
‡G = inputs 1G and 2G connected together
H = high level, L = low level, X = irrelevant

absolute maximum ratings over operating free-air temperature range (unless otherwise noted)

Supply voltage, V_{CC} (see Note 1)	7 V
Input voltage: '155, '156	5.5 V
'LS155, 'LS156	7 V
Off-state output voltage: '155	5.5 V
'LS155	7 V
Operating free-air temperature range: SN54', SN54LS' Circuits	-55°C to 125°C
SN74', SN74LS' Circuits	0°C to 70°C
Storage temperature range	-65°C to 150°C

NOTE 1: Voltage values are with respect to network ground terminal.

TEXAS INSTRUMENTS
INCORPORATED
POST OFFICE BOX 5012 • DALLAS, TEXAS 75222

3

recommended operating conditions

	SN54155 MIN	SN54155 NOM	SN54155 MAX	SN74155 MIN	SN74155 NOM	SN74155 MAX	UNIT
Supply voltage, V_{CC}	4.5	5	5.5	4.75	5	5.25	V
High-level output current, I_{OH}			−800			−800	µA
Low-level output current, I_{OL}			16			16	mA
Operating free-air temperature, T_A	−55		125	0		70	°C

electrical characteristics over recommended operating free-air temperature range (unless otherwise noted)

PARAMETER		TEST CONDITIONS[†]	SN54155 SN74155 MIN	TYP[‡]	MAX	UNIT
V_{IH}	High-level input voltage		2			V
V_{IL}	Low-level input voltage				0.8	V
V_{IK}	Input clamp voltage	V_{CC} = MIN, I_I = −8 mA			−1.5	V
V_{OH}	High-level output voltage	V_{CC} = MIN, V_{IH} = 2 V, V_{IL} = 0.8 V, I_{OH} = −800 µA	2.4	3.4		V
V_{OL}	Low-level output voltage	V_{CC} = MIN, V_{IH} = 2 V, V_{IL} = 0.8 V, I_{OL} = 16 mA		0.2	0.4	V
I_I	Input current at maximum input voltage	V_{CC} = MAX, V_I = 5.5 V			1	mA
I_{IH}	High-level input current	V_{CC} = MAX, V_I = 2.4 V			40	µA
I_{IL}	Low-level input current	V_{CC} = MAX, V_I = 0.4 V			−1.6	mA
I_{OS}	Short-circuit output current[§]	V_{CC} = MAX SN54155	−20		−55	mA
		SN74155	−18		−57	
I_{CC}	Supply current	V_{CC} = MAX, See Note 2 SN54155		25	35	mA
		SN74155		25	40	

[†]For conditions shown as MIN or MAX, use the appropriate value specified under recommended operating conditions.
[‡]All typical values are at V_{CC} = 5 V, T_A = 25°C.
[§]Not more than one output should be shorted at a time.
NOTE 2: I_{CC} is measured with outputs open, A, B, and 1C inputs at 4.5 V, and 2C, 1G, and 2G inputs grounded.

switching characteristics, V_{CC} = 5 V, T_A = 25°C

PARAMETER[¶]	FROM (INPUT)	TO (OUTPUT)	LEVELS OF LOGIC	TEST CONDITIONS	MIN	TYP	MAX	UNIT
t_{PLH}	A, B, 2C, 1G, or 2G	Y	2			13	20	ns
t_{PHL}	A, B, 2C, 1G, or 2G	Y	2	C_L = 15 pF, R_L = 400 Ω, See Note 3		18	27	ns
t_{PLH}	A or B	Y	3			21	32	ns
t_{PHL}	A or B	Y	3			21	32	ns
t_{PLH}	1C	Y	3			16	24	ns
t_{PHL}	1C	Y	3			20	30	ns

[¶]t_{PLH} ≡ propagation delay time, low-to-high-level output
t_{PHL} ≡ propagation delay time, high-to-low-level output
NOTE 3: Load circuit and voltage waveforms are shown on page 3-10.

7

TYPES SN54LS155, SN74LS155
DUAL 2-LINE-TO-4-LINE DECODERS/DEMULTIPLEXERS

REVISED OCTOBER 1976

recommended operating conditions

	SN54LS155 MIN	NOM	MAX	SN74LS155 MIN	NOM	MAX	UNIT
Supply voltage, V_{CC}	4.5	5	5.5	4.75	5	5.25	V
High-level output current, I_{OH}			−400			−400	µA
Low-level output current, I_{OL}			4			8	mA
Operating free-air temperature, T_A	−55		125	0		70	°C

electrical characteristics over recommended operating free-air temperature range (unless otherwise noted)

PARAMETER	TEST CONDITIONS[†]		SN54LS155 MIN	TYP[‡]	MAX	SN74LS155 MIN	TYP[‡]	MAX	UNIT
V_{IH} High-level input voltage			2			2			V
V_{IL} Low-level input voltage					0.7			0.8	V
V_{IK} Input clamp voltage	V_{CC} = MIN, I_I = −18 mA				−1.5			−1.5	V
V_{OH} High-level output voltage	V_{CC} = MIN, V_{IH} = 2 V, $V_{IL} = V_{IL\,max}$, I_{OH} = −400 µA		2.5	3.4		2.7	3.4		V
V_{OL} Low-level output voltage	V_{CC} = MIN, V_{IH} = 2 V, $V_{IL} = V_{IL\,max}$	I_{OL} = 4 mA		0.25	0.4		0.25	0.4	V
		I_{OL} = 8 mA					0.35	0.5	
I_I Input current at maximum input voltage	V_{CC} = MAX, V_I = 7 V				0.1			0.1	mA
I_{IH} High-level input current	V_{CC} = MAX, V_I = 2.7 V				20			20	µA
I_{IL} Low-level input current	V_{CC} = MAX, V_I = 0.4 V				−0.4			−0.4	mA
I_{OS} Short-circuit output current[§]	V_{CC} = MAX		−6		−40	−5		−42	mA
I_{CC} Supply current	V_{CC} = MAX, See Note 2			6.1	10		6.1	10	mA

[†] For conditions shown as MIN or MAX, use the appropriate value specified under recommended operating conditions.
[‡] All typical values are at V_{CC} = 5 V, T_A = 25°C.
[§] Not more than one output should be shorted at a time.
NOTE 2: I_{CC} is measured with outputs open, A, B, and 1C inputs at 4.5 V, and 2C, 1G, and 2G inputs grounded.

switching characteristics, V_{CC} = 5 V, T_A = 25°C

PARAMETER[¶]	FROM (INPUT)	TO (OUTPUT)	LEVELS OF LOGIC	TEST CONDITIONS	SN54LS155 SN74LS155 MIN	TYP	MAX	UNIT
t_{PLH}	A, B, 2C, 1G, or 2G	Y	2			10	15	ns
t_{PHL}	A, B, 2C, 1G, or 2G	Y	2	C_L = 15 pF, R_L = 2 kΩ, See Note 4		19	30	ns
t_{PLH}	A or B	Y	3			17	26	ns
t_{PHL}	A or B	Y	3			19	30	ns
t_{PLH}	1C	Y	3			18	27	ns
t_{PHL}	1C	Y	3			18	27	ns

[¶] t_{PLH} ≡ propagation delay time, low-to-high-level output
t_{PHL} ≡ propagation delay time, high-to-low-level output
NOTE 4: Load circuit and voltage waveforms are shown on page 3-11.

7

TEXAS INSTRUMENTS
INCORPORATED
POST OFFICE BOX 5012 • DALLAS, TEXAS 75222

recommended operating conditions

	SN54156 MIN	SN54156 NOM	SN54156 MAX	SN74156 MIN	SN74156 NOM	SN74156 MAX	UNIT
Supply voltage, V_{CC}	4.5	5	5.5	4.75	5	5.25	V
High-level output voltage; V_{OH}			5.5			5.5	V
Low-level output current, I_{OL}			16			16	mA
Operating free-air temperature, T_A	−55		125	0		70	°C

electrical characteristics over recommended operating free-air temperature range (unless otherwise noted)

PARAMETER		TEST CONDITIONS[†]	SN54156 SN74156 MIN	SN54156 SN74156 TYP[‡]	SN54156 SN74156 MAX	UNIT
V_{IH}	High-level input voltage		2			V
V_{IL}	Low-level input voltage				0.8	V
V_{IK}	Input clamp voltage	V_{CC} = MIN, I_I = −8 mA			−1.5	V
I_{OH}	High-level output current	V_{CC} = MIN, V_{IH} = 2 V, V_{IL} = 0.8 V, V_{OH} = 5.5 V			250	μA
V_{OL}	Low-level output voltage	V_{CC} = MIN, V_{IH} = 2 V, V_{IL} = 0.8 V, I_{OL} = 16 mA		0.2	0.4	V
I_I	Input current at maximum input voltage	V_{CC} = MAX, V_I = 5.5 V			1	mA
I_{IH}	High-level input current	V_{CC} = MAX, V_I = 2.4 V			40	μA
I_{IL}	Low-level input current	V_{CC} = MAX, V_I = 0.4 V			−1.6	mA
I_{CC}	Supply current	V_{CC} = MAX, See Note 2 SN54156		25	35	mA
		SN74156		25	40	

†For conditions shown as MIN or MAX, use the appropriate value specified under recommended operating conditions.
‡All typical values are at V_{CC} = 5 V, T_A = 25°C.
NOTE 2: I_{CC} is measured with outputs open, A, B, and 1C inputs at 4.5 V, and 2C, 1G, and 2G inputs grounded.

switching characteristics, V_{CC} = 5 V, T_A = 25°C

PARAMETER[¶]	FROM (INPUT)	TO (OUTPUT)	LEVELS OF LOGIC	TEST CONDITIONS	MIN	TYP	MAX	UNIT
t_{PLH}	A, B, 2C, 1G, or 2G	Y	2			15	23	ns
t_{PHL}	A, B, 2C, 1G, or 2G	Y	2	C_L = 15 pF, R_L = 400 Ω, See Note 3		20	30	ns
t_{PLH}	A or B	Y	3			23	34	ns
t_{PHL}	A or B	Y	3			23	34	ns
t_{PLH}	1C	Y	3			18	27	ns
t_{PHL}	1C	Y	3			22	33	ns

¶t_{PLH} ≡ propagation delay time, low-to-high-level output
t_{PHL} ≡ propagation delay time, high-to-low-level output
NOTE 3: Load circuit and voltage waveforms are shown on page 3-10.

7

TEXAS INSTRUMENTS
INCORPORATED
POST OFFICE BOX 5012 • DALLAS, TEXAS 75222

TYPES SN54LS156, SN74LS156
DUAL 2-LINE-TO-4-LINE DECODERS/DEMULTIPLEXERS

recommended operating conditions

	SN54LS156			SN74LS156			UNIT
	MIN	NOM	MAX	MIN	NOM	MAX	
Supply voltage, V_{CC}	4.5	5	5.5	4.75	5	5.25	V
High-level output voltage, V_{OH}			5.5			5.5	V
Low-level output current, I_{OL}			4			8	mA
Operating free-air temperature, T_A	−55		125	0		70	°C

electrical characteristics over recommended operating free-air temperature range (unless otherwise noted)

PARAMETER		TEST CONDITIONS†		SN54LS156			SN74LS156			UNIT
				MIN	TYP‡	MAX	MIN	TYP‡	MAX	
V_{IH}	High-level input voltage			2			2			V
V_{IL}	Low-level input voltage					0.7			0.8	V
V_{IK}	Input clamp voltage	V_{CC} = MIN,	I_I = −18 mA			−1.5			−1.5	V
I_{OH}	High-level output current	V_{CC} = MIN, V_{IH} = 2 V, $V_{IL} = V_{IL}$ max, V_{OH} = 5.5 V				100			100	µA
V_{OL}	Low-level output voltage	V_{CC} = MIN, V_{IH} = 2 V, $V_{IL} = V_{IL}$ max	I_{OL} = 4 mA	0.25	0.4		0.25	0.4		V
			I_{OL} = 8 mA				0.35	0.5		
I_I	Input current at maximum input voltage	V_{CC} = MAX,	V_I = 7 V			0.1			0.1	mA
I_{IH}	High-level input current	V_{CC} = MAX,	V_I = 2.7 V			20			20	µA
I_{IL}	Low-level input current	V_{CC} = MAX,	V_I = 0.4 V			−0.4			−0.4	mA
I_{CC}	Supply current	V_{CC} = MAX,	See Note 2		6.1	10		6.1	10	mA

†For conditions shown as MIN or MAX, use the appropriate value specified under recommended operating conditions.
‡All typical values are at V_{CC} = 5 V, T_A = 25°C.
NOTE 2: I_{CC} is measured with outputs open, A, B, and 1C inputs at 4.5 V, and 2C, 1G, and 2G inputs grounded.

switching characteristics, V_{CC} = 5 V, T_A = 25°C

PARAMETER¶	FROM (INPUT)	TO (OUTPUT)	LEVELS OF LOGIC	TEST CONDITIONS	SN54LS156 SN74LS156			UNIT
					MIN	TYP	MAX	
t_{PLH}	A, B, 2C 1G, or 2G	Y	2			25	40	ns
t_{PHL}	A, B, 2C, 1G, or 2G	Y	2	C_L = 15 pF, R_L = 2 kΩ, See Note 4		34	51	ns
t_{PLH}	A or B	Y	3			31	46	ns
t_{PHL}	A or B	Y	3			34	51	ns
t_{PLH}	1C	Y	3			32	48	ns
t_{PHL}	1C	Y	3			32	48	ns

¶ t_{PLH} ≡ propagation delay time, low-to-high-level output
t_{PHL} ≡ propagation delay time, high-to-low-level output
NOTE 4: Load circuit and voltage waveforms are shown on page 3-11.

TEXAS INSTRUMENTS
INCORPORATED
POST OFFICE BOX 5012 • DALLAS, TEXAS 75222

107

TYPES SN54157, SN54L157, SN54LS157, SN54LS158, SN54S157, SN54S158, SN74157, SN74L157, SN74LS157, SN74LS158, SN74S157, SN74S158
QUADRUPLE 2-LINE-TO-1-LINE DATA SELECTORS/MULTIPLEXERS

BULLETIN NO. DL-S 7711847, MARCH 1974—REVISED AUGUST 1977

features

- **Buffered Inputs and Outputs**
- **Three Speed/Power Ranges Available**

TYPES	TYPICAL AVERAGE PROPAGATION TIME	TYPICAL POWER DISSIPATION
'157	9 ns	150 mW
'L157	18 ns	75 mW
'LS157	9 ns	49 mW
'S157	5 ns	250 mW
'LS158	7 ns	24 mW
'S158	4 ns	195 mW

applications

- **Expand Any Data Input Point**
- **Multiplex Dual Data Buses**
- **Generate Four Functions of Two Variables (One Variable Is Common)**
- **Source Programmable Counters**

description

These monolithic data selectors/multiplexers contain inverters and drivers to supply full on-chip data selection to the four output gates. A separate strobe input is provided. A 4-bit word is selected from one of two sources and is routed to the four outputs. The '157, 'L157, 'LS157, and 'S157 present true data whereas the 'LS158 and 'S158 present inverted data to minimize propagation delay time.

FUNCTION TABLE

INPUTS				OUTPUT Y	
STROBE	SELECT	A	B	'157, 'L157, 'LS157, 'S157	'LS158 'S158
H	X	X	X	L	H
L	L	L	X	L	H
L	L	H	X	H	L
L	H	X	L	L	H
L	H	X	H	H	L

H = high level, L = low level, X = irrelevant

SN54157, SN54LS157, SN54S157 . . . J OR W PACKAGE
SN54L157 . . . J PACKAGE
SN74157, SN74L157, SN74LS157, SN74S157 . . . J OR N PACKAGE
(TOP VIEW)

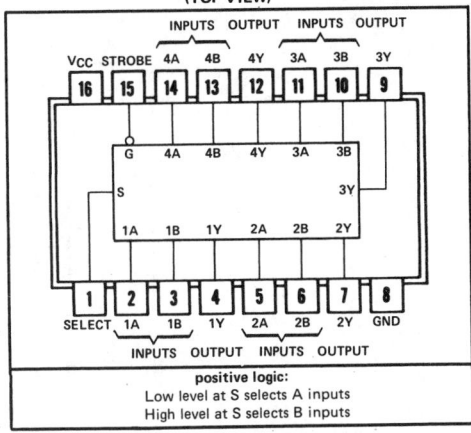

positive logic:
Low level at S selects A inputs
High level at S selects B inputs

SN54LS158, SN54S158 . . . J OR W PACKAGE
SN74LS158, SN74S158 . . . J OR N PACKAGE
(TOP VIEW)

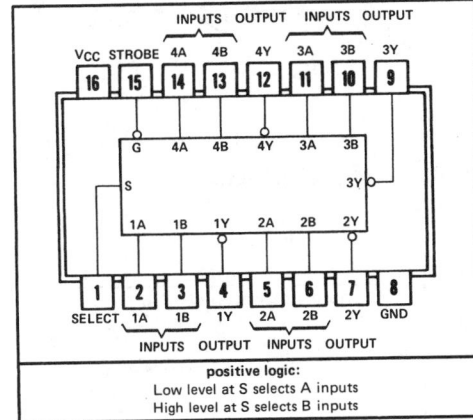

positive logic:
Low level at S selects A inputs
High level at S selects B inputs

absolute maximum ratings over operating free-air temperature range (unless otherwise noted)

Supply voltage, V_{CC} (see Note 1)	7 V
Input voltage: '157, 'L157, 'S158	5.5 V
'LS157, 'LS158	7 V
Operating free-air temperature range: SN54', SN54L', SN54LS', SN54S' Circuits	−55°C to 125°C
SN74', SN74L', SN74LS', SN74S' Circuits	0°C to 70°C
Storage temperature range	−65°C to 150°C

NOTE 1: Voltage values are with respect to network ground terminal.

TEXAS INSTRUMENTS
INCORPORATED
POST OFFICE BOX 5012 • DALLAS, TEXAS 75222

7

functional block diagram

'157, 'L157

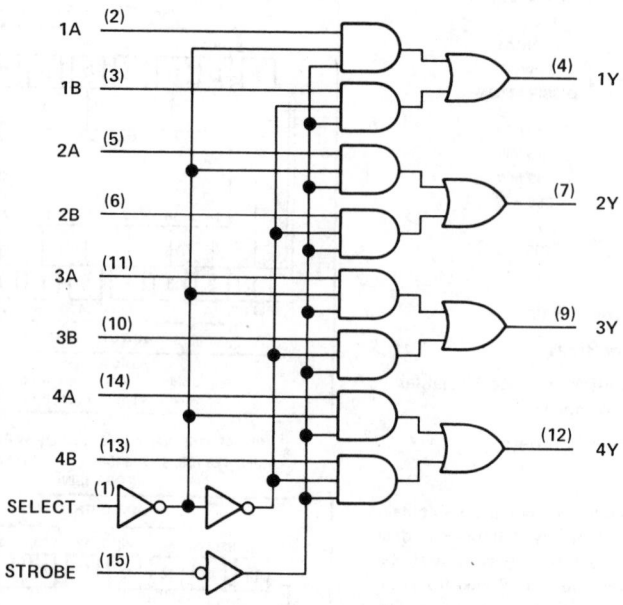

schematics of inputs and outputs

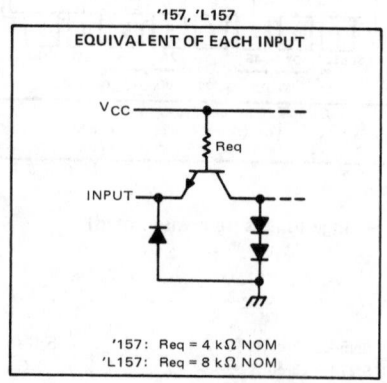

'157, 'L157
EQUIVALENT OF EACH INPUT

'157: Req = 4 kΩ NOM
'L157: Req = 8 kΩ NOM

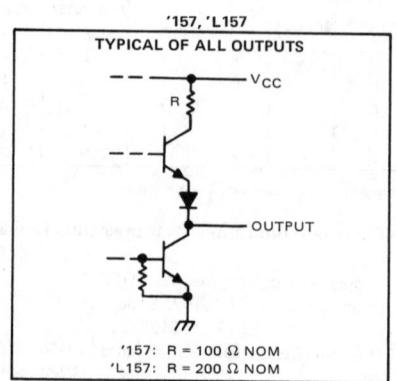

'157, 'L157
TYPICAL OF ALL OUTPUTS

'157: R = 100 Ω NOM
'L157: R = 200 Ω NOM

TEXAS INSTRUMENTS
INCORPORATED
POST OFFICE BOX 5012 • DALLAS, TEXAS 75222

functional block diagrams

schematics of inputs and outputs

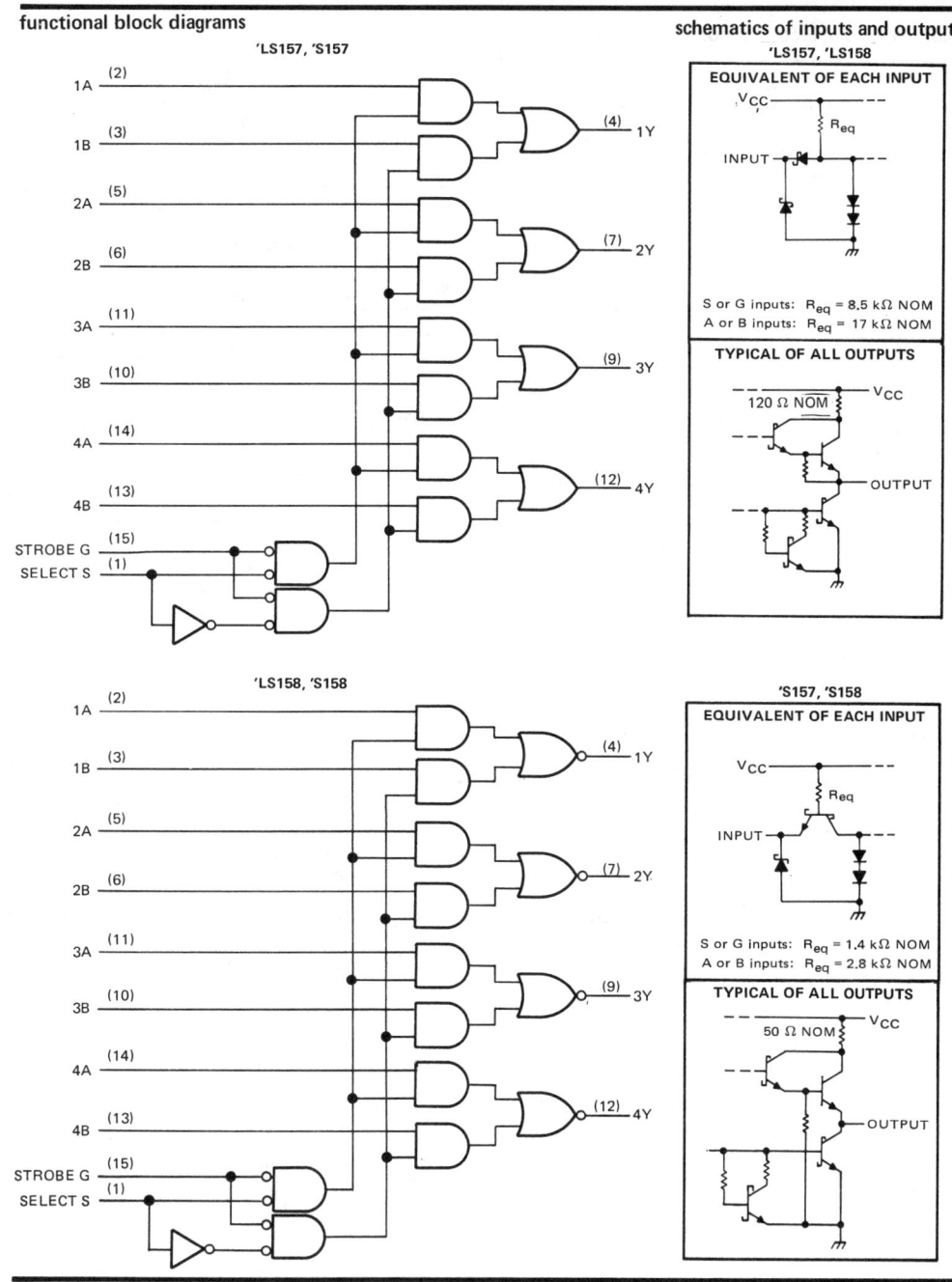

TEXAS INSTRUMENTS
INCORPORATED
POST OFFICE BOX 5012 • DALLAS, TEXAS 75222

recommended operating conditions

	SN54157			SN74157			UNIT
	MIN	NOM	MAX	MIN	NOM	MAX	
Supply voltage, V_{CC}	4.5	5	5.5	4.75	5	5.25	V
High-level output current, I_{OH}			−800			−800	μA
Low-level output current, I_{OL}			16			16	mA
Operating free-air temperature, T_A	−55		125	0		70	°C

electrical characteristics over recommended operating free-air temperature range (unless otherwise noted)

PARAMETER		TEST CONDITIONS[†]	SN54157			SN74157			UNIT
			MIN	TYP[‡]	MAX	MIN	TYP[‡]	MAX	
V_{IH}	High-level input voltage		2			2			V
V_{IL}	Low-level input voltage				0.8			0.8	V
V_{IK}	Input clamp voltage	V_{CC} = MIN, I_I = −12 mA			−1.5			−1.5	V
V_{OH}	High-level output voltage	V_{CC} = MIN, V_{IH} = 2 V, V_{IL} = 0.8 V, I_{OH} = −800 μA	2.4	3.4		2.4	3.4		V
V_{OL}	Low-level output voltage	V_{CC} = MIN, V_{IH} = 2 V, V_{IL} = 0.8 V, I_{OL} = 16 mA		0.2	0.4		0.2	0.4	V
I_I	Input current at maximum input voltage	V_{CC} = MAX, V_I = 5.5 V			1			1	mA
I_{IH}	High-level input current	V_{CC} = MAX, V_I = 2.4 V			40			40	μA
I_{IL}	Low-level input current	V_{CC} = MAX, V_I = 0.4 V			−1.6			−1.6	mA
I_{OS}	Short-circuit output current§	V_{CC} = MAX	−20		−55	−18		−55	mA
I_{CC}	Supply current	V_{CC} = MAX, See Note 2		30	48		30	48	mA

†For conditions shown as MIN or MAX, use the appropriate value specified under recommended operating conditions.
‡All typical values are at V_{CC} = 5 V, T_A = 25°C.
§Not more than one output should be shorted at a time and duration of short-circuit should not exceed one second.
NOTE 2: I_{CC} is measured with 4.5 V applied to all inputs and all outputs open.

switching characteristics, V_{CC} = 5 V, T_A = 25°C

PARAMETER¶	FROM (INPUT)	TEST CONDITIONS	MIN	TYP	MAX	UNIT
t_{PLH}	Data			9	14	ns
t_{PHL}	Data	C_L = 15 pF, R_L = 400 Ω, See Note 3		9	14	
t_{PLH}	Strobe			13	20	ns
t_{PHL}	Strobe			14	21	
t_{PLH}	Select			15	23	ns
t_{PHL}	Select			18	27	

¶t_{PLH} ≡ propagation delay time, low-to-high-level output
t_{PHL} ≡ propagation delay time, high-to-low-level output
NOTE 3: Load circuit and voltage waveforms are shown on page 3-10.

7

QUADRUPLE 2-LINE-TO-1-LINE DATA SELECTORS/MULTIPLEXERS

recommended operating conditions

	SN54L157			SN74L157			UNIT
	MIN	NOM	MAX	MIN	NOM	MAX	
Supply voltage, V_{CC}	4.5	5	5.5	4.75	5	5.25	V
High-level output current, I_{OH}			−400			−400	μA
Low-level output current, I_{OL}			8			8	mA
Operating free-air temperature, T_A	−55		125	0		70	°C

electrical characteristics over recommended operating free-air temperature range (unless otherwise noted)

PARAMETER		TEST CONDITIONS[†]	MIN	TYP[‡]	MAX	UNIT
V_{IH}	High-level input voltage		2			V
V_{IL}	Low-level input voltage				0.8	V
V_{IK}	Input clamp voltage	V_{CC} = MIN, I_I = −12 mA			−1.5	V
V_{OH}	High-level output voltage	V_{CC} = MIN, V_{IH} = 2 V, V_{IL} = 0.8 V, I_{OH} = −400 μA	2.4	3.4		V
V_{OL}	Low-level output voltage	V_{CC} = MIN, V_{IH} = 2 V, V_{IL} = 0.8 V, I_{OL} = 8 mA		0.2	0.4	V
I_I	Input current at maximum input voltage	V_{CC} = MAX, V_I = 5.5 V			1	mA
I_{IH}	High-level input current	V_{CC} = MAX, V_I = 2.4 V			20	μA
I_{IL}	Low-level input current	V_{CC} = MAX, V_I = 0.4 V			−0.8	mA
I_{OS}	Short-circuit output current[§]	V_{CC} = MAX	−9		−28	mA
I_{CC}	Supply current	V_{CC} = MAX, See Note 2		15	24	mA

[†]For conditions shown as MIN or MAX, use the appropriate value specified under recommended operating conditions.
[‡]All typical values are at V_{CC} = 5 V, T_A = 25°C.
[§]Not more than one output should be shorted at a time.
NOTE 2: I_{CC} is measured with 4.5 V applied to all inputs and all outputs open.

switching characteristics, V_{CC} = 5 V, T_A = 25°C

PARAMETER[¶]	FROM (INPUT)	TEST CONDITIONS	MIN	TYP	MAX	UNIT
t_{PLH}	Data			18	28	ns
t_{PHL}		C_L = 15 pF, R_L = 800 Ω, See Note 3		18	28	
t_{PLH}	Strobe			26	40	ns
t_{PHL}				28	42	
t_{PLH}	Select			30	46	ns
t_{PHL}				36	54	

[¶]t_{PLH} ≡ propagation delay time, low-to-high-level output
t_{PHL} ≡ propagation delay time, high-to-low-level output

NOTE 3:   Load circuit and voltage waveforms are shown on page 3-10.

7

TEXAS INSTRUMENTS
INCORPORATED
POST OFFICE BOX 5012 • DALLAS, TEXAS 75222

recommended operating conditions

	SN54LS' MIN	NOM	MAX	SN74LS' MIN	NOM	MAX	UNIT
Supply voltage, V_{CC}	4.5	5	5.5	4.75	5	5.25	V
High-level output current, I_{OH}			−400			−400	μA
Low-level output current, I_{OL}			4			8	mA
Operating free-air temperature, T_A	−55		125	0		70	°C

electrical characteristics over recommended operating free-air temperature range (unless otherwise noted)

PARAMETER		TEST CONDITIONS[†]		SN54LS' MIN	TYP[‡]	MAX	SN74LS' MIN	TYP[‡]	MAX	UNIT
V_{IH}	High-level input voltage			2			2			V
V_{IL}	Low-level input voltage					0.7			0.8	V
V_{IK}	Input clamp voltage	V_{CC} = MIN,	I_I = −18 mA			−1.5			−1.5	V
V_{OH}	High-level output voltage	V_{CC} = MIN, V_{IL} = MAX,	V_{IH} = 2 V, I_{OH} = −400 μA	2.5	3.4		2.7	3.4		V
V_{OL}	Low-level output voltage	V_{CC} = MIN, V_{IL} = MAX	V_{IH} = 2 V, I_{OL} = 4 mA		0.25	0.4		0.25	0.4	V
			I_{OL} = 8 mA					0.35	0.5	
I_I	Input current at maximum input voltage	S or G input	V_{CC} = MAX, V_I = 7 V			0.2			0.2	mA
		A or B input				0.1			0.1	
I_{IH}	High-level input current	S or G input	V_{CC} = MAX, V_I = 2.7 V			40			40	μA
		A or B input				20			20	
I_{IL}	Low-level input current	S or G input	V_{CC} = MAX, V_I = 0.4 V			−0.8			−0.8	mA
		A or B input				−0.4			−0.4	
I_{OS}	Short-circuit output current[§]		V_{CC} = MAX	−20		−100	−20		−100	mA
I_{CC}	Supply current		V_{CC} = MAX, See Note 2	'LS157	9.7	16		9.7	16	mA
				'LS158	4.8	8		4.8	8	

[†]For conditions shown as MIN or MAX, use the appropriate value specified under recommended operating conditions.
[‡]All typical values are at V_{CC} = 5 V, T_A = 25°C.
[§]Not more than one output should be shorted at a time and duration of short-circuit should not exceed one second.
NOTE 2: I_{CC} is measured with 4.5 V applied to all inputs and all outputs open.

switching characteristics, V_{CC} = 5 V, T_A = 25°C

PARAMETER[¶]	FROM (INPUT)	TEST CONDITIONS	'LS157 MIN	TYP	MAX	'LS158 MIN	TYP	MAX	UNIT
t_{PLH}	Data	C_L = 15 pF, R_L = 2 kΩ, See Note 4		9	14		7	12	ns
t_{PHL}				9	14		7	12	
t_{PLH}	Strobe			13	20		11	17	ns
t_{PHL}				14	21		12	18	
t_{PLH}	Select			15	23		13	20	ns
t_{PHL}				18	27		16	24	

[¶] t_{PLH} ≡ propagation delay time, low-to-high-level output
t_{PHL} ≡ propagation delay time, high-to-low-level output
NOTE 4: Load circuit and voltage waveforms are shown on page 3-11.

7

TEXAS INSTRUMENTS
INCORPORATED
POST OFFICE BOX 5012 • DALLAS, TEXAS 75222

1076

TYPES SN54S157, SN54S158, SN74S157, SN74S158
QUADRUPLE 2-LINE-TO-1-LINE DATA SELECTORS/MULTIPLEXERS

REVISED AUGUST 1977

recommended operating conditions

	SN54S157 SN54S158			SN74S157 SN74S158			UNIT
	MIN	NOM	MAX	MIN	NOM	MAX	
Supply voltage, V_{CC}	4.5	5	5.5	4.75	5	5.25	V
High-level output current, I_{OH}			−1			−1	mA
Low-level output current, I_{OL}			20			20	mA
Operating free-air temperature, T_A	−55		125	0		70	°C

electrical characteristics over recommended operating free-air temperature range (unless otherwise noted)

PARAMETER		TEST CONDITIONS[†]		SN54S157 SN74S157			SN54S158 SN74S158			UNIT
				MIN	TYP[‡]	MAX	MIN	TYP[‡]	MAX	
V_{IH}	High-level input voltage			2			2			V
V_{IL}	Low-level input voltage					0.8			0.8	V
V_{IK}	Input clamp voltage	V_{CC} = MIN, I_I = −18 mA				−1.2			−1.2	V
V_{OH}	High-level output voltage	V_{CC} = MIN, V_{IH} = 2 V,	Series 54S	2.5	3.4		2.5	3.4		V
		V_{IL} = 0.8 V, I_{OH} = −1 mA	Series 74S	2.7	3.4		2.7	3.4		
V_{OL}	Low-level output voltage	V_{CC} = MIN, V_{IH} = 2 V, V_{IL} = 0.8 V, I_{OL} = 20 mA				0.5			0.5	V
I_I	Input current at maximum input voltage	V_{CC} = MAX, V_I = 5.5 V				1			1	mA
I_{IH}	High-level input current	S or G input	V_{CC} = MAX, V_I = 2.7 V			100			100	μA
		A or B input				50			50	
I_{IL}	Low-level input current	S or G input	V_{CC} = MAX, V_I = 0.5 V			−4			−4	mA
		A or B input				−2			−2	
I_{OS}	Short-circuit ouput current§	V_{CC} = MAX		−40		−100	−40		−100	mA
I_{CC}	Supply current	V_{CC} = MAX, All inputs at 4.5 V, See Note 2			50	78		39	61	mA
		V_{CC} = MAX, A inputs at 4.5 V, B,G,S, inputs at 0 V, See Note 2							81	

† For conditions shown as MIN or MAX, use the appropriate value specified under recommended operating conditions.
‡ All typical values are at V_{CC} = 5 V, T_A = 25°C.
§ Not more than one output should be shorted at a time, and duration of the short-circuit should not exceed one second.
Note 2: I_{CC} is measured with all outputs open.

switching characteristics, V_{CC} = 5 V, T_A = 25°C

PARAMETER¶	FROM (INPUT)	TEST CONDITIONS	SN54S157 SN74S157			SN54S158 SN74S158			UNIT
			MIN	TYP	MAX	MIN	TYP	MAX	
t_{PLH}	Data	C_L = 15 pF, R_L = 280 Ω, See Note 3		5	7.5		4	6	ns
t_{PHL}				4.5	6.5		4	6	
t_{PLH}	Strobe			8.5	12.5		6.5	11.5	ns
t_{PHL}				7.5	12		7	12	
t_{PLH}	Select			9.5	15		8	12	ns
t_{PHL}				9.5	15		8	12	

¶ t_{PLH} ≡ propagation delay time, low-to-high-level output
t_{PHL} ≡ propagation delay time, high-to-low-level output
NOTE 3: Load circuit and voltage waveforms are shown on page 3-10.

TEXAS INSTRUMENTS
INCORPORATED
POST OFFICE BOX 5012 • DALLAS, TEXAS 75222

TTL
MSI

TYPES SN54159, SN74159
4-LINE-TO-16-LINE DECODERS/DEMULTIPLEXERS
WITH OPEN-COLLECTOR OUTPUTS
BULLETIN NO. DL-S 7211800, DECEMBER 1972

- Open-Collector Outputs for Interfacing with MOS or Memory Decoders/Drivers

- Decodes 4 Binary-Coded Inputs into One of 16 Mutually Exclusive Outputs

- Performs the Demultiplexing Function by Distributing Data from One Input Line to Any One of 16 Outputs

- Typical Average Propagation Delay Times:
  24 ns through 3 Levels of Logic
  19 ns from Strobe Input

- Output Off-State Current is Less Than 50 μA

- Fully Compatible with Most TTL, DTL, and MSI Circuits

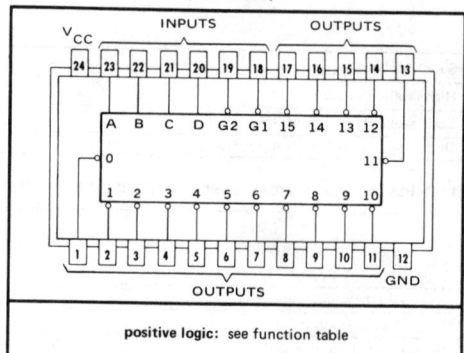

SN54159 . . . J OR W PACKAGE
SN74159 . . . J OR N PACKAGE
(TOP VIEW)

positive logic: see function table

description

Each of these monolithic, 4-line-to-16-line decoders utilizes TTL circuitry to decode four binary-coded inputs into one of sixteen mutually exclusive open-collector outputs when both the strobe inputs, G1 and G2, are low. The demultiplexing function is performed by using the 4 input lines to address the output line, passing data from one of the strobe inputs with the other strobe input low. When either strobe input is high, all outputs are high. These demultiplexers are ideally suited for implementing MOS memory decoding or for interfacing with discrete memory address drivers. For ultra-high-speed applications, the SN54S138/SN74S138 or SN54S139/SN74S139 is recommended.

These circuits are fully compatible for use with most other TTL and DTL circuits. Input clamping diodes are provided to minimize transmission-line effects and thereby simplify system design. Input buffers are used to lower the fan-in requirement to only one normalized Series 54/74 load. A fan-out to 10 normalized Series 54/74 loads in the low-level state is available from each of the sixteen outputs. Typical power dissipation is 170 mW.

The SN54159 is characterized for operation over the full military temperature range of −55°C to 125°C; the SN74159 is characterized for operation from 0°C to 70°C.

function table

Same as SN54154, SN74154. See page 7-172.

functional block diagram

Same as SN54154, SN74154. See page 7-172.

absolute maximum ratings over operating free-air temperature range (unless otherwise noted)

Supply voltage, V_{CC} (see Note 1) . . . . 7 V
Input voltage . . . . 5.5 V
Off-state output voltage . . . . 5.5 V
Operating free-air temperature range: SN54159 Circuits . . . . −55°C to 125°C
                                       SN74159 Circuits . . . . 0°C to 70°C
Storage temperature range . . . . −65°C to 150°C

NOTE 1: Voltage values are with respect to network ground terminal

TEXAS INSTRUMENTS
INCORPORATED
POST OFFICE BOX 5012 • DALLAS, TEXAS 75222

1076

recommended operating conditions

	SN54159			SN74159			UNIT
	MIN	NOM	MAX	MIN	NOM	MAX	
Supply voltage, V_{CC}	4.5	5	5.5	4.75	5	5.25	V
Low-level output current, I_{OL}			16			16	mA
Operating free-air temperature, T_A	55		125	0		70	°C

electrical characteristics over recommended operating free-air temperature range (unless otherwise noted)

	PARAMETER	TEST CONDITIONS[†]	MIN	TYP[‡]	MAX	UNIT
V_{IH}	High-level input voltage		2			V
V_{IL}	Low-level input voltage				0.8	V
V_{IK}	Input clamp voltage	V_{CC} = MIN, I_I = −12 mA			−1.5	V
I_{OH}	High-level output current	V_{CC} = MIN, V_{IH} = 2 V, V_{IL} = 0.8 V, V_{OH} = 5.5 V			50	μA
V_{OL}	Low-level output voltage	V_{CC} = MIN, V_{IH} = 2 V, V_{IL} = 0.8 V, I_{OL} = 16 mA			0.4	V
I_I	Input current at maximum input voltage	V_{CC} = MAX, V_I = 5.5 V			1	mA
I_{IH}	High-level input current	V_{CC} = MAX, V_I = 2.4 V			40	μA
I_{IL}	Low-level input current	V_{CC} = MAX, V_I = 0.4 V			−1.6	mA
I_{CC}	Supply current	V_{CC} = MAX, All inputs grounded		34	56	mA

[†]For conditions shown as MIN or MAX, use the appropriate value specified under recommended operating conditions for the applicable type.
[‡]All typical values are at V_{CC} = 5 V, T_A = 25°C.

switching characteristics, V_{CC} = 5 V, T_A = 25°C

	PARAMETER	TEST CONDITIONS	MIN	TYP	MAX	UNIT
t_{PLH}	Propagation delay time, low-to-high-level output, from A, B, C, or D inputs through 3 levels of logic			23	36	ns
t_{PHL}	Propagation delay time, high-to-low-level output, from A, B, C, or D inputs through 3 levels of logic	C_L = 15 pF, R_L = 400 Ω, See Note 2		24	36	ns
t_{PLH}	Propagation delay time, low-to-high-level output, from either strobe input			15	25	ns
t_{PHL}	Propagation delay time, high-to-low-level output, from either strobe input			22	36	ns

NOTE 2: See load circuit and waveforms shown on page 3-10.

schematics of inputs and outputs

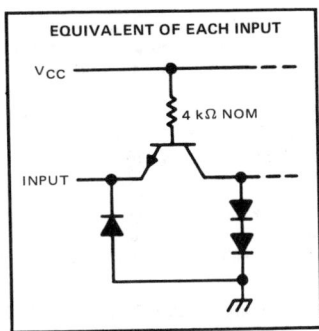

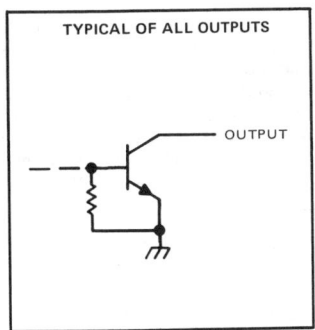

TEXAS INSTRUMENTS
INCORPORATED
POST OFFICE BOX 5012 • DALLAS, TEXAS 75222

TTL MSI

TYPES SN54160 THRU SN54163, SN54LS160A THRU SN54LS163A, SN54S162, SN54S163, SN74160 THRU SN74163, SN74LS160A THRU SN74LS163A, SN74S162, SN74S163 SYNCHRONOUS 4-BIT COUNTERS

BULLETIN NO. DL-S 7711385, OCTOBER 1976—REVISED AUGUST 1977

'160, '161, 'LS160A, 'LS161A . . . SYNCHRONOUS COUNTERS WITH DIRECT CLEAR
'162, '163, 'LS162A, 'LS163A, 'S162, 'S163 . . . FULLY SYNCHRONOUS COUNTERS

- **Internal Look-Ahead for Fast Counting**
- **Carry Output for n-Bit Cascading**
- **Synchronous Counting**
- **Synchronously Programmable**
- **Load Control Line**
- **Diode-Clamped Inputs**

SERIES 54', 54LS', 54S' . . . J OR W PACKAGE
SERIES 74', 74LS', 74S' . . . J OR N PACKAGE
(TOP VIEW)

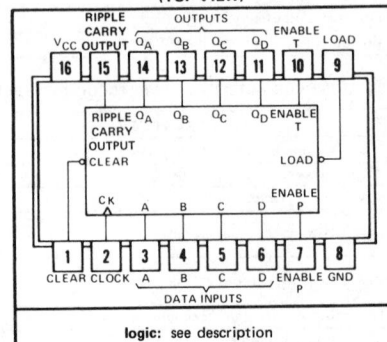

logic: see description

TYPE	TYPICAL PROPAGATION TIME, CLOCK TO Q OUTPUT	TYPICAL MAXIMUM CLOCK FREQUENCY	TYPICAL POWER DISSIPATION
'160 thru '163	14 ns	32 MHz	305 mW
'LS160A thru 'LS163A	14 ns	32 MHz	93 mW
'S162 and 'S163	9 ns	70 MHz	475 mW

description

These synchronous, presettable counters feature an internal carry look-ahead for application in high-speed counting designs. The '160, '162, 'LS160A, 'LS162A, and 'S162 are decade counters and the '161, '163, 'LS161A, 'LS163A, and 'S163 are 4-bit binary counters. Synchronous operation is provided by having all flip-flops clocked simultaneously so that the outputs change coincident with each other when so instructed by the count-enable inputs and internal gating. This mode of operation eliminates the output counting spikes that are normally associated with asynchronous (ripple clock) counters. A buffered clock input triggers the four flip-flops on the rising (positive-going) edge of the clock input waveform.

These counters are fully programmable; that is, the outputs may be preset to either level. As presetting is synchronous, setting up a low level at the load input disables the counter and causes the outputs to agree with the setup data after the next clock pulse regardless of the levels of the enable inputs. Low-to-high transitions at the load input of the '160 thru '163 should be avoided when the clock is low if the enable inputs are high at or before the transition. This restriction is not applicable to the 'LS160A thru 'LS163A or 'S162 or 'S163 . The clear function for the '160, '161, 'LS160A, and 'LS161A is asynchronous and a low level at the clear input sets all four of the flip-flop outputs low regardless of the levels of clock, load, or enable inputs. The clear function for the '162, '163, 'LS162A, 'LS163A, 'S162, and 'S163 is synchronous and a low level at the clear input sets all four of the flip-flop outputs low after the next clock pulse, regardless of the levels of the enable inputs. This synchronous clear allows the count length to be modified easily as decoding the maximum count desired can be accomplished with one external NAND gate. The gate output is connected to the clear input to synchronously clear the counter to 0000 (LLLL). Low-to-high transitions at the clear input of the '162 and '163 should be avoided when the clock is low if the enable and load inputs are high at or before the transition.

The carry look-ahead circuitry provides for cascading counters for n-bit synchronous applications without additional gating. Instrumental in accomplishing this function are two count-enable inputs and a ripple carry output. Both count-enable inputs (P and T) must be high to count, and input T is fed forward to enable the ripple carry output. The ripple carry output thus enabled will produce a high-level output pulse with a duration approximately equal to the high-level portion of the Q_A output. This high-level overflow ripple carry pulse can be used to enable successive cascaded stages. High-to-low-level transitions at the enable P or T inputs of the '160 thru '163 should occur only when the clock input is high. Transitions at the enable P or T inputs of the 'LS160A thru 'LS163A or 'S162 and 'S163 are allowed regardless of the level of the clock input.

'LS160A thru 'LS163A, 'S162 and 'S163 feature a fully independent clock circuit. Changes at control inputs (enable P or T, or clear) that will modify the operating mode have no effect until clocking occurs. The function of the counter (whether enabled, disabled, loading, or counting) will be dictated solely by the conditions meeting the stable setup and hold times.

The 'LS160A thru 'LS163A are completely new designs. Compared to the original 'LS160 thru 'LS163, they feature 0-nanosecond minimum hold time and reduced input currents I_{IH} and I_{IL}.

7

TEXAS INSTRUMENTS
INCORPORATED
POST OFFICE BOX 5012 • DALLAS, TEXAS 75222

functional block diagrams

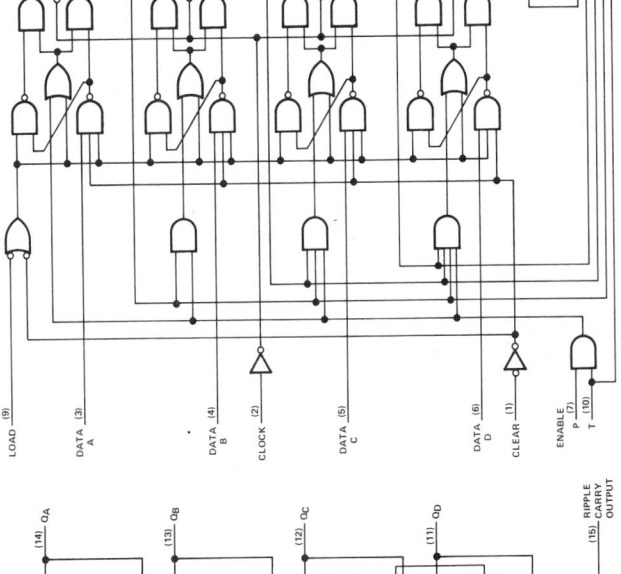

SN54163, SN74163 SYNCHRONOUS BINARY COUNTERS

SN54161, SN74161 synchronous binary counters are similar; however, the clear is asynchronous as shown for the SN74160, SN74160 decade counters at left.

SN54160, SN74160 SYNCHRONOUS DECADE COUNTERS

SN54162, SN74162 synchronous decade counters are similar; however the clear is synchronous as shown for the SN54163, SN74163 binary counters at right.

TEXAS INSTRUMENTS
INCORPORATED
POST OFFICE BOX 5012 • DALLAS, TEXAS 75222

TYPES SN54LS160A THRU SN54LS163A, SN74LS160A THRU SN74LS163A SYNCHRONOUS 4-BIT COUNTERS

functional block diagram

SN54LS163A, SN74LS163A SYNCHRONOUS BINARY COUNTERS

SN54LS161A, SN74LS161A synchronous binary counters are similar; however, the clear is asynchronous as shown for the SN54LS160A, SN74LS160A decade counters at left.

SN54LS160A, SN74LS160A SYNCHRONOUS DECADE COUNTERS

SN54LS162A, SN74LS162A synchronous decade counters are similar; however the clear is synchronous as shown for the SN54LS163A, SN74LS163A binary counters at right.

TEXAS INSTRUMENTS
INCORPORATED
POST OFFICE BOX 5012 • DALLAS, TEXAS 75222

functional block diagrams

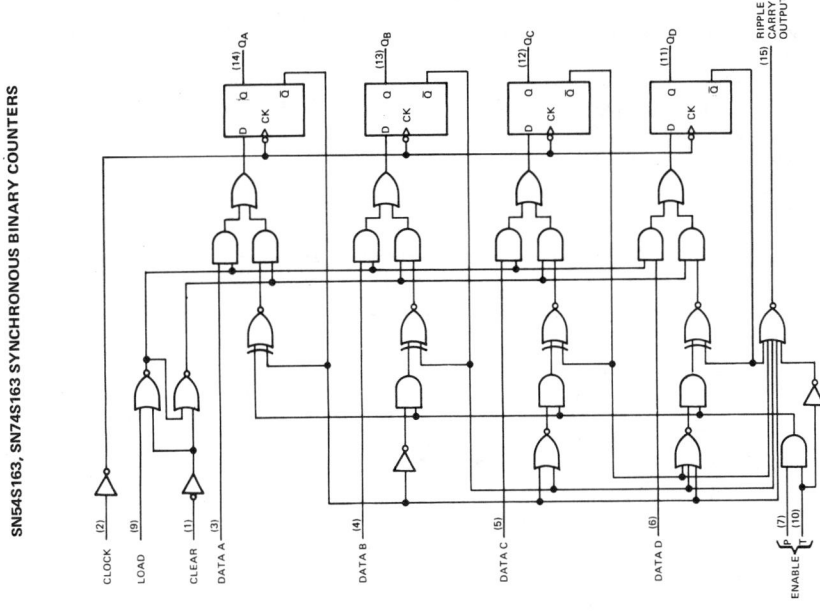

SN54S163, SN74S163 SYNCHRONOUS BINARY COUNTERS

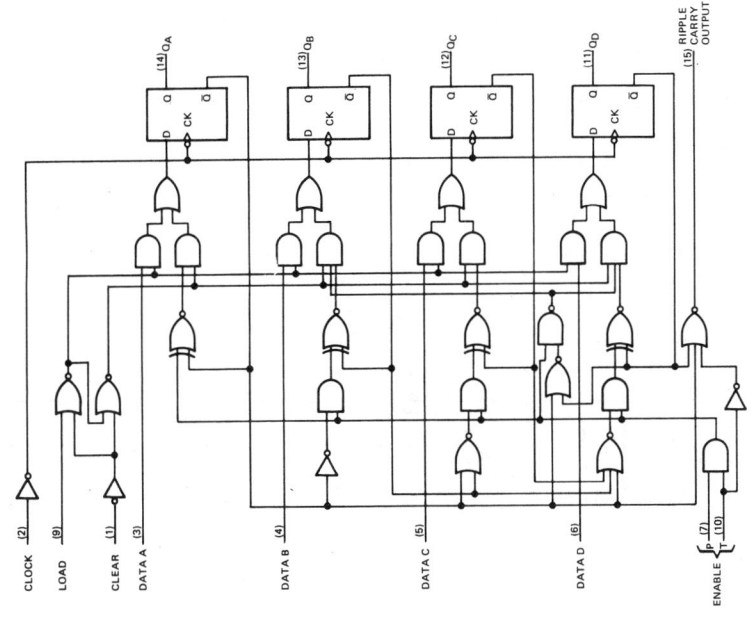

SN54S162, SN74S162 SYNCHRONOUS DECADE COUNTERS

TYPES SN54160, SN54162, SN54LS160A, SN54LS162A, SN54S162, SN74160, SN74162, SN74LS160A, SN74LS162A, SN74S162 SYNCHRONOUS 4-BIT COUNTERS

'160, '162, 'LS160A, 'LS162A, 'S162 DECADE COUNTERS

typical clear, preset, count, and inhibit sequences

Illustrated below is the following sequence:

1. Clear outputs to zero ('160 and 'LS160A are asynchronous; '162, 'LS162A,and 'S162 are synchronous)
2. Preset to BCD seven
3. Count to eight, nine, zero, one, two, and three
4. Inhibit

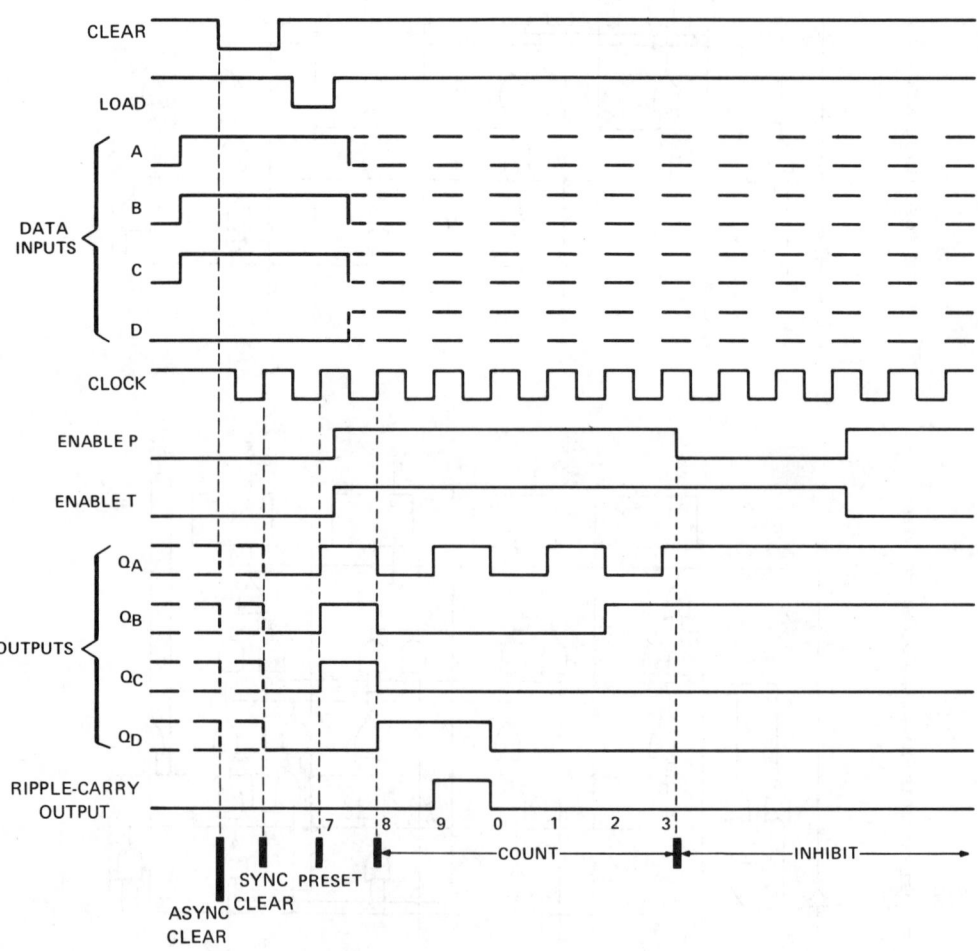

TEXAS INSTRUMENTS
INCORPORATED
POST OFFICE BOX 5012 • DALLAS, TEXAS 75222

TYPES SN54161, SN54163, SN54LS161A, SN54LS163A, SN54S163, SN74161, SN74163, SN74LS161A, SN74LS163A, SN74S163 SYNCHRONOUS 4-BIT COUNTERS

'161, 'LS161A, '163, 'LS163A, 'S163 BINARY COUNTERS

typical clear, preset, count, and inhibit sequences

Illustrated below is the following sequence:

1. Clear outputs to zero ('161 and 'LS161A are asynchronous; '163, 'LS163A, and 'S163 are synchronous)
2. Preset to binary twelve
3. Count to thirteen, fourteen fifteen, zero, one, and two
4. Inhibit

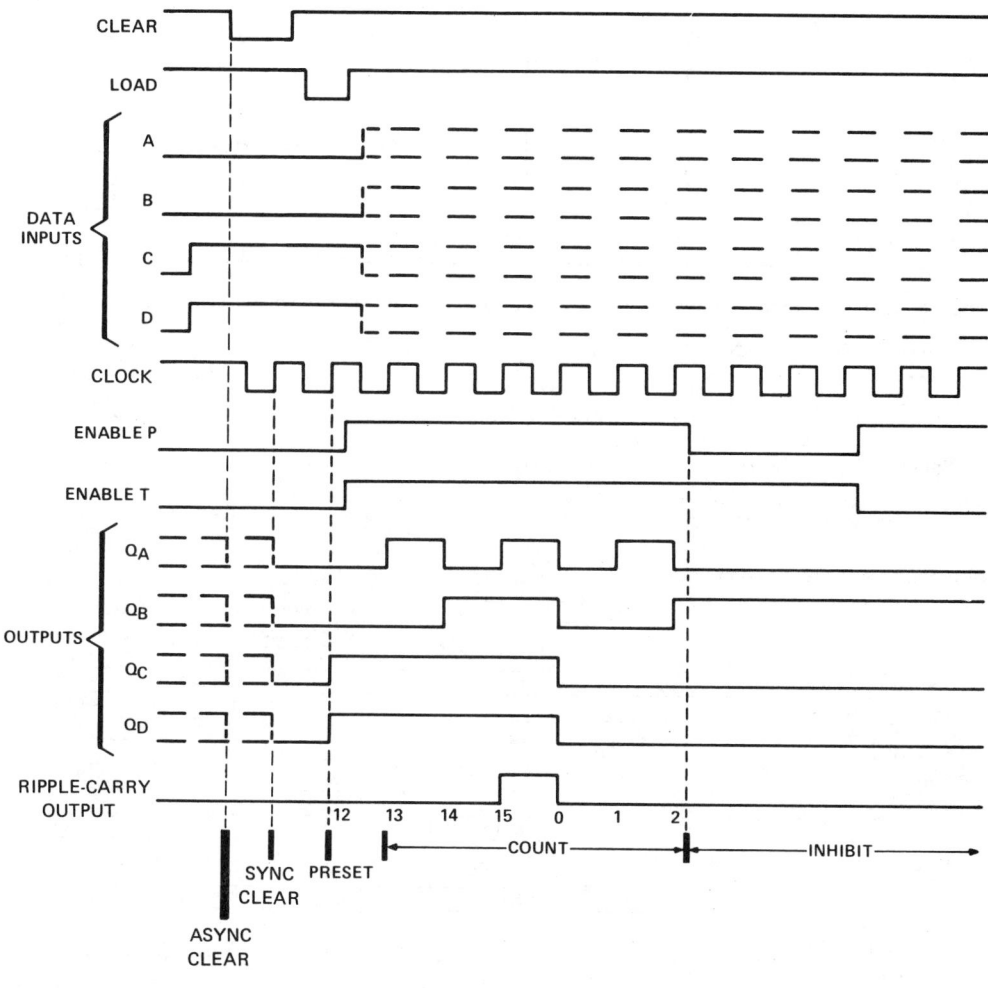

TEXAS INSTRUMENTS
INCORPORATED
POST OFFICE BOX 5012 • DALLAS, TEXAS 75222

schematics of inputs and outputs

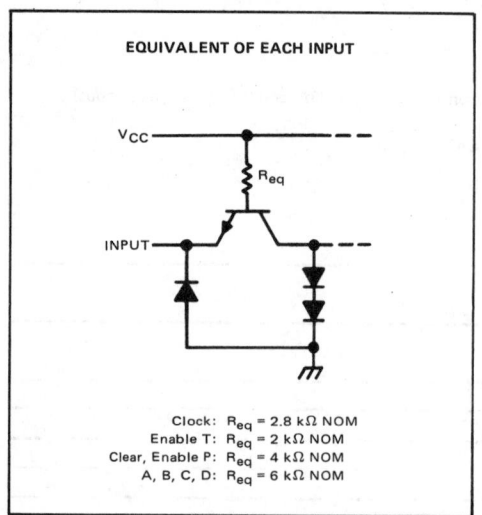

EQUIVALENT OF EACH INPUT

Clock: R_{eq} = 2.8 kΩ NOM
Enable T: R_{eq} = 2 kΩ NOM
Clear, Enable P: R_{eq} = 4 kΩ NOM
A, B, C, D: R_{eq} = 6 kΩ NOM

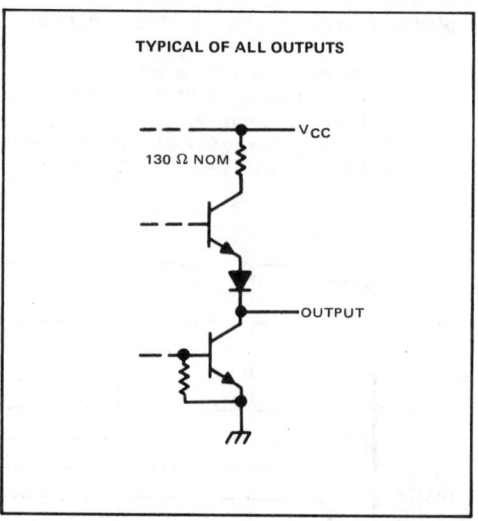

TYPICAL OF ALL OUTPUTS

130 Ω NOM

absolute maximum ratings over operating free-air temperature range (unless otherwise noted)

Supply voltage, V_{CC} (see Note 1) . . . . 7 V
Input voltage . . . . 5.5 V
Interemitter voltage (see Note 2) . . . . 5.5 V
Operating free-air temperature range: SN54' Circuits . . . . −55°C to 125°C
                               SN74' Circuits . . . . 0°C to 70°C
Storage temperature range . . . . −65°C to 150°C

NOTES: 1. Voltage values, except interemitter voltage, are with respect to network ground terminal.
         2. This is the voltage between two emitters of a multiple-emitter transistor. For these circuits, this rating applies between the count enable inputs P and T.

recommended operating conditions

		SN54160, SN54161 SN54162, SN54163			SN74160, SN74161 SN74162, SN74163			UNIT
		MIN	NOM	MAX	MIN	NOM	MAX	
Supply voltage, V_{CC}		4.5	5	5.5	4.75	5	5.25	V
High-level output current, I_{OH}				−800			−800	µA
Low-level output current, I_{OL}				16			16	mA
Clock frequency, f_{clock}		0		25	0		25	MHz
Width of clock pulse, $t_{w(clock)}$		25			25			ns
Width of clear pulse, $t_{w(clear)}$		20			20			ns
Setup time, t_{su} (see Figures 1 and 2)	Data inputs A, B, C, D	20			20			ns
	Enable P	20			20			
	Load	25			25			
	Clear◊	20			20			
Hold time at any input, t_h		0			0			ns
Operating free-air temperature, T_A		−55		125	0		70	°C

◊This applies only for '162 and '163, which have synchronous clear inputs.

TEXAS INSTRUMENTS
INCORPORATED
POST OFFICE BOX 5012 • DALLAS, TEXAS 75222

electrical characteristics over recommended operating free-air temperature range (unless otherwise noted)

PARAMETER		TEST CONDITIONS†	SN54160, SN54161 SN54162, SN54163			SN74160, SN74161 SN74162, SN74163			UNIT
			MIN	TYP‡	MAX	MIN	TYP‡	MAX	
V_{IH}	High-level input voltage		2			2			V
V_{IL}	Low-level input voltage				0.8			0.8	V
V_{IK}	Input clamp voltage	V_{CC} = MIN, I_I = −12 mA			−1.5			−1.5	V
V_{OH}	High-level output voltage	V_{CC} = MIN, V_{IH} = 2 V, V_{IL} = 0.8 V, I_{OH} = −800 μA	2.4	3.4		2.4	3.4		V
V_{OL}	Low-level output voltage	V_{CC} = MIN, V_{IH} = 2 V, V_{IL} = 0.8 V, I_{OL} = 16 mA		0.2	0.4		0.2	0.4	V
I_I	Input current at maximum input voltage	V_{CC} = MAX, V_I = 5.5 V			1			1	mA
I_{IH}	High-level input current — Clock or enable T	V_{CC} = MAX, V_I = 2.4 V			80			80	μA
	High-level input current — Other inputs				40			40	
I_{IL}	Low-level input current — Clock or enable T	V_{CC} = MAX, V_I = 0.4 V			−3.2			−3.2	mA
	Low-level input current — Other inputs				−1.6			−1.6	
I_{OS}	Short-circuit output current §	V_{CC} = MAX	−20		−57	−18		−57	mA
I_{CCH}	Supply current, all outputs high	V_{CC} = MAX, See Note 3		59	85		59	94	mA
I_{CCL}	Supply current, all outputs low	V_{CC} = MAX, See Note 4		63	91		63	101	mA

†For conditions shown as MIN or MAX, use the appropriate value specified under recommended operating conditions.
‡All typical values are at V_{CC} = 5 V, T_A = 25°C.
§Not more than one output should be shorted at a time.
NOTES: 3. I_{CCH} is measured with the load input high, then again with the load input low, with all other inputs high and all outputs open.
4. I_{CCL} is measured with the clock input high, then again with the clock input low, with all other inputs low and all outputs open.

switching characteristics, V_{CC} = 5 V, T_A = 25°C

PARAMETER¶	FROM (INPUT)	TO (OUTPUT)	TEST CONDITIONS	MIN	TYP	MAX	UNIT
f_{max}				25	32		ns
t_{PLH}	Clock	Ripple			23	35	ns
t_{PHL}		carry			23	35	
t_{PLH}	Clock (load input high)	Any Q	C_L = 15 pF, R_L = 400 Ω, See Figures 1 and 2 and Notes 5 and 6		13	20	ns
t_{PHL}					15	23	
t_{PLH}	Clock (load input low)	Any Q			17	25	ns
t_{PHL}					19	29	
t_{PLH}	Enable T	Ripple			11	16	ns
t_{PHL}		carry			11	16	
t_{PHL}	Clear	Any Q			26	38	ns

¶f_{max} ≡ Maximum clock frequency
t_{PLH} ≡ propagation delay time, low-to-high-level output
t_{PHL} ≡ propagation delay time, high-to-low-level output
NOTES: 5. Load circuit is shown on page 3-10.
6. Propagation delay for clearing is measured from the clear input for the '160 and '161 or from the clock input transition for the '162 and '163.

TYPES SN54LS160A, THRU SN54LS163A, SN74LS160A, THRU SN74LS163A, SYNCHRONOUS 4-BIT COUNTERS

schematics of inputs and outputs

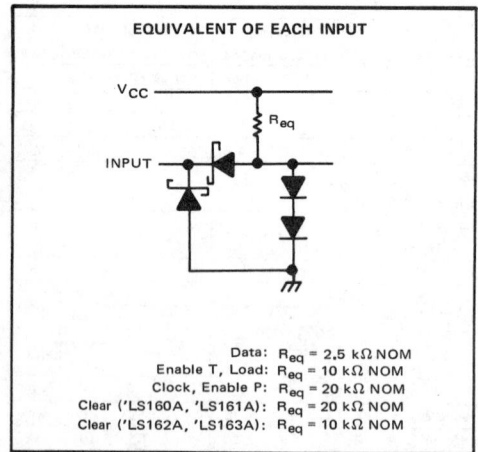

EQUIVALENT OF EACH INPUT

Data: R_{eq} = 2.5 kΩ NOM
Enable T, Load: R_{eq} = 10 kΩ NOM
Clock, Enable P: R_{eq} = 20 kΩ NOM
Clear ('LS160A, 'LS161A): R_{eq} = 20 kΩ NOM
Clear ('LS162A, 'LS163A): R_{eq} = 10 kΩ NOM

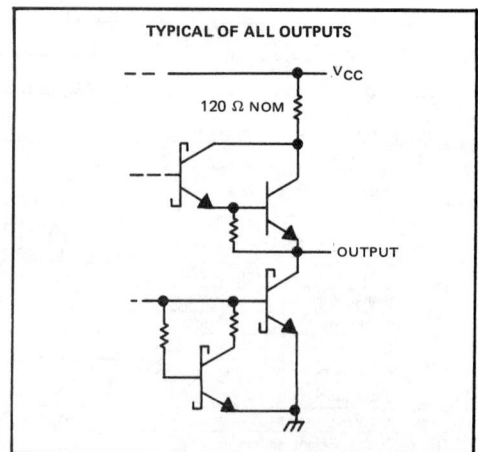

TYPICAL OF ALL OUTPUTS

120 Ω NOM

absolute maximum ratings over operating free-air temperature range (unless otherwise noted)

Supply voltage, V_{CC} (see Note 7) . . . . 7 V
Input voltage . . . . 7 V
Operating free-air temperature range: SN54LS' Circuits . . . . −55°C to 125°C
　　　　　　　　　　　　　　　　SN74LS' Circuits . . . . 0°C to 70°C
Storage temperature range . . . . −65°C to 150°C

NOTE 7: Voltage values are with respect to network ground terminal.

recommended operating conditions

		SN54LS'			SN74LS'			UNIT
		MIN	NOM	MAX	MIN	NOM	MAX	
Supply voltage, V_{CC}		4.5	5	5.5	4.75	5	5.25	V
High-level output current, I_{OH}				−400			−400	μA
Low-level output current, I_{OL}				.4			8	mA
Clock frequency, f_{clock}		0		25	0		25	MHz
Width of clock pulse, $t_{w(clock)}$		25			25			ns
Width of clear pulse, $t_{w(clear)}$		20			20			ns
Setup time, t_{su} (see Figures 1 and 2)	Data inputs A, B, C, D	20			20			ns
	Enable P or T	20			20			
	Load	20			20			
	Clear◊	20			20			
Hold time at any input, t_h		0			0			ns
Operating free-air temperature, T_A		−55		125	0		70	°C

◊ This applies only for 'LS162 and 'LS163, which have synchronous clear inputs.

TEXAS INSTRUMENTS
INCORPORATED
POST OFFICE BOX 5012 • DALLAS, TEXAS 75222

electrical characteristics over recommended operating free-air temperature range (unless otherwise noted)

PARAMETER		TEST CONDITIONS†	SN54LS' MIN	SN54LS' TYP‡	SN54LS' MAX	SN74LS' MIN	SN74LS' TYP‡	SN74LS' MAX	UNIT
V_{IH} High-level input voltage			2			2			V
V_{IL} Low-level input voltage					0.7			0.8	V
V_{IK} Input clamp voltage		V_{CC} = MIN, I_I = −18 mA			−1.5			−1.5	V
V_{OH} High-level output voltage		V_{CC} = MIN, V_{IH} = 2 V, V_{IL} = V_{IL} max, I_{OH} = −400 μA	2.5	3.4		2.7	3.4		V
V_{OL} Low-level output voltage		V_{CC} = MIN, V_{IH} = 2 V, V_{IL} = V_{IL} max, I_{OL} = 4 mA		0.25	0.4		0.25	0.4	V
		I_{OL} = 8 mA					0.35	0.5	
I_I Input current at maximum input voltage	Data or enable P	V_{CC} = MAX, V_I = 7 V			0.1			0.1	mA
	Load, clock, or enable T				0.2			0.2	
	Clear ('LS160A, 'LS161A)				0.1			0.1	
	Clear ('LS162A, 'LS163A)				0.2			0.2	
I_{IH} High-level input current	Data or enable P	V_{CC} = MAX, V_I = 2.7 V			20			20	μA
	Load, clock, or enable T				40			40	
	Clear ('LS160A, 'LS161A)				20			20	
	Clear ('LS162A, 'LS163A)				40			40	
I_{IL} Low-level input current	Data or enable P	V_{CC} = MAX, V_I = 0.4 V			−0.4			−0.4	mA
	Load, clock, or enable T				−0.8			−0.8	
	Clear ('LS160A, 'LS161A)				−0.4			−0.4	
	Clear ('LS162A, 'LS163A)				−0.8			−0.8	
I_{OS} Short-circuit output current§		V_{CC} = MAX	−20		−100	−20		−100	mA
I_{CCH} Supply current, all outputs high		V_{CC} = MAX, See Note 3		18	31		18	31	mA
I_{CCL} Supply current, all outputs low		V_{CC} = MAX, See Note 4		19	32		19	32	mA

†For conditions shown as MIN or MAX, use the appropriate value specified under recommended operating conditions.
‡All typical values are at V_{CC} = 5 V, T_A = 25°C.
§Not more than one output should be shorted at a time, and duration of the short-circuit should not exceed one second.
NOTES: 3. I_{CCH} is measured with the load input high, then again with the load input low, with all other inputs high and all outputs open.
   4. I_{CCL} is measured with the clock input high, then again with the clock input low, with all other inputs low and all outputs open.

switching characteristics, V_{CC} = 5 V, T_A = 25°C

PARAMETER¶	FROM (INPUT)	TO (OUTPUT)	TEST CONDITIONS	MIN	TYP	MAX	UNIT
f_{max}				25	32		MHz
t_{PLH}	Clock	Ripple	C_L = 15 pF, R_L = 2 kΩ, See Figures 1 and 2 and Notes 8 and 9		20	35	ns
t_{PHL}		carry			18	35	
t_{PLH}	Clock (load input high)	Any Q			13	24	ns
t_{PHL}					18	27	
t_{PLH}	Clock (load input low)	Any Q			13	24	ns
t_{PHL}					18	27	
t_{PLH}	Enable T	Ripple			9	14	ns
t_{PHL}		carry			9	14	
t_{PHL}	Clear	Any Q			20	28	ns

¶f_{max} ≡ Maximum clock frequency
t_{PLH} ≡ propagation delay time, low-to-high-level output.
t_{PHL} ≡ propagation delay time, high-to-low-level output.
NOTES: 8. Load circuit is shown on page 3-11.
   9. Propagation delay for clearing is measured from the clear input for the 'LS160A and 'LS161A or from the clock transition for the 'LS162A and 'LS163A.

7

SYNCHRONOUS 4-BIT COUNTERS
REVISED AUGUST 1977

schematics of inputs and outputs

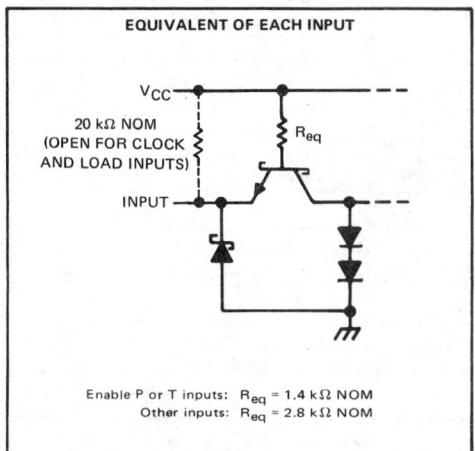

EQUIVALENT OF EACH INPUT

V_{CC}

20 kΩ NOM
(OPEN FOR CLOCK
AND LOAD INPUTS)

R_{eq}

INPUT

Enable P or T inputs: R_{eq} = 1.4 kΩ NOM
Other inputs: R_{eq} = 2.8 kΩ NOM

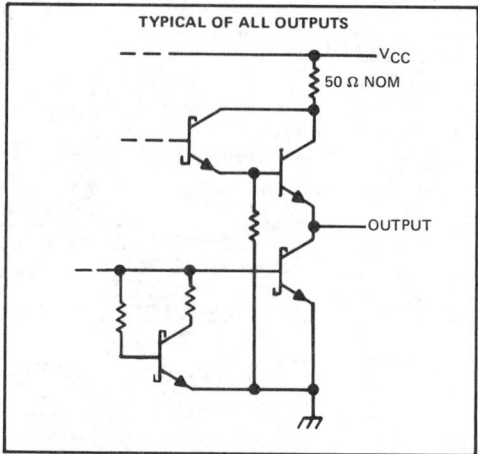

TYPICAL OF ALL OUTPUTS

V_{CC}

50 Ω NOM

OUTPUT

absolute maximum ratings over operating free-air temperature range (unless otherwise noted)

Supply voltage, V_{CC} (see Note 1)	7 V
Input voltage	5.5 V
Interemitter voltage (see Note 2)	5.5 V
Operating free-air temperature range: SN54S162, SN54S163 (see Note 10)	−55°C to 125°C
SN74S162, SN74S163	0°C to 70°C
Storage temperature range	−65°C to 150°C

recommended operating conditions

		SN54S162, SN54S163			SN74S162, SN74S163			UNIT
		MIN	NOM	MAX	MIN	NOM	MAX	
Supply voltage, V_{CC}		4.5	5	5.5	4.75	5	5.25	V
High-level output current, I_{OH}				−1			−1	mA
Low-level output current, I_{OL}				20			20	mA
Clock frequency, f_{clock}		0		40	0		40	MHz
Width of clock pulse, $t_{w(clock)}$ (high or low)		10			10			ns
Width of clear pulse, $t_{w(clear)}$		10			10			ns
Setup time, t_{su} (see Figure 4)	Data inputs, A, B, C, D	4			4			ns
	Enable P or T	12			12			
	Load	14			14			
	Clear	14			14			
	Load inactive-state	12			12			
	Clear inactive-state	12			12			
Release time, $t_{release}$ (see Figure 4)	Enable P or T			4			4	ns
Hold time, t_h (see Figure 4)	Data inputs A, B, C, D	3			3			ns
	Load	0			0			
	Clear	0			0			
Operating free-air temperature, T_A (see Note 10)		−55		125	0		70	°C

NOTES: 1. Voltage values, except interemitter voltage, are with respect to network ground terminal.
2. This is the voltage between two emitters of a multiple-emitter transistor. For these circuits, this rating applies between the count enable inputs P and T.
10. An SN54S162 or SN54S163 in the W package operating at free-air temperatures above 91°C requires a heat sink that provides a thermal resistance from case to free-air, $R_{\theta CA}$, of not more than 26°C/W.

TEXAS INSTRUMENTS
INCORPORATED
POST OFFICE BOX 5012 • DALLAS, TEXAS 75222

electrical characteristics over recommended operating free-air temperature range (unless otherwise noted)

	PARAMETER	TEST CONDITIONS[†]	SN54S162 SN54S163 MIN	TYP[‡]	MAX	SN74S162 SN74S163 MIN	TYP[‡]	MAX	UNIT
V_{IH}	High-level input voltage		2			2			V
V_{IL}	Low-level input voltage				0.8			0.8	V
V_{IK}	Input clamp voltage	V_{CC} = MIN, I_I = −18 mA			−1.2			−1.2	V
V_{OH}	High-level output voltage	V_{CC} = MIN, V_{IH} = 2 V, V_{IL} = 0.8 V, I_{OH} = −1 mA	2.5	3.4		2.7	3.4		V
V_{OL}	Low-level output voltage	V_{CC} = MIN, V_{IH} = 2 V, V_{IL} = 0.8 V, I_{OL} = 20 mA			0.5			0.5	V
I_I	Input current at maximum input voltage	V_{CC} = MAX, V_I = 5.5 V			1			1	mA
I_{IH}	High-level input current — Enable T	V_{CC} = MAX, V_I = 2.7 V			100			100	μA
	Other inputs				50			50	
I_{IL}	Low-level input current — Enable T	V_{CC} = MAX, V_I = 0.5 V			−4			−4	mA
	Other inputs				−2			−2	
I_{OS}	Short-circuit output current[§]	V_{CC} = MAX	−40		−100	−40		−100	mA
I_{CC}	Supply current	V_{CC} = MAX		95	160		95	160	mA

[†]For conditions shown as MIN or MAX, use the appropriate value specified under recommended operating conditions.
[‡]All typical values are at V_{CC} = 5 V, T_A = 25°C.
[§]Not more than one output should be shorted at a time, and duration of the short-circuit should not exceed one second.

switching characteristics, V_{CC} = 5 V, T_A = 25°C

PARAMETER[¶]	FROM (INPUT)	TO (OUTPUT)	TEST CONDITIONS	MIN	TYP	MAX	UNIT
f_{max}				40	70		MHz
t_{PLH}	Clock	Ripple	C_L = 15 pF, R_L = 280 Ω, See Figures 1, 3, and 4 and Note 5		14	25	ns
t_{PHL}		carry			17	25	
t_{PLH}	Clock	Any Q			8	15	ns
t_{PHL}					10	15	
t_{PLH}	Enable T	Ripple			10	15	ns
t_{PHL}		carry			10	15	

[¶]f_{max} ≡ maximum clock frequency
t_{PLH} ≡ propagation delay time, low-to-high-level output
t_{PHL} ≡ propagation delay time, high-to-low-level output

NOTE 5: Load circuit is shown on page 3-10.

7

TYPES SN54160 THRU SN54163, SN54LS160A THRU SN54LS163A, SN54S162, SN54S163, SN74160 THRU SN74163, SN74LS160A THRU SN74LS163A, SN74S162, SN74S163 SYNCHRONOUS 4-BIT COUNTERS

PARAMETER MEASUREMENT INFORMATION

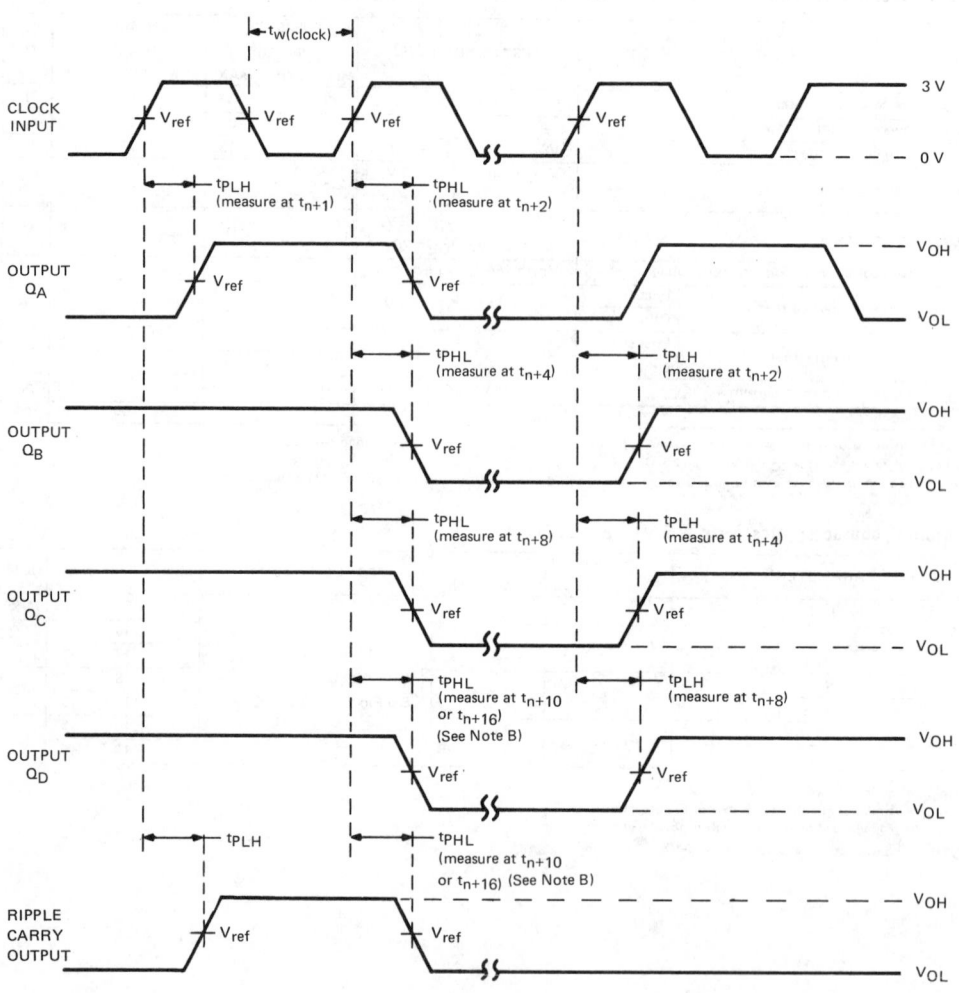

VOLTAGE WAVEFORMS

NOTES: A. The input pulses are supplied by a generator having the following characteristics: PRR ≤ 1 MHz, duty cycle ≤ 50%, $Z_{out} \approx 50\ \Omega$; for '160 thru '163, $t_r \le 10$ ns, $t_f \le 10$ ns; for 'LS160A thru' LS163A $t_r \le 15$ ns, $t_f \le 6$ ns; and for 'S162, 'S163, $t_r \le 2.5$ ns, $t_f \le 2.5$ ns. Vary PRR to measure f_{max}.
B. Outputs Q_D and carry are tested at t_{n+10} for '160, '162, 'LS160A, 'LS162A and 'S162, and at t_{n+16} for '161, '163, 'LS161A 'LS163A, and 'S163, where t_n is the bit time when all outputs are low.
C. For '160 thru '163, 'S162, and 'S163, $V_{ref} = 1.5$ V; for 'LS160A thru 'LS163A, $V_{ref} = 1.3$ V.

FIGURE 1—SWITCHING TIMES

TEXAS INSTRUMENTS
INCORPORATED
POST OFFICE BOX 5012 • DALLAS, TEXAS 75222

PARAMETER MEASUREMENT INFORMATION

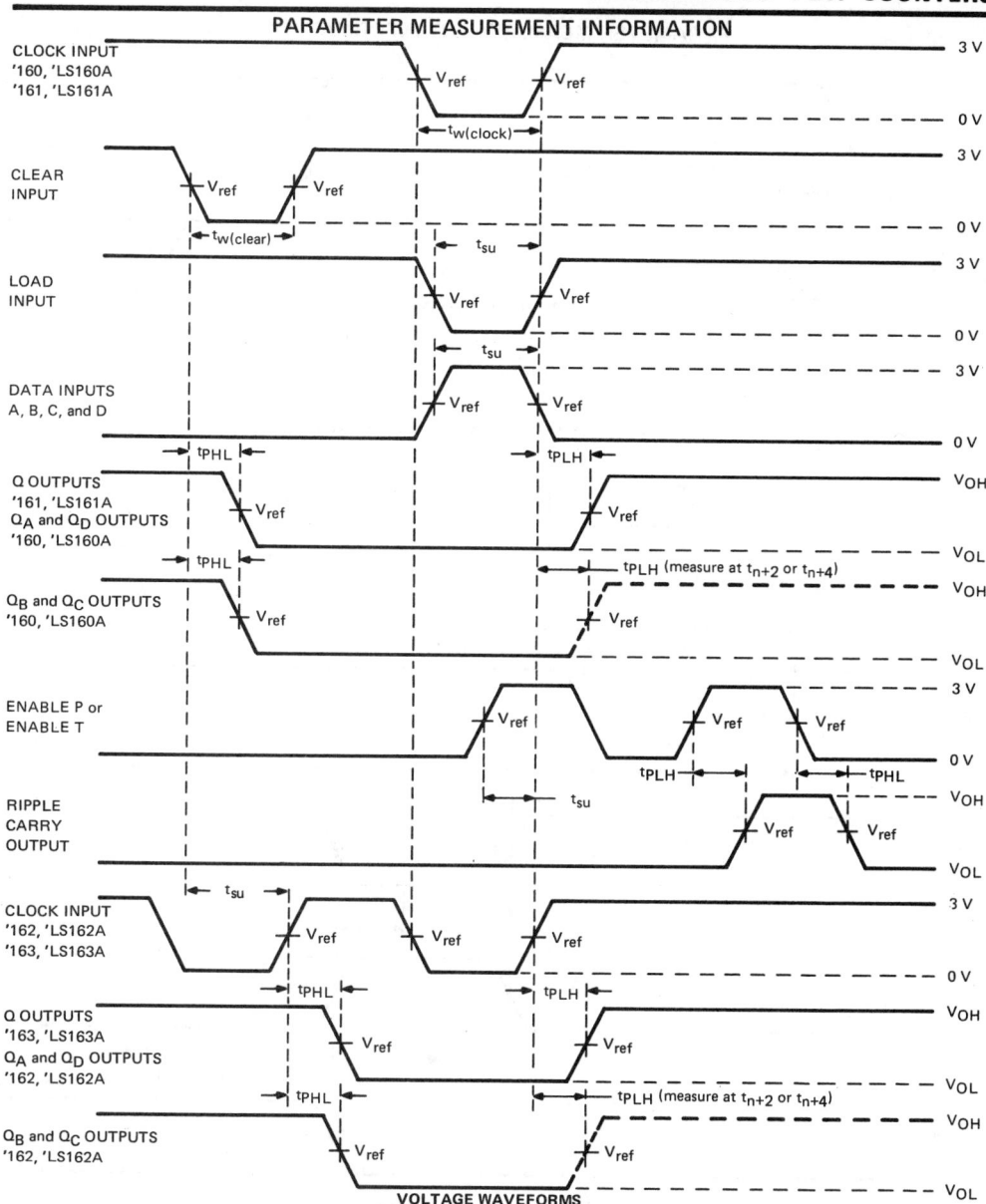

VOLTAGE WAVEFORMS

NOTES: A. The input pulses are supplied by generators having the following characteristics: PRR ≤ 1 MHz, duty cycle ≤ 50%, $Z_{out} \approx 50\ \Omega$; for '160 thru '163, $t_r \leqslant 10$ ns, $t_f \leqslant 10$ ns; and for 'LS160A thru 'LS163A, $t_r \leqslant 15$ ns, $t_f \leqslant 6$ ns.
  B. Enable P and enable T setup times are measured at t_{n+0}.
  C. For '160 thru '163, V_{ref} = 1.5 V; for 'LS160A thru 'LS163A, V_{ref} = 1.3 V.

FIGURE 2—SWITCHING TIMES

TEXAS INSTRUMENTS
INCORPORATED
POST OFFICE BOX 5012 • DALLAS, TEXAS 75222

TYPES SN54S162, SN54S163, SN74S162, SN74S163
SYNCHRONOUS 4-BIT COUNTERS

PARAMETER MEASUREMENT INFORMATION

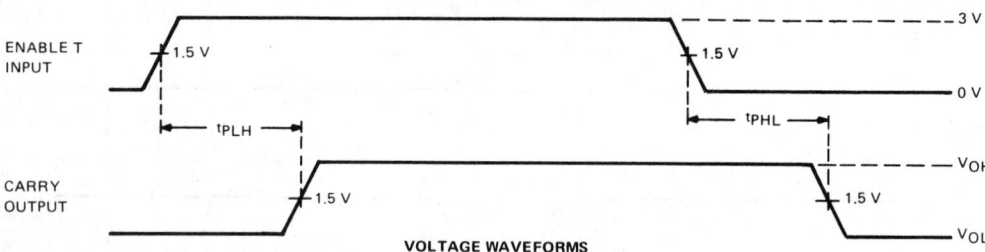

VOLTAGE WAVEFORMS

NOTES: A. The input pulse is supplied by a generator having the following characteristics: $t_r \leqslant 2.5$ ns, $t_f \leqslant 2.5$ ns, PRR $\leqslant 1$ MHz, duty cycle $\leqslant 50\%$, $Z_{out} \approx 50 \ \Omega$.

B. t_{PLH} and t_{PHL} from enable T input to carry output assume that the counter is at the maximum count (Q_A and Q_D high for 'S162, all Q outputs high for 'S163).

FIGURE 3—PROPAGATION DELAY TIMES FROM ENABLE T INPUT TO CARRY OUTPUT

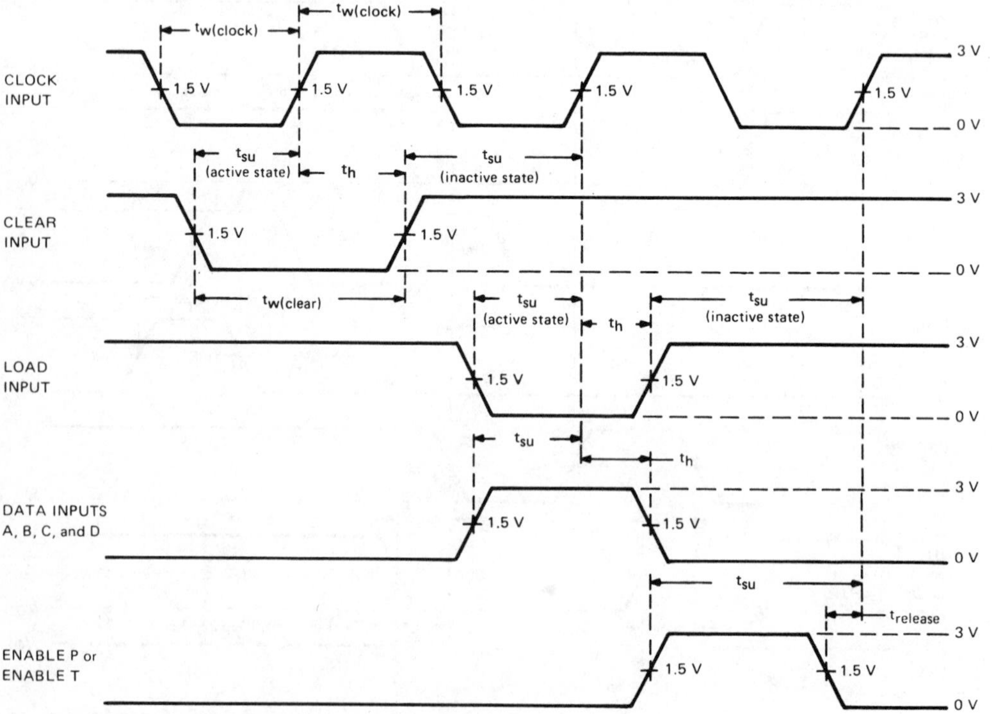

VOLTAGE WAVEFORMS

NOTE A: The input pulses are supplied by generators having the following characteristics: $t_r \leqslant 2.5$ ns, $t_f \leqslant 2.5$ ns, PRR $\leqslant 1$ MHz, duty cycle $\leqslant 50\%$, $Z_{out} \approx 50 \ \Omega$.

FIGURE 4—PULSE WIDTHS, SETUP TIMES, HOLD TIMES, AND RELEASE TIME

TEXAS INSTRUMENTS
INCORPORATED

POST OFFICE BOX 5012 • DALLAS, TEXAS 75222

TYPICAL APPLICATION DATA

N-BIT SYNCHRONOUS COUNTERS

This application demonstrates how the look-ahead carry circuit can be used to implement a high-speed n-bit counter. The '160, '162, 'LS160A, 'LS162A, or 'S162 will count in BCD and the '161, '163, 'LS161A, 'LS163A or 'S163 will count in binary. Virtually any count mode (modulo-N, N₁-to-N₂, N₁-to-maximum) can be used with this fast look-ahead circuit.

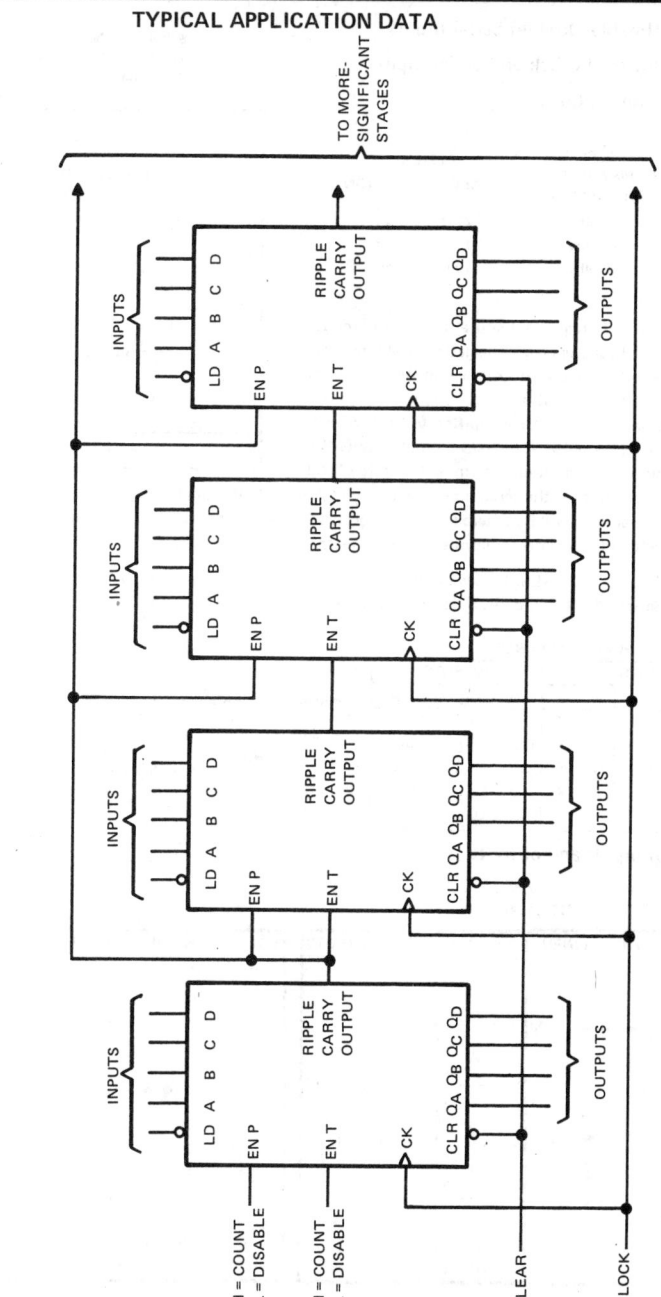

TEXAS INSTRUMENTS
INCORPORATED
POST OFFICE BOX 5012 • DALLAS, TEXAS 75222

TTL MSI TYPES SN54164, SN54L164, SN54LS164, SN74164, SN74L164, SN74LS164
8-BIT PARALLEL-OUT SERIAL SHIFT REGISTERS

BULLETIN NO. DL-S 7611835, MARCH 1974—REVISED OCTOBER 1976

- Gated (Enable/Disable) Serial Inputs
- Fully Buffered Clock and Serial Inputs
- Asynchronous Clear

TYPE	TYPICAL MAXIMUM CLOCK FREQUENCY	TYPICAL POWER DISSIPATION
'164	36 MHz	21 mW per bit
'L164	18 MHz	11 mW per bit
'LS164	36 MHz	10 mW per bit

SN54164, SN54LS164 . . . J OR W PACKAGE
SN54L164, SN74L164 . . . J, N, OR T PACKAGE
SN74164, SN74LS164 . . . J OR N PACKAGE
(TOP VIEW)

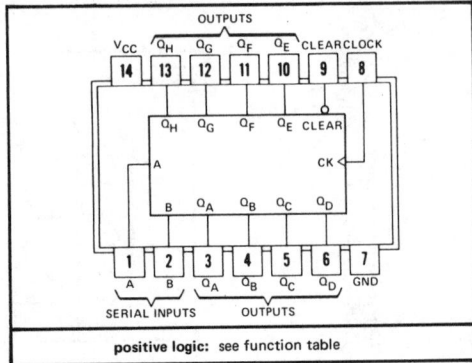

positive logic: see function table

description

These 8-bit shift registers feature gated serial inputs and an asynchronous clear. The gated serial inputs (A and B) permit complete control over incoming data as a low at either (or both) input(s) inhibits entry of the new data and resets the first flip-flop to the low level at the next clock pulse. A high-level input enables the other input which will then determine the state of the first flip-flop. Data at the serial inputs may be changed while the clock is high or low, but only information meeting the setup requirements will be entered. Clocking occurs on the low-to-high-level transition of the clock input. All inputs are diode-clamped to minimize transmission-line effects.

Series 54, 54L, and 54LS devices are characterized for operation over the full military temperature range of −55°C to 125°C; Series 74, 74L, and 74LS devices are characterized for operation from 0°C to 70°C.

FUNCTION TABLE

INPUTS				OUTPUTS			
CLEAR	CLOCK	A	B	Q_A	Q_B	...	Q_H
L	X	X	X	L	L		L
H	L	X	X	Q_{A0}	Q_{B0}		Q_{H0}
H	↑	H	H	H	Q_{An}		Q_{Gn}
H	↑	L	X	L	Q_{An}		Q_{Gn}
H	↑	X	L	L	Q_{An}		Q_{Gn}

H = high level (steady state), L = low level (steady state)
X = irrelevant (any input, including transitions)
↑ = transition from low to high level.
Q_{A0}, Q_{B0}, Q_{H0} = the level of Q_A, Q_B, or Q_H, respectively, before the indicated steady-state input conditions were established.
Q_{An}, Q_{Gn} = the level of Q_A or Q_G before the most-recent ↑ transition of the clock; indicates a one-bit shift.

schematics of inputs and outputs

'164, 'L164

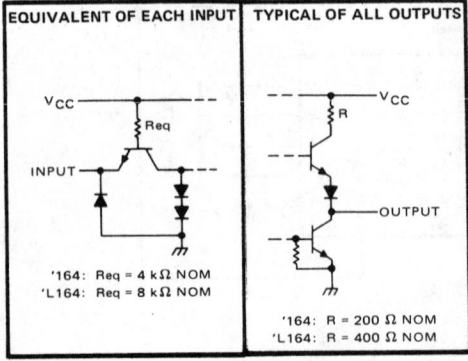

'LS164

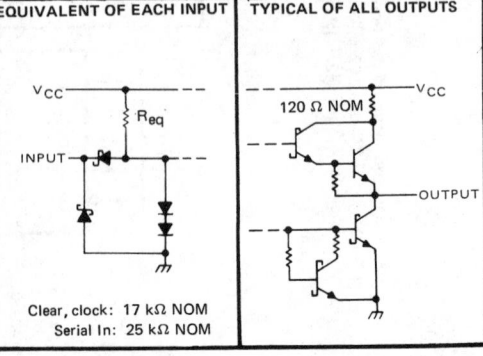

TEXAS INSTRUMENTS
INCORPORATED
POST OFFICE BOX 5012 • DALLAS, TEXAS 75222

7

TYPES SN54164, SN54L164, SN54LS164, SN74164, SN74L164, SN74LS164
8-BIT PARALLEL-OUT SERIAL SHIFT REGISTERS

REVISED OCTOBER 1976

typical clear, shift, and clear sequences

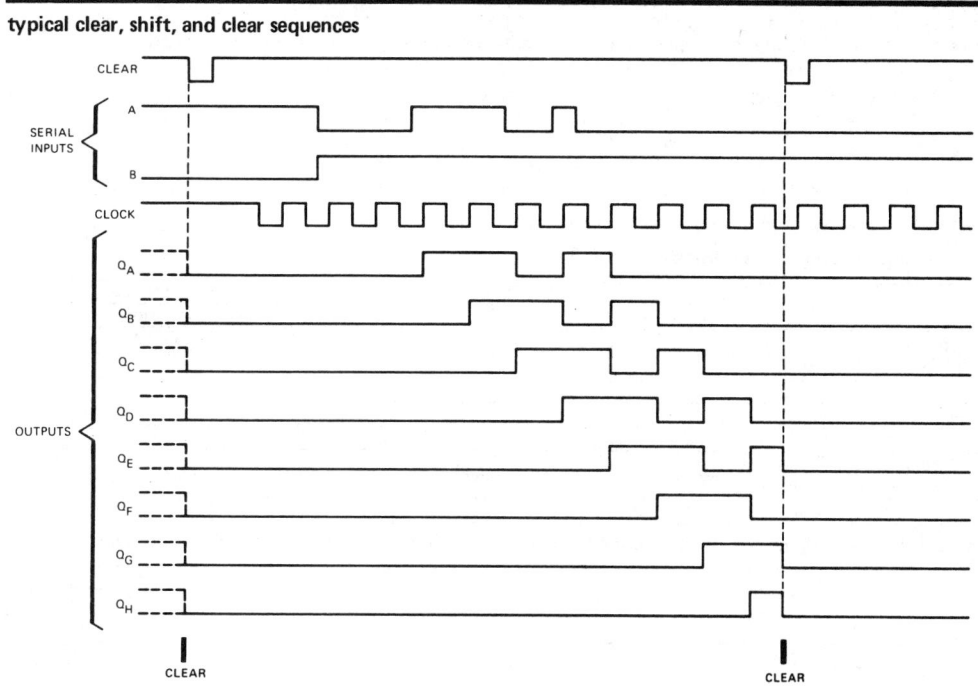

functional block diagram

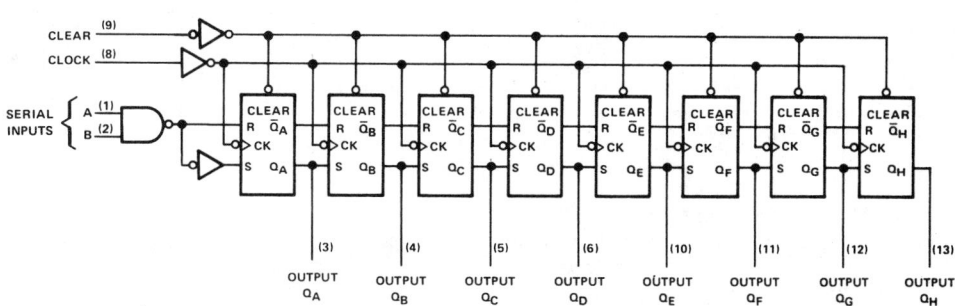

TEXAS INSTRUMENTS
INCORPORATED
POST OFFICE BOX 5012 • DALLAS, TEXAS 75222

absolute maximum ratings over operating free-air temperature range (unless otherwise noted)

Supply voltage, V_{CC} (see Note 1) . . . . 7 V
Input voltage . . . . 5.5 V
Operating free-air temperature range: SN54164 . . . . −55°C to 125°C
SN74164 . . . . 0°C to 70°C
Storage temperature range . . . . −65°C to 150°C

NOTE 1: Voltage values are with respect to network ground terminal.

recommended operating conditions

	SN54164			SN74164			UNIT
	MIN	NOM	MAX	MIN	NOM	MAX	
Supply voltage, V_{CC}	4.5	5	5.5	4.75	5	5.25	V
High-level output current, I_{OH}			−400			−400	µA
Low-level output current, I_{OL}			8			8	mA
Clock frequency, f_{clock}	0		25	0		25	MHz
Width of clock or clear input pulse, t_W	20			20			ns
Data setup time, t_{su} (see Figure 1)	15			15			ns
Data hold time, t_h (see Figure 1)	5			5			ns
Operating free-air temperature, T_A	−55		125	0		70	°C

electrical characteristics over recommended operating free-air temperature range (unless otherwise noted)

PARAMETER		TEST CONDITIONS[†]		SN54164			SN74164			UNIT
				MIN	TYP[‡]	MAX	MIN	TYP[‡]	MAX	
V_{IH}	High-level input voltage			2			2			V
V_{IL}	Low-level input voltage					0.8			0.8	V
V_{IK}	Input clamp voltage	V_{CC} = MIN,	I_I = −12 mA			−1.5			−1.5	V
V_{OH}	High-level output voltage	V_{CC} = MIN, V_{IH} = 2 V, V_{IL} = 0.8 V, I_{OH} = −400 µA		2.4	3.2		2.4	3.2		V
V_{OL}	Low-level output voltage	V_{CC} = MIN, V_{IH} = 2 V, V_{IL} = 0.8 V, I_{OL} = 8 mA			0.2	0.4		0.2	0.4	V
I_I	Input current at maximum input voltage	V_{CC} = MAX,	V_I = 5.5 V,			1			1	mA
I_{IH}	High-level input current	V_{CC} = MAX,	V_I = 2.4 V			40			40	µA
I_{IL}	Low-level input current	V_{CC} = MAX,	V_I = 0.4 V			−1.6			−1.6	mA
I_{OS}	Short-circuit output current[§]	V_{CC} = MAX		−10		−27.5	−9		−27.5	mA
I_{CC}	Supply current	V_{CC} = MAX, See Note 2	$V_{I(clock)}$ = 0.4 V		30			30		mA
			$V_{I(clock)}$ = 2.4 V		37	54		37	54	

[†]For conditions shown at MIN or MAX, use the appropriate value specified under recommended operating conditions.
[‡]All typical values are at V_{CC} = 5 V, T_A = 25°C.
[§]Not more than two outputs should be shorted at a time.
NOTE 2: I_{CC} is measured with outputs open, serial inputs grounded, and a momentary ground, then 4.5 V, applied to clear.

switching characteristics, V_{CC} = 5 V, T_A = 25°C

PARAMETER		TEST CONDITIONS		MIN	TYP	MAX	UNIT
f_{max}	Maximum clock frequency		C_L = 15 pF	25	36		MHz
t_{PHL}	Propagation delay time, high-to-low-level Q outputs from clear input		C_L = 15 pF		24	36	ns
		R_L = 800 Ω, See Figure 1	C_L = 50 pF		28	42	
t_{PLH}	Propagation delay time, low-to-high-level Q outputs from clock input		C_L = 15 pF	8	17	27	ns
			C_L = 50 pF	10	20	30	
t_{PHL}	Propagation delay time, high-to-low-level Q outputs from the clock input		C_L = 15 pF	10	21	32	ns
			C_L = 50 pF	10	25	37	

TEXAS INSTRUMENTS
INCORPORATED
POST OFFICE BOX 5012 • DALLAS, TEXAS 75222

7

absolute maximum ratings over operating free-air temperature range (unless otherwise noted)

Supply voltage, V_{CC} (see Note 1)	7 V
Input voltage	5.5 V
Operating free-air temperature range: SN54L164	$-55°C$ to $125°C$
SN74L164	$0°C$ to $70°C$
Storage temperature range	$-65°C$ to $150°C$

NOTE 1: Voltage values are with respect to network ground terminal.

recommended operating conditions

	SN54L164			SN74L164			UNIT
	MIN	NOM	MAX	MIN	NOM	MAX	
Supply voltage, V_{CC}	4.5	5	5.5	4.75	5	5.25	V
High-level output current, I_{OH}			-200			-200	μA
Low-level output current, I_{OL}			4			4	mA
Clock frequency, f_{clock}	0		12	0		12	MHz
Width of clock or clear input pulse, t_w	40			40			ns
Data setup time, t_{su} (see Figure 1)	30			30			ns
Data hold time, t_h (see Figure 1)	10			10			ns
Operating free-air temperature, T_A	-55		125	0		70	$°C$

electrical characteristics over recommended operating free-air temperature range (unless otherwise noted)

PARAMETER		TEST CONDITIONS[†]	SN54L164			SN74L164			UNIT
			MIN	TYP[‡]	MAX	MIN	TYP[‡]	MAX	
V_{IH}	High-level input voltage		2			2			V
V_{IL}	Low-level input voltage				0.8			0.8	V
V_{IK}	Input clamp voltage	$V_{CC} = MIN$, $I_I = -12$ mA			-1.5			-1.5	V
V_{OH}	High-level output voltage	$V_{CC} = MIN$, $V_{IH} = 2$ V, $V_{IL} = 0.8$ V, $I_{OH} = -200\ \mu A$,	2.4	3.2		2.4	3.2		V
V_{OL}	Low-level output voltage	$V_{CC} = MIN$, $V_{IH} = 2$ V, $V_{IL} = 0.8$ V, $I_{OL} = 4$ mA		0.2	0.4		0.2	0.4	V
I_I	Input current at maximum input voltage	$V_{CC} = MAX$, $V_I = 5.5$ V			1			1	mA
I_{IH}	High-level input current	$V_{CC} = MAX$, $V_I = 2.4$ V			20			20	μA
I_{IL}	Low-level input current	$V_{CC} = MAX$, $V_I = 0.4$ V			-0.8			-0.8	mA
I_{OS}	Short-circuit output current[§]	$V_{CC} = MAX$	-5		-20	-4		-20	mA
I_{CC}	Supply current	$V_{CC} = MAX$, See Note 3		19	27		19	27	mA

[†]For conditions shown at MIN or MAX, use the appropriate value specified under recommended operating conditions.
[‡]All typical values are at $V_{CC} = 5$ V, $T_A = 25°C$
[§]Not more than two outputs should be shorted at a time.
NOTE 3: I_{CC} is measured with outputs open, serial inputs grounded, the clock input at 2.4 V, and a momentary ground, then 4.5 V, applied to clear.

switching characteristics, $V_{CC} = 5$ V, $T_A = 25°C$

PARAMETER		TEST CONDITIONS	MIN	TYP	MAX	UNIT
f_{max}	Maximum clock frequency	$C_L = 15$ pF	12	18		MHz
t_{PHL}	Propagation delay time, high-to-low-level Q outputs from clear input	$C_L = 15$ pF		48	72	ns
		$C_L = 50$ pF		56	84	
t_{PLH}	Propagation delay time, low-to-high-level Q outputs from clock input	$C_L = 15$ pF	8	34	54	ns
		$C_L = 50$ pF	10	20	60	
t_{PHL}	Propagation delay time, high-to-low-level Q outputs from the clock input	$C_L = 15$ pF	10	42	64	ns
		$C_L = 50$ pF	10	50	74	

$R_L = 800\ \Omega$, See Figure 1

7

TYPES SN54LS164, SN74LS164
8-BIT PARALLEL-OUT SERIAL SHIFT REGISTERS

REVISED OCTOBER 1976

absolute maximum ratings over operating free-air temperature range (unless otherwise noted)

Supply voltage, V_{CC} (see Note 1)	7 V
Input voltage	7 V
Operating free-air temperature range: SN54LS164	−55°C to 125°C
SN74LS164	0°C to 70°C
Storage temperature range	−65°C to 150°C

NOTE 1: Voltage values are with respect to network ground terminal.

recommended operating conditions

	SN54LS164			SN74LS164			UNIT
	MIN	NOM	MAX	MIN	NOM	MAX	
Supply voltage, V_{CC}	4.5	5	5.5	4.75	5	5.25	V
High-level output current, I_{OH}			−400			−400	µA
Low-level output current, I_{OL}			4			8	mA
Clock frequency, f_{clock}	0		25	0		25	MHz
Width of clock or clear input pulse, t_w	20			20			ns
Data setup time, t_{su} (see Figure 1)	15			15			ns
Data hold time, t_h (see Figure 1)	5			5			ns
Operating free-air temperature, T_A	−55		125	0		70	°C

electrical characteristics over recommended operating free-air temperature range (unless otherwise noted)

PARAMETER		TEST CONDITIONS[†]		SN54LS164			SN74LS164			UNIT
				MIN	TYP[‡]	MAX	MIN	TYP[‡]	MAX	
V_{IH}	High-level input voltage			2			2			V
V_{IL}	Low-level input voltage					0.7			0.8	V
V_{IK}	Input clamp voltage	V_{CC} = MIN,	I_I = −18 mA			−1.5			−1.5	V
V_{OH}	High-level output voltage	V_{CC} = MIN, V_{IH} = 2 V, V_{IL} = V_{IL} max, I_{OH} = −400 µA		2.5	3.5		2.7	3.5		V
V_{OL}	Low-level output voltage	V_{CC} = MIN, V_{IH} = 2 V, V_{IL} = V_{IL} max	I_{OL} = 4 mA		0.25	0.4		0.25	0.4	V
			I_{OL} = 8 mA					0.35	0.5	
I_I	Input current at maximum input voltage	V_{CC} = MAX,	V_I = 7 V			0.1			0.1	mA
I_{IH}	High-level input current	V_{CC} = MAX,	V_I = 2.7 V			20			20	µA
I_{IL}	Low-level input current	V_{CC} = MAX,	V_I = 0.4 V			−0.4			−0.4	mA
I_{OS}	Short-circuit output current[§]	V_{CC} = MAX		−20		−100	−20		−100	mA
I_{CC}	Supply current	V_{CC} = MAX,	See Note 3		16	27		16	27	mA

[†] For conditions shown as MIN or MAX, use the appropriate value specified under recommended operating conditions.
[‡] All typical values are at V_{CC} = 5 V, T_A = 25°C.
[§] Not more than one output should be shorted at a time, and duration of the short-circuit should not exceed one second.
NOTE 3: I_{CC} is measured with outputs open, serial inputs grounded, the clock input at 2.4 V, and a momentary ground, then 4.5 V applied to clear.

switching characteristics, V_{CC} = 5 V, T_A = 25°C

PARAMETER		TEST CONDITIONS	MIN	TYP	MAX	UNIT
f_{max}	Maximum clock frequency	C_L = 15 pF, R_L = 2 kΩ, See Figure 1	25	36		MHz
t_{PHL}	Propagation delay time, high-to-low-level Q outputs from clear input			24	36	ns
t_{PLH}	Propagation delay time, low-to-high-level Q outputs from clock input			17	27	ns
t_{PHL}	Propagation delay time, high-to-low-level Q outputs from clock input			21	32	ns

7

TEXAS INSTRUMENTS
INCORPORATED
POST OFFICE BOX 5012 • DALLAS, TEXAS 75222

1076

TYPES SN54164, SN54L164, SN54LS164, SN74164, SN74L164, SN74LS164
8-BIT PARALLEL-OUT SERIAL SHIFT REGISTERS

PARAMETER MEASUREMENT INFORMATION

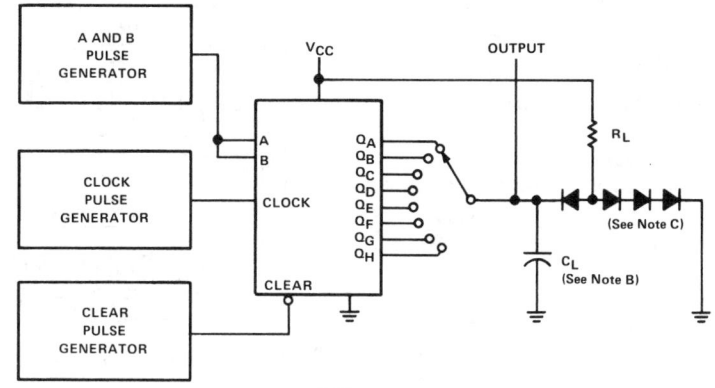

TEST CIRCUIT

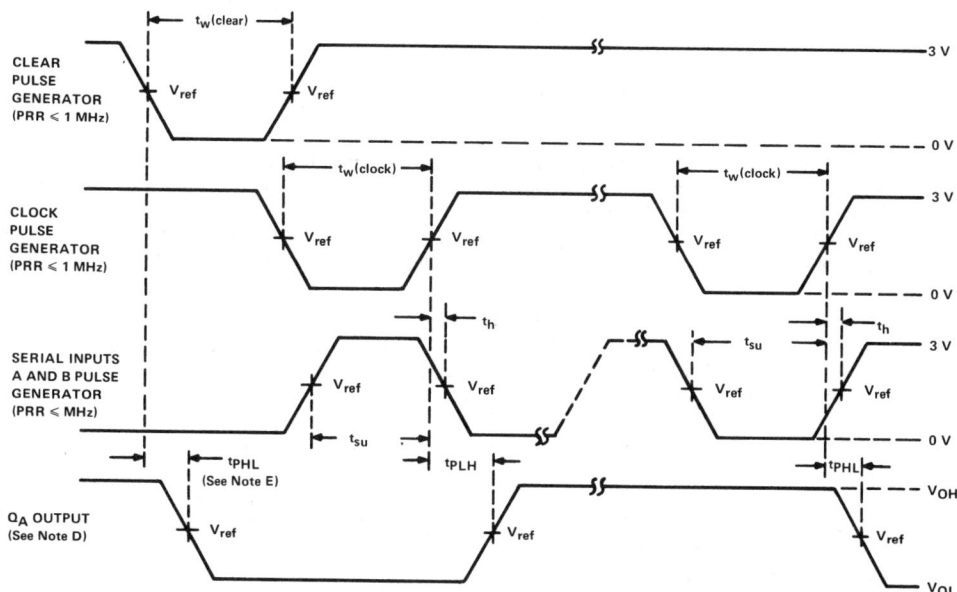

VOLTAGE WAVEFORMS

NOTES:
A. The pulse generators have the following characteristics: duty cycle ⩽ 50%, $Z_{out} \approx 50\ \Omega$; for '164 and 'L164, $t_r \leqslant 10$ ns, $t_f \leqslant 10$ ns, and for 'LS164, $t_r \leqslant 15$ ns, $t_f \leqslant 6$ ns.
B. C_L includes probe and jig capacitance.
C. All diodes are 1N3064 or 1N916.
D. Q_A output is illustrated. Relationship of serial input A and B data to other Q outputs is illustrated in the typical shift sequence.
E. Outputs are set to the high level prior to the measurement of t_{PHL} from the clear input.
F. For '164 and 'L164, V_{ref} = 1.5 V; for 'LS164, V_{ref} = 1.3 V.

FIGURE 1—SWITCHING TIMES

TEXAS INSTRUMENTS
INCORPORATED
POST OFFICE BOX 5012 • DALLAS, TEXAS 75222

TTL
MSI

TYPES SN54165, SN54LS165, SN74165, SN74LS165
PARALLEL-LOAD 8-BIT SHIFT REGISTERS

BULLETIN NO. DL-S 7611375, OCTOBER 1976

- Complementary Outputs
- Direct Overriding Load (Data) Inputs
- Gated Clock Inputs
- Parallel-to-Serial Data Conversion

TYPE	TYPICAL MAXIMUM CLOCK FREQUENCY	TYPICAL POWER DISSIPATION
'165	26 MHz	210 mW
'LS165	35 MHz	105 mW

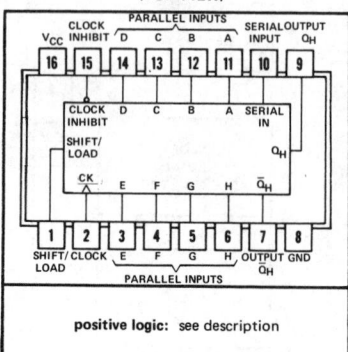

SN54165, SN54LS165 . . . J OR W PACKAGE
SN74165, SN74LS165 . . . J OR N PACKAGE
(TOP VIEW)

positive logic: see description

description

The '165 and 'LS165 are 8-bit serial shift registers that shift the data in the direction of Q_A toward Q_H when clocked. Parallel-in access to each stage is made available by eight individual direct data inputs that are enabled by a low level at the shift/load input. These registers also feature gated clock inputs and complementary outputs from the eighth bit. All inputs are diode-clamped to minimize transmission-line effects, thereby simplifying system design.

Clocking is accomplished through a 2-input positive-NOR gate, permitting one input to be used as a clock-inhibit function. Holding either of the clock inputs high inhibits clocking and holding either clock input low with the shift/load input high enables the other clock input. The clock-inhibit input should be changed to the high level only while the clock input is high. Parallel loading is inhibited as long as the shift/load input is high. Data at the parallel inputs are loaded directly into the register on a high-to-low transition of the shift/load input independently of the levels of the clock, clock inhibit, or serial inputs.

FUNCTION TABLE

INPUTS					INTERNAL OUTPUTS		OUTPUT
SHIFT/ LOAD	CLOCK INHIBIT	CLOCK	SERIAL	PARALLEL A . . . H	Q_A	Q_B	Q_H
L	X	X	X	a . . . h	a	b	h
H	L	L	X	X	Q_{A0}	Q_{B0}	Q_{H0}
H	L	↑	H	X	H	Q_{An}	Q_{Gn}
H	L	↑	L	X	L	Q_{An}	Q_{Gn}
H	H	X	X	X	Q_{A0}	Q_{B0}	Q_{H0}

See explanation of function tables on page 3-8.

schematic of inputs and output

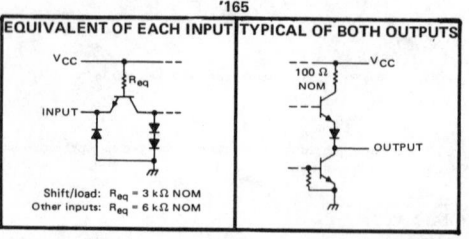

'165

EQUIVALENT OF EACH INPUT	TYPICAL OF BOTH OUTPUTS

Shift/load: R_{eq} = 3 kΩ NOM
Other inputs: R_{eq} = 6 kΩ NOM

'LS165

EQUIVALENT OF EACH INPUT	TYPICAL OF BOTH OUTPUTS

Clock, clock inhibit: R_{eq} = 17 kΩ NOM
Parallel inputs,
serial input: R_{eq} = 24 kΩ NOM
Shift/load: R_{eq} = 5.7 kΩ NOM

TEXAS INSTRUMENTS
INCORPORATED
POST OFFICE BOX 5012 • DALLAS, TEXAS 75222

functional block diagram

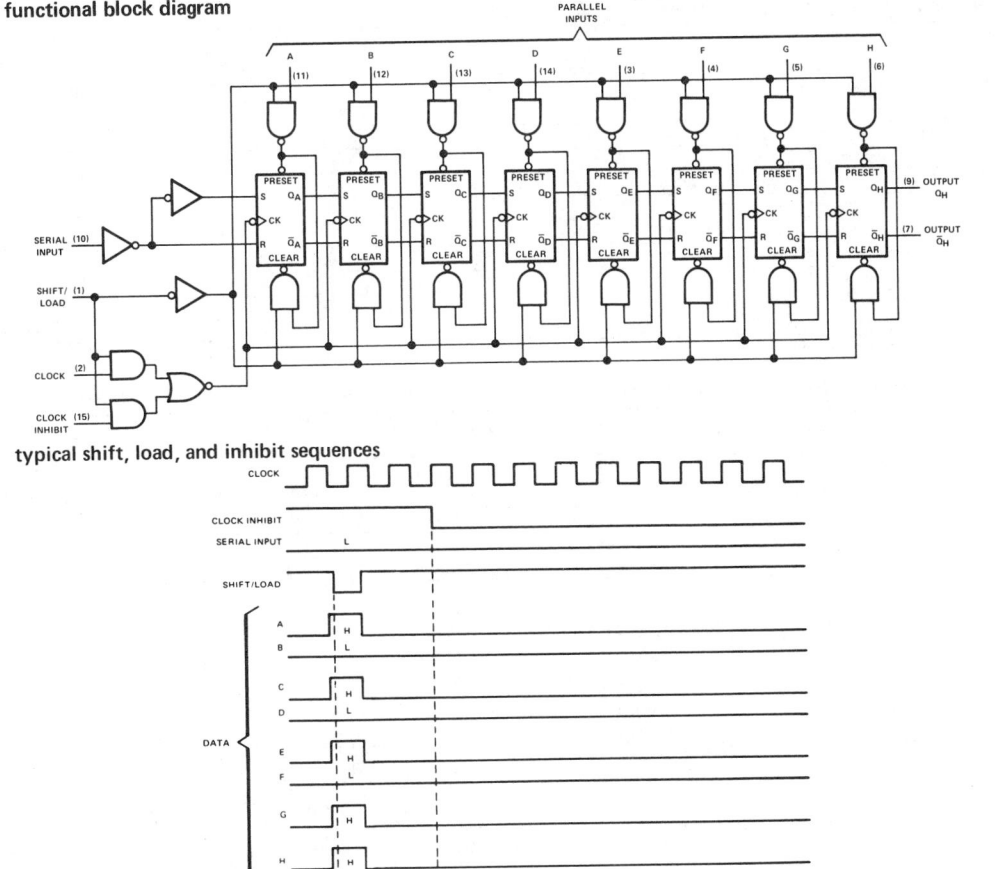

typical shift, load, and inhibit sequences

absolute maximum ratings over operating free-air temperature range (unless otherwise noted)

Supply voltage, V$_{CC}$ (see Note 1)	7 V
Input voltage: SN54165, SN74165	5.5 V
SN54LS165, SN74LS165	7 V
Interemitter voltage (see Note 2)	5.5 V
Operating free-air temperature range: SN54165, SN54LS165	−55°C to 125°C
SN74165, SN74LS165	0°C to 70°C
Storage temperature range	−65°C to 150°C

NOTES: 1. Voltage values, except interemitter voltage, are with respect to network ground terminal.
2. This is the voltage between two emitters of a multiple-emitter transistor. This rating applies for the '165 to the shift/load input in conjunction with the clock-inhibit inputs.

TEXAS INSTRUMENTS
INCORPORATED
POST OFFICE BOX 5012 • DALLAS, TEXAS 75222

TYPES SN54165, SN74165
PARALLEL-LOAD 8-BIT SHIFT REGISTERS

recommended operating conditions

	SN54165			SN74165			UNIT
	MIN	NOM	MAX	MIN	NOM	MAX	
Supply voltage, V_{CC}	4.5	5	5.5	4.75	5	5.25	V
High-level output current, I_{OH}			−800			−800	μA
Low-level output current, I_{OL}			16			16	mA
Clock frequency, f_{clock}	0		20	0		20	MHz
Width of clock input pulse, $t_{w(clock)}$	25			25			ns
Width of load input pulse, $t_{w(load)}$	15			15			ns
Clock-enable setup time, t_{su} (see Figure 1)	30			30			ns
Parallel input setup time, t_{su} (see Figure 1)	10			10			ns
Serial input setup time, t_{su} (see Figure 2)	20			20			ns
Shift setup time, t_{su} (see Figure 2)	45			45			ns
Hold time at any input, t_h	0			0			ns
Operating free-air temperature, T_A	−55		125	0		70	°C

electrical characteristics over recommended operating free-air temperature range (unless otherwise noted)

PARAMETER		TEST CONDITIONS†	SN54165			SN74165			UNIT
			MIN	TYP‡	MAX	MIN	TYP‡	MAX	
V_{IH}	High-level input voltage		2			2			V
V_{IL}	Low-level input voltage				0.8			0.8	V
V_{IK}	Input clamp voltage	V_{CC} = MIN, I_I = −12 mA			−1.5			−1.5	V
V_{OH}	High-level output voltage	V_{CC} = MIN, V_{IH} = 2 V, V_{IL} = 0.8 V, I_{OH} = −800 μA	2.4	3.4		2.4	3.4		V
V_{OL}	Low-level output voltage	V_{CC} = MIN, V_{IH} = 2 V, V_{IL} = 0.8 V, I_{OL} = 16 mA		0.2	0.4		0.2	0.4	V
I_I	Input current at maximum input voltage	V_{CC} = MAX, V_I = 5.5 V			1			1	mA
I_{IH}	High-level input current — Shift/load	V_{CC} = MAX, V_I = 2.4 V			80			80	μA
	Other inputs				40			40	
I_{IL}	Low-level input current — Shift/load	V_{CC} = MAX, V_I = 0.4 V			−3.2			−3.2	mA
	Other inputs				−1.6			−1.6	
I_{OS}	Short-circuit output current§	V_{CC} = MAX	−20		−55	−18		−55	mA
I_{CC}	Supply current	V_{CC} = MAX, See Note 3		42	63		42	63	mA

NOTE 3: With the outputs open, clock inhibit and clock at 4.5 V, and a clock pulse applied to the shift/load input, I_{CC} is measured first with the parallel inputs at 4.5 V, then with the parallel inputs grounded.
†For conditions shown as MIN or MAX, use the appropriate value specified under recommended operating conditions.
‡All typical values are at V_{CC} = 5 V, T_A = 25°C.
§Not more than one output should be shorted at a time.

switching characteristics, V_{CC} = 5 V, T_A = 25°C

PARAMETER¶	FROM (INPUT)	TO (OUTPUT)	TEST CONDITIONS	MIN	TYP	MAX	UNIT
f_{max}				20	26		MHz
t_{PLH}	Load	Any			21	31	ns
t_{PHL}					27	40	
t_{PLH}	Clock	Any	C_L = 15 pF, R_L = 400 Ω, See figures 1 thru 3		16	24	ns
t_{PHL}					21	31	
t_{PLH}	H	Q_H			11	17	ns
t_{PHL}					24	36	
t_{PLH}	H	$\overline{Q}_H$			18	27	ns
t_{PHL}					18	27	

¶f_{max} ≡ maximum clock frequency
t_{PLH} ≡ propagation delay time, low-to-high-level output
t_{PHL} ≡ propagation delay time, high-to-low-level output

7

1076

TEXAS INSTRUMENTS
INCORPORATED
POST OFFICE BOX 5012 • DALLAS, TEXAS 75222

recommended operating conditions

	SN54LS165			SN74LS165			UNIT
	MIN	NOM	MAX	MIN	NOM	MAX	
Supply voltage, V_{CC}	4.5	5	5.5	4.75	5	5.25	V
High-level output current, I_{OH}			−400			−400	μA
Low-level output current, I_{OL}			4			8	mA
Clock frequency, f_{clock}	0		25	0		25	MHz
Width of clock input pulse, $t_{w(clock)}$	25			25			ns
Width of load input pulse, $t_{w(load)}$	15			15			ns
Clock-enable setup time, t_{su} (see Figure 1)	30			30			ns
Parallel input setup time, t_{su} (see Figure 1)	10			10			ns
Serial input setup time, t_{su} (see Figure 2)	20			20			ns
Shift setup time, t_{su} (see Figure 2)	45			45			ns
Hold time at any input, t_h	0			0			ns
Operating free-air temperature, T_A	−55		125	0		70	°C

electrical characteristics over recommended operating free-air temperature range (unless otherwise noted)

PARAMETER		TEST CONDITIONS[†]		SN54LS165			SN74LS165			UNIT
				MIN	TYP[‡]	MAX	MIN	TYP[‡]	MAX	
V_{IH}	High-level input voltage			2			2			V
V_{IL}	Low-level input voltage					0.7			0.8	V
V_{IK}	Input clamp voltage	V_{CC} = MIN,	I_I = −18 mA			−1.5			−1.5	V
V_{OH}	High-level output voltage	V_{CC} = MIN, V_{IL} = V_{IL}max,	V_{IH} = 2 V, I_{OH} = −400 μA	2.5	3.5		2.7	3.5		V
V_{OL}	Low-level output voltage	V_{CC} = MIN, V_{IH} = 2 V, V_{IL} = V_{IL}max,	I_{OL} = 4 mA		0.25	0.4		0.25	0.4	V
			I_{OL} = 8 mA					0.35	0.5	
I_I	Input current at maximum input voltage	Shift/load	V_{CC} = MAX, V_I = 7 V			0.3			0.3	mA
		Other inputs				0.1			0.1	
I_{IH}	Low-level input current	Shift/load	V_{CC} = MAX, V_I = 2.7 V			60			60	μA
		Other inputs				20			20	
I_{IL}	Low-level input current	Shift/load	V_{CC} = MAX, V_I = 0.4 V			−1.2			−1.2	mA
		Other inputs				−0.4			−0.4	
I_{OS}	Short-circuit output current[§]	V_{CC} = MAX		−20		−100	−20		−100	mA
I_{CC}	Supply current	V_{CC} = MAX,	See Note 3		21	36		21	36	mA

NOTE 3: With the outputs open, clock inhibit and clock at 4.5 V, and a clock pulse applied to the shift/load input, I_{CC} is measured first with the parallel inputs at 4.5 V, then with the parallel inputs grounded.

[†] For conditions shown as MIN or MAX, use the appropriate value specified under recommended operating conditions.
[‡] All typical values are at V_{CC} = 5 V, T_A = 25°C.
[§] Not more than one output should be shorted at a time, and the duration of the short-circuit should not exceed one second.

switching characteristics, V_{CC} = 5 V, T_A = 25°C

PARAMETER[¶]	FROM (INPUT)	TO (OUTPUT)	TEST CONDITIONS	MIN	TYP	MAX	UNIT
f_{max}				25	35		MHz
t_{PLH}	Load	Any			22	35	ns
t_{PHL}					22	35	
t_{PLH}	Clock	Any	C_L = 15 pF, R_L = 2 kΩ, See figures 1 thru 3		27	40	ns
t_{PHL}					28	40	
t_{PLH}	H	Q_H			14	25	ns
t_{PHL}					21	30	
t_{PLH}	H	$\overline{Q}_H$			21	30	ns
t_{PHL}					16	25	

[¶] f_{max} ≡ maximum clock frequency
t_{PLH} ≡ propagation delay time, low-to-high-level output
t_{PHL} ≡ propagation delay time, high-to-low-level output

TEXAS INSTRUMENTS
INCORPORATED
POST OFFICE BOX 5012 • DALLAS, TEXAS 75222

PARAMETER MEASUREMENT INFORMATION

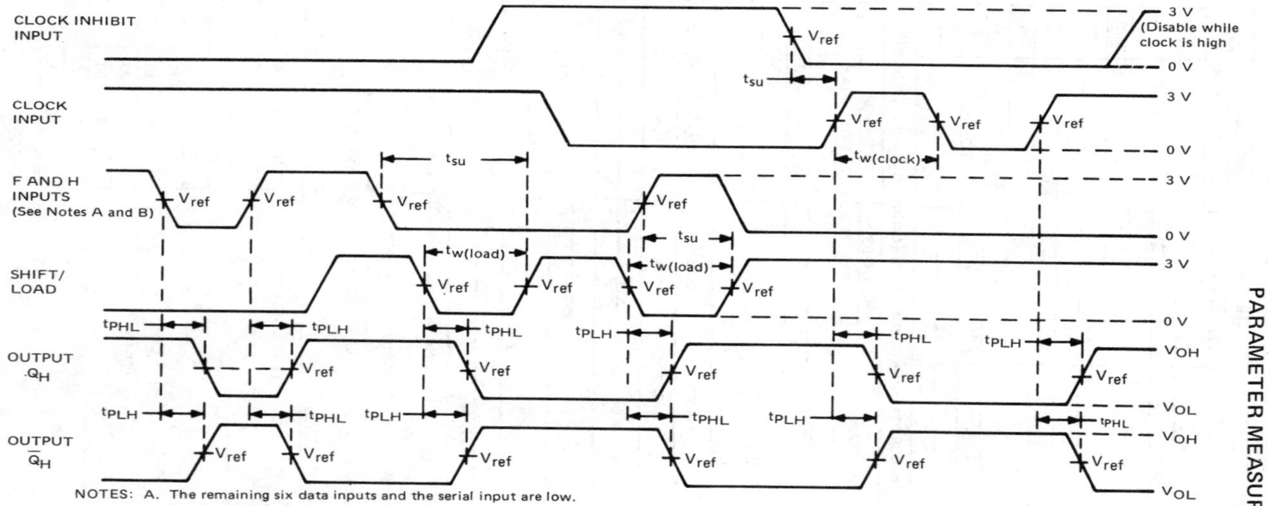

FIGURE 1–VOLTAGE WAVEFORMS

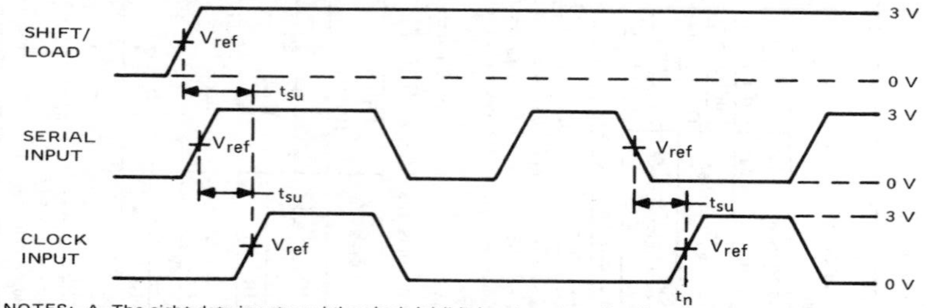

NOTES: A. The remaining six data inputs and the serial input are low.
B. Prior to test, high-level data is loaded into H input.
C. The input pulse generators have the following characteristics: PRR ⩽ 1 MHz, duty cycle ⩽ 50% $Z_{out} \approx 50\ \Omega$; for '165, $t_r \leqslant 10$ ns, $t_f \leqslant 10$ ns; for 'LS165, $t_r \leqslant 15$ ns, $t_f \leqslant 6$ ns.
D. For '165, $V_{ref} = 1.5$ V; for 'LS165, $V_{ref} = 1.3$ V.

FIGURE 2–VOLTAGE WAVEFORMS

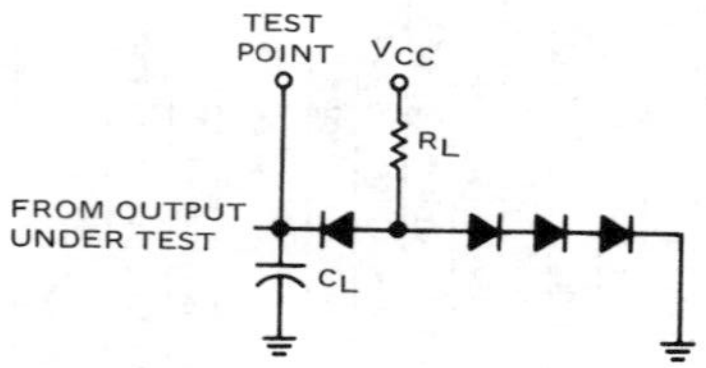

NOTES: A. The eight data inputs and the clock-inhibit input are low. Results are monitored at output Q_H at t_{n+7}.
B. The input pulse generators have the following characteristics: PRR ⩽ 1 MHz, duty cycle ⩽ 50%, $Z_{out} \approx 50\ \Omega$; for '165, $t_r \leqslant 10$ ns, $t_f \leqslant 10$ ns; for 'LS165, $t_r \leqslant 15$ ns, $t_f \leqslant 6$ ns.
C. For '165, $V_{ref} = 1.5$ V; for 'LS165, $V_{ref} = 1.3$ V.

FIGURE 3–LOAD CIRCUIT FOR SWITCHING TESTS

NOTES: A. C_L includes probe and jig capacitance.
B. All diodes are IN3064.

TEXAS INSTRUMENTS
INCORPORATED
POST OFFICE BOX 5012 • DALLAS, TEXAS 75222

1076

TTL MSI

TYPES SN54166, SN54LS166, SN74166, SN74LS166
8-BIT SHIFT REGISTERS

BULLETIN NO. DL-S7711808, OCTOBER 1976—REVISED AUGUST 1977

- Synchronous Load
- Direct Overriding Clear
- Parallel to Serial Conversion

TYPE	TYPICAL MAXIMUM CLOCK FREQUENCY	TYPICAL POWER DISSIPATION
'166	35 MHz	360 mW
'LS166	35 MHz	110 mW

functional block diagram

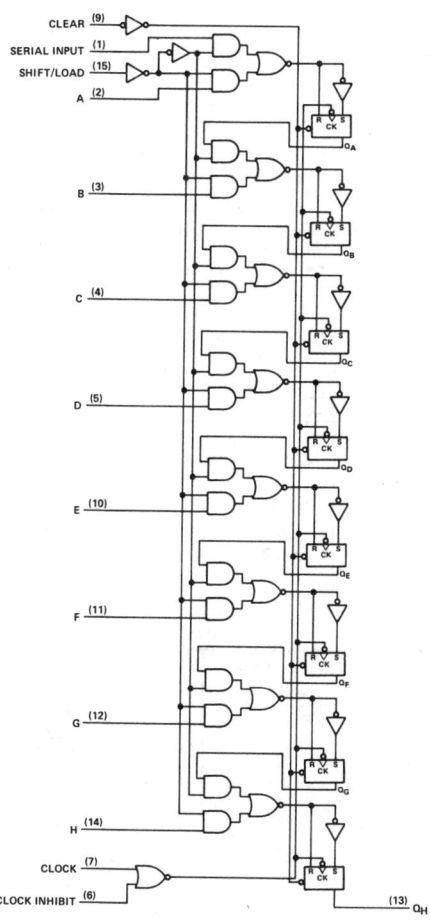

CLEAR (9)
SERIAL INPUT (1)
SHIFT/LOAD (15)
A (2)
B (3)
C (4)
D (5)
E (10)
F (11)
G (12)
H (14)
CLOCK (7)
CLOCK INHIBIT (6)
(13) Q_H

Q_A Q_B Q_C Q_D Q_E Q_F Q_G

⊸▷⊸ . . . dynamic input activated by transition from a high level to a low level.

SN54166, SN54LS166 . . . J OR W PACKAGE
SN74166, SN74LS166 . . . J OR N PACKAGE
(TOP VIEW)

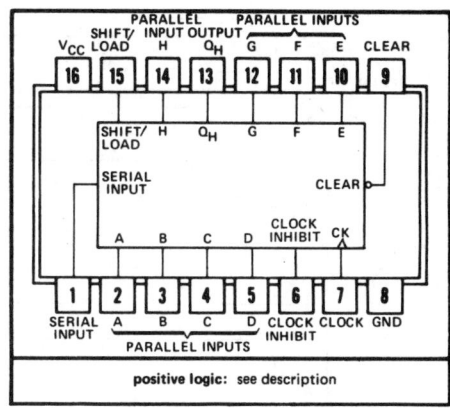

positive logic: see description

description

The '166 and 'LS166 8-bit shift registers are compatible with most other TTL and DTL logic families. All '166 and 'LS166 inputs are buffered to lower the drive requirements to one Series 54/74 or Series 54LS/74LS standard load, respectively. Input clamping diodes minimize switching transients and simplify system design.

These parallel-in or serial-in, serial-out shift registers have a complexity of 77 equivalent gates on a monolithic chip. They feature gated clock inputs and an overriding clear input. The parallel-in or serial-in modes are established by the shift/load input. When high, this input enables the serial data input and couples the eight flip-flops for serial shifting with each clock pulse. When low, the parallel (broadside) data inputs are enabled and synchronous loading occurs on the next clock pulse. During parallel loading, serial data flow is inhibited. Clocking is accomplished on the low-to-high-level edge of the clock pulse through a two-input positive NOR gate permitting one input to be used as a clock-enable or clock-inhibit function. Holding either of the clock inputs high inhibits clocking; holding either low enables the other clock input. This, of course, allows the system clock to be free-running and the register can be stopped on command with the other clock input. The clock-inhibit input should be changed to the high level only while the clock input is high. A buffered, direct clear input overrides all other inputs, including the clock, and sets all flip-flops to zero.

TEXAS INSTRUMENTS
INCORPORATED
POST OFFICE BOX 5012 • DALLAS, TEXAS 75222

TYPES SN54166, SN54LS166, SN74166, SN74LS166
8-BIT SHIFT REGISTERS

typical clear, shift, load, inhibit, and shift sequences

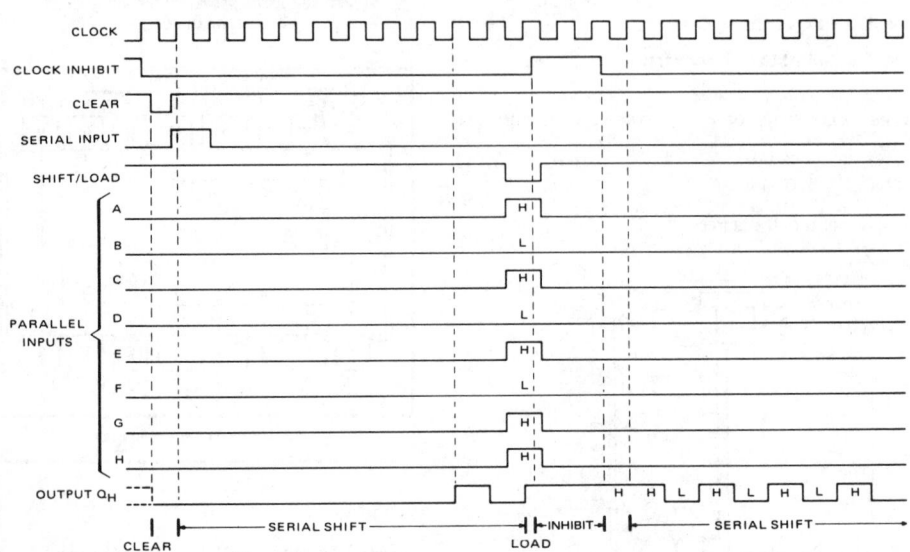

FUNCTION TABLE

| INPUTS | | | | | | INTERNAL OUTPUTS | | OUTPUT |
CLEAR	SHIFT/ LOAD	CLOCK INHIBIT	CLOCK	SERIAL	PARALLEL A...H	Q_A	Q_B	Q_H
L	X	X	X	X	X	L	L	L
H	X	L	L	X	X	Q_{A0}	Q_{B0}	Q_{H0}
H	L	L	↑	X	a...h	a	b	h
H	H	L	↑	H	X	H	Q_{An}	Q_{Gn}
H	H	L	↑	L	X	L	Q_{An}	Q_{Gn}
H	X	H	↑	X	X	Q_{A0}	Q_{B0}	Q_{H0}

See explanation of function tables on page 3-8.

schematics of inputs and outputs

'166

EQUIVALENT OF EACH INPUT	OUTPUT

V_{CC} 4 kΩ NOM
INPUT

V_{CC} 100 Ω
OUTPUT

'LS166

EQUIVALENT OF EACH INPUT	OUTPUT

$\overline{V_{CC}}$ R_{eq}
INPUT

Parallel and serial inputs: R_{eq} = 24 kΩ NOM
Others: R_{eq} = 17 kΩ NOM

V_{CC} 120 Ω NOM
OUTPUT

TEXAS INSTRUMENTS
INCORPORATED
POST OFFICE BOX 5012 • DALLAS, TEXAS 75222

1076

absolute maximum ratings over operating free-air temperature range (unless otherwise noted)

Supply voltage, V_{CC} (see Note 1) . . . . 7 V
Input voltage . . . . 5.5 V
Operating free-air temperature range: SN54166 (see Note 2) . . . . −55°C to 125°C
SN74166 . . . . 0°C to 70°C
Storage temperature range . . . . −65°C to 150°C

recommended operating conditions

	SN54166			SN74166			UNIT
	MIN	NOM	MAX	MIN	NOM	MAX	
Supply voltage, V_{CC}	4.5	5	5.5	4.75	5	5.25	V
High-level output current, I_{OH}			−800			−800	µA
Low-level output current, I_{OL}			16			16	mA
Clock frequency, f_{clock}	0		25	0		25	MHz
Width of clock or clear pulse, t_w (see Figure 1)	20			20			ns
Mode-control setup time, t_{su}	30			30			ns
Data setup time, t_{su} (see Figure 1)	20			20			ns
Hold time at any input, t_h (see Figure 1)	0			0			ns
Operating free-air temperature, T_A (see Note 2)	−55		125	0		70	°C

electrical characteristics over recommended operating free-air temperature range (unless otherwise noted)

PARAMETER		TEST CONDITIONS[†]	SN54166			SN74166			UNIT
			MIN	TYP[‡]	MAX	MIN	TYP[‡]	MAX	
V_{IH}	High-level input voltage		2			2			V
V_{IL}	Low-level input voltage				0.8			0.8	V
V_{IK}	Input clamp voltage	V_{CC} = MIN, I_I = −12 mA			−1.5			−1.5	V
V_{OH}	High-level output voltage	V_{CC} = MIN, V_{IH} = 2 V, V_{IL} = 0.8 V, I_{OH} = −800 µA	2.4	3.4		2.4	3.4		V
V_{OL}	Low-level output voltage	V_{CC} = MIN, V_{IH} = 2 V, V_{IL} = 0.8 V, I_{OL} = 16 mA		0.2	0.4		0.2	0.4	V
I_I	Input current at maximum input voltage	V_{CC} = MAX, V_I = 5.5 V			1			1	mA
I_{IH}	High-level input current	V_{CC} = MAX, V_I = 2.4 V			40			40	µA
I_{IL}	Low-level input current	V_{CC} = MAX, V_I = 0.4 V			−1.6			−1.6	mA
I_{OS}	Short-circuit output current[§]	V_{CC} = MAX	−20		−57	−18		−57	mA
I_{CC}	Supply current	V_{CC} = MAX, See Note 3		90	127		90	127	mA

[†] For conditions shown as MIN or MAX, use the appropriate value specified under recommended operating conditions.
[‡] All typical values are at V_{CC} = 5 V, T_A = 25°C.
[§] Not more than one output should be shorted at a time.
NOTES: 1. Voltage values are with respect to network ground terminal.
      2. An SN54166 in the W package operating at free-air temperatures above 113°C requires a heat-sink that provides a thermal resistance from case to free air, $R_{\theta CA}$, of not more than 48°C/W.
      3. With all outputs open, 4.5 V applied to the serial input, all other inputs except the clock grounded, I_{CC} is measured after a momentary ground, then 4.5 V, is applied to the clock.

switching characteristics, V_{CC} = 5 V, T_A = 25°C

PARAMETER		TEST CONDITIONS	MIN	TYP	MAX	UNIT
f_{max}	Maximum clock frequency		25	35		MHz
t_{PHL}	Propagation delay time, high-to-low-level output from clear	C_L = 15 pF, R_L = 400 Ω, See Figure 1		23	35	ns
t_{PHL}	Propagation delay time, high-to-low-level output from clock			20	30	ns
t_{PLH}	Propagation delay time, low-to-high-level output from clock			17	26	ns

7

887

TEXAS INSTRUMENTS
INCORPORATED
POST OFFICE BOX 5012 • DALLAS, TEXAS 75222

7-219

absolute maximum ratings over operating free-air temperature range (unless otherwise noted)

Supply voltage, V_{CC} (see Note 1) . . . . 7 V
Input voltage . . . . 7 V
Operating free-air temperature range: SN54LS166 . . . . −55°C to 125°C
SN74LS166 . . . . 0°C to 70°C
Storage temperature range . . . . −65°C to 150°C

NOTE 1: Voltage values are with respect to network ground terminal.

recommended operating conditions

	SN54LS166			SN74LS166			UNIT
	MIN	NOM	MAX	MIN	NOM	MAX	
Supply voltage, V_{CC}	4.5	5	5.5	4.75	5	5.25	V
High-level output current, I_{OH}			−400			−400	μA
Low-level output current, I_{OL}			4			8	mA
Clock frequency, f_{clock}	0		25	0		25	MHz
Width of clock or clear pulse, t_w (see Figure 1)	20			20			ns
Mode-control setup time, t_{su}	30			30			ns
Data setup time, t_{su} (see Figure 1)	20			20			ns
Hold time at any input, t_h (see Figure 1)	0			0			ns
Operating free-air temperature, T_A	−55		125	0		70	°C

electrical characteristics over recommended operating free-air temperature range (unless otherwise noted)

PARAMETER		TEST CONDITIONS[†]		SN54LS166			SN74LS166			UNIT
				MIN	TYP[‡]	MAX	MIN	TYP[‡]	MAX	
V_{IH}	High-level input voltage			2			2			V
V_{IL}	Low-level input voltage					0.7			0.8	V
V_{IK}	Input clamp voltage	V_{CC} = MIN, I_I = −18 mA				−1.5			−1.5	V
V_{OH}	High-level output voltage	V_{CC} = MIN, V_{IH} = 2 V, V_{IL} = V_{IL} max, I_{OH} = −400 μA		2.5	3.4		2.7	3.4		V
V_{OL}	Low-level output voltage	V_{CC} = MIN, V_{IH} = 2 V, V_{IL} = V_{IL} max	I_{OL} = 4 mA	0.25	0.4		0.25	0.4		V
			I_{OL} = 8 mA					0.35	0.5	
I_I	Input current at maximum input voltage	V_{CC} = MAX, V_I = 7 V				0.1			0.1	mA
I_{IH}	High-level input current	V_{CC} = MAX, V_I = 2.7 V				20			20	μA
I_{IL}	Low-level input current	V_{CC} = MAX, V_I 0.4 V				−0.4			−0.4	mA
I_{OS}	Short-circuit output current[§]	V_{CC} = MAX		−20		−100	−20		−100	mA
I_{CC}	Supply current	V_{CC} = MAX, See Note 3			22	38		22	38	mA

[†] For conditions shown as MIN or MAX, use the appropriate value specified under recommended operating conditions.
[‡] All typical values are at V_{CC} = 5 V, T_A = 25°C.
[§] Not more than one output should be shorted at a time, and duration of short-circuit should not exceed one second.
NOTE 3: With all outputs open, 4.5 V applied to the serial input and all other inputs except the clock grounded, I_{CC} is measured after a momentary ground, then 4.5 V, is applied to clock.

switching characteristics, V_{CC} = 5 V, T_A = 25°C

PARAMETER		TEST CONDITIONS	MIN	TYP	MAX	UNIT
f_{max}	Maximum clock frequency		25	35		MHz
t_{PHL}	Propagation delay time, high-to-low-level output from clear	C_L = 15 pF, R_L = 2 kΩ, See Figure 1		19	30	ns
t_{PHL}	Propagation delay time, high-to-low-level output from clock		8	23	35	ns
t_{PLH}	Propagation delay time, low-to-high-level output from clock		8	24	35	ns

TEXAS INSTRUMENTS
INCORPORATED
POST OFFICE BOX 5012 • DALLAS, TEXAS 75222

7

PARAMETER MEASUREMENT INFORMATION

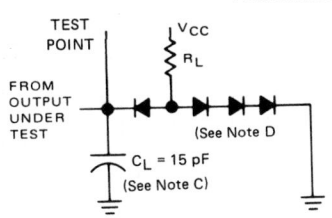

LOAD FOR OUTPUT UNDER TEST

TEST TABLE FOR SYNCHRONOUS INPUTS

DATA INPUT FOR TEST	SHIFT/LOAD	OUTPUT TESTED (SEE NOTE F)
H	0 V	Q_H at t_{n+1}
Serial Input	4.5 V	Q_H at t_{n+8}

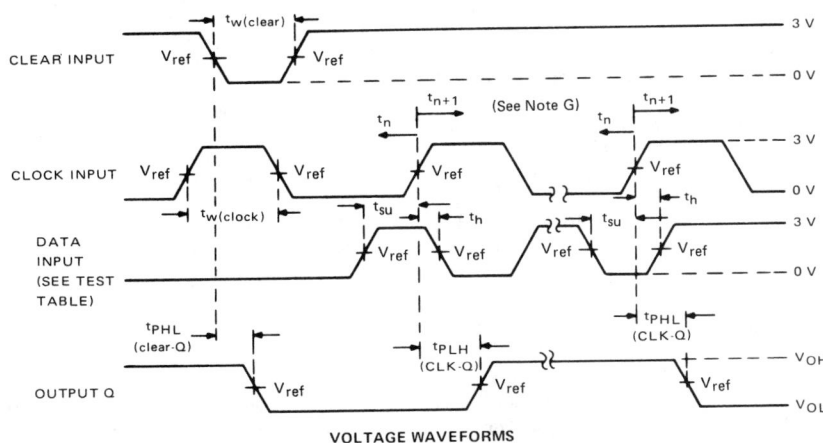

VOLTAGE WAVEFORMS

NOTE: A. All pulse generators have the following characteristics: $Z_{out} \approx 50 \, \Omega$; for '166, $t_r \leqslant 7$ ns and $t_f \leqslant 7$ ns; for 'LS166, $t_r \leqslant 15$ ns and $t_f \leqslant 6$ ns.
    B. The clock pulse has the following characteristics: $t_{w(clock)} \leqslant 20$ ns and PRR = 1 MHz. The clear pulse has the following characteristics: $t_{w(clear)} \geqslant 20$ ns and $t_{hold} = 0$ ns. When testing f_{max}, vary the clock PRR.
    C. C_L includes probe and jig capacitance.
    D. All diodes are 1N3064 or 1N916.
    E. A clear pulse is applied prior to each test.
    F. Propagation delay times (t_{PLH} and t_{PHL}) are measured at t_{n+1}. Proper shifting of data is verified at t_{n+8} with a functional test.
    G. t_n = bit time before clocking transition
       t_{n+1} = bit time after one clocking transition
       t_{n+8} = bit time after eight clocking transitions
    H. For '166 V_{ref} = 1.5 V; for 'LS166 V_{ref} = 1.3 V.

FIGURE 1

7

- Perform Fixed-Rate or Variable-Rate Frequency Division

- For Applications in Arithmetic, Radar, Digital-to-Analog (D/A), Analog-to-Digital (A/D), and other Conversion Operations

- Typical Maximum Clock Frequency . . . 32 Megahertz

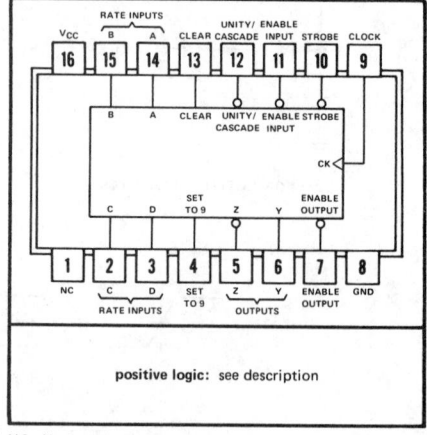

SN54167 . . . J OR W PACKAGE
SN74167 . . . J OR N PACKAGE
(TOP VIEW)

positive logic: see description

NC—No internal connection

description

These monolithic, fully synchronous, programmable counters utilize Series 54/74 TTL circuitry to achieve 32-megahertz typical maximum operating frequencies. These decade counters feature buffered clock, clear, enable and set-to-nine inputs to control the operation of the counter, and a strobe input to enable or inhibit the rate input/decoding AND-OR-INVERT gates. The outputs have additional gating for cascading and transferring unity-count rates.

The counter is enabled when the clear, strobe set-to-nine, and enable inputs are low. With the counter enabled, the output frequency is equal to the input frequency multiplied by the rate input M and divided by 10, ie.:

$$f_{out} = \frac{M \cdot f_{in}}{10}$$

where: $M = D \cdot 2^3 + C \cdot 2^2 + B \cdot 2^1 + A \cdot 2^0$ for decimal zero through nine.

When the rate input is binary 0 (all rate inputs low), Z remains high. In order to cascade devices to perform two-decade rate multiplication (0-99), the enable output is connected to the enable and strobe inputs of the next stage, the Z output of each stage is connected to the unity/cascade input of the other stage, and the sub-multiple frequency is taken from the Y output. For longer words, see typical application data, Figure 1.

The unity/cascade input, when connected to the clock input, may be utilized to pass the clock frequency (inverted) to the Y output when the rate input/decoding gates are inhibited by the strobe. The unity/cascade input may also be used as a control for the Y output.

All of the inputs of these counters are diode-clamped, and each input, except the clock input, represents one normalized Series 54/74 load. The buffered clock input, used with the strobe gate, is only two Series 54/74 loads. Full fan-out to 10 Series 54/74 loads is available from each of the output. These devices are completely compatible with most TTL and DTL families. Typical dissipation is 270 milliwatts. The SN54167 is characterized for operation over the full military temperature range of −55°C to 125°C, and the SN74167 is characterized for operation from 0°C to 70°C.

TEXAS INSTRUMENTS
INCORPORATED
POST OFFICE BOX 5012 • DALLAS, TEXAS 75222

1076

STATE AND/OR RATE FUNCTION TABLE (See Note A)

INPUTS							NUMBER OF CLOCK PULSES	UNITY/ CASCADE	OUTPUTS			
			BCD RATE						LOGIC LEVEL OR NUMBER OF PULSES			
CLEAR	ENABLE	STROBE	D	C	B	A			Y	Z	ENABLE	NOTES
H	X	H	X	X	X	X	X	H	L	H	H	B
L	L	L	L	L	L	L	10	H	L	H	1	C
L	L	L	L	L	L	H	10	H	1	1	1	C
L	L	L	L	L	H	L	10	H	2	2	1	C
L	L	L	L	L	H	H	10	H	3	3	1	C
L	L	L	L	H	L	L	10	H	4	4	1	C
L	L	L	L	H	L	H	10	H	5	5	1	C
L	L	L	L	H	H	L	10	H	6	6	1	C
L	L	L	L	H	H	H	10	H	7	7	1	C
L	L	L	H	L	L	L	10	H	8	8	1	C
L	L	L	H	L	L	H	10	H	9	9	1	C
L	L	L	H	L	H	L	10	H	8	8	1	C, D
L	L	L	H	L	H	H	10	H	9	9	1	C, D
L	L	L	H	H	L	L	10	H	8	8	1	C, D
L	L	L	H	H	L	H	10	H	9	9	1	C, D
L	L	L	H	H	H	L	10	H	8	8	1	C, D
L	L	L	H	H	H	H	10	H	9	9	1	C, D
L	L	L	H	L	L	H	10	L	H	9	1	E

NOTES: A. H = high level, L = low level, X = irrelevant. All remaining entries are numeric counts.

B. This is a simplified illustration of the clear function. The states of clock and strobe can affect the logic level of Y and Z. A low unity/cascade will cause output Y to remain high.

C. Each rate illustrated assumes a constant value at rate inputs; however, these illustrations in no way prohibit variable-rate inputs.

D. These input conditions exceed the range of the decimal rate inputs.

E. Unity/cascade can be used to inhibit output Y.

functional block diagram and schematics of inputs and outputs

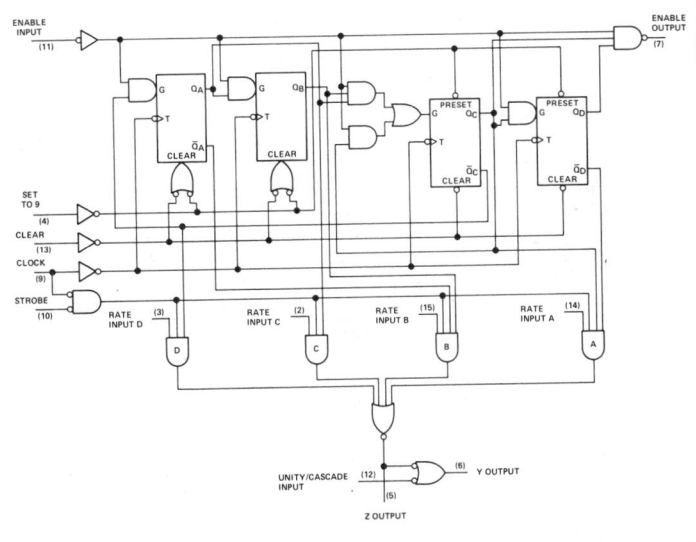

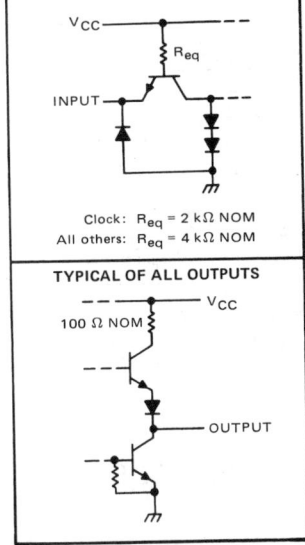

EQUIVALENT OF EACH INPUT

Clock: R_{eq} = 2 kΩ NOM
All others: R_{eq} = 4 kΩ NOM

TYPICAL OF ALL OUTPUTS

100 Ω NOM

7

TEXAS INSTRUMENTS
INCORPORATED
POST OFFICE BOX 5012 • DALLAS, TEXAS 75222

absolute maximum ratings over operating free-air temperature range (unless otherwise noted)

Supply voltage, V_{CC} (see Note 1)	7 V
Input voltage	5.5 V
Operating free-air temperature range: SN54167	$-55°C$ to $125°C$
SN74167	$0°C$ to $70°C$
Storage temperature range	$-65°C$ to $150°C$

NOTE 1: Voltage values are with respect to network ground terminal.

recommended operating conditions

		SN54167			SN74167			UNIT
		MIN	NOM	MAX	MIN	NOM	MAX	
Supply voltage, V_{CC}		4.5	5	5.5	4.75	5	5.25	V
High-level output current, I_{OH}				−400			−400	µA
Low-level output current, I_{OL}				16			16	mA
Clock frequency, f_{clock}		0		25	0		25	MHz
Width of clock pulse, $t_{w(clock)}$		20			20			ns
Width of clear pulse, $t_{w(clear)}$		15			15			ns
Width of set-to-nine pulse $t_{w(set-to-9)}$		15			15			ns
Enable setup time, t_{su}: (See Note 2)								
From positive-going transition of clock pulse		25			25			ns
From negative-going transition of previous clock pulse		0	$t_{w(clock)}-10$		0	$t_{w(clock)}-10$		ns
Enable hold time, t_h: (See Note 2)								
From positive-going transition of clock pulse		0	$t_{w(clock)}-10$		0	$t_{w(clock)}-10$		ns
From negative-going transition of previous clock pulse		20	$t_{cp}-10$		20	$t_{cp}-10$		ns
Operating free-air temperature, T_A		−55		125	0		70	°C

NOTE 2: $t_{w(clock)}$ is the interval in which the clock is high. t_{cp} is the total clock cycle starting with a negative transition. See Figure 1 on SN5497, SN7497 data sheet.

electrical characteristics over recommended operating free-air temperature range (unless otherwise noted)

PARAMETER		TEST CONDITIONS†		MIN	TYP‡	MAX	UNIT
V_{IH}	High-level input voltage			2			V
V_{IL}	Low-level input voltage					0.8	V
V_I	Input clamp voltage	V_{CC} = MIN,	I_I = −12 mA			−1.5	V
V_{OH}	High-level output voltage	V_{CC} = MIN, V_{IH} = 2 V, V_{IL} = 0.8 V,	I_{OH} = −400 µA	2.4	3.4		V
V_{OL}	Low-level output voltage	V_{CC} = MIN, V_{IH} = 2 V, V_{IL} = 0.8 V,	I_{OL} = 16 mA		0.2	0.4	V
I_I	Input current at maximum input voltage	V_{CC} = MAX,	V_I = 5.5 V			1	mA
I_{IH}	High-level input current	clock input	V_{CC} = MAX, V_I = 2.4 V			80	µA
		other inputs				40	
I_{IL}	Low-level input current	clock inputs	V_{CC} = MAX, V_I = 0.4 V			−3.2	mA
		other inputs				−1.6	
I_{OS}	Short circuit output current§	V_{CC} = MAX		−18		−55	mA
I_{CCH}	Supply current, output high	V_{CC} = MAX,	See Note 3		43		mA
I_{CCL}	Supply current, output low	V_{CC} = MAX,	See Note 4		65	99	mA

NOTES: 3. I_{CCH} is measured with outputs open and all inputs low.
4. I_{CCL} is measured with outputs open and all inputs high except the set-to-nine input which is low.

†For test conditions shown as MIN or MAX, use the appropriate value specified under recommended operating conditions for the applicable device type.

‡All typical values are at V_{CC} = 5 V, T_A = 25°C.

§Not more than one output should be shorted at a time.

TEXAS INSTRUMENTS
INCORPORATED
POST OFFICE BOX 5012 • DALLAS, TEXAS 75222

switching characteristics, $V_{CC} = 5$ V, $T_A = 25°C$

PARAMETERS¶	FROM INPUT	TO OUTPUT	TEST CONDITIONS	MIN	TYP	MAX	UNIT
f_{max}				25	32		MHz
t_{PLH}	Enable	Enable			13	20	ns
t_{PHL}					14	21	
t_{PLH}	Strobe	Z			12	18	ns
t_{PHL}					15	23	
t_{PLH}	Clock	Y			26	39	ns
t_{PHL}					20	30	
t_{PLH}	Clock	Z			12	18	ns
t_{PHL}					17	26	
t_{PLH}	Rate	Z	$C_L = 15$ pF,		9	14	ns
t_{PHL}			$R_L = 400\ \Omega$,		6	10	
t_{PLH}	Unity/Cascade	Y	See Note 5		9	14	ns
t_{PHL}					6	10	
t_{PLH}	Strobe	Y			19	30	ns
t_{PHL}					22	33	
t_{PLH}	Clock	Enable			19	30	ns
t_{PHL}					22	33	
t_{PLH}	Clear	Y			24	36	ns
t_{PHL}		$\overline{Z}$			15	23	
t_{PHL}	Set-to-9	Enable			18	27	ns
t_{PLH}	Any Rate Input	Y			15	23	ns
t_{PHL}					15	23	

¶ f_{max} is maximum clock frequency.
  t_{PLH} is propagation delay time, low-to-high-level output.
  t_{PHL} is propagation delay time, high-to-low-level output.
NOTE 5: Load circuit, voltage waveforms, and input conditions for measuring switching characteristics are the same as those for the SN5497
        and SN7497, page 7-106.

TYPICAL APPLICATION DATA

This application demonstrates how the decimal-rate multipliers may be cascaded for longer words. Three decades are illustrated (0.999 to 999) although longer words can be implemented by using the pattern shown. The output is decoded either from output Y with a NOR gate or from output Z with a NAND gate. Either method of decoding produces the complement of the output used.

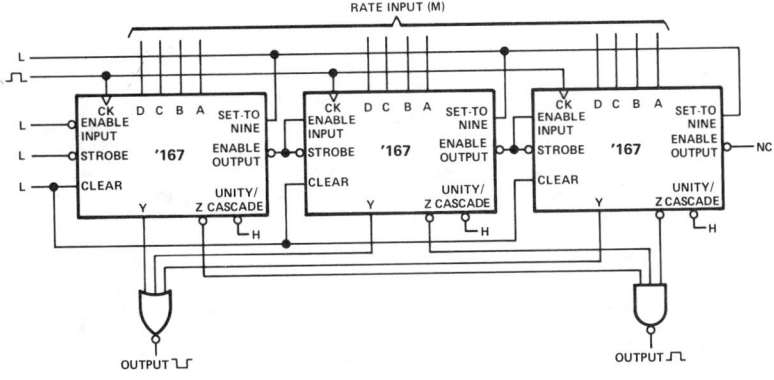

FIGURE 1

TEXAS INSTRUMENTS
INCORPORATED
POST OFFICE BOX 5012 • DALLAS, TEXAS 75222

TTL
MSI

TYPES SN54LS168A SN54LS169A, SN54S168, SN54S169, SN74LS168A, SN74LS169A, SN74S168, SN74S169
SYNCHRONOUS 4-BIT UP/DOWN COUNTERS
BULLETIN NO. DL-S 7712068, OCTOBER 1976—REVISED AUGUST 1977

'LS168A, 'S168 . . . SYNCHRONOUS UP/DOWN DECADE COUNTERS
'LS169A, 'S169 . . . SYNCHRONOUS UP/DOWN BINARY COUNTERS

Programmable Look-Ahead Up/Down
Binary/Decade Counters

- Fully Synchronous Operation for Counting
  and Programming

- Internal Look-Ahead for Fast Counting

- Carry Output for n-Bit Cascading

- Fully Independent Clock Circuit

SERIES SN54LS', SN54S' . . . J OR W PACKAGE
SERIES SN74LS', SN74S' . . . J OR N PACKAGE
(TOP VIEW)

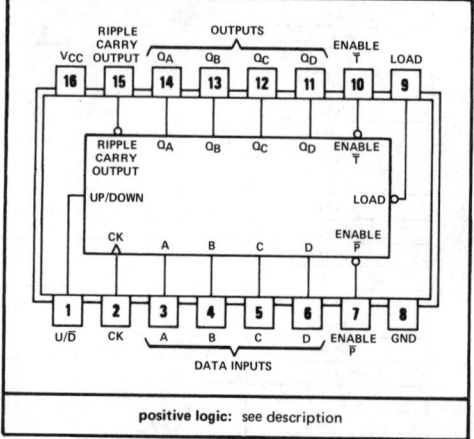

positive logic: see description

TYPE	TYPICAL MAXIMUM CLOCK FREQUENCY		TYPICAL POWER DISSIPATION
	COUNTING UP	COUNTING DOWN	
'LS168A, 'LS169A	35 MHz	35 MHz	100 mW
'S168, 'S169	70 MHz	55 MHz	500 mW

description

These synchronous presettable counters feature an internal carry look-ahead for cascading in high-speed counting applications. The 'LS168A and 'S168 are decade counters and the 'LS169A and 'S169 are 4-bit binary counters. Synchronous operation is provided by having all flip-flops clocked simultaneously so that the outputs change coincident with each other when so instructed by the count-enable inputs and internal gating. This mode of operation helps eliminate the output counting spikes that are normally associated with asynchronous (ripple-clock) counters. A buffered clock input triggers the four master-slave flip-flops on the rising (positive-going) edge of the clock waveform.

These counters are fully programmable; that is, the outputs may each be preset to either level. The load input circuitry allows loading with the carry-enable output of cascaded counters. As loading is synchronous, setting up a low level at the load input disables the counter and causes the outputs to agree with the data inputs after the next clock pulse.

The carry look-ahead circuitry provides for cascading counters for n-bit synchronous applications without additional gating. Instrumental in accomplishing this function are two count-enable inputs and a carry output. Both count enable inputs ($\overline{P}$ and $\overline{T}$) must be low to count. The direction of the count is determined by the level of the up/down input. When the input is high, the counter counts up; when low, it counts down. Input $\overline{T}$ is fed forward to enable the carry output. The carry output thus enabled will produce a low-level output pulse with a duration approximately equal to the high portion of the Q_A output when counting up and approximately equal to the low portion of the Q_A output when counting down. This low-level overflow carry pulse can be used to enable successive cascaded stages. Transitions at the enable $\overline{P}$ or $\overline{T}$ inputs are allowed regardless of the level of the clock input. All inputs are diode-clamped to minimize transmission-line effects, thereby simplifying system design.

These counters feature a fully independent clock circuit. Changes at control inputs (enable $\overline{P}$, enable $\overline{T}$, load, up/down) that will modify the operating mode have no effect until clocking occurs. The function of the counter (whether enabled, disabled, loading, or counting) will be dictated solely by the conditions meeting the stable setup and hold times.

The 'LS168A and 'LS169A are completely new designs. Compared to the original 'LS168 and 'LS169, they feature 0-nanosecond minimum hold time and reduced input currents I_{IH} and I_{IL}.

7

TEXAS INSTRUMENTS
INCORPORATED
POST OFFICE BOX 5012 • DALLAS, TEXAS 75222

TYPES SN54LS168A, SN54LS169A, SN74LS168A, SN74LS169A
SYNCHRONOUS 4-BIT UP/DOWN COUNTERS

REVISED AUGUST 1977

functional block diagrams

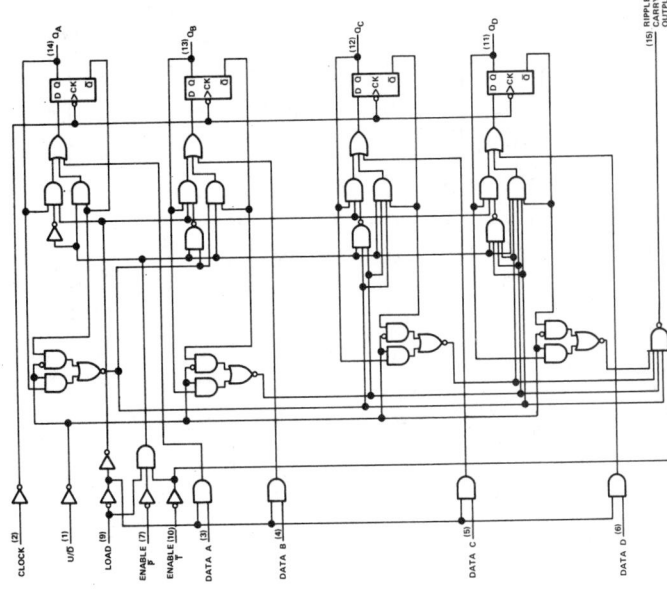

SN54LS169A, SN74LS169A, BINARY COUNTERS

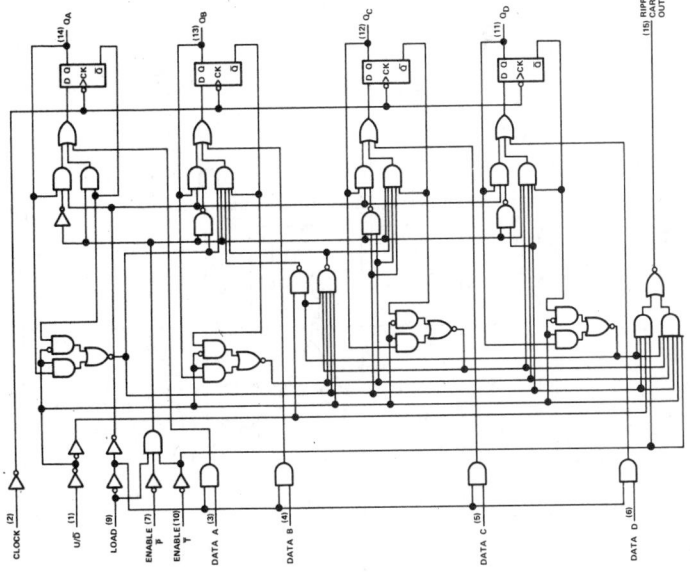

SN54LS168A, SN74LS168A, DECADE COUNTERS

7

TEXAS INSTRUMENTS
INCORPORATED
POST OFFICE BOX 5012 • DALLAS, TEXAS 75222

TYPES SN54S168, SN54S169, SN74S168, SN74S169
SYNCHRONOUS 4-BIT UP/DOWN COUNTERS

functional block diagrams

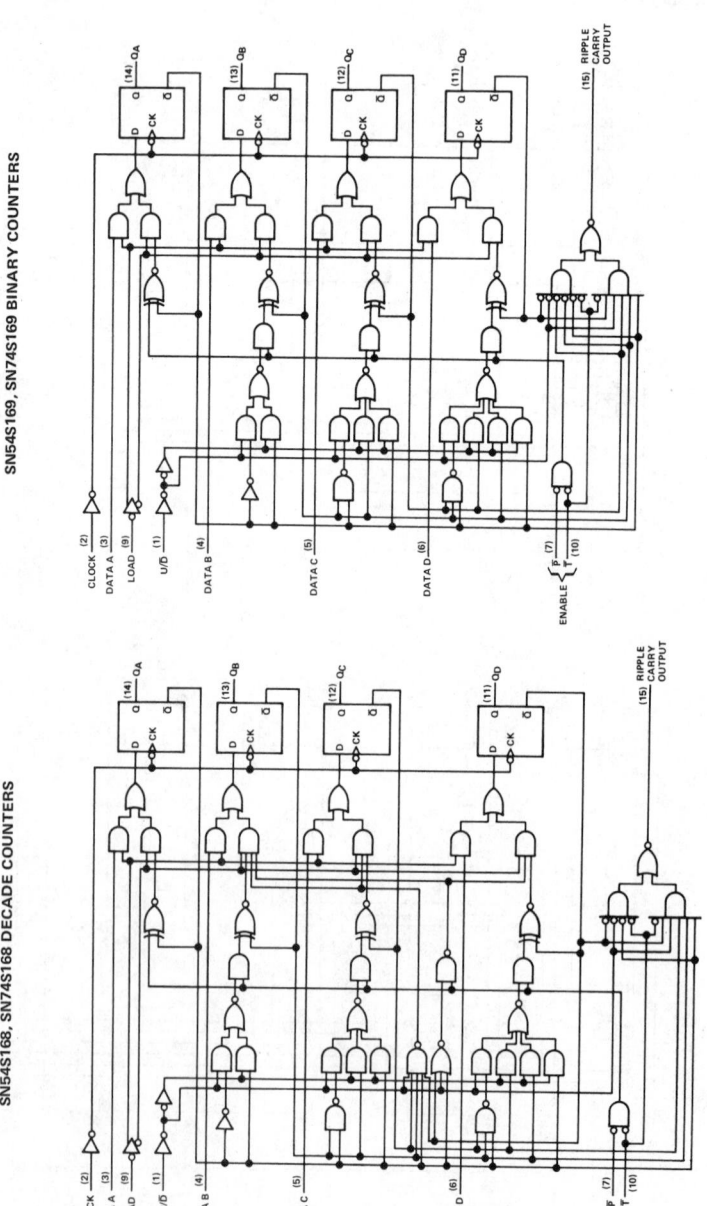

TEXAS INSTRUMENTS
INCORPORATED
POST OFFICE BOX 5012 • DALLAS, TEXAS 75222

TYPES SN54LS168A, SN54S168, SN74LS168A, SN74S168
SYNCHRONOUS 4-BIT UP/DOWN COUNTERS

'LS168A, 'S168 DECADE COUNTERS

typical load, count, and inhibit sequences

Illustrated below is the following sequence:

1. Load (preset) to BCD seven
2. Count up to eight, nine (maximum), zero, one, and two
3. Inhibit
4. Count down to one, zero (minimum), nine, eight, and seven

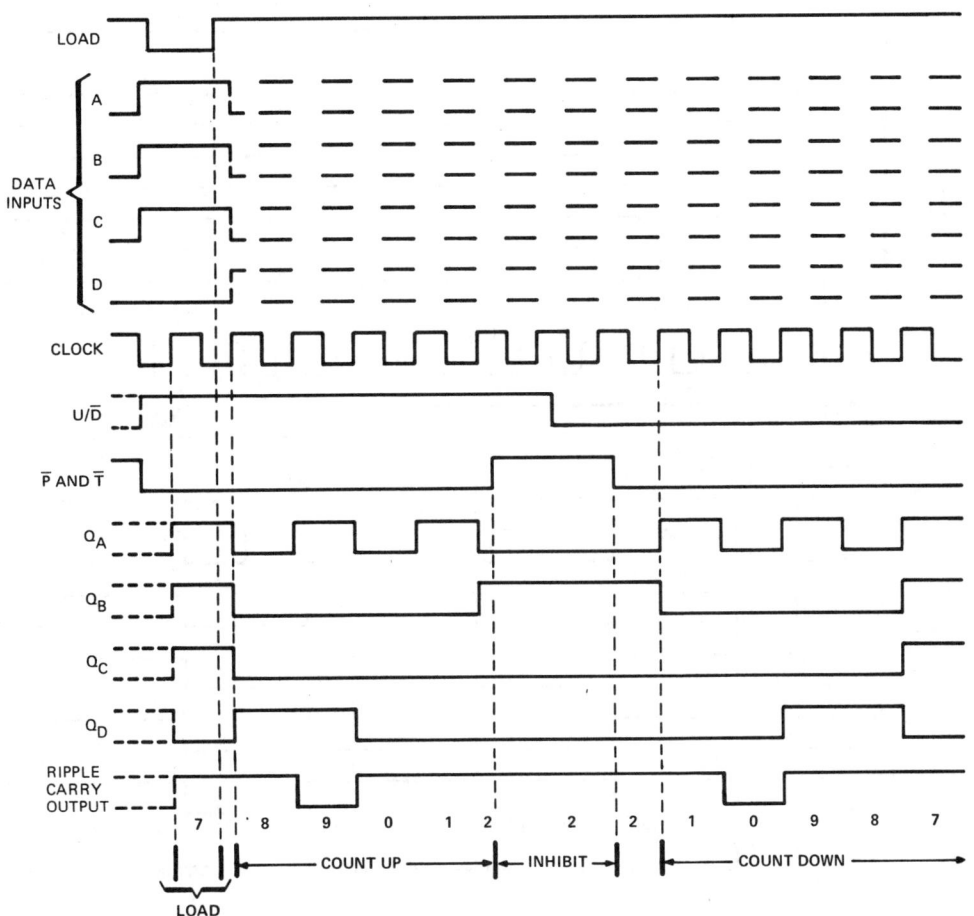

TEXAS INSTRUMENTS
INCORPORATED
POST OFFICE BOX 5012 • DALLAS, TEXAS 75222

TYPES SN54LS169A, SN54S169, SN74LS169A, SN74S169
SYNCHRONOUS 4-BIT UP/DOWN COUNTERS

'LS169A, 'S169 BINARY COUNTERS

typical load, count, and inhibit sequences

Illustrated below is the following sequence:

1. Load (preset) to binary thirteen
2. Count up to fourteen, fifteen (maximum), zero, one, and two
3. Inhibit
4. Count down to one, zero (minimum), fifteen, fourteen, and thirteen

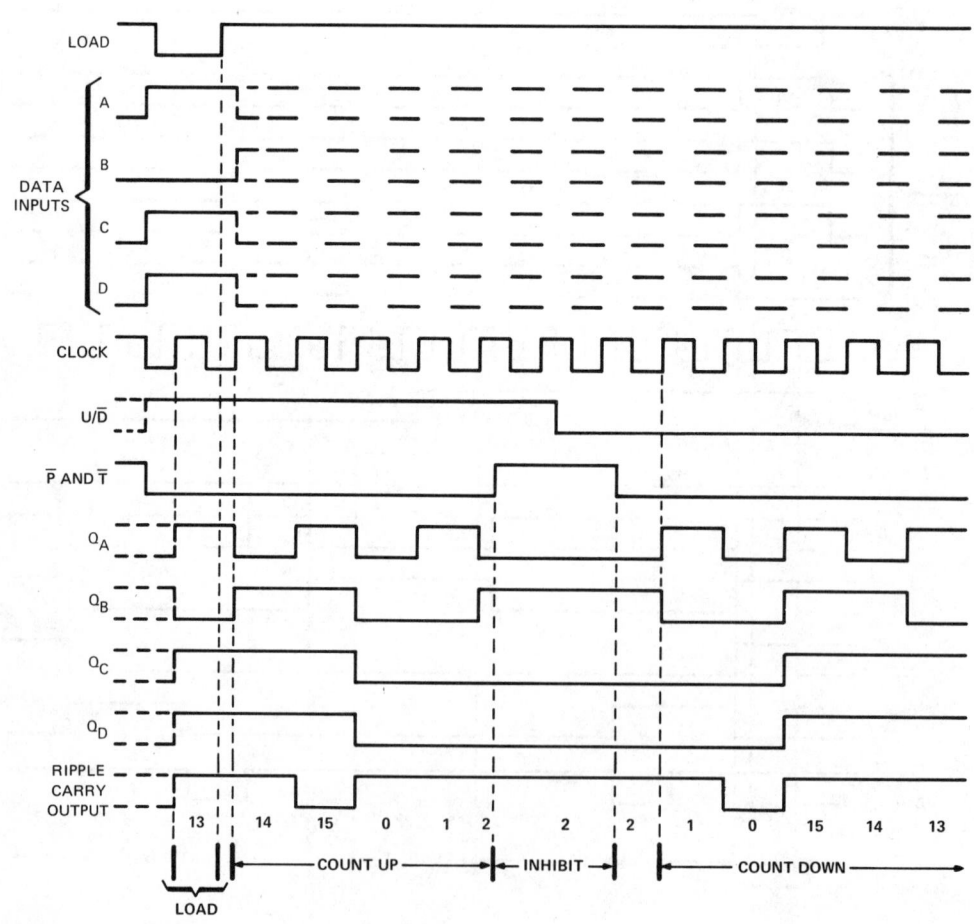

TEXAS INSTRUMENTS
INCORPORATED
POST OFFICE BOX 5012 • DALLAS, TEXAS 75222

schematics of inputs and outputs

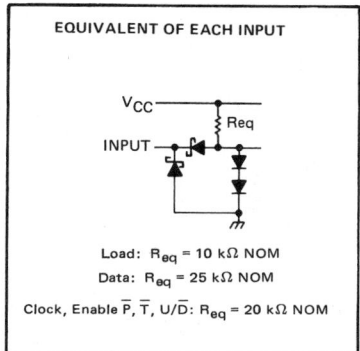

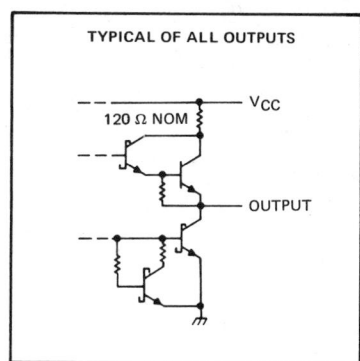

absolute maximum ratings over operating free-air temperature range (unless otherwise noted)

Supply voltage, V_{CC} (see Note 1) . . . . 7 V

Input voltage . . . . 7 V

Operating free-air temperature range: SN54LS168A, SN54LS169A . . . . −55°C to 125°C

SN74LS168A, SN74LS169A . . . . 0°C to 70°C

Storage temperature range . . . . −65°C to 150°C

NOTE 1: Voltage values are with respect to network ground terminal.

recommended operating conditions

		SN54LS168A SN54LS169A			SN74LS168A SN74LS169A			UNIT
		MIN	NOM	MAX	MIN	NOM	MAX	
Supply voltage, V_{CC}		4.5	5	5.5	4.75	5	5.25	V
High-level output current, I_{OH}				−400			−400	μA
Low-level output current, I_{OL}				4			8	mA
Clock frequency, f_{clock}		0		25	0		25	MHz
Width of clock pulse, $t_{w(clock)}$ (high or low) (see Figure 1)		25			25			ns
Setup time, t_{su} (see Figure 1)	Data inputs A, B, C, D	20			20			ns
	Enable $\overline{P}$ or $\overline{T}$	20			20			
	Load	25			25			
	Up/Down	30			30			
Hold time at any input with respect to clock, t_h (see Figure 1)		0			0			ns
Operating free-air temperature, T_A		−55		125	0		70	°C

TEXAS INSTRUMENTS
INCORPORATED

POST OFFICE BOX 5012 • DALLAS, TEXAS 75222

electrical characteristics over recommended operating free-air temperature range (unless otherwise noted)

PARAMETER		TEST CONDITIONS†		SN54LS168A SN54LS169A MIN	TYP‡	MAX	SN74LS168A SN74LS169A MIN	TYP‡	MAX	UNIT
V_{IH} High-level input voltage				2			2			V
V_{IL} Low-level input voltage						0.7			0.8	V
V_{IK} Input clamp voltage		V_{CC} = MIN,	I_I = −18 mA			−1.5			−1.5	V
V_{OH} High-level output voltage		V_{CC} = MIN, V_{IL} = V_{IL} max,	V_{IH} = 2 V, I_{OH} = −400 µA	2.5	3.4		2.7	3.4		V
V_{OL} Low-level output voltage		V_{CC} = MIN, V_{IH} = 2 V,	I_{OL} = 4 mA		0.25	0.4		0.25	0.4	V
		V_{IL} = V_{IL} max	I_{OL} = 8 mA					0.35	0.5	
I_I Input current at maximum input voltage	A, B, C, D, P̄, U/D̄					0.1			0.1	mA
	Clock, T̄	V_{CC} = MAX,	V_I = 7 V			0.1			0.1	
	Load					0.2			0.2	
I_{IH} High-level input current	A, B, C, D, P̄, U/D̄					20			20	µA
	Clock, T̄	V_{CC} = MAX,	V_I = 2.7 V			20			20	
	Load					40			40	
I_{IL} Low-level input current	A, B, C, D, P̄, U/D̄					−0.4			−0.4	mA
	Clock, T̄	V_{CC} = MAX,	V_I = 0.4 V			−0.4			−0.4	
	Load					−0.8			−0.8	
I_{OS} Short-circuit output current§		V_{CC} = MAX		−20		−100	−20		−100	mA
I_{CC} Supply current		V_{CC} = MAX,	See Note 2		20	34		20	34	mA

†For conditions shown as MIN or MAX, use the appropriate value specified under recommended operating conditions.
‡All typical values are at V_{CC} = 5 V, T_A = 25°C.
§Not more than one output should be shorted at a time, and duration of the short-circuit should not exceed one second.
NOTE 2: I_{CC} is measured after applying a momentary 4.5 V, then ground, to the clock input with all other inputs grounded and the outputs open.

switching characteristics, V_{CC} = 5 V, T_A = 25°C

PARAMETER¶	FROM (INPUT)	TO (OUTPUT)	TEST CONDITIONS	MIN	TYP	MAX	UNIT
f_{max}				25	32		MHz
t_{PLH}	Clock	Ripple carry			23	35	ns
t_{PHL}					23	35	
t_{PLH}	Clock	Any Q	C_L = 15 pF,		13	20	ns
t_{PHL}			R_L = 2 kΩ,		15	23	
t_{PLH}	Enable T̄	Ripple carry	See Figures 2 and 3 and Note 3		10	14	ns
t_{PHL}					10	14	
t_{PLH}◊	Up/Down	Ripple carry			17	25	ns
t_{PHL}◊					19	29	

¶ f_{max} ≡ Maximum clock frequency
t_{PLH} ≡ propagation delay time, low-to-high-level output.
t_{PHL} ≡ propagation delay time, high-to-low-level output.
◊Propagation delay time from up/down to ripple carry must be measured with the counter at either a minimum or a maximum count. As the logic level of the up/down input is changed, the ripple carry output will follow. If the count is minimum (0), the ripple carry output transition will be in phase. If the count is maximum (9 for 'LS168A or 15 for 'LS169A), the ripple carry output will be out of phase.
NOTE 3: Load circuit is shown on page 3-11.

TEXAS INSTRUMENTS
INCORPORATED
POST OFFICE BOX 5012 • DALLAS, TEXAS 75222

schematics of inputs and outputs

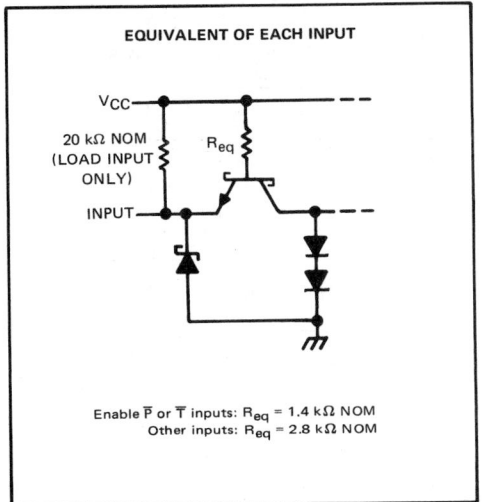

EQUIVALENT OF EACH INPUT

Enable $\overline{P}$ or $\overline{T}$ inputs: R_{eq} = 1.4 kΩ NOM
Other inputs: R_{eq} = 2.8 kΩ NOM

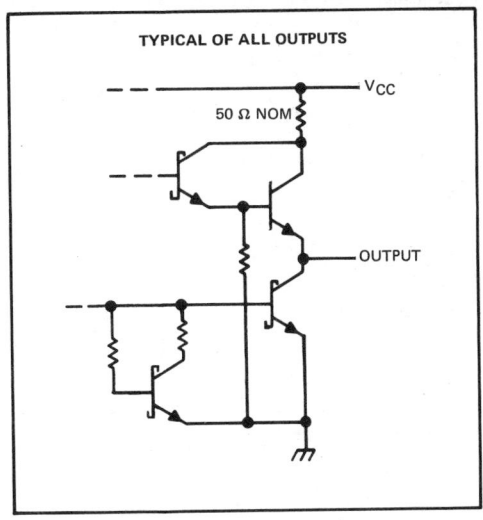

TYPICAL OF ALL OUTPUTS

absolute maximum ratings over operating free-air temperature range (unless otherwise noted)

Supply voltage, V_{CC} (see Note 4) . . . . 7 V
Input voltage . . . . 5.5 V
Interemitter voltage (see Note 5) . . . . 5.5 V
Operating free-air temperature range: SN54S168, SN54S169 (see Note 6) . . . . −55°C to 125°C
                        SN74S168, SN74S169 . . . . 0°C to 70°C
Storage temperature range . . . . −65°C to 150°C

recommended operating conditions

		SN54S168 SN54S169			SN74S168 SN74S169			UNIT
		MIN	NOM	MAX	MIN	NOM	MAX	
Supply voltage, V_{CC}		4.5	5	5.5	4.75	5	5.25	V
High-level output current, I_{OH}				−1			−1	mA
Low-level output current, I_{OL}				20			20	mA
Clock frequency, f_{clock}		0		40	0		40	MHz
Width of clock pulse, $t_{w(clock)}$ (high or low) (see Figure 1)		10			10			ns
Setup time, t_{su} (see Figure 1)	Data inputs A, B, C, D	4			4			ns
	Enable $\overline{P}$ or $\overline{T}$	14			14			
	Load	6			6			
	Up/Down	20			20			
Hold time at any input with respect to clock, t_h (see Figure 1)		1			1			ns
Operating free-air temperature, T_A (see Note 6)		−55		125	0		70	°C

NOTES: 4. Voltage values, except interemitter voltage, are with respect to network ground terminal.
        5. This is the voltage between two emitters of a multiple-emitter transistor. For these circuits, this rating applies between the count enable inputs $\overline{P}$ and $\overline{T}$.
        6. An SN54S168 or SN54S169 in the W package operating at free-air temperatures above 91°C requires a heat sink that provides a thermal resistance from case to free-air, $R_{\theta CA}$, of not more than 26°C/W.

electrical characteristics over recommended operating free-air temperature range (unless otherwise noted)

PARAMETER		TEST CONDITIONS[†]	SN54S168 SN54S169			SN74S168 SN74S169			UNIT
			MIN	TYP[‡]	MAX	MIN	TYP[‡]	MAX	
V_{IH} High-level input voltage			2			2			V
V_{IL} Low-level input voltage					0.8			0.8	V
V_{IK} Input clamp voltage		V_{CC} = MIN, I_I = −18 mA			−1.2			−1.2	V
V_{OH} High-level output voltage		V_{CC} = MIN, V_{IH} = 2 V, V_{IL} = 0.8 V, I_{OH} = −1 mA	2.5	3.4		2.7	3.4		V
V_{OL} Low-level output voltage		V_{CC} = MIN, V_{IH} = 2 V, V_{IL} = 0.8 V, I_{OL} = 20 mA			0.5			0.5	V
I_I Input current at maximum input voltage		V_{CC} = MAX, V_I = 5.5 V			1			1	mA
I_{IH} High-level input current	Enable $\overline{T}$	V_{CC} = MAX, V_I = 2.7 V			100			100	μA
	Other inputs				50			50	
I_{IL} Low-level input current	Enable $\overline{T}$	V_{CC} = MAX, V_I = 0.5 V			−4			−4	mA
	Other inputs				−2			−2	
I_{OS} Short-circuit output current[§]		V_{CC} = MAX	−40		−100	−40		−100	mA
I_{CC} Supply current		V_{CC} = MAX, See Note 2		100	160		100	160	mA

[†]For conditions shown as MIN or MAX, use the appropriate value specified under recommended operating conditions.
[‡]All typical values are at V_{CC} = 5 V, T_A = 25°C.
[§]Not more than one output should be shorted at a time, and duration of the short-circuit should not exceed one second.
NOTE 2: I_{CC} is measured after applying a momentary 4.5 V, then ground, to the clock input with all other inputs grounded and the outputs open.

switching characteristics, V_{CC} = 5 V, T_A = 25°C

PARAMETER[¶]	FROM (INPUT)	TO (OUTPUT)	TEST CONDITIONS	UP/DOWN = HIGH			UP/DOWN = LOW			UNIT
				MIN	TYP	MAX	MIN	TYP	MAX	
f_{max}				40	70		40	55		MHz
t_{PLH}	Clock	Ripple carry	C_L = 15 pF, R_L = 280 Ω, See Figures 2 and 3 and Note 7	14	21		14	21		ns
t_{PHL}				20	28		20	28		
t_{PLH}	Clock	Any Q		8	15		8	15		ns
t_{PHL}				11	15		11	15		
t_{PLH}	Enable $\overline{T}$	Ripple carry		7.5	11		6	12		ns
t_{PHL}				15	22		15	25		
t_{PLH}[◊]	Up/Down	Ripple carry		9	15		8	15		ns
t_{PHL}[◊]				10	15		16	22		

[¶]f_{max} ≡ maximum clock frequency
t_{PLH} ≡ propagation delay time, low-to-high-level output
t_{PHL} ≡ propagation delay time, high-to-low-level output
[◊]Propagation delay time from up/down to ripple carry must be measured with the counter at either a minimum or a maximum count. As the logic level of the up/down input is changed, the ripple carry output will follow. If the count is minimum (0), the ripple carry output transition will be in phase. If the count is maximum (9 for 'S168 or 15 for 'S169), the ripple carry output will be out of phase.
NOTE 7: Load circuit is shown on page 3-10.

7

TEXAS INSTRUMENTS
INCORPORATED
POST OFFICE BOX 5012 • DALLAS, TEXAS 75222

TYPES SN54LS168A, SN54LS169A, SN54S168, SN54S169, SN74LS168A, SN74LS169A, SN74S168, SN74S169 SYNCHRONOUS 4-BIT UP/DOWN COUNTERS

PARAMETER MEASUREMENT INFORMATION

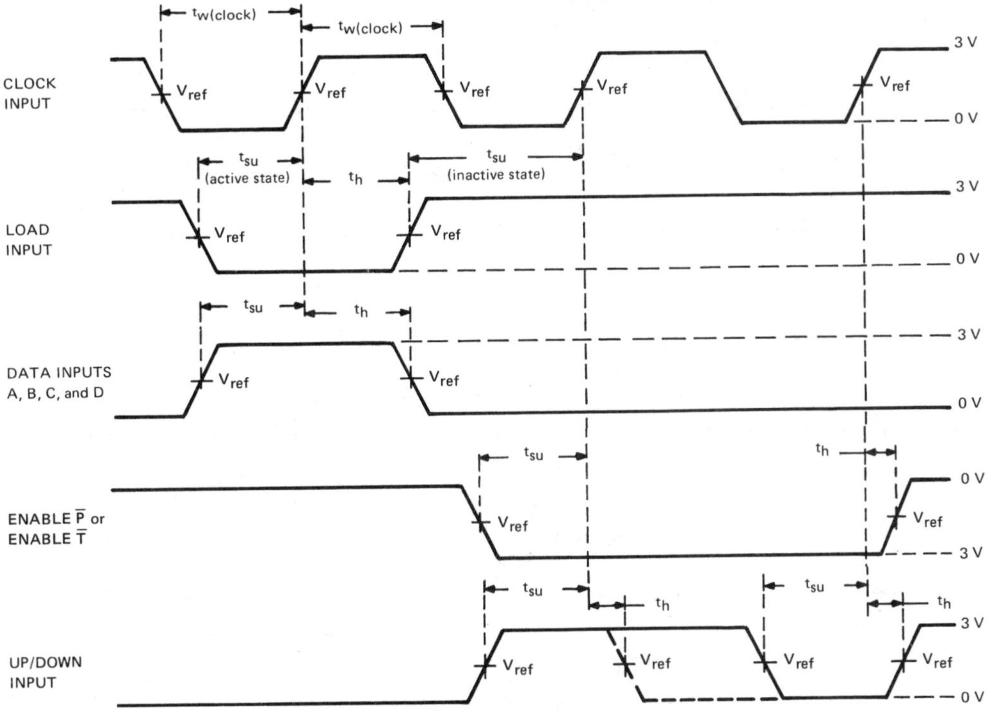

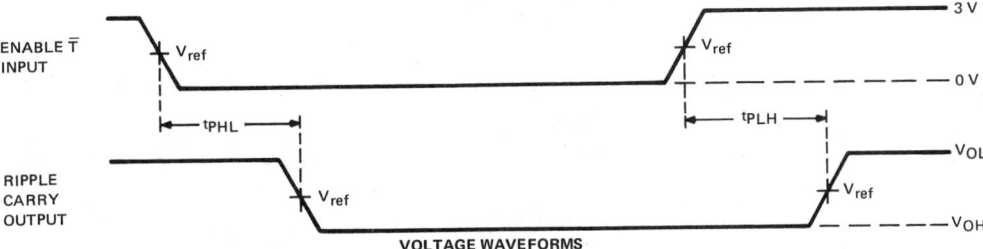

VOLTAGE WAVEFORMS

NOTES: A. The input pulses are supplied by a generator having the following characteristics: PRR ≤ 1 MHz, duty cycle ≤ 50%, $Z_{out} \approx 50\ \Omega$; for 'LS168A and 'LS169A, $t_r \le 15$ ns, $t_f \le 6$ ns, and for 'S168 and 'S169, $t_r \le 2.5$ ns, $t_f \le 2.5$ ns.

B. For 'LS168A and 'LS169A, V_{ref} = 1.3 V; for 'S168 and 'S169, V_{ref} = 1.5 V.

FIGURE 1—PULSE WIDTHS, SETUP TIMES, HOLD TIMES

VOLTAGE WAVEFORMS

NOTES: A. The input pulse is supplied by a generator having the following characteristics: PRR ≤ 1 MHz, duty cycle ≤ 50%, $Z_{out} \approx 50\ \Omega$; for 'LS168A and 'LS169A, $t_r \le 15$ ns, $t_f \le 6$ ns; and for 'S168 and 'S169, $t_r \le 2.5$ ns, $t_f \le 2.5$ ns.

B. t_{PLH} and t_{PHL} from enable $\overline{T}$ input to ripple carry output assume that the counter is at the maximum count (Q_A and Q_D high for 'LS168A and 'S168, all Q outputs high for 'LS169A and 'S169).

C. For 'LS168A and 'LS169A, V_{ref} = 1.3 V; for 'S168 and 'S169, V_{ref} = 1.5 V.

D. Propagation delay time from up/down to ripple carry must be measured with the counter at either a minimum or a maximum count. As the logic level of the up/down input is changed, the ripple carry output will follow. If the count is minimum (0) the ripple carry output transition will be in phase. If the count is maximum (9 for 'LS168A and 'S168, or 15 for 'LS169A and 'S169) the ripple carry output will be out of phase.

FIGURE 2—PROPAGATION DELAY TIMES TO CARRY OUTPUT

PARAMETER MEASUREMENT INFORMATION

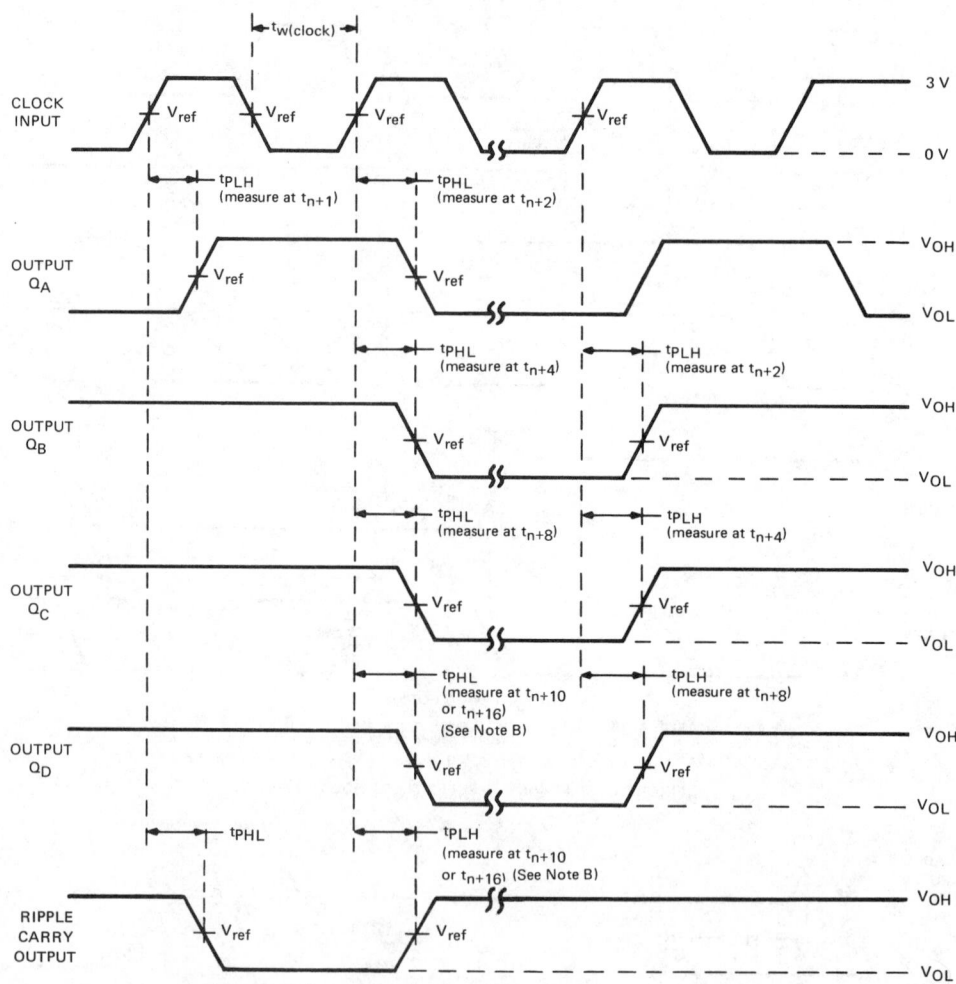

UP-COUNT VOLTAGE WAVEFORMS

NOTES: A. The input pulses are supplied by a generator having the following characteristics: PRR ≤ 1 MHz, duty cycle ≤ 50%, $Z_{out} \approx 50 \, \Omega$; for 'LS168A and 'LS169A, $t_r \leq 15$ ns, $t_f \leq 6$ ns; and for 'S168 and 'S169, $t_r \leq 2.5$ ns, $t_f \leq 2.5$ ns. Vary PRR to measure f_{max}.
B. Outputs Q_D and carry are tested at t_{n+10} for the 'LS168A and 'S168, and at t_{n+16} for the 'LS169A and 'S169, where t_n is the bit-time when all outputs are low.
C. For 'LS168A and 'LS169A, $V_{ref} = 1.3$ V; for 'S168 and 'S169, $V_{ref} = 1.5$ V.

FIGURE 3—PROPAGATION DELAY TIMES FROM CLOCK

- Separate Read/Write Addressing Permits Simultaneous Reading and Writing

- Fast Access Times . . . Typically 20 ns

- Organized as 4 Words of 4 Bits

- Expandable to 1024 Words of n-Bits

- For Use as:
  Scratch-Pad Memory
  Buffer Storage between Processors
  Bit Storage in Fast Multiplication Designs

- Open-Collector Outputs with Low Maximum Off-State Current:
  '170 . . . 30 μA
  'LS170 . . . 20 μA

- SN54LS670 and SN74LS670 Are Similar But Have 3-State Outputs

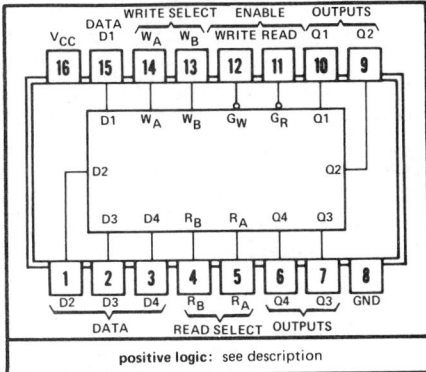

SN54170, SN54LS170 . . . J OR W PACKAGE
SN74170, SN74LS170 . . . J OR N PACKAGE
(TOP VIEW)

positive logic: see description

description

The '170 and 'LS170 MSI 16-bit TTL register files incorporate the equivalent of 98 gates. The register file is organized as 4 words of 4 bits each and separate on-chip decoding is provided for addressing the four word locations to either write-in or retrieve data. This permits simultaneous writing into one location and reading from another word location.

Four data inputs are available which are used to supply the 4-bit word to be stored. Location of the word is determined by the write-address inputs A and B in conjunction with a write-enable signal. Data applied at the inputs should be in its true form. That is, if a high-level signal is desired from the output, a high level is applied at the data input for that particular bit location. The latch inputs are arranged so that new data will be accepted only if both internal address gate inputs are high. When this condition exists, data at the D input is transferred to the latch output. When the write-enable input, G_W, is high, the data inputs are inhibited and their levels can cause no change in the information stored in the internal latches. When the read-enable input, G_R, is high, the data outputs are inhibited and remain high.

The individual address lines permit direct acquisition of data stored in any four of the latches. Four individual decoding gates are used to complete the address for reading a word. When the read address is made in conjunction with the read-enable signal, the word appears at the four outputs.

This arrangement—data-entry addressing separate from data-read addressing and individual sense line—eliminates recovery times, permits simultaneous reading and writing, and is limited in speed only by the write time (30 nanoseconds typical) and the read time (25 nanoseconds typical). The register file has a nondestructive readout in that data is not lost when addressed.

All '170 inputs and all inputs except the read enable and write enable of the 'LS170 are buffered to lower the drive requirements to one Series 54/74 or Series 54LS/74LS standard load, respectively. Input-clamping diodes minimize switching transients to simplify system design. High-speed, double-ended AND-OR-INVERT gates are employed for the read-address function and drive high-sink-current, open-collector outputs. Up to 256 of these outputs may be wire-AND connected for increasing the capacity up to 1024 words. Any number of these registers may be paralleled to provide n-bit word length.

The SN54170 and SN54LS170 are characterized for operation over the full military temperature range of −55°C to 125°C; the SN74170 and SN74LS170 are characterized for operation from 0°C to 70°C.

TEXAS INSTRUMENTS
INCORPORATED
POST OFFICE BOX 5012 • DALLAS, TEXAS 75222

TYPES SN54170, SN54LS170, SN74170, SN74LS170
4-BY-4 REGISTER FILES WITH OPEN-COLLECTOR OUTPUTS

logic

WRITE FUNCTION TABLE (SEE NOTES A, B, AND C)

WRITE INPUTS			WORD			
W_B	W_A	G_W	0	1	2	3
L	L	L	Q = D	Q_0	Q_0	Q_0
L	H	L	Q_0	Q = D	Q_0	Q_0
H	L	L	Q_0	Q_0	Q = D	Q_0
H	H	L	Q_0	Q_0	Q_0	Q = D
X	X	H	Q_0	Q_0	Q_0	Q_0

READ FUNCTION TABLE (SEE NOTES A AND D)

READ INPUTS			OUTPUTS			
R_B	R_A	G_R	Q1	Q2	Q3	Q4
L	L	L	W0B1	W0B2	W0B3	W0B4
L	H	L	W1B1	W1B2	W1B3	W1B4
H	L	L	W2B1	W2B2	W2B3	W2B4
H	H	L	W3B1	W3B2	W3B3	W3B4
X	X	H	H	H	H	H

NOTES: A. H = high level, L = low level, X = irrelevant.
B. (Q = D) = The four selected internal flip-flop outputs will assume the states applied to the four external data inputs.
C. Q_0 = the level of Q before the indicated input conditions were established.
D. W0B1 = The first bit of word 0, etc.

functional block diagram   '170

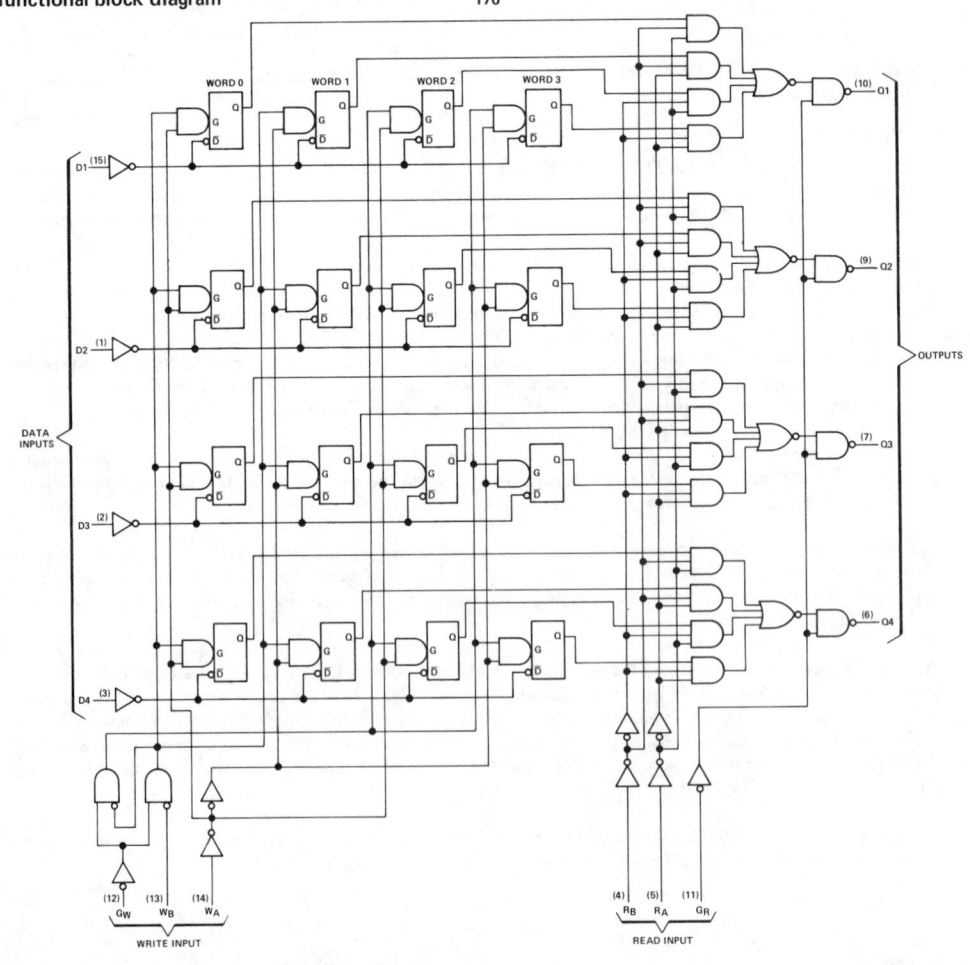

7

TEXAS INSTRUMENTS
INCORPORATED
POST OFFICE BOX 5012 • DALLAS, TEXAS 75222

functional block diagram

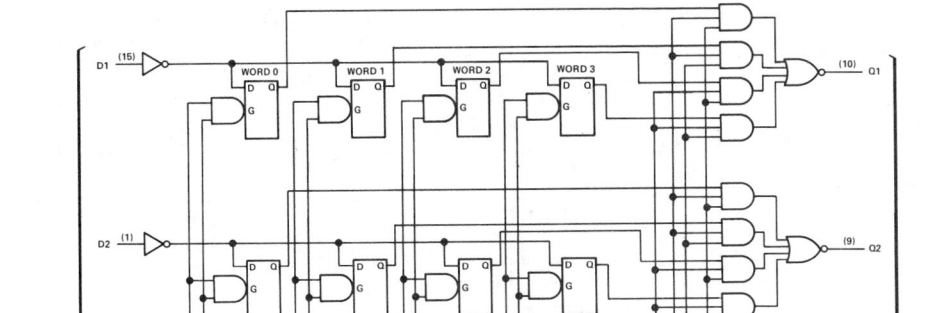

'LS170

absolute maximum ratings over operating free-air temperature range (unless otherwise noted)

Supply voltage, V_{CC} (see Note 1) . . . . 7 V
Input voltage: '170 . . . . 5.5 V
           'LS170 . . . . 7 V
Off-state output voltage: '170 . . . . 5.5 V
              'LS170 . . . . 7 V
Operating free-air temperature range: SN54170, SN54LS170 (see Note 2) . . . . −55°C to 125°C
                               SN74170, SN74LS170 . . . . 0°C to 70°C
Storage temperature range . . . . −65°C to 150°C

NOTES: 1. Voltage values are with respect to network ground terminal.
        2. An SN54170 in the W package operating at free-air temperatures above 105°C requires a heat sink that provides a thermal
           resistance from case to free-air, $R_{\theta CA}$, of not more than 38°C/W

TYPES SN54170, SN74170
4-BY-4 REGISTER FILES WITH OPEN-COLLECTOR OUTPUTS

recommended operating conditions

		SN54170			SN74170			UNIT
		MIN	NOM	MAX	MIN	NOM	MAX	
Supply voltage, V_{CC}		4.5	5	5.5	4.75	5	5.25	V
High-level output voltage, V_{OH}				5.5			5.5	V
Low-level output current, I_{OL}				16			16	mA
Width of write-enable or read-enable pulse, t_W		25			25			ns
Setup times, high- or low-level data (see Figure 2)	Data input with respect to write enable, $t_{su(D)}$	10			10			ns
	Write select with respect to write enable, $t_{su(W)}$	15			15			ns
Hold times, high- or low-level data (see Note 3 and Figure 2)	Data input with respect to write enable, $t_{h(D)}$	15			15			ns
	Write select with respect to write enable, $t_{h(W)}$	5			5			ns
Latch time for new data, t_{latch} (see Note 4)		25			25			ns
Operating free-air temperature range, T_A (see Note 2)		−55		125	0		70	°C

NOTES: 2. An SN54170 in the W package operating at free-air temperatures above 105°C requires a heat sink that provides a thermal resistance from case to free-air, $R_{\theta CA}$, of not more than 38°C/W.
3. Write select setup time will protect the data written into the previous address. If protection of data in the previous address is not required, $t_{su(W)}$ can be ignored as any address selection sustained for the final 30 ns of the write-enable pulse and during $t_{h(W)}$ will result in data being written into that location. Depending on the duration of the input conditions, one or a number of previous addresses may have been written into.
4. Latch time is the time allowed for the internal output of the latch to assume the state of new data. See Figure 2. This is important only when attempting to read from a location immediately after that location has received new data.

electrical characteristics over recommended operating free-air temperature range (unless otherwise noted)

PARAMETER		TEST CONDITIONS[†]	MIN	TYP[‡]	MAX	UNIT
V_{IH}	High-level input voltage		2			V
V_{IL}	Low-level input voltage				0.8	V
V_{IK}	Input clamp voltage	V_{CC} = MIN, I_I = −12 mA			−1.5	V
I_{OH}	High-level output current	V_{CC} = MIN, V_{OH} = 5.5 V, V_{IH} = 2 V, V_{IL} = 0.8 V			30	μA
V_{OL}	Low-level output voltage	V_{CC} = MIN, V_{IH} = 2 V, V_{IL} = 0.8 V, I_{OL} = 16 mA		0.2	0.4	V
I_I	Input current at maximum input voltage	V_{CC} = MAX, V_I = 5.5 V			1	mA
I_{IH}	High-level input current	V_{CC} = MAX, V_I = 2.4 V			40	μA
I_{IL}	Low-level input current	V_{CC} = MAX, V_I = 0.4 V			−1.6	mA
I_{CC}	Supply current	V_{CC} = MAX, See Note 5 — SN54170		127[§]	140	mA
		SN74170		127[§]	150	mA

[†]For conditions shown as MIN or MAX, use the appropriate value specified under recommended operating conditions.
[‡]All typical values are at V_{CC} = 5 V, T_A = 25°C.
[§]Typical supply current shown is an average for 50% duty cycle.
NOTE 5: Maximum I_{CC} is guaranteed for the following worst-case conditions: 4.5 V is applied to all data inputs and both enable inputs, all address inputs are grounded, and all outputs are open.

TEXAS INSTRUMENTS
INCORPORATED
POST OFFICE BOX 5012 • DALLAS, TEXAS 75222

7

switching characteristics, V_{CC} = 5 V, T_A = 25°C

PARAMETER¶	FROM (INPUT)	TO (OUTPUT)	TEST CONDITIONS	MIN	TYP	MAX	UNIT
t_{PLH}	Read enable	Any Q	C_L = 15 pF, R_L = 400 Ω, See Figures 1 and 2		10	15	ns
t_{PHL}					20	30	
t_{PLH}	Read Select	Any Q			23	35	ns
t_{PHL}					30	40	
t_{PLH}	Write enable	Any Q	C_L = 15 pF, R_L = 400 Ω, See Figures 1 and 3		25	40	ns
t_{PHL}					34	45	
t_{PLH}	Data	Any Q			20	30	ns
t_{PHL}					30	45	

¶t_{PLH} ≡ propagation delay time, low-to-high-level output
t_{PHL} ≡ propagation delay time, high-to-low-level output

schematics of inputs and outputs

'170

'170

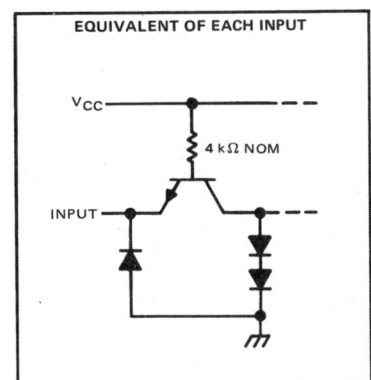

EQUIVALENT OF EACH INPUT

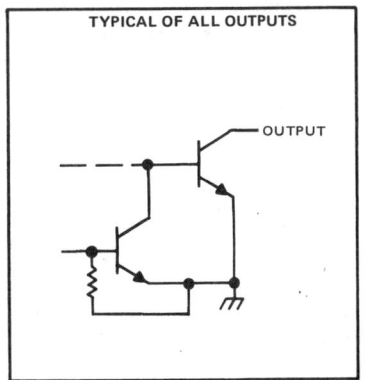

TYPICAL OF ALL OUTPUTS

7

recommended operating conditions

		SN54LS170			SN74LS170			UNIT
		MIN	NOM	MAX	MIN	NOM	MAX	
Supply voltage, V_{CC}		4.5	5	5.5	4.75	5	5.25	V
High-level output voltage, V_{OH}				5.5			5.5	V
Low-level output current, I_{OL}				4			8	mA
Width of write-enable or read-enable pulse, t_w		25			25			ns
Setup times, high- or low-level data (see Figure 2)	Data input with respect to write enable, $t_{su(D)}$	10			10			ns
	Write select with respect to write enable, $t_{su(W)}$	15			15			ns
Hold times, high- or low-level data (see Note 3 and Figure 2)	Data input with respect to write enable, $t_{h(D)}$	15			15			ns
	Write select with respect to write enable, $t_{h(W)}$	5			5			ns
Latch time for new data, t_{latch} (see Note 4)		25			25			ns
Operating free-air temperature range, T_A		−55		125	0		70	°C

NOTES: 3. Write-select setup time will protect the data written into the previous address. If protection of data in the previous address is not required, $t_{su(W)}$ can be ignored as any address selection sustained for the final 30 ns of the write-enable pulse and during $t_{h(W)}$ will result in data being written into that location. Depending on the duration of the input conditions, one or a number of previous addresses may have been written into.

4. Latch time is the time allowed for the internal output of the latch to assume the state of new data. See Figure 2. This is important only when attempting to read from a location immediately after that location has received new data.

electrical characteristics over recommended operating free-air temperature range (unless otherwise noted)

PARAMETER			TEST CONDITIONS†	SN54LS170			SN74LS170			UNIT
				MIN	TYP‡	MAX	MIN	TYP‡	MAX	
V_{IH}	High-level input voltage			2			2			V
V_{IL}	Low-level input voltage					0.7			0.8	V
V_{IK}	Input clamp voltage		V_{CC} = MIN, I_I = −18 mA			−1.5			−1.5	V
I_{OH}	High-level output current		V_{CC} = MIN, V_{OH} = 5.5 V, $V_{IL} = V_{IL}$ max, V_{IH} = 2 V			20			20	µA
V_{OL}	Low-level output voltage		V_{CC} = MIN, V_{IH} = 2 V, $V_{IL} = V_{IL}$ max	I_{OL} = 4 mA	0.25	0.4		0.25	0.4	V
				I_{OL} = 8 mA				0.35	0.5	
I_I	Input current at maximum input voltage	Any D, R, or W	V_{CC} = MAX, V_I = 7 V			0.1			0.1	mA
		G_R or G_W				0.2			0.2	
I_{IH}	High-level input current	Any D, R, or W	V_{CC} = MAX, V_I = 2.7 V			20			20	µA
		G_R or G_W				40			40	
I_{IL}	Low-level input current	Any D, R, or W	V_{CC} = MAX, V_I = 0.4 V			−0.4			−0.4	mA
		G_R or G_W				−0.8			−0.8	
I_{CC}	Supply current		V_{CC} = MAX, See Note 6	25	40		25	40		mA

†For conditions shown as MIN or MAX, use the appropriate value specified under recommended operating conditions.
‡All typical values are at V_{CC} = 5 V, T_A = 25°C.
NOTE 6: I_{CC} is measured under the following worst-case conditions: 4.5 V is applied to all data inputs and both enable inputs, all address inputs are grounded, and all outputs are open.

7

TEXAS INSTRUMENTS
INCORPORATED

POST OFFICE BOX 5012 • DALLAS, TEXAS 75222

switching characteristics, V_{CC} = 5 V, T_A = 25°C

PARAMETER¶	FROM (INPUT)	TO (OUTPUT)	TEST CONDITIONS	MIN	TYP	MAX	UNIT
t_{PLH}	Read enable	Any Q	C_L = 15 pF, R_L = 2 kΩ, See Figures 1 and 2		20	30	ns
t_{PHL}					20	30	
t_{PLH}	Read select	Any Q			25	40	ns
t_{PHL}					24	40	
t_{PLH}	Write enable	Any Q	C_L = 15 pF, R_L = 2 kΩ, See Figures 1 and 3		30	45	ns
t_{PHL}					26	40	
t_{PLH}	Data	Any Q			30	45	ns
t_{PHL}					22	35	

¶ t_{PLH} ≡ propagation delay time, low-to-high-level output
t_{PHL} ≡ propagation delay time, high-to-low-level output

schematics of inputs and outputs

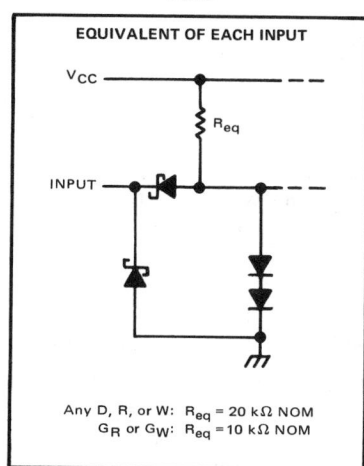

'LS170

EQUIVALENT OF EACH INPUT

Any D, R, or W: R_{eq} = 20 kΩ NOM
G_R or G_W: R_{eq} = 10 kΩ NOM

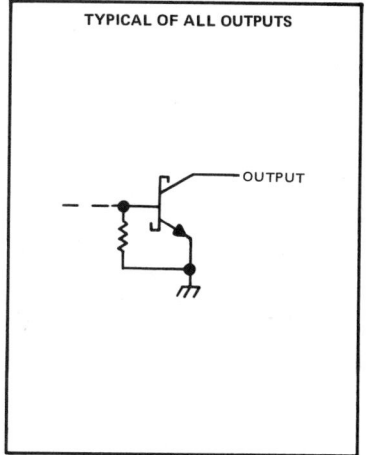

'LS170

TYPICAL OF ALL OUTPUTS

7

PARAMETER MEASUREMENT INFORMATION

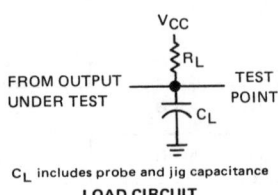

C_L includes probe and jig capacitance
LOAD CIRCUIT

FIGURE 1

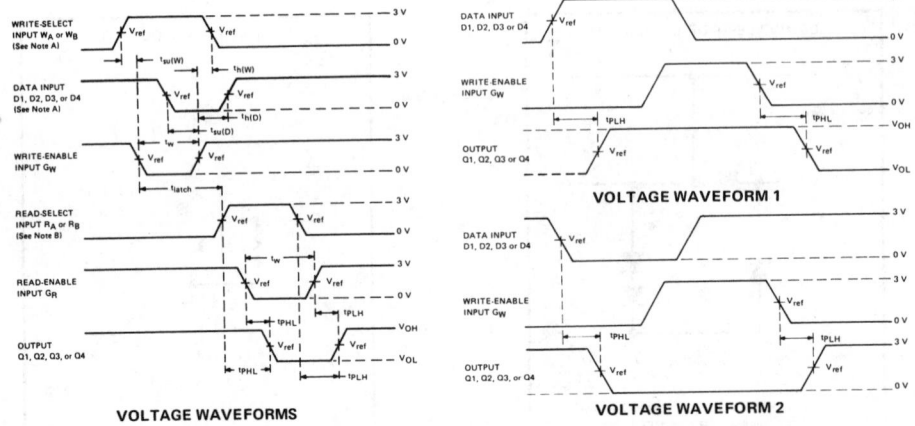

VOLTAGE WAVEFORMS

FIGURE 2

VOLTAGE WAVEFORM 1

VOLTAGE WAVEFORM 2

FIGURE 3

NOTES:
A. High-level input pulses at the select and data inputs are illustrated in Figure 2; however, times associated with low-level pulses are measured from the same reference points.

B. When measuring delay times from a read-select input, the read-enable input is low. When measuring delay times from the read-enable input, both read-select inputs have been established at steady states.

C. In Figure 3, each select address is tested. Prior to the start of each of the above tests, both write and read address inputs are stablized with $W_A = R_A$ and $W_B = R_B$. During the test G_R is low.

D. Input waveforms are supplied by generators having the following characteristics: PRR ≤ 1 MHz, Z_{out} ≈ 50 Ω, duty cycle ≤ 50%, t_r ≤ 10 ns and t_f ≤ 10 ns for '170, and t_r ≤ 15 ns and t_f ≤ 6 ns for 'LS170.

D. For '170, $V_{ref} = 1.5$ V; for 'LS170, $V_{ref} = 1.3$ V.

TEXAS INSTRUMENTS
INCORPORATED
POST OFFICE BOX 5012 • DALLAS, TEXAS 75222

TYPE SN74172
16-BIT MULTIPLE-PORT REGISTER FILE WITH 3-STATE OUTPUTS

BULLETIN NO. DL-S 7211744, MAY 1972 — REVISED DECEMBER 1972

- Independent Read/Write Addressing Permits Simultaneous Reading and Writing

- Organized as Eight Words of Two Bits Each

- Fast Access Times:
  From Read Enable . . . 15 ns Typical
  From Read Select . . . 33 ns Typical

- Three-State Outputs Simplify Use in Bus-Organized Systems

- Applications:
  Stacked Data Registers
  Scratch-Pad Memory
  Buffer Storage Between Processors
  Fast Multiplication Schemes

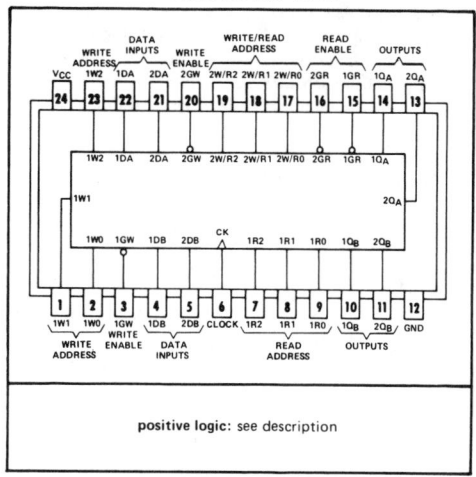

J OR N DUAL-IN-LINE PACKAGE (TOP VIEW)

positive logic: see description

description

The SN74172, containing the equivalent of 201 gates on a monolithic chip, is a high-performance 16-bit register file organized as eight words of two bits each.

Multiple address decoding circuitry is used so that the read and write operation can be performed independently on two word locations. This provides a true simultaneous read/write capability. Basically, the file consists of two distinct sections (see Figure A).

Section 1 permits the writing of data into any two-bit word location while reading two bits of data from another location simultaneously. To provide this flexibility, independent decoding is incorporated.

Section 2 of the register file is similar to section 1 with the exception that common read/write address circuitry is employed. This means that section 2 can be utilized in one of three modes:

1) Writing new data into two bits
2) Reading from two bits
3) Writing into and simultaneously reading from the same two bits.

Regardless of the mode, the operation of section 2 is entirely independent of section 1.

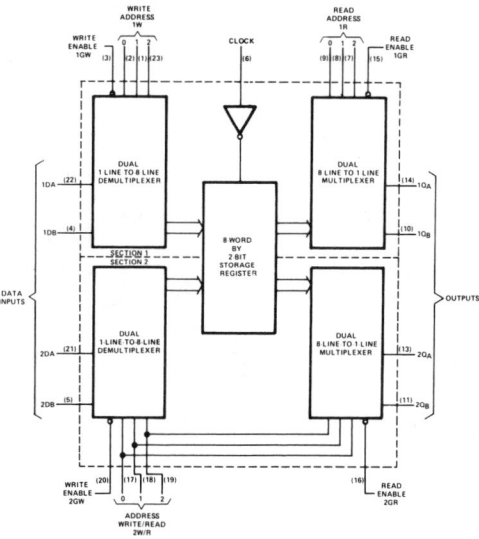

FIGURE A

description (continued)

The three-state outputs of this register file permit connection of up to 129 compatible outputs and one Series 54/74 high-logic-level load to a common system bus. The outputs are controlled by the read-enable circuitry so that they operate as standard TTL totem-pole outputs when the appropriate read-enable input is low or they are placed in a high-impedance state when the associated read-enable input is at a high logic level. To minimize the possibility that two outputs from separate register files will attempt to take a common bus to opposite logic levels, the read-enable circuitry is designed such that disable times are shorter than enable times.

All inputs are buffered to lower the drive requirements of the clock, read/write address, and write-enable inputs to one normalized Series 54/74 load, and of all other inputs to one-half of one normalized Series 54/74 load.

Functions of the inputs and outputs of the SN74172 are as shown in the following table.

FUNCTION	SECTION 1	SECTION 2	DESCRIPTION
Write Address	1W0, 1W1, 1W2	2W/R0, 2W/R1, 2W/R2	Binary write address selects one of eight two-bit word locations.
Write Enable	1GW	2GW	When low, permits the writing of new data into the selected word location on a positive transition of the clock input.
Data Inputs	1DA, 1DB	2DA, 2DB	Data at these inputs is entered on a positive transition of the clock input into the location selected by the write address inputs if the write enable input is low. Since the two sections are independent, it is possible for both write functions to be activated with both write addresses selecting the same word location. If this occurs and the information at the data inputs is not the same for both sections (i.e., $1DA \neq 2DA$ and/or $1DB \neq 2DB$) the low-level data will predominate in each bit and be stored.
Read Address	1R0, 1R1, 1R2	Common with write address	Binary write address selects one of eight two-bit word locations.
Read Enable	1GR	2GR	When read enable is low, the outputs assume the levels of the data stored in the location selected by read address inputs. When read enable is high, the associated outputs remain in the high-impedance state and neither significantly load nor drive the lines to which they are connected.
Data Outputs	1Q$_A$, 1Q$_B$	2Q$_A$, 2Q$_B$	
Clock		CK	The positive-going transition of the clock input will enter new data into the addressed location if the write enable input is low. The clock is common to both sections.

TEXAS INSTRUMENTS
INCORPORATED
POST OFFICE BOX 5012 • DALLAS, TEXAS 75222

absolute maximum ratings over operating free-air temperature range (unless otherwise noted)

Supply voltage (see Note 1)	7 V
Input voltage	5.5 V
Output voltage (see Note 2)	5.5 V
Operating free-air temperature range	0°C to 70°C
Storage temperature	−65°C to 150°C

NOTES: 1. Voltage values are with respect to network ground terminal.
2. This is the maximum voltage which should be applied to any output when it is in the high-impedance state.

recommended operating conditions

		MIN	NOM	MAX	UNIT
Supply voltage, V_{CC}		4.75	5	5.25	V
High-level output current, I_{OH}				−5.2	mA
Low-level output current, I_{OL}				16	mA
Clock frequency, f_{clock}		0		20	MHz
Width of clock pulse, $t_{w(clock)}$		25			ns
Setup time, t_{su}(see Figure 1)	Write select	$t_{w(clock)}$+10			ns
	High-level data	30			
	Low-level data	45			
	Write enable	35			
Hold time, t_h(see Figure 1)	Write select	0			ns
	Write enable	0			
Data release time, $t_{release}$ (see Figure 1)	High-level data			10	ns
	Low-level data			10	
Operating free-air temperature, T_A		0		70	°C

electrical characteristics over recommended operating free-air temperature range (unless otherwise noted)

	PARAMETER		TEST CONDITIONS[†]		MIN	TYP[‡]	MAX	UNIT
V_{IH}	High-level input voltage				2			V
V_{IL}	Low-level input voltage						0.8	V
V_{IK}	Input clamp voltage		V_{CC} = MIN,	I_I = −12 mA			−1.5	V
V_{OH}	High-level output voltage		V_{CC} = MIN, V_{IL} = 0.8 V,	V_{IH} = 2 V, I_{OH} = −5.2 mA	2.4	3		V
V_{OL}	Low-level output voltage		V_{CC} = MIN, V_{IL} = 0.8 V,	V_{IH} = 2 V, I_{OL} = 16 mA		0.2	0.4	V
$I_{O(off)}$	Off-state (high-impedance state) output current		V_{CC} = MAX,	V_O = 2.4 V			40	μA
			V_{CC} = MAX,	V_O = 0.4 V			−40	
I_I	Input current at maximum input voltage		V_{CC} = MAX,	V_I = 5.5 V			1	mA
I_{IH}	High-level input current		V_{CC} = MAX,	V_I = 2.4 V			40	μA
I_{IL}	Low-level input current	2W/R0, 2W/R1, 2W/R2, 1GW, 2GW, or clock	V_{CC} = MAX,	V_I = 0.4 V			−1.6	mA
		Any other input					−0.8	
I_{OS}	Short-circuit output current §		V_{CC} = MAX		−18		−55	mA
I_{CC}	Supply current		V_{CC} = MAX, Outputs open	All inputs at 4.5 V,		112	170	mA

†For conditions shown as MIN or MAX, use the appropriate value specified under recommended operating conditions.
‡All typical values are at V_{CC} = 5 V, T_A = 25°C.
§Not more than one output should be shorted at a time.

TEXAS INSTRUMENTS
INCORPORATED
POST OFFICE BOX 5012 • DALLAS, TEXAS 75222

7

TYPE SN74172
16-BIT MULTIPLE-PORT REGISTER FILE WITH 3-STATE OUTPUTS

switching characteristics, V_{CC} = 5 V, T_A = 25°C, R_L = 400 Ω

PARAMETER		TEST CONDITIONS	MIN	TYP	MAX	UNIT
f_{max}	Maximum clock frequency		20			MHz
t_{PLH}	Propagation delay time, low-to-high-level output from read select	C_L = 50 pF, See Figure 1		33	45	ns
t_{PHL}	Propagation delay time, high-to-low-level output from read select			30	45	
t_{PLH}	Propagation delay time, low-to-high-level output from clock			35	50	ns
t_{PHL}	Propagation delay time, high-to-low-level output from clock			35	50	
t_{ZH}	Output enable time to high level			14	30	ns
t_{ZL}	Output enable time to low level			16	30	
t_{HZ}	Output disable time from high level	C_L = 5 pF, See Figure 1		6	20	ns
t_{LZ}	Output disable time from low level			11	20	

PARAMETER MEASUREMENT INFORMATION

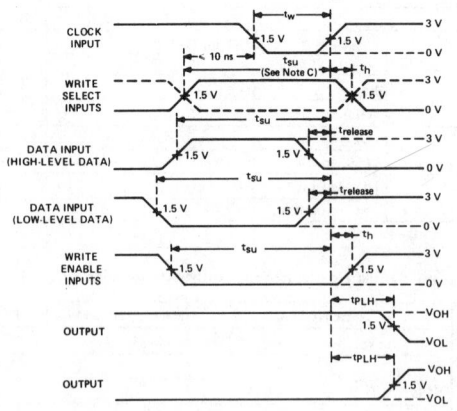

SWITCHING TIMES FROM CLOCK INPUT

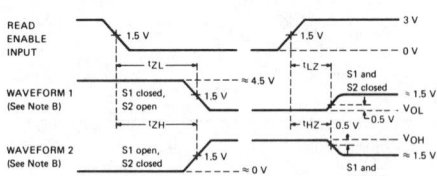

ENABLE AND DISABLE TIMES FROM READ ENABLE

NOTES: A. Input waveforms are supplied by pulse generators having the following characteristics: $t_r \leqslant 7$ ns, $t_f \leqslant 7$ ns, PRR = 1 MHz, $Z_{out} \approx 50$ Ω.
   B. Waveform 1 is for an output with internal conditions such that the output is low except when disabled. Waveform 2 is for an output with internal conditions such that the output is high except when disabled.
   C. Write select setup time, as specified, will protect data written into previous address.
   D. Load circuit is shown on page 3-10.

VOLTAGE WAVEFORMS
FIGURE 1

schematics of inputs and outputs

EQUIVALENT OF EACH INPUT	TYPICAL OF ALL OUTPUTS
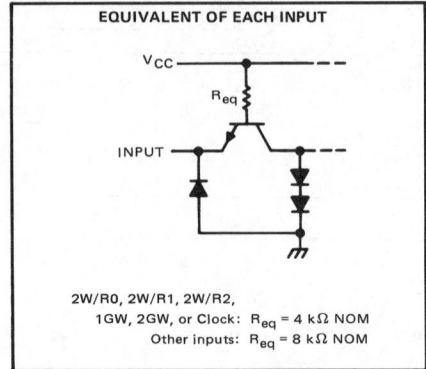	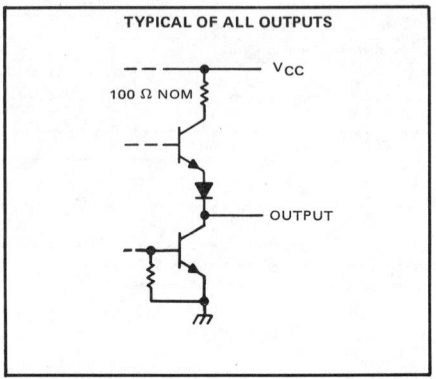

2W/R0, 2W/R1, 2W/R2, 1GW, 2GW, or Clock: R_{eq} = 4 kΩ NOM
Other inputs: R_{eq} = 8 kΩ NOM

7

TEXAS INSTRUMENTS
INCORPORATED
POST OFFICE BOX 5012 • DALLAS, TEXAS 75222

TTL
MSI

TYPES SN54173, SN54LS173, SN74173, SN74LS173
4-BIT D-TYPE REGISTERS WITH 3-STATE OUTPUTS

BULLETIN NO. DL-S 7611721, OCTOBER 1976

- Three-State Outputs Interface Directly with System Bus
- Gated Output-Control Lines for Enabling or Disabling the Outputs
- Fully Independent Clock Virtually Eliminates Restrictions for Operating in One of Two Modes:

    Parallel Load
    Do Nothing (Hold)

- For Application as Bus Buffer Registers

TYPE	TYPICAL PROPAGATION DELAY TIME	MAXIMUM CLOCK FREQUENCY	TYPICAL POWER DISSIPATION
'173	23 ns	35 MHz	250 mW
'LS173	18 ns	50 MHz	85 mW

SN54173, SN54LS173 . . . J OR W PACKAGE
SN74173, SN74LS173 . . . J OR N PACKAGE
(TOP VIEW)

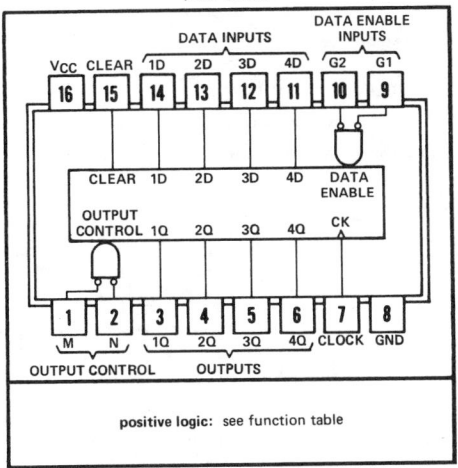

positive logic: see function table

description

The '173 and 'LS173 four-bit registers include D-type flip-flops featuring totem-pole three-state out-puts capable of driving highly capacitive or relatively low-impedance loads. The high-impedance third state and increased high-logic-level drive provide these flip-flops with the capability of being connected directly to and driving the bus lines in a bus-organized system without need for interface or pull-up components. Up to 128 of the SN74173 or SN74LS173 outputs may be connected to a common bus and still drive two Series 54/74 or 54LS/74LS TTL normalized loads, respectively. Similarly, up to 49 of the SN54173 or SN54LS173 outputs can be connected to a common bus and drive one additional Series 54/74 or 54LS/74LS TTL normalized load, respectively. To minimize the possibility that two outputs will attempt to take a common bus to opposite logic levels, the output control circuitry is designed so that the average output disable times are shorter than the average output enable times.

FUNCTION TABLE

INPUTS					OUTPUT
CLEAR	CLOCK	DATA ENABLE		DATA	Q
		G1	G2	D	
H	X	X	X	X	L
L	L	X	X	X	Q_0
L	↑	H	X	X	Q_0
L	↑	X	H	X	Q_0
L	↑	L	L	L	L
L	↑	L	L	H	H

When either M or N (or both) is (are) high the output is disabled to the high-impedance state; however sequential operation of the flip-flops is not affected.

Gated enable inputs are provided on the '173 and 'LS173 for controlling the entry of data into the flip-flops. When both data-enable inputs are low, data at the D inputs are loaded into their respective flip-flops on the next positive transition of the buffered clock input. Gate output control inputs are also provided. When both are low, the normal logic states (high or low levels) of the four outputs are available for driving the loads or bus lines. The outputs are disabled independently from the level of the clock by a high logic level at either output control input. The outputs then present a high impedance and neither load nor drive the bus line. Detailed operation is given in the function table.

Higher density D-type registers, some with improved performance and including the new octal D-type registers, are shown in the functional index/selection guide, see pages 1-11 and 1-12.

TEXAS INSTRUMENTS
INCORPORATED
POST OFFICE BOX 5012 • DALLAS, TEXAS 75222

TYPES SN54173, SN54LS173, SN74173, SN74LS173
4-BIT D-TYPE REGISTERS WITH 3-STATE OUTPUTS

absolute maximum ratings over operating free-air temperature range (unless otherwise noted)

Supply voltage, V_{CC} (see Note 1) . . . . 7 V
Input voltage: '173 . . . . 5.5 V
            'LS173 . . . . 7 V
Off-state output voltage . . . . 5.5 V
Operating free-air temperature range: SN54173, SN54LS173 . . . . $-55°C$ to $125°C$
                             SN74173, SN74LS173 . . . . $0°C$ to $70°C$
Storage temperature range . . . . $-65°C$ to $150°C$

NOTE 1: Voltage values are with respect to network ground terminals.

functional block diagram and schematics of inputs and outputs

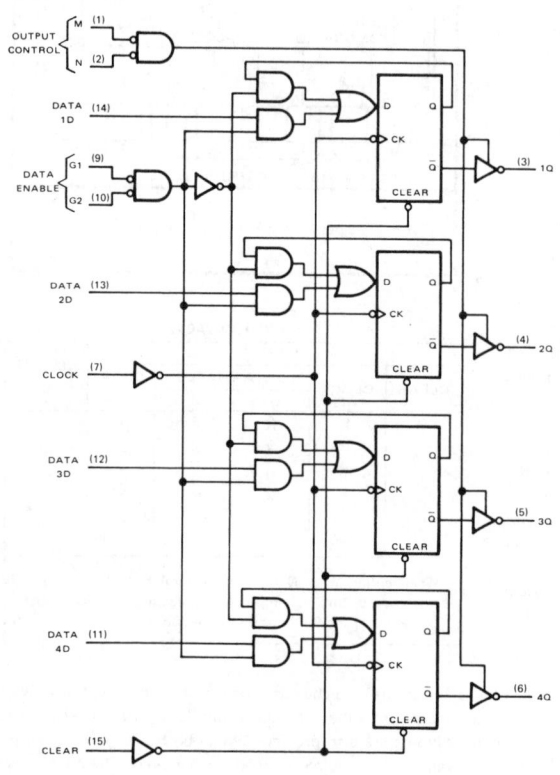

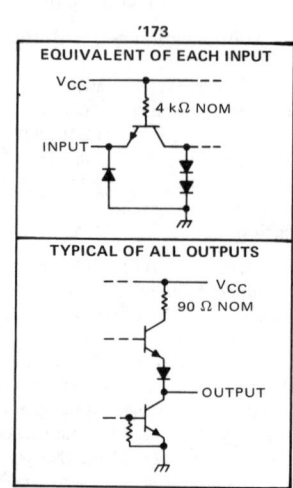

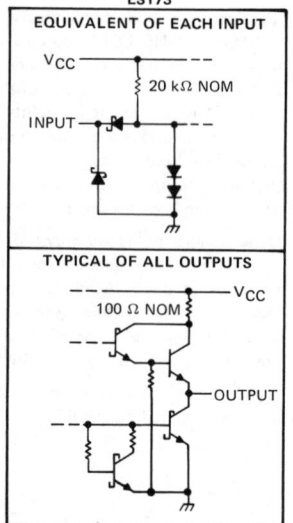

⟶◁⟩⟶ . . . . dynamic input activated by a transition from a high level to a low level.

TEXAS INSTRUMENTS
INCORPORATED
POST OFFICE BOX 5012 • DALLAS, TEXAS 75222

recommended operating conditions

		SN54173 MIN	NOM	MAX	SN74173 MIN	NOM	MAX	UNIT
Supply voltage, V_{CC}		4.5	5	5.5	4.75	5	5.25	V
High-level output current, I_{OH}				−2			−5.2	mA
Low-level output current, I_{OL}				16			16	mA
Input clock frequency, f_{clock}		0		25	0		25	MHz
Width of clock or clear pulse, t_w		20			20			ns
Setup time, t_{su}	Data enable	17			17			ns
	Data	10			10			
	Clear inactive state	10			10			
Hold time, t_h	Data enable	2			2			ns
	Data	10			10			
Operating free-air temperature, T_A		−55		125	0		70	°C

electrical characteristics over recommended operating free-air temperature range (unless otherwise noted)

	PARAMETER	TEST CONDITIONS[†]	MIN	TYP[‡]	MAX	UNIT
V_{IH}	High-level input voltage		2			V
V_{IL}	Low-level input voltage				0.8	V
V_{IK}	Input clamp voltage	V_{CC} = MIN, I_I = −12 mA			−1.5	V
V_{OH}	High-level output voltage	V_{CC} = MIN, V_{IH} = 2 V, V_{IL} = 0.8 V, I_{OH} = MAX	2.4			V
V_{OL}	Low-level output voltage	V_{CC} = MIN, V_{IH} = 2 V, V_{IL} = 0.8 V, I_{OL} = 16 mA			0.4	V
$I_{O(off)}$	Off-state (high-impedance state) output current	V_{CC} = MAX, V_O = 2.4 V			40	µA
		V_{IH} = 2 V $\quad$ V_O = 0.4 V			−40	
I_I	Input current at maximum input voltage	V_{CC} = MAX, V_I = 5.5 V			1	mA
I_{IH}	High-level input current	V_{CC} = MAX, V_I = 2.4 V			40	µA
I_{IL}	Low-level input current	V_{CC} = MAX, V_I = 0.4 V			−1.6	mA
I_{OS}	Short-circuit output current[§]	V_{CC} = MAX	−30		−70	mA
I_{CC}	Supply current	V_{CC} = MAX, See Note 2		50	72	mA

[†]For conditions shown as MIN or MAX, use the appropriate value specified under recommended operating conditions.
[‡]All typical values are at V_{CC} = 5 V, T_A = 25°C.
[§]Not more than one output should be shorted at a time.
NOTE 2: I_{CC} is measured with all outputs open; clear grounded following momentary connection to 4.5 V; N, G1, G2, and all data inputs grounded; and the clock input and M at 4.5 V.

switching characteristics, V_{CC} = 5 V, T_A = 25°C, R_L = 400 Ω

	PARAMETER	TEST CONDITIONS	MIN	TYP	MAX	UNIT
f_{max}	Maximum clock frequency		25	35		MHz
t_{PHL}	Propagation delay time, high-to-low-level output from clear input			18	27	ns
t_{PLH}	Propagation delay time, low-to-high-level output from clock input	C_L = 50 pF,		28	43	ns
t_{PHL}	Propagation delay time, high-to-low-level output from clock input	See Note 3		19	31	
t_{PZH}	Output enable time to high level		7	16	30	ns
t_{PZL}	Output enable time to low level		7	21	30	
t_{PHZ}	Output disable time from high level	C_L = 5 pF,	3	5	14	ns
t_{PLZ}	Output disable time from low level	See Note 3	3	11	20	

NOTE 3: Load circuits and voltage waveforms are shown on page 3-10.

7

TEXAS INSTRUMENTS
INCORPORATED
POST OFFICE BOX 5012 • DALLAS, TEXAS 75222

recommended operating conditions

		SN54LS173			SN74LS173			UNIT
		MIN	NOM	MAX	MIN	NOM	MAX	
Supply voltage, V_{CC}		4.5	5	5.5	4.75	5	5.25	V
High-level output current, I_{OH}				−1			−2.6	mA
Low-level output current, I_{OL}				12			24	mA
Input clock frequency, f_{clock}		0		30	0		30	MHz
Width of clock or clear pulse, t_w		20			20			ns
Setup time, t_{su}	Data enable	17			17			
	Data	17			17			ns
	Clear inactive state	10			10			
Hold time, t_h	Data enable	0			0			
	Data	0			0			ns
Operating free-air temperature, T_A		−55		125	0		70	°C

electrical characteristics over recommended operating free-air temperature range (unless otherwise noted)

PARAMETER		TEST CONDITIONS[†]		SN54LS173			SN74LS173			UNIT
				MIN	TYP[‡]	MAX	MIN	TYP[‡]	MAX	
V_{IH}	High-level input voltage			2			2			V
V_{IL}	Low-level input voltage					0.7			0.8	V
V_{IK}	Input clamp voltage	V_{CC} = MIN,	I_I = −18 mA			−1.5			−1.5	V
V_{OH}	High-level output voltage	V_{CC} = MIN, $V_{IL} = V_{IL}$max	V_{IH} = 2 V, I_{OH} = MAX	2.4	3.4		2.4	3.1		V
V_{OL}	Low-level output voltage	V_{CC} = MIN, V_{IL} = 0.8 V	I_{OL} = 12 mA		0.25	0.4		0.25	0.4	V
			I_{OL} = 24 mA					0.35	0.5	
$I_{O(off)}$	Off-state (high-impedance state) output current	V_{CC} = MAX, V_{IH} = 2 V	V_O = 2.7 V			20			20	μA
			V_O = 0.4 V			−20			−20	
I_I	Input current at maximum input voltage	V_{CC} = MAX,	V_I = 7 V			0.1			0.1	mA
I_{IH}	High-level input current	V_{CC} = MAX,	V_I = 2.7 V			20			20	μA
I_{IL}	Low-level input current	V_{CC} = MAX,	V_I = 0.4 V			−0.4			−0.4	mA
I_{OS}	Short-circuit output current[§]	V_{CC} = MAX		−30		−130	−30		−130	mA
I_{CC}	Supply current	V_{CC} = MAX,	See Note 2		17	30		17	30	mA

[†]For conditions shown as MIN or MAX, use the appropriate value specified under recommended operating conditions.
[‡]All typical values are at V_{CC} = 5 V, T_A = 25°C.
[§]Not more than one output should be shorted at a time.
NOTE 2: I_{CC} is measured with all outputs open; clear grounded following momentary connection to 4.5 V; N, G1, G2, and all data inputs grounded; and the clock input and M at 4.5 V.

switching characteristics, V_{CC} = 5 V, T_A = 25°C, R_L = 667 Ω

PARAMETER		TEST CONDITIONS	MIN	TYP	MAX	UNIT
f_{max}	Maximum clock frequency		30	50		MHz
t_{PHL}	Propagation delay time, high-to-low-level output from clear input			20	30	ns
t_{PLH}	Propagation delay time, low-to-high-level output from clock input	C_L = 45 pF,		16	29	
t_{PHL}	Propagation delay time, high-to-low-level output from clock input	See Note 4		20	30	ns
t_{PZH}	Output enable time to high level			13	21	
t_{PZL}	Output enable time to low level			24	36	ns
t_{PHZ}	Output disable time from high level	C_L = 5 pF,		11	17	
t_{PLZ}	Output disable time from low level	See Note 4		15	23	ns

NOTE 4: Load circuits and voltage waveforms are shown on page 3-11.

This page provides tentative information on a product in the developmental stage. Texas Instruments reserves the right to change or discontinue this product without notice.

TEXAS INSTRUMENTS
INCORPORATED
POST OFFICE BOX 5012 • DALLAS, TEXAS 75222

7

TYPES SN54174, SN54175, SN54LS174, SN54LS175, SN54S174, SN54S175, SN74174, SN74175, SN74LS174, SN74LS175, SN74S174, SN74S175
HEX/QUADRUPLE D-TYPE FLIP-FLOPS WITH CLEAR

BULLETIN NO. DL-S 7611803, DECEMBER 1972—REVISED OCTOBER 1976

'174, 'LS174, 'S174 . . . HEX D-TYPE FLIP-FLOPS
'175, 'LS175, 'S175 . . . QUADRUPLE D-TYPE FLIP-FLOPS

- **'174, 'LS174, 'S174 Contain Six Flip-Flops with Single-Rail Outputs**

- **'175, 'LS175, 'S175 Contain Four Flip-Flops with Double-Rail Outputs**

- **Three Performance Ranges Offered: See Table Lower Right**

- **Buffered Clock and Direct Clear Inputs**

- **Individual Data Input to Each Flip-Flop**

- **Applications include:**
  Buffer/Storage Registers
  Shift Registers
  Pattern Generators

description

These monolithic, positive-edge-triggered flip-flops utilize TTL circuitry to implement D-type flip-flop logic. All have a direct clear input, and the '175, 'LS175, and 'S175 feature complementary outputs from each flip-flops.

Information at the D inputs meeting the setup time requirements is transferred to the Q outputs on the positive-going edge of the clock pulse. Clock triggering occurs at a particular voltage level and is not directly related to the transition time of the positive-going pulse. When the clock input is at either the high or low level, the D input signal has no effect at the output.

These circuits are fully compatible for use with most TTL or DTL circuits.

SN54174, SN54LS174, SN54S174 . . . J OR W PACKAGE
SN74174, SN74LS174, SN74S174 . . . J OR N PACKAGE
(TOP VIEW)

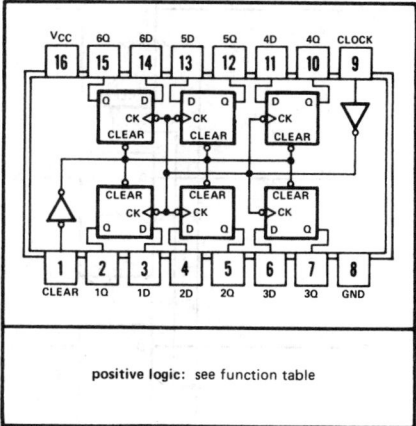

positive logic: see function table

SN54175, SN54LS175, SN54S175 . . . J OR W PACKAGE
SN74175, SN74LS175, SN74S175 . . . J OR N PACKAGE
(TOP VIEW)

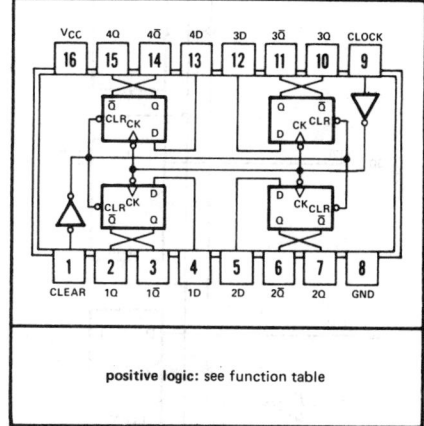

positive logic: see function table

FUNCTION TABLE
(EACH FLIP-FLOP)

INPUTS			OUTPUTS	
CLEAR	CLOCK	D	Q	$\bar{Q}$†
L	X	X	L	H
H	↑	H	H	L
H	↑	L	L	H
H	L	X	Q_0	$\bar{Q}_0$

H = high level (steady state)
L = low level (steady state)
X = irrelevant
↑ = transition from low to high level
Q_0 = the level of Q before the indicated steady-state
  input conditions were established.
† = '175, 'LS175, and 'S175 only

TYPES	TYPICAL MAXIMUM CLOCK FREQUENCY	TYPICAL POWER DISSIPATION PER FLIP-FLOP
'174, '175	35 MHz	38 mW
'LS174, 'LS175	40 MHz	14 mW
'S174, 'S175	110 MHz	75 mW

7

functional block diagrams

'174, 'LS174, 'S174

'175, 'LS175, 'S175

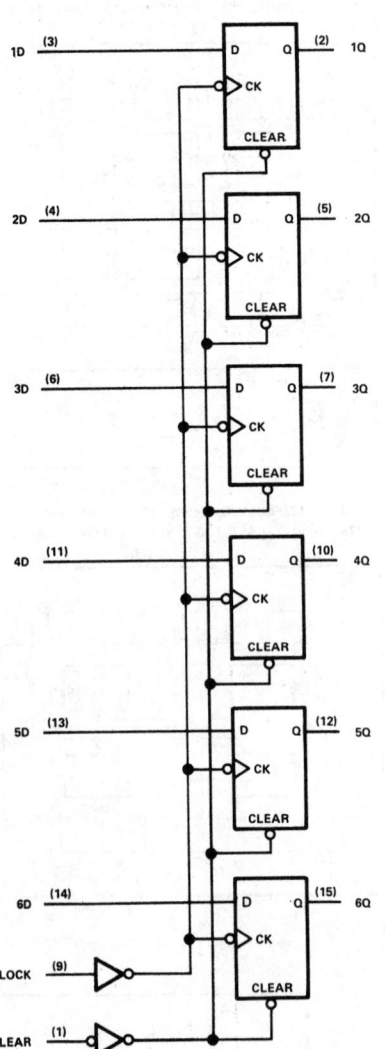

. . . dynamic input activated by transition from a high level to a low level.

TEXAS INSTRUMENTS
INCORPORATED
POST OFFICE BOX 5012 • DALLAS, TEXAS 75222

schematics of inputs and outputs

SN54174, SN54175, SN74174, SN74175

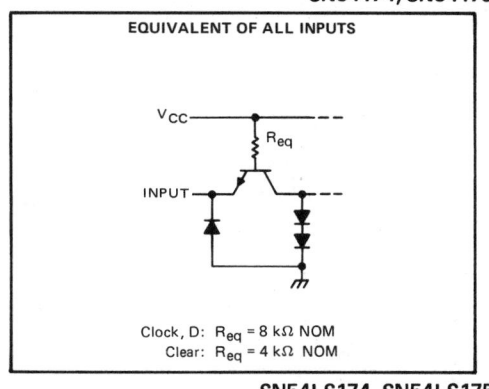

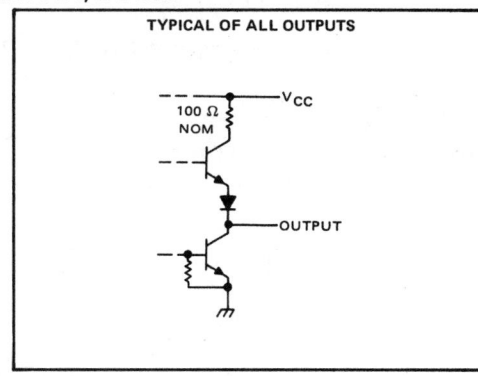

SN54LS174, SN54LS175, SN74LS174, SN74LS175

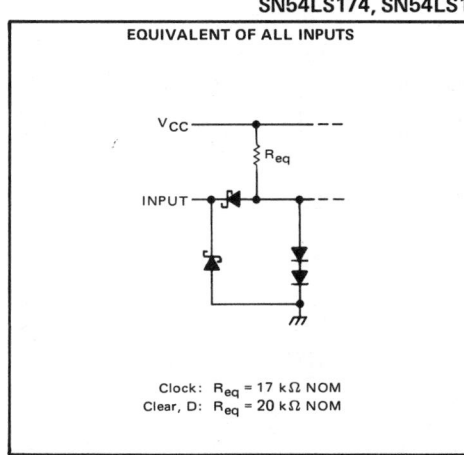

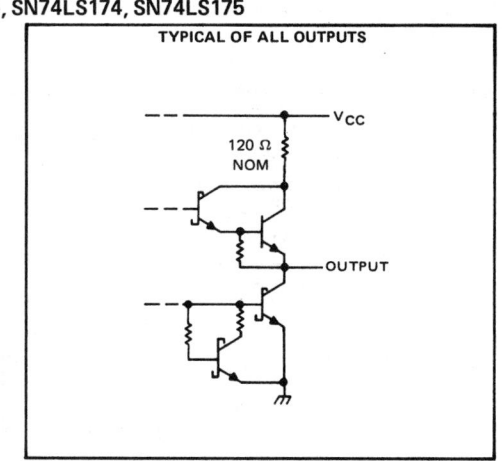

7

SN54S174, SN54S175, SN74S174, SN74S175

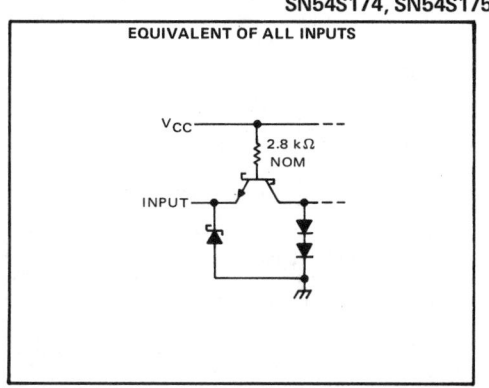

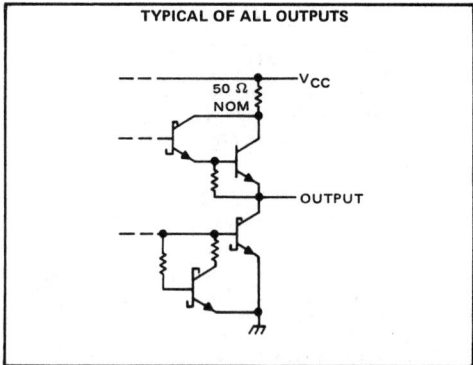

TEXAS INSTRUMENTS
INCORPORATED
POST OFFICE BOX 5012 • DALLAS, TEXAS 75222

TYPES SN54174, SN54175, SN74174, SN74175
HEX/QUADRUPLE D-TYPE FLIP-FLOPS WITH CLEAR

absolute maximum ratings over operating free-air temperature range (unless otherwise noted)

Supply voltage, V_{CC} (see Note 1)	7 V
Input voltage	5.5 V
Operating free-air temperature range: SN54174, SN54175 Circuits	$-55°C$ to $125°C$
SN74174, SN74175 Circuits	$0°C$ to $70°C$
Storage temperature range	$-65°C$ to $150°C$

NOTE 1: Voltage values are with respect to network ground terminal.

recommended operating conditions

		SN54174, SN54175			SN74174, SN74175			UNIT
		MIN	NOM	MAX	MIN	NOM	MAX	
Supply voltage, V_{CC}		4.5	5	5.5	4.75	5	5.25	V
High-level output current, I_{OH}				−800			−800	μA
Low-level output current, I_{OL}				16			16	mA
Clock frequency, f_{clock}		0		25	0		25	MHz
Width of clock or clear pulse, t_w		20			20			ns
Setup time, t_{su}	Data input	20			20			ns
	Clear inactive-state	25			25			ns
Data hold time, t_h		5			5			ns
Operating free-air temperature, T_A		−55		125	0		70	°C

electrical characteristics over recommended operating free-air temperature range (unless otherwise noted)

PARAMETER		TEST CONDITIONS[†]		MIN	TYP[‡]	MAX	UNIT
V_{IH}	High-level input voltage			2			V
V_{IL}	Low-level input voltage					0.8	V
V_{IK}	Input clamp voltage	V_{CC} = MIN, I_I = −12 mA				−1.5	V
V_{OH}	High-level output voltage	V_{CC} = MIN, V_{IH} = 2 V, V_{IL} = 0.8 V, I_{OH} = −800 μA		2.4	3.4		V
V_{OL}	Low-level output voltage	V_{CC} = MIN, V_{IH} = 2 V, V_{IL} = 0.8 V, I_{OL} = 16 mA			0.2	0.4	V
I_I	Input current at maximum input voltage	V_{CC} = MAX, V_I = 5.5 V				1	mA
I_{IH}	High-level input current	V_{CC} = MAX, V_I = 2.4 V				40	μA
I_{IL}	Low-level input current	V_{CC} = MAX, V_I = 0.4 V				−1.6	mA
I_{OS}	Short-circuit output current[§]	V_{CC} = MAX	SN54′	−20		−57	mA
			SN74′	−18		−57	
I_{CC}	Supply current	V_{CC} = MAX, See Note 2	′174		45	65	mA
			′175		30	45	

[†] For conditions shown as MIN or MAX, use the appropriate value specified under recommended operating conditions for the applicable device type.

[‡] All typical values are at V_{CC} = 5 V, T_A = 25°C.

[§] Not more than one output should be shorted at a time.

NOTE 2: With all outputs open and 4.5 V applied to all data and clear inputs, I_{CC} is measured after a momentary ground, then 4.5 V, is applied to clock.

switching characteristics, V_{CC} = 5 V, T_A = 25°C

PARAMETER		TEST CONDITIONS	MIN	TYP	MAX	UNIT
f_{max}	Maximum clock frequency	C_L = 15 pF, R_L = 400 Ω, See Note 3	25	35		MHz
t_{PLH}	Propagation delay time, low-to-high-level output from clear (SN54175, SN74175 only)			16	25	ns
t_{PHL}	Propagation delay time, high-to-low-level output from clear			23	35	ns
t_{PLH}	Propagation delay time, low-to-high-level output from clock			20	30	ns
t_{PHL}	Propagation delay time, high-to-low-level output from clock			24	35	ns

NOTE 3: Load circuit and voltage waveforms are shown on page 3-10.

107

TEXAS INSTRUMENTS
INCORPORATED
POST OFFICE BOX 5012 • DALLAS, TEXAS 75222

absolute maximum ratings over operating free-air temperature range (unless otherwise noted)

Supply voltage, V_{CC} (see Note 1)	7 V
Input voltage	7 V
Operating free-air temperature range: SN54LS174, SN54LS175 Circuits	$-55°C$ to $125°C$
SN74LS174, SN74LS175 Circuits	$0°C$ to $70°C$
Storage temperature range	$-65°C$ to $150°C$

NOTE 1: Voltage values are with respect to network ground terminal.

recommended operating conditions

		SN54LS174 SN54LS175			SN74LS174 SN74LS175			UNIT
		MIN	NOM	MAX	MIN	NOM	MAX	
Supply voltage, V_{CC}		4.5	5	5.5	4.75	5	5.25	V
High-level output current, I_{OH}				−400			−400	μA
Low-level output current, I_{OL}				4			8	mA
Clock frequency, f_{clock}		0		30	0		30	MHz
Width of clock or clear pulse, t_w		20			20			ns
Setup time, t_{su}	Data input	20			20			ns
	Clear inactive-state	25			25			ns
Data hold time, t_h		5			5			ns
Operating free-air temperature, T_A		−55		125	0		70	°C

electrical characteristics over recommended operating free-air temperature range (unless otherwise noted)

PARAMETER		TEST CONDITIONS†		SN54LS174 SN54LS175			SN74LS174 SN74LS175			UNIT
				MIN	TYP‡	MAX	MIN	TYP‡	MAX	
V_{IH}	High-level input voltage			2			2			V
V_{IL}	Low-level input voltage					0.7			0.8	V
V_{IK}	Input clamp voltage	V_{CC} = MIN,	$I_I = -18$ mA			−1.5			−1.5	V
V_{OH}	High-level output voltage	V_{CC} = MIN, $V_{IH} = 2$ V, $V_{IL} = V_{IL}$max, $I_{OH} = -400$ μA		2.5	3.5		2.7	3.5		V
V_{OL}	Low-level output voltage	V_{CC} = MIN, $V_{IH} = 2$ V, $V_{IL} = V_{IL}$ max	$I_{OL} = 4$ mA		0.25	0.4		0.25	0.4	V
			$I_{OL} = 8$ mA					0.35	0.5	
I_I	Input current at maximum input voltage	V_{CC} = MAX, $V_I = 7$ V				0.1			0.1	mA
I_{IH}	High-level input current	V_{CC} = MAX, $V_I = 2.7$ V				20			20	μA
I_{IL}	Low-level input current	V_{CC} = MAX, $V_I = 0.4$ V				−0.4			−0.4	mA
I_{OS}	Short-circuit output current§	V_{CC} = MAX		−20		−100	−20		−100	mA
I_{CC}	Supply current	V_{CC} = MAX, See Note 2	'LS174		16	26		16	26	mA
			'LS175		11	18		11	18	

†For conditions shown as MIN or MAX, use the appropriate value specified under recommended operating conditions.

‡All typical values are at $V_{CC} = 5$ V, $T_A = 25°C$.

§Not more than one output should be shorted at a time, and duration of the short-circuit should not exceed one second.

NOTE 2: With all outputs open and 4.5 V applied to all data and clear inputs, I_{CC} is measured after a momentary ground, then 4.5 V, is applied to clock.

switching characteristics, $V_{CC} = 5$ V, $T_A = 25°C$

PARAMETER	TEST CONDITIONS	MIN	TYP	MAX	UNIT
f_{max} Maximum clock frequency	$C_L = 15$ pF, $R_L = 2$ kΩ, See Note 4	30	40		MHz
t_{PLH} Propagation delay time, low-to-high-level output from clear (SN54LS175, SN74LS175 only)			16	25	ns
t_{PHL} Propagation delay time, high-to-low-level output from clear			23	35	ns
t_{PLH} Propagation delay time, low-to-high-level output from clock			20	30	ns
t_{PHL} Propagation delay time, high-to-low-level output from clock			21	30	ns

NOTE 4: Load circuit and voltage waveforms are shown on page 3-11.

7

TEXAS INSTRUMENTS
INCORPORATED
POST OFFICE BOX 5012 • DALLAS, TEXAS 75222

TYPES SN54S174, SN54S175, SN74S174, SN74S175
HEX/QUADRUPLE D-TYPE FLIP-FLOPS WITH CLEAR

absolute maximum ratings over operating free-air temperature range (unless otherwise noted)

Supply voltage, V_{CC} (see Note 1) . . . . 7 V
Input voltage . . . . 5.5 V
Operating free-air temperature range: SN54S174, SN54S175 Circuits . . . . −55°C to 125°C
SN74S174, SN74S175 Circuits . . . . 0°C to 70°C
Storage temperature range . . . . −65°C to 150°C

NOTE 1: Voltage values are with respect to network ground terminal.

recommended operating conditions

		SN54S174, SN54S175			SN74S174, SN74S175			UNIT
		MIN	NOM	MAX	MIN	NOM	MAX	
Supply voltage, V_{CC}		4.5	5	5.5	4.75	5	5.25	V
High-level output current, I_{OH}				−1			−1	mA
Low-level output current, I_{OL}				20			20	mA
Clock frequency, f_{clock}		0	75		0	75		MHz
Pulse width, t_w	Clock	7			7			ns
	Clear	10			10			
Setup time, t_{su}	Data input	5			5			ns
	Clear inactive-state	5			5			
Data hold time, t_h		3			3			ns
Operating free-air temperature, T_A		−55		125	0		70	°C

electrical characteristics over recommended operating free-air temperature range (unless otherwise noted)

PARAMETER		TEST CONDITIONS[†]		MIN	TYP[‡]	MAX	UNIT
V_{IH}	High-level input voltage			2			V
V_{IL}	Low-level input voltage					0.8	V
V_{IK}	Input clamp voltage	V_{CC} = MIN, I_I = −18 mA				−1.2	V
V_{OH}	High-level output voltage	V_{CC} = MIN, V_{IH} = 2 V,	SN54S'	2.5	3.4		V
		V_{IL} = 0.8 V, I_{OH} = −1 mA	SN74S'	2.7	3.4		
V_{OL}	Low-level output voltage	V_{CC} = MIN, V_{IH} = 2 V, V_{IL} = 0.8 V, I_{OL} = 20 mA				0.5	V
I_I	Input current at maximum input voltage	V_{CC} = MAX, V_I = 5.5 V				1	mA
I_{IH}	High-level input current	V_{CC} = MAX, V_I = 2.7 V				50	μA
I_{IL}	Low-level input current	V_{CC} = MAX, V_I = 0.5 V				−2	mA
I_{OS}	Short-circuit output current[§]	V_{CC} = MAX		−40		−100	mA
I_{CC}	Supply current	V_{CC} = MAX, See Note 2	'174		90	144	mA
			'175		60	96	

[†]For conditions shown as MIN or MAX, use the appropriate value specified under recommended operating conditions for the applicable device type.
[‡]All typical values are at V_{CC} = 5 V, T_A = 25°C.
[§]Not more than one output should be shorted at a time, and duration of the short-circuit should not exceed one second.
NOTE 2: With all outputs open and 4.5 V applied to all data and clear inputs, I_{CC} is measured after a momentary ground, then 4.5 V, is applied to clock.

switching characteristics, V_{CC} = 5 V, T_A = 25°C

PARAMETER		TEST CONDITIONS	MIN	TYP	MAX	UNIT
f_{max}	Maximum clock frequency		75	110		MHz
t_{PLH}	Propagation delay time, low-to-high-level $\overline{Q}$ output from clear (SN54S175, SN74S175 only)	C_L = 15 pF, R_L = 280 Ω, See Note 3		10	15	ns
t_{PHL}	Propagation delay time, high-to-low-level Q output from clear			13	22	ns
t_{PLH}	Propagation delay time, low-to-high-level output from clock			8	12	ns
t_{PHL}	Propagation time, high-to-low-level output from clock			11.5	17	ns

NOTE 3: Load circuit and voltage waveforms are shown on page 3-10.

TEXAS INSTRUMENTS
INCORPORATED
POST OFFICE BOX 5012 • DALLAS, TEXAS 75222

7

TTL
MSI

TYPES SN54176, SN54177, SN74176, SN74177
35-MHz PRESETTABLE DECADE AND
BINARY COUNTERS/LATCHES
BULLETIN NO. DL-S 7211478, MAY 1971—REVISED DECEMBER 1972

- Reduced-Power Versions of SN54196, SN54197, SN74196, and SN74197 50-MHz Counters

- D-C Coupled Counters Designed to Replace Signetics 8280, 8281, 8290, and 8291 Counters in Most Applications

- Performs BCD, Bi-Quinary, or Binary Counting

- Fully Programmable

- Fully Independent Clear Input

- Guaranteed to Count at Input Frequencies from 0 to 35 MHz

- Input Clamping Diodes Simplify System Design

SN54176, SN54177 . . . J OR W PACKAGE
SN74176, SN74177 . . . J OR N PACKAGE
(TOP VIEW)

asynchronous input: Low input to clear sets Q_A, Q_B, Q_C, and Q_D low.

description

These high-speed monolithic counters consist of four d-c coupled master-slave flip-flops which are internally interconnected to provide either a divide-by-two and a divide-by-five counter (SN54176, SN74176) or a divide-by-two and a divide-by-eight counter (SN54177, SN74177). These counters are fully programmable; that is, the outputs may be preset to any state by placing a low on the count/load input and entering the desired data at the data inputs. The outputs will change to agree with the data inputs independent of the state of the clocks.

These counters may also be used as 4-bit latches by using the count/load input as the strobe and entering data at the data inputs. The outputs will directly follow the data inputs when the count/load is low, but will remain unchanged when the count/load is high and the clock inputs are inactive.

These high-speed counters will accept count frequencies of 0 to 35 megahertz at the clock-1 input and 0 to 17.5 megahertz at the clock-2 input. During the count operation, transfer of information to the outputs occurs on the negative-going edge of the clock pulse. The counters feature a direct clear which when taken low sets all outputs low regardless of the states of the clocks.

All inputs are diode-clamped to minimize transmission-line effects and simplify system design. The circuits are compatible with most TTL and DTL logic families. Typical power dissipation is 150 milliwatts. The SN54176 and SN54177 circuits are characterized for operation over the full military temperature range of −55°C to 125°C; the SN74176 and SN74177 circuits are characterized for operation from 0°C to 70°C.

TEXAS INSTRUMENTS
INCORPORATED
POST OFFICE BOX 5012 • DALLAS, TEXAS 75222

typical count configurations

SN54176 and SN74176

The output of flip-flop A is not internally connected to the succeeding flip-flops; therefore, the count may be operated in three independent modes:

1. When used as a binary-coded-decimal decade counter, the clock-2 input must be externally connected to the Q_A output. The clock-1 input receives the incoming count, and a count sequence is obtained in accordance with the BCD count sequence function table shown at right.

2. If a symmetrical divide-by-ten count is desired for frequency synthesizers (or other applications requiring division of a binary count by a power of ten), the Q_D output must be externally connected to the clock-1 input. The input count is then applied at the clock-2 input and a divide-by-ten square wave is obtained at output Q_A in accordance with the bi-quinary function table.

SN54176, SN74176
FUNCTION TABLES

DECADE (BCD)
(See Note A)

COUNT	OUTPUT			
	Q_D	Q_C	Q_B	Q_A
0	L	L	L	L
1	L	L	L	H
2	L	L	H	L
3	L	L	H	H
4	L	H	L	L
5	L	H	L	H
6	L	H	H	L
7	L	H	H	H
8	H	L	L	L
9	H	L	L	H

BI-QUINARY (5-2)
(See Note B)

COUNT	OUTPUT			
	Q_A	Q_D	Q_C	Q_B
0	L	L	L	L
1	L	L	L	H
2	L	L	H	L
3	L	L	H	H
4	L	H	L	L
5	H	L	L	L
6	H	L	L	H
7	H	L	H	L
8	H	L	H	H
9	H	H	L	L

H = high level, L = low level

NOTES: A. Output Q_A connected to clock-2 input.
B. Output Q_D connected to clock-1 input.

3. For operation as a divide-by-two counter and a divide-by-five counter, no external interconnections are required. Flip-flop A is used as a binary element for the divide-by-two function. The clock-2 input is used to obtain binary divide-by-five operation at the Q_B, Q_C, and Q_D outputs. In this mode, the two counters operate independently; however, all four flip-flops are loaded and cleared simultaneously.

SN54177 and SN74177

The output of flip-flop A is not internally connected to the succeeding flip-flops, therefore the counter may be operated in two independent modes:

1. When used as a high-speed 4-bit ripple-through counter, output Q_A must be externally connected to the clock-2 input. The input count pulses are applied to the clock-1 input. Simultaneous divisions by 2, 4, 8, and 16 are performed at the Q_A, Q_B, Q_C, and Q_D outputs as shown in the function table at right.

2. When used as a 3-bit ripple-through counter, the input count pulses are applied to the clock-2 input. Simultaneous frequency divisions by 2, 4, and 8 are available at the Q_B, Q_C, and Q_D outputs. Independent use of flip-flop A is available if the load and clear functions coincide with those of the 3-bit ripple-through counter.

SN54177, SN74177
FUNCTION TABLE
(See Note A)

COUNT	OUTPUT			
	Q_D	Q_C	Q_B	Q_A
0	L	L	L	L
1	L	L	L	H
2	L	L	H	L
3	L	L	H	H
4	L	H	L	L
5	L	H	L	H
6	L	H	H	L
7	L	H	H	H
8	H	L	L	L
9	H	L	L	H
10	H	L	H	L
11	H	L	H	H
12	H	H	L	L
13	H	H	L	H
14	H	H	H	L
15	H	H	H	H

H = high level, L = low level

NOTE A: Output Q_A connected to clock-2 input.

7

TEXAS INSTRUMENTS
INCORPORATED
POST OFFICE BOX 5012 • DALLAS, TEXAS 75222

functional block diagrams

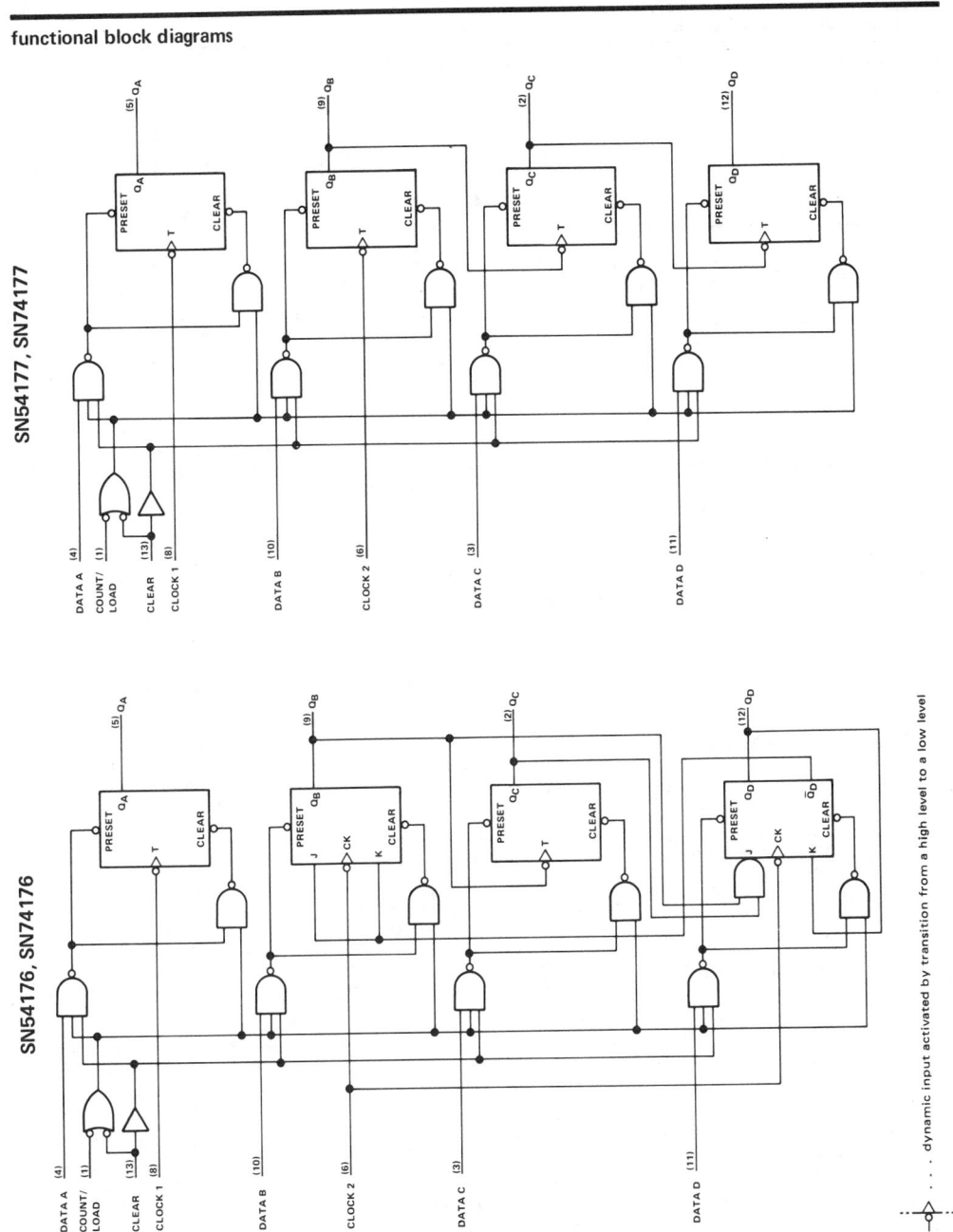

SN54177, SN74177

SN54176, SN74176

. . . . dynamic input activated by transition from a high level to a low level

TEXAS INSTRUMENTS
INCORPORATED
POST OFFICE BOX 5012 • DALLAS, TEXAS 75222

TYPES SN54176, SN54177, SN74176, SN74177
35-MHz PRESETTABLE DECADE AND
BINARY COUNTERS/LATCHES

schematics of inputs and outputs

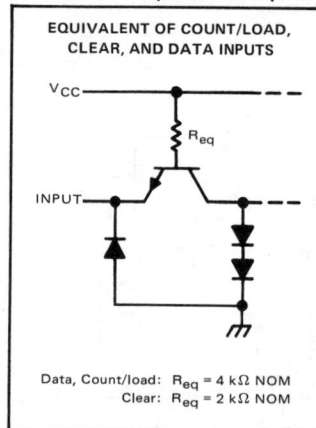

EQUIVALENT OF COUNT/LOAD, CLEAR, AND DATA INPUTS

V_CC

R_eq

INPUT

Data, Count/load: R_eq = 4 kΩ NOM
Clear: R_eq = 2 kΩ NOM

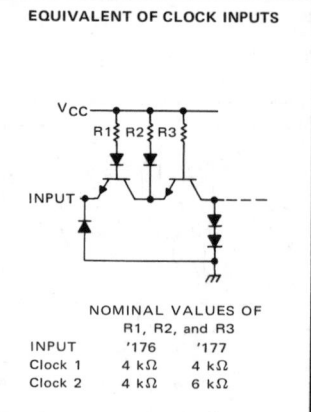

EQUIVALENT OF CLOCK INPUTS

V_CC

R1 R2 R3

INPUT

NOMINAL VALUES OF
R1, R2, and R3

INPUT	'176	'177
Clock 1	4 kΩ	4 kΩ
Clock 2	4 kΩ	6 kΩ

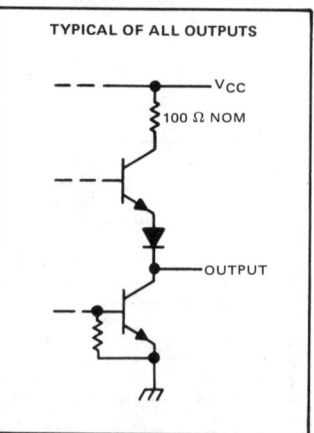

TYPICAL OF ALL OUTPUTS

V_CC

100 Ω NOM

OUTPUT

absolute maximum ratings over operating free-air temperature range (unless otherwise noted)

Supply voltage, V_{CC} (see Note 1) . . . . 7 V
Input voltage . . . . 5.5 V
Interemitter voltage (see Note 2) . . . . 5.5 V
Operating free-air temperature range: SN54176, SN54177 Circuits . . . . −55°C to 125°C
                              SN74176, SN74177 Circuits . . . . 0°C to 70°C
Storage temperature range . . . . −65°C to 150°C

NOTES: 1. Voltage values are with respect to network ground terminal.
        2. This is the voltage between two emitters of a multiple-emitter transistor. For this circuit, this rating applies between the clear and
          count/load inputs.

recommended operating conditions

		MIN	NOM	MAX	UNIT
Supply voltage, V_{CC}	SN54'	4.5	5	5.5	V
	SN74'	4.75	5	5.25	
High-level output current, I_{OH}				−800	µA
Low-level output current, I_{OL}				16	mA
Count frequency (see Figure 1)	Clock-1 input	0		35	MHz
	Clock-2 input	0		17.5	
Pulse width, t_w (see Figure 1)	Clock-1 input	14			ns
	Clock-2 input	28			
	Clear	20			
	Load	25			
Input hold time, t_h (see Figure 1)	High-level data	$t_{w(load)}$			ns
	Low-level data	$t_{w(load)}$			
Input setup time, t_{su} (see Figure 1)	High-level data	15			ns
	Low-level data	20			
Count enable time, t_{enable} (see Note 3 and Figure 1)		25			ns
Operating free-air temperature, T_A	SN54'	−55		125	°C
	SN74'	0		70	

NOTE 3: Minimum count enable time is the interval immediately preceding the negative-going edge of the clock pulse during which interval the
        count/load and clear inputs must both be high to ensure counting.

TEXAS INSTRUMENTS
INCORPORATED
POST OFFICE BOX 5012 • DALLAS, TEXAS 75222

electrical characteristics over recommended operating free-air temperature range (unless otherwise noted)

PARAMETER		TEST CONDITIONS†		SN54176, SN74176 MIN	TYP‡	MAX	SN54177, SN74177 MIN	TYP‡	MAX	UNIT
V_{IH}	High-level input voltage			2			2			V
V_{IL}	Low-level input voltage					0.8			0.8	V
V_{IK}	Input clamp voltage	V_{CC} = MIN, I_I = −12 mA				−1.5			−1.5	V
V_{OH}	High-level output voltage	V_{CC} = MIN, V_{IH} = 2 V, V_{IL} = 0.8 V, I_{OH} = −800 μA		2.4	3.4		2.4	3.4		V
V_{OL}	Low-level output voltage	V_{CC} = MIN, V_{IH} = 2 V, V_{IL} = 0.8 V, I_{OL} = 16 mA¶			0.2	0.4		0.2	0.4	V
I_I	Input current at maximum input voltage	V_{CC} = MAX, V_I = 5.5 V				1			1	mA
I_{IH}	High-level input current	Data, count/load	V_{CC} = MAX, V_I = 2.4 V			40			40	μA
		Clear, clock 1				80			80	
		Clock 2				120			80	
I_{IL}	Low-level input current	Data, count/load	V_{CC} = MAX, V_I = 0.4 V			−1.6			−1.6	mA
		Clear				−3.2			−3.2	
		Clock 1				−4.8			−4.8	
		Clock 2				−4.8			−3.2	
I_{OS}	Short-circuit output current §	V_{CC} = MAX	SN54′	−20		−57	−20		−57	mA
			SN74′	−18		−57	−18		−57	
I_{CC}	Supply current	V_{CC} = MAX, See Note 4			30	48		30	48	mA

NOTE 4: I_{CC} is measured with all inputs grounded and all outputs open.

†For conditions shown as MIN or MAX, use the appropriate value specified under recommended operating conditions.

‡All typical values are at V_{CC} = 5 V, T_A = 25°C.

¶Q_A outputs are tested at I_{OL} = 16 mA plus the limit value of I_{IL} for the clock-2 input. This permits driving the clock-2 input while fanning out to 10 Series 54/74 loads.

§Not more than one output should be shorted at a time.

switching characteristics, V_{CC} = 5 V, R_L = 400 Ω, C_L = 15 pF, T_A = 25°C, see figure 1

PARAMETER◊	FROM (INPUT)	TO (OUTPUT)	SN54176, SN74176 MIN	TYP	MAX	SN54177, SN54177 MIN	TYP	MAX	UNIT
f_{max}	Clock 1	Q_A	35	50		35	50		MHz
t_{PLH}	Clock 1	Q_A		8	13		8	13	ns
t_{PHL}				11	17		11	17	
t_{PLH}	Clock 2	Q_B		11	17		11	17	ns
t_{PHL}				17	26		17	26	
t_{PLH}	Clock 2	Q_C		27	41		27	41	ns
t_{PHL}				34	51		34	51	
t_{PLH}	Clock 2	Q_D		13	20		44	66	ns
t_{PHL}				17	26		50	75	
t_{PLH}	A, B, C, D	Q_A, Q_B, Q_C, Q_D		19	29		19	29	ns
t_{PHL}				31	46		31	46	
t_{PLH}	Load	Any		29	43		29	43	ns
t_{PHL}				32	48		32	48	
t_{PHL}	Clear	Any		32	48		32	48	ns

◊f_{max} ≡ maximum count frequency

t_{PLH} ≡ propagation delay time, low-to-high-level output

t_{PHL} ≡ propagation delay time, high-to-low-level output

7

TEXAS INSTRUMENTS
INCORPORATED

POST OFFICE BOX 5012 • DALLAS, TEXAS 75222

PARAMETER MEASUREMENT INFORMATION

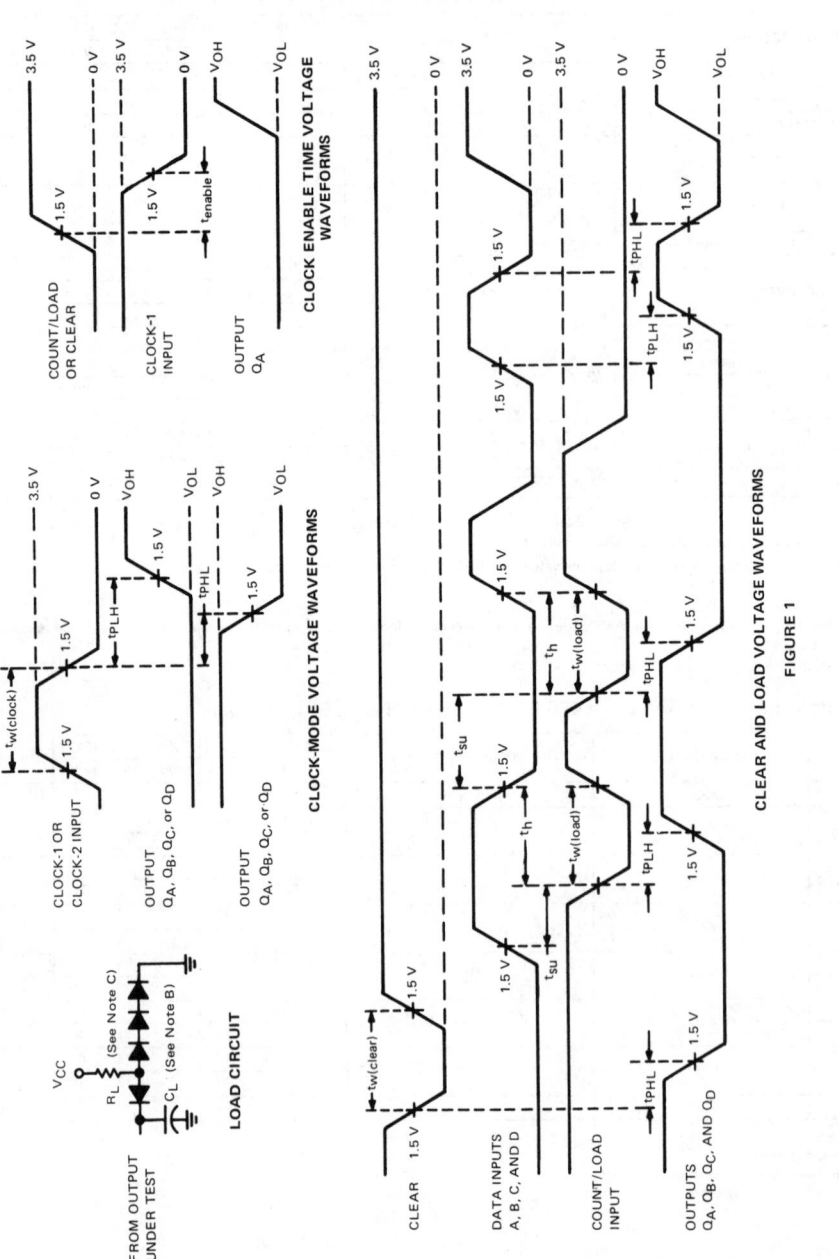

NOTES: A. The input pulse is supplied by a generator having the following characteristics: PRR ≤ 1 MHz, duty cycle ≤ 50%, t_r < 5 ns, and unless specified, t_f < 5 ns. When testing f_{max}, vary PRR.
B. C_L includes probe and jig capacitance.
C. All diodes are 1N3064.
D. Unless otherwise specified, Q_A is connected to clock 2.

TEXAS INSTRUMENTS
INCORPORATED
POST OFFICE BOX 5012 • DALLAS, TEXAS 75222

TTL
MSI

TYPES SN54178, SN54179, SN74178, SN74179
4-BIT PARALLEL-ACCESS SHIFT REGISTERS

BULLETIN NO. DL-S 7211846, DECEMBER 1972

- **Typical Maximum Clock Frequency . . . 39 MHz**
- **Three Operating Modes:**
  Synchronous Parallel Load
  Right Shift
  Hold (Do Nothing)
- **Negative-Edge-Triggered Clocking**
- **D-C Coupling Symplifies System Designs**

description

These shift registers utilize fully d-c coupled storage elements and feature synchronous parallel inputs and parallel outputs. The SN54179/SN74179 has a direct clear line and complementary output from the D flip-flop, thereby differing from the SN54178/SN74178.

Parallel loading is accomplished by taking the shift input low, applying the four bits of data, and taking the load input high. The data is loaded into the associated flip-flop synchronously and appears at the outputs after a high-to-low transition of the clock. During loading, serial data flow is inhibited.

Shift right is also accomplished on the falling edge of the clock pulse when the shift input is high regardless of the level of the load input. Serial data for this mode is entered at the serial data input.

When both the shift and load inputs are low, clocking of the register can continue; however, data appearing at each output is fed back to the flip-flop input creating a mode in which the data is held unchanged. Thus, the system clock may be left free-running without changing the contents of the register.

SN54178 . . . J OR W PACKAGE
SN74178 . . . J OR N PACKAGE
(TOP VIEW)

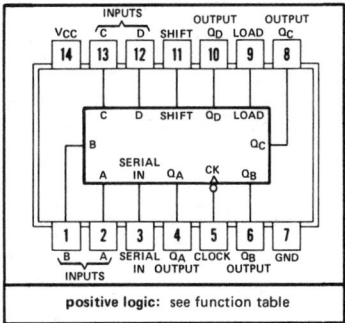

positive logic: see function table

SN54179 . . . J OR W PACKAGE
SN74179 . . . J OR N PACKAGE
(TOP VIEW)

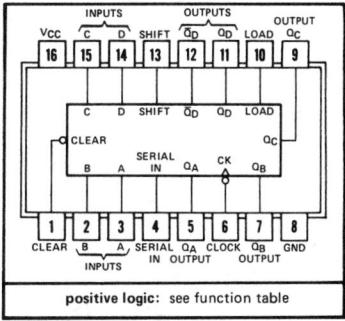

positive logic: see function table

'178, '179†
FUNCTION TABLE

INPUTS									OUTPUTS				
CLEAR†	SHIFT	LOAD	CLOCK	SERIAL	PARALLEL				Q_A	Q_B	Q_C	Q_D	$\overline{Q}_D$†
					A	B	C	D					
L	X	X	X	X	X	X	X	X	L	L	L	L	H
H	X	X	H	X	X	X	X	X	Q_{A0}	Q_{B0}	Q_{C0}	Q_{D0}	$\overline{Q}_{D0}$
H	L	L	↓	X	X	X	X	X	Q_{A0}	Q_{B0}	Q_{C0}	Q_{D0}	$\overline{Q}_{D0}$
H	L	H	↓	X	a	b	c	d	a	b	c	d	$\overline{d}$
H	H	X	↓	H	X	X	X	X	H	Q_{An}	Q_{Bn}	Q_{Cn}	$\overline{Q}_{Cn}$
H	H	X	↓	L	X	X	X	X	L	Q_{An}	Q_{Bn}	Q_{Cn}	Q_{Cn}

†The columns for clear, $\overline{Q}_D$, and the top line of the table apply for the '179 only.

H = high level (steady state), L = low level (steady state)
X = irrelevant (any input, including transitions)
↓ = transition from high to low level
a, b, c, d = the level of steady-state input at inputs A, B, C, or D, respectively.
Q_{A0}, Q_{B0}, Q_{C0}, Q_{D0} = the level of Q_A, Q_B, Q_C, or Q_D, respectively, before the indicated steady-state input conditions were established.
Q_{An}, Q_{Bn}, Q_{Cn} = the level of Q_A, Q_B, or Q_C, respectively, before the most-recent ↓ transition of the clock.

TEXAS INSTRUMENTS
INCORPORATED
POST OFFICE BOX 5012 • DALLAS, TEXAS 75222

TYPES SN54178, SN54179, SN74178, SN74179
4-BIT PARALLEL-ACCESS SHIFT REGISTERS

functional block diagram   ('178) ['179]

SERIAL (3) [4]

DATA A (2) [3]   S   Q_A   (4) [5] Q_A
                                                                 CK
LOAD (9) [10]   R
                                                                CLEAR

DATA B (1) [2]   S   Q_B   (6) [7] Q_B
                                                                 CK
                                                                 R
                                                                CLEAR

DATA C (13) [15]   S   Q_C   (8) [9] Q_C
                                                                 CK
                                                                 R
                                                                CLEAR

DATA D (12) [14]   S   Q_D   (10) [11] Q_D
                                                                 CK
SHIFT (11) [13]   R $\overline{Q}_D$ [12] $\overline{Q}_D$
                                                                CLEAR   ['179
                                                                               ONLY]
CLOCK (5) [6]

CLEAR [1]
['179
ONLY]

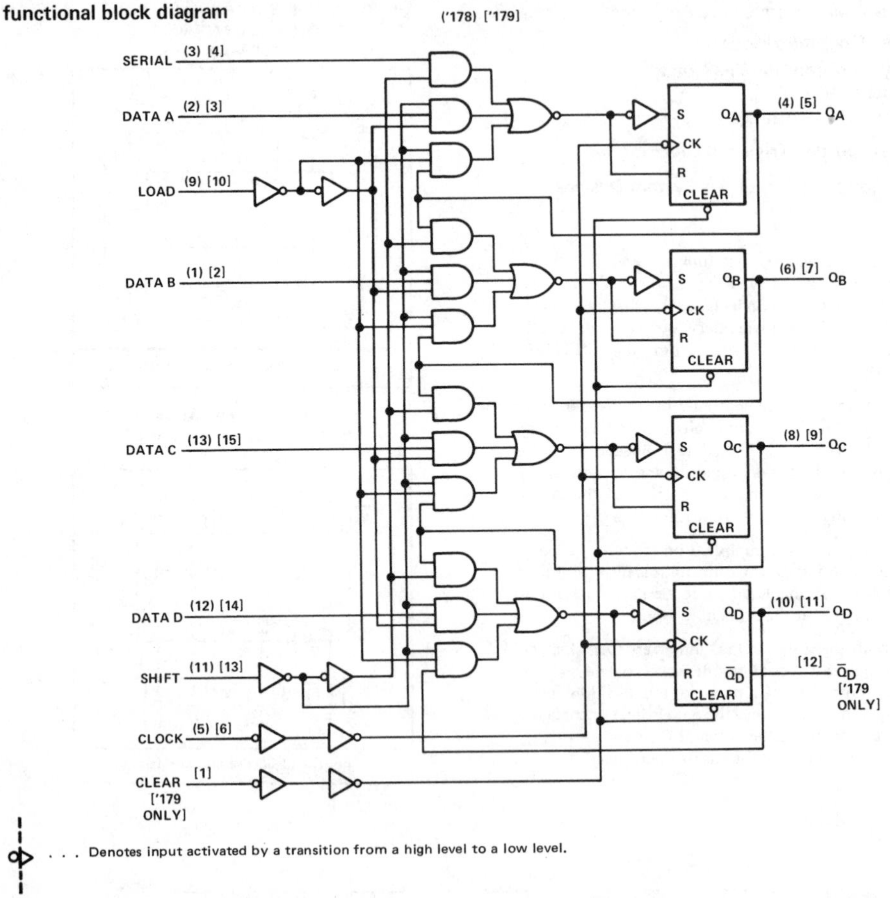

⊕ . . . Denotes input activated by a transition from a high level to a low level.

schematics of inputs and outputs

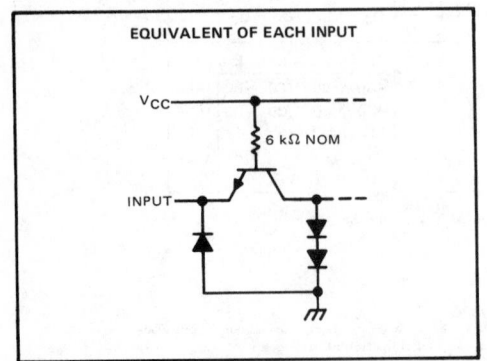

EQUIVALENT OF EACH INPUT

V_CC

6 kΩ NOM

INPUT

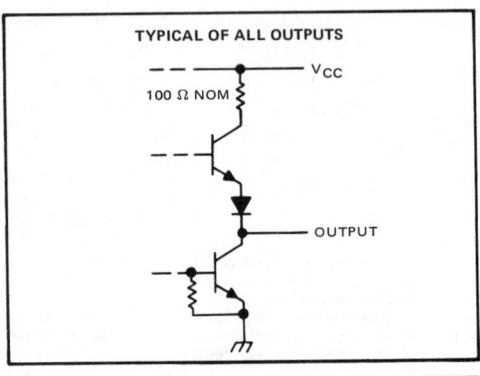

TYPICAL OF ALL OUTPUTS

V_CC

100 Ω NOM

OUTPUT

1272

7-266

TEXAS INSTRUMENTS
INCORPORATED
POST OFFICE BOX 5012 • DALLAS, TEXAS 75222

absolute maximum ratings over operating free-air temperature range (unless otherwise noted)

Supply voltage, V_{CC} (see Note 1)	7 V
Input voltage	5.5 V
Operating free-air temperature range: SN54178, SN54179 Circuits	$-55°C$ to $125°C$
SN74178, SN74179 Circuits	$0°C$ to $70°C$
Storage temperature range	$-65°C$ to $150°C$

NOTE 1: Voltage values are with respect to network ground terminal.

recommended operating conditions

		SN54178, SN54179			SN74178, SN74179			UNIT
		MIN	NOM	MAX	MIN	NOM	MAX	
Supply voltage, V_{CC}		4.5	5	5.5	4.75	5	5.25	V
High-level output current, I_{OH}				−800			−800	μA
Low-level output current, I_{OL}				16			16	mA
Clock frequency, f_{clock}		0		25	0		25	MHz
Width of clock or clear pulse, t_w (see Figure 1)		20			20			ns
Setup time, t_{su} (see Figure 1)	Shift (H or L) or load	35			35			ns
	Data	30			30			
	Clear-inactive-state (SN54179 and SN74179)	15			15			
Hold time at any input, t_h		5			5			ns
Operating free-air temperature, T_A		−55		125	0		70	$°C$

electrical characteristics over recommended operating free-air temperature range (unless otherwise noted)

PARAMETER		TEST CONDITIONS†	SN54178, SN54179			SN74178, SN74179			UNIT
			MIN	TYP‡	MAX	MIN	TYP‡	MAX	
V_{IH}	High-level input voltage		2			2			V
V_{IL}	Low-level input voltage				0.8			0.8	V
V_{IK}	Input clamp voltage	V_{CC} = MIN, I_I = −12 mA			−1.5			−1.5	V
V_{OH}	High-level output voltage	V_{CC} = MIN, V_{IH} = 2 V, V_{IL} = 0.8 V, I_{OH} = −800 μA	2.4	3.4		2.4	3.4		V
V_{OL}	Low-level output voltage	V_{CC} = MIN, V_{IH} = 2 V, V_{IL} = 0.8 V, I_{OL} = 16 mA		0.2	0.4		0.2	0.4	V
I_I	Input current at maximum input voltage	V_{CC} = MAX, V_I = 5.5 V			1			1	mA
I_{IH}	High-level input current	V_{CC} = MAX, V_I = 2.4 V			40			40	μA
I_{IL}	Low-level input current	V_{CC} = MAX, V_I = 0.4 V			−1.6			−1.6	mA
I_{OS}	Short-circuit output current§	V_{CC} = MAX	−20		−57	−18		−57	mA
I_{CC}	Supply current	V_{CC} = MAX, See Note 2		46	70		46	75	mA

†For conditions shown as MIN or MAX, use the appropriate value specified under recommended operating conditions for the applicable device type.

‡All typical values are at V_{CC} = 5 V, T_A = 25°C.

§Not more than one output should be shorted at a time.

NOTE 2: I_{CC} is measured as follows:
  a) 4.5 V is applied to serial inputs, load, shift, and clear,
  b) Parallel inputs A through D are grounded,
  c) 4.5 V is momentarily applied to clock which is then grounded.

TEXAS INSTRUMENTS
INCORPORATED
POST OFFICE BOX 5012 • DALLAS, TEXAS 75222

7

switching characteristics, V_{CC} = 5 V, T_A = 25°C

PARAMETER¶	FROM (INPUT)	TO (OUTPUT)	TEST CONDITIONS	MIN	TYP	MAX	UNIT
f_{max}				25	39		MHz
t_{PLH}	Clear	$\overline{Q}_D$	C_L = 15 pF, R_L = 400 Ω, See Figure 1		15	23	ns
t_{PHL}		Q_A, Q_B, Q_C, Q_D			24	36	
t_{PLH}	Clock	Any output			17	26	ns
t_{PHL}					23	35	

¶f_{max} ≡ Maximum clock frequency
t_{PHL} ≡ Propagation delay time, high-to-low-level output
t_{PLH} ≡ Propagation delay time, low-to-high-level output

PARAMETER MEASUREMENT INFORMATION

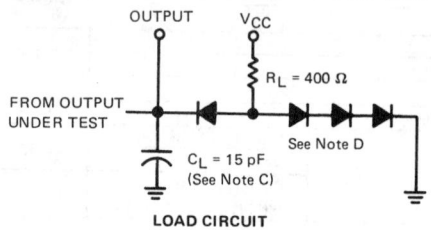

LOAD CIRCUIT

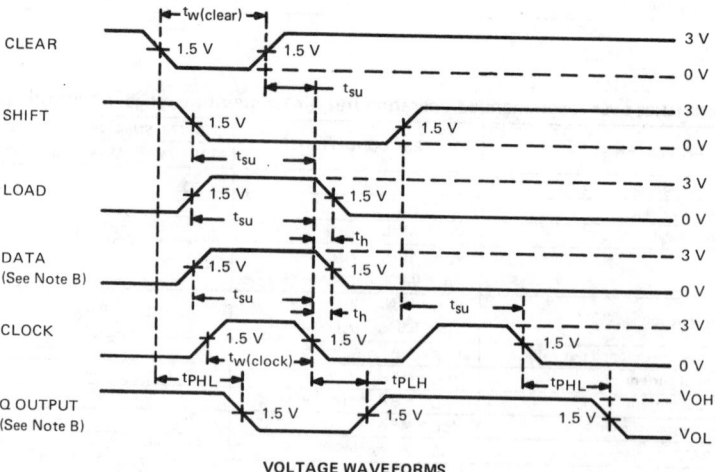

VOLTAGE WAVEFORMS

NOTES: A. Input pulses are supplied by generators having the following characteristics: t_{TLH} ≤ 10 ns, t_{THL} ≤ 10 ns, PRR ≤ 1 MHz, Z_{out} ≈ 50 Ω.
     B. Data input and Q output are any related pair. Serial and other data inputs are at GND. Serial data input is tested in conjunction with Q_A output in the shift mode.
     C. C_L includes probe and jig capacitance.
     D. All diodes are 1N3064.

FIGURE 1—SWITCHING TIMES

TEXAS INSTRUMENTS
INCORPORATED
POST OFFICE BOX 5012 • DALLAS, TEXAS 75222

1076

logic

SN54180 . . . J OR W PACKAGE
SN74180 . . . J OR N PACKAGE
(TOP VIEW)

FUNCTION TABLE

INPUTS			OUTPUTS	
Σ OF H's AT A THRU H	EVEN	ODD	Σ EVEN	Σ ODD
EVEN	H	L	H	L
ODD	H	L	L	H
EVEN	L	H	L	H
ODD	L	H	H	L
X	H	H	L	L
X	L	L	H	H

H = high level, L = low level, X = irrelevant

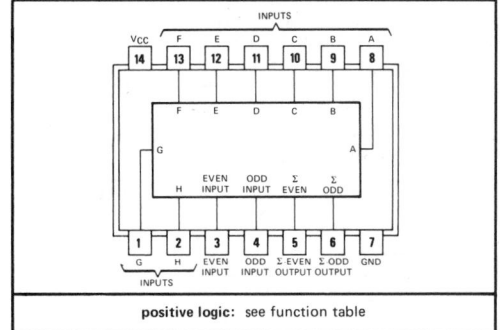

positive logic: see function table

description

These universal, monolithic, 9-bit (8 data bits plus 1 parity bit) parity generators/checkers, utilize familiar Series 54/74 TTL circuitry and feature odd/even outputs and control inputs to facilitate operation in either odd- or even-parity applications. Depending on whether even or odd parity is being generated or checked, the even or odd inputs can be utilized as the parity or 9th-bit input. The word-length capability is easily expanded by cascading.

The SN54180/SN74180 are fully compatible with other TTL or DTL circuits. Input buffers are provided so that each data input represents only one normalized series 54/74 load. A full fan-out to 10 normalized series 54/74 loads is available from each of the outputs at a low logic level. A fan-out to 20 normalized loads is provided at a high logic level to facilitate the connection of unused inputs to used inputs. Typical power dissipation is 170 mW.

The SN54180 is characterized for operation over the full military temperature range of -55°C to 125°C; and the SN74180 is characterized for operation from 0°C to 70°C.

absolute maximum ratings over operating free-air temperature range (unless otherwise noted)

Supply voltage, V_{CC} (see Note 1) . . . . 7 V
Input voltage . . . . 5.5 V
Operating free-air temperature range: SN54180 Circuits . . . . -55°C to 125°C
              SN74180 Circuits . . . . 0°C to 70°C
Storage temperature range . . . . -65°C to 150°C

NOTE 1: Voltage values are with respect to network ground terminal.

recommended operating conditions

	SN54180			SN74180			UNIT
	MIN	NOM	MAX	MIN	NOM	MAX	
Supply voltage, V_{CC}	4.5	5	5.5	4.75	5	5.25	V
High-level output current, I_{OH}			−800			−800	µA
Low-level output current, I_{OL}			16			16	mA
Operating free-air temperature, T_A	−55		125	0		70	°C

1076

TEXAS INSTRUMENTS
INCORPORATED
POST OFFICE BOX 5012 • DALLAS, TEXAS 75222

electrical characteristics over recommended operating free-air temperature range (unless otherwise noted)

PARAMETER		TEST CONDITIONS[†]	SN54180 MIN	SN54180 TYP[‡]	SN54180 MAX	SN74180 MIN	SN74180 TYP[‡]	SN74180 MAX	UNIT
V_{IH}	High-level input voltage		2			2			V
V_{IL}	Low-level input voltage				0.8			0.8	V
V_{IK}	Input clamp voltage	V_{CC} = MIN, I_I = −12 mA			−1.5			−1.5	V
V_{OH}	High-level output voltage	V_{CC} = MIN, V_{IH} = 2 V, V_{IL} = 0.8 V, I_{OH} = −800 µA	2.4	3.3		2.4	3.3		V
V_{OL}	Low-level output voltage	V_{CC} = MIN, V_{IH} = 2 V, V_{IL} = 0.8 V, I_{OL} = 16 mA		0.2	0.4		0.2	0.4	V
I_I	Input current at maximum input voltage	V_{CC} = MAX, V_I = 5.5 V			1			1	mA
I_{IH}	High-level input current — Any data input	V_{CC} = MAX, V_I = 2.4 V			40			40	µA
I_{IH}	High-level input current — Even or odd input	V_{CC} = MAX, V_I = 2.4 V			80			80	µA
I_{IL}	Low-level input current — Any data input	V_{CC} = MAX, V_I = 0.4 V			−1.6			−1.6	mA
I_{IL}	Low-level input current — Even or odd input	V_{CC} = MAX, V_I = 0.4 V			−3.2			−3.2	mA
I_{OS}	Short-circuit output current§	V_{CC} = MAX	−20		−55	−18		−55	mA
I_{CC}	Supply current	V_{CC} = MAX, See Note 2		34	49		34	56	mA

NOTE 2: I_{CC} is measured with even and odd inputs at 4.5 V, all other inputs and outputs open.
†For conditions shown as MIN or MAX, use the appropriate value specified under recommended operating conditions for the applicable type.
‡All typical values are at V_{CC} = 5 V, T_A = 25°C.
§Not more than one output should be shorted at a time.

switching characteristics, V_{CC} = 5 V, T_A = 25°C

PARAMETER¶	FROM (INPUT)	TO (OUTPUT)	TEST CONDITIONS	MIN	TYP	MAX	UNIT
t_{PLH}	Data	Σ Even	C_L = 15 pF, R_L = 400 Ω, Odd input grounded, See Note 3		40	60	ns
t_{PHL}	Data	Σ Even			45	68	ns
t_{PLH}	Data	Σ Odd			32	48	ns
t_{PHL}	Data	Σ Odd			25	38	ns
t_{PLH}	Data	Σ Even	C_L = 15 pF, R_L = 400 Ω, Even input grounded, See Note 3		32	48	ns
t_{PHL}	Data	Σ Even			25	38	ns
t_{PLH}	Data	Σ Odd			40	60	ns
t_{PHL}	Data	Σ Odd			45	68	ns
t_{PLH}	Even or Odd	Σ Even or Σ Odd	C_L = 15 pF, R_L = 400 Ω, See Note 3		13	20	ns
t_{PHL}	Even or Odd	Σ Even or Σ Odd			7	10	ns

NOTE 3: Load circuits and waveforms are shown on page 3-10.
¶t_{PLH} ≡ Propagation delay time, low-to-high-level output
t_{PHL} ≡ Propagation delay time, high-to-low-level output

functional block diagram and schematics of inputs and outputs

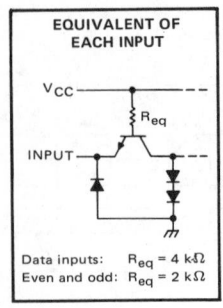

EQUIVALENT OF EACH INPUT

V_{CC}

R_{eq}

INPUT

Data inputs: R_{eq} = 4 kΩ
Even and odd: R_{eq} = 2 kΩ

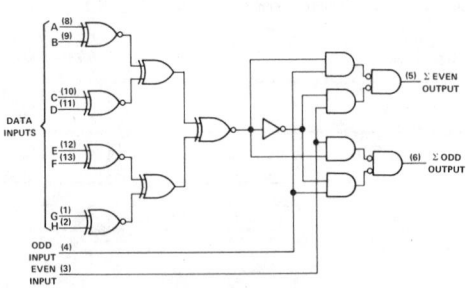

A (8)
B (9)
C (10)
D (11)
E (12)
F (13)
G (1)
H (2)
DATA INPUTS
(5) Σ EVEN OUTPUT
(6) Σ ODD OUTPUT
ODD (4) INPUT
EVEN (3) INPUT

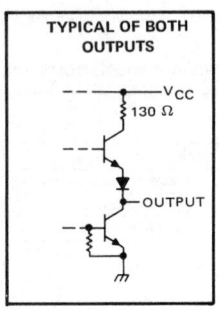

TYPICAL OF BOTH OUTPUTS

V_{CC}
130 Ω
OUTPUT

1076

TEXAS INSTRUMENTS
INCORPORATED
POST OFFICE BOX 5012 • DALLAS, TEXAS 75222

TYPES SN54181, SN54LS181, SN54S181, SN74181, SN74LS181, SN74S181
ARITHMETIC LOGIC UNITS/FUNCTION GENERATORS
BULLETIN NO. DL-S 7611831, DECEMBER 1972 – REVISED OCTOBER 1976

- Full Look-Ahead for High-Speed Operations on Long Words

- Input Clamping Diodes Minimize Transmission-Line Effects

- Darlington Outputs Reduce Turn-Off Time

- Arithmetic Operating Modes:
    Addition
    Subtraction
    Shift Operand A One Position
    Magnitude Comparison
    Plus Twelve Other Arithmetic Operations

- Logic Function Modes:
    Exclusive-OR
    Comparator
    AND, NAND, OR, NOR
    Plus Ten Other Logic Operations

SN54181, SN54LS181, SN54S181 . . . J OR W PACKAGE
SN74181, SN74LS181, SN74S181 . . . J OR N PACKAGE
(TOP VIEW)

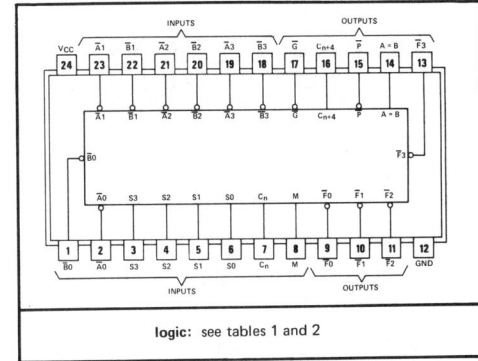

logic: see tables 1 and 2

TYPICAL ADDITION TIMES

NUMBER OF BITS	ADDITION TIMES			PACKAGE COUNT		CARRY METHOD BETWEEN ALU's
	USING '181 AND '182	USING 'LS181 AND '182	USING 'S181 AND 'S182	ARITHMETIC/ LOGIC UNITS	LOOK-AHEAD CARRY GENERATORS	
1 to 4	24 ns	24 ns	11 ns	1		NONE
5 to 8	36 ns	40 ns	18 ns	2		RIPPLE
9 to 16	36 ns	44 ns	19 ns	3 or 4	1	FULL LOOK-AHEAD
17 to 64	60 ns	68 ns	28 ns	5 to 16	2 to 5	FULL LOOK-AHEAD

description

The '181, 'LS181, and 'S181 are arithmetic logic units (ALU)/function generators that have a complexity of 75 equivalent gates on a monolithic chip. These circuits perform 16 binary arithmetic operations on two 4-bit words as shown in Tables 1 and 2. These operations are selected by the four function-select lines (S0, S1, S2, S3) and include addition, subtraction, decrement, and straight transfer. When performing arithmetic manipulations, the internal carries must be enabled by applying a low-level voltage to the mode control input (M). A full carry look-ahead scheme is made available in these devices for fast, simultaneous carry generation by means of two cascade-outputs (pins 15 and 17) for the four bits in the package. When used in conjunction with the SN54182, SN54S182, SN74182, or SN74S182, full carry look-ahead circuits, high-speed arithmetic operations can be performed. The typical addition times shown above illustrate the little additional time required for addition of longer words when full carry look-ahead is employed. The method of cascading '182 or 'S182 circuits with these ALU's to provide multi-level full carry look-ahead is illustrated under typical applications data for the '182 and 'S182.

If high speed is not of importance, a ripple-carry input (C_n) and a ripple-carry output (C_{n+4}) are available. However, the ripple-carry delay has also been minimized so that arithmetic manipulations for small word lengths can be performed without external circuitry.

7

TEXAS INSTRUMENTS
INCORPORATED
POST OFFICE BOX 5012 • DALLAS, TEXAS 75222

description (continued)

The '181, 'LS181, and 'S181 will accommodate active-high or active-low data if the pin designations are interpreted as follows:

PIN NUMBER	2	1	23	22	21	20	19	18	9	10	11	13	7	16	15	17
Active-low data (Table 1)	$\bar{A}_0$	$\bar{B}_0$	$\bar{A}_1$	$\bar{B}_1$	$\bar{A}_2$	$\bar{B}_2$	$\bar{A}_3$	$\bar{B}_3$	$\bar{F}_0$	$\bar{F}_1$	$\bar{F}_2$	$\bar{F}_3$	C_n	C_{n+4}	$\bar{P}$	$\bar{G}$
Active-high data (Table 2)	A_0	B_0	A_1	B_1	A_2	B_2	A_3	B_3	F_0	F_1	F_2	F_3	$\bar{C}_n$	$\bar{C}_{n+4}$	X	Y

Subtraction is accomplished by 1's complement addition where the 1's complement of the subtrahend is generated internally. The resultant output is $A-B-1$, which requires an end-around or forced carry to provide $A-B$.

The '181, 'LS181, or 'S181 can also be utilized as a comparator. The A = B output is internally decoded from the function outputs (F0, F1, F2, F3) so that when two words of equal magnitude are applied at the A and B inputs, it will assume a high level to indicate equality (A = B). The ALU should be in the subtract mode with C_n = H when performing this comparison. The A = B output is open-collector so that is can be wire-AND connected to give a comparison for more than four bits. The carry output (C_{n+4}) can also be used to supply relative magnitude information. Again, the ALU should be placed in the subtract mode by placing the function select inputs S3, S2, S1, S0 at L, H, H, L, respectively.

INPUT C_n	OUTPUT C_{n+4}	ACTIVE-LOW DATA (FIGURE 1)	ACTIVE-HIGH DATA (FIGURE 2)
H	H	$A \geqslant B$	$A < B$
H	L	$A < B$	$A > B$
L	H	$A > B$	$A < B$
L	L	$A \leqslant B$	$A \geqslant B$

These circuits have been designed to not only incorporate all of the designer's requirements for arithmetic operations, but also to provide 16 possible functions of two Boolean variables without the use of external circuitry. These logic functions are selected by use of the four function-select inputs (S0, S1, S2, S3) with the mode-control input (M) at a high level to disable the internal carry. The 16 logic functions are detailed in Tables 1 and 2 and include exclusive-OR, NAND, AND, NOR, and OR functions.

Series 54, 54LS, and 54S devices are characterized for operation over the full military temperature range of $-55°$C to $125°$C; Series 74, 74LS, and 74S devices are characterized for operation from $0°$C to $70°$C.

signal designations

The '181, 'LS181, and 'S181 together with the '182 and 'S182 can be used with the signal designations of either Figure 1 or Figure 2. The inversion indicators (O) and the bars over the terminal letter symbols (e.g., $\bar{C}$) each indicate that the associated input or output is active with respect to the selected function of the device when that input or output is low. That is, a low at $\bar{C}$ means "do carry" while a high means "do not carry".

The logic functions and arithmetic operations obtained with signal designations of Figure 1 are given in Table 1; those obtained with signal designations of Figure 2 are given in Table 2.

TEXAS INSTRUMENTS
INCORPORATED
POST OFFICE BOX 5012 • DALLAS, TEXAS 75222

1076

7

TYPES SN54181, SN54LS181, SN54S181, SN74181, SN74LS181, SN74S181
ARITHMETIC LOGIC UNITS/FUNCTION GENERATORS

signal designations (continued)

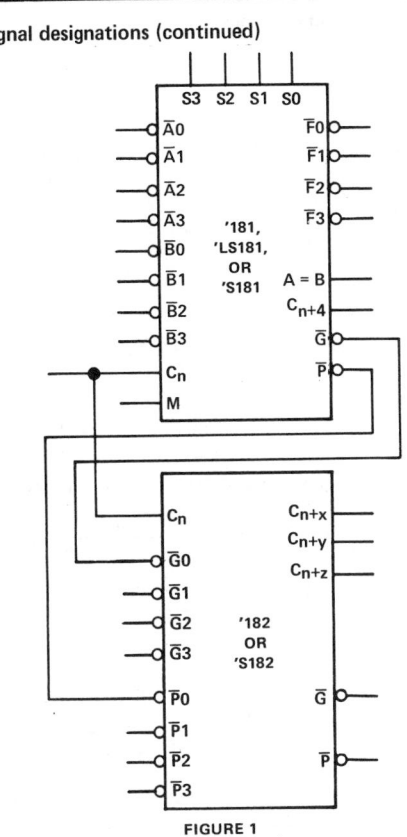

FIGURE 1
(Use with Table 1)

FIGURE 2
(Use with Table 2)

TABLE 1

SELECTION				ACTIVE-LOW DATA		
				M = H	M = L; ARITHMETIC OPERATIONS	
S3	S2	S1	S0	LOGIC FUNCTIONS	C_n = L (no carry)	C_n = H (with carry)
L	L	L	L	$F = \overline{A}$	F = A MINUS 1	F = A
L	L	L	H	$F = \overline{AB}$	F = AB MINUS 1	F = AB
L	L	H	L	$F = \overline{A} + B$	$F = A\overline{B}$ MINUS 1	$F = A\overline{B}$
L	L	H	H	F = 1	F = MINUS 1 (2's COMP)	F = ZERO
L	H	L	L	$F = \overline{A + B}$	$F = A$ PLUS $(A + \overline{B})$	$F = A$ PLUS $(A + \overline{B})$ PLUS 1
L	H	L	H	$F = \overline{B}$	$F = AB$ PLUS $(A + \overline{B})$	$F = AB$ PLUS $(A + \overline{B})$ PLUS 1
L	H	H	L	$F = \overline{A \oplus B}$	F = A MINUS B MINUS 1	F = A MINUS B
L	H	H	H	$F = A + \overline{B}$	$F = A + \overline{B}$	$F = (A + \overline{B})$ PLUS 1
H	L	L	L	$F = \overline{A}B$	$F = A$ PLUS $(A + B)$	$F = A$ PLUS $(A + B)$ PLUS 1
H	L	L	H	$F = A \oplus B$	F = A PLUS B	F = A PLUS B PLUS 1
H	L	H	L	F = B	$F = A\overline{B}$ PLUS $(A + B)$	$F = A\overline{B}$ PLUS $(A + B)$ PLUS 1
H	L	H	H	F = A + B	$F = (A + B)$	$F = (A + B)$ PLUS 1
H	H	L	L	F = 0	F = A PLUS A*	F = A PLUS A PLUS 1
H	H	L	H	$F = A\overline{B}$	F = AB PLUS A	F = AB PLUS A PLUS 1
H	H	H	L	F = AB	$F = A\overline{B}$ PLUS A	$F = A\overline{B}$ PLUS A PLUS 1
H	H	H	H	F = A	F = A	F = A PLUS 1

TABLE 2

SELECTION				ACTIVE-HIGH DATA		
				M = H	M = L; ARITHMETIC OPERATIONS	
S3	S2	S1	S0	LOGIC FUNCTIONS	$\overline{C}_n$ = H (no carry)	$\overline{C}_n$ = L (with carry)
L	L	L	L	$F = \overline{A}$	F = A	F = A PLUS 1
L	L	L	H	$F = \overline{A + B}$	F = A + B	F = (A + B) PLUS 1
L	L	H	L	$F = \overline{A}B$	$F = A + \overline{B}$	$F = (A + \overline{B})$ PLUS 1
L	L	H	H	F = 0	F = MINUS 1 (2's COMPL)	F = ZERO
L	H	L	L	$F = \overline{AB}$	$F = A$ PLUS $A\overline{B}$	$F = A$ PLUS $A\overline{B}$ PLUS 1
L	H	L	H	$F = \overline{B}$	$F = (A + B)$ PLUS $A\overline{B}$	$F = (A + B)$ PLUS $A\overline{B}$ PLUS 1
L	H	H	L	$F = A \oplus B$	F = A MINUS B MINUS 1	F = A MINUS B
L	H	H	H	$F = A\overline{B}$	$F = A\overline{B}$ MINUS 1	$F = A\overline{B}$
H	L	L	L	$F = \overline{A} + B$	F = A PLUS AB	F = A PLUS AB PLUS 1
H	L	L	H	$F = \overline{A \oplus B}$	F = A PLUS B	F = A PLUS B PLUS 1
H	L	H	L	F = B	$F = (A + \overline{B})$ PLUS AB	$F = (A + \overline{B})$ PLUS AB PLUS 1
H	L	H	H	F = AB	F = AB MINUS 1	F = AB
H	H	L	L	F = 1	F = A PLUS A*	F = A PLUS A PLUS 1
H	H	L	H	$F = A + \overline{B}$	$F = (A + B)$ PLUS A	$F = (A + B)$ PLUS A PLUS 1
H	H	H	L	F = A + B	$F = (A + \overline{B})$ PLUS A	$F = (A + \overline{B})$ PLUS A PLUS 1
H	H	H	H	F = A	F = A MINUS 1	F = A

*Each bit is shifted to the next more significant position.

TEXAS INSTRUMENTS
INCORPORATED
POST OFFICE BOX 5012 • DALLAS, TEXAS 75222

7

absolute maximum ratings over operating free-air temperature range (unless otherwise noted)

Supply voltage, V_{CC} (see Note 1) . . . . 7 V
Input voltage . . . . 5.5 V
Interemitter voltage (see Note 2) . . . . 5.5 V
Operating free-air temperature range: SN54181 . . . . −55°C to 125°C
                                  SN74181 . . . . 0°C to 70°C
Storage temperature range . . . . −65°C to 150°C

NOTES: 1. Voltage values, except interemitter voltage, are with respect to network ground terminal.
           2. This is the voltage between two emitters of a multiple-emitter transistor. For this circuit, this rating applies to each $\overline{A}$ input in conjunction with inputs S2 or S3, and to each $\overline{B}$ input in conjunction with inputs S0 or S3.

recommended operating conditions

	SN54181			SN74181			UNIT
	MIN	NOM	MAX	MIN	NOM	MAX	
Supply voltage, V_{CC}	4.5	5	5.5	4.75	5	5.25	V
High-level output current, I_{OH} (All outputs except A = B)			−800			−800	μA
Low-level output current, I_{OL}			16			16	mA
Operating free-air temperature, T_A	−55		125	0		70	°C

electrical characteristics over recommended operating free-air temperature range (unless otherwise noted)

PARAMETER		TEST CONDITIONS[†]		SN54181			SN74181			UNIT
				MIN	TYP[‡]	MAX	MIN	TYP[‡]	MAX	
V_{IH}	High-level input voltage			2			2			V
V_{IL}	Low-level input voltage					0.8			0.8	V
V_{IK}	Input clamp voltage	V_{CC} = MIN,	I_I = −12 mA			−1.5			−1.5	V
V_{OH}	High-level output voltage, any output except A = B	V_{CC} = MIN, V_{IH} = 2 V, V_{IL} = 0.8 V, I_{OH} = −800 μA		2.4	3.4		2.4	3.4		V
I_{OH}	High-level output current, A = B output only	V_{CC} = MIN, V_{IH} = 2 V, V_{IL} = 0.8 V, V_{OH} = 5.5 V				250			250	μA
V_{OL}	Low-level output voltage	V_{CC} = MIN, V_{IH} = 2 V, V_{IL} = 0.8 V, I_{OL} = 16 mA			0.2	0.4		0.2	0.4	V
I_I	Input current at maximum input voltage	V_{CC} = MAX, V_I = 5.5 V				1			1	mA
I_{IH}	High-level input current	Mode input	V_{CC} = MAX, V_I = 2.4 V			40			40	μA
		Any $\overline{A}$ or $\overline{B}$ input				120			120	
		Any S input				160			160	
		Carry input				200			200	
I_{IL}	Low-level input current	Mode input	V_{CC} = MAX, V_I = 0.4 V			−1.6			−1.6	mA
		Any $\overline{A}$ or $\overline{B}$ input				−4.8			−4.8	
		Any S input				−6.4			−6.4	
		Carry input				−8			−8	
I_{OS}	Short-circuit output current, any output except A = B[§]	V_{CC} = MAX		−20		−55	−18		−57	mA
I_{CC}	Supply current	V_{CC} = MAX, See Note 3	Condition A		88	127		88	140	mA
			Condition B		94	135		94	150	mA

[†]For conditions shown as MIN or MAX, use the appropriate value specified under recommended operating conditions.
[‡]All typical values are at V_{CC} = 5 V, T_A = 25°C.
[§]Not more than one output should be shorted at a time.
NOTE 3: With outputs open, I_{CC} is measured for the following conditions:
      A. S0 through S3, M, and $\overline{A}$ inputs are at 4.5 V, all other inputs are grounded.
      B. S0 through S3 and M are at 4.5 V, all other inputs are grounded.

7

TEXAS INSTRUMENTS
INCORPORATED
POST OFFICE BOX 5012 • DALLAS, TEXAS 75222

switching characteristics, V_{CC} = 5 V, T_A = 25°C (C_L = 15 pF, R_L = 400 Ω, see note 4)

PARAMETER¶	FROM (INPUT)	TO (OUTPUT)	TEST CONDITIONS	MIN	TYP	MAX	UNIT
t_{PLH}	C_n	C_{n+4}			12	18	ns
t_{PHL}					13	19	
t_{PLH}	Any $\overline{A}$ or $\overline{B}$	C_{n+4}	M = 0 V, S0 = S3 = 4.5 V,		28	43	ns
t_{PHL}			S1 = S2 = 0 V ($\overline{SUM}$ mode)		27	41	
t_{PLH}	Any $\overline{A}$ or $\overline{B}$	C_{n+4}	M = 0 V, S0 = S3 = 0 V,		35	50	ns
t_{PHL}			S1 = S2 = 4.5 V ($\overline{DIFF}$ mode)		33	50	
t_{PLH}	C_n	Any $\overline{F}$	M = 0 V		13	19	ns
t_{PHL}			($\overline{SUM}$ or $\overline{DIFF}$ mode)		12	18	
t_{PLH}	Any $\overline{A}$ or $\overline{B}$	$\overline{G}$	M = 0 V, S0 = S3 = 4.5 V,		13	19	ns
t_{PHL}			S1 = S2 = 0 V ($\overline{SUM}$ mode)		13	19	
t_{PLH}	Any $\overline{A}$ or $\overline{B}$	$\overline{G}$	M = 0 V, S0 = S3 = 0 V,		17	25	ns
t_{PHL}			S1 = S2 = 4.5 V ($\overline{DIFF}$ mode)		17	25	
t_{PLH}	Any $\overline{A}$ or $\overline{B}$	$\overline{P}$	M = 0 V, S0 = S3 = 4.5 V,		13	19	ns
t_{PHL}			S1 = S2 = 0 V ($\overline{SUM}$ mode)		17	25	
t_{PLH}	Any $\overline{A}$ or $\overline{B}$	$\overline{P}$	M = 0 V, S0 = S3 = 0 V,		17	25	ns
t_{PHL}			S1 = S2 = 4.5 V ($\overline{DIFF}$ mode)		17	25	
t_{PLH}	$\overline{A}_i$ or $\overline{B}_i$	$\overline{F}_i$	M = 0 V, S0 = S3 = 4.5 V,		28	42	ns
t_{PHL}			S1 = S2 = 0 V ($\overline{SUM}$ mode)		21	32	
t_{PLH}	$\overline{A}_i$ or $\overline{B}_i$	$\overline{F}_i$	M = 0 V, S0 = S3 = 0 V,		32	48	ns
t_{PHL}			S1 = S2 = 4.5 V ($\overline{DIFF}$ mode)		23	34	
t_{PLH}	$\overline{A}_i$ or $\overline{B}_i$	$\overline{F}_i$	M = 4.5 V (logic mode)		32	48	ns
t_{PHL}					23	34	
t_{PLH}	Any $\overline{A}$ or $\overline{B}$	A = B	M = 0 V, S0 = S3 = 0 V,		35	50	ns
t_{PHL}			S1 = S2 = 4.5 V ($\overline{DIFF}$ mode)		32	48	

¶ t_{PLH} ≡ propagation delay time, low-to-high-level output
  t_{PHL} ≡ propagation delay time, high-to-low-level output
NOTE 4: Load circuit and voltage waveforms are shown on page 3-10.

schematics of inputs and outputs

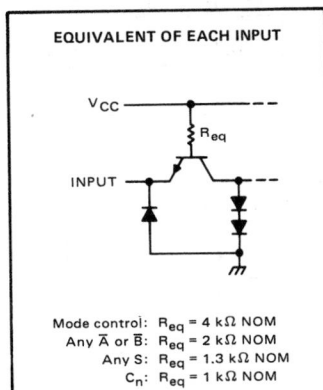

EQUIVALENT OF EACH INPUT

Mode control: R_{eq} = 4 kΩ NOM
Any $\overline{A}$ or $\overline{B}$: R_{eq} = 2 kΩ NOM
Any S: R_{eq} = 1.3 kΩ NOM
C_n: R_{eq} = 1 kΩ NOM

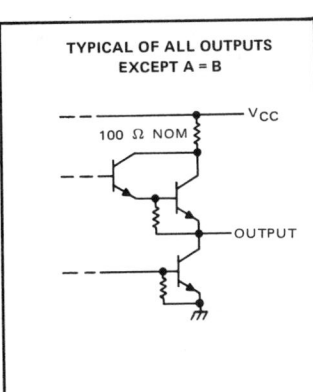

TYPICAL OF ALL OUTPUTS
EXCEPT A = B

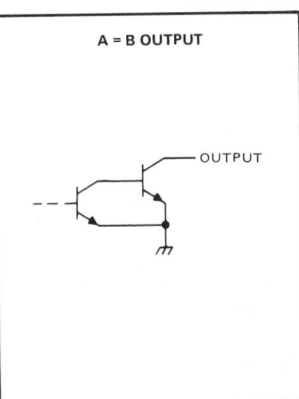

A = B OUTPUT

7

TEXAS INSTRUMENTS
INCORPORATED
POST OFFICE BOX 5012 • DALLAS, TEXAS 75222

absolute maximum ratings over recommended operating free-air temperature range (unless otherwise noted)

Supply voltage, V_{CC} (see Note 1)	7 V
Input voltage	5.5 V
Interemitter voltage (see Note 2)	5.5 V
Operating free-air temperature range: SN54LS181	−55°C to 125°C
SN74LS181	0°C to 70°C
Storage temperature range	−65°C to 150°C

NOTES: 1. Voltage values, except interemitter voltage, are with respect to network ground terminal.
2. This is the voltage between two emitters of a multiple-emitter transistor. For this circuit, this rating applies to each $\overline{A}$ input in conjunction with inputs S2 or S3, and to each $\overline{B}$ input in conjunction with inputs S0 or S3.

recommended operating conditions

	SN54LS181			SN74LS181			UNIT
	MIN	NOM	MAX	MIN	NOM	MAX	
Supply voltage, V_{CC}	4.5	5	5.5	4.75	5	5.25	V
High-level output current, I_{OH} (All outputs except A = B)			−400			−400	µA
Low-level output current, I_{OL}			4			8	mA
Operating free-air temperature, T_A	−55		125	0		70	°C

electrical characteristics over recommended operating free-air temperature range (unless otherwise noted)

PARAMETER			TEST CONDITIONS†		SN54LS181			SN74LS181			UNIT
					MIN	TYP‡	MAX	MIN	TYP‡	MAX	
V_{IH}	High-level input voltage				2			2			V
V_{IL}	Low-level input voltage						0.7			0.8	V
V_{IK}	Input clamp voltage		V_{CC} = MIN, I_I = −18 mA				−1.5			−1.5	V
V_{OH}	High-level output voltage, any output except A = B		V_{CC} = MIN, V_{IH} = 2 V, V_{IL} = V_{IL} max, I_{OH} = −400 µA		2.5	3.4		2.7	3.4		V
I_{OH}	High-level output current, A = B output only		V_{CC} = MIN, V_{IH} = 2 V, V_{IL} = V_{IL} max, V_{OH} = 5.5 V				100			100	µA
V_{OL}	Low-level output voltage	All outputs	V_{CC} = MIN, V_{IH} = 2 V, V_{IL} = V_{IL} max	I_{OL} = 4 mA		0.25	0.4		0.25	0.4	V
				I_{OL} = 8 mA					0.35	0.5	
		Output $\overline{G}$		I_{OL} = 16 mA		0.47	0.7		0.47	0.7	
		Output $\overline{P}$		I_{OL} = 8 mA		0.35	0.6		0.35	0.5	
I_I	Input current at max. input voltage	Mode input	V_{CC} = MAX, V_I = 5.5 V				0.1			0.1	mA
		Any $\overline{A}$ or $\overline{B}$ input					0.3			0.3	
		Any S input					0.4			0.4	
		Carry input					0.5			0.5	
I_{IH}	High-level input current	Mode input	V_{CC} = MAX, V_I = 2.7 V				20			20	µA
		Any $\overline{A}$ or $\overline{B}$ input					60			60	
		Any S input					80			80	
		Carry input					100			100	
I_{IL}	Low-level input current	Mode input	V_{CC} = MAX, V_I = 0.4 V				−0.4			−0.4	mA
		Any $\overline{A}$ or $\overline{B}$ input					−1.2			−1.2	
		Any S input					−1.6			−1.6	
		Carry input					−2			−2	
I_{OS}	Short-circuit output current, any output except A = B§		V_{CC} = MAX		−6		−40	−5		−42	mA
I_{CC}	Supply current		V_{CC} = MAX, See Note 3	Condition A		20	32		20	34	mA
				Condition B		21	35		21	37	

†For conditions shown as MIN or MAX, use the appropriate value specified under recommended operating conditions.
‡All typical values are at V_{CC} = 5 V, T_A = 25°C.
§Not more than one output should be shorted at a time.
NOTE 3: With outputs open, I_{CC} is measured for the following conditions:
A. S0 through S3, M, and $\overline{A}$ inputs are at 4.5 V, all other inputs are grounded.
B. S0 through S3 and M are at 4.5 V, all other inputs are grounded.

7

TEXAS INSTRUMENTS
INCORPORATED
POST OFFICE BOX 5012 • DALLAS, TEXAS 75222

1076

switching characteristics, V_{CC} = 5 V, T_A = 25°C, (C_L = 15 pF, R_L = 2 kΩ, see note 4)

PARAMETER¶	FROM (INPUT)	TO (OUTPUT)	TEST CONDITIONS	MIN	TYP	MAX	UNIT
t_{PLH}	C_n	C_{n+4}			18	27	ns
t_{PHL}					13	20	
t_{PLH}	Any $\overline{A}$ or $\overline{B}$	C_{n+4}	M = 0 V, S0 = S3 = 4.5 V,		25	38	ns
t_{PHL}			S1 = S2 = 0 V ($\overline{SUM}$ mode)		25	38	
t_{PLH}	Any $\overline{A}$ or $\overline{B}$	C_{n+4}	M = 0 V, S0 = S3 = 0 V		27	41	ns
t_{PHL}			S1 = S2 = 4.5 V ($\overline{DIFF}$ mode)		27	41	
t_{PLH}	C_n	Any $\overline{F}$	M = 0 V		17	26	ns
t_{PHL}			($\overline{SUM}$ or $\overline{DIFF}$ mode)		13	20	
t_{PLH}	Any $\overline{A}$ or $\overline{B}$	$\overline{G}$	M = 0 V, S0 = S3 = 4.5 V,		19	29	ns
t_{PHL}			S1 = S2 = 0 V ($\overline{SUM}$ mode)		15	23	
t_{PLH}	Any $\overline{A}$ or $\overline{B}$	$\overline{G}$	M = 0 V, S0 = S3 = 0 V,		21	32	ns
t_{PHL}			S1 = S2 = 4.5 V ($\overline{DIFF}$ mode)		21	32	
t_{PLH}	Any $\overline{A}$ or $\overline{B}$	$\overline{P}$	M = 0 V, S0 = S3 = 4.5 V,		20	30	ns
t_{PHL}			S1 = S2 = 0 V, ($\overline{SUM}$ mode)		20	30	
t_{PLH}	Any $\overline{A}$ or $\overline{B}$	$\overline{P}$	M = 0 V, S0 = S3 = 0 V,		20	30	ns
t_{PHL}			S1 = S2 = 4.5 V ($\overline{DIFF}$ mode)		22	33	
t_{PLH}	$\overline{A}_i$ or $\overline{B}_i$	$\overline{F}_i$	M = 0 V, S0 = S3 = 4.5 V,		21	32	ns
t_{PHL}			S1 = S2 = 0 V (SUM mode)		13	20	
t_{PLH}	$\overline{A}_i$ or $\overline{B}_i$	$\overline{F}_i$	M = 0 V, S0 = S3 = 0 V,		21	32	ns
t_{PHL}			S1 = S2 = 4.5 V ($\overline{DIFF}$ mode)		21	32	
t_{PLH}	$\overline{A}_i$ or $\overline{B}_i$	$\overline{F}_i$	M = 4.5 V (logic mode)		22	33	ns
t_{PHL}					26	38	
t_{PLH}	Any $\overline{A}$ or $\overline{B}$	A = B	M = 0 V, S0 = S3 = 0 V,		33	50	ns
t_{PHL}			S1 = S2 = 4.5 V ($\overline{DIFF}$ mode)		41	62	

¶ t_{PLH} ≡ propagation delay time, low-to-high-level output
t_{PHL} ≡ propagation delay time, high-to-low-level output
NOTE 4: Load circuit and voltage waveforms are shown on page 3-11.

schematics of inputs and outputs

EQUIVALENT OF EACH INPUT	TYPICAL OF ALL OUTPUTS EXCEPT A = B	A = B OUTPUT
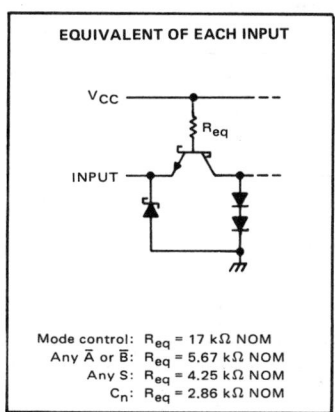	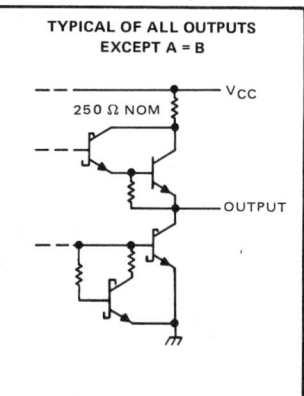	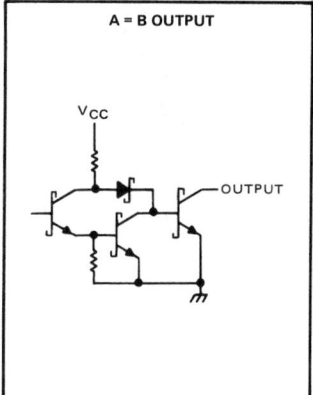

Mode control: R_{eq} = 17 kΩ NOM
Any $\overline{A}$ or $\overline{B}$: R_{eq} = 5.67 kΩ NOM
Any S: R_{eq} = 4.25 kΩ NOM
C_n: R_{eq} = 2.86 kΩ NOM

7

TEXAS INSTRUMENTS
INCORPORATED
POST OFFICE BOX 5012 • DALLAS, TEXAS 75222

TYPES SN54S181, SN74S181
ARITHMETIC LOGIC UNITS/FUNCTION GENERATORS

REVISED OCTOBER 1976

absolute maximum ratings over operating free-air temperature range (unless otherwise noted)

Supply voltage, V_{CC} (see Note 1) . . . . 7 V
Input voltage . . . . 5.5 V
Interemitter voltage (see Note 2) . . . . 5.5 V
Operating free-air temperature: SN54S181 . . . . −55°C to 125°C
SN74S181 . . . . 0°C to 70°C
Storage temperature range . . . . −65°C to 150°C

NOTES: 1. Voltage values, except interemitter voltage, are with respect to network ground terminal.
2. This is the voltage between two emitters of a multiple-emitter transistor. For this circuit, this rating applies to each $\overline{A}$ input in conjunction with inputs S2 or S3, and to each $\overline{B}$ input in conjunction with inputs S0 or S3.

recommended operating conditions

	SN54S181			SN74S181			UNIT
	MIN	NOM	MAX	MIN	NOM	MAX	
Supply voltage, V_{CC}	4.5	5	5.5	4.75	5	5.25	V
High-level output current, I_{OH} (All outputs except A = B)			−1			−1	mA
Low-level output current, I_{OL}			20			20	mA
Operating free-air temperature, T_A	−55		125	0		70	°C

electrical characteristics over recommended operating free-air temperature range (unless otherwise noted)

PARAMETER		TEST CONDITIONS†		SN54S181			SN74S181			UNIT
				MIN	TYP‡	MAX	MIN	TYP‡	MAX	
V_{IH}	High-level input voltage			2			2			V
V_{IL}	Low-level input voltage					0.8			0.8	V
V_{IK}	Input clamp voltage	V_{CC} = MIN,	I_I = −18 mA			−1.2			−1.2	V
V_{OH}	High-level output voltage, any output except A = B	V_{CC} = MIN, V_{IH} = 2 V, V_{IL} = 0.8 V, I_{OH} = −1 mA		2.5	3.4		2.7	3.4		V
I_{OH}	High-level output current, A = B output only	V_{CC} = MIN, V_{IH} = 2 V, V_{IL} = 0.8 V, V_{OH} = 5.5 V				250			250	µA
V_{OL}	Low-level output voltage	V_{CC} = MIN, V_{IH} = 2 V, V_{IL} = 0.8 V, I_{OL} = 20 mA				0.5			0.5	V
I_I	Input current at maximum input voltage	V_{CC} = MAX, V_I = 5.5 V				1			1	mA
I_{IH}	High-level input current	Mode input	V_{CC} = MAX, V_I = 2.5 V			50			50	µA
		Any $\overline{A}$ or $\overline{B}$ input				150			150	
		Any S input				200			200	
		Carry input				250			250	
I_{IL}	Low-level input current	Mode input	V_{CC} = MAX, V_I = 0.5 V			−2			−2	mA
		Any $\overline{A}$ or $\overline{B}$ input				−6			−6	
		Any S input				−8			−8	
		Carry input				−10			−10	
I_{OS}	Short-circuit output current, any output except A = B §	V_{CC} = MAX		−40		−100	−40		−100	mA
I_{CC}	Supply current	V_{CC} = MAX, T_A = 125°C, See Note 3	W package only			195				mA
		V_{CC} = MAX, See Note 3	All packages		120	220		120	220	

†For conditions shown as MIN or MAX, use the appropriate value specified under recommended operating conditions.
‡All typical values are at V_{CC} = 5 V, T_A = 25°C.
§Not more than one output should be shorted at a time.
NOTE 3: I_{CC} is measured for the following conditions (the typical and maximum values apply to both):
A. S0 through S3, M, and $\overline{A}$ inputs are at 4.5 V, all other inputs are grounded, and all outputs are open.
B. S0 through S3 and M are at 4.5 V, all other inputs grounded, and all outputs are open.

7

TEXAS INSTRUMENTS
INCORPORATED
POST OFFICE BOX 5012 • DALLAS, TEXAS 75222

switching characteristics, V_{CC} = 5 V, T_A = 25°C (C_L = 15 pF, R_L = 280 Ω, see note 4)

PARAMETER¶	FROM (INPUT)	TO (OUTPUT)	TEST CONDITIONS	MIN	TYP	MAX	UNIT
t_{PLH}	C_n	C_{n+4}			7	10.5	ns
t_{PHL}					7	10.5	
t_{PLH}	Any $\overline{A}$ or $\overline{B}$	C_{n+4}	M = 0 V, S0 = S3 = 4.5 V,		12.5	18.5	ns
t_{PHL}			S1 = S2 = 0 V ($\overline{SUM}$ mode)		12.5	18.5	
t_{PLH}	Any $\overline{A}$ or $\overline{B}$	C_{n+4}	M = 0 V, S0 = S3 = 0 V,		15.5	23	ns
t_{PHL}			S1 = S2 = 4.5 V (DIFF mode)		15.5	23	
t_{PLH}	C_n	Any $\overline{F}$	M = 0 V		7	12	ns
t_{PHL}			($\overline{SUM}$ or $\overline{DIFF}$ mode)		7	12	
t_{PLH}	Any $\overline{A}$ or $\overline{B}$	$\overline{G}$	M = 0 V, S0 = S3 = 4.5 V,		8	12	ns
t_{PHL}			S1 = S2 = 0 V ($\overline{SUM}$ mode)		7.5	12	
t_{PLH}	Any $\overline{A}$ or $\overline{B}$	$\overline{G}$	M = 0 V, S0 = S3 = 0 V,		10.5	15	ns
t_{PHL}			S1 = S2 = 4.5 V ($\overline{DIFF}$ mode)		10.5	15	
t_{PLH}	Any $\overline{A}$ or $\overline{B}$	$\overline{P}$	M = 0 V, S0 = S3 = 4.5 V,		7.5	12	ns
t_{PHL}			S1 = S2 = 0 V ($\overline{SUM}$ mode)		7.5	12	
t_{PLH}	Any $\overline{A}$ or $\overline{B}$	$\overline{P}$	M = 0 V, S0 = S3 = 0 V,		10.5	15	ns
t_{PHL}			S1 = S2 = 4.5 V ($\overline{DIFF}$ mode)		10.5	15	
t_{PLH}	$\overline{A}_i$ or $\overline{B}_i$	$\overline{F}_i$	M = 0 V, S0 = S3 = 4.5 V,		11	16.5	ns
t_{PHL}			S1 = S2 = 0 V ($\overline{SUM}$ mode)		11	16.5	
t_{PLH}	$\overline{A}_i$ or $\overline{B}_i$	$\overline{F}_i$	M = 0 V, S0 = S3 = 0 V,		14	20	ns
t_{PHL}			S1 = S2 = 4.5 V ($\overline{DIFF}$ mode)		14	22	
t_{PLH}	$\overline{A}_i$ or $\overline{B}_i$	$\overline{F}_i$	M = 4.5 V (logic mode)		14	20	ns
t_{PHL}					14	22	
t_{PLH}	Any $\overline{A}$ or $\overline{B}$	A = B	M = 0 V, S0 = S3 = 0 V,		15	23	ns
t_{PHL}			S1 = S2 = 4.5 V ($\overline{DIFF}$ mode)		20	30	

¶ t_{PLH} ≡ propagation delay time, low-to-high-level output
  t_{PHL} ≡ propagation delay time, high-to-low-level output
NOTE 4: Load circuit and voltage waveforms are shown on page 3-10.

schematics of inputs and outputs

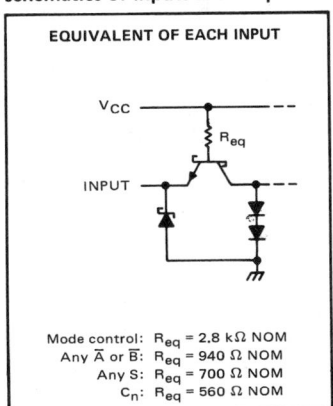

EQUIVALENT OF EACH INPUT

V_{CC}

R_{eq}

INPUT

Mode control: R_{eq} = 2.8 kΩ NOM
Any $\overline{A}$ or $\overline{B}$: R_{eq} = 940 Ω NOM
Any S: R_{eq} = 700 Ω NOM
C_n: R_{eq} = 560 Ω NOM

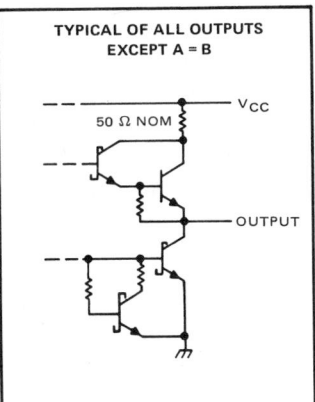

**TYPICAL OF ALL OUTPUTS
EXCEPT A = B**

V_{CC}

50 Ω NOM

OUTPUT

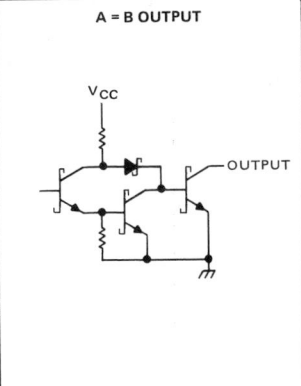

A = B OUTPUT

V_{CC}

OUTPUT

TEXAS INSTRUMENTS
INCORPORATED
POST OFFICE BOX 5012 • DALLAS, TEXAS 75222

7

TYPES SN54181, SN54LS181, SN54S181, SN74181, SN74LS181, SN74S181
ARITHMETIC LOGIC UNITS/FUNCTION GENERATORS

functional block diagram

TEXAS INSTRUMENTS
INCORPORATED
POST OFFICE BOX 5012 • DALLAS, TEXAS 75222

10

PARAMETER MEASUREMENT INFORMATION

$\overline{\text{SUM}}$ MODE TEST TABLE
FUNCTION INPUTS: S0 = S3 = 4.5 V, S1 = S2 = M = 0 V

PARAMETER	INPUT UNDER TEST	OTHER INPUT SAME BIT		OTHER DATA INPUTS		OUTPUT UNDER TEST	OUTPUT WAVEFORM (See Note 4)
		APPLY 4.5 V	APPLY GND	APPLY 4.5 V	APPLY GND		
t_{PLH} / t_{PHL}	$\overline{A}_i$	$\overline{B}_i$	None	Remaining $\overline{A}$ and $\overline{B}$	C_n	$\overline{F}_i$	In-Phase
t_{PLH} / t_{PHL}	$\overline{B}_i$	$\overline{A}_i$	None	Remaining $\overline{A}$ and $\overline{B}$	C_n	$\overline{F}_i$	In-Phase
t_{PLH} / t_{PHL}	$\overline{A}_i$	$\overline{B}_i$	None	None	Remaining $\overline{A}$ and $\overline{B}$, C_n	$\overline{P}$	In-Phase
t_{PLH} / t_{PHL}	$\overline{B}_i$	$\overline{A}_i$	None	None	Remaining $\overline{A}$ and $\overline{B}$, C_n	$\overline{P}$	In-Phase
t_{PLH} / t_{PHL}	$\overline{A}_i$	None	$\overline{B}_i$	Remaining $\overline{B}$	Remaining $\overline{A}$, C_n	$\overline{G}$	In-Phase
t_{PLH} / t_{PHL}	$\overline{B}_i$	None	$\overline{A}_i$	Remaining $\overline{B}$	Remaining $\overline{A}$, C_n	$\overline{G}$	In-Phase
t_{PLH} / t_{PHL}	C_n	None	None	All $\overline{A}$	All $\overline{B}$	Any $\overline{F}$ or C_{n+4}	In-Phase
t_{PLH} / t_{PHL}	$\overline{A}_i$	None	$\overline{B}_i$	Remaining $\overline{B}$	Remaining $\overline{A}$, C_n	C_{n+4}	Out-of-Phase
t_{PLH} / t_{PHL}	$\overline{B}_i$	None	$\overline{A}_i$	Remaining $\overline{B}$	Remaining $\overline{A}$, C_n	C_{n+4}	Out-of-Phase

$\overline{\text{DIFF}}$ MODE TEST TABLE
FUNCTION INPUTS: S1 = S2 = 4.5 V, S0 = S3 = M = 0 V

PARAMETER	INPUT UNDER TEST	OTHER INPUT SAME BIT		OTHER DATA INPUTS		OUTPUT UNDER TEST	OUTPUT WAVEFORM (See Note 4)
		APPLY 4.5 V	APPLY GND	APPLY 4.5 V	APPLY GND		
t_{PLH} / t_{PHL}	$\overline{A}_i$	None	$\overline{B}_i$	Remaining $\overline{A}$	Remaining $\overline{B}$, C_n	$\overline{F}_i$	In-Phase
t_{PLH} / t_{PHL}	$\overline{B}_i$	$\overline{A}_i$	None	Remaining $\overline{A}$	Remaining $\overline{B}$, C_n	$\overline{F}_i$	Out-of-Phase
t_{PLH} / t_{PHL}	$\overline{A}_i$	None	$\overline{B}_i$	None	Remaining $\overline{A}$ and $\overline{B}$, C_n	$\overline{P}$	In-Phase
t_{PLH} / t_{PHL}	$\overline{B}_i$	$\overline{A}_i$	None	None	Remaining $\overline{A}$ and $\overline{B}$, C_n	$\overline{P}$	Out-of-Phase
t_{PLH} / t_{PHL}	$\overline{A}_i$	$\overline{B}_i$	None	None	Remaining $\overline{A}$ and $\overline{B}$, C_n	$\overline{G}$	In-Phase
t_{PLH} / t_{PHL}	$\overline{B}_i$	None	$\overline{A}_i$	None	Remaining $\overline{A}$ and $\overline{B}$, C_n	$\overline{G}$	Out-of-Phase
t_{PLH} / t_{PHL}	$\overline{A}_i$	None	$\overline{B}_i$	Remaining $\overline{A}$	Remaining $\overline{B}$, C_n	A = B	In-Phase
t_{PLH} / t_{PHL}	$\overline{B}_i$	$\overline{A}_i$	None	Remaining $\overline{A}$	Remaining $\overline{B}$, C_n	A = B	Out-of Phase
t_{PLH} / t_{PHL}	C_n	None	None	All $\overline{A}$ and $\overline{B}$	None	C_{n+4} or any $\overline{F}$	In-Phase
t_{PLH} / t_{PHL}	$\overline{A}_i$	$\overline{B}_i$	None	None	Remaining $\overline{A}$, $\overline{B}$, C_n	C_{n+4}	Out-of-Phase
t_{PLH} / t_{PHL}	$\overline{B}_i$	None	$\overline{A}_i$	None	Remaining $\overline{A}$, $\overline{B}$, C_n	C_{n+4}	In -Phase

LOGIC MODE TEST TABLE
FUNCTION INPUTS: S1 = S2 = M = 4.5 V, S0 = S3 = 0 V

PARAMETER	INPUT UNDER TEST	OTHER INPUT SAME BIT		OTHER DATA INPUTS		OUTPUT UNDER TEST	OUTPUT WAVEFORM (See Note 4)
		APPLY 4.5 V	APPLY GND	APPLY 4.5 V	APPLY GND		
t_{PLH} / t_{PHL}	$\overline{A}_i$	$\overline{B}_i$	None	None	Remaining $\overline{A}$ and $\overline{B}$, C_n	$\overline{F}_i$	Out-of-Phase
t_{PLH} / t_{PHL}	$\overline{B}_i$	$\overline{A}_i$	None	None	Remaining $\overline{A}$ and $\overline{B}$, C_n	$\overline{F}_i$	Out-of-Phase

NOTE 4: Load circuit and voltage waveforms are shown on pages 3-10 and 3-11.

TTL
MSI

TYPES SN54182, SN54S182, SN74182, SN74S182
LOOK-AHEAD CARRY GENERATORS
BULLETIN NO. DL-S 7611823, DECEMBER 1972—REVISED OCTOBER 1976

- Directly Compatible for Use With:
  SN54181/SN74181, SN54LS181/SN74LS181,
  SN54S281/SN74S281, SN54S381, SN74S381,
  SN54S481/SN74S481

SN54182, SN54S182 . . . J OR W PACKAGE
SN74182, SN74S182 . . . J OR N PACKAGE
(TOP VIEW)

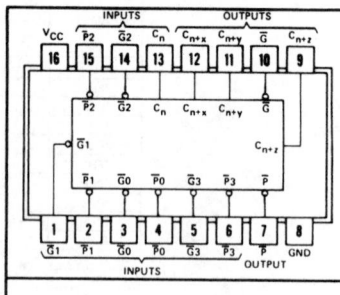

logic: see description and function tables

PIN DESIGNATIONS

ALTERNATIVE	DESIGNATIONS[†]	PIN NOS.	FUNCTION
$\overline{G0}, \overline{G1}, \overline{G2}, \overline{G3}$	G0, G1, G2, G3	3, 1, 14, 5	CARRY GENERATE INPUTS
$\overline{P0}, \overline{P1}, \overline{P2}, \overline{P3}$	P0, P1, P2, P3	4, 2, 15, 6	CARRY PROPAGATE INPUTS
C_n	$\overline{C_n}$	13	CARRY INPUT
$C_{n+x}, C_{n+y}, C_{n+z}$	$\overline{C}_{n+x}, \overline{C}_{n+y}, \overline{C}_{n+z}$	12, 11, 9	CARRY OUTPUTS
$\overline{G}$	Y	10	CARRY GENERATE OUTPUT
$\overline{P}$	X	7	CARRY PROPAGATE OUTPUT
V_{CC}		16	SUPPLY VOLTAGE
GND		8	GROUND

[†]Interpretations are illustrated on page 7-273

description

The SN54182, SN54S182, SN74182, and SN74S182 are high-speed, look-ahead carry generators capable of anticipating a carry across four binary adders or group of adders. They are cascadable to perform full look-ahead across n-bit adders. Carry, generate-carry, and propagate-carry functions are provided as enumerated in the pin designation table above.

When used in conjunction with the '181, 'LS181, or 'S181 arithmetic logic unit (ALU), these generators provide high-speed carry look-ahead capability for any word length. Each '182 or 'S182 generates the look-ahead (anticipated carry) across a group of four ALU's and, in addition, other carry look-ahead circuits may be employed to anticipate carry across sections of four look-ahead packages up to n-bits. The method of cascading '182 or 'S182 circuits to perform multi-level look-ahead is illustrated under typical application data.

The carry functions (inputs, outputs, generate, and propagate) of the look-ahead generators are implemented in the compatible forms for direct connection to the ALU. Reinterpretations of carry functions as explained on the '181, 'LS181, and 'S181 data sheet are also applicable to and compatible with the look-ahead generator. Logic equations for the '182 and 'S182 are:

$C_{n+x} = G0 + P0\,C_n$
$C_{n+y} = G1 + P1\,G0 + P1\,P0\,C_n$
$C_{n+z} = G2 + P2\,G1 + P2\,P1\,G0 + P2\,P1\,P0\,C_n$
$\overline{G} = \overline{G3 + P3\,G2 + P3\,P2\,G1 + P3\,P2\,P1\,G0}$
$\overline{P} = \overline{P3\,P2\,P1\,P0}$

or

$\overline{C}_{n+x} = \overline{Y0\,(X0 + C_n)}$
$\overline{C}_{n+y} = \overline{Y1\,[X1 + Y0\,(X0 + C_n)]}$
$\overline{C}_{n+z} = \overline{Y2\,\{X2 + Y1\,[X1 + Y0\,(X0 + C_n)]\}}$
$Y = Y3\,(X3 + Y2)\,(X3 + X2 + Y1)\,(X3 + X2 + X1 + Y0)$
$X = X3 + X2 + X1 + X0$

logic

FUNCTION TABLE FOR $\overline{G}$ OUTPUT

INPUTS							OUTPUT
$\overline{G3}$	$\overline{G2}$	$\overline{G1}$	$\overline{G0}$	$\overline{P3}$	$\overline{P2}$	$\overline{P1}$	$\overline{G}$
L	X	X	X	X	X	X	L
X	L	X	X	L	X	X	L
X	X	L	X	L	L	X	L
X	X	X	L	L	L	L	L
All other combinations							H

FUNCTION TABLE FOR $\overline{P}$ OUTPUT

INPUTS				OUTPUT
$\overline{P3}$	$\overline{P2}$	$\overline{P1}$	$\overline{P0}$	$\overline{P}$
L	L	L	L	L
All other combinations				H

H = high level, L = low level, X = irrelevant
Any inputs not shown in a given table are irrelevant with respect to that output.

TEXAS INSTRUMENTS
INCORPORATED
POST OFFICE BOX 5012 • DALLAS, TEXAS 75222

1076

TYPES SN54182, SN54S182, SN74182, SN74S182
LOOK-AHEAD CARRY GENERATORS

logic

FUNCTION TABLE
FOR C_{n+x} OUTPUT

INPUTS			OUTPUT
$\overline{G0}$	$\overline{P0}$	C_n	C_{n+x}
L	X	X	H
X	L	H	H
All other combinations			L

FUNCTION TABLE
FOR C_{n+y} OUTPUT

INPUTS					OUTPUT
$\overline{G1}$	$\overline{G0}$	$\overline{P1}$	$\overline{P0}$	C_n	C_{n+y}
L	X	X	X	X	H
X	L	L	X	X	H
X	X	L	L	H	H
All other combinations					L

FUNCTION TABLE FOR C_{n+z} OUTPUT

INPUTS							OUTPUT
$\overline{G2}$	$\overline{G1}$	$\overline{G0}$	$\overline{P2}$	$\overline{P1}$	$\overline{P0}$	C_n	C_{n+z}
L	X	X	X	X	X	X	H
X	L	X	L	X	X	X	H
X	X	L	L	L	X	X	H
X	X	X	L	L	L	H	H
All other combinations							L

H = high level, L = low level, X = irrelevant
Any inputs not shown in a given table are irrelevant with respect to
that output.

functional block diagram

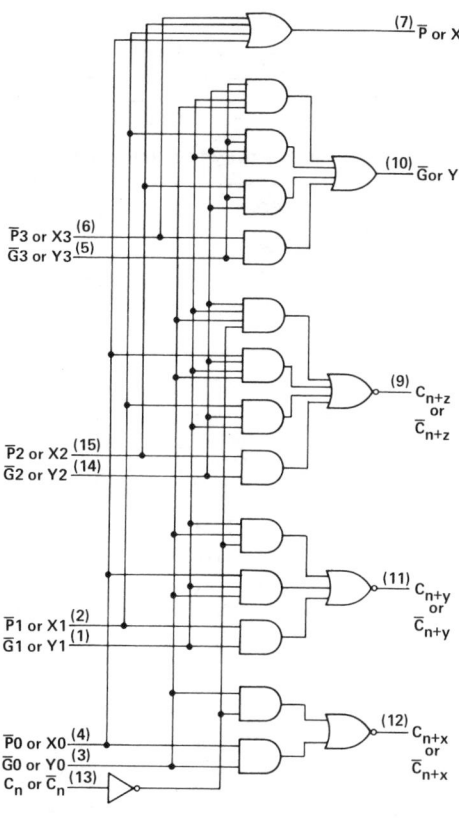

absolute maximum ratings over operating free-air temperature range (unless otherwise noted)

Supply voltage, V_{CC} (see Note 1) . . . . 7 V
Input voltage . . . . 5.5 V
Interemitter voltage (see Note 2) . . . . 5.5 V
Operating free-air temperature range: SN54', SN54S' Circuits . . . . $-55°C$ to $125°C$
                        SN74', SN74S' Circuits . . . . $0°C$ to $70°C$
Storage temperature range . . . . $-65°C$ to $150°C$

NOTES: 1. Voltage values, except interemitter voltage, are with respect to network ground terminal.
        2. This is the voltage between two emitters of a multiple-emitter input transistor. For these circuits, this rating applies to each $\overline{G}$
           input in conjunction with any other $\overline{G}$ input or in conjunction with any $\overline{P}$ input.

7

recommended operating conditions

	SN54182			SN74182			UNIT
	MIN	NOM	MAX	MIN	NOM	MAX	
Supply voltage, V_{CC}	4.5	5	5.5	4.75	5	5.25	V
High-level output current, I_{OH}			−800			−800	μA
Low-level output current, I_{OL}			16			16	mA
Operating free-air temperature, T_A	−55		125	0		70	°C

electrical characteristics over recommended operating free-air temperature range (unless otherwise noted)

PARAMETER		TEST CONDITIONS[†]	SN54182			SN74182			UNIT
			MIN	TYP[‡]	MAX	MIN	TYP[‡]	MAX	
V_{IH} High-level input voltage			2			2			V
V_{IL} Low-level input voltage					0.8			0.8	V
V_{IK} Input clamp voltage		V_{CC} = MIN, I_I = −12 mA			−1.5			−1.5	V
V_{OH} High-level output voltage		V_{CC} = MIN, V_{IH} = 2 V, V_{IL} = 0.8 V, I_{OH} = −800 μA	2.4	3.4		2.4	3.4		V
V_{OL} Low-level output voltage		V_{CC} = MIN, V_{IH} = 2 V, V_{IL} = 0.8 V, I_{OL} = 16 mA		0.2	0.4		0.2	0.4	V
I_I Input current at maximum input voltage		V_{CC} = MAX, V_I = 5.5 V			1			1	mA
I_{IH} High-level input current	C_n input	V_{CC} = MAX, V_I = 2.4 V			80			80	μA
	$\overline{P}3$ input				120			120	
	$\overline{P}2$ input				160			160	
	$\overline{P}0, \overline{P}1,$ or $\overline{G}3$ input				200			200	
	$\overline{G}0$ or $\overline{G}2$ input				360			360	
	$\overline{G}1$ input				400			400	
I_{IL} Low-level input current	C_n input	V_{CC} = MAX, V_I = 0.4 V			−3.2			−3.2	mA
	$\overline{P}3$ input				−4.8			−4.8	
	$\overline{P}2$ input				−6.4			−6.4	
	$\overline{P}0, \overline{P}1,$ or $\overline{G}3$ input				−8			−8	
	$\overline{G}0$ or $\overline{G}2$ input				−14.4			−14.4	
	$\overline{G}1$ input				−16			−16	
I_{OS} Short-circuit output current§		V_{CC} = MAX	−40		−100	−40		−100	mA
I_{CCH} Supply current, all outputs high		V_{CC} = 5 V, See Note 3		27			27		mA
I_{CCL} Supply current, all outputs low		V_{CC} = MAX, See Note 4		45	65		45	72	mA

†For conditions shown as MIN or MAX, use the appropriate value specified under recommended operating conditions.
‡All typical values are at V_{CC} = 5 V, T_A = 25°C.
§Not more than one output should be shorted at a time and duration of the short-circuit test should not exceed one second.
NOTES: 3. I_{CCH} is measured with all outputs open, inputs $\overline{P}3$ and $\overline{G}3$ at 4.5 V, and all other inputs grounded.
      4. I_{CCL} is measured with all outputs open; inputs $\overline{G}0$, $\overline{G}1$, and $\overline{G}2$ at 4.5 V; and all other inputs grounded.

switching characteristics, V_{CC} = 5 V, T_A = 25°C

PARAMETER	TEST CONDITIONS	MIN	TYP	MAX	UNIT
t_{PLH} Propagation delay time, low-to-high-level output	C_L = 15 pF, R_L = 400 Ω, See Note 5		11	17	ns
t_{PHL} Propagation delay time, high-to-low-level output			15	22	ns

NOTE 5: Load circuit and voltage waveforms are shown on page 3-10.

TEXAS INSTRUMENTS
INCORPORATED
POST OFFICE BOX 5012 • DALLAS, TEXAS 75222

recommended operating conditions

	SN54S182			SN74S182			UNIT
	MIN	NOM	MAX	MIN	NOM	MAX	
Supply voltage, V_{CC}	4.5	5	5.5	4.75	5	5.25	V
High-level output current, I_{OH}			−1			−1	mA
Low-level output current, I_{OL}			20			20	mA
Operating free-air temperature, T_A	−55		125	0		70	°C

electrical characteristics over recommended operating free-air temperature range (unless otherwise noted)

	PARAMETER		TEST CONDITIONS[†]	SN54S182			SN74S182			UNIT
				MIN	TYP[‡]	MAX	MIN	TYP[‡]	MAX	
V_{IH}	High-level input voltage			2			2			V
V_{IL}	Low-level input voltage					0.8			0.8	V
V_{IK}	Input clamp voltage		V_{CC} = MIN, I_I = −18 mA			−1.2			−1.2	V
V_{OH}	High-level output voltage		V_{CC} = MIN, V_{IH} = 2 V, V_{IL} = 0.8 V, I_{OH} = −1 mA	2.5	3.4		2.7	3.4		V
V_{OL}	Low-level output voltage		V_{CC} = MIN, V_{IH} = 2 V, V_{IL} = 0.8 V, I_{OL} = 20 mA			0.5			0.5	V
I_I	Input current at maximum input voltage		V_{CC} = MAX, V_I = 5.5 V			1			1	mA
I_{IH}	High-level input current	C_n input	V_{CC} = MAX, V_I = 2.7 V			50			50	µA
		$\overline{P}3$ input				100			100	
		$\overline{P}2$ input				150			150	
		$\overline{P}0$, $\overline{P}1$, or $\overline{G}3$ input				200			200	
		$\overline{G}0$ or $\overline{G}2$ input				350			350	
		$\overline{G}1$ input				400			400	
I_{IL}	Low-level input current	C_n input	V_{CC} = MAX, V_I = 0.5 V			−2			−2	mA
		$\overline{P}3$ input				−4			−4	
		$\overline{P}2$ input				−6			−6	
		$\overline{P}0$, $\overline{P}1$, or $\overline{G}3$ input				−8			−8	
		$\overline{G}0$ or $\overline{G}2$ input				−14			−14	
		$\overline{G}1$ input				−16			−16	
I_{OS}	Short-circuit output current§		V_{CC} = MAX	−40		−100	−40		−100	mA
I_{CCH}	Supply current, all outputs high		V_{CC} = 5 V, See Note 3		35			35		mA
I_{CCL}	Supply current, all outputs low		V_{CC} = MAX, See Note 4		69	99		69	109	mA

†For conditions shown as MIN or MAX, use the appropriate value specified under recommended operating conditions for the applicable type.
‡All typical values are at V_{CC} = 5 V, T_A = 25°C.
§Not more than one output should be shorted at a time and duration of the short-circuit test should not exceed one second.
NOTES: 3. I_{CCH} is measured with all outputs open, inputs $\overline{P}3$ and $\overline{G}3$ at 4.5 V, and all other inputs grounded.
     4. I_{CCL} is measured with all outputs open; inputs $\overline{G}0$, $\overline{G}1$, and $\overline{G}2$ at 4.5 V; and all other inputs grounded.

switching characteristics, V_{CC} = 5 V, T_A = 25°C

PARAMETER¶	FROM (INPUT)	TO (OUTPUT)	TEST CONDITIONS	MIN	TYP	MAX	UNIT
t_{PLH}	$\overline{G}0$, $\overline{G}1$, $\overline{G}2$, $\overline{G}3$, P0, P1, P2, or P3	C_{n+x}, C_{n+y}, or C_{n+z}			4.5	7	ns
t_{PHL}					4.5	7	
t_{PLH}	$\overline{G}0$, $\overline{G}1$, $\overline{G}2$, $\overline{G}3$, P1, P2, or P3	$\overline{G}$	R_L = 280 Ω, C_L = 15 pF, See Note 5		5	7.5	ns
t_{PHL}					7	10.5	
t_{PLH}	$\overline{P}0$, $\overline{P}1$, $\overline{P}2$, or $\overline{P}3$	$\overline{P}$			4.5	6.5	ns
t_{PHL}					6.5	10	
t_{PLH}	C_n	C_{n+x}, C_{n+y}, or C_{n+z}			6.5	10	ns
t_{PHL}					7	10.5	

¶t_{PLH} ≡ propagation delay time, low-to-high-level output
  t_{PHL} ≡ propagation delay time, high-to-low-level output
NOTE 5: Load circuit and voltage waveforms are shown on page 3-10.

TEXAS INSTRUMENTS
INCORPORATED
POST OFFICE BOX 5012 • DALLAS, TEXAS 75222

TYPES SN54182, SN54S182, SN74182, SN74S182
LOOK-AHEAD CARRY GENERATORS

schematics of inputs and outputs

'182

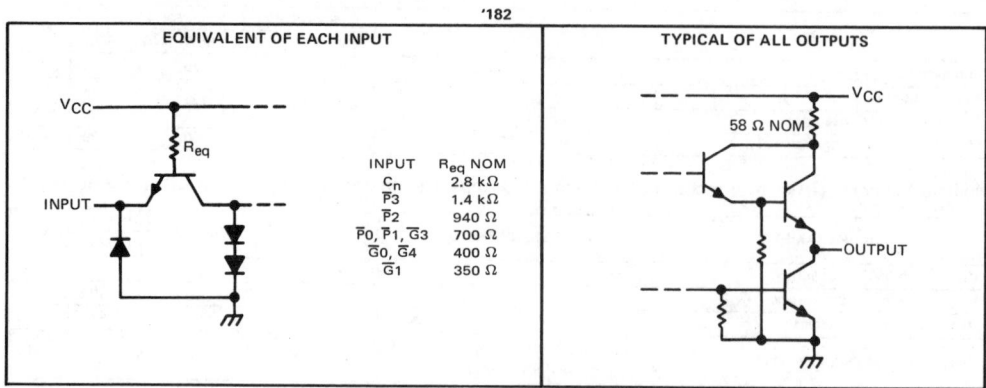

EQUIVALENT OF EACH INPUT	TYPICAL OF ALL OUTPUTS

INPUT	R_{eq} NOM
C_n	2.8 kΩ
$\overline{P}3$	1.4 kΩ
$\overline{P}2$	940 Ω
$\overline{P}0, \overline{P}1, \overline{G}3$	700 Ω
$\overline{G}0, \overline{G}4$	400 Ω
$\overline{G}1$	350 Ω

'S182

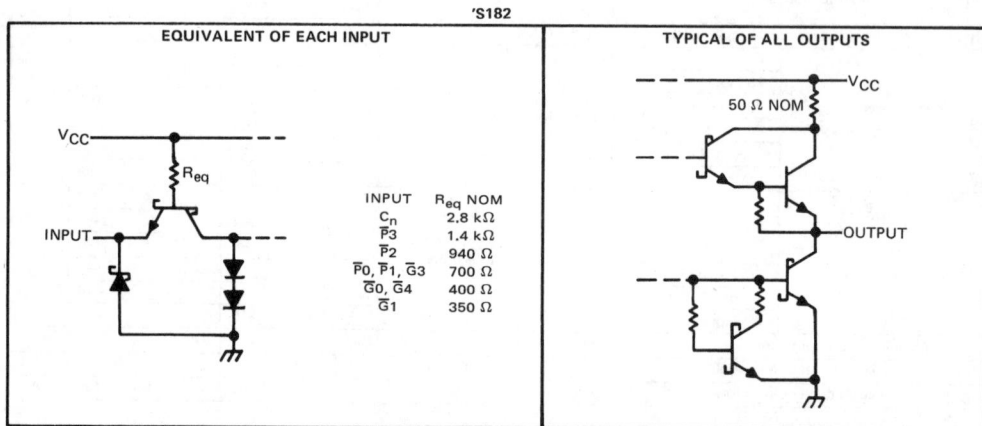

EQUIVALENT OF EACH INPUT	TYPICAL OF ALL OUTPUTS

INPUT	R_{eq} NOM
C_n	2.8 kΩ
$\overline{P}3$	1.4 kΩ
$\overline{P}2$	940 Ω
$\overline{P}0, \overline{P}1, \overline{G}3$	700 Ω
$\overline{G}0, \overline{G}4$	400 Ω
$\overline{G}1$	350 Ω

TYPICAL APPLICATION DATA

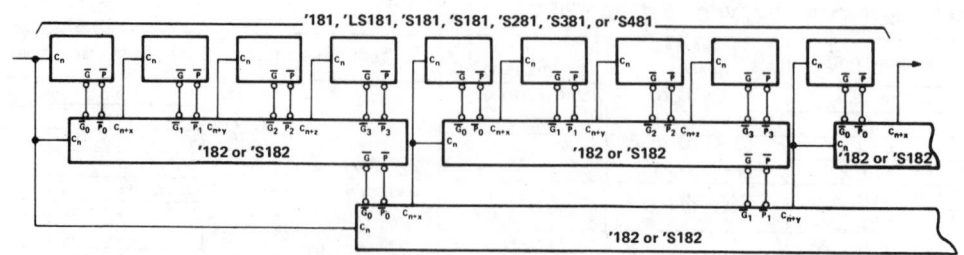

'181, 'LS181, 'S181, 'S181, 'S281, 'S381, or 'S481

'182 or 'S182

64-BIT ALU, FULL-CARRY LOOK-AHEAD IN THREE LEVELS
Remaining inputs and outputs of '181, 'LS181, 'S181 'S281, 'S381, and 'S481 are not shown.

TEXAS INSTRUMENTS
INCORPORATED
POST OFFICE BOX 5012 • DALLAS, TEXAS 75222

TYPES SN54H183, SN54LS183, SN74H183, SN74LS183
DUAL CARRY-SAVE FULL ADDERS

BULLETIN NO. DL-S 7711848, OCTOBER 1976–REVISED AUGUST 1977

- For Use in High-Speed Wallace-Tree Summing Networks

- High-Speed, High-Fan-Out Darlington Outputs

- Input Clamping Diodes Simplify System Design

TYPES	TYPICAL AVERAGE PROPAGATION DELAY TIME	TYPICAL POWER DISSIPATION
'H183	11 ns	110 mW per bit
'LS183	15 ns	23 mW per bit

SN54H183, SN54LS183 . . . J OR W PACKAGE
SN74H183, SN74LS183 . . . J OR N PACKAGE
(TOP VIEW)

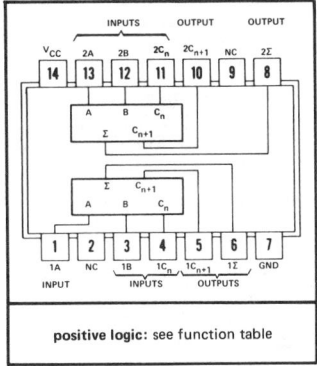

positive logic: see function table

NC—No internal connection

functional block diagram (each adder)

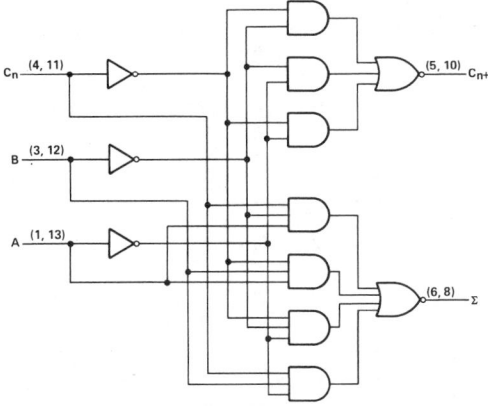

FUNCTION TABLE
(EACH ADDER)

INPUTS			OUTPUTS	
C_n	B	A	Σ	C_{n+1}
L	L	L	L	L
L	L	H	H	L
L	H	L	H	L
L	H	H	L	H
H	L	L	H	L
H	L	H	L	H
H	H	L	L	H
H	H	H	H	H

H = high level, L = low level

schematics of inputs and outputs

'H183

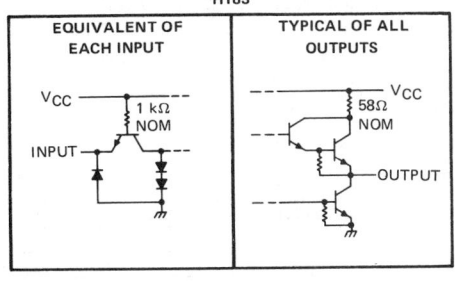

EQUIVALENT OF EACH INPUT	TYPICAL OF ALL OUTPUTS

'LS183

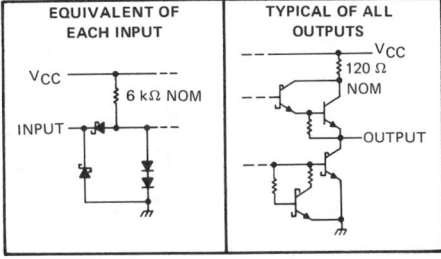

EQUIVALENT OF EACH INPUT	TYPICAL OF ALL OUTPUTS

description

These dual full adders feature an individual carry output from each bit for use in multiple-input, carry-save techniques to produce the true sum and true carry outputs with no more than two gate delays. The circuits utilize high-speed, high-fan-out, transistor-transistor logic (TTL), but are compatible with both DTL and TTL families. Series 54H and 54LS devices are characterized for operation over the full military temperature range of −55°C to 125°C; Series 74H and 74LS devices are characterized for operation from 0°C to 70°C.

TEXAS INSTRUMENTS
INCORPORATED
POST OFFICE BOX 5012 • DALLAS, TEXAS 75222

TYPES SN54H183, SN74H183
DUAL CARRY-SAVE FULL ADDERS

REVISED AUGUST 1977

absolute maximum ratings over operating free-air temperature range (unless otherwise noted)

Supply voltage V_{CC} (see Note 1)	7 V
Input voltage	5.5 V
Interemitter voltage (see Note 2)	5.5 V
Operating free-air temperature range: SN54H183 Circuits	−55°C to 125°C
SN74H183 Circuits	0°C to 70°C
Storage temperature range	−65°C to 150°C

NOTES: 1. Voltage values, except interemitter voltage, are with respect to network ground terminal.
2. This is the voltage between two emitters of a multiple-emitter transistor. For this circuit, this rating applies between any two inputs to the same adder.

recommended operating conditions

	SN54H183			SN74H183			UNIT
	MIN	NOM	MAX	MIN	NOM	MAX	
Supply voltage, V_{CC}	4.5	5	5.5	4.75	5	5.25	V
High-level output current, I_{OH}			−1			−1	mA
Low-level output current, I_{OL}			20			20	mA
Operating free-air temperature, T_A	−55		125	0		70	°C

electrical characteristics over recommended operating free-air temperature range (unless otherwise noted)

	PARAMETER	TEST CONDITIONS[†]		MIN	TYP[‡]	MAX	UNIT
V_{IH}	High-level input voltage			2			V
V_{IL}	Low-level input voltage					0.8	V
V_{IK}	Input clamp voltage	V_{CC} = MIN,	I_I = −8 mA			−1.5	V
V_{OH}	High-level output voltage	V_{CC} = MIN, V_{IH} = 2 V, V_{IL} = 0.8 V, I_{OH} = −1 mA		2.4	3.5		V
V_{OL}	Low-level output voltage	V_{CC} = MIN, V_{IH} = 2 V, V_{IL} = 0.8 V, I_{OL} = 20 mA			0.2	0.4	V
I_I	Input current at maximum input voltage	V_{CC} = MAX, V_I = 5.5 V				1	mA
I_{IH}	High-level input current	V_{CC} = MAX, V_I = 2.4 V				150	µA
I_{IL}	Low-level input current	V_{CC} = MAX, V_I = 0.4 V				−6	mA
I_{OS}	Short-circuit output current[§]	V_{CC} = MAX		−40		−100	mA
I_{CCL}	Supply current, all outputs low	V_{CC} = MAX, See Note 3	SN54H183		48	69	mA
			SN74H183		48	75	
I_{CCH}	Supply current, all outputs high	V_{CC} = MAX, See Note 4			40	65	mA

[†] For conditions shown as MIN or MAX, use the appropriate value specified under recommended operating conditions for the applicable type.
[‡] All typical values are at V_{CC} = 5 V, T_A = 25°C.
[§] Not more than one output should be shorted at a time, and duration of the short circuit should not exceed one second.

NOTES: 3. I_{CCL} is measured with all outputs open and all inputs grounded.
4. I_{CCH} is measured with all outputs open and all inputs at 4.5 V.

switching characteristics, V_{CC} = 5 V, T_A = 25°C

	PARAMETER	TEST CONDITIONS	MIN	TYP	MAX	UNIT
t_{PLH}	Propagation delay time, low-to-high-level output	C_L = 25 pF, R_L = 280 Ω, See Note 5		10	15	ns
t_{PHL}	Propagation delay time, high-to-low-level output			12	18	ns

NOTE 5: Load circuit and waveforms are shown on page 3-10.

7

TEXAS INSTRUMENTS
INCORPORATED
POST OFFICE BOX 5012 • DALLAS, TEXAS 75222

absolute maximum ratings over operating free-air temperature range (unless otherwise noted)

Supply voltage V_{CC} (see Note 1) . . . . 7 V
Input voltage . . . . 7 V
Operating free-air temperature range: SN54LS183 Circuits . . . . −55°C to 125°C
SN74LS183 Circuits . . . . 0°C to 70°C
Storage temperature range . . . . −65°C to 150°C

NOTE 1: Voltage values, except interemitter voltage, are with respect to network ground terminal.

recommended operating conditions

	SN54LS183			SN74LS183			UNIT
	MIN	NOM	MAX	MIN	NOM	MAX	
Supply voltage, V_{CC}	4.5	5	5.5	4.75	5	5.25	V
High-level output current, I_{OH}			−400			−400	µA
Low-level output current, I_{OL}			4			8	mA
Operating free-air temperature, T_A	−55		125	0		70	°C

electrical characteristics over recommended operation free-air temperature range (unless otherwise noted)

PARAMETER		TEST CONDITIONS[†]		MIN	TYP[‡]	MAX	MIN	TYP[‡]	MAX	UNIT
V_{IH}	High-level input voltage			2			2			V
V_{IL}	Low-level input voltage					0.7			0.8	V
V_{IK}	Input clamp voltage	V_{CC} = MIN,	I_I = −18 mA			−1.5			−1.5	V
V_{OH}	High-level output voltage	V_{CC} = MIN, V_{IH} = 2 V, V_{IL} = V_{IL}max, I_{OH} = −400 µA		2.5	3.4		2.7	3.4		V
V_{OL}	Low-level output voltage	V_{CC} = MIN, V_{IH} = 2 V, V_{IL} = V_{IL}max,	I_{OL} = 4 mA		0.25	0.4		0.25	0.4	V
			I_{OL} = 8 mA					0.35	0.5	
I_I	Input current at maximum input voltage	V_{CC} = MAX,	V_I = 7 V			0.3			0.3	mA
I_{IH}	High-level input current	V_{CC} = MAX,	V_I = 2.7 V			60			60	µA
I_{IL}	Low-level input current	V_{CC} = MAX,	V_I = 0.4 V			−1.2			−1.2	mA
I_{OS}	Short-circuit output current[§]	V_{CC} = MAX		−20		−100	−20		−100	mA
I_{CCL}	Supply current, all outputs low	V_{CC} = MAX,	See Note 3		10	17		10	17	mA
I_{CCH}	Supply current, all outputs high	V_{CC} = MAX,	See Note 4		8	14		8	14	mA

[†] For conditions shown as MIN or MAX, use the appropriate value specified under recommended operating conditions for the applicable type.
[‡] All typical values are at V_{CC} = 5 V, T_A = 25°C.
[§] Not more than one output should be shorted at a time, and duration of the short circuit should not exceed one second.
NOTES: 3. I_{CCL} is measured with all outputs open and all inputs grounded.
4. I_{CCH} is measured with all outputs open and all inputs at 4.5 V.

switching characteristics, V_{CC} = 5 V, T_A = 25°C

PARAMETER		TEST CONDITIONS	MIN	TYP	MAX	UNIT
t_{PLH}	Propagation delay time, low-to-high-level output	C_L = 15 pF, R_L = 2 kΩ, See Note 6		9	15	ns
t_{PHL}	Propagation delay time, high-to-low-level output			20	33	ns

NOTE 6: Load circuit and waveforms are shown on page 3-11.

TYPES SN54184, SN54185A, SN74184, SN74185A
BCD-TO-BINARY AND BINARY-TO-BCD CONVERTERS

BULLETIN NO. DL-S 7211392, FEBRUARY 1971 — REVISED DECEMBER 1972

SN54184, SN74184 BCD-TO-BINARY CONVERTERS
SN54185A, SN74185A BINARY-TO-BCD CONVERTERS

description

These monolithic converters are derived from the custom MSI 256-bit read-only memories SN5488 and SN7488. Emitter connections are made to provide direct read-out of converted codes at outputs Y8 through Y1 as shown in the function tables. These converters demonstrate the versatility of a read-only memory in that an unlimited number of reference tables or conversion tables may be built into a system using economical, customized read-only memories. Both of these converters comprehend that the least significant bits (LSB) of the binary and BCD codes are logically equal, and in each case the LSB bypasses the converter as illustrated in the typical applications. This means that a 6-bit converter is produced in each case. Both devices are cascadable to N bits.

SN54184, SN54185A . . . J OR W PACKAGE
SN74184, SN74185A . . . J OR N PACKAGE
(TOP VIEW)

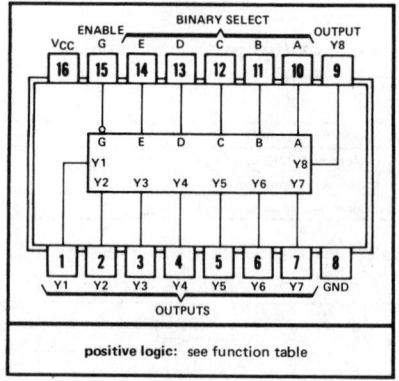

positive logic: see function table

An overriding enable input is provided on each converter which, when taken high, inhibits the function, causing all outputs to go high. For this reason, and to minimize power consumption, unused outputs Y7 and Y8 of the '185A and all "don't care" conditions of the '184 are programmed high. The outputs are of the open-collector type.

The SN54184 and SN54185A are characterized for operation over the full military temperature range of −55°C to 125°C; the SN74184 and SN74185A are characterized for operation from 0°C to 70°C.

SN54184 and SN74184 BCD-to-binary converters

The 6-bit BCD-to-binary function of the SN54184 and SN74184 is analogous to the algorithm:

   a. Shift BCD number right one bit and examine each decade. Subtract three from each 4-bit decade containing a binary value greater than seven.

   b. Shift right, examine, and correct after each shift until the least significant decade contains a number smaller than eight and all other converted decades contain zeros.

TABLE I
SN54184, SN74184
PACKAGE COUNT AND DELAY TIMES
FOR BCD-TO-BINARY CONVERSION

INPUT (DECADES)	PACKAGES REQUIRED	TOTAL DELAY TIMES (ns)	
		TYP	MAX
2	2	56	80
3	6	140	200
4	11	196	280
5	19	280	400
6	28	364	520

TEXAS INSTRUMENTS
INCORPORATED
POST OFFICE BOX 5012 • DALLAS, TEXAS 75222

SN54184 and SN74184 BCD-to-binary converters (continued)

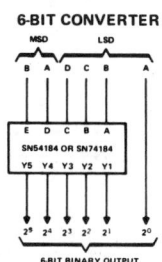

6-BIT CONVERTER

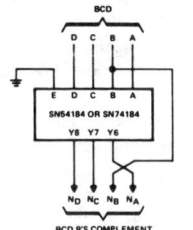

BCD 9'S COMPLEMENT CONVERTER

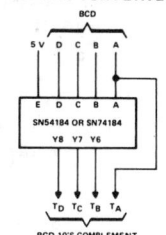

BCD 10'S COMPLEMENT CONVERTER

FUNCTION TABLE
BCD-TO-BINARY
CONVERTER

BCD WORDS	INPUTS (See Note A)						OUTPUTS (See Note B)				
	E	D	C	B	A	G	Y5	Y4	Y3	Y2	Y1
0-1	L	L	L	L	L	L	L	L	L	L	L
2-3	L	L	L	L	H	L	L	L	L	L	H
4-5	L	L	L	H	L	L	L	L	L	H	L
6-7	L	L	L	H	H	L	L	L	L	H	H
8-9	L	L	H	L	L	L	L	L	H	L	L
10-11	L	H	L	L	L	L	L	L	H	L	H
12-13	L	H	L	L	H	L	L	L	H	H	L
14-15	L	H	L	H	L	L	L	L	H	H	H
16-17	L	H	L	H	H	L	L	H	L	L	L
18-19	L	H	H	L	L	L	L	H	L	L	H
20-21	H	L	L	L	L	L	L	H	L	H	L
22-23	H	L	L	L	H	L	L	H	L	H	H
24-25	H	L	L	H	L	L	L	H	H	L	L
26-27	H	L	L	H	H	L	L	H	H	L	H
28-29	H	L	H	L	L	L	L	H	H	H	L
30-31	H	H	L	L	L	L	L	H	H	H	H
32-33	H	H	L	L	H	L	H	L	L	L	L
34-35	H	H	L	H	L	L	H	L	L	L	H
36-37	H	H	L	H	H	L	H	L	L	H	L
38-39	H	H	H	L	L	L	H	L	L	H	H
ANY	X	X	X	X	X	H	H	H	H	H	H

H = high level, L = low level, X = irrelevant

NOTES: A. Input conditions other than those shown produce highs at outputs Y1 through Y5.

B. Outputs Y6, Y7, and Y8 are not used for BCD-to-binary conversion.

In addition to BCD-to-binary conversion, the SN54184 and SN74184 are programmed to generate BCD 9's complement or BCD 10's complement. Again, in each case, one bit of the complement code is logically equal to one of the BCD bits; therefore, these complements can be produced on three lines. As outputs Y6, Y7, and Y8 are not required in the BCD-to-binary conversion, they are utilized to provide these complement codes as specified in the function table (above, right) when the devices are connected as shown above the function table.

FUNCTION TABLE
BCD 9'S OR BCD 10'S
COMPLEMENT CONVERTER

BCD WORD	INPUTS (See Note C)						OUTPUTS (See Note D)		
	E†	D	C	B	A	G	Y8	Y7	Y6
0	L	L	L	L	L	L	H	L	H
1	L	L	L	L	H	L	H	L	L
2	L	L	L	H	L	L	L	H	H
3	L	L	L	H	H	L	L	H	L
4	L	L	H	L	L	L	L	H	H
5	L	L	H	L	H	L	L	H	L
6	L	L	H	H	L	L	L	L	H
7	L	L	H	H	H	L	L	L	L
8	L	H	L	L	L	L	L	L	H
9	L	H	L	L	H	L	L	L	L
0	H	L	L	L	L	L	L	L	L
1	H	L	L	L	H	L	H	L	L
2	H	L	L	H	L	L	H	L	L
3	H	L	L	H	H	L	L	H	H
4	H	L	H	L	L	L	L	H	H
5	H	L	H	L	H	L	L	H	L
6	H	L	H	H	L	L	L	H	L
7	H	L	H	H	H	L	L	L	H
8	H	H	L	L	L	L	L	L	L
9	H	H	L	L	H	L	L	L	L
ANY	X	X	X	X	X	H	H	H	H

H = high level, L = low level, X = irrelevant

NOTES: C. Input conditions other than those shown produce highs at outputs Y6, Y7, and Y8.

D. Outputs Y1 through Y5 are not used for BCD 9's or BCD 10's complement conversion.

†When these devices are used as complement converters, input E is used as a mode control. With this input low, the BCD 9's complement is generated; when it is high, the BCD 10's complement is generated.

TEXAS INSTRUMENTS
INCORPORATED
POST OFFICE BOX 5012 • DALLAS, TEXAS 75222

7

SN54185A and SN74185A binary-to-BCD converters

The function performed by these 6-bit binary-to-BCD converters is analogous to the algorithm:

- a. Examine the three most significant bits. If the sum is greater than four, add three and shift left one bit.
- b. Examine each BCD decade. If the sum is greater than four, add three and shift left one bit.
- c. Repeat step b until the least-significant binary bit is in the least-significant BCD location.

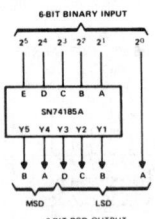

6-BIT CONVERTER

TABLE II

SN54185A, SN74185A

PACKAGE COUNT AND DELAY TIMES

FOR BINARY-TO-BCD CONVERSION

INPUT	PACKAGES	TOTAL DELAY TIME (ns)	
(BITS)	REQUIRED	TYP	MAX
4 to 6	1	25	40
7 or 8	3	50	80
9	4	75	120
10	6	100	160
11	7	125	200
12	8	125	200
13	10	150	240
14	12	175	280
15	14	175	280
16	16	200	320
17	19	225	360
18	21	225	360
19	24	250	400
20	27	275	440

FUNCTION TABLE

BINARY WORDS	INPUTS						OUTPUTS							
	BINARY SELECT					ENABLE								
	E	D	C	B	A	G	Y8	Y7	Y6	Y5	Y4	Y3	Y2	Y1
0 - 1	L	L	L	L	L	L	H	H	L	L	L	L	L	L
2 - 3	L	L	L	L	H	L	H	H	L	L	L	L	L	H
4 - 5	L	L	L	H	L	L	H	H	L	L	L	L	H	L
6 - 7	L	L	L	H	H	L	H	H	L	L	L	L	H	H
8 - 9	L	L	H	L	L	L	H	H	L	L	L	H	L	L
10 - 11	L	L	H	L	H	L	H	H	L	L	L	H	L	H
12 - 13	L	L	H	H	L	L	H	H	L	L	H	L	L	H
14 - 15	L	L	H	H	H	L	H	H	L	L	H	L	H	L
16 - 17	L	H	L	L	L	L	H	H	L	L	H	L	H	H
18 - 19	L	H	L	L	H	L	H	H	L	L	H	H	L	L
20 - 21	L	H	L	H	L	L	H	H	L	H	L	L	L	L
22 - 23	L	H	L	H	H	L	H	H	L	H	L	L	L	H
24 - 25	L	H	H	L	L	L	H	H	L	H	L	L	H	L
26 - 27	L	H	H	L	H	L	H	H	L	H	L	L	H	H
28 - 29	L	H	H	H	L	L	H	H	L	H	L	H	L	L
30 - 31	L	H	H	H	H	L	H	H	L	H	H	L	L	L
32 - 33	H	L	L	L	L	L	H	H	L	H	H	L	L	H
34 - 35	H	L	L	L	H	L	H	H	L	H	H	L	H	L
36 - 37	H	L	L	H	L	L	H	H	L	H	H	L	H	H
38 - 39	H	L	L	H	H	L	H	H	L	H	H	H	L	L
40 - 41	H	L	H	L	L	L	H	H	H	L	L	L	L	L
42 - 43	H	L	H	L	H	L	H	H	H	L	L	L	L	H
44 - 45	H	L	H	H	L	L	H	H	H	L	L	L	H	L
46 - 47	H	L	H	H	H	L	H	H	H	L	L	L	H	H
48 - 49	H	H	L	L	L	L	H	H	H	L	L	H	L	L
50 - 51	H	H	L	L	H	L	H	H	H	L	H	L	L	H
52 - 53	H	H	L	H	L	L	H	H	H	L	H	L	L	H
54 - 55	H	H	L	H	H	L	H	H	H	L	H	L	H	L
56 - 57	H	H	H	L	L	L	H	H	H	L	H	L	H	H
58 - 59	H	H	H	L	H	L	H	H	H	L	H	H	L	L
60 - 61	H	H	H	H	L	L	H	H	H	H	L	L	L	L
62 - 63	H	H	H	H	H	L	H	H	H	H	L	L	L	H
ALL	X	X	X	X	X	H	H	H	H	H	H	H	H	H

H = high level, L = low level, X = irrelevant

absolute maximum ratings over operating free-air temperature range (unless otherwise noted)

Supply voltage, V_{CC} (see Note 1) . . . . 7 V

Input voltage . . . . 5.5 V

Operating free-air temperature range: SN54184, SN54185A . . . . −55°C to 125°C

SN74184, SN74185A . . . . 0°C to 70°C

Storage temperature range . . . . −65°C to 150°C

NOTE 1: Voltage values are with respect to network ground terminal.

TEXAS INSTRUMENTS
INCORPORATED
POST OFFICE BOX 5012 • DALLAS, TEXAS 75222

recommended operating conditions

	SN54184, SN54185A			SN74184, SN74185A			UNIT
	MIN	NOM	MAX	MIN	NOM	MAX	
Supply voltage, V_{CC}	4.5	5	5.5	4.75	5	5.25	V
Low-level output current, I_{OL}			12			12	mA
Operating free-air temperature, T_A	−55		125	0		70	°C

electrical characteristics over recommended operating free-air temperature range (unless otherwise noted)

	PARAMETER	TEST CONDITIONS[†]	MIN	TYP[‡]	MAX	UNIT
V_{IH}	High-level input voltage		2			V
V_{IL}	Low-level input voltage				0.8	V
V_{IK}	Input clamp voltage	V_{CC} = MIN, I_I = −12 mA			−1.5	V
I_{OH}	High-level output current	V_{CC} = MIN, V_{IH} = 2 V, V_{IL} = 0.8 V, V_{OH} = 5.5 V			100	µA
V_{OL}	Low-level output voltage	V_{CC} = MIN, V_{IH} = 2 V, V_{IL} = 0.8 V, I_{OL} = 12 mA			0.4	V
I_I	Input current at maximum input voltage	V_{CC} = MAX, V_I = 5.5 V			1	mA
I_{IH}	High-level input current	V_{CC} = MAX, V_I = 2.4 V			40	µA
I_{IL}	Low-level input current	V_{CC} = MAX, V_I = 0.4 V			−1	mA
I_{CCH}	Supply current, all outputs high	V_{CC} = MAX		50		mA
I_{CCL}	Supply current, all programmed outputs low			62	99	

[†]For conditions shown as MIN or MAX, use the appropriate value specified under recommended operating conditions for the applicable type.
[‡]All typical values are at V_{CC} = 5 V, T_A = 25°C.

switching characteristics, V_{CC} = 5 V, T_A = 25°C

	PARAMETER	TEST CONDITIONS	MIN	TYP	MAX	UNIT
t_{PLH}	Propagation delay time, low-to-high-level output from enable G	C_L = 15 pF,		19	30	ns
t_{PHL}	Propagation delay time, high-to-low-level output from enable G	R_{L1} = 400 Ω,		22	35	ns
t_{PLH}	Propagation delay time, low-to-high-level output from binary select	R_{L2} = 600 Ω,		27	40	ns
t_{PHL}	Propagation delay time, high-to-low-level output from binary select	See Figure 1 and Note 2		23	40	ns

PARAMETER MEASUREMENT INFORMATION

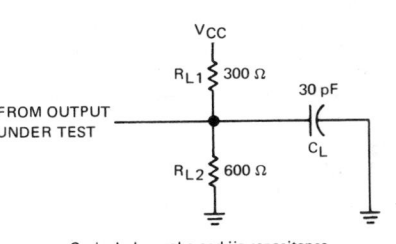

C_L includes probe and jig capacitance.

LOAD CIRCUIT
FIGURE 1

NOTE 2: Voltage waveforms are shown on page 3-10.

schematics of inputs and outputs

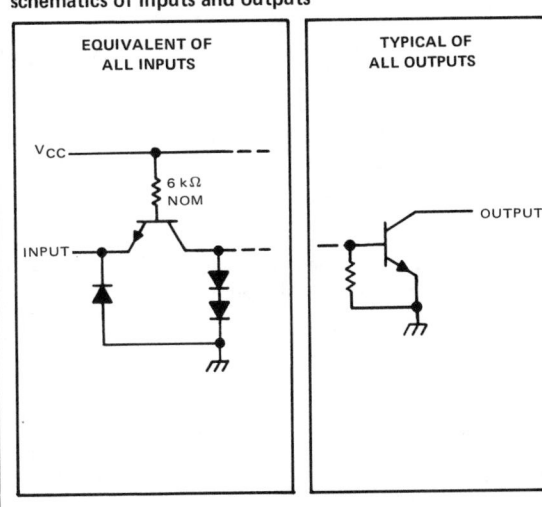

EQUIVALENT OF ALL INPUTS

TYPICAL OF ALL OUTPUTS

7

TEXAS INSTRUMENTS
INCORPORATED
POST OFFICE BOX 5012 • DALLAS, TEXAS 75222

TYPES SN54184, SN54185A, SN74184, SN74185A
BCD-TO-BINARY AND BINARY-TO-BCD CONVERTERS

TYPICAL APPLICATION DATA
SN54184, SN74184

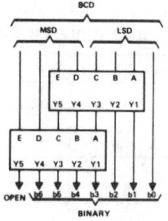

FIGURE 1—BCD-TO-BINARY CONVERTER
FOR TWO BCD DECADES

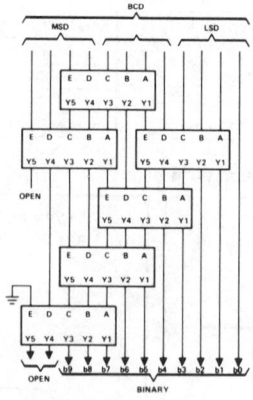

FIGURE 2—BCD-TO-BINARY CONVERTER
FOR THREE BCD DECADES

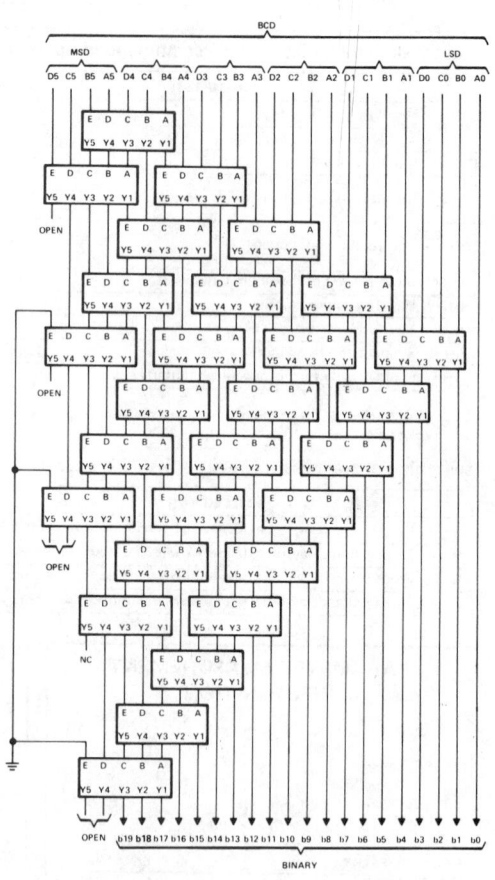

FIGURE 3—BCD-TO-BINARY CONVERTER
FOR SIX BCD DECADES

MSD—most significant decade
LSD—least significant decade
Each rectangle represents an SN54184 or SN74184.

TEXAS INSTRUMENTS
INCORPORATED
POST OFFICE BOX 5012 • DALLAS, TEXAS 75222

TYPICAL APPLICATION DATA
SN54185A, SN74185A

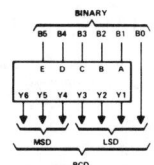

FIGURE 4—6-BIT BINARY-TO-BCD CONVERTER

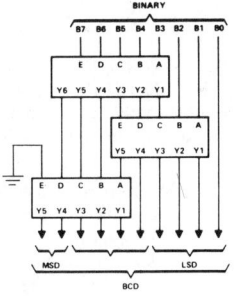

FIGURE 5—8-BIT BINARY-TO-BCD CONVERTER

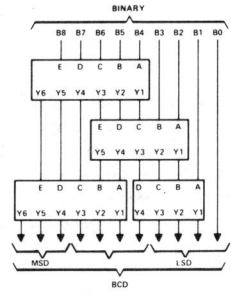

FIGURE 6—9-BIT BINARY-TO-BCD CONVERTER

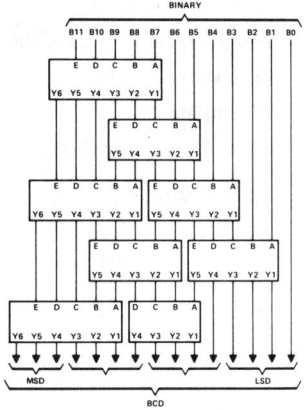

FIGURE 7—12-BIT BINARY-TO-BCD CONVERTER (SEE NOTE B)

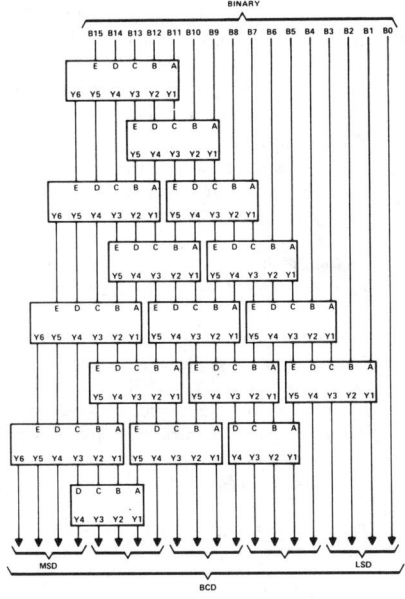

FIGURE 8—16-BIT BINARY-TO-BCD CONVERTER (SEE NOTE B)

MSD—Most significant decade
LSD—Least significant decade
NOTES: A. Each rectangle represents an SN54185A or an SN74185A.
          B. All unused E inputs are grounded.

TYPES SN54190, SN54191, SN54LS190, SN54LS191, SN74190, SN74191, SN74LS190, SN74LS191
SYNCHRONOUS UP/DOWN COUNTERS WITH DOWN/UP MODE CONTROL

BULLETIN NO. DL-S 7711865, DECEMBER 1972—REVISED AUGUST 1977

- Counts 8-4-2-1 BCD or Binary
- Single Down/Up Count Control Line
- Count Enable Control Input
- Ripple Clock Output for Cascading
- Asynchronously Presettable with Load Control
- Parallel Outputs
- Cascadable for n-Bit Applications

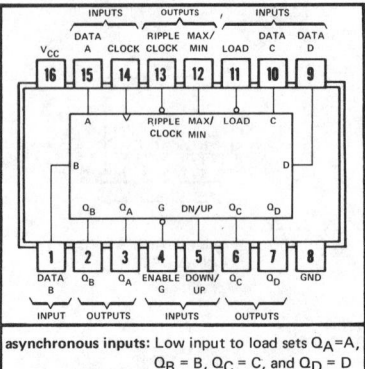

SN54', SN54LS' . . . J OR W PACKAGE
SN74', SN74LS' . . . J OR N PACKAGE
(TOP VIEW)

asynchronous inputs: Low input to load sets $Q_A = A$,
$Q_B = B$, $Q_C = C$, and $Q_D = D$.

TYPE	AVERAGE PROPAGATION DELAY	TYPICAL MAXIMUM CLOCK FREQUENCY	TYPICAL POWER DISSIPATION
'190, '191	20 ns	25 MHz	325 mW
'LS190, 'LS191	20 ns	25 MHz	100 mW

description

The '190, 'LS190, '191, and 'LS191 are synchronous, reversible up/down counters having a complexity of 58 equivalent gates. The '191 and 'LS191 are 4-bit binary counters and the '190 and 'LS190 are BCD counters. Synchronous operation is provided by having all flip-flops clocked simultaneously so that the outputs change coincide with each other when so instructed by the steering logic. This mode of operation eliminates the output counting spikes normally associated with asynchronous (ripple clock) counters.

The outputs of the four master-slave flip-flops are triggered on a low-to-high-level transition of the clock input if the enable input is low. A high at the enable input inhibits counting. Level changes at the enable input should be made only when the clock input is high. The direction of the count is determined by the level of the down/up input. When low, the counter counts up and when high, it counts down. Level changes at the down/up input of the 'LS190 and 'LS191 should be made only when the clock input is high.

These counters are fully programmable; that is, the outputs may be preset to either level by placing a low on the load input and entering the desired data at the data inputs. The output will change to agree with the data inputs independently of the level of the clock input. This feature allows the counters to be used as modulo-N dividers by simply modifying the count length with the preset inputs.

The clock, down/up, and load inputs are buffered to lower the drive requirement which significantly reduces the number of clock drivers, etc., required for long parallel words.

Two outputs have been made available to perform the cascading function: ripple clock and maximum/minimum count. The latter output produces a high-level output pulse with a duration approximately equal to one complete cycle of the clock when the counter overflows or underflows. The ripple clock output produces a low-level output pulse equal in width to the low-level portion of the clock input when an overflow or underflow condition exists. The counters can be easily cascaded by feeding the ripple clock output to the enable input of the succeeding counter if parallel clocking is used, or to the clock input if parallel enabling is used. The maximum/minimum count output can be used to accomplish look-ahead for high-speed operation.

Series 54' and 54LS' are characterized for operation over the full military temperature range of −55°C to 125°C; Series 74' and 74LS' are characterized for operation from 0°C to 70°C.

TEXAS INSTRUMENTS
INCORPORATED
POST OFFICE BOX 5012 • DALLAS, TEXAS 75222

877

functional block diagrams

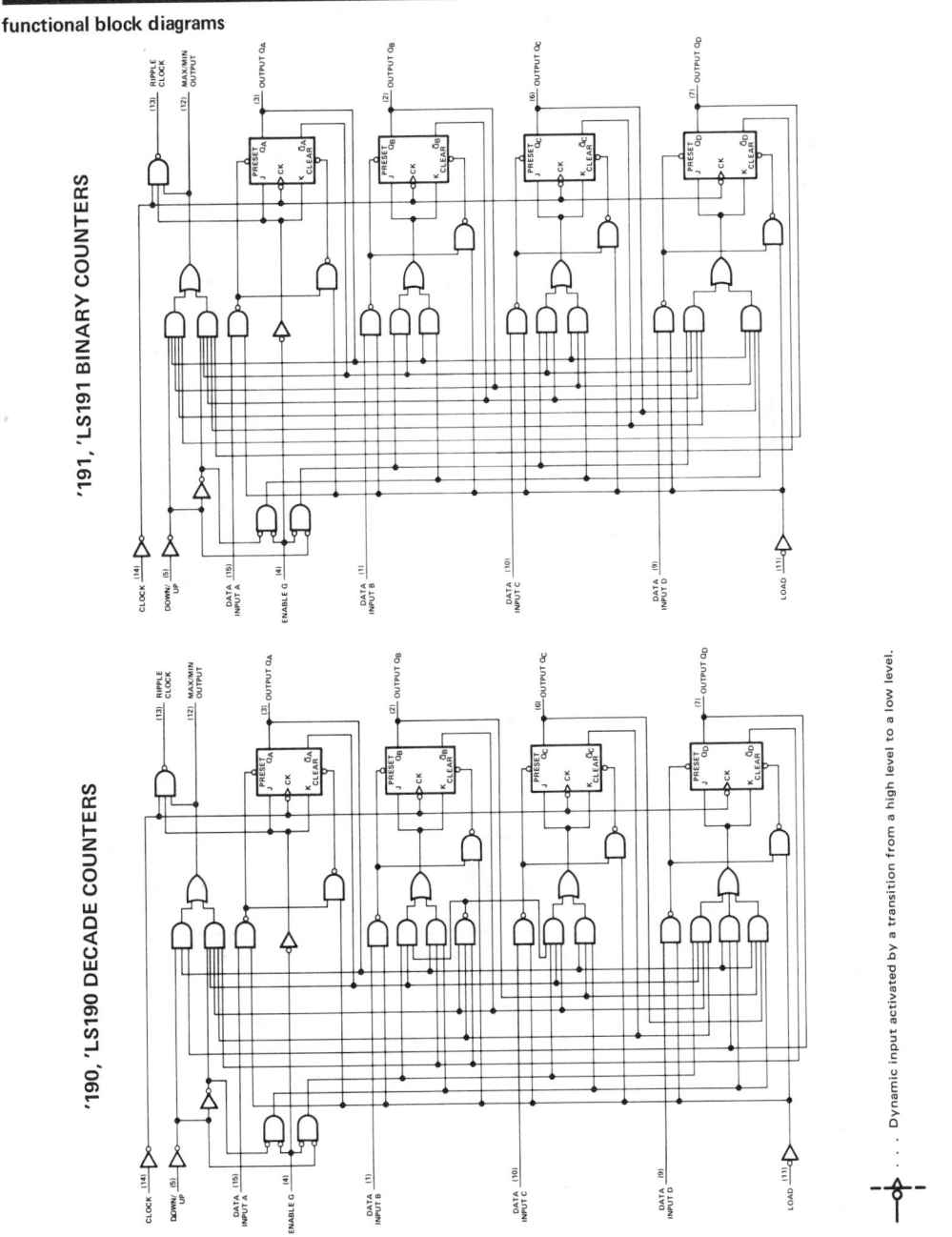

'191, 'LS191 BINARY COUNTERS

'190, 'LS190 DECADE COUNTERS

· · · · Dynamic input activated by a transition from a high level to a low level.

TEXAS INSTRUMENTS
INCORPORATED
POST OFFICE BOX 5012 · DALLAS, TEXAS 75222

'190, 'LS190 DECADE COUNTERS

typical load, count, and inhibit sequences

Illustrated below is the following sequence:

1. Load (preset) to BCD seven.
2. Count up to eight, nine (maximum), zero, one, and two.
3. Inhibit.
4. Count down to one, zero (minimum), nine, eight, and seven.

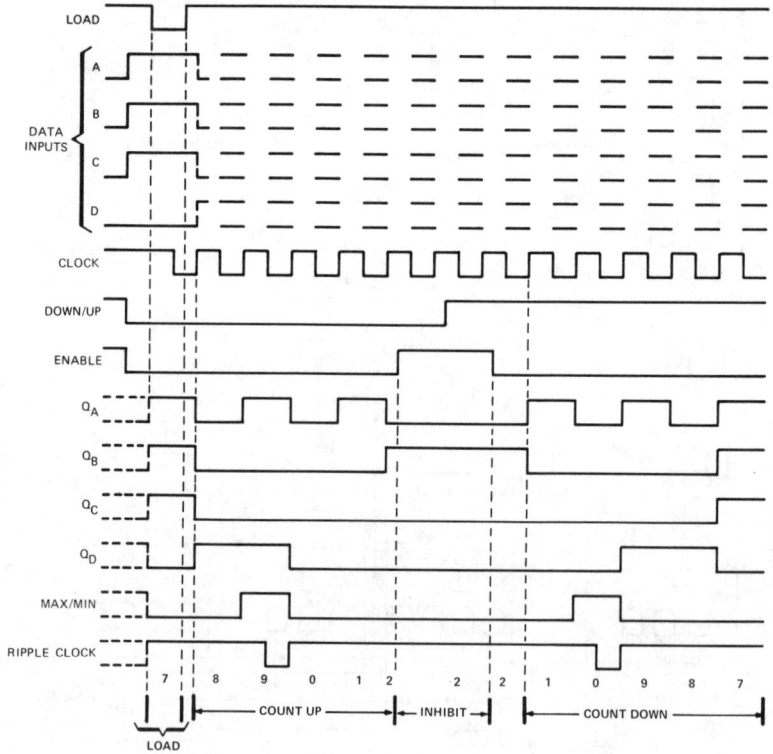

TEXAS INSTRUMENTS
INCORPORATED
POST OFFICE BOX 5012 • DALLAS, TEXAS 75222

'191, 'LS191 BINARY COUNTERS

typical load, count, and inhibit sequences

Illustrated below is the following sequence:

1. Load (preset) to binary thirteen.
2. Count up to fourteen, fifteen (maximum), zero, one, and two.
3. Inhibit.
4. Count down to one, zero (minimum), fifteen, fourteen, and thirteen.

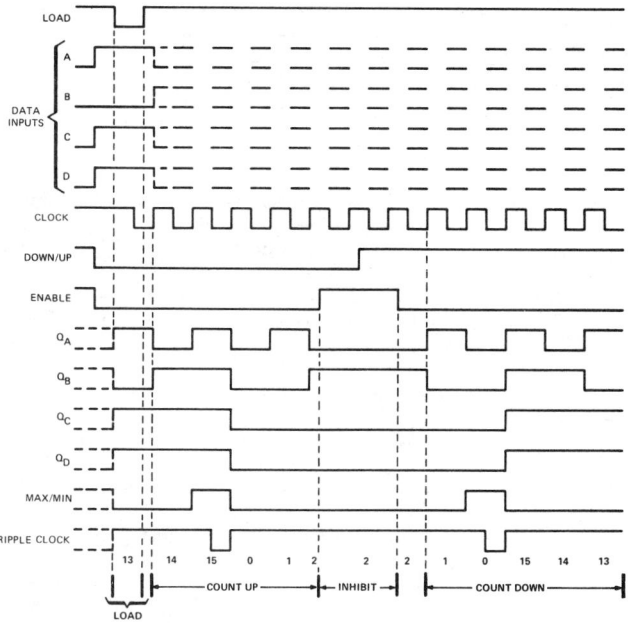

absolute maximum ratings over operating free-air temperature range (unless otherwise noted)

Supply voltage, V_{CC} (see Note 1) . . . . 7 V
Input voltage: SN54', SN74' Circuits . . . . 5.5 V
            SN54LS', SN74LS' Circuits . . . . 7 V
Operating free-air temperature range: SN54', SN54LS' Circuits . . . . -55°C to 125°C
                     SN74', SN74LS' Circuits . . . . 0°C to 70°C
Storage temperature range   . . . . -65°C to 150°C

NOTE 1: Voltage values are with respect to network ground terminal.

recommended operating conditions

	SN54190, SN54191			SN74190, SN74191			UNIT
	MIN	NOM	MAX	MIN	NOM	MAX	
Supply voltage, V_{CC}	4.5	5	5.5	4.75	5	5.25	V
High-level output current, I_{OH}			−800			−800	μA
Low-level output current, I_{OL}			16			16	mA
Input clock frequency, f_{clock}	0		20	0		20	MHz
Width of clock input pulse, $t_{w(clock)}$	25			25			ns
Width of load input pulse, $t_{w(load)}$	35			35			ns
Data setup time, t_{setup} (See Figures 1 and 2)	20			20			ns
Data hold time, t_{hold}	0			0			ns
Operating free-air temperature, T_A	−55		125	0		70	°C

electrical characteristics over recommended operating free-air temperature range (unless otherwise noted)

PARAMETER		TEST CONDITIONS[†]	SN54190, SN54191			SN74190, SN74191			UNIT
			MIN	TYP[‡]	MAX	MIN	TYP[‡]	MAX	
V_{IH}	High-level input voltage	V_{CC} = MIN	2			2			V
V_{IL}	Low-level input voltage	V_{CC} = MIN			0.8			0.8	V
V_{IK}	Input clamp voltage	V_{CC} = MIN, I_I = −12 mA			−1.5			−1.5	V
V_{OH}	High-level output voltage	V_{CC} = MIN, V_{IH} = 2 V, V_{IL} = 0.8 V, I_{OH} = −800 μA	2.4	3.4		2.4	3.4		V
V_{OL}	Low-level output voltage	V_{CC} = MIN, V_{IH} = 2 V, V_{IL} = 0.8 V, I_{OL} = 16 mA		0.2	0.4		0.2	0.4	V
I_I	High-level input current at maximum input voltage	V_{CC} = MAX, V_I = 5.5 V			1			1	mA
I_{IH}	High-level input current at any input except enable	V_{CC} = MAX, V_I = 2.4 V			40			40	μA
I_{IH}	High-level input current at enable input				120			120	μA
I_{IL}	Low-level input current at any input except enable	V_{CC} = MAX, V_I = 0.4 V			−1.6			−1.6	mA
I_{IL}	Low-level input current at enable input				−4.8			−4.8	mA
I_{OS}	Short-circuit output current§	V_{CC} = MAX	−20		−65	−18		−65	mA
I_{CC}	Supply current	V_{CC} = MAX, See Note 2		65	99		65	105	mA

[†] For conditions shown as MAX or MIN, use appropriate value specified under recommended operating conditions.
[‡] All typical values are at V_{CC} = 5 V, T_A = 25°C.
§ Not more than one output should be shorted at a time.
NOTE 2: I_{CC} is measured with all inputs grounded and all outputs open.

TEXAS INSTRUMENTS
INCORPORATED
POST OFFICE BOX 5012 • DALLAS, TEXAS 75222

switching characteristics, $V_{CC} = 5$ V, $T_A = 25°C$

PARAMETER ¶	FROM (INPUT)	TO (OUTPUT)	TEST CONDITIONS	'190, '191 MIN	TYP	MAX	UNIT
f_{max}				20	25		MHz
t_{PLH}	Load	Q_A, Q_B, Q_C, Q_D			22	33	ns
t_{PHL}					33	50	
t_{PLH}	Data A, B, C, D	Q_A, Q_B, Q_C, Q_D			14	22	ns
t_{PHL}					35	50	
t_{PLH}	Clock	Ripple Clock	$C_L = 15$ pF, $R_L = 400$ Ω,		13	20	ns
t_{PHL}			See Figures 1 and 3 thru 7		16	24	
t_{PLH}	Clock	Q_A, Q_B, Q_C, Q_D			16	24	ns
t_{PHL}					24	36	
t_{PLH}	Clock	Max/Min			28	42	ns
t_{PHL}					37	52	
t_{PLH}	Down/Up	Ripple Clock			30	45	ns
t_{PHL}					30	45	
t_{PLH}	Down/Up	Max/Min			21	33	ns
t_{PHL}					22	33	

¶ f_{max} ≡ maximum clock frequency
t_{PLH} ≡ propagation delay time, low-to-high-level output
t_{PHL} ≡ propagation delay time, high-to-low-level output

schematics of inputs and outputs

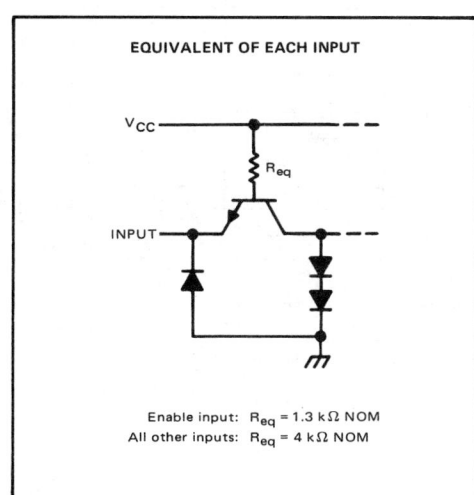

EQUIVALENT OF EACH INPUT

Enable input: $R_{eq} = 1.3$ kΩ NOM
All other inputs: $R_{eq} = 4$ kΩ NOM

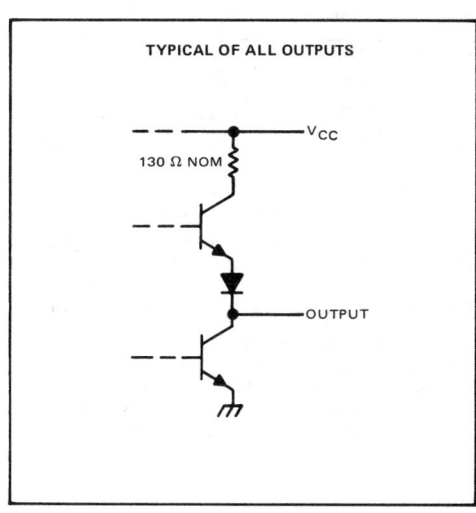

TYPICAL OF ALL OUTPUTS

130 Ω NOM

7

recommended operating conditions

		SN54LS190 SN54LS191		SN74LS190 SN74LS191			UNIT
	MIN	NOM	MAX	MIN	NOM	MAX	
Supply voltage, V_{CC}	4.5	5	5.5	4.75	5	5.25	V
High-level output current, I_{OH}			−400			−400	μA
Low-level output current, I_{OL}			4			8	mA
Clock frequency, f_{clock}	0	20		0	20		MHz
Width of clock input pulse, $t_{w(clock)}$	25			25			ns
Width of load input pulse, $t_{w(load)}$	35			35			ns
Data setup time, t_{setup} (See Figures 1 and 2)	20			20			ns
Data hold time, t_{hold}	0			0			ns
Count enable time, t_{enable} (see Note 3)	40			40			ns
Operating free-air temperature, T_A	−55		125	0		70	°C

electrical characteristics over recommended operating free-air temperature range (unless otherwise noted)

PARAMETER			TEST CONDITIONS†		SN54LS190 SN54LS191			SN74LS190 SN74LS191			UNIT
					MIN	TYP‡	MAX	MIN	TYP‡	MAX	
V_{IH}	High-level input voltage				2			2			V
V_{IL}	Low-level input voltage						0.7			0.8	V
V_{IK}	Input clamp voltage		V_{CC} = MIN,	I_I = −18 mA			−1.5			−1.5	V
V_{OH}	High-level output voltage		V_{CC} = MIN, V_{IH} = 2 V, V_{IL} = V_{IL} max, I_{OH} = −400 μA		2.5	3.4		2.7	3.4		V
V_{OL}	Low-level output voltage		V_{CC} = MIN, V_{IH} = 2 V, V_{IL} = V_{IL} max	I_{OL} = 4 mA	0.25		0.4		0.25	0.4	V
				I_{OL} = 8 mA					0.35	0.5	
I_I	High-level input current at maximum input voltage	Enable	V_{CC} = MAX,	V_I = 7 V			0.3			0.3	mA
		Others					0.1			0.1	
I_{IH}	High-level input current	Enable	V_{CC} = MAX,	V_I = 2.7 V			60			60	μA
		Others					20			20	
I_{IL}	Low-level input current	Enable	V_{CC} = MAX,	V_I = 0.4 V			−1.2			−1.2	mA
		Others					−0.4			−0.4	
I_{OS}	Short-circuit output current§		V_{CC} = MAX,		−20		−100	−20		−100	mA
I_{CC}	Supply current		V_{CC} = MAX,	See Note 2		20	35		20	35	mA

†For conditions shown as MAX or MIN, use appropriate value specified under recommended operating conditions for the applicable device type.

‡All typical values are at V_{CC} = 5 V, T_A = 25°C.

§Not more than one output should be shorted at a time, and duration of the short-circuit should not exceed one second.

NOTES: 2. I_{CC} is measured with all inputs grounded and all outputs open.

　　　　3. Minimum count enable time is the interval immediately preceeding the rising edge of the clock pulse during which interval the count enable input must be low to ensure counting.

TEXAS INSTRUMENTS
INCORPORATED
POST OFFICE BOX 5012 • DALLAS, TEXAS 75222

switching characteristics, V_{CC} = 5 V, T_A = 25°C

PARAMETER¶	FROM (INPUT)	TO (OUTPUT)	TEST CONDITIONS	'LS190, 'LS191 MIN	TYP	MAX	UNIT
f_{max}				20	25		MHz
t_{PLH}	Load	Q_A, Q_B, Q_C, Q_D			22	33	ns
t_{PHL}					33	50	
t_{PLH}	Data A, B, C, D	Q_A, Q_B, Q_C, Q_D			20	32	ns
t_{PHL}					27	40	
t_{PLH}	Clock	Ripple Clock	C_L = 15 pF, R_L = 2 kΩ, See Figures 1 and 3 thru 7		13	20	ns
t_{PHL}					16	24	
t_{PLH}	Clock	Q_A, Q_B, Q_C, Q_D			16	24	ns
t_{PHL}					24	36	
t_{PLH}	Clock	Max/Min			28	42	ns
t_{PHL}					37	52	
t_{PLH}	Down/Up	Ripple Clock			30	45	ns
t_{PHL}					30	45	
t_{PLH}	Down/Up	Max/Min			21	33	ns
t_{PHL}					22	33	
t_{PLH}	Enable	Ripple Clock			21	33	ns
t_{PHL}					22	33	

¶f_{max} ≡ maximum clock frequency
t_{PLH} ≡ propagation delay time, low-to-high-level output
t_{PHL} ≡ propagation delay time, high-to-low-level output

schematics of inputs and outputs

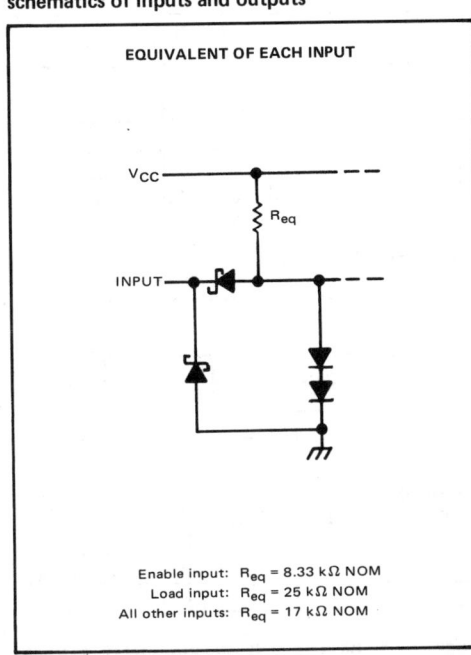

EQUIVALENT OF EACH INPUT

Enable input: R_{eq} = 8.33 kΩ NOM
Load input: R_{eq} = 25 kΩ NOM
All other inputs: R_{eq} = 17 kΩ NOM

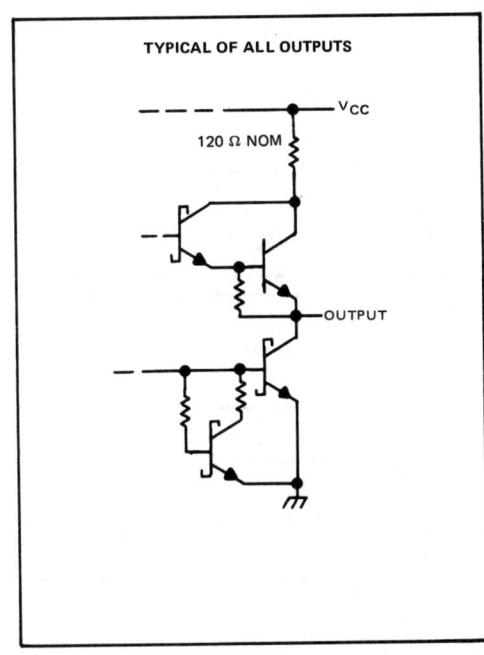

TYPICAL OF ALL OUTPUTS

120 Ω NOM

TEXAS INSTRUMENTS
INCORPORATED
POST OFFICE BOX 5012 • DALLAS, TEXAS 75222

PARAMETER MEASUREMENT INFORMATION

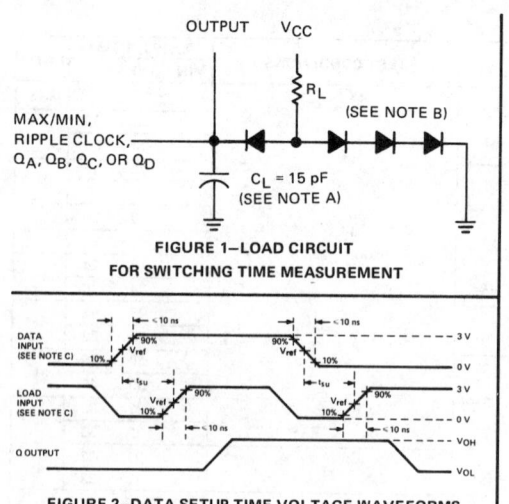

FIGURE 1—LOAD CIRCUIT
FOR SWITCHING TIME MEASUREMENT

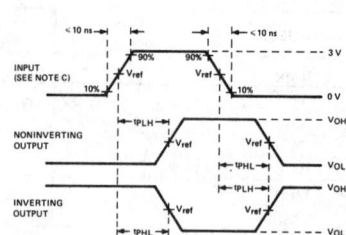

FIGURE 2—DATA SETUP TIME VOLTAGE WAVEFORMS

See waveform sequences in figures 4 through 7 for propagation times from a specific input to a specific output. For simplification, pulse rise times, reference levels, etc., have not been shown in figures 4 through 7.

FIGURE 3—GENERAL VOLTAGE WAVEFORMS FOR
PROPAGATION TIMES

NOTES: A. C$_L$ includes probe and jig capacitance.
  B. All diodes are 1N3064.
  C. The input pulses are supplied by generators having the following characteristics: Z$_{out}$ = 50 Ω, duty cycle ⩽ 50%, PRR ⩽ 1 MHz.
  D. V$_{ref}$ = 1.5 V for '190 and '191; 1.3 V for 'LS190 and 'LS191.

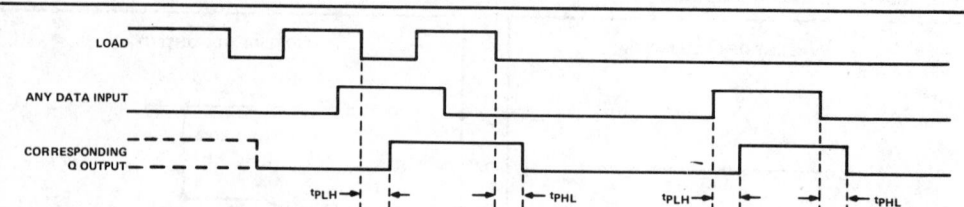

NOTE E: Conditions on other inputs are irrelevant.

FIGURE 4—LOAD TO OUTPUT AND DATA TO OUTPUT

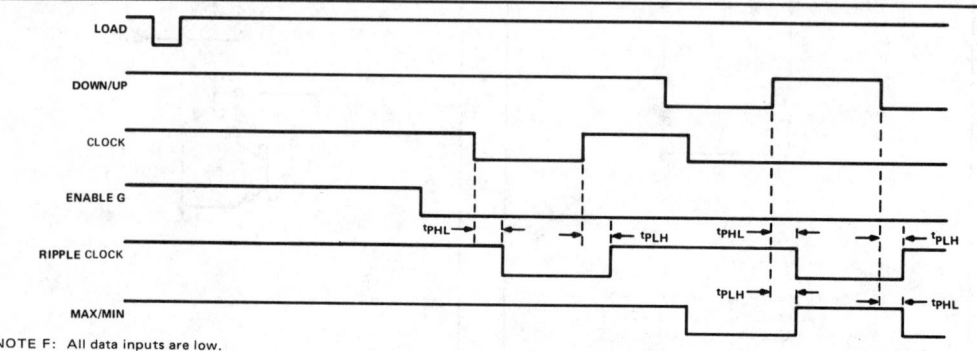

NOTE F: All data inputs are low.

FIGURE 5—ENABLE TO RIPPLE CLOCK, CLOCK TO RIPPLE CLOCK, DOWN/UP TO RIPPLE CLOCK, AND DOWN/UP TO MAX/MIN

TEXAS INSTRUMENTS
INCORPORATED
POST OFFICE BOX 5012 • DALLAS, TEXAS 75222

TYPES SN54190, SN54191, SN54LS190, SN54LS191, SN74190, SN74191, SN74LS190, SN74LS191
SYNCHRONOUS UP/DOWN COUNTERS WITH DOWN/UP MODE CONTROL

PARAMETER MEASUREMENT INFORMATION

switching characteristics (continued)

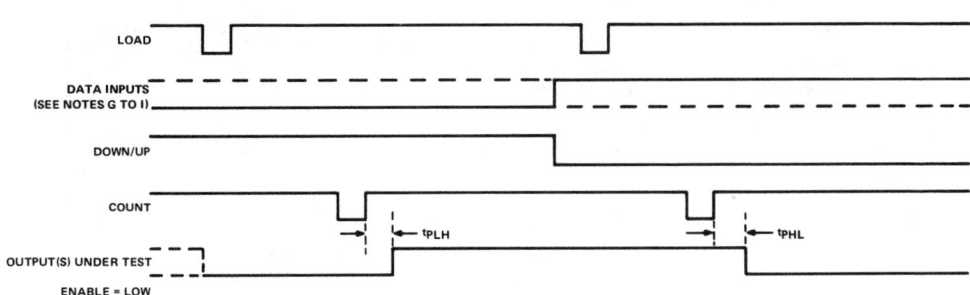

NOTES: G. to test Q_A, Q_B, and Q_C outputs of '190 and 'LS190: Data inputs A, B, and C are shown by the solid line. Data input D is shown by the dashed line.

H. To test Q_D output of '190 and 'LS190: Data inputs A and D are shown by the solid line. Data inputs B and C are held at the low logic level.

I. To test Q_A, Q_B, Q_C, and Q_D outputs of '191 and 'LS191: All four data inputs are shown by the solid line.

FIGURE 6—CLOCK TO OUTPUT

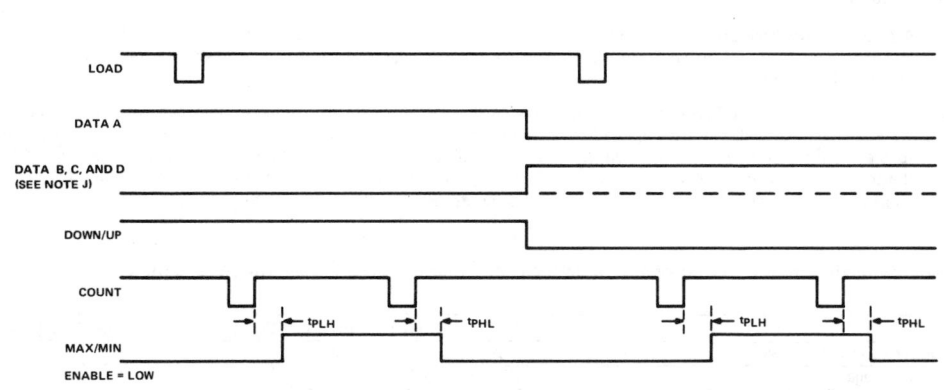

NOTE J: Data inputs B and C are shown by the dashed line for the '190 and 'LS190 and the solid line for the '191 and 'LS191: Data input D is shown by the solid line for both devices.

FIGURE 7—CLOCK TO MAX/MIN

TEXAS INSTRUMENTS
INCORPORATED
POST OFFICE BOX 5012 • DALLAS, TEXAS 75222

7

TYPES SN54192, SN54193, SN54L192, SN54L193, SN54LS192, SN54LS193 SN74192, SN74193, SN74L192, SN74L193, SN74LS192, SN74LS193
SYNCHRONOUS 4-BIT UP/DOWN COUNTERS (DUAL CLOCK WITH CLEAR)

BULLETIN NO. DL-S 7711828, DECEMBER 1972—REVISED AUGUST 1977

- Cascading Circuitry Provided Internally
- Synchronous Operation
- Individual Preset to Each Flip-Flop
- Fully Independent Clear Input

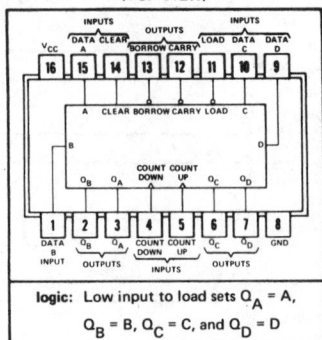

SN54', SN54LS' . . . J OR W PACKAGE
SN54L' . . . J PACKAGE
SN74', SN74L', SN74LS' . . . J OR N PACKAGE
(TOP VIEW)

logic: Low input to load sets Q_A = A, Q_B = B, Q_C = C, and Q_D = D

TYPES	TYPICAL MAXIMUM COUNT FREQUENCY	TYPICAL POWER DISSIPATION
'192, '193	32 MHz	325 mW
'L192, 'L193	7 MHz	43 mW
'LS192, 'LS193	32 MHz	95 mW

description

These monolithic circuits are synchronous reversible (up/down) counters having a complexity of 55 equivalent gates. The '192, 'L192, and 'LS192 circuits are BCD counters and the '193, 'L193 and 'LS193 are 4-bit binary counters. Synchronous operation is provided by having all flip-flops clocked simultaneously so that the outputs change coincidently with each other when so instructed by the steering logic. This mode of operation eliminates the output counting spikes which are normally associated with asynchronous (ripple-clock) counters.

The outputs of the four master-slave flip-flops are triggered by a low-to-high-level transition of either count (clock) input. The direction of counting is determined by which count input is pulsed while the other count input is high.

All four counters are fully programmable; that is, each output may be preset to either level by entering the desired data at the data inputs while the load input is low. The output will change to agree with the data inputs independently of the count pulses. This feature allows the counters to be used as modulo-N dividers by simply modifying the count length with the preset inputs.

A clear input has been provided which forces all outputs to the low level when a high level is applied. The clear function is independent of the count and load inputs. The clear, count, and load inputs are buffered to lower the drive requirements. This reduces the number of clock drivers, etc., required for long words.

These counters were designed to be cascaded without the need for external circuitry. Both borrow and carry outputs are available to cascade both the up- and down-counting functions. The borrow output produces a pulse equal in width to the count-down input when the counter underflows. Similarly, the carry output produces a pulse equal in width to the count-up input when an overflow condition exists. The counters can then be easily cascaded by feeding the borrow and carry outputs to the count-down and count-up inputs respectively of the succeeding counter.

absolute maximum ratings over operating free-air temperature range (unless otherwise noted)

	SN54'	SN54L'	SN54LS'	SN74'	SN74L'	SN74LS'	UNIT
Supply voltage, V_{CC} (see Note 1)	7	8	7	7	8	7	V
Input voltage	5.5	5.5	7	5.5	5.5	7	V
Operating free-air temperature range	−55 to 125			0 to 70			°C
Storage temperature range	−65 to 150			−65 to 150			°C

NOTE 1: Voltage values are with respect to network ground terminal.

TEXAS INSTRUMENTS
INCORPORATED
POST OFFICE BOX 5012 • DALLAS, TEXAS 75222

TYPES SN54192, SN54193, SN54L192, SN54L193, SN54LS192, SN54LS193, SN74192, SN74193, SN74L192, SN74L193, SN74LS192, SN74LS193 SYNCHRONOUS 4-BIT UP/DOWN COUNTERS (DUAL CLOCK WITH CLEAR)

functional block diagrams

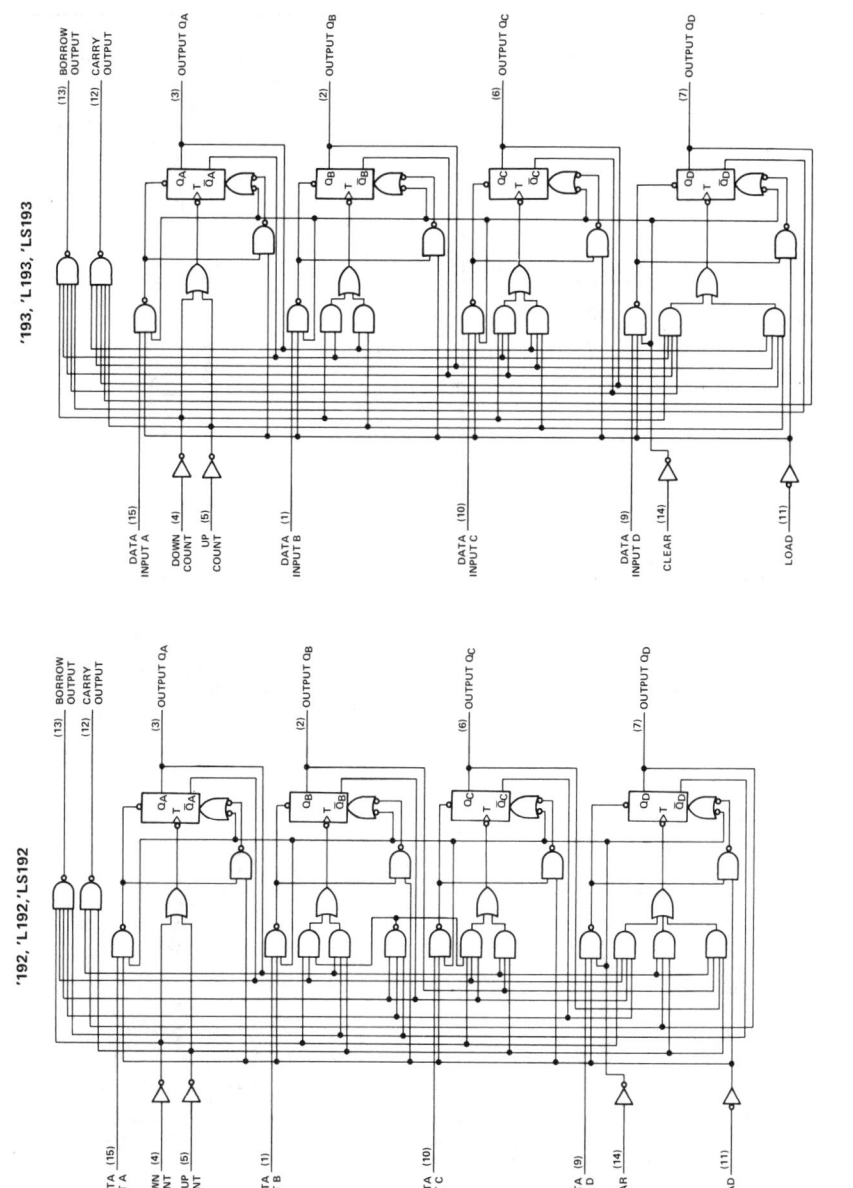

schematics of inputs and outputs

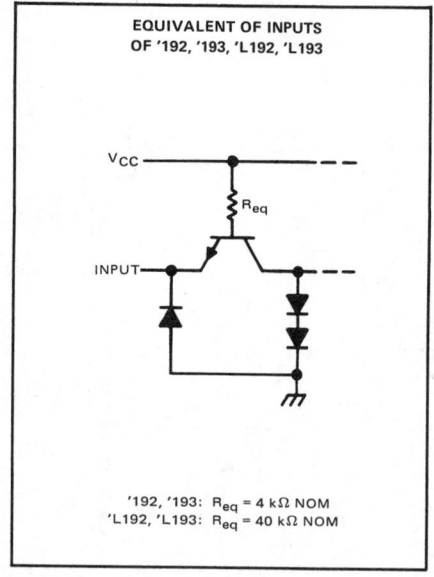

EQUIVALENT OF INPUTS
OF '192, '193, 'L192, 'L193

'192, '193: R_eq = 4 kΩ NOM
'L192, 'L193: R_eq = 40 kΩ NOM

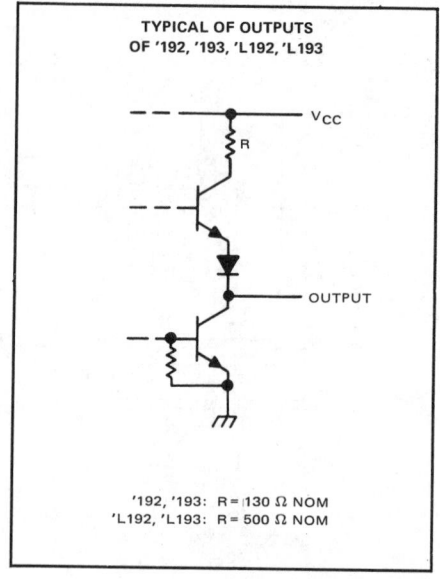

TYPICAL OF OUTPUTS
OF '192, '193, 'L192, 'L193

'192, '193: R = 130 Ω NOM
'L192, 'L193: R = 500 Ω NOM

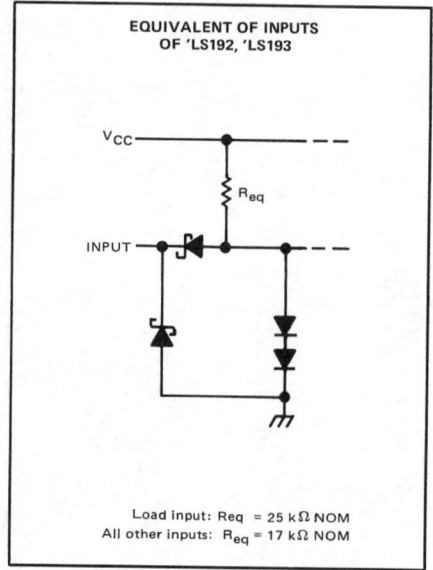

EQUIVALENT OF INPUTS
OF 'LS192, 'LS193

Load input: Req = 25 kΩ NOM
All other inputs: R_eq = 17 kΩ NOM

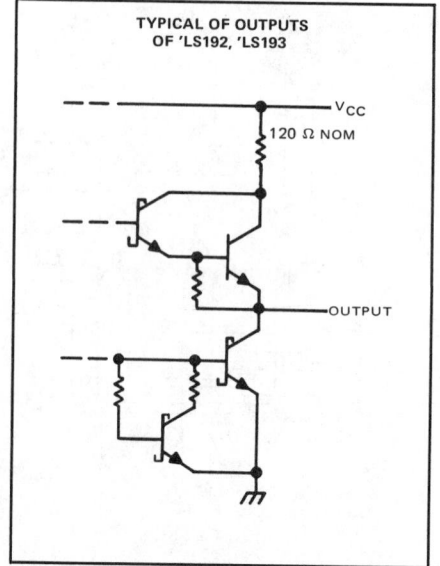

TYPICAL OF OUTPUTS
OF 'LS192, 'LS193

120 Ω NOM

TEXAS INSTRUMENTS
INCORPORATED
POST OFFICE BOX 5012 • DALLAS, TEXAS 75222

TYPES SN54192, SN54L192, SN54LS192, SN74192, SN74L192, SN74LS192
SYNCHRONOUS 4-BIT UP/DOWN COUNTERS (DUAL CLOCK WITH CLEAR)

'192,'L192,'LS192 DECADE COUNTERS

typical clear, load, and count sequences

Illustrated below is the following sequence:

1. Clear outputs to zero.
2. Load (preset) to BCD seven.
3. Count up to eight, nine, carry, zero, one, and two.
4. Count down to one, zero, borrow, nine, eight, and seven.

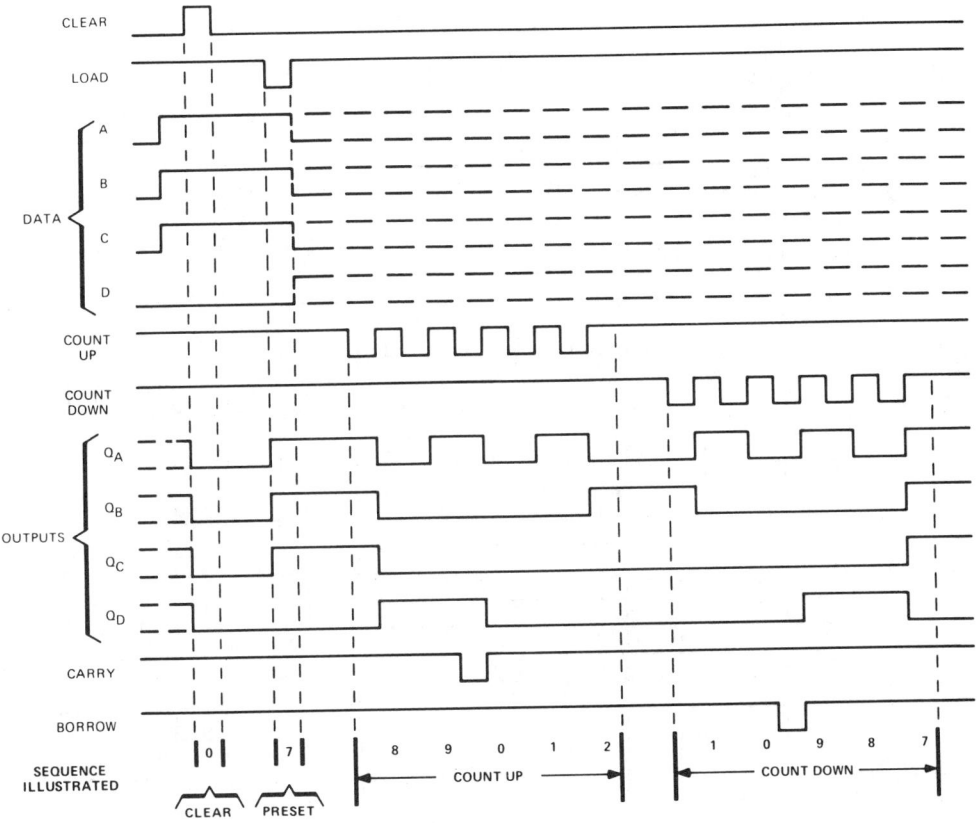

NOTES: A. Clear overrides load, data, and count inputs.
       B. When counting up, count-down input must be high; when counting down, count-up input must be high.

TEXAS INSTRUMENTS
INCORPORATED
POST OFFICE BOX 5012 • DALLAS, TEXAS 75222

TYPES SN54193, SN54L193, SN54LS193, SN74193, SN74L193, SN74LS193
SYNCHRONOUS 4-BIT UP/DOWN COUNTERS (DUAL CLOCK WITH CLEAR)

'193, 'L193, 'LS193 BINARY COUNTERS

typical clear, load, and count sequences

Illustrated below is the following sequence:

1. Clear outputs to zero.
2. Load (preset) to binary thirteen.
3. Count up to fourteen, fifteen, carry, zero, one, and two.
4. Count down to one, zero, borrow, fifteen, fourteen, and thirteen.

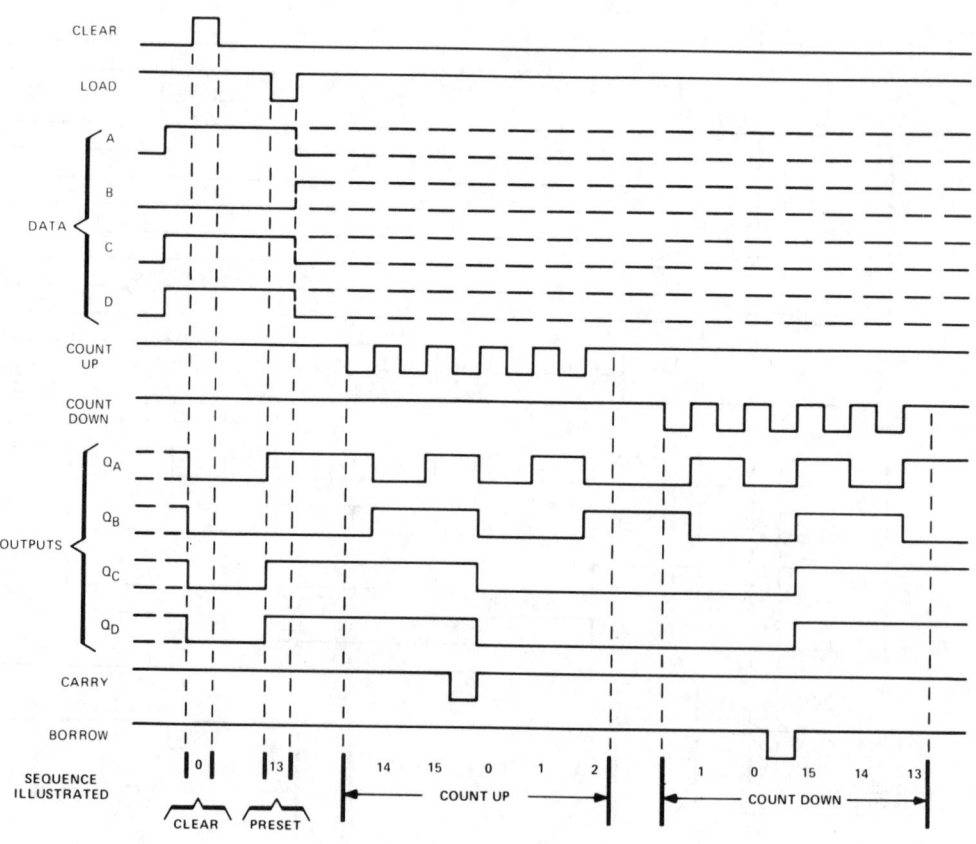

NOTES: A. Clear overrides load, data, and count inputs.

B. When counting up, count-down input must be high; when counting down, count-up input must be high.

TEXAS INSTRUMENTS
INCORPORATED
POST OFFICE BOX 5012 • DALLAS, TEXAS 75222

1272

recommended operating conditions

	SN54192 SN54193			SN74192 SN74193			UNIT
	MIN	NOM	MAX	MIN	NOM	MAX	
Supply voltage, V_{CC}	4.5	5	5.5	4.75	5	5.25	V
High-level output current, I_{OH}			−400			−400	μA
Low-level output current, I_{OL}			16			16	mA
Clock frequency, f_{clock}	0		25	0		25	MHz
Width of any input pulse, t_w	20			20			ns
Data setup time, t_{su} (see Figure 1)	20			20			ns
Data hold time, t_h	0			0			ns
Operating free-air temperature, T_A	−55		125	0		70	°C

electrical characteristics over recommended operating free-air temperature range (unless otherwise noted)

PARAMETER	TEST CONDITIONS[†]	SN54192 SN54193			SN74192 SN74193			UNIT
		MIN	TYP[‡]	MAX	MIN	TYP[‡]	MAX	
V_{IH} High-level input voltage		2			2			V
V_{IL} Low-level input voltage				0.8			0.8	V
V_{IK} Input clamp voltage	V_{CC} = MIN, I_I = −12 mA			−1.5			−1.5	V
V_{OH} High-level output voltage	V_{CC} = MIN, V_{IH} = 2 V, V_{IL} = 0.8 V, I_{OH} = −400 μA	2.4	3.4		2.4	3.4		V
V_{OL} Low-level output voltage	V_{CC} = MIN, V_{IH} = 2 V V_{IL} = 0.8 V, I_{OL} = 16 mA		0.2	0.4		0.2	0.4	V
I_I Input current at maximum input voltage	V_{CC} = MAX, V_I = 5.5 V			1			1	mA
I_{IH} High-level input current	V_{CC} = MAX, V_I = 2.4 V			40			40	μA
I_{IL} Low-level input current	V_{CC} = MAX, V_I = 0.4 V			−1.6			−1.6	mA
I_{OS} Short-circuit output current[§]	V_{CC} = MAX	−20		−65	−18		−65	mA
I_{CC} Supply current	V_{CC} = MAX, See Note 2		65	89		65	102	mA

[†]For conditions shown as MIN or MAX, use the appropriate value specified under recommended operating conditions for the applicable type.
[‡]All typical values are at V_{CC} = 5 V, T_A = 25°C.
[§]Not more than one output should be shorted at a time.
NOTE 2: I_{CC} is measured with all outputs open, clear and load inputs grounded, and all other inputs at 4.5 V.

switching characteristics, V_{CC} = 5 V, T_A = 25°C

PARAMETER[¶]	FROM INPUT	TO OUTPUT	TEST CONDITIONS	MIN	TYP	MAX	UNIT
f_{max}				25	32		MHz
t_{PLH}	Count-up	Carry			17	26	ns
t_{PHL}					16	24	
t_{PLH}	Count-down	Borrow	C_L = 15 pF,		16	24	ns
t_{PHL}			R_L = 400 Ω,		16	24	
t_{PLH}	Either Count	Q	See Figures 1 and 2		25	38	ns
t_{PHL}					31	47	
t_{PLH}	Load	Q			27	40	ns
t_{PHL}					29	40	
t_{PHL}	Clear	Q			22	35	ns

[¶]f_{max} ≡ maximum clock frequency
t_{PLH} ≡ propagation delay time, low-to-high-level output
t_{PHL} ≡ propagation delay time, high-to-low-level output

TEXAS INSTRUMENTS
INCORPORATED
POST OFFICE BOX 5012 • DALLAS, TEXAS 75222

7

TYPES SN54L192, SN54L193, SN74L192, SN74L193
SYNCHRONOUS 4-BIT UP/DOWN COUNTERS (DUAL CLOCK WITH CLEAR)

recommended operating conditions

	SN54L192 SN54L193			SN74L192 SN74L193			UNIT
	MIN	NOM	MAX	MIN	NOM	MAX	
Supply voltage, V_{CC}	4.5	5	5.5	4.75	5	5.25	V
High-level output current, I_{OH}			−100			−200	µA
Low-level output current, I_{OL}			2			3.6	mA
Clock frequency, f_{clock}	0		3	0		3	MHz
Width of any input pulse, t_w	200			200			ns
Data setup time, t_{su} (see Figure 1)	100			100			ns
Data hold time, t_h	0			0			ns
Operating free-air temperature range, T_A	−55		125	0		70	°C

electrical characteristics over recommended operating free-air temperature range (unless otherwise noted)

PARAMETER		TEST CONDITIONS[†]	SN54L192 SN54L193			SN74L192 SN74L193			UNIT
			MIN	TYP[‡]	MAX	MIN	TYP[‡]	MAX	
V_{IH}	High-level input voltage		2			2			V
V_{IL}	Low-level input voltage				0.7			0.7	V
V_{IK}	Input clamp voltage	V_{CC} = MIN,　I_I = −12 mA			−1.5			−1.5	V
V_{OH}	High-level output voltage	V_{CC} = MIN,　V_{IH} = 2 V, V_{IL} = 0.7 V, I_{OH} = MAX	2.4	3.3		2.4	3.2		V
V_{OL}	Low-level output voltage	V_{CC} = MIN,　V_{IH} = 2 V V_{IL} = 0.7 V, I_{OL} = MAX		0.15	0.3		0.2	0.4	V
I_I	Input current at maximum input voltage	V_{CC} = MAX,　V_I = 5.5 V			100			100	µA
I_{IH}	High-level input current	V_{CC} = MAX,　V_I = 2.4 V			10			10	µA
I_{IL}	Low-level input current	V_{CC} = MAX,　V_I = 0.3 V			−0.18			−0.18	mA
I_{OS}	Short-circuit output current[§]	V_{CC} = MAX	−3		−15	−3		−15	mA
I_{CC}	Supply current	V_{CC} = MAX,　See Note 2		8.5	15		8.5	15	mA

[†]For conditions shown as MIN or MAX, use the appropriate value specified under recommended operating conditions for the applicable type.
[‡]All typical values are at V_{CC} = 5 V, T_A = 25°C.
[§]Not more than one output should be shorted at a time.
NOTE 2:　I_{CC} is measured with all outputs open, clear and load inputs grounded, and all other inputs at 4.5 V.

switching characteristics, V_{CC} = 5 V, T_A = 25°C

PARAMETER[¶]	FROM INPUT	TO OUTPUT	TEST CONDITIONS	MIN	TYP	MAX	UNIT
f_{max}				3	7		MHz
t_{PLH}	Count-up	Carry			65	130	ns
t_{PHL}					65	130	
t_{PLH}	Count-down	Borrow	C_L = 50 pF,		65	130	ns
t_{PHL}			R_L = 4 kΩ,		65	130	
t_{PLH}	Either Count	Q	See Figures 1 and 2		104	200	ns
t_{PHL}					135	240	
t_{PLH}	Load	Q			130	240	ns
t_{PHL}					105	200	
t_{PHL}	Clear	Q			110	200	ns

[¶]f_{max} ≡ maximum clock frequency
t_{PLH} ≡ propagation delay time, low-to-high-level output
t_{PHL} ≡ propagation delay time, high-to-low-level output

1076

TEXAS INSTRUMENTS
INCORPORATED
POST OFFICE BOX 5012 • DALLAS, TEXAS 75222

TYPES SN54LS192, SN54LS193, SN74LS192, SN74LS193
SYNCHRONOUS 4-BIT UP/DOWN COUNTERS (DUAL CLOCK WITH CLEAR)

REVISED AUGUST 1977

recommended operating conditions

	SN54LS192 SN54LS193			SN74LS192 SN74LS193			UNIT
	MIN	NOM	MAX	MIN	NOM	MAX	
Supply voltage, V_{CC}	4.5	5	5.5	4.75	5	5.25	V
High-level output current, I_{OH}			−400			−400	μA
Low-level output current, I_{OL}			4			8	mA
Clock frequency, f_{clock}	0		25	0		25	MHz
Width of any input pulse, t_W	20			20			ns
Clear inactive-state setup time	40			40			ns
Data setup time, t_{su} (see Figure 1)	20			20			ns
Data hold time, t_h	0			0			ns
Operating free-air temperature range, T_A	−55		125	0		70	°C

electrical characteristics over recommended operating free-air temperature range (unless otherwise noted)

PARAMETER		TEST CONDITIONS[†]		SN54LS192 SN54LS193			SN74LS192 SN74LS193			UNIT
				MIN	TYP[‡]	MAX	MIN	TYP[‡]	MAX	
V_{IH}	High-level input voltage			2			2			V
V_{IL}	Low-level input voltage					0.7			0.8	V
V_{IK}	Input clamp voltage	V_{CC} = MIN,	I_I = −18 mA			−1.5			−1.5	V
V_{OH}	High-level output voltage	V_{CC} = MIN, V_{IH} = 2 V, V_{IL} = V_{IL} max, I_{OH} = −400 μA		2.5	3.4		2.7	3.4		V
V_{OL}	Low-level output voltage	V_{CC} = MIN, V_{IH} = 2 V, V_{IL} = V_{IL} max	I_{OL} = 4 mA		0.25	0.4		0.15	0.4	V
			I_{OL} = 8 mA					0.35	0.5	
I_I	Input current at maximum input voltage	V_{CC} = MAX,	V_I = 7 V			0.1			0.1	mA
I_{IH}	High-level input current	V_{CC} = MAX,	V_I = 2.7 V			20			20	μA
I_{IL}	Low-level input current	V_{CC} = MAX,	V_I = 0.4 V			−0.4			−0.4	mA
I_{OS}	Short-circuit output current[§]	V_{CC} = MAX		−20		−100	−20		−100	mA
I_{CC}	Supply current	V_{CC} = MAX,	See Note 2		19	34		19	34	mA

[†]For conditions shown as MIN or MAX, use the appropriate value specified under recommended operating conditions for the applicable type.
[‡]All typical values are at V_{CC} = 5 V, T_A = 25°C.
[§]Not more than one output should be shorted at a time, and duration of the short-circuit should not exceed one second.
NOTE 2: I_{CC} is measured with all outputs open, clear and load inputs grounded, and all other inputs at 4.5 V.

switching characteristics, V_{CC} = 5 V, T_A = 25°C

PARAMETER[¶]	FROM INPUT	TO OUTPUT	TEST CONDITIONS	MIN	TYP	MAX	UNIT
f_{max}				25	32		MHz
t_{PLH}	Count-up	Carry			17	26	ns
t_{PHL}					18	24	
t_{PLH}	Count-down	Borrow	C_L = 15 pF, R_L = 2 kΩ, See Figures 1 and 2		16	24	ns
t_{PHL}					15	24	
t_{PLH}	Either Count	Q			27	38	ns
t_{PHL}					30	47	
t_{PLH}	Load	Q			24	40	ns
t_{PHL}					25	40	
t_{PHL}	Clear	Q			23	35	ns

[¶]f_{max} ≡ maximum clock frequency
t_{PLH} ≡ propagation delay time, low-to-high-level output
t_{PHL} ≡ propagation delay time, high-to-low-level output

7

TEXAS INSTRUMENTS
INCORPORATED
POST OFFICE BOX 5012 • DALLAS, TEXAS 75222

TYPES SN54192, SN54193, SN54L192, SN54L193, SN54LS192, SN54LS193, SN74192, SN74193, SN74L192, SN74L193, SN74LS192, SN74LS193
SYNCHRONOUS 4-BIT UP/DOWN COUNTERS (DUAL CLOCK WITH CLEAR)

PARAMETER MEASUREMENT INFORMATION

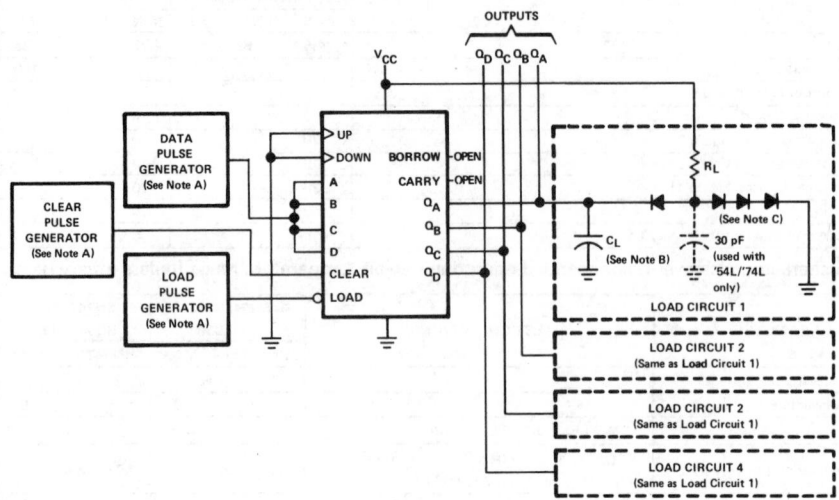

TEST CIRCUIT

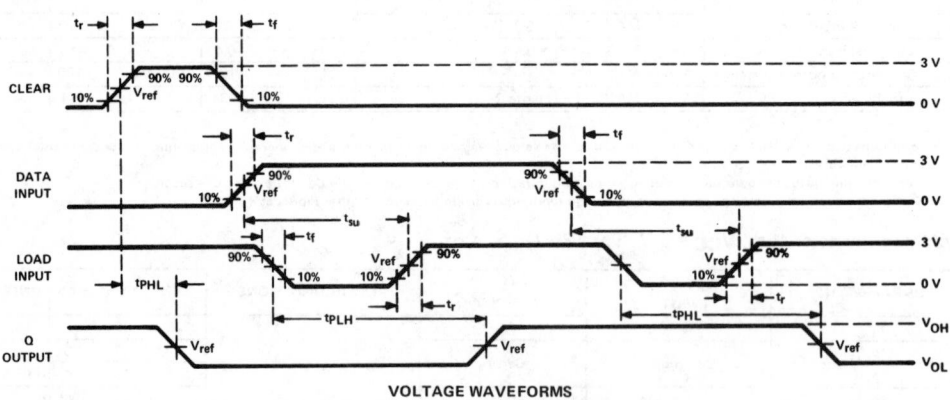

VOLTAGE WAVEFORMS

NOTES: A. The pulse generators have the following characteristics: $Z_{out} \approx 50\ \Omega$ and for the data pulse generator PRR ≤ 500 kHz, duty cycle = 50%; for the load pulse generator PRR is two times data PRR, duty cycle = 50%.
   B. C_L includes probe and jig capacitance.
   C. Diodes are 1N3064 for '192, '193, 'LS192, and 'LS193; 1N916 for 'L192 and 'L193.
   D. t_r and t_f ≤ 7 ns for '192, '193, 'LS192, and 'LS193; ≤ 25 ns for 'L192 and 'L193.
   E. V_{ref} is 1.5 volts for '192 and '193; 1.3 volts for 'L192, 'L193; 'LS192, and 'LS193.

FIGURE 1—CLEAR, SETUP, AND LOAD TIMES

1076

TEXAS INSTRUMENTS
INCORPORATED
POST OFFICE BOX 5012 • DALLAS, TEXAS 75222

TYPES SN54192, SN54193, SN54L192, SN54L193, SN54LS192, SN54LS193, SN74192, SN74193, SN74L192, SN74L193, SN74LS192, SN74LS193
SYNCHRONOUS 4-BIT UP/DOWN COUNTERS (DUAL CLOCK WITH CLEAR)

PARAMETER MEASUREMENT INFORMATION

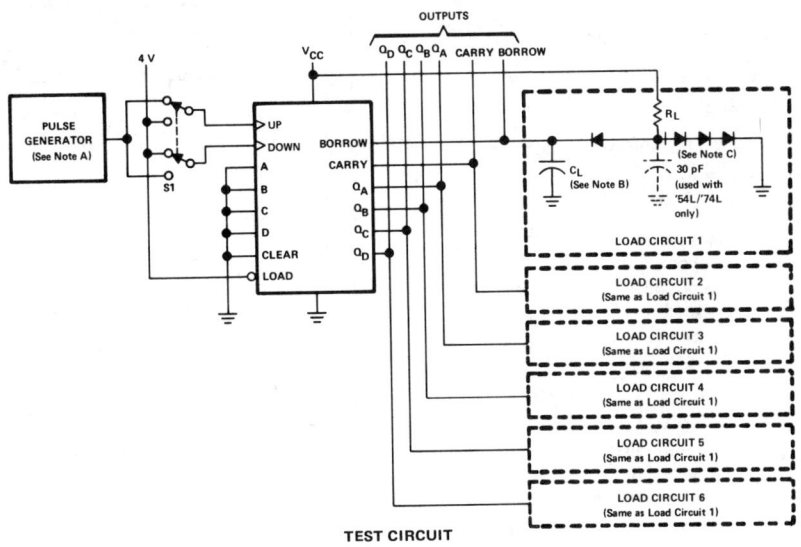

TEST CIRCUIT

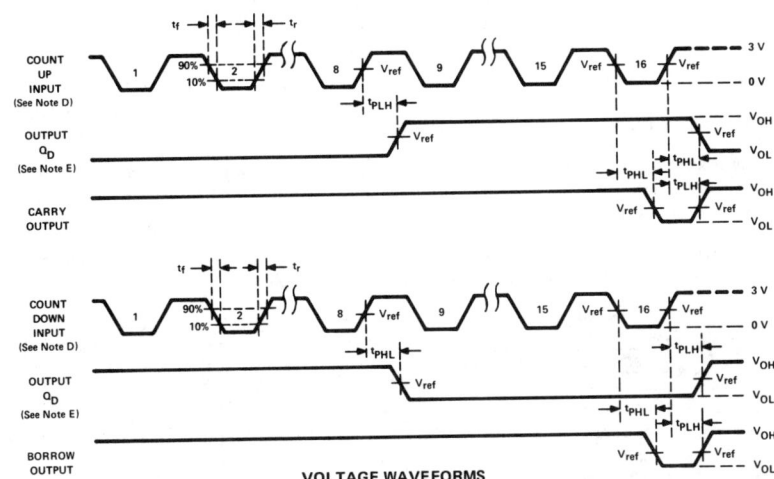

VOLTAGE WAVEFORMS

NOTES: A. The pulse generator has the following characteristics: PRR ≤ 1 MHz, $Z_{out} \approx 50\ \Omega$, duty cycle = 50%.
      B. C_L includes probe and jig capacitance.
      C. Diodes are 1N3064 for '192, '193, 'LS192, and 'LS193; 1N916 for 'L192 and 'L193.
      D. Count-up and count-down pulse shown are for the '193, 'L193, 'LS193 binary counters. Count cycle for '192, 'L192, and 'LS192 decade counters is 1 through 10.
      E. Waveforms for outputs Q_A, Q_B, and Q_C are omitted to simplify the drawing.
      F. t_r and $t_f \leqslant 7$ ns for '192, '193, 'LS192, and 'LS193; ≤ 25 ns for 'L192 and 'L193.
      G. V_{ref} is 1.5 volts for '192 and '193; 1.3 volts for 'L192, 'L193, LS192, and 'LS193.

FIGURE 2—PROPAGATION DELAY TIMES

TEXAS INSTRUMENTS
INCORPORATED
POST OFFICE BOX 5012 • DALLAS, TEXAS 75222

- **Parallel Inputs and Outputs**
- **Four Operating Modes:**
  - Synchronous Parallel Load
  - Right Shift
  - Left Shift
  - Do Nothing
- **Positive Edge-Triggered Clocking**
- **Direct Overriding Clear**

TYPE	TYPICAL MAXIMUM CLOCK FREQUENCY	TYPICAL POWER DISSIPATION
'194	36 MHz	195 mW
'LS194A	36 MHz	75 mW
'S194	105 MHz	425 mW

SN54194, SN54LS194A, SN54S194 . . . J OR W PACKAGE
SN74194, SN74LS194A, SN74S194 . . . J OR N PACKAGE
(TOP VIEW)

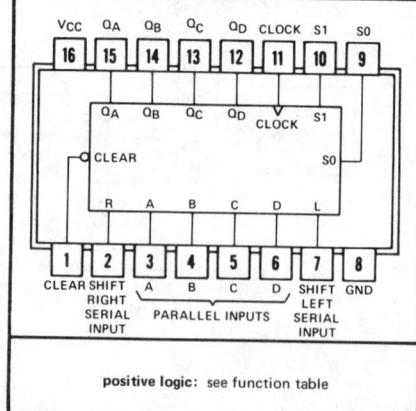

positive logic: see function table

description

These bidirectional shift registers are designed to incorporate virtually all of the features a system designer may want in a shift register. The circuit contains 46 equivalent gates and features parallel inputs, parallel outputs, right-shift and left-shift serial inputs, operating-mode-control inputs, and a direct overriding clear line. The register has four distinct modes of operation, namely:

Parallel (broadside) load
Shift right (in the direction Q_A toward Q_D)
Shift left (in the direction Q_D toward Q_A)
Inhibit clock (do nothing)

Synchronous parallel loading is accomplished by applying the four bits of data and taking both mode control inputs, S0 and S1, high. The data are loaded into the associated flip-flops and appear at the outputs after the positive transistion of the clock input. During loading, serial data flow is inhibited.

Shift right is accomplished synchronously with the rising edge of the clock pulse when S0 is high and S1 is low. Serial data for this mode is entered at the shift-right data input. When S0 is low and S1 is high, data shifts left synchronously and new data is entered at the shift-left serial input.

Clocking of the flip-flop is inhibited when both mode control inputs are low. The mode controls of the SN54194/SN74194 should be changed only while the clock input is high.

FUNCTION TABLE

CLEAR	MODE		CLOCK	SERIAL		PARALLEL				OUTPUTS			
	S1	S0		LEFT	RIGHT	A	B	C	D	Q_A	Q_B	Q_C	Q_D
L	X	X	X	X	X	X	X	X	X	L	L	L	L
H	X	X	L	X	X	X	X	X	X	Q_{A0}	Q_{B0}	Q_{C0}	Q_{D0}
H	H	H	↑	X	X	a	b	c	d	a	b	c	d
H	L	H	↑	X	H	X	X	X	X	H	Q_{An}	Q_{Bn}	Q_{Cn}
H	L	H	↑	X	L	X	X	X	X	L	Q_{An}	Q_{Bn}	Q_{Cn}
H	H	L	↑	H	X	X	X	X	X	Q_{Bn}	Q_{Cn}	Q_{Dn}	H
H	H	L	↑	L	X	X	X	X	X	Q_{Bn}	Q_{Cn}	Q_{Dn}	L
H	L	L	X	X	X	X	X	X	X	Q_{A0}	Q_{B0}	Q_{C0}	Q_{D0}

H = high level (steady state)
L = low level (steady state)
X = irrelevant (any input, including transitions)
↑ = transition from low to high level
a, b, c, d = the level of steady-state input at inputs A, B, C, or D, respectively.
$Q_{A0}, Q_{B0}, Q_{C0}, Q_{D0}$ = the level of Q_A, Q_B, Q_C, or Q_D, respectively, before the indicated steady-state input conditions were established.
$Q_{An}, Q_{Bn}, Q_{Cn}, Q_{Dn}$ = the level of Q_A, Q_B, Q_C, respectively, before the most-recent ↑ transition of the clock.

TEXAS INSTRUMENTS
INCORPORATED
POST OFFICE BOX 5012 • DALLAS, TEXAS 75222

1076

functional block diagrams

'194

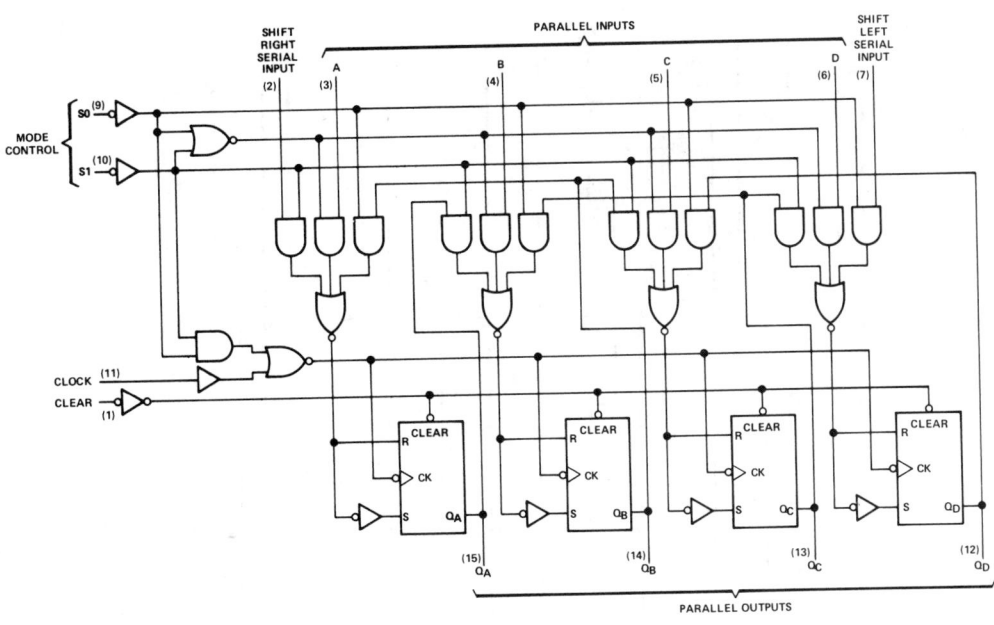

'LS194A, 'S194

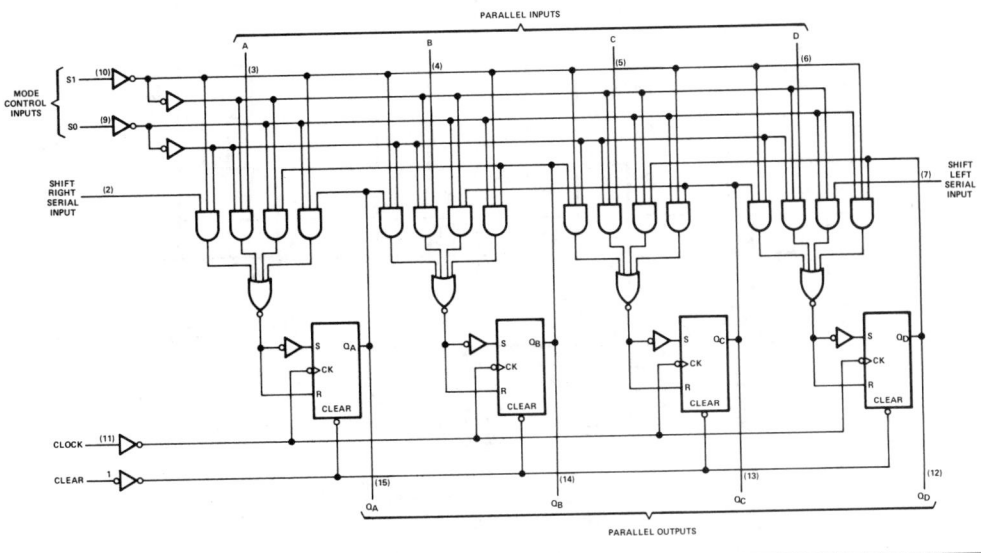

TEXAS INSTRUMENTS
INCORPORATED
POST OFFICE BOX 5012 • DALLAS, TEXAS 75222

TYPES SN54194, SN54LS194A, SN54S194,
SN74194, SN74LS194A, SN74S194
4-BIT BIDIRECTIONAL UNIVERSAL SHIFT REGISTERS

typical clear, load, right-shift, left-shift, inhibit, and clear sequences

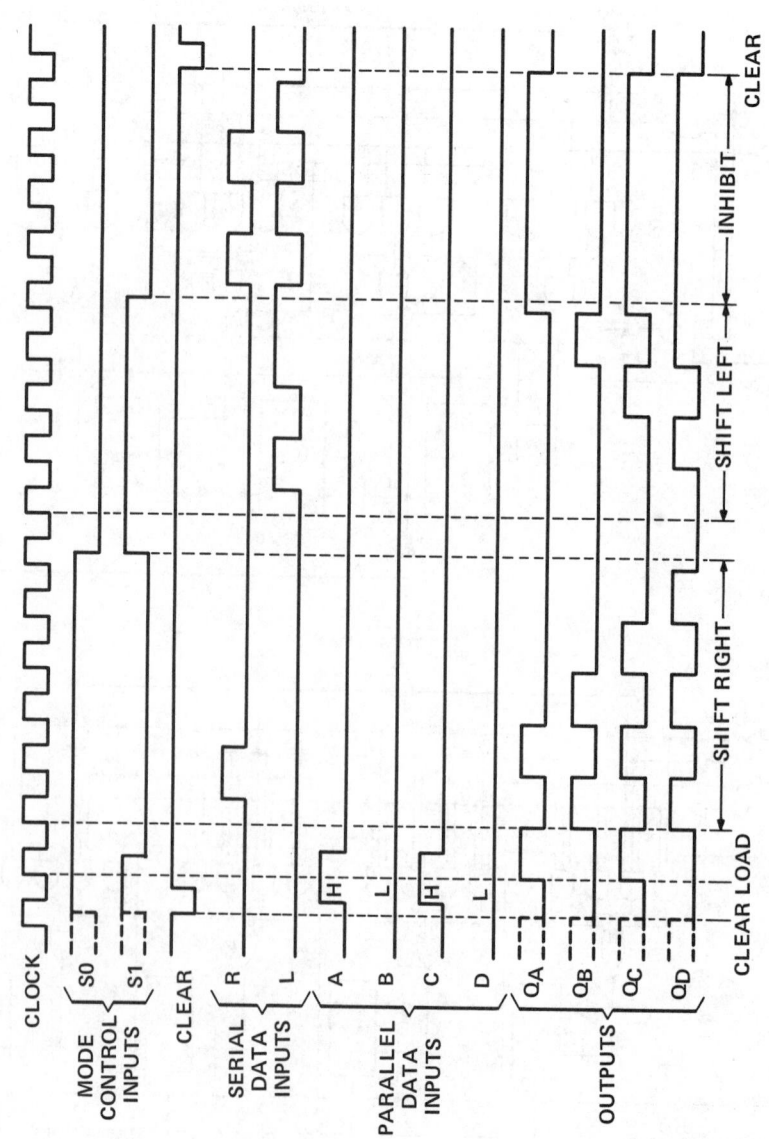

TEXAS INSTRUMENTS
INCORPORATED
POST OFFICE BOX 5012 • DALLAS, TEXAS 75222

schematics of inputs and outputs

'194

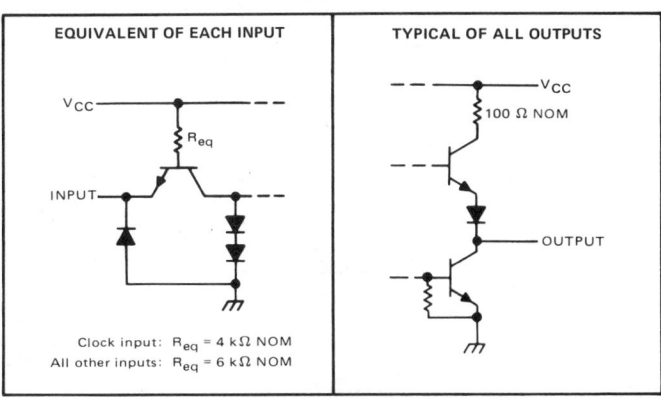

'LS194A

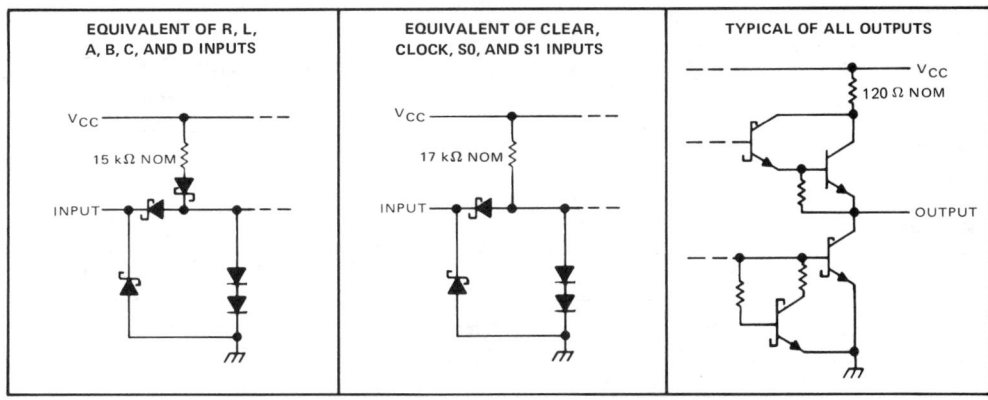

'S194

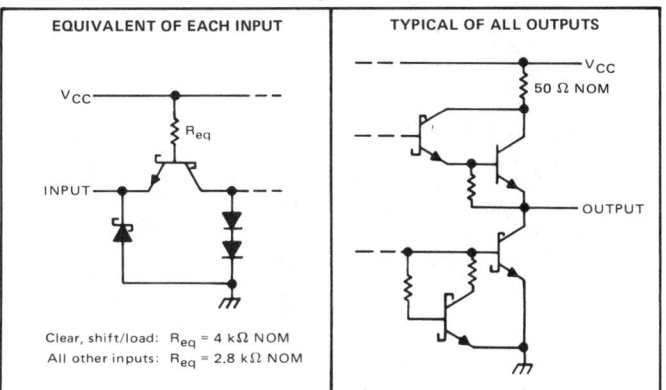

TEXAS INSTRUMENTS
INCORPORATED
POST OFFICE BOX 5012 • DALLAS, TEXAS 75222

TYPES SN54194, SN74194
4-BIT BIDIRECTIONAL UNIVERSAL SHIFT REGISTERS

REVISED MARCH 1974

absolute maximum ratings over operating free-air temperature range (unless otherwise noted)

Supply voltage, V_{CC} (see Note 1) . . . . 7 V
Input voltage . . . . 5.5 V
Operating free-air temperature range: SN54194 . . . . −55°C to 125°C
             SN74194 . . . . 0°C to 70°C
Storage temperature range . . . . −65°C to 150°C

NOTE 1: Voltage values are with respect to network ground terminal.

recommended operating conditions

		SN54194			SN74194			UNIT
		MIN	NOM	MAX	MIN	NOM	MAX	
Supply voltage, V_{CC}		4.5	5	5.5	4.75	5	5.25	V
High-level output current, I_{OH}				−800			−800	μA
Low-level output current, I_{OL}				16			16	mA
Clock frequency, f_{clock}		0		25	0		25	MHz
Width of clock or clear pulse, t_w		20			20			ns
Setup time, t_{su}	Mode control	30			30			ns
	Serial and parallel data	20			20			ns
	Clear inactive-state	25			25			ns
Hold time at any input, t_h		0			0			ns
Operating free-air temperature, T_A		−55		125	0		70	°C

electrical characteristics over recommended operating free-air temperature range (unless otherwise noted)

PARAMETER		TEST CONDITIONS[†]	SN54194			SN74194			UNIT
			MIN	TYP[‡]	MAX	MIN	TYP[‡]	MAX	
V_{IH}	High-level input voltage		2			2			V
V_{IL}	Low-level input voltage				0.8			0.8	V
V_{IK}	Input clamp voltage	V_{CC} = MIN, I_I = −12 mA			−1.5			−1.5	V
V_{OH}	High-level output voltage	V_{CC} = MIN, V_{IH} = 2 V, V_{IL} = 0.8 V, I_{OH} = −800 μA	2.4	3.4		2.4	3.4		V
V_{OL}	Low-level output voltage	V_{CC} = MIN, V_{IH} = 2 V, V_{IL} = 0.8 V, I_{OL} = 16 mA		0.2	0.4		0.2	0.4	V
I_I	Input current at maximum input voltage	V_{CC} = MAX, V_I = 5.5 V			1			1	mA
I_{IH}	High-level input current	V_{CC} = MAX, V_I = 2.4 V			40			40	μA
I_{IL}	Low-level input current	V_{CC} = MAX, V_I = 0.4 V			−1.6			−1.6	mA
I_{OS}	Short-circuit output current[§]	V_{CC} = MAX	−20		−57	−18		−57	mA
I_{CC}	Supply current	V_{CC} = MAX, See Note 2		39	63		39	63	mA

[†]For conditions shown as MIN or MAX, use the appropriate value specified under recommended operating conditions.
[‡]All typical values are at V_{CC} = 5 V, T_A = 25°C.
[§]Not more than one output should be shorted at a time.
NOTE 2: With all outputs open, inputs A through D grounded, and 4.5 V applied to S0, S1, clear, and the serial inputs, I_{CC} is tested with a momentary GND, then 4.5 V applied to clock.

switching characteristics, V_{CC} = 5 V, T_A = 25°C

PARAMETER		TEST CONDITIONS	MIN	TYP	MAX	UNIT
f_{max}	Maximum clock frequency	C_L = 15 pF, R_L = 400 Ω, See Figure 1	25	36		MHz
t_{PHL}	Propagation delay time, high-to-low-level output from clear			19	30	ns
t_{PLH}	Propagation delay time, low-to-high-level output from clock			14	22	ns
t_{PHL}	Propagation delay time, high-to-low-level output from clock			17	26	ns

7

TEXAS INSTRUMENTS
INCORPORATED
POST OFFICE BOX 5012 • DALLAS, TEXAS 75222

1076

absolute maximum ratings over operating free-air temperature range (unless otherwise noted)

Supply voltage, V_{CC} (see Note 1) . . . . 7 V

Input voltage . . . . 7 V

Operating free-air temperature range: SN54LS194A . . . . −55°C to 125°C

SN74LS194A . . . . 0°C to 70°C

Storage temperature range . . . . −65°C to 150°C

NOTE 1: Voltage values are with respect to network ground terminal.

recommended operating conditions

			SN54LS194A			SN74LS194A			UNIT
			MIN	NOM	MAX	MIN	NOM	MAX	
Supply voltage, V_{CC}			4.5	5	5.5	4.75	5	5.25	V
High-level output current, I_{OH}					−400			−400	μA
Low-level output current, I_{OL}					4			8	mA
Clock frequency, f_{clock}			0		25	0		25	MHz
Width of clock or clear pulse, t_w			20			20			ns
Setup time, t_{su}		Mode control	30			30			ns
		Serial and parallel data	20			20			ns
		Clear inactive-state	25			25			ns
Hold time at any input, t_h			0			0			ns
Operating free-air temperature, T_A			−55		125	0		70	°C

electrical characteristics over recommended operating free-air temperature range (unless otherwise noted)

PARAMETER		TEST CONDITIONS[†]	SN54LS194A			SN74LS194A			UNIT
			MIN	TYP[‡]	MAX	MIN	TYP[‡]	MAX	
V_{IH}	High-level input voltage		2			2			V
V_{IL}	Low-level input voltage				0.7			0.8	V
V_{IK}	Input clamp voltage	V_{CC} = MIN, I_I = −18 mA			−1.5			−1.5	V
V_{OH}	High-level output voltage	V_{CC} = MIN, V_{IH} = 2 V, $V_{IL} = V_{IL}$ max, $I_{OH} = -400\,\mu A$	2.5	3.5		2.7	3.5		V
V_{OL}	Low-level output voltage	V_{CC} = MIN, V_{IH} = 2 V, $V_{IL} = V_{IL}$ max — I_{OL} = 4 mA		0.25	0.4		0.25	0.4	V
		I_{OL} = 8 mA					0.35	0.5	
I_I	Input current at maximum input voltage	V_{CC} = MAX, V_I = 7 V			0.1			0.1	mA
I_{IH}	High-level input current	V_{CC} = MAX, V_I = 2.7 V			20			20	μA
I_{IL}	Low-level input current	V_{CC} = MAX, V_I = 0.4 V			−0.4			−0.4	mA
I_{OS}	Short-circuit output current[§]	V_{CC} = MAX	−20		−100	−20		−100	mA
I_{CC}	Supply current	V_{CC} = MAX, See Note 2		15	23		15	23	mA

[†]For conditions shown as MIN or MAX, use the appropriate value specified under recommended operating conditions.

[‡]All typical values are at V_{CC} = 5 V, T_A = 25°C.

[§]Not more than one output should be shorted at a time, and duration of the short-circuit should not exceed one second.

NOTE 2: With all outputs open, inputs A through D grounded, and 4.5 V applied to S0, S1, clear, and the serial inputs, I_{CC} is tested with a momentary GND, then 4.5 V, applied to clock.

switching characteristics, V_{CC} = 5 V, T_A = 25°C

PARAMETER		TEST CONDITIONS	MIN	TYP	MAX	UNIT
f_{max}	Maximum clock frequency	C_L = 15 pF, R_L = 2 kΩ, See Figure 1	25	36		MHz
t_{PHL}	Propagation delay time, high-to-low-level output from clear			19	30	ns
t_{PLH}	Propagation delay time, low-to-high-level output from clock			14	22	ns
t_{PHL}	Propagation delay time, high-to-low-level output from clock			17	26	ns

7

TEXAS INSTRUMENTS
INCORPORATED
POST OFFICE BOX 5012 • DALLAS, TEXAS 75222

TYPES SN54S194, SN74S194
4-BIT BIDIRECTIONAL UNIVERSAL SHIFT REGISTERS

REVISED MARCH 1974

absolute maximum ratings over operating free-air temperature range (unless otherwise noted)

Supply voltage, V_{CC} (see Note 1) . . . . 7 V
Input voltage . . . . 5.5 V
Operating free-air temperature range: SN54S194 . . . . -55°C to 125°C
                                     SN74S194 . . . . 0°C to 70°C
Storage temperature range . . . . -65°C to 150°C

NOTE 1: Voltage values are with respect to network ground terminal.

recommended operating conditions

		SN54S194			SN74S194			UNIT
		MIN	NOM	MAX	MIN	NOM	MAX	
Supply voltage, V_{CC}		4.5	5	5.5	4.75	5	5.25	V
High-level output current, I_{OH}				-1			-1	mA
Low-level output current, I_{OL}				20			20	mA
Clock frequency, f_{clock}		0		70	0		70	MHz
Width of clock pulse, $t_{w(clock)}$		7			7			ns
Width of clear pulse, $t_{w(clear)}$		12			12			ns
Setup time, t_{su}	Mode control	11			11			ns
	Serial and parallel data	5			5			ns
	Clear inactive-state	9			9			ns
Hold time at any input, t_h		3			3			ns
Operating free-air temperature, T_A		-55		125	0		70	$^{\circ}$C

electrical characteristics over recommended operating free-air temperature range (unless otherwise noted)

PARAMETER		TEST CONDITIONS[†]	SN54S194			SN74S194			UNIT
			MIN	TYP[‡]	MAX	MIN	TYP[‡]	MAX	
V_{IH}	High-level input voltage		2			2			V
V_{IL}	Low-level input voltage				0.8			0.8	V
V_{IK}	Input clamp voltage	V_{CC} = MIN, $I_I = -18$ mA			-1.2			-1.2	V
V_{OH}	High-level output voltage	V_{CC} = MIN, $V_{IH} = 2$ V, $V_{IL} = 0.8$ V, $I_{OH} = -1$ mA	2.5	3.4		2.7	3.4		V
V_{OL}	Low-level output voltage	V_{CC} = MIN, $V_{IH} = 2$ V, $V_{IL} = 0.8$ V, $I_{OL} = 20$ mA			0.5			0.5	V
I_I	Input current at maximum input voltage	V_{CC} = MAX, $V_I = 5.5$ V			1			1	mA
I_{IH}	High-level input current	V_{CC} = MAX, $V_I = 2.4$ V			50			50	μA
I_{IL}	Low-level input current	V_{CC} = MAX, $V_I = 0.4$ V			-2			-2	mA
I_{OS}	Short-circuit output current[§]	V_{CC} = MAX	-40		-100	-40		-100	mA
I_{CC}	Supply current	V_{CC} = MAX, See Note 2		85	135		85	135	mA
		V_{CC} = MAX, $T_A = 125^{\circ}$C, W package, See Note 2			110				

[†] For conditions shown as MIN or MAX, use the appropriate value specified under recommended operating conditions.
[‡] All typical values are at $V_{CC} = 5$ V, $T_A = 25^{\circ}$C.
[§] Not more than one output should be shorted at a time, and duration of the short-circuit should not exceed one second.
NOTE 2: With all outputs open, inputs A through D grounded, and 4.5 V applies to S0, S1, clear, and the serial inputs, I_{CC} is tested with a momentary GND, then 4.5 V, applied to clock.

switching characteristics, $V_{CC} = 5$ V, $T_A = 25^{\circ}$C

PARAMETER		TEST CONDITIONS	MIN	TYP	MAX	UNIT
f_{max}	Maximum clock frequency	$C_L = 15$ pF, $R_L = 280\ \Omega$, See Figure 1	70	105		MHz
t_{PHL}	Propagation delay time, high-to-low-level output from clear			12.5	18.5	ns
t_{PLH}	Propagation delay time, low-to-high-level output from clock		4	8	12	ns
t_{PHL}	Propagation delay time, high-to-low-level output from clock		4	11	16.5	ns

7

TEXAS INSTRUMENTS
INCORPORATED
POST OFFICE BOX 5012 • DALLAS, TEXAS 75222

1076

PARAMETER MEASUREMENT INFORMATION

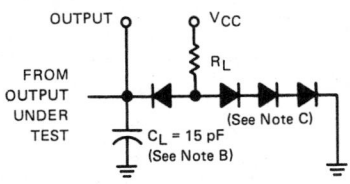

LOAD FOR OUTPUT UNDER TEST

TEST TABLE FOR SYNCHRONOUS INPUTS

DATA INPUT FOR TEST	S1	S0	OUTPUT TESTED (SEE NOTE E)
A	4.5 V	4.5 V	Q_A at t_{n+1}
B	4.5 V	4.5 V	Q_B at t_{n+1}
C	4.5 V	4.5 V	Q_C at t_{n+1}
D	4.5 V	4.5 V	Q_D at t_{n+1}
L Serial Input	4.5 V	0 V	Q_A at t_{n+4}
R Serial Input	0 V	4.5 V	Q_D at t_{n+4}

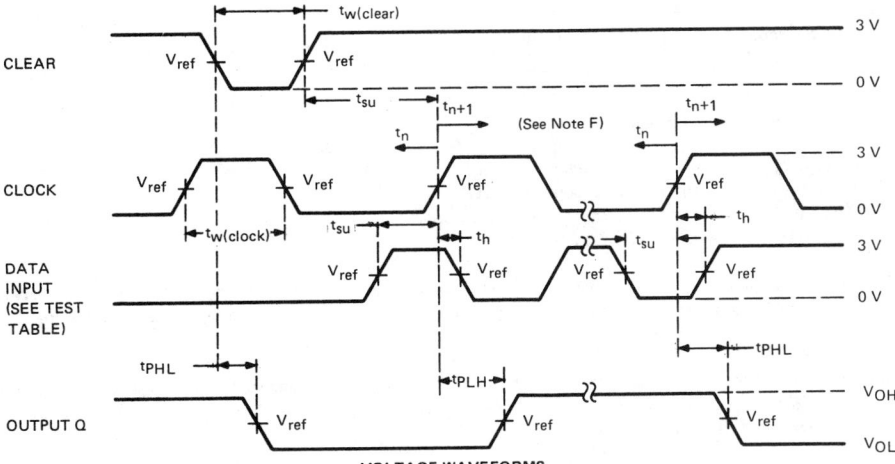

VOLTAGE WAVEFORMS

NOTES: A. The clock pulse generator has the following characteristics: $Z_{out} \approx 50\ \Omega$ and PRR $\leqslant$ 1 MHz, For '194, $t_r \leqslant$ 7 ns and $t_f \leqslant$ 7 ns. For 'LS194A, $t_r \leqslant$ 15 ns and $t_f \leqslant$ 6 ns. For 'S194, $t_r \leqslant$ 2.5 ns and $t_f \leqslant$ 2.5 ns. When testing f_{max}, vary PRR.
B. C_L includes probe and jig capacitance.
C. All diodes are 1N3064 or 1N916.
D. A clear pulse is applied prior to each test.
E. For '194 and 'S194, V_{ref} = 1.5 V; for 'LS194A, V_{ref} = 1.3 V.
F. Propagation delay times (t_{PLH} and t_{PHL}) are measured at t_{n+1}. Proper shifting of data is verified at t_{n+4} with a functional test.
G. t_n = bit time before clocking transition.
   t_{n+1} = bit time after one clocking transition.
   t_{n+4} = bit time after four clocking transitions.

FIGURE 1–SWITCHING TIMES

7

TEXAS INSTRUMENTS
INCORPORATED
POST OFFICE BOX 5012 • DALLAS, TEXAS 75222

TTL
MSI

TYPES SN54195, SN54LS195A, SN54S195, SN74195, SN74LS195A, SN74S195
4-BIT PARALLEL-ACCESS SHIFT REGISTERS
BULLETIN NO. DL-S 7611820, MARCH 1974—REVISED OCTOBER 1976

- Synchronous Parallel Load
- Positive-Edge-Triggered Clocking
- Parallel Inputs and Outputs from Each Flip-Flop
- Direct Overriding Clear
- J and $\overline{K}$ Inputs to First Stage
- Complementary Outputs from Last Stage
- For Use in High-Performance:
  Accumulators/Processors
  Serial-to-Parallel, Parallel-to-Serial Converters

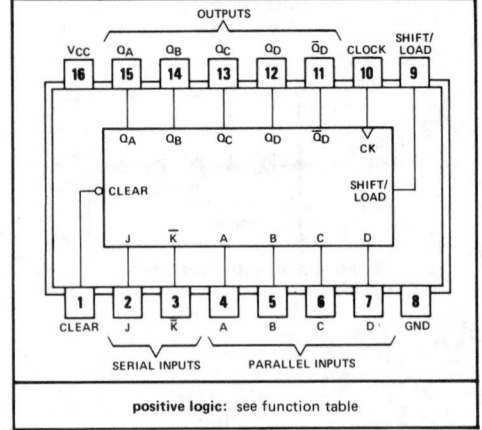

SN54195, SN54LS195A, SN54S195 . . . J OR W PACKAGE
SN74195, SN74LS195A, SN74S195 . . . J OR N PACKAGE
(TOP VIEW)

positive logic: see function table

description

These 4-bit registers feature parallel inputs, parallel outputs, J-$\overline{K}$ serial inputs, shift/load control input, and a direct overriding clear. All inputs are buffered to lower the input drive requirements. The registers have two modes of operation:

Parallel (broadside) load
Shift (in the direction Q_A toward Q_D)

Parallel loading is accomplished by applying the four bits of data and taking the shift/load control input low. The data is loaded into the associated flip-flop and appears at the outputs after the positive transition of the clock input. During loading, serial data flow is inhibited.

Shifting is accomplished synchronously when the shift/load control input is high. Serial data for this mode is entered at the J-$\overline{K}$ inputs. These inputs permit the first stage to perform as a J-$\overline{K}$, D-, or T-type flip-flop as shown in the function table.

The high-performance 'S195, with a 105-megahertz typical maximum shift-frequency, is particularly attractive for very-high-speed data processing systems. In most cases existing systems can be upgraded merely by using this Schottky-clamped shift register.

TYPE	TYPICAL MAXIMUM CLOCK FREQUENCY	TYPICAL POWER DISSIPATION
'195	39 MHz	195 mW
'LS195A	39 MHz	70 mW
'S195	105 MHz	350 mW

FUNCTION TABLE

INPUTS									OUTPUTS				
CLEAR	SHIFT/ LOAD	CLOCK	SERIAL		PARALLEL				Q_A	Q_B	Q_C	Q_D	$\overline{Q}_D$
			J	$\overline{K}$	A	B	C	D					
L	X	X	X	X	X	X	X	X	L	L	L	L	H
H	L	↑	X	X	a	b	c	d	a	b	c	d	$\overline{d}$
H	H	L	X	X	X	X	X	X	Q_{A0}	Q_{B0}	Q_{C0}	Q_{D0}	$\overline{Q}_{D0}$
H	H	↑	L	H	X	X	X	X	Q_{A0}	Q_{A0}	Q_{Bn}	Q_{Cn}	$\overline{Q}_{Cn}$
H	H	↑	L	L	X	X	X	X	L	Q_{An}	Q_{Bn}	Q_{Cn}	$\overline{Q}_{Cn}$
H	H	↑	H	H	X	X	X	X	H	Q_{An}	Q_{Bn}	Q_{Cn}	$\overline{Q}_{Cn}$
H	H	↑	H	L	X	X	X	X	$\overline{Q}_{An}$	Q_{An}	Q_{Bn}	Q_{Cn}	$\overline{Q}_{Cn}$

H = high level (steady state)
L = low level (steady state)
X = irrelevant (any input, including transitions)
↑ = transition from low to high level
a, b, c, d = the level of steady-state input at A, B, C, or D, respectively

Q_{A0}, Q_{B0}, Q_{C0}, Q_{D0} = the level of Q_A, Q_B, Q_C, or Q_D, respectively, before the indicated steady-state input conditions were established

Q_{An}, Q_{Bn}, Q_{Cn} = the level of Q_A, Q_B, or Q_C, respectively, before the most-recent transition of the clock

TEXAS INSTRUMENTS
INCORPORATED
POST OFFICE BOX 5012 • DALLAS, TEXAS 75222

functional block diagram

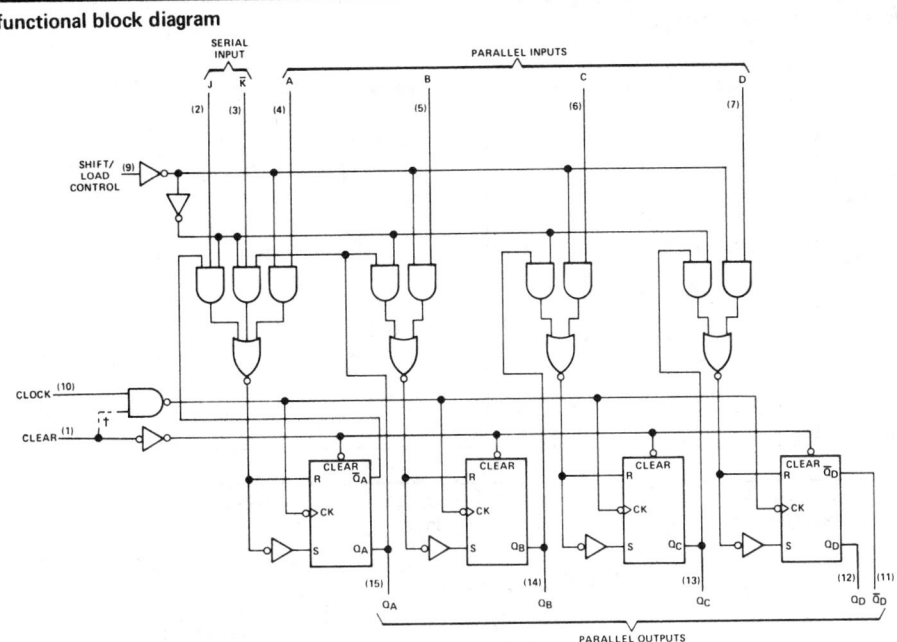

†This connection is made on '195 only.

typical clear, shift, and load sequences

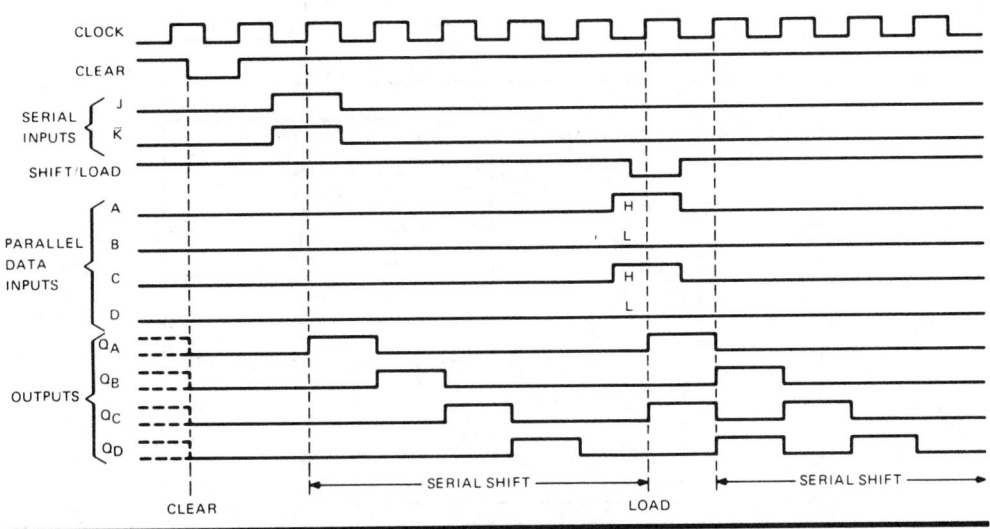

TEXAS INSTRUMENTS
INCORPORATED
POST OFFICE BOX 5012 • DALLAS, TEXAS 75222

TYPES SN54195, SN54LS195A, SN54S195, SN74195, SN74LS195A, SN74S195
4-BIT PARALLEL-ACCESS SHIFT REGISTERS

REVISED OCTOBER 1976

schematics of inputs and outputs

'195

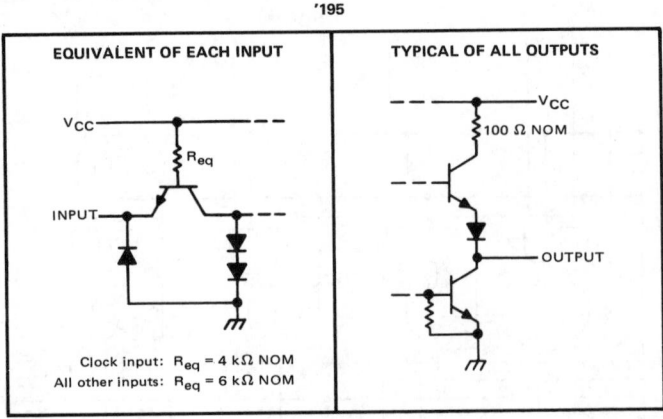

'LS195A

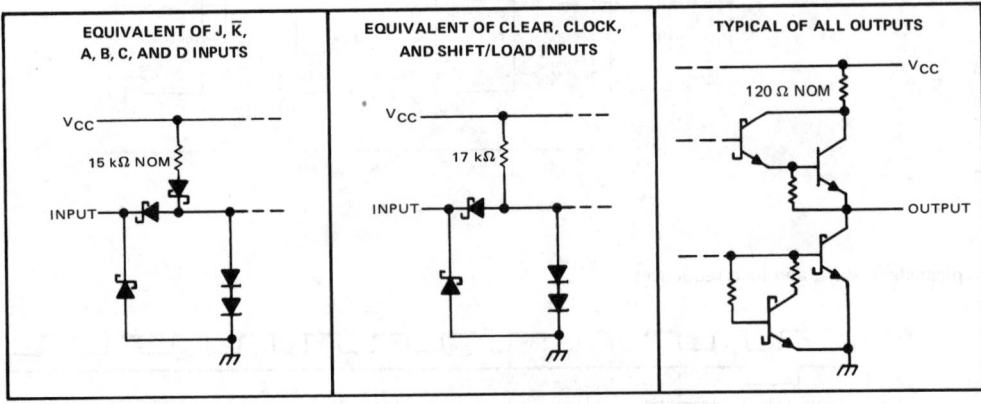

'S195

TEXAS INSTRUMENTS
INCORPORATED
POST OFFICE BOX 5012 • DALLAS, TEXAS 75222

absolute maximum ratings over operating free-air temperature range (unless otherwise noted)

Supply voltage, V_{CC} (see Note 1)	7 V
Input voltage	5.5 V
Operating free-air temperature range: SN54195	−55°C to 125°C
SN74195	0°C to 70°C
Storage temperature range	−65°C to 150°C

NOTE 1: Voltage values are with respect to network ground terminal.

recommended operating conditions

		SN54195			SN74195			UNIT
		MIN	NOM	MAX	MIN	NOM	MAX	
Supply voltage, V_{CC}		4.5	5	5.5	4.75	5	5.25	V
High-level output current, I_{OH}				−800			−800	μA
Low-level output current, I_{OL}				16			16	mA
Clock frequency, f_{clock}		0		30	0		30	MHz
Width of clock input pulse, $t_{w(clock)}$		16			16			ns
Width of clear input pulse, $t_{w(clear)}$		12			12			ns
Setup time, t_{su} (see Figure 1)	Shift/load	25			25			ns
	Serial and parallel data	20			20			
	Clear inactive-state	25			25			
Shift/load release time, $t_{release}$ (see Figure 1)				10			10	ns
Serial and parallel data hold time, t_h (see Figure 1)		0			0			ns
Operating free-air temperature, T_A		−55		125	0		70	°C

electrical characteristics over recommended operating free-air temperature range (unless otherwise noted)

	PARAMETER	TEST CONDITIONS†		MIN	TYP‡	MAX	UNIT
V_{IH}	High-level input voltage			2			V
V_{IL}	Low-level input voltage					0.8	V
V_{IK}	Input clamp voltage	V_{CC} = MIN,	I_I = −12 mA			−1.5	V
V_{OH}	High-level output voltage	V_{CC} = MIN,	V_{IH} = 2 V,	2.4	3.4		V
		V_{IL} = 0.8 V,	I_{OH} = −800 μA				
V_{OL}	Low-level output voltage	V_{CC} = MIN,	V_{IH} = 2 V,		0.2	0.4	V
		V_{IL} = 0.8 V,	I_{OL} = 16 mA				
I_I	Input current at maximum input voltage	V_{CC} = MAX,	V_I = 5.5 V			1	mA
I_{IH}	High-level input current	V_{CC} = MAX,	V_I = 2.4 V			40	μA
I_{IL}	Low-level input current	V_{CC} = MAX,	V_I = 0.4 V			−1.6	mA
I_{OS}	Short-circuit output current§	V_{CC} = MAX	SN54195	−20		−57	mA
			SN74195	−18		−57	
I_{CC}	Supply current	V_{CC} = MAX,	See Note 2		39	63	mA

†For conditions shown as MIN or MAX, use the appropriate value specified under recommended operating conditions.

‡All typical values are at V_{CC} = 5 V, T_A = 25°C.

§Not more than one output should be shorted at a time.

NOTE 2: With all outputs open, shift/load grounded, and 4.5 V applied to the J, $\overline{K}$, and data inputs, I_{CC} is measured by applying a momentary ground, followed by 4.5 V, to clear and then applying a momentary ground, followed by 4.5 V, to clock.

switching characteristics, V_{CC} = 5 V, T_A = 25°C

	PARAMETER	TEST CONDITIONS	MIN	TYP	MAX	UNIT
f_{max}	Maximum clock frequency		30	39		MHz
t_{PHL}	Propagation delay time, high-to-low-level output from clear	C_L = 15 pF,		19	30	ns
t_{PLH}	Propagation delay time, low-to-high-level output from clock	R_L = 400 Ω,		14	22	ns
t_{PHL}	Propagation delay time, high-to-low-level output from clock	See Figure 1		17	26	ns

TYPES SN54LS195A, SN74LS195A
4-BIT PARALLEL-ACCESS SHIFT REGISTERS

REVISED OCTOBER 1976

absolute maximum ratings over operating free-air temperature range (unless otherwise noted)

Supply voltage, V_{CC} (see Note 1) . . . . 7 V
Input voltage . . . . 7 V
Operating free-air temperature range: SN54LS195A . . . . −55°C to 125°C
SN74LS195A . . . . 0°C to 70°C
Storage temperature range . . . . −65°C to 150°C

NOTE 1: Voltage values are with respect to network ground terminal.

recommended operating conditions

		SN54LS195A			SN74LS195A			UNIT
		MIN	NOM	MAX	MIN	NOM	MAX	
Supply voltage, V_{CC}		4.5	5	5.5	4.75	5	5.25	V
High-level output current, I_{OH}				−400			−400	μA
Low-level output current, I_{OL}				4			8	mA
Clock frequency, f_{clock}		0		30	0		30	MHz
Width of clock or clear pulse, $t_{w(clock)}$		16			16			ns
Width of clear input pulse, $t_{w(clear)}$		12			12			ns
Setup time, t_{su} (see Figure 1)	Shift/load	25			25			ns
	Serial and parallel data	15			15			
	Clear inactive-state	25			25			
Shift/load release time, $t_{release}$ (see Figure 1)				10			10	ns
Serial and parallel data hold time, t_h (see Figure 1)		0			0			ns
Operating free-air temperature, T_A		−55		125	0		70	°C

electrical characteristics over recommended operating free-air temperature range (unless otherwise noted)

PARAMETER		TEST CONDITIONS[†]	SN54LS195A			SN74LS195A			UNIT
			MIN	TYP[‡]	MAX	MIN	TYP[‡]	MAX	
V_{IH}	High-level input voltage		2			2			V
V_{IL}	Low-level input voltage				0.7			0.8	V
V_{IK}	Input clamp voltage	V_{CC} = MIN, I_I = −18 mA			−1.5			−1.5	V
V_{OH}	High-level output voltage	V_{CC} = MIN, V_{IH} = 2 V, $V_{IL} = V_{IL}$ max, I_{OH} = −400 μA	2.5	3.4		2.7	3.4		V
V_{OL}	Low-level output voltage	V_{CC} = MIN, V_{IH} = 2 V, $V_{IL} = V_{IL}$ max, I_{OL} = 4 mA		0.25	0.4		0.25	0.4	V
		I_{OL} = 8 mA					0.35	0.5	
I_I	Input current at maximum input voltage	V_{CC} = MAX, V_I = 7 V			0.1			0.1	mA
I_{IH}	High-level input current	V_{CC} = MAX, V_I = 2.7 V			20			20	μA
I_{IL}	Low-level input current	V_{CC} = MAX, V_I = 0.4 V			−0.4			−0.4	mA
I_{OS}	Short-circuit output current[§]	V_{CC} = MAX	−20		−100	−20		−100	mA
I_{CC}	Supply current	V_{CC} = MAX, See Note 2		14	21		14	21	mA

[†]For conditions shown as MIN or MAX, use the appropriate value specified under recommended operating conditions.
[‡]All typical values are at V_{CC} = 5 V, T_A = 25°C.
[§]Not more than one output should be shorted at a time, and duration of the short-circuit should not exceed one second.
NOTE 2: With all outputs open, shift/load grounded, and 4.5 V applied to the J, K, and data inputs, I_{CC} is measured by applying a momentary ground, followed by 4.5 V, to clear and then applying a momentary ground, followed by 4.5 V, to clock.

switching characteristics, V_{CC} = 5 V, T_A = 25°C

PARAMETER		TEST CONDITIONS	MIN	TYP	MAX	UNIT
f_{max}	Maximum clock frequency	C_L = 15 pF, R_L = 2 kΩ, See Figure 1	30	39		MHz
t_{PHL}	Propagation delay time, high-to-low-level output from clear			19	30	ns
t_{PLH}	Propagation delay time, low-to-high-level output from clock			14	22	ns
t_{PHL}	Propagation delay time, high-to-low-level output from clock			17	26	ns

TEXAS INSTRUMENTS
INCORPORATED
POST OFFICE BOX 5012 • DALLAS, TEXAS 75222

absolute maximum ratings over operating free-air temperature range (unless otherwise noted)

Supply voltage, V_{CC} (see Note 1) . . . . 7 V
Input voltage . . . . 5.5 V
Operating free-air temperature range: SN54S195 . . . . −55°C to 125°C
SN74S195 . . . . 0°C to 70°C
Storage temperature range . . . . −65°C to 150°C

NOTE 1: Voltage values are with respect to network ground terminal.

recommended operating conditions

		SN54S195			SN74S195			UNIT
		MIN	NOM	MAX	MIN	NOM	MAX	
Supply voltage, V_{CC}		4.5	5	5.5	4.75	5	5.25	V
High-level output current, I_{OH}				−1			−1	mA
Low-level output current, I_{OL}				20			20	mA
Clock frequency, f_{clock}		0		70	0		70	MHz
Width of clock input pulse, $t_{w(clock)}$		7			7			ns
Width of clear input pulse, $t_{w(clear)}$		12			12			ns
Setup time, t_{su} (see Figure 1)	Shift/load	11			11			ns
	Serial and parallel data	5			5			
	Clear inactive-state	9			9			
Shift/load release time, $t_{release}$ (see Figure 1)				6			6	ns
Serial and parallel data hold time, t_h (see Figure 1)		3			3			ns
Operating free-air temperature, T_A		−55		125	0		70	°C

electrical characteristics over recommended operating free-air temperature range (unless otherwise noted)

PARAMETER		TEST CONDITIONS[†]		MIN	TYP[‡]	MAX	UNIT
V_{IH}	High-level input voltage			2			V
V_{IL}	Low-level input voltage					0.8	V
V_{IK}	Input clamp voltage	V_{CC} = MIN,	I_I = −18 mA			−1.2	V
V_{OH}	High-level output voltage	V_{CC} = MIN, V_{IH} = 2 V, V_{IL} = 0.8 V, I_{OH} = −1 mA	SN54S195	2.5	3.4		V
			SN74S195	2.7	3.4		
V_{OL}	Low-level output voltage	V_{CC} = MIN, V_{IH} = 2 V, V_{IL} = 0.8 V, I_{OL} = 20 mA				0.5	V
I_I	Input current at maximum input voltage	V_{CC} = MAX,	V_I = 5.5 V			1	mA
I_{IH}	High-level input current	V_{CC} = MAX,	V_I = 2.7 V			50	µA
I_{IL}	Low-level input current	V_{CC} = MAX,	V_I = 0.5 V			−2	mA
I_{OS}	Short-circuit output current[§]	V_{CC} = MAX		−40		−100	mA
I_{CC}	Supply current	V_{CC} = MAX,	See Note 2	SN54S195		70	99	mA
				SN74S195		70	109	

[†]For conditions shown as MIN or MAX, use the appropriate value specified under recommended operating conditions.
[‡]All typical values are at V_{CC} = 5 V, T_A = 25°C.
[§]Not more than one output should be shorted at a time, and duration of the short-circuit should not exceed one second.
NOTE 2: With all outputs open, shift/load grounded, and 4.5 V applied to the J, $\overline{K}$, and data inputs, I_{CC} is measured by applying a momentary ground, followed by 4.5 V, to clear, and then applying a momentary ground, followed by 4.5 V, to clock.

switching characteristics, V_{CC} = 5 V, T_A = 25°C

PARAMETER	TEST CONDITIONS	MIN	TYP	MAX	UNIT
f_{max} Maximum clock frequency	C_L = 15 pF, R_L = 280 Ω, See Figure 1	70	105		MHz
t_{PHL} Propagation delay time, high-to-low-level output from clear			12.5	18.5	ns
t_{PLH} Propagation delay time, low-to-high-level output from clock			8	12	ns
t_{PHL} Propagation delay time, high-to-low-level output from clock			11	16.5	ns

TEXAS INSTRUMENTS
INCORPORATED
POST OFFICE BOX 5012 • DALLAS, TEXAS 75222

TYPES SN54195, SN54LS195A, SN54S195, SN74195, SN74LS195A, SN74S195
4-BIT PARALLEL-ACCESS SHIFT REGISTERS

PARAMETER MEASUREMENT INFORMATION

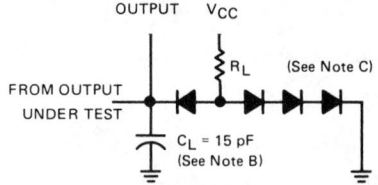

LOAD FOR OUTPUT UNDER TEST

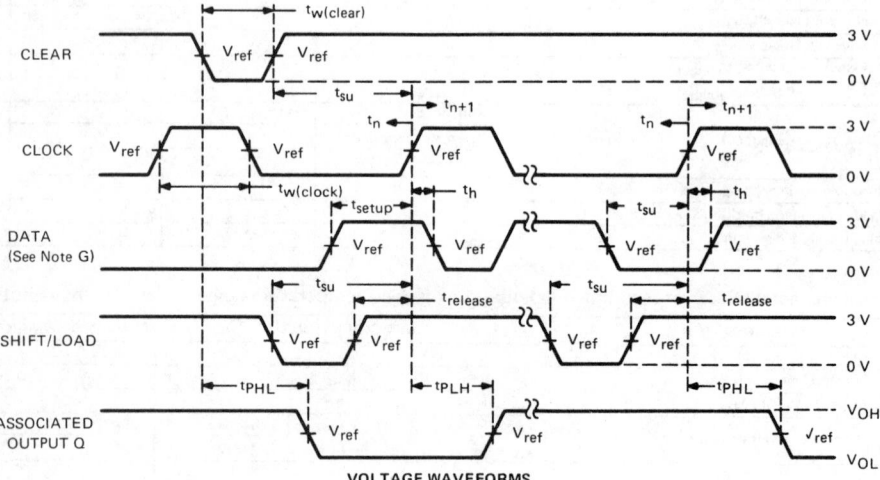

VOLTAGE WAVEFORMS

NOTES: A. The clock pulse generator has the following characteristics: $Z_{out} \approx 50\ \Omega$ and PRR $\leqslant$ 1 MHz. For '195, $t_r \leqslant$ 7 ns and $t_f \leqslant$ 7 ns. For 'LS195A, $t_r \leqslant$ 15 ns and $t_f \leqslant$ 6 ns. For 'S195, t_r = 2.5 ns and t_f = 2.5 ns. When testing f_{max}, vary the clock PRR.
   B. C_L includes probe and jig capacitance.
   C. All diodes are 1N3064.
   D. A clear pulse is applied prior to each test.
   E. For '195 and 'S195, V_{ref} = 1.5 V; for 'LS195A, V_{ref} = 1.3 V.
   F. Propagation delay times (t_{PLH} and t_{PHL}) are measured at t_{n+1}. Proper shifting of data is verified at t_{n+4} with a functional test.
   G. J and $\overline{K}$ inputs are tested the same as data A, B, C, and D inputs except that shift/load input remains high.
   H. t_n = bit time before clocking transition.
       t_{n+1} = bit time after one clocking transition.
       t_{n+4} = bit time after four clocking transitions.

FIGURE 1—SWITCHING TIMES

TEXAS INSTRUMENTS
INCORPORATED
POST OFFICE BOX 5012 • DALLAS, TEXAS 75222

TYPES SN54196, SN54197, SN54LS196, SN54LS197, SN54S196, SN54S197, SN74196, SN74197, SN74LS196, SN74LS197, SN74S196, SN74S197
50/30/100-MHz PRESETTABLE DECADE OR BINARY COUNTERS/LATCHES

BULLETIN NO. DL-S 7711806, OCTOBER 1976—REVISED AUGUST 1977

- Performs BCD, Bi-Quinary, or Binary Counting

- Fully Programmable

- Fully Independent Clear Input

- Input Clamping Diodes Simplify System Design

- Output Q_A Maintains Full Fan-out Capability In Addition to Driving Clock-2 Input

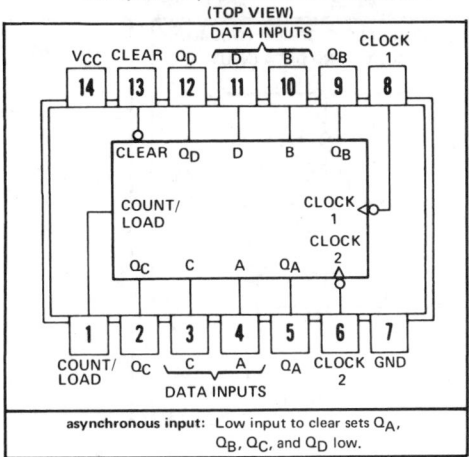

SN54', SN54LS', SN54S' . . . J OR W PACKAGE
SN74', SN74LS', SN74S' . . . J OR N PACKAGE
(TOP VIEW)

asynchronous input: Low input to clear sets Q_A, Q_B, Q_C, and Q_D low.

TYPES	GUARANTEED COUNT FREQUENCY		TYPICAL POWER DISSIPATION
	CLOCK 1	CLOCK 2	
'196, '197	0-50 MHz	0-25 MHz	240 mW
'LS196, 'LS197	0-30 MHz	0-15 MHz	80 mW
'S196, 'S197	0-100 MHz	0-50 MHz	375 mW

description

These high-speed monolithic counters consist of four d-c coupled, master-slave flip-flops, which are internally interconnected to provide either a divide-by-two and a divide-by-five counter ('196, 'LS196, 'S196) or a divide-by-two and a divide-by-eight counter ('197, 'LS197, 'S197). These four counters are fully programmable; that is, the outputs may be preset to any state by placing a low on the count/load input and entering the desired data at the data inputs. The outputs will change to agree with the data inputs independent of the state of the clocks.

During the count operation, transfer of information to the outputs occurs on the negative-going edge of the clock pulse. These counters feature a direct clear which when taken low sets all outputs low regardless of the states of the clocks.

These counters may also be used as 4-bit latches by using the count/load input as the strobe and entering data at the data inputs. The outputs will directly follow the data inputs when the count/load is low, but will remain unchanged when the count/load is high and the clock inputs are inactive.

All inputs are diode-clamped to minimize transmission-line effects and simplify system design. These circuits are compatible with most TTL and DTL logic families. Series 54, 54LS, and 54S circuits are characterized for operation over the full military temperature range of −55°C to 125°C; Series 74, 74LS, and 74S circuits are characterized for operation from 0°C to 70°C.

typical count configurations

'196, 'LS196, and 'S196 typical count configurations and function tables are the same as those for '176. See page 7-260.
'197, 'LS197, and 'S197 typical count configurations and function tables are the same as those for '177. See page 7-260.

functional block diagrams

'196, 'LS196, and 'S196 functional block diagram is the same as that for '176. See page 7-261.
'197, 'LS197, and 'S197 functional block diagram is the same as that for '177. See page 7-261.

TEXAS INSTRUMENTS
INCORPORATED
POST OFFICE BOX 5012 • DALLAS, TEXAS 75222

TYPES SN54196, SN54197, SN74196, SN74197
50-MHz PRESETTABLE DECADE OR BINARY COUNTERS/LATCHES

REVISED AUGUST 1977

schematics of inputs and outputs

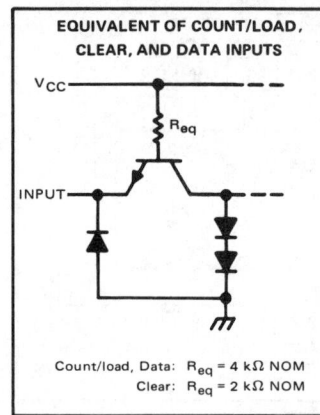

EQUIVALENT OF COUNT/LOAD, CLEAR, AND DATA INPUTS

Count/load, Data: R_{eq} = 4 kΩ NOM
Clear: R_{eq} = 2 kΩ NOM

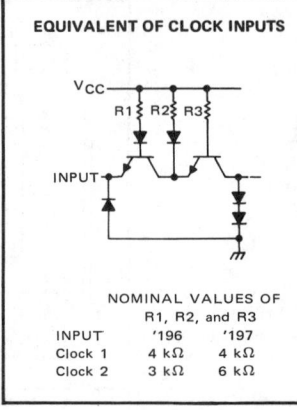

EQUIVALENT OF CLOCK INPUTS

NOMINAL VALUES OF R1, R2, and R3

INPUT	'196	'197
Clock 1	4 kΩ	4 kΩ
Clock 2	3 kΩ	6 kΩ

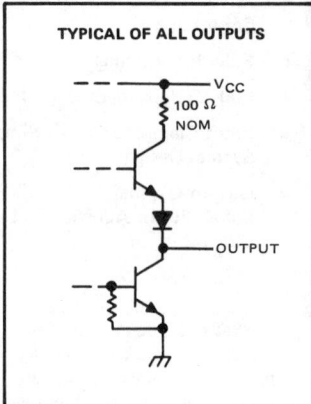

TYPICAL OF ALL OUTPUTS

absolute maximum ratings over operating free-air temperature range (unless otherwise noted)

Supply voltage, V_{CC} (see Note 1)	7 V
Input voltage	5.5 V
Interemitter voltage (see Note 2)	5.5 V
Operating free-air temperature range: SN54196, SN54197 Circuits	−55°C to 125°C
SN74196, SN74197 Circuits	0°C to 70°C
Storage temperature range	−65°C to 150°C

NOTES: 1. Voltage values are with respect to network ground terminal.
2. This is the voltage between two emitters of a multiple-emitter transistor. For this circuit, this rating applies between the clear and count/load inputs.

recommended operating conditions

		SN54196, SN54197			SN74196, SN74197			UNIT
		MIN	NOM	MAX	MIN	NOM	MAX	
Supply voltage, V_{CC}		4.5	5	5.5	4.75	5	5.25	V
High-level output current, I_{OH}				−800			−800	µA
Low-level output current, I_{OL}				16			16	mA
Count frequency	Clock-1 input	0		50	0		50	MHz
	Clock-2 input	0		25	0		25	
Pulse width, t_w	Clock-1 input	10			10			ns
	Clock-2 input	20			20			
	Clear	15			15			
	Load	20			20			
Input hold time, t_h	High-level data	$t_{w(load)}$			$t_{w(load)}$			ns
	Low-level data	$t_{w(load)}$			$t_{w(load)}$			
Input setup time, t_{su}	High-level data	10			10			ns
	Low-level data	15			15			
Count enable time, t_{enable} (See Note 3)		20			20			ns
Operating free-air temperature, T_A		−55		125	0		70	°C

NOTE 3: Minimum count enable time is the interval immediately preceding the negative-going edge of the clock pulse during which interval the count/load and clear inputs must both be high to ensure counting.

TEXAS INSTRUMENTS
INCORPORATED
POST OFFICE BOX 5012 • DALLAS, TEXAS 75222

7

electrical characteristics over recommended operating free-air temperature range (unless otherwise noted)

PARAMETER		TEST CONDITIONS†		SN54196, SN74196			SN54197, SN74197			UNIT
				MIN	TYP‡	MAX	MIN	TYP‡	MAX	
V_{IH}	High-level input voltage			2			2			V
V_{IL}	Low-level input voltage					0.8			0.8	V
V_{IK}	Input clamp voltage	V_{CC} = MIN, I_I = −12 mA				−1.5			−1.5	V
V_{OH}	High-level output voltage	V_{CC} = MIN, V_{IH} = 2 V, V_{IL} = 0.8 V, I_{OH} = −800 μA		2.4	3.4		2.4	3.4		V
V_{OL}	Low-level output voltage	V_{CC} = MIN, V_{IH} = 2 V, V_{IL} = 0.8 V, I_{OL} = 16 mA¶			0.2	0.4		0.2	0.4	V
I_I	Input current at maximum input voltage	V_{CC} = MAX, V_I = 5.5 V				1			1	mA
I_{IH}	High-level input current	data, count/load	V_{CC} = MAX, V_I = 2.4 V			40			40	μA
		clear, clock 1				80			80	
		clock 2				120			80	
I_{IL}	Low-level input current	data, count/load	V_{CC} = MAX, V_I = 0.4 V			−1.6			−1.6	mA
		clear				−3.2			−3.2	
		clock 1				−4.8			−4.8	
		clock 2				−6.4			−3.2	
I_{OS}	Short-circuit output current §	V_{CC} = MAX	SN54'	−20		−57	−20		−57	mA
			SN74'	−18		−57	−18		−57	
I_{CC}	Supply current	V_{CC} = MAX, See Note 4			48	59		48	59	mA

NOTE 4: I_{CC} is measured with all inputs grounded and all outputs open.

†For conditions shown as MIN or MAX, use the appropriate value specified under recommended operating conditions.

‡All typical values are at V_{CC} = 5 V, T_A = 25°C.

¶Q_A outputs are tested at I_{OL} = 16 mA plus the limit value of I_{IL} for the clock-2 input. This permits driving the clock-2 input while fanning out to 10 Series 54/74 loads.

§Not more than one output should be shorted at a time.

switching characteristics, V_{CC} = 5 V, T_A = 25°C

PARAMETER◇	FROM (INPUT)	TO (OUTPUT)	TEST CONDITIONS	SN54196 SN74196			SN54197 SN74197			UNIT
				MIN	TYP	MAX	MIN	TYP	MAX	
f_{max}	Clock 1	Q_A		50	70		50	70		MHz
t_{PLH}	Clock 1	Q_A			7	12		7	12	ns
t_{PHL}					10	15		10	15	
t_{PLH}	Clock 2	Q_B			12	18		12	18	ns
t_{PHL}					14	21		14	21	
t_{PLH}	Clock 2	Q_C	C_L = 15 pF, R_L = 400 Ω, See Note 5		24	36		24	36	ns
t_{PHL}					28	42		28	42	
t_{PLH}	Clock 2	Q_D			14	21		36	54	ns
t_{PHL}					12	18		42	63	
t_{PLH}	A, B, C, D	Q_A, Q_B, Q_C, Q_D			16	24		16	24	ns
t_{PHL}					25	38		25	38	
t_{PLH}	Load	Any			22	33		22	33	ns
t_{PHL}					24	36		24	36	
t_{PHL}	Clear	Any			25	37		25	37	ns

◇f_{max} ≡ maximum count frequency.

t_{PLH} ≡ propagation delay time, low-to-high-level output.

t_{PHL} ≡ propagation delay time, high-to-low-level output.

NOTE 5: Load circuit, input conditions, and voltage waveforms are the same as those shown for the '176, '177 (page 7-264) except that testing f_{max}, V_{IL} = 0.3 V.

TEXAS INSTRUMENTS
INCORPORATED
POST OFFICE BOX 5012 • DALLAS, TEXAS 75222

7

schematics of inputs and outputs

EQUIVALENT OF COUNT/LOAD AND CLEAR INPUTS	EQUIVALENT OF CLOCK INPUTS	EQUIVALENT OF DATA INPUTS	TYPICAL OF ALL OUTPUTS
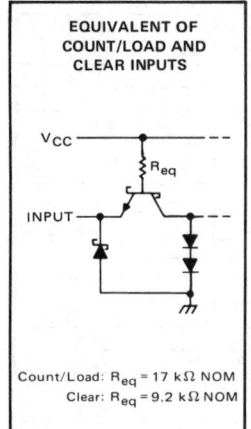	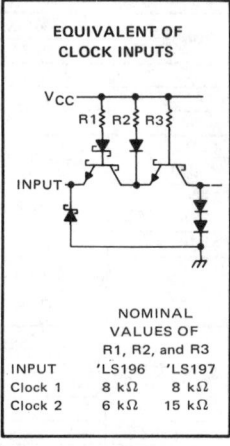	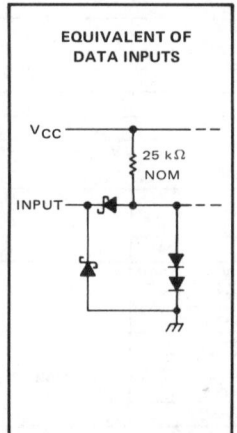	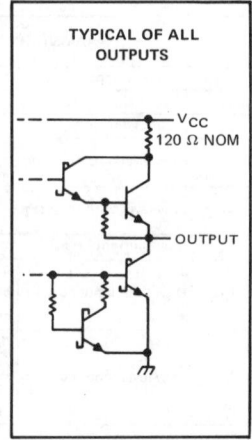

Count/Load: R_{eq} = 17 kΩ NOM
Clear: R_{eq} = 9.2 kΩ NOM

NOMINAL VALUES OF R1, R2, and R3

INPUT	'LS196	'LS197
Clock 1	8 kΩ	8 kΩ
Clock 2	6 kΩ	15 kΩ

absolute maximum ratings over operating free-air temperature range (unless otherwise noted)

Supply voltage, V_{CC} (see Note 1) . . . . 7 V
Input voltage . . . . 5.5 V
Interemitter voltage (see Note 2). . . . . 5.5 V
Operating free-air temperature range: SN54LS196, SN54LS197 Circuits . . . . −55°C to 125°C
                             SN74LS196, SN74LS197 Circuits . . . . 0°C to 70°C
Storage temperature range . . . . −65°C to 150°C

NOTES: 1. Voltage values are with respect to network ground terminal.
        2. This is the voltage between two emitters of a multiple-emitter transistor. For this circuit, this rating applies between the clear and count/load inputs.

recommended operating conditions

		SN54LS196, SN54LS197			SN74LS196, SN74LS197			UNIT
		MIN	NOM	MAX	MIN	NOM	MAX	
Supply voltage, V_{CC}		4.5	5	5.5	4.75	5	5.25	V
High-level output current, I_{OH}				−400			−400	µA
Low-level output current, I_{OL}				4			8	mA
Count frequency	Clock-1 input	0		30	0		30	MHz
	Clock-2 input	0		15	0		15	
Pulse width, t_W	Clock-1 input	20			20			ns
	Clock-2 input	30			30			
	Clear	15			15			
	Load	20			20			
Input hold time, t_h	High-level data	t_W(load)			t_W(load)			ns
	Low-level data	t_W(load)			t_W(load)			
Input setup time, t_{su}	High-level data	10			10			ns
	Low-level data	15			15			
Count enable time, t_{enable} (See Note 3)		30			30			ns
Operating free-air temperature, T_A		−55		125	0		70	°C

NOTE 3: Minimum count enable time is the interval immediately preceding the negative-going edge of the clock pulse during which interval the count/load and clear inputs must both be high to ensure counting.

TEXAS INSTRUMENTS
INCORPORATED
POST OFFICE BOX 5012 • DALLAS, TEXAS 75222

electrical characteristics over recommended operating free-air temperature range (unless otherwise noted)

PARAMETER		TEST CONDITIONS[†]		SN54LS196 SN54LS197			SN74LS196 SN74LS197			UNIT
				MIN	TYP[‡]	MAX	MIN	TYP[‡]	MAX	
V_{IH} High-level input voltage				2			2			V
V_{IL} Low-level input voltage						0.7			0.8	V
V_{IK} Input clamp voltage		V_{CC} = MIN, I_I = −18 mA				−1.5			−1.5	V
V_{OH} High-level output voltage		V_{CC} = MIN, V_{IH} = 2 V, V_{IL} = $V_{IL\,max}$, I_{OH} = −400 μA		2.5	3.4		2.7	3.4		V
V_{OL} Low-level output voltage		V_{CC} = MIN, V_{IH} = 2 V, V_{IL} = $V_{IL\,max}$	I_{OL} = 4 mA¶		0.25	0.4		0.25	0.4	V
			I_{OL} = 8 mA¶					0.35	0.5	
I_I Input current at maximum input voltage	Data, count/load	V_{CC} = MAX, V_I = 5.5 V				0.1			0.1	mA
	Clear, clock 1					0.2			0.2	
	Clock 2 of 'LS196					0.4			0.4	
	Clock 2 of 'LS197					0.2			0.2	
I_{IH} High-level input current	Data, count/load	V_{CC} = MAX, V_I = 2.7 V				20			20	μA
	Clear, clock 1					40			40	
	Clock 2 of 'LS196					80			80	
	Clock 2 of 'LS197					40			40	
I_{IL} Low-level Input current	Data, count/load	V_{CC} = MAX, V_I = 0.4 V				−0.4			−0.4	mA
	Clear					−0.8			−0.8	
	Clock 1					−2.4			−2.4	
	Clock 2 of 'LS196					−2.8			−2.8	
	Clock 2 of 'LS197					−1.3			−1.3	
I_{OS} Short-circuit output current§		V_{CC} = MAX		−20		−100	−20		−100	mA
I_{CC} Supply current		V_{CC} = MAX, See Note 4			16	27		16	27	mA

†For conditions shown as MIN or MAX, use the appropriate value specified under recommended operating conditions.
‡All typical values are at V_{CC} = 5 V, T_A = 25°C.
§Not more than one output should be shorted at a time, and duration of the short-circuit should not exceed one second.
¶Q_A outputs are tested at specified I_{OL} plus the limit value of I_{IL} for the clock-2 input. This permits driving the clock-2 input while maintaining full fan-out capability.
NOTE 4: I_{CC} is measured with all inputs grounded and all outputs open.

switching characteristics, V_{CC} = 5 V, T_A = 25°C

PARAMETER◊	FROM (INPUT)	TO (OUTPUT)	TEST CONDITIONS	SN54LS196 SN74LS196			SN54LS197 SN74LS197			UNIT
				MIN	TYP	MAX	MIN	TYP	MAX	
f_{max}	Clock 1	Q_A		30	40		30	40		MHz
t_{PLH}	Clock 1	Q_A			8	15		8	15	ns
t_{PHL}					13	20		14	21	
t_{PLH}	Clock 2	Q_B			16	24		12	19	ns
t_{PHL}					22	33		23	35	
t_{PLH}	Clock 2	Q_C	C_L = 15 pF, R_L = 2 kΩ, See Note 6		38	57		34	51	ns
t_{PHL}					41	62		42	63	
t_{PLH}	Clock 2	Q_D			12	18		55	78	ns
t_{PHL}					30	45		63	95	
t_{PLH}	A, B, C, D	Q_A, Q_B, Q_C Q_D			20	30		18	27	ns
t_{PHL}					29	44		29	44	
t_{PLH}	Load	Any			27	41		26	39	ns
t_{PHL}					30	45		30	45	
t_{PHL}	Clear	Any			34	51		34	51	ns

◊f_{max} ≡ maximum count frequency
t_{PLH} ≡ propagation delay time, low-to-high-level output, t_{PHL} ≡ propagation delay time, high-to-low-level output
NOTE 6: Load circuit, input conditions, and voltage waveforms are the same as those shown for the '176, '177 (page 7-264) except that t_r ⩽ 15 ns, t_f ⩽ 6 ns, and V_{ref} = 1.3 V (as opposed to 1.5 V).

TEXAS INSTRUMENTS
INCORPORATED
POST OFFICE BOX 5012 • DALLAS, TEXAS 75222

schematics of inputs and outputs

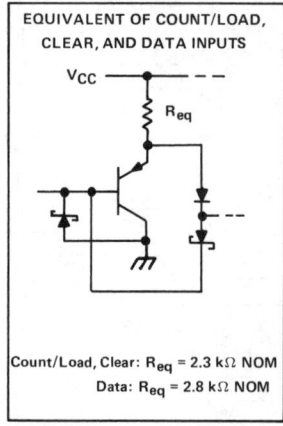

EQUIVALENT OF COUNT/LOAD, CLEAR, AND DATA INPUTS

V_{CC}

R_{eq}

Count/Load, Clear: R_{eq} = 2.3 kΩ NOM

Data: R_{eq} = 2.8 kΩ NOM

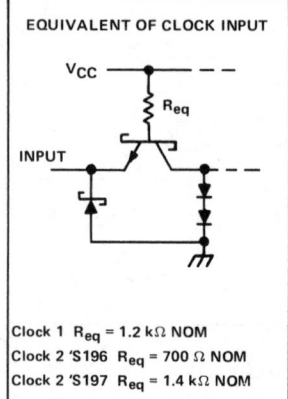

EQUIVALENT OF CLOCK INPUT

V_{CC}

R_{eq}

INPUT

Clock 1 R_{eq} = 1.2 kΩ NOM
Clock 2 'S196 R_{eq} = 700 Ω NOM
Clock 2 'S197 R_{eq} = 1.4 kΩ NOM

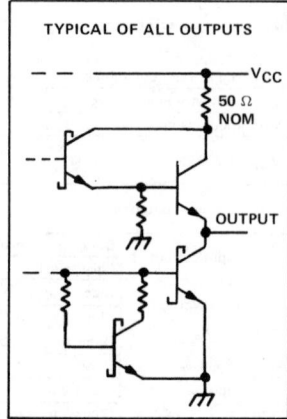

TYPICAL OF ALL OUTPUTS

V_{CC}

50 Ω NOM

OUTPUT

absolute maximum ratings over operating free-air temperature range (unless otherwise noted)

Supply voltage, V_{CC} (see Note 1) . . . . 7 V
Input voltage . . . . 5.5 V
Operating free-air temperature range: SN54S196, SN54S197 Circuits . . . . −55°C to 125°C
                      SN74S196, SN74S197 Circuits . . . . 0°C to 70°C
Storage temperature range . . . . −65°C to 150°C

NOTE 1: Voltage values are with respect to network ground terminal.

recommended operating conditions

		SN54S196, SN54S197			SN74S196, SN74S197			UNIT
		MIN	NOM	MAX	MIN	NOM	MAX	
Supply voltage, V_{CC}		4.5	5	5.5	4.75	5	5.25	V
High-level output current, I_{OH}				−1			−1	mA
Low-level output current, I_{OL}				20			20	mA
Clock frequency	Clock-1 input	0		100	0		100	MHz
	Clock-2 input	0		50	0		50	
Pulse width, t_W	Clock-1 input	5			5			ns
	Clock-2 input	10			10			
	Clear	30			30			
	Load	5			5			
Input hold time, t_h	High-level data	3↑			3↑			ns
	Low-level data	3↑			3↑			
Input setup time, t_{su}	High-level data	6↑			6↑			ns
	Low-level data	6↑			6↑			
Count enable time, t_{enable} (see Note 3)		12			12			ns
Operating free-air temperature, T_A		−55		125	0		70	°C

NOTE 3: Minimum count enable time is the interval immediately preceding the negative-going edge of the clock pulse during which interval the count/load and clear inputs are both high to permit counting.

TEXAS INSTRUMENTS
INCORPORATED
POST OFFICE BOX 5012 • DALLAS, TEXAS 75222

electrical characteristics over recommended operating free-air temperature range (unless otherwise noted)

PARAMETER		TEST CONDITIONS[†]		SN54S196, SN74S196			SN54S197, SN74S197			UNIT
				MIN	TYP[‡]	MAX	MIN	TYP[‡]	MAX	
V_{IH}	High-level input voltage			2			2			V
V_{IL}	Low-level input voltage					0.8			0.8	V
V_{IK}	Input clamp voltage	V_{CC} = MIN,	I_I = −18 mA			−1.2			−1.2	V
V_{OH}	High-level output voltage	V_{CC} = MIN, V_{IH} = 2 V, V_{IL} = 0.8 V, I_{OH} = −1 mA	54S	2.5	3.4		2.5	3.4		V
			74S	2.7	3.4		2.7	3.4		
V_{OL}	Low-level output voltage	V_{CC} = MIN, V_{IH} = 2 V, V_{IL} = 0.8 V, I_{OL} = 20 mA[¶]				0.5			0.5	V
I_I	Input current at maximum input voltage	V_{CC} = MAX,	V_I = 5.5 V			1			1	mA
I_{IH}	High-level input current	V_{CC} = MAX,	V_I = 2.7 V			50			50	µA
I_{IL}	Low-level input current	data, count/load clear	V_{CC} = MAX, V_I = 0.5 V			0.75			0.75	mA
		clock 1				−8			−8	mA
		clock 2				−10			−6	mA
I_{OS}	Short-circuit output current[§]	V_{CC} = MAX		−30		−110	−30		−110	mA
I_{CC}	Supply current	V_{CC} = MAX, See Note 4	54S		75	110		75	110	mA
			74S		75	120		75	120	

NOTE 4: I_{CC} is measured with all inputs grounded and all outputs open.

[†]For conditions shown as MIN or MAX, use the appropriate value specified under recommended operating conditions.

[‡]All typical values are at V_{CC} = 5 V, T_A = 25°C.

[¶]Q_A outputs are tested at I_{OL} = 20 mA plus the limit value of I_{IL} for the clock-2 input. This permits driving the clock-2 input while fanning out to 10 Series 54S/74S loads.

[§]Not more than one output should be shorted at a time, and duration of the short-circuit should not exceed one second.

switching characteristics, V_{CC} = 5 V, T_A = 25°C

PARAMETER[◊]	FROM (INPUT)	TO (OUTPUT)	TEST CONDITIONS	SN54S196, SN74S196			SN54S197, SN74S197			UNIT
				MIN	TYP	MAX	MIN	TYP	MAX	
f_{max}	Clock 1	Q_A		100	140		100	140		MHz
t_{PLH}	Clock 1	Q_A			5	10		5	10	ns
t_{PHL}					6	10		6	10	
t_{PLH}	Clock 2	Q_B			5	10		5	10	ns
t_{PHL}					8	12		8	12	
t_{PLH}	Clock 2	Q_C	C_L = 15 pF, R_L = 280 Ω, See Note 7		12	18		12	18	ns
t_{PHL}					16	24		15	22	
t_{PLH}	Clock 2	Q_D			5	10		18	27	ns
t_{PHL}					8	12		22	33	
t_{PLH}	A, B, C, D	Q_A, Q_B, Q_C, Q_D			7	12		7	12	ns
t_{PHL}					12	18		12	18	
t_{PLH}	Load	Any			10	18		10	18	ns
t_{PHL}					12	18		12	18	
t_{PHL}	Clear	Any			26	37		26	37	ns

[◊]f_{max} ≡ maximum input county frequency.

t_{PLH} ≡ propagation delay time, low-to-high-level output.

t_{PHL} ≡ propagation delay time, high-to-low-level output.

NOTE 7: Load circuit, input conditions, and voltage waveforms are the same as those shown for the '176, '177 on page 7-264.

TEXAS INSTRUMENTS
INCORPORATED
POST OFFICE BOX 5012 • DALLAS, TEXAS 75222

description

These 8-bit shift registers are compatible with most other TTL, DTL, and MSI logic families. All inputs are buffered to lower the drive requirements to one normalized Series 54/74 load, and input clamping diodes minimize switching transients to simplify system design. Maximum input clock frequency is typically 35 megahertz and power dissipation is typically 360 mW.

Series 54 devices are characterized for operation over the full military temperature range of $-55°C$ to $125°C$; Series 74 devices are characterized for operation from $0°C$ to $70°C$.

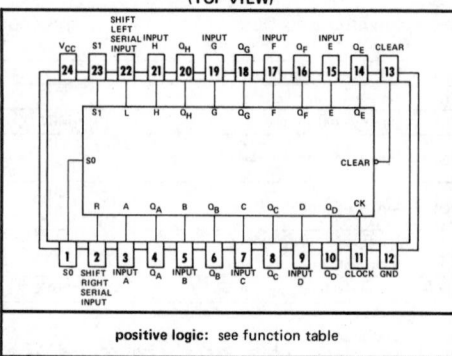

SN54198 . . . J OR W PACKAGE
SN74198 . . . J OR N PACKAGE
(TOP VIEW)

positive logic: see function table

SN54198 and SN74198

These bidirectional registers are designed to incorporate virtually all of the features a system designer may want in a shift register. These circuits contain 87 equivalent gates and feature parallel inputs, parallel outputs, right-shift and left-shift serial inputs, operating-mode-control inputs, and a direct overriding clear line. The register has four distinct modes of operation, namely:

Parallel (Broadside) Load
Shift Right (In the direction Q_A toward Q_H)
Shift Left (In the direction Q_H toward Q_A)
Inhibit Clock (Do nothing)

Synchronous parallel loading is accomplished by applying the eight bits of data and taking both mode control inputs, S0 and S1, high. The data is loaded into the associated flip-flop and appears at the outputs after the positive transition of the clock input. During loading, serial data flow is inhibited.

Shift right is accomplished synchronously with the rising edge of the clock pulse when S0 is high and S1 is low. Serial data for this mode is entered at the shift-right data input. When S0 is low and S1 is high, data shifts left synchronously and new data is entered at the shift-left serial input.

Clocking of the flip-flop is inhibited when both mode control inputs are low. The mode controls should be changed only while the clock input is high.

'198
FUNCTION TABLE

INPUTS								OUTPUTS			
CLEAR	MODE		CLOCK	SERIAL		PARALLEL		Q_A	Q_B ...	Q_G	Q_H
	S_1	S_0		LEFT	RIGHT	A ... H					
L	X	X	X	X	X	X		L	L	L	L
H	X	X	L	X	X	X		Q_{A0}	Q_{B0}	Q_{G0}	Q_{H0}
H	H	H	↑	X	X	a...h		a	b	g	h
H	L	H	↑	X	H	X		H	Q_{An}	Q_{Fn}	Q_{Gn}
H	L	H	↑	X	L	X		L	Q_{An}	Q_{Fn}	Q_{Gn}
H	H	L	↑	H	X	X		Q_{Bn}	Q_{Cn}	Q_{Hn}	H
H	H	L	↑	L	X	X		Q_{Bn}	Q_{Cn}	Q_{Hn}	L
H	L	L	X	X	X	X		Q_{A0}	Q_{B0}	Q_{G0}	Q_{H0}

H = high level (steady state), L = low level (steady state)
X = irrelevant (any input, including transitions)
↑ = transition from low to high level
a . . . h = the level of steady-state input at inputs A thru H, respectively.
Q_{A0}, Q_{B0}, Q_{G0}, Q_{H0} = the level of Q_A, Q_B, Q_G, or Q_H, respectively, before the indicated steady-state input conditions were established.
Q_{An}, Q_{Bn}, etc. = the level of Q_A, Q_B, etc., respectively, before the most-recent ↑ transition of the clock.

TEXAS INSTRUMENTS
INCORPORATED
POST OFFICE BOX 5012 • DALLAS, TEXAS 75222

SN54199 and SN74199

These registers feature parallel inputs, parallel outputs, J-$\overline{K}$ serial inputs, shift/load control input, a direct overriding clear line, and gated clock inputs. The register has three modes of operation:

    Parallel (Broadside) Load
    Shift (In the direction Q_A toward Q_H)
    Inhibit Clock (Do nothing)

Parallel loading is accomplished by applying the eight bits of data and taking the shift/load control input low when the clock input is not inhibited. The data is loaded into the associated flip-flop and appears at the outputs after the positive transition of the clock input. During loading, serial data flow is inhibited.

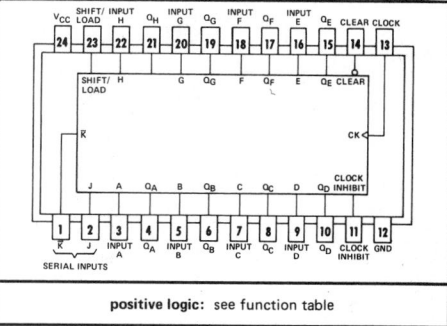

SN54199 . . . J OR W PACKAGE
SN74199 . . . J OR N PACKAGE
(TOP VIEW)

positive logic: see function table

Shifting is accomplished synchronously when shift/load is high and the clock input is not inhibited. Serial data for this mode is entered at the J-$\overline{K}$ inputs. See the function table for levels required to enter serial data into the first flip-flop.

Both of the clock inputs are identical in function and may be used interchangeably to serve as clock or clock-inhibit inputs. Holding either high inhibits clocking, but when one is held low, a clock input applied to the other input is passed to the eight flip-flops of the register. The clock-inhibit input should be changed to the high level only while the clock input is high.

These shift registers contain the equivalent of 79 TTL gates. Average power dissipation per gate is typically 4.55 mW.

'199
FUNCTION TABLE

INPUTS						OUTPUTS			
CLEAR	SHIFT/ LOAD	CLOCK INHIBIT	CLOCK	SERIAL J	$\overline{K}$	PARALLEL A...H	Q_A	Q_B	Q_C ... Q_H
L	X	X	X	X	X	X	L	L	L L
H	X	L	L	X	X	X	Q_{A0}	Q_{B0}	Q_{C0} Q_{H0}
H	L	L	↑	X	X	a...h	a	b	c h
H	H	L	↑	L	H	X	Q_{A0}	Q_{A0}	Q_{Bn} Q_{Gn}
H	H	L	↑	L	L	X	L	Q_{An}	Q_{Bn} Q_{Gn}
H	H	L	↑	H	H	X	H	Q_{An}	Q_{Bn} Q_{Gn}
H	H	L	↑	H	L	X	$\overline{Q}_{An}$	Q_{An}	Q_{Bn} Q_{Gn}
H	X	H	↑	X	X	X	Q_{A0}	Q_{B0}	Q_{B0} Q_{H0}

H = high level (steady state), L = low level (steady state)
X = irrelevant (any input, including transitions)
↑ = transition from low to high level
a . . . h = the level of steady-state input at inputs A thru H, respectively.
Q_{A0}, Q_{B0}, Q_{C0} . . . Q_{H0} = the level of Q_A, Q_B, or Q_C thru Q_H, respectively, before the indicated steady-state input conditions were established.
Q_{An}, Q_{Bn} . . . Q_{Gn} = the level of Q_A or Q_B thru Q_G, respectively, before the most-recent ↑ transition of the clock.

7

TEXAS INSTRUMENTS
INCORPORATED
POST OFFICE BOX 5012 • DALLAS, TEXAS 75222

TYPES SN54198, SN54199, SN74198, SN74199
8-BIT SHIFT REGISTERS

functional block diagrams

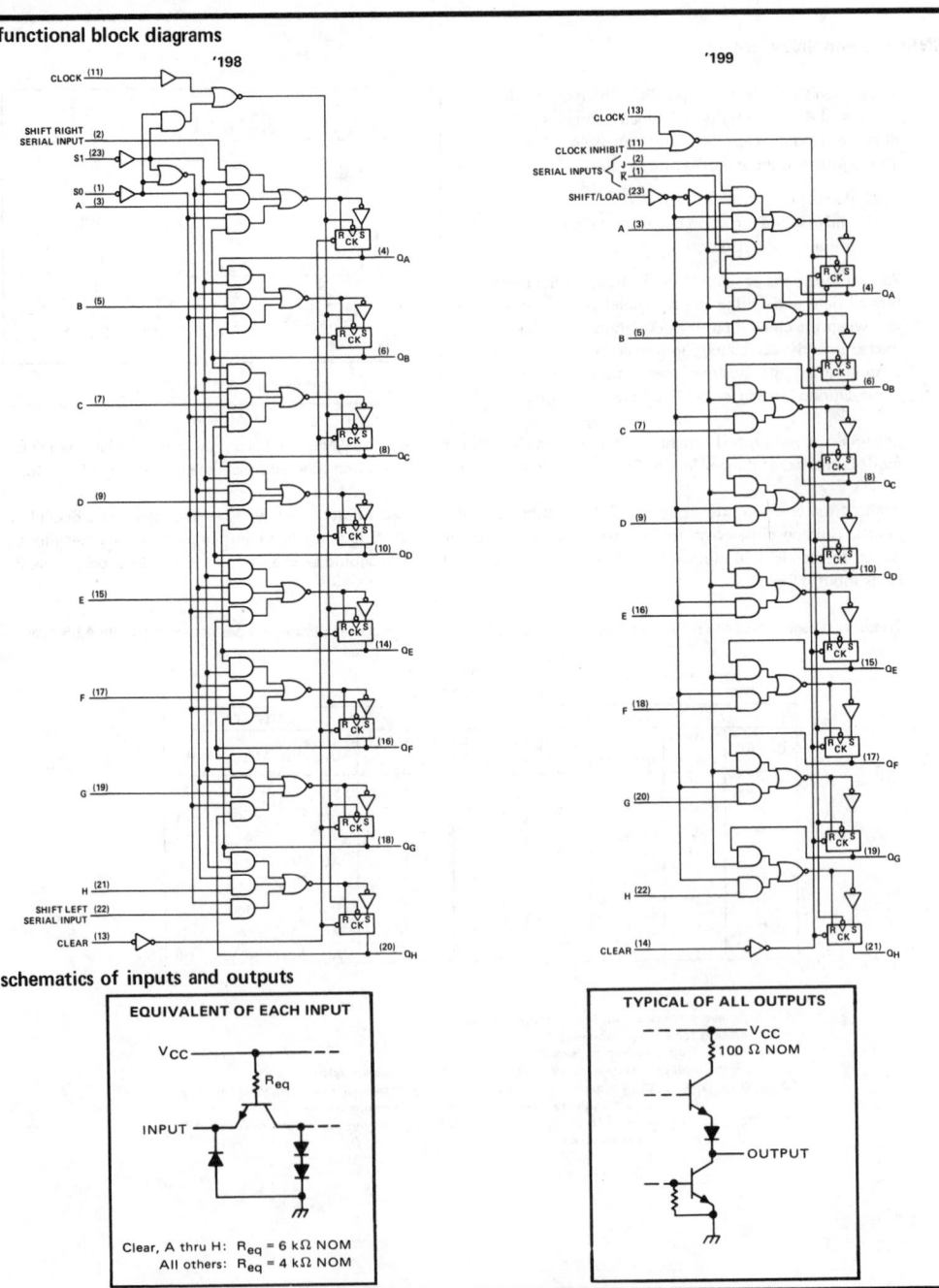

'198

'199

schematics of inputs and outputs

EQUIVALENT OF EACH INPUT

V_{CC}

R_{eq}

INPUT

Clear, A thru H: R_{eq} = 6 kΩ NOM
All others: R_{eq} = 4 kΩ NOM

TYPICAL OF ALL OUTPUTS

V_{CC}
100 Ω NOM

OUTPUT

TEXAS INSTRUMENTS
INCORPORATED
POST OFFICE BOX 5012 • DALLAS, TEXAS 75222

SN54198, SN74198

typical clear, load, right-shift, left-shift, inhibit, and clear sequences

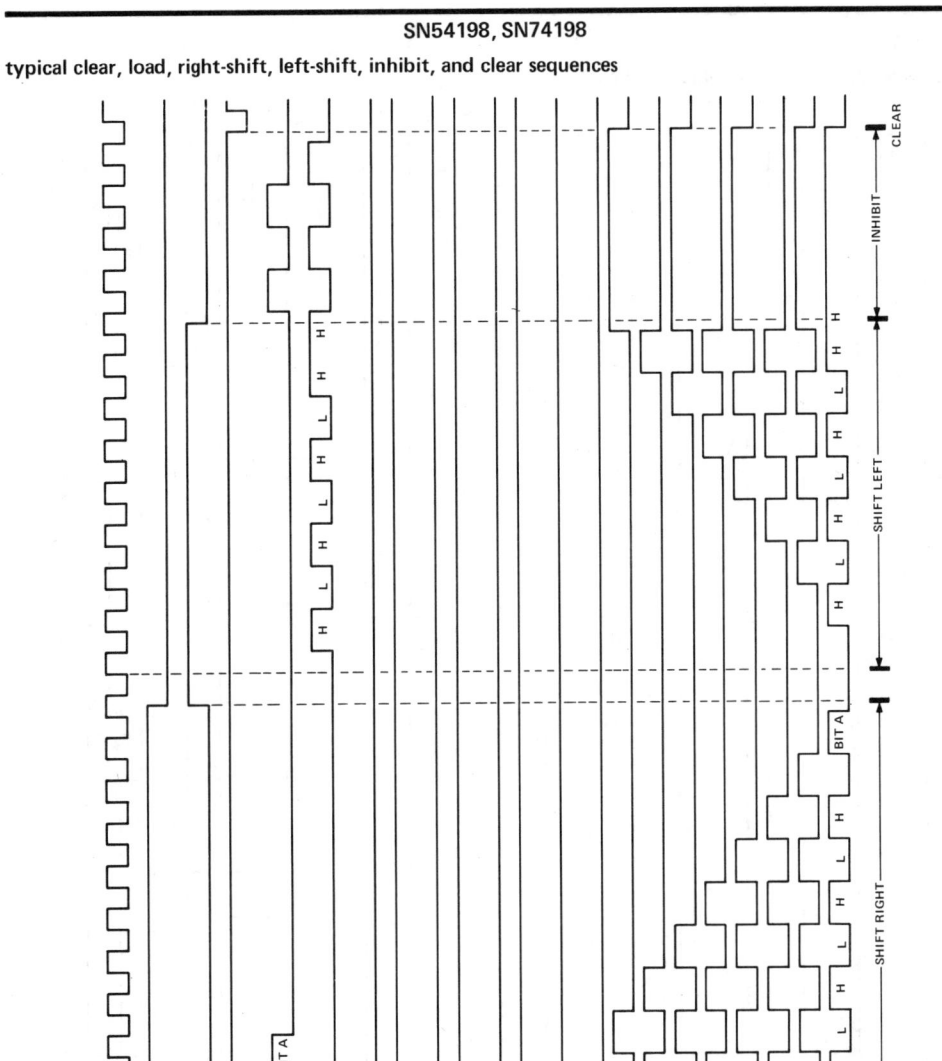

TEXAS INSTRUMENTS
INCORPORATED
POST OFFICE BOX 5012 • DALLAS, TEXAS 75222

SN54199, SN74199

typical clear, shift, load, and inhibit sequences

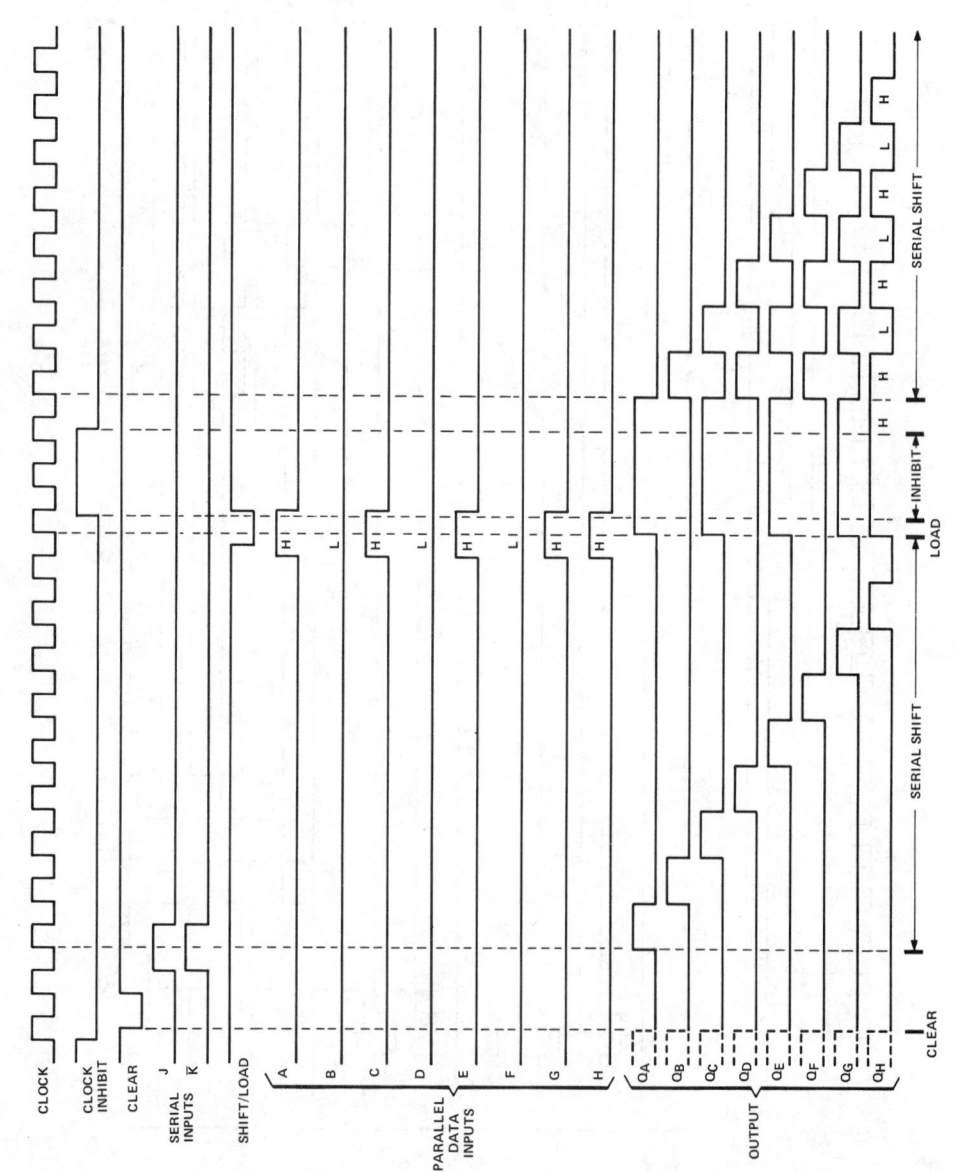

TEXAS INSTRUMENTS
INCORPORATED
POST OFFICE BOX 5012 • DALLAS, TEXAS 75222

absolute maximum ratings over operating free-air temperature range (unless otherwise noted)

Supply voltage, V_{CC} (see Note 1)	7 V
Input voltage	5.5 V
Operating free-air temperature range: SN54' Circuits	−55°C to 125°C
SN74' Circuits	0°C to 70°C
Storage temperature range	−65°C to 150°C

NOTE 1: Voltage values are with respect to network ground terminal.

recommended operating conditions

	SN54198 SN54199			SN74198 SN74199			UNIT
	MIN	NOM	MAX	MIN	NOM	MAX	
Supply voltage, V_{CC}	4.5	5	5.5	4.75	5	5.25	V
High-level output current, I_{OH}			−800			−800	µA
Low-level output current, I_{OL}			16			16	mA
Clock frequency, f_{clock}	0		25	0		25	MHz
Width of clock or clear pulse, t_w (see Figure 1)	20			20			ns
Mode-control setup time, t_{su}	30			30			ns
Data setup time, t_{su} (see Figure 1)	20			20			ns
Hold time at any input, t_h (see Figure 1)	0			0			ns
Operating free-air temperature, T_A	−55		125	0		70	°C

electrical characteristics over recommended operating free-air temperature range (unless otherwise noted)

PARAMETER		TEST CONDITIONS[†]	SN54198 SN54199			SN74198 SN74199			UNIT
			MIN	TYP[‡]	MAX	MIN	TYP[‡]	MAX	
V_{IH}	High-level input voltage		2			2			V
V_{IL}	Low-level input voltage				0.8			0.8	V
V_{IK}	Input clamp voltage	V_{CC} = MIN, I_I = −12 mA			−1.5			−1.5	V
V_{OH}	High-level output voltage	V_{CC} = MIN, V_{IH} = 2 V, V_{IL} = 0.8 V, I_{OH} = −800 µA	2.4	3.4		2.4	3.4		V
V_{OL}	Low-level output voltage	V_{CC} = MIN, V_{IH} = 2 V, V_{IL} = 0.8 V, I_{OL} = 16 mA		0.2	0.4		0.2	0.4	V
I_I	Input current at maximum input voltage	V_{CC} = MAX, V_I = 5.5 V			1			1	mA
I_{IH}	High-level input current	V_{CC} = MAX, V_I = 2.4 V			40			40	µA
I_{IL}	Low-level input current	V_{CC} = MAX, V_I = 0.4 V			−1.6			−1.6	mA
I_{OS}	Short-circuit output current[§]	V_{CC} = MAX	−20		−57	−18		−57	mA
I_{CC}	Supply current	V_{CC} = MAX, See Table Below		90	127		90	127	mA

[†]For conditions shown as MIN or MAX, use the appropriate value specified under recommended operating conditions.

[‡]All typical values are at V_{CC} = 5 V, T_A = 25°C.
[§]Not more than one output should be shorted at a time.

TEST CONDITIONS FOR I_{CC}
(ALL OUTPUTS ARE OPEN)

TYPE	APPLY 4.5 V	FIRST GROUND, THEN APPLY 4.5 V	GROUND
SN54198, SN74198	Serial Input, S_0, S_1	Clock	Clear, Inputs A thru H
SN54199, SN74199	J, $\overline{K}$, Inputs A thru H	Clock	Clock inhibit, Clear, Shift/Load

TEXAS INSTRUMENTS
INCORPORATED
POST OFFICE BOX 5012 • DALLAS, TEXAS 75222

TYPES SN54198, SN54199, SN74198, SN74199
8-BIT SHIFT REGISTERS

switching characteristics, $V_{CC} = 5$ V, $T_A = 25°C$

PARAMETER		TEST CONDITIONS	MIN	TYP	MAX	UNIT
f_{max}	Maximum clock frequency		25	35		MHz
t_{PHL}	Propagation delay time, high-to-low-level output from clear	$C_L = 15$ pF, $R_L = 400$ Ω, See Figure 1		23	35	ns
t_{PHL}	Propagation delay time, high-to-low-level output from clock			20	30	ns
t_{PLH}	Propagation delay time, low-to-high-level output from clock			17	26	ns

PARAMETER MEASUREMENT INFORMATION

SN54198, SN74198
TEST TABLE FOR SYNCHRONOUS INPUTS

DATA INPUT FOR TEST	S1	S0	OUTPUT TESTED (SEE NOTE E)
A	4.5 V	4.5 V	Q_A at t_{n+1}
B	4.5 V	4.5 V	Q_B at t_{n+1}
C	4.5 V	4.5 V	Q_C at t_{n+1}
D	4.5 V	4.5 V	Q_D at t_{n+1}
E	4.5 V	4.5 V	Q_E at t_{n+1}
F	4.5 V	4.5 V	Q_F at t_{n+1}
G	4.5 V	4.5 V	Q_G at t_{n+1}
H	4.5 V	4.5 V	Q_H at t_{n+1}
L Serial Input	4.5 V	0 V	Q_A at t_{n+8}
R Serial Input	0 V	4.5 V	Q_H at t_{n+8}

SN54199, SN74199
TEST TABLE FOR SYNCHRONOUS INPUTS

DATA INPUT FOR TEST	SHIFT/LOAD	OUTPUT TESTED (SEE NOTE E)
A	0 V	Q_A at t_{n+1}
B	0 V	Q_B at t_{n+1}
C	0 V	Q_C at t_{n+1}
D	0 V	Q_D at t_{n+1}
E	0 V	Q_E at t_{n+1}
F	0 V	Q_F at t_{n+1}
G	0 V	Q_G at t_{n+1}
H	0 V	Q_H at t_{n+1}
J and $\overline{K}$	4.5 V	Q_H at t_{n+8}

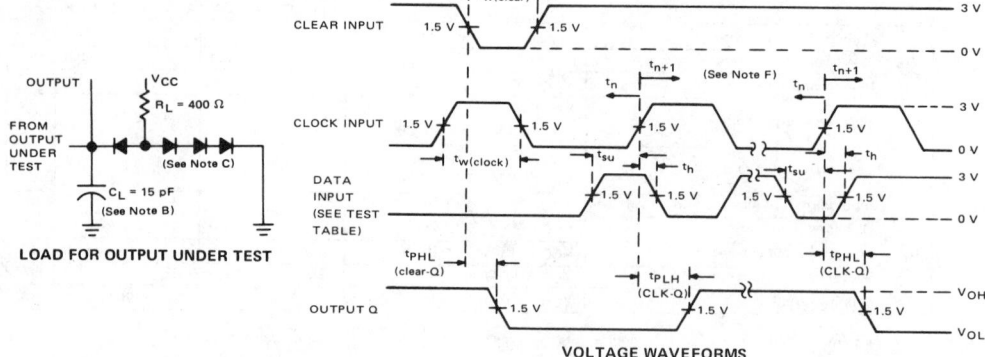

LOAD FOR OUTPUT UNDER TEST

VOLTAGE WAVEFORMS

NOTES: A. The clock pulse has the following characteristics: $t_{w(clock)} \geqslant 20$ ns and PRR = 1 MHz. The clear pulse has the following characteristics: $t_{w(clear)} \geqslant 20$ ns and $t_{hold} = 0$ ns. When testing f_{max}, vary the clock PRR.
B. C_L includes probe and jig capacitance.
C. All diodes are 1N3064.
D. A clear pulse is applied prior to each test.
E. Propagation delay times (t_{PLH} and t_{PHL}) are measured at t_{n+1}. Proper shifting of data is verified at t_{n+8} with a functional test.
F. t_n = bit time before clocking transition
   t_{n+1} = bit time after one clocking transition
   t_{n+8} = bit time after eight clocking transitions

FIGURE 1

7

TEXAS INSTRUMENTS
INCORPORATED
POST OFFICE BOX 5012 • DALLAS, TEXAS 75222

- Universal Transceivers for Implementing System Bus Controllers
- Dual-Rank 4-Bit Transparent Latches Provide
  - Exchange of Data Between 2 Buses In One Clock Pulse
  - Bus-to-Bus Isolation
  - Rapid Data Transfer
  - Full Storage Capability
- Hysteresis at Data Inputs Enhances Noise Rejection
- Separate Output Control Inputs Provide Independent Enable/Disable for Either Bus Output
- 3-State Outputs Drive Bus Lines Directly

SN54S226 . . . J PACKAGE
SN74S226 . . . J OR N PACKAGE

(TOP VIEW)

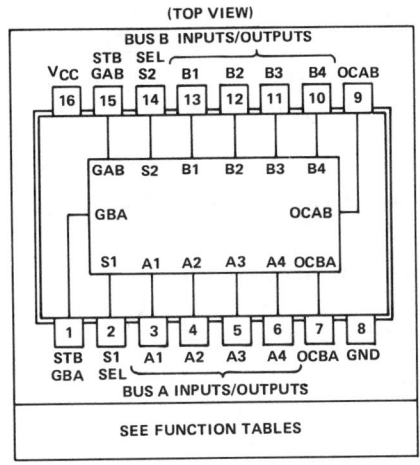

SEE FUNCTION TABLES

description

These high-performance Schottky TTL quadruple bus transceivers employ dual-rank bidirectional four-bit transparent latches and feature three-state outputs designed specifically for driving highly-capacitive or relatively low-impedance loads. The bus-management functions implemented and the high-impedance controls offered provide the designer with a controller/transceiver that interfaces and drives system bus-organized lines directly. They are particularly attractive for implementing:

> Bidirectional bus transceivers
> Data-bus controllers

The bus-management functions, under control of the function-select (S1, S2) inputs, provide complete data integrity for each of the four modes described in the function table. Directional transparency provides for routing data from or to either bus, and the dual store and dual readout capabilities can be used to perform the exchange of data between the two bus lines in the equivalent of a single clock pulse. Storage of data is accomplished by selecting the latch function, setting up the data, and taking the appropriate strobe input low. As long as the strobe is held low, the data is latched for the selected function. Further control is offered through the availability of independent output controls that can be used to enable or

functional block diagram

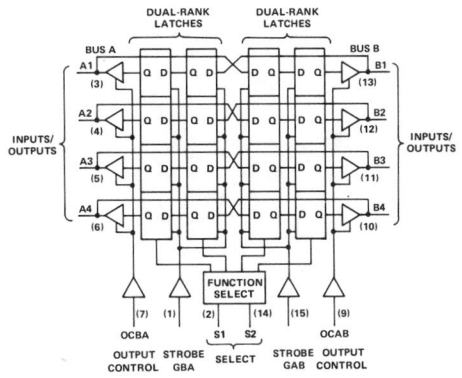

TYPES SN54S226, SN74S226
4-BIT PARALLEL LATCHED BUS TRANSCEIVERS

REVISED AUGUST 1977

BUS-MANAGEMENT FUNCTION TABLE

OPERATION	S2	S1	LATCH FUNCTIONS
DRIVE BUS A	L	L	Pass Bus B Data to Bus A
DRIVE BUS B	H	L	Pass Bus A Data to Bus B
EXCHANGE	H	H	Store Bus A and Bus B Data
BUS A AND B	L	H	Readout Stored Data

OUTPUT-CONTROL FUNCTION TABLE

OCAB	OCBA	OUTPUT FUNCTION
L	X	Disable Bus B Outputs (Hi-Z)
H	X	Enable Bus B Outputs
X	L	Disable Bus A Outputs (Hi-Z)
X	H	Enable Bus A Outputs

disable the outputs as shown in the output-control function table, regardless of the latch function in process. Store operations can be performed with the outputs disabled to a high impedance (Hi-Z). In the Hi-Z state the inputs/outputs neither load nor drive the bus lines significantly. The p-n-p inputs feature typically 400 millivolts of hysteresis to enhance noise rejection.

absolute maximum ratings over operating free-air temperature range (unless otherwise noted)

Supply voltage, V_{CC} (see Note 1) . . . . 7 V
Input voltage . . . . 5.5 V
Off-state output voltage . . . . 5.5 V
Operating free-air temperature range: SN54S226 (see Note 2) . . . . −55°C to 125°C
  SN74S226 . . . . 0°C to 70°C
Storage temperature range . . . . −65°C to 150°C

NOTES: 1. Voltage values are with respect to network ground terminal.
     2. An SN54S226 in the J package operating at temperatures above 113°C requires a heat-sink that provides a thermal resistance from case to free air, $R_{\theta CA}$, of not more than 48°C/W.

7

TEXAS INSTRUMENTS
INCORPORATED
POST OFFICE BOX 5012 • DALLAS, TEXAS 75222

recommended operating conditions

		SN54S226			SN74S226			UNIT
		MIN	NOM	MAX	MIN	NOM	MAX	
Supply voltage, V_{CC}		4.5	5	5.5	4.75	5	5.25	V
High-level output voltage, V_{OH}				5.5			5.5	V
High-level output current, I_{OH}				−6.5			−10.3	mA
Data setup time, t_{su}	Data (A or B)	0↓			0↓			ns
	Select	0↓			0↓			
Data hold time, t_h	Data (A or B)	30↓			30↓			ns
	Select	30↓			30↓			
Operating free-air temperature, T_A (see Note 2)		−55		125	0		70	°C

↓The arrow indicates that the high-to-low transition of the enable input is used for reference.

electrical characteristics over recommended operating free-air temperature range (unless otherwise noted)

PARAMETER		TEST CONDITIONS[†]		MIN	TYP[‡]	MAX	UNIT
V_{IH} High-level input voltage				2			V
V_{IL} Low-level input voltage						0.8	V
V_{IK} Input clamp voltage		V_{CC} = MIN, I_I = −18 mA				−1.2	V
V_{OH} High-level output voltage	SN54S226	V_{CC} = MIN, V_{IH} = 2 V,	SN54S226	2.4	3.3		V
	SN74S226	V_{IL} = 0.8 V, I_{OH} = MAX	SN74S226	2.4	2.9		
V_{OL} Low-level output voltage		V_{CC} = MIN, V_{IH} = 2 V, V_{IL} = 0.8 V, I_{OL} = 20 mA				0.5	V
I_{OZH} Off-state output current, high-level voltage applied		V_{CC} = MAX, V_{IH} = 2 V, V_O = 2.4 V				100	μA
I_{OZL} Off-state output current, low-level voltage applied		V_{CC} = MAX, V_{IH} = 2 V, V_O = 0.5 V				−100	μA
I_I Input current at maximum input voltage		V_{CC} = MAX, V_I = 5.5 V				1	mA
I_{IH} High-level input current		V_{CC} = MAX, V_I = 2.7 V				100	μA
I_{IL} Low-level input current		V_{CC} = MAX, V_I = 0.5 V				−380	μA
I_{OS} Short-circuit output current §		V_{CC} = MAX		−50		−180	mA
I_{CC} Supply current		V_{CC} = MAX, See Note 3			125	185	mA

†For conditions shown as MIN or MAX, use the appropriate value specified under recommended operating conditions.
‡All typical values are at V_{CC} = 5 V, T_A = 25°C.
§Not more than one output should be shorted at a time and duration of the short-circuit should not exceed one second.
NOTES: 2. An SN54S226 in the J package operating at temperatures above 113°C requires a heat-sink that provides a thermal resistance from case to free air, $R_{\theta CA}$, of not more than 48°C/W.
3. I_{CC} is measured with all inputs (and outputs) grounded.

7

TEXAS INSTRUMENTS
INCORPORATED
POST OFFICE BOX 5012 • DALLAS, TEXAS 75222

TYPES SN54S226, SN74S226
4-BIT PARALLEL LATCHED BUS TRANSCEIVERS

REVISED AUGUST 1977

switching characteristics, $V_{CC} = 5$ V, $T_A = 25°C$

PARAMETER	FROM (INPUT)	TO (OUTPUT)	TEST CONDITIONS		MIN	TYP	MAX	UNIT
t_{PLH}	A or B	B or A				20	30	ns
t_{PHL}						15	30	
t_{PLH}	Select	Any	$C_L = 50$ pF,	$R_L = 280$ Ω,		25	37	ns
t_{PHL}			See Note 4			19	30	
t_{PLH}	Strobe GBA	A or B				25	37	ns
t_{PHL}	or GAB					19	30	
t_{PZH}	Output Control	A or B				12	20	ns
t_{PZL}	OCBA or OCAB					12	20	
t_{PHZ}	Output Control	A or B	$C_L = 5$ pF,	$R_L = 280$ Ω,		10	15	ns
t_{PLZ}	OCBA or OCAB		See Note 4			10	15	

$t_{PLH} \equiv$ propagation delay time, low-to-high-level output
$t_{PHL} \equiv$ propagation delay time, low-to-high-level output
$t_{ZH} \equiv$ output enable time to high level
$t_{ZL} \equiv$ output enable time to low level
$t_{HZ} \equiv$ output disable time from high level
$t_{LZ} \equiv$ output disable time from low level
NOTE 4: Load circuits and voltage waveforms are shown on page 3-10.

applications

The following examples demonstrate four fundamental bus-management functions that can be performed with the 'S226. Exchange of data on the two bus lines can be accomplished with a single high-to-low transition at S2 when S1 is high.

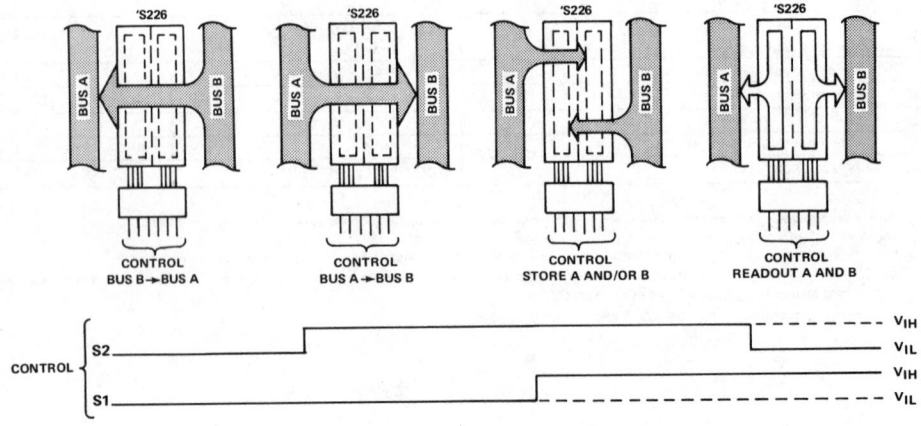

7

TEXAS INSTRUMENTS
INCORPORATED
POST OFFICE BOX 5012 • DALLAS, TEXAS 75222

- Bi-directional Bus Transceiver in a High-Density 20-Pin Package
- 3-State Outputs Drive Bus Lines Directly
- P-N-P Inputs Reduce D-C Loading on Bus Lines
- Hysteresis at Bus Inputs Improve Noise Margins
- Typical Propagation Delay Times, Port-to-Port . . . 8 ns
- Typical Enable/Disable Times . . . 17 ns

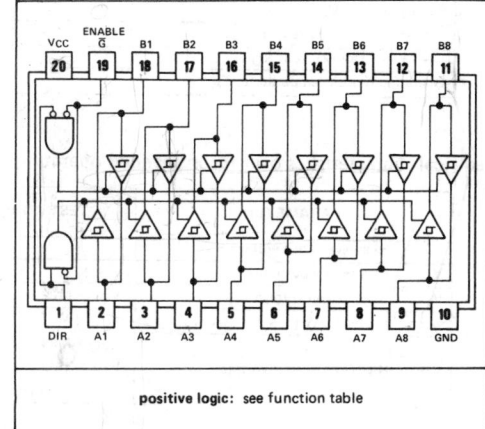

SN54LS245 . . . J PACKAGE
SN74LS245 . . . J OR N PACKAGE
(TOP VIEW)

positive logic: see function table

TYPE	I_{OL} (SINK CURRENT)	I_{OH} (SOURCE CURRENT)
SN54LS245	12 mA	−12 mA
SN74LS245	24 mA	−15 mA

description

These octal bus transceivers are designed for asynchronous two-way communication between data buses. The control function implementation minimizes external timing requirements.

The device allows data transmission from the A bus to the B bus or from the B bus to the A bus depending upon the logic level at the direction control (DIR) input. The enable input ($\overline{G}$) can be used to disable the device so that the buses are effectively isolated.

The SN54LS245 is characterized for operation over the full military temperature range of −55°C to 125°C. The SN74LS245 is characterized for operation from 0°C to 70°C.

schematics of inputs and outputs

EQUIVALENT OF EACH INPUT	TYPICAL OF ALL OUTPUTS
V_{CC} — 9 kΩ NOM — INPUT	V_{CC} — 50 Ω NOM — OUTPUT

FUNCTION TABLE

ENABLE $\overline{G}$	DIRECTION CONTROL DIR	OPERATION
L	L	B data to A bus
L	H	A data to B bus
H	X	Isolation

H = high level, L = low level, X = irrelevant

absolute maximum ratings over operating free-air temperature range (unless otherwise noted)

Supply voltage, V_{CC} (see Note 1) . . . . 7 V
Input voltage . . . . 7 V
Operating free-air temperature range: SN54LS245 . . . . −55°C to 125°C
SN74LS245 . . . . 0°C to 70°C
Storage temperature range . . . . −65°C to 150°C

NOTE 1: Voltage values are with respect to network ground terminal.

TYPES SN54LS245, SN74LS245
OCTAL BUS TRANSCEIVERS WITH 3-STATE OUTPUTS

REVISED AUGUST 1977

recommended operating conditions

PARAMETER	SN54LS245 MIN	NOM	MAX	SN74LS245 MIN	NOM	MAX	UNIT
Supply voltage, V_{CC}	4.5	5	5.5	4.75	5	5.25	V
High-level output current, I_{OH}			−12			−15	mA
Low-level output current, I_{OL}			12			24	mA
Operating free-air temperature, T_A	−55		125	0		70	°C

electrical characteristics over recommended operating free-air temperature range (unless otherwise noted)

PARAMETER		TEST CONDITIONS[†]		SN54LS245 MIN	TYP[‡]	MAX	SN74LS245 MIN	TYP[‡]	MAX	UNIT
V_{IH}	High-level input voltage			2			2			V
V_{IL}	Low-level input voltage					0.7			0.8	V
V_{IK}	Input clamp voltage	V_{CC} = MIN,	I_I = −18 mA			−1.5			−1.5	V
	Hysteresis $(V_{T+} - V_{T-})$A or B input	V_{CC} = MIN		0.2	0.4		0.2	0.4		V
V_{OH}	High-level output voltage	V_{CC} = MIN, V_{IH} = 2 V,	I_{OH} = −3 mA	2.4	3.4		2.4	3.4		V
		$V_{IL} = V_{IL}$ max	I_{OH} = MAX	2			2			
V_{OL}	Low-level output voltage	V_{CC} = MIN, V_{IH} = 2 V,	I_{OL} = 12 mA			0.4			0.4	V
		$V_{IL} = V_{IL}$ max	I_{OL} = 24 mA						0.5	
I_{OZH}	Off-state output current, high-level voltage applied	V_{CC} = MAX, $\overline{G}$ at 2 V	V_O = 2.7 V			10			10	µA
I_{OZL}	Off-state output current, low-level voltage applied		V_O = 0.4 V			−200			−200	
I_I	Input current at	A or B	V_{CC} = MAX,	V_I = 5.5 V			0.1			0.1	mA
	maximum input voltage	DIR or $\overline{G}$		V_I = 7 V			0.1			0.1	
I_{IH}	High-level input current	V_{CC} = MAX,	V_{IH} = 2.7 V			20			20	µA
I_{IL}	Low-level input current	V_{CC} = MAX,	V_{IL} = 0.4 V			−0.2			−0.2	mA
I_{OS}	Short-circuit output current[¶]	V_{CC} = MAX		−40		−225	−40		−225	mA
I_{CC}	Supply current	Total, outputs high	V_{CC} = MAX, Outputs open		48	70		48	70	mA
		Total, outputs low			62	90		62	90	
		Outputs at Hi-Z			64	95		64	95	

[†] For conditions shown as MIN or MAX, use the appropriate value specified under recommended operating conditions.
[‡] All typical values are at V_{CC} = 5 V, T_A = 25°C.
[¶] Not more than one output should be shorted at a time, and duration of the short-circuit should not exceed one second.

switching characteristics, V_{CC} = 5 V, T_A = 25°C

	PARAMETER	TEST CONDITIONS	MIN	TYP	MAX	UNIT
t_{PLH}	Propagation delay time, low-to-high-level output	C_L = 45 pF, R_L = 667 Ω, See Note 2		8	12	ns
t_{PHL}	Propagation delay time, high-to-low-level output			8	12	ns
t_{PZL}	Output enable time to low level			27	40	ns
t_{PZH}	Output enable time to high level			25	40	ns
t_{PLZ}	Output disable time from low level	C_L = 5 pF, R_L = 667 Ω, See Note 2		15	25	ns
t_{PHZ}	Output disable time from high level			15	25	ns

NOTE 2: Load circuit and waveforms are shown on page 3-11.

7

TEXAS INSTRUMENTS
INCORPORATED
POST OFFICE BOX 5012 • DALLAS, TEXAS 75222

TTL
MSI

TYPES SN54246 THRU SN54249, SN54LS247 THRU SN54LS249,
SN74246 THRU SN74249, SN74LS247 THRU SN74LS249
BCD-TO-SEVEN-SEGMENT DECODERS/DRIVERS

BULLETIN NO. DL-S 7612078, MARCH 1974— REVISED OCTOBER 1976

'246, '247, 'LS247 feature	'248, 'LS248 feature	'249, 'LS249 feature
• **Open-Collector Outputs Drive Indicators Directly**	• **Internal Pull-Ups Eliminate Need for External Resistors**	• **Open-Collector Outputs**
• **Lamp-Test Provision**	• **Lamp-Test Provision**	• **Lamp-Test Provision**
• **Leading/Trailing Zero Suppression**	• **Leading/Trailing Zero Suppression**	• **Leading/Trailing Zero Suppression**

- **All Circuit Types Feature Lamp Intensity Modulation Capability**

TYPE	DRIVER OUTPUTS				TYPICAL	PACKAGES
	ACTIVE LEVEL	OUTPUT CONFIGURATION	SINK CURRENT	MAX VOLTAGE	POWER DISSIPATION	
SN54246	low	open-collector	40 mA	30 V	320 mW	J, W
SN54247	low	open-collector	40 mA	15 V	320 mW	J, W
SN54248	high	2-kΩ pull-up	6.4 mA	5.5 V	265 mW	J, W
SN54249	high	open-collector	10 mA	5.5 V	265 mW	J, W
SN54LS247	low	open-collector	12 mA	15 V	35 mW	J, W
SN54LS248	high	2-kΩ pull-up	2 mA	5.5 V	125 mW	J, W
SN54LS249	high	open-collector	4 mA	5.5 V	40 mW	J, W
SN74246	low	open-collector	40 mA	30 V	320 mW	J, N
SN74247	low	open-collector	40 mA	15 V	320 mW	J, N
SN74248	high	2-kΩ pull-up	6.4 mA	5.5 V	265 mW	J, N
SN74249	high	open-collector	10 mA	5.5 V	265 mW	J, N
SN74LS247	low	open-collector	24 mA	15 V	35 mW	J, N
SN74LS248	high	2-kΩ pull-up	6 mA	5.5 V	125 mW	J, N
SN74LS249	high	open-collector	8 mA	5.5 V	40 mW	J, N

'246, '247, 'LS247 (TOP VIEW)   '248, '249, 'LS248, 'LS249 (TOP VIEW)

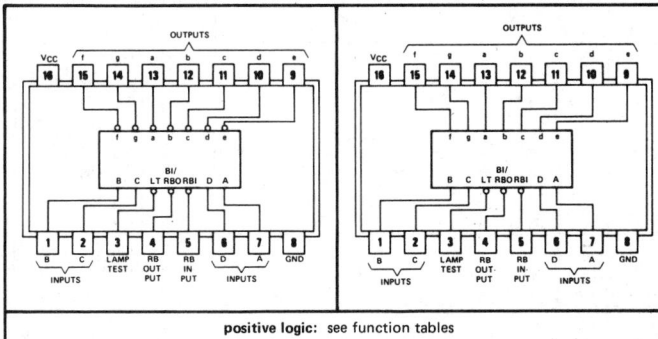

positive logic: see function tables

description

The '246 through '248 are electrically and functionally identical to the SN5446A/SN7446A, SN5447A/SN7447A, and SN5448/SN7448, respectively, and have the same pin assignments as their equivalents. Also the 'LS247 and 'LS248 are electrically and functionally identical to the SN54LS47/SN74LS47 and SN54LS48/SN74LS48, respectively, and have the same pin assignments as their equivalents. They can be used interchangeably in present or future designs to offer designers a choice between two indicator fonts. The '249 and 'LS249 are 16-pin versions of the 14-pin SN5449 and SN54LS49/SN74LS49, respectively. Included in the '249 and 'LS249 circuits is the full functional capability for lamp test and ripple blanking, which is not available in the '49 and 'LS49 circuits. The '46A, '47A, '48, '49, 'LS47, 'LS48, and 'LS49 compose the ᗷ and the ᑫ without tails and the '246 through '249 and 'LS247, 'LS248, and 'LS249

1076

TEXAS INSTRUMENTS
INCORPORATED
POST OFFICE BOX 5012 • DALLAS, TEXAS 75222

TYPES SN54246 THRU SN54249, SN54LS247 THRU SN54LS249, SN74246 THRU SN74249, SN74LS247 THRU SN74LS249
BCD-TO-SEVEN-SEGMENT DECODERS/DRIVERS

description (continued)

compose the 6 and the 9 with tails. Composition of all other characters, including display patterns for BCD inputs above nine, is identical. The '246, '247, and 'LS247 feature active-low outputs designed for driving indicators directly, and the '248, '249, 'LS248, and 'LS249 feature active-high outputs for driving lamp buffers. All of the circuits have full ripple-blanking input/output controls and a lamp test input. Segment identification and resultant displays are shown below. Display patterns for BCD input counts above 9 are unique symbols to authenticate input conditions.

All of these circuits incorporate automatic leading and/or trailing-edge zero-blanking control (RBI and RBO). Lamp test (LT) of these types may be performed at any time when the BI/RBO node is at a high level. All types contain an overriding blanking input (BI) which can be used to control the lamp intensity by pulsing or to inhibit the outputs. Inputs and outputs are entirely compatible for use with TTL or DTL logic outputs.

Series 54 and Series 54LS devices are characterized for operation over the full military temperature range of $-55°C$ to $125°C$; Series 74 and Series 74LS devices are characterized for operation from $0°C$ to $70°C$.

NUMERICAL DESIGNATIONS AND RESULTANT DISPLAYS

SEGMENT
IDENTIFICATION

'246, '247, 'LS247
FUNCTION TABLE

DECIMAL OR FUNCTION	INPUTS						BI/RBO†	OUTPUTS							NOTE
	LT	RBI	D	C	B	A		a	b	c	d	e	f	g	
0	H	H	L	L	L	L	H	ON	ON	ON	ON	ON	ON	OFF	
1	H	X	L	L	L	H	H	OFF	ON	ON	OFF	OFF	OFF	OFF	
2	H	X	L	L	H	L	H	ON	ON	OFF	ON	ON	OFF	ON	
3	H	X	L	L	H	H	H	ON	ON	ON	ON	OFF	OFF	ON	
4	H	X	L	H	L	L	H	OFF	ON	ON	OFF	OFF	ON	ON	
5	H	X	L	H	L	H	H	ON	OFF	ON	ON	OFF	ON	ON	
6	H	X	L	H	H	L	H	ON	OFF	ON	ON	ON	ON	ON	
7	H	X	L	H	H	H	H	ON	ON	ON	OFF	OFF	OFF	OFF	
8	H	X	H	L	L	L	H	ON	ON	ON	ON	ON	ON	ON	1
9	H	X	H	L	L	H	H	ON	ON	ON	ON	OFF	ON	ON	
10	H	X	H	L	H	L	H	OFF	OFF	OFF	ON	ON	OFF	ON	
11	H	X	H	L	H	H	H	OFF	OFF	ON	ON	OFF	OFF	ON	
12	H	X	H	H	L	L	H	OFF	ON	OFF	OFF	OFF	ON	ON	
13	H	X	H	H	L	H	H	ON	OFF	OFF	ON	OFF	ON	ON	
14	H	X	H	H	H	L	H	OFF	OFF	OFF	ON	ON	ON	ON	
15	H	X	H	H	H	H	H	OFF	OFF	OFF	OFF	OFF	OFF	OFF	
BI	X	X	X	X	X	X	L	OFF	OFF	OFF	OFF	OFF	OFF	OFF	2
RBI	H	L	L	L	L	L	L	OFF	OFF	OFF	OFF	OFF	OFF	OFF	3
LT	L	X	X	X	X	X	H	ON	ON	ON	ON	ON	ON	ON	4

H = high level, L = low level, X = irrelevant

NOTES: 1. The blanking input (BI) must be open or held at a high logic level when output functions 0 through 15 are desired. The ripple-blanking input (RBI) must be open or high if blanking of a decimal zero is not desired.
2. When a low logic level is applied directly to the blanking input (BI), all segment outputs are off regardless of the level of any other input.
3. When ripple-blanking input (RBI) and inputs A, B, C, and D are at a low level with the lamp test input high, all segment outputs go off and the ripple-blanking output (RBO) goes to a low level (response condition).
4. When the blanking input/ripple blanking output (BI/RBO) is open or held high and a low is applied to the lamp-test input, all segment outputs are on.

†BI/RBO is wire-AND logic serving as blanking input (BI) and/or ripple-blanking output (RBO).

TEXAS INSTRUMENTS
INCORPORATED
POST OFFICE BOX 5012 • DALLAS, TEXAS 75222

'248, '249, 'LS248, 'LS249
FUNCTION TABLE

DECIMAL OR FUNCTION	INPUTS					BI/RBO†	OUTPUTS							NOTE
	LT	RBI	D	C	B	A		a	b	c	d	e	f	g	
0	H	H	L	L	L	L	H	H	H	H	H	H	H	L	1
1	H	X	L	L	L	H	H	L	H	H	L	L	L	L	1
2	H	X	L	L	H	L	H	H	H	L	H	H	L	H	
3	H	X	L	L	H	H	H	H	H	H	H	L	L	H	
4	H	X	L	H	L	L	H	L	H	H	L	L	H	H	
5	H	X	L	H	L	H	H	H	L	H	H	L	H	H	
6	H	X	L	H	H	L	H	H	L	H	H	H	H	H	
7	H	X	L	H	H	H	H	H	H	H	L	L	L	L	1
8	H	X	H	L	L	L	H	H	H	H	H	H	H	H	
9	H	X	H	L	L	H	H	H	H	H	H	L	H	H	
10	H	X	H	L	H	L	H	L	L	L	H	H	L	H	
11	H	X	H	L	H	H	H	L	L	H	H	L	L	H	
12	H	X	H	H	L	L	H	L	H	L	L	L	H	H	
13	H	X	H	H	L	H	H	H	L	L	H	L	H	H	
14	H	X	H	H	H	L	H	L	L	L	H	H	H	H	
15	H	X	H	H	H	H	H	L	L	L	L	L	L	L	
BI	X	X	X	X	X	X	L	L	L	L	L	L	L	L	2
RBI	H	L	L	L	L	L	L	L	L	L	L	L	L	L	3
LT	L	X	X	X	X	X	H	H	H	H	H	H	H	H	4

H = high level, L = low level, X = irrelevant

NOTES: 1. The blanking input (BI) must be open or held at a high logic level when output functions 0 through 15 are desired. The ripple-blanking input (RBI) must be open or high if blanking of a decimal zero is not desired.

2. When a low logic level is applied directly to the blanking input (BI), all segment outputs are low regardless of the level of any other input.

3. When ripple-blanking input (RBI) and inputs A, B, C, and D are at a low level with the lamp test input high, all segment outputs go low and the ripple-blanking output (RBO) goes to a low level (response condition).

4. When the blanking input/ripple-blanking output (BI/RBO) is open or held high and a low is applied to the lamp-test input, all segment outputs are high.

†BI/RBO is wire-AND logic serving as blanking input (BI) and/or ripple-blanking output (RBO).

'246, '247, 'LS247

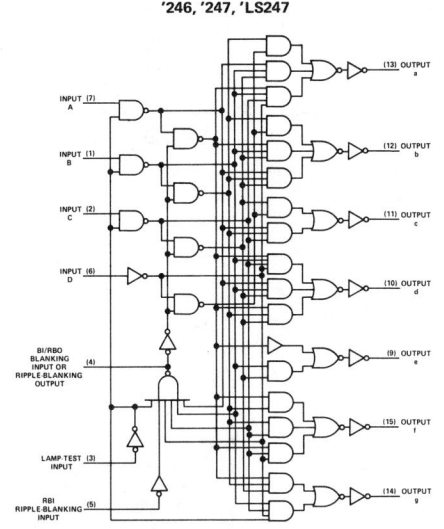

'248, '249, 'LS248, 'LS249

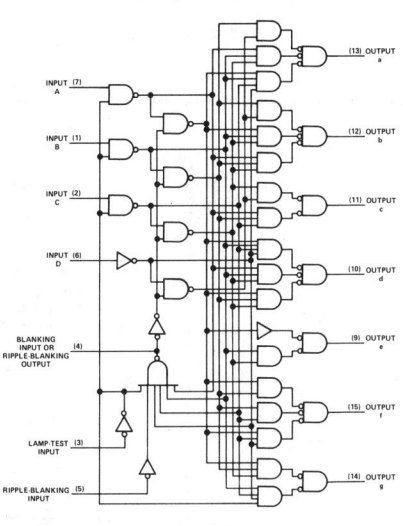

TEXAS INSTRUMENTS
INCORPORATED
POST OFFICE BOX 5012 • DALLAS, TEXAS 75222

TYPES SN54246 THRU SN54249, SN74246 THRU SN74249
BCD-TO-SEVEN-SEGMENT DECODERS/DRIVERS

schematics of inputs and outputs

'246, '247, '248, '249

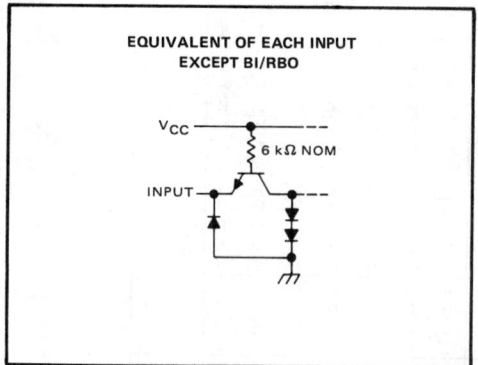

EQUIVALENT OF EACH INPUT
EXCEPT BI/RBO

'246, '247, '248, '249

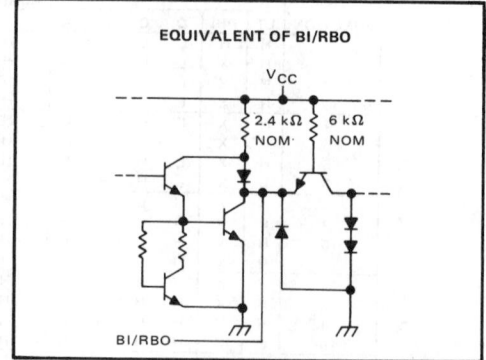

EQUIVALENT OF BI/RBO

'246, '247

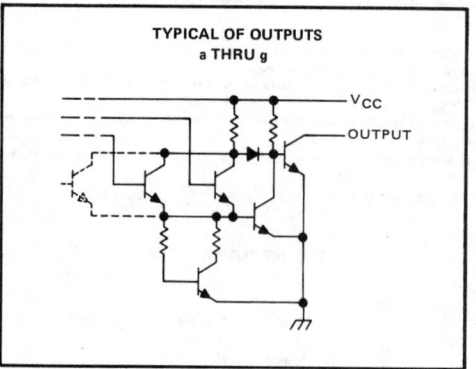

TYPICAL OF OUTPUTS
a THRU g

'248

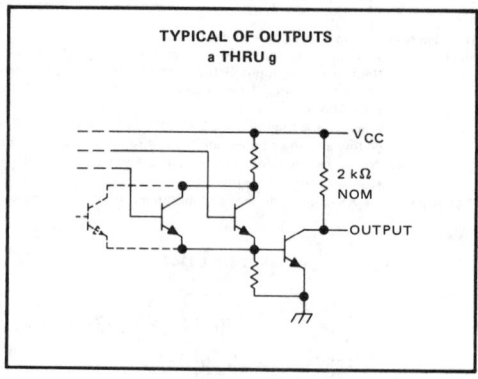

TYPICAL OF OUTPUTS
a THRU g

'249

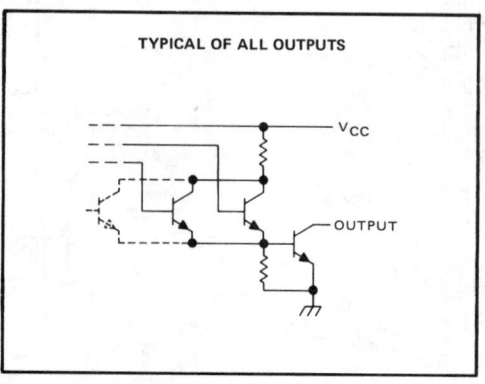

TYPICAL OF ALL OUTPUTS

TEXAS INSTRUMENTS
INCORPORATED
POST OFFICE BOX 5012 • DALLAS, TEXAS 75222

schematics of inputs and outputs

'LS247, 'LS248, 'LS249

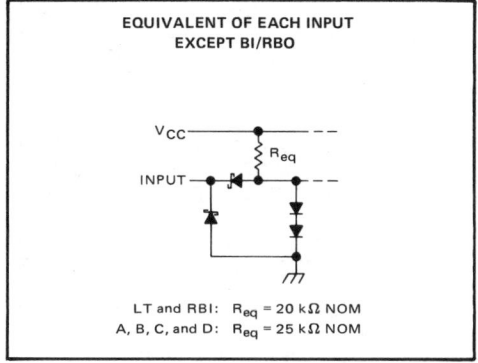

EQUIVALENT OF EACH INPUT EXCEPT BI/RBO

LT and RBI: R_{eq} = 20 kΩ NOM
A, B, C, and D: R_{eq} = 25 kΩ NOM

'LS247, 'LS248, 'LS249

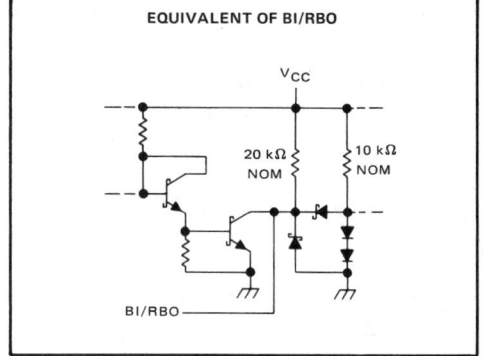

EQUIVALENT OF BI/RBO

'LS247

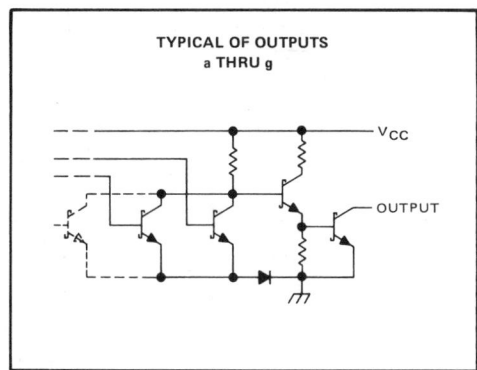

TYPICAL OF OUTPUTS a THRU g

'LS248

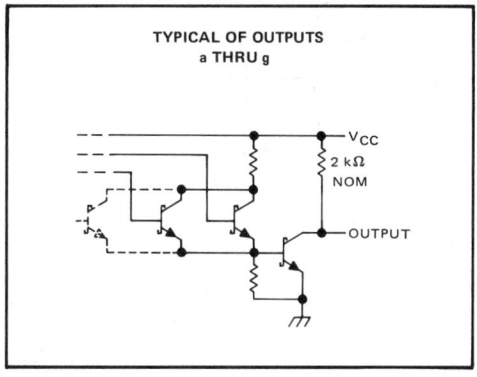

TYPICAL OF OUTPUTS a THRU g

'LS249

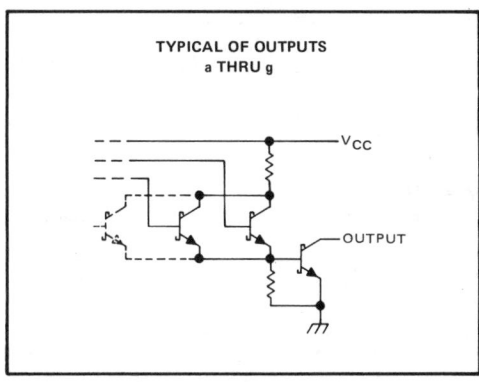

TYPICAL OF OUTPUTS a THRU g

TEXAS INSTRUMENTS
INCORPORATED
POST OFFICE BOX 5012 • DALLAS, TEXAS 75222

TYPES SN54246, SN54247, SN74246, SN74247
BCD-TO-SEVEN-SEGMENT DECODERS/DRIVERS

REVISED MARCH 1974

absolute maximum ratings over operating free-air temperature range (unless otherwise noted)

Supply voltage, V_{CC} (see Note 1)	7 V
Input voltage	5.5 V
Current forced into any output in the off state	1 mA
Operating free-air temperature range: SN54246, SN54247	−55°C to 125°C
SN74246, SN74247	0°C to 70°C
Storage temperature range	−65°C to 150°C

NOTE 1: Voltage values are with respect to network ground terminal.

recommended operating conditions

		SN54246			SN54247			SN74246			SN74247			UNIT
		MIN	NOM	MAX	MIN	NOM	MAX	MIN	NOM	MAX	MIN	NOM	MAX	
Supply voltage, V_{CC}		4.5	5	5.5	4.5	5	5.5	4.75	5	5.25	4.75	5	5.25	V
Off-state output voltage, $V_{O(off)}$	a thru g			30			15			30			15	V
On-state output current, $I_{O(on)}$	a thru g			40			40			40			40	mA
High-level output current, I_{OH}	BI/RBO			−200			−200			−200			−200	μA
Low-level output current, I_{OL}	BI/RBO			8			8			8			8	mA
Operating free-air temperature, T_A		−55		125	−55		125	0		70	0		70	°C

electrical characteristics over recommended operating free-air temperature range (unless otherwise noted)

PARAMETER			TEST CONDITIONS†	MIN	TYP‡	MAX	UNIT
V_{IH}	High-level input voltage			2			V
V_{IL}	Low-level input voltage					0.8	V
V_{IK}	Input clamp voltage		V_{CC} = MIN, I_I = −12 mA			1.5 V	V
V_{OH}	High-level output voltage	BI/RBO	V_{CC} = MIN, V_{IH} = 2 V, V_{IL} = 0.8 V, I_{OH} = −200 μA	2.4	3.7		V
V_{OL}	Low-level output voltage	BI/RBO	V_{CC} = MIN, V_{IH} = 2 V, V_{IL} = 0.8 V, I_{OL} = 8 mA		0.27	0.4	V
$I_{O(off)}$	Off-state output current	a thru g	V_{CC} = MAX, V_{IH} = 2 V, V_{IL} = 0.8 V, $V_{O(off)}$ = MAX			250	μA
$V_{O(on)}$	On-state output voltage	a thru g	V_{CC} = MAX, V_{IH} = 2 V, V_{IL} = 0.8 V, $I_{O(on)}$ = 40 mA		0.3	0.4	V
I_I	Input current at maximum input voltage	Any input except BI/RBO	V_{CC} = MAX, V_I = 5.5 V			1	mA
I_{IH}	High-level input current	Any input except BI/RBO	V_{CC} = MAX, V_I = 2.4 V			40	μA
I_{IL}	Low-level input current	Any input except BI/RBO	V_{CC} = MAX, V_I = 0.4 V			−1.6	mA
		BI/RBO				−4	
I_{OS}	Short-circuit output current	BI/RBO	V_{CC} = MAX			−4	mA
I_{CC}	Supply current		V_{CC} = MAX, See Note 2		64	103	mA

†For conditions shown as MIN or MAX, use the appropriate value specified under recommended operating conditions.
‡All typical values are at V_{CC} = 5 V, T_A = 25°C.
NOTE 2: I_{CC} is measured with all outputs open and all inputs at 4.5 V.

switching characteristics, V_{CC} = 5 V, T_A = 25°C

PARAMETER		TEST CONDITIONS	MIN	TYP	MAX	UNIT
t_{off}	Turn-off time from A input	C_L = 15 pF, R_L = 120 Ω, See Note 3			100	ns
t_{on}	Turn-on time from A input				100	
t_{off}	Turn-off time from RBI input				100	ns
t_{on}	Turn-on time from RBI input				100	

NOTE 3: Load circuit and voltage waveforms are shown on page 3-10; t_{off} corresponds to t_{PLH} and t_{on} corresponds to t_{PHL}.

7

TEXAS INSTRUMENTS
INCORPORATED
POST OFFICE BOX 5012 • DALLAS, TEXAS 75222

1076

absolute maximum ratings over operating free-air temperature range (unless otherwise noted)

Supply voltage, V_{CC} (see Note 1) . . . . 7 V
Input voltage . . . . 7 V
Peak output current ($t_W \leqslant 1$ ms, duty cycle $\leqslant 10\%$) . . . . 200 mA
Current forced into any output in the off state . . . . 1 mA
Operating free-air temperature range: SN54LS247 . . . . $-55°$C to $125°$C
SN74LS247 . . . . $0°$C to $70°$C
Storage temperature range . . . . $-65°$C to $150°$C

NOTE 1: Voltage values are with respect to network ground terminal.

recommended operating conditions

		SN54LS247			SN74LS247			UNIT
		MIN	NOM	MAX	MIN	NOM	MAX	
Supply voltage, V_{CC}		4.5	5	5.5	4.75	5	5.25	V
Off-state output voltage, $V_{O(off)}$	a thru g			15			15	V
On-state output current, $I_{O(on)}$	a thru g			12			24	mA
High-level output current, I_{OH}	BI/RBO			-50			-50	μA
Low-level output current, I_{OL}	BI/RBO			1.6			3.2	mA
Operating free-air temperature, T_A		-55		125	0		70	$°$C

electrical characteristics over recommended operating free-air temperature range (unless otherwise noted)

PARAMETER		TEST CONDITIONS†		SN54LS247			SN74LS247			UNIT
				MIN	TYP‡	MAX	MIN	TYP‡	MAX	
V_{IH}	High-level input voltage			2			2			V
V_{IL}	Low-level input voltage					0.7			0.8	V
V_{IK}	Input clamp voltage	$V_{CC} = $ MIN,	$I_I = -18$ mA			-1.5			-1.5	V
V_{OH}	High-level output voltage BI/RBO	$V_{CC} = $ MIN, $V_{IH} = 2$ V, $V_{IL} = V_{IL}$ max, $I_{OH} = -50$ μA		2.4	4.2		2.4	4.2		V
V_{OL}	Low-level output voltage BI/RBO	$V_{CC} = $ MIN, $V_{IH} = 2$ V, $V_{IL} = V_{IL}$ max	$I_{OL} = 1.6$ mA		0.25	0.4		0.25	0.4	V
			$I_{OL} = 3.2$ mA					0.35	0.5	
$I_{O(off)}$	Off-state output current a thru g	$V_{CC} = $ MAX, $V_{IH} = 2$ V, $V_{IL} = V_{IL}$ max, $V_{O(off)} = 15$ V				250			250	μA
$V_{O(on)}$	On-state output voltage a thru g	$V_{CC} = $ MAX, $V_{IH} = 2$ V, $V_{IL} = V_{IL}$ max	$I_{O(on)} = 12$ mA		0.25	0.4		0.25	0.4	V
			$I_{O(on)} = 24$ mA					0.35	0.5	
I_I	Input current at maximum input voltage	$V_{CC} = $ MAX,	$V_I = 7$ V			0.1			0.1	mA
I_{IH}	High-level input current	$V_{CC} = $ MAX,	$V_I = 2.7$ V			20			20	μA
I_{IL}	Low-level input current	Any input except BI/RBO	$V_{CC} = $ MAX, $V_I = 0.4$ V			-0.4			-0.4	mA
		BI/RBO				-1.2			-1.2	
I_{OS}	Short-circuit output current BI/RBO	$V_{CC} = $ MAX		-0.3		-2	-0.3		-2	mA
I_{CC}	Supply current	$V_{CC} = $ MAX,	See Note 2		7	13		7	13	mA

†For conditions shown as MIN or MAX, use the appropriate value specified under recommended operating conditions.
‡All typical values are at $V_{CC} = 5$ V, $T_A = 25°$C.
NOTE 2: I_{CC} is measured with all outputs open and all inputs at 4.5 V.

switching characteristics, $V_{CC} = 5$ V, $T_A = 25°$C

PARAMETER		TEST CONDITIONS	MIN	TYP	MAX	UNIT
t_{off}	Turn-off time from A input	$C_L = 15$ pF, $R_L = 665$ Ω, See Note 4			100	ns
t_{on}	Turn-on time from A input				100	
t_{off}	Turn-off time from RBI input				100	ns
t_{on}	Turn-on time from RBI input				100	

NOTE 4: Load circuit and voltage waveforms are shown on page 3-11; t_{off} corresponds to t_{PLH} and t_{on} corresponds to t_{PHL}.

TYPES SN54248, SN74248
BCD-TO-SEVEN-SEGMENT DECODERS/DRIVERS

REVISED MARCH 1974

absolute maximum ratings over operating free-air temperature range (unless otherwise noted)

Supply voltage, V_{CC} (see Note 1) . . . . 7 V
Input voltage . . . . 5.5 V
Operating free-air temperature range: SN54248 . . . . −55°C to 125°C
                               SN74248 . . . . 0°C to 70°C
Storage temperature range . . . . −65°C to 150°C

NOTE 1: Voltage values are with respect to network ground terminals.

recommended operating conditions

		SN54248			SN74248			UNIT
		MIN	NOM	MAX	MIN	NOM	MAX	
Supply voltage, V_{CC}		4.5	5	5.5	4.75	5	5.25	V
High-level output current, I_{OH}	a thru g			−400			−400	μA
	BI/RBO			−200			−200	
Low-level output current, I_{OL}	a thru g			6.4			6.4	mA
	BI/RBO			8			8	
Operating free-air temperature, T_A		−55		125	0		70	°C

electrical characteristics over recommended operating free-air temperature range (unless otherwise noted)

	PARAMETER		TEST CONDITIONS†	MIN	TYP‡	MAX	UNIT
V_{IH}	High-level input voltage			2			V
V_{IL}	Low-level input voltage					0.8	V
V_{IK}	Input clamp voltage		V_{CC} = MIN, I_I = −12 mA			−1.5	V
V_{OH}	High-level output voltage	a thru g	V_{CC} = MIN, V_{IH} = 2 V,	2.4	4.2		V
		BI/RBO	V_{IL} = 0.8 V, I_{OH} = MAX	2.4	3.7		
I_O	Output current	a thru g	V_{CC} = MIN, V_O = 0.85 V, Input conditions as for V_{OH}	−1.3	−2		mA
V_{OL}	Low-level output voltage		V_{CC} = MIN, V_{IH} = 2 V, V_{IL} = 0.8 V, I_{OL} = MAX		0.27	0.4	V
I_I	Input current at maximum input voltage	Any input except BI/RBO	V_{CC} = MAX, V_I = 5.5 V			1	mA
I_{IH}	High-level input current	Any input except BI/RBO	V_{CC} = MAX, V_I = 2.4 V			40	μA
I_{IL}	Low-level input current	Any input except BI/RBO	V_{CC} = MAX, V_I = 0.4 V			−1.6	mA
		BI/RBO				−4	
I_{OS}	Short-circuit output current	BI/RBO	V_{CC} = MAX			−4	mA
I_{CC}	Supply current		V_{CC} = MAX, See Note 2		53	90	mA

†For conditions shown as MIN or MAX, use the appropriate value specified under recommended operating conditions.
‡All typical values are at V_{CC} = 5 V, T_A = 25°C.
NOTE 2: I_{CC} is measured with all outputs open and all inputs at 4.5 V.

switching characteristics, V_{CC} = 5 V, T_A = 25°C

	PARAMETER	TEST CONDITIONS	MIN	TYP	MAX	UNIT
t_{PHL}	Propagation delay time, high-to-low-level output from A input	C_L = 15 pF, R_L = 1 kΩ, See Note 5			100	ns
t_{PLH}	Propagation delay time, low-to-high-level output from A input				100	
t_{PHL}	Propagation delay time, high-to-low-level output from RBI input				100	ns
t_{PLH}	Propagation delay time, low-to-high-level output from RBI input				100	

NOTE 5: Load circuit and voltage waveforms are shown on page 3-10.

7

TEXAS INSTRUMENTS
INCORPORATED
POST OFFICE BOX 5012 • DALLAS, TEXAS 75222

absolute maximum ratings over operating free-air temperature range (unless otherwise noted)

Supply voltage, V_{CC} (see Note 1)	7 V
Input voltage	7 V
Operating free-air temperature range: SN54LS248	-55°C to 125°C
SN74LS248	0°C to 70°C
Storage temperature range	-65°C to 150°C

NOTE 1: Voltage values are with respect to network ground terminal.

recommended operating conditions

		SN54LS248			SN74LS248			UNIT
		MIN	NOM	MAX	MIN	NOM	MAX	
Supply voltage, V_{CC}		4.5	5	5.5	4.75	5	5.25	V
High-level output current, I_{OH}	a thru g			−100			−100	μA
	BI/RBO			−50			−50	
Low-level output current, I_{OL}	a thru g			2			6	mA
	BI/RBO			1.6			3.2	
Operating free-air temperature, T_A		−55		125	0		70	$^\circ$C

electrical characteristics over recommended operating free-air temperature range (unless otherwise noted)

PARAMETER		TEST CONDITIONS†		SN54LS248			SN74LS248			UNIT
				MIN	TYP‡	MAX	MIN	TYP‡	MAX	
V_{IH}	High-level input voltage			2			2			V
V_{IL}	Low-level input voltage					0.7			0.8	V
V_{IK}	Input clamp voltage	V_{CC} = MIN,	I_I = −18 mA			−1.5			−1.5	V
V_{OH}	High-level output voltage	a thru g and BI/RBO	V_{CC} = MIN, V_{IH} = 2 V, V_{IL} = V_{IL} max, I_{OH} = MAX	2.4	4.2		2.4	4.2		V
I_O	Output current	a thru g	V_{CC} = MIN, V_O = 0.85 V, Input conditions as for V_{OH}	−1.3	−2		−1.3	−2		mA
V_{OL}	Low-level output voltage	a thru g	V_{CC} = MIN, V_{IH} = 2 V, V_{IL} = V_{IL} max $\quad I_{OL}$ = 2 mA		0.25	0.4		0.25	0.4	V
			$\quad I_{OL}$ = 6 mA					0.35	0.5	
		BI/RBO	V_{CC} = MIN, V_{IH} = 2 V, V_{IL} = V_{IL} max $\quad I_{OL}$ = 1.6 mA		0.25	0.4		0.25	0.4	V
			$\quad I_{OL}$ = 3.2 mA					0.35	0.5	
I_I	Input current at maximum input voltage	Any input except BI/BRO	V_{CC} = MAX, V_I = 7 V			0.1			0.1	mA
I_{IH}	High-level input current	Any input except BI/RBO	V_{CC} = MAX, V_I = 2.7 V			20			20	μA
I_{IL}	Low-level input current	Any input except BI/RBO	V_{CC} = MAX, V_I = 0.4 V			−0.4			−0.4	mA
		BI/RBO				−1.2			−1.2	
I_{OS}	Short-circuit output current	BI/RBO	V_{CC} = MAX	−0.3		−2	−0.3		−2	mA
I_{CC}	Supply current		V_{CC} = MAX, See Note 2		25	38		25	38	mA

†For conditions shown as MIN or MAX, use the appropriate value specified under recommended operating conditions.
‡All typical values are at V_{CC} = 5 V, T_A 25°C.
NOTE 2: I_{CC} is measured with all outputs open and all inputs at 4.5 V.

switching characteristics, V_{CC} = 5 V, T_A = 25°C

PARAMETER		TEST CONDITIONS	MIN	TYP	MAX	UNIT
t_{PHL}	Propagation delay time, high-to-low-level output from A input	C_L = 15 pF, R_L = 4 kΩ, See Note 6			100	ns
t_{PLH}	Propagation delay time, low-to-high-level output from A input				100	
t_{PHL}	Propagation delay time, high-to-low-level output from RBI input	C_L = 15 pF, R_L = 6 kΩ, See Note 6			100	ns
t_{PLH}	Propagation delay time, low-to-high-level output from RBI input				100	

NOTE 6: Load circuit and voltage waveforms are shown on page 3-11.

7

TYPES SN54249, SN74249
BCD-TO-SEVEN-SEGMENT DECODERS/DRIVERS

absolute maximum ratings over operating free-air temperature range (unless otherwise noted)

Supply voltage, V_{CC} (see Note 1)	7 V
Input voltage	5.5 V
Current forced into any output in the off state	1 mA
Operating free-air temperature range: SN54249	-55°C to 125°C
SN74249	0°C to 70°C
Storage temperature range	-65°C to 150°C

NOTE 1: Voltage values are with respect to network ground terminal.

recommended operating conditions

		SN54249			SN74249			UNIT
		MIN	NOM	MAX	MIN	NOM	MAX	
Supply voltage, V_{CC}		4.5	5	5.5	4.75	5	5.25	V
High-level output voltage, V_{OH}				5.5			5.5	V
High-level output current, I_{OH}	BI/RBO			−200			−200	µA
Low-level output current, I_{OL}	a thru g			10			10	mA
	BI/RBO			8			8	
Operating free-air temperature, T_A		−55		125	0		70	°C

electrical characteristics over recommended operating free-air temperature range (unless otherwise noted)

PARAMETER			TEST CONDITIONS[†]	MIN	TYP[‡]	MAX	UNIT
V_{IH}	High-level input voltage			2			V
V_{IL}	Low-level input voltage					0.8	V
V_{IK}	Input clamp voltage		V_{CC} = MIN, I_I = −12 mA			−1.5	V
V_{OH}	High-level output voltage	BI/RBO	V_{CC} = MIN, V_{IH} = 2 V, V_{IL} = 0.8 V, I_{OH} = MAX	2.4	3.7		V
I_{OH}	High-level output current	a thru g	V_{CC} = MIN, V_{IH} = 2 V, V_{IL} = 0.8 V, V_{OH} = 5.5 V			250	µA
V_{OL}	Low-level output voltage		V_{CC} = MIN, V_{IH} = 2 V, V_{IL} = 0.8 V, I_{OL} = MAX		0.27	0.4	V
I_I	Input current at maximum input voltage	Any input except BI/RBO	V_{CC} = MAX, V_I = 7 V			1	mA
I_{IH}	High-level input current	Any input except BI/RBO	V_{CC} = MAX, V_I = 2.4 V			40	µA
I_{IL}	Low-level input current	Any input except BI/RBO	V_{CC} = MAX, V_I = 0.4 V			−1.6	mA
		BI/RBO				−4	
I_{OS}	Short-circuit output current	BI/RBO	V_{CC} = MAX			−4	mA
I_{CC}	Supply current		V_{CC} = MAX, See Note 2		53	90	mA

†For conditions shown as MIN or MAX, use the appropriate value specified under recommended operating conditions.
‡All typical values are at V_{CC} = 5 V, T_A = 25°C.
NOTE 2: I_{CC} is measured with all outputs open and all inputs at 4.5 V.

switching characteristics, V_{CC} = 5 V, T_A = 25°C

PARAMETER		TEST CONDITIONS	MIN	TYP	MAX	UNIT
t_{PHL}	Propagation delay time, high-to-low-level output from A input	C_L = 15 pF, R_L = 667 Ω, See Note 5			100	ns
t_{PLH}	Propagation delay time, low-to-high-level output from A input				100	
t_{PHL}	Propagation delay time, high-to-low-level output from RBI input				100	ns
t_{PLH}	Propagation delay time, low-to-high-level output from RBI input				100	

NOTE 5: Load circuit and voltage waveforms are shown on page 3-10.

TEXAS INSTRUMENTS
INCORPORATED
POST OFFICE BOX 5012 • DALLAS, TEXAS 75222

1076

TYPES SN54LS249, SN74LS249
BCD-TO-SEVEN-SEGMENT DECODERS/DRIVERS

REVISED OCTOBER 1976

absolute maximum ratings over operating free-air temperature range (unless otherwise noted)

Supply voltage, V_{CC} (see Note 1)	7 V
Input voltage	7 V
Current forced into any output in the offstate	1 mA
Operating free-air temperature range: SN54LS249	-55°C to 125°C
SN74LS249	0°C to 70°C
Storage temperature range	-65°C to 150°C

NOTE 1: Voltage values are with respect to network ground terminal.

recommended operating conditions

		SN54LS249			SN74LS249			UNIT
		MIN	NOM	MAX	MIN	NOM	MAX	
Supply voltage, V_{CC}		4.5	5	5.5	4.75	5	5.25	V
High-level output voltage, V_{OH}	a thru g			5.5			5.5	V
High-level output current, I_{OH}	BI/RBO			-50			-50	μA
Low-level output current, I_{OL}	a thru g			4			8	mA
	BI/RBO			1.6			3.2	
Operating free-air temperature, T_A		-55		125	0		70	$^\circ$C

electrical characteristics over recommended operating free-air temperature range (unless otherwise noted)

PARAMETER		TEST CONDITIONS[†]		SN54LS249			SN74LS249			UNIT
				MIN	TYP[‡]	MAX	MIN	TYP[‡]	MAX	
V_{IH}	High-level input voltage			2			2			V
V_{IL}	Low-level input voltage					0.7			0.8	V
V_{IK}	Input clamp voltage	V_{CC} = MIN,	I_I = -18 mA			-1.5			-1.5	V
V_{OH}	High-level output voltage	BI/RBO	V_{CC} = MIN, V_{IH} = 2 V, V_{IL} = V_{IL} max, I_{OH} = $-50\,\mu$A	2.4	4.2		2.4	4.2		V
I_{OH}	High-level output current	a thru g	V_{CC} = MIN, V_{IH} = 2 V, V_{IL} = V_{IL} max, V_{OH} = 5.5 V			250			250	μA
V_{OL}	Low-level output voltage	BI/RBO	V_{CC} = MIN, V_{IH} = 2 V, V_{IL} = V_{IL} max, I_{OL} = 1.6 mA		0.25	0.4		0.25	0.4	V
			I_{OL} = 3.2 mA					0.35	0.5	
		a thru g	V_{CC} = MIN, V_{IH} = 2 V, V_{IL} = V_{IL} max, I_{OL} = 4 mA		0.25	0.4		0.25	0.4	V
			I_{OL} = 8 mA					0.35	0.5	
I_I	Input current at maximum input voltage	Any input except BI/RBO	V_{CC} = MAX, V_I = 7 V			0.1			0.1	mA
I_{IH}	High-level input current	Any input except BI/RBO	V_{CC} = MAX, V_I = 2.7 V			20			20	μA
I_{IL}	Low-level input current	Any input except BI/RBO	V_{CC} = MAX, V_I = 0.4 V			-0.4			-0.4	mA
		BI/RBO				-1.2			-1.2	
I_{OS}	Short-circuit output current	BI/RBO	V_{CC} = MAX	-0.3		-2	-0.3		-2	mA
I_{CC}	Supply current		V_{CC} = MAX, See Note 2		8	15		8	15	mA

[†]For conditions shown as MIN or MAX, use the appropriate value specified under recommended operating conditions.
[‡]All typical values are at V_{CC} = 5 V, T_A = 25°C.
NOTE 2: I_{CC} is measured with all outputs open and inputs at 4.5 V.

switching characteristics, V_{CC} = 5 V, T_A = 25°C

PARAMETER		TEST CONDITIONS	MIN	TYP	MAX	UNIT
t_{PHL}	Propagation delay time, high-to-low-level output from A input	C_L = 15 pF, R_L = 2 kΩ, See Note 6			100	ns
t_{PLH}	Propagation delay time, low-to-high-level output from A input				100	
t_{PHL}	Propagation delay time, high-to-low-level output from RBI input	C_L = 15 pF, R_L = 6 kΩ, See Note 6			100	ns
t_{PLH}	Propagation delay time, low-to-high-level output from RBI input				100	

NOTE 6: Load circuit and voltage waveforms are shown on page 3-11.

TEXAS INSTRUMENTS
INCORPORATED
POST OFFICE BOX 5012 • DALLAS, TEXAS 75222

U.S.A.

TTL
MSI

TYPES SN54251, SN54LS251, SN54S251,
SN74251, SN74LS251 (TIM9905), SN74S251
DATA SELECTORS/MULTIPLEXERS WITH 3-STATE OUTPUTS
BULLETIN NO. DL-S 7611834, DECEMBER 1972—REVISED OCTOBER 1976

- Three-State Versions of '151, 'LS151, 'S151
- Three-State Outputs Interface Directly with System Bus
- Perform Parallel-to-Serial Conversion
- Permit Multiplexing from N-lines to One Line
- Complementary Outputs Provide True and Inverted Data
- Fully Compatible with Most TTL and DTL Circuits

SN54251, SN54LS251, SN54S251 . . . J OR W PACKAGE
SN74251, SN74LS251, SN54S251 . . . J OR N PACKAGE
(TOP VIEW)

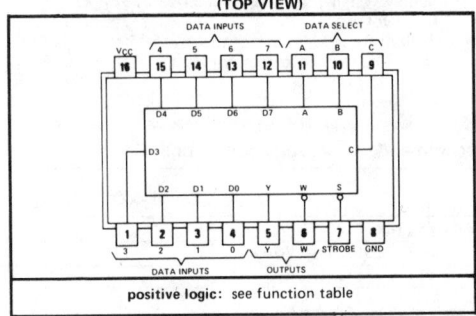

positive logic: see function table

TYPE	MAX NO. OF COMMON OUTPUTS	TYPICAL AVG PROP DELAY TIME (D TO Y)	TYPICAL POWER DISSIPATION
SN54251	49	17 ns	250 mW
SN74251	129	17 ns	250 mW
SN54LS251	49	17 ns	35 mW
SN74LS251	129	17 ns	35 mW
SN54S251	39	8 ns	275 mW
SN74S251	129	8 ns	275 mW

functional block diagram

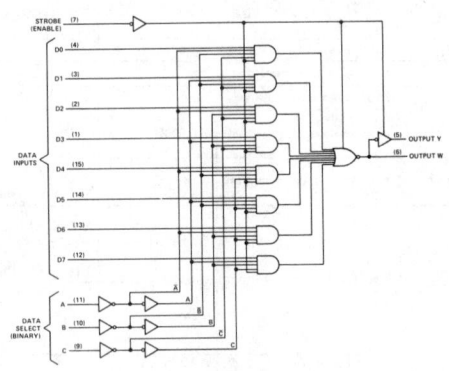

description

These monolithic data selectors/multiplexers contain full on-chip binary decoding to select one-of-eight data sources and feature a strobe-controlled three-state output. The strobe must be at a low logic level to enable these devices. The three-state outputs permit a number of outputs to be connected to a common bus. When the strobe input is high, both outputs are in a high-impedance state in which both the upper and lower transistors of each totem-pole output are off, and the output neither drives nor loads the bus significantly. When the strobe is low, the outputs are activated and operate as standard TTL totem-pole outputs.

To minimize the possibility that two outputs will attempt to take a common bus to opposite logic levels, the output control circuitry is designed so that the 'average output disable time is shorter than the average output enable time. The SN54251 and SN74251 have output clamp diodes to attenuate reflections on the bus line.

FUNCTION TABLE

INPUTS				OUTPUTS	
SELECT			STROBE	Y	W
C	B	A	S		
X	X	X	H	Z	Z
L	L	L	L	D0	$\overline{D0}$
L	L	H	L	D1	$\overline{D1}$
L	H	L	L	D2	$\overline{D2}$
L	H	H	L	D3	$\overline{D3}$
H	L	L	L	D4	$\overline{D4}$
H	L	H	L	D5	$\overline{D5}$
H	H	L	L	D6	$\overline{D6}$
H	H	H	L	D7	$\overline{D7}$

H = high logic level, L = low logic level
X = irrelevant, Z = high impedance (off)
D0, D1 . . . D7 = the level of the respective D input

1076

TEXAS INSTRUMENTS
INCORPORATED
POST OFFICE BOX 5012 • DALLAS, TEXAS 75222

absolute maximum ratings over operating free-air temperature range (unless otherwise noted)

Supply voltage, V_{CC} (see Note 1) . . . . 7 V
Input voltage . . . . 5.5 V
Off-state output voltage . . . . 5.5 V
Operating free-air temperature range: SN54251 . . . . −55°C to 125°C
SN74251 . . . . 0°C to 70°C
Storage temperature range . . . . −65°C to 150°C

NOTE 1: Voltage values are with respect to network ground terminal.

recommended operating conditions

	SN54251			SN74251			UNIT
	MIN	NOM	MAX	MIN	NOM	MAX	
Supply voltage, V_{CC}	4.5	5	5.5	4.75	5	5.25	V
High-level output current, I_{OH}			−2			−5.2	mA
Low-level output current, I_{OL}			16			16	mA
Operating free-air temperature, T_A	−55		125	0		70	°C

electrical characteristics over recommended operating free-air temperature range (unless otherwise noted)

PARAMETER		TEST CONDITIONS[†]		MIN	TYP[‡]	MAX	UNIT
V_{IH}	High-level input voltage			2			V
V_{IL}	Low-level input voltage					0.8	V
V_{IK}	Input clamp voltage	V_{CC} = MIN,	I_I = −12 mA			−1.5	V
V_{OH}	High-level output voltage	V_{CC} = MIN, V_{IH} = 2 V, V_{IL} = 0.8 V, I_{OH} = MAX		2.4	3.2		V
V_{OL}	Low-level output voltage	V_{CC} = MIN, V_{IH} = 2 V, V_{IL} = 0.8 V, I_{OL} = 16 mA			0.2	0.4	V
I_{OZ}	Off-state (high-impedance-state) output current	V_{CC} = MAX, V_{IH} = 2 V	V_O = 2.4 V			40	μA
			V_O = 0.4 V			−40	
V_O	Output clamp voltage	V_{CC} = MAX, V_{IH} = 4.5 V	I_O = −12 mA			−1.5	V
			I_O = 12 mA			V_{CC}+1.5	
I_I	Input current at maximum input voltage	V_{CC} = MAX,	V_I = 5.5 V			1	mA
I_{IH}	High-level input current	V_{CC} = MAX,	V_I = 2.4 V			40	μA
I_{IL}	Low-level input current	V_{CC} = MAX,	V_I = 0.4 V			−1.6	mA
I_{OS}	Short-circuit output current[§]	V_{CC} = MAX		−18		−55	mA
I_{CC}	Supply current	V_{CC} = MAX, All inputs at 4.5 V, All outputs open			38	62	mA

[†]For conditions shown as MIN or MAX, use the appropriate value specified under recommended operating conditions for the applicable type.
[‡]All typical values are at V_{CC} = 5 V, T_A = 25°C.
[§]Not more than one output should be shorted at a time.

TEXAS INSTRUMENTS
INCORPORATED
POST OFFICE BOX 5012 • DALLAS, TEXAS 75222

TYPES SN54251, SN74251
DATA SELECTORS/MULTIPLEXERS WITH 3-STATE OUTPUTS

switching characteristics, V_{CC} = 5 V, T_A = 25°C

PARAMETER¶	FROM (INPUT)	TO (OUTPUT)	TEST CONDITIONS	MIN	TYP	MAX	UNIT
t_{PLH}	A, B, or C	Y			29	45	ns
t_{PHL}	(4 levels)				28	45	
t_{PLH}	A, B, or C	W			20	33	ns
t_{PHL}	(3 levels)				21	33	
t_{PLH}	Any D	Y	C_L = 50 pF,		17	28	ns
t_{PHL}			R_L = 400 Ω,		18	28	
t_{PLH}	Any D	W	See Note 2		10	15	ns
t_{PHL}					9	15	
t_{ZH}	Strobe	Y			17	27	ns
t_{ZL}					26	40	
t_{ZH}	Strobe	W			17	27	ns
t_{ZL}					24	40	
t_{HZ}	Strobe	Y	C_L = 5 pF,		5	8	ns
t_{LZ}			R_L = 400 Ω,		15	23	
t_{HZ}	Strobe	W	See Note 2		5	8	ns
t_{LZ}					15	23	

¶t_{PLH} ≡ Propagation delay time, low-to-high-level output
t_{PHL} ≡ Propagation delay time, high-to-low-level output
t_{ZH} ≡ Output enable time to high level
t_{ZL} ≡ Output enable time to low level
t_{HZ} ≡ Output disable time from high level
t_{LZ} ≡ Output disable time from low level
NOTE 2: See load circuits and waveforms on page 3-10.

schematics of inputs and outputs

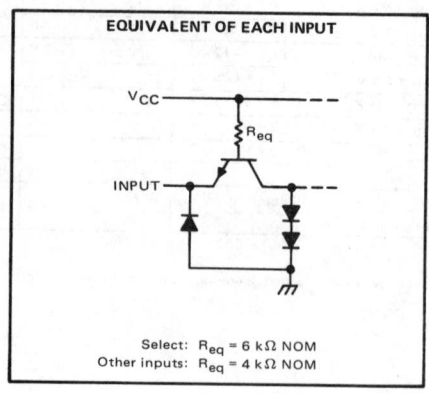

EQUIVALENT OF EACH INPUT

Select: R_{eq} = 6 kΩ NOM
Other inputs: R_{eq} = 4 kΩ NOM

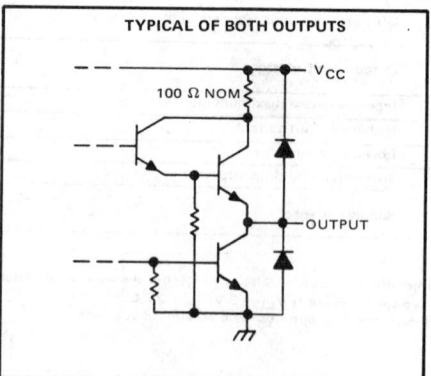

TYPICAL OF BOTH OUTPUTS

TEXAS INSTRUMENTS
INCORPORATED
POST OFFICE BOX 5012 • DALLAS, TEXAS 75222

1272

absolute maximum ratings over operating free-air temperature range (unless otherwise noted)

Supply voltage, V_{CC} (see Note 1)	7 V
Input voltage	7 V
Off-state output voltage	5.5 V
Operating free-air temperature range: SN54LS251	55°C to 125°C
SN74LS251	0°C to 70°C
Storage temperature range	−65°C to 150°C

NOTE 1: Voltage values are with respect to network ground terminal.

recommended operating conditions

	SN54LS251			SN74LS251			UNIT
	MIN	NOM	MAX	MIN	NOM	MAX	
Supply voltage, V_{CC}	4.5	5	5.5	4.75	5	5.25	V
High-level output current, I_{OH}			−1			−2.6	mA
Low-level output current, I_{OL}			4			8	mA
Operating free-air temperature, T_A	−55		125	0		70	°C

electrical characteristics over recommended operating free-air temperature range (unless otherwise noted)

PARAMETER		TEST CONDITIONS[†]		SN54LS251			SN74LS251			UNIT
				MIN	TYP[‡]	MAX	MIN	TYP[‡]	MAX	
V_{IH}	High-level input voltage			2			2			V
V_{IL}	Low-level input voltage					0.7			0.8	V
V_{IK}	Input clamp voltage	V_{CC} = MIN,	I_I = −18 mA			−1.5			−1.5	V
V_{OH}	High-level output voltage	V_{CC} = MIN, V_{IH} = 2 V, V_{IL} = MAX, I_{OH} = MAX		2.4	3.4		2.4	3.1		V
V_{OL}	Low-level voltage	V_{CC} = MIN, V_{IH} = 2 V, V_{IL} = VIL max	I_{OL} = 4 mA		0.25	0.4		0.25	0.4	V
			I_{OL} = 8 mA					0.35	0.5	
I_{OZ}	Off-state (high-impedance-state) output current	V_{CC} = MAX, V_{IH} = 2 V	V_O = 2.7 V			20			20	µA
			V_O = 0.4 V			−20			−20	
I_I	Input current at maximum input voltage	V_{CC} = MAX,	V_I = 7 V			0.1			0.1	mA
I_{IH}	High-level input current	V_{CC} = MAX,	V_I = 2.7 V			20			20	µA
I_{IL}	Low-level input current	V_{CC} = MAX,	V_I = 0.4 V			−0.4			−0.4	mA
I_{OS}	Short-circuit output current [§]	V_{CC} = MAX		−30		−130	−30		−130	mA
I_{CC}	Supply current	V_{CC} = MAX, See Note 3	Condition A		6.1	10		6.1	10	mA
			Condition B		7.1	12		7.1	12	

[†]For conditions shown as MIN or MAX, use the appropriate value specified under recommended operating conditions for the applicable type.
[‡]All typical values are at V_{CC} = 5 V, T_A = 25°C.
[§]Not more than one output should be shorted at a time, and duration of the short-circuit should not exceed one second.
NOTE 3: I_{CC} is measured with the outputs open and all data and select inputs at 4.5 V under the following conditions:
    A. Strobe grounded.
    B. Strobe at 4.5 V.

7

TEXAS INSTRUMENTS
INCORPORATED
POST OFFICE BOX 5012 • DALLAS, TEXAS 75222

switching characteristics, $V_{CC} = 5$ V, $T_A = 25°C$

PARAMETER¶	FROM (INPUT)	TO (OUTPUT)	TEST CONDITIONS	MIN	TYP	MAX	UNIT
t_{PLH}	A, B, or C	Y			29	45	ns
t_{PHL}	(4 levels)				28	45	
t_{PLH}	A, B, or C	W			20	33	ns
t_{PHL}	(3 levels)				21	33	
t_{PLH}	Any D	Y	$C_L = 15$ pF,		17	28	ns
t_{PHL}			$R_L = 2$ kΩ,		18	28	
t_{PLH}	Any D	W	See Note 4		10	15	ns
t_{PHL}					9	15	
t_{ZH}	Strobe	Y			30	45	ns
t_{ZL}					26	40	
t_{ZH}	Strobe	W			17	27	ns
t_{ZL}					24	40	
t_{HZ}	Strobe	Y	$C_L = 5$ pF,		30	45	ns
t_{LZ}			$R_L = 2$ kΩ,		15	25	
t_{HZ}	Strobe	W	See Note 4		37	55	ns
t_{LZ}					15	25	

¶ $t_{PLH} \equiv$ Propagation delay time, low-to-high-level output
   $t_{PHL} \equiv$ Propagation delay time, high-to-low-level output
   $t_{ZH} \equiv$ Output enable time to high level
   $t_{ZL} \equiv$ Output enable time to low level
   $t_{HZ} \equiv$ Output disable time from high level
   $t_{LZ} \equiv$ Output disable time from low level
NOTE 4: See load circuits and waveforms on page 3-11.

schematics of inputs and outputs

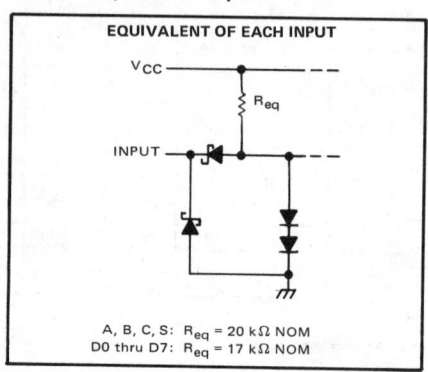

EQUIVALENT OF EACH INPUT

A, B, C, S: $R_{eq} = 20$ kΩ NOM
D0 thru D7: $R_{eq} = 17$ kΩ NOM

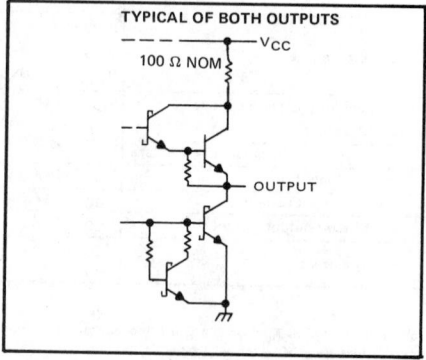

TYPICAL OF BOTH OUTPUTS

100 Ω NOM

TEXAS INSTRUMENTS
INCORPORATED
POST OFFICE BOX 5012 • DALLAS, TEXAS 75222

1076

absolute maximum ratings over operating free-air temperature range (unless otherwise noted)

Supply voltage, V_{CC} (see Note 1) . . . . 7 V
Input voltage . . . . 5.5 V
Off-state output voltage . . . . 5.5 V
Operating free-air temperature range: SN54S251 . . . . −55°C to 125°C
SN74S251 . . . . 0°C to 70°C
Storage temperature range . . . . −65°C to 150°C

NOTE 1: Voltage values are with respect to network ground terminal.

recommended operating conditions

	SN54S251			SN74S251			UNIT
	MIN	NOM	MAX	MIN	NOM	MAX	
Supply voltage, V_{CC}	4.5	5	5.5	4.75	5	5.25	V
High-level output current, I_{OH}			−2			−6.5	mA
Low-level output current, I_{OL}			20			20	mA
Operating free-air temperature, T_A	−55		125	0		70	°C

electrical characteristics over recommended operating free-air temperature range (unless otherwise noted)

	PARAMETER	TEST CONDITIONS[†]			MIN	TYP[‡]	MAX	UNIT
V_{IH}	High-level input voltage				2			V
V_{IL}	Low-level input voltage						0.8	V
V_{IK}	Input clamp voltage	V_{CC} = MIN,	I_I = −18 mA				−1.2	V
V_{OH}	High-level output voltage	V_{CC} = MIN, V_{IH} = 2 V,	SN54S'		2.4	3.4		V
		V_{IL} = 0.8 V, I_{OH} = MAX	SN74S'		2.4	3.2		
V_{OL}	Low-level output voltage	V_{CC} = MIN, V_{IH} = 2 V,					0.5	V
		V_{IL} = 0.8 V, I_{OL} = 20 mA						
I_{OZ}	Off-state (high-impedance-state) output current	V_{CC} = MAX,	V_O = 2.4 V				50	μA
		V_{IH} = 2 V	V_O = 0.5 V				−50	
I_I	Input current at maximum input voltage	V_{CC} = MAX,	V_I = 5.5 V				1	mA
I_{IH}	High-level input current	V_{CC} = MAX,	V_I = 2.7 V				50	μA
I_{IL}	Low-level input current	V_{CC} = MAX,	V_I = 0.5 V				−2	mA
I_{OS}	Short-circuit output current[§]	V_{CC} = MAX			−40		−100	mA
I_{CC}	Supply current	V_{CC} = MAX, All inputs at 4.5 V, All outputs open				55	85	mA

[†]For conditions shown as MIN or MAX, use the appropriate value specified under recommended operating conditions for the applicable type.
[‡]All typical values are at V_{CC} = 5 V, T_A = 25°C.
[§]Not more than one output should be shorted at a time, and duration of the short-circuit should not exceed one second.

TEXAS INSTRUMENTS
INCORPORATED
POST OFFICE BOX 5012 • DALLAS, TEXAS 75222

switching characteristics, V_{CC} = 5 V, T_A = 25°C

PARAMETER¶	FROM (INPUT)	TO (OUTPUT)	TEST CONDITIONS	MIN	TYP	MAX	UNIT
t_{PLH}	A, B, or C	Y			12	18	ns
t_{PHL}	(4 levels)				13	19.5	
t_{PLH}	A, B, or C	W	C_L = 15 pF,		10	15	ns
t_{PHL}	(3 levels)		R_L = 280 Ω,		9	13.5	
t_{PLH}	Any D	Y	See Note 2		8	12	ns
t_{PHL}					8	12	
t_{PLH}	Any D	W			4.5	7	ns
t_{PHL}					4.5	7	
t_{ZH}	Strobe	Y	C_L = 50 pF,		13	19.5	ns
t_{ZL}			R_L = 280 Ω,		14	21	
t_{ZH}	Strobe	W	See Note 2		13	19.5	ns
t_{ZL}					14	21	
t_{HZ}	Strobe	Y	C_L = 5 pF,		5.5	8.5	ns
t_{LZ}			R_L = 280 Ω,		9	14	
t_{HZ}	Strobe	W	See Note 2		5.5	8.5	ns
t_{LZ}					9	14	

¶t_{PLH} ≡ Propagation delay time, low-to-high-level output
t_{PHL} ≡ Propagation delay time, high-to-low-level output
t_{ZH} ≡ Output enable time to high level
t_{ZL} ≡ Output enable time to low level
t_{HZ} ≡ Output disable time from high level
t_{LZ} ≡ Output disable time from low level
NOTE 2: See load circuits and waveforms on page 3-10.

schematics of inputs and outputs

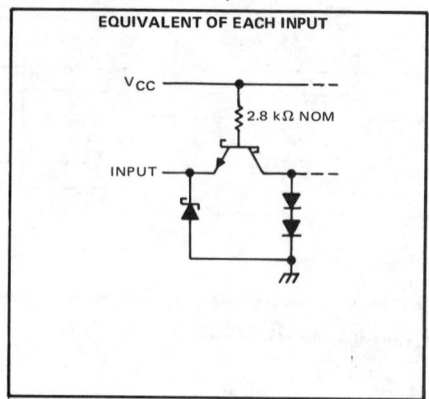

EQUIVALENT OF EACH INPUT

V_{CC}
2.8 kΩ NOM
INPUT

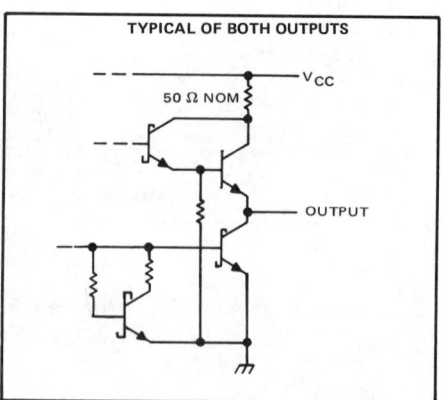

TYPICAL OF BOTH OUTPUTS

V_{CC}
50 Ω NOM
OUTPUT

TEXAS INSTRUMENTS
INCORPORATED
POST OFFICE BOX 5012 • DALLAS, TEXAS 75222

1272

TYPES SN54LS253, SN74LS253
DUAL 4-LINE-TO-1-LINE DATA SELECTORS/MULTIPLEXERS WITH 3-STATE OUTPUTS

BULLETIN NO. DL-S 7611790, SEPTEMBER 1972—REVISED OCTOBER 1976

- Three-State Version of SN54LS153/SN74LS153
- Schottky-Diode-Clamped Transistors
- Permits Multiplexing from N Lines to 1 Line
- Performs Parallel-to-Serial Conversion
- Typical Average Propagation Delay Times:
  Data Input to Output . . . 12 ns
  Control Input to Output . . . 16 ns
  Select Input to Output . . . 21 ns
- Fully Compatible with Most TTL and DTL Circuits
- Low Power Dissipation . . . 35 mW Typical (Enabled)

SN54LS253 . . . J OR W PACKAGE
SN74LS253 . . . J OR N PACKAGE
(TOP VIEW)

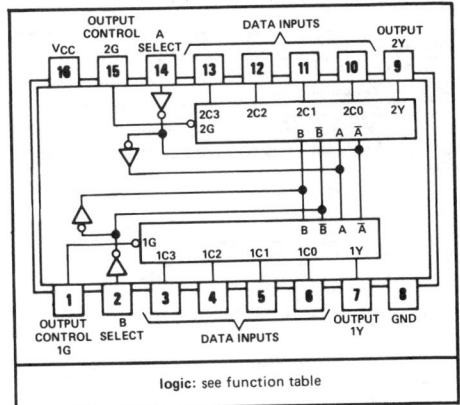

logic: see function table

description

Each of these Schottky-clamped data selectors/multiplexers contains inverters and drivers to supply fully complementary, on-chip, binary decoding data selection to the AND-OR gates. Separate output control inputs are provided for each of the two four-line sections.

The three-state outputs can interface with and drive data lines of bus-organized systems. With all but one of the common outputs disabled (at a high-impedance state) the low-impedance of the single enabled output will drive the bus line to a high or low logic level.

logic

FUNCTION TABLE

SELECT INPUTS		DATA INPUTS				OUTPUT CONTROL	OUTPUT
B	A	C0	C1	C2	C3	G	Y
X	X	X	X	X	X	H	Z
L	L	L	X	X	X	L	L
L	L	H	X	X	X	L	H
L	H	X	L	X	X	L	L
L	H	X	H	X	X	L	H
H	L	X	X	L	X	L	L
H	L	X	X	H	X	L	H
H	H	X	X	X	L	L	L
H	H	X	X	X	H	L	H

Address inputs A and B are common to both sections.
H = high level, L = low level, X = irrelevant, Z = high impedance (off)

functional block diagram

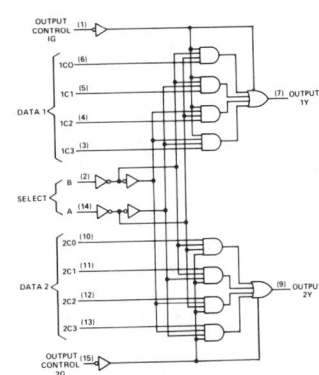

absolute maximum ratings over operating free-air temperature range (unless otherwise noted)

Supply voltage, V_{CC} (see Note 1) . . . . 7 V
Input voltage . . . . 7 V
Off-state output voltage . . . . 5.5 V
Operating free-air temperature range: SN54LS253 . . . . −55°C to 125°C
SN74LS253 . . . . 0°C to 70°C
Storage temperature range . . . . −65°C to 150°C

NOTE 1: Voltage values are with respect to network ground terminal.

TEXAS INSTRUMENTS
INCORPORATED
POST OFFICE BOX 5012 • DALLAS, TEXAS 75222

TYPES SN54LS253, SN74LS253
DUAL 4-LINE-TO-1-LINE DATA SELECTORS/
MULTIPLEXERS WITH 3-STATE OUTPUTS

REVISED OCTOBER 1976

recommended operating conditions

	SN54LS253			SN74LS253			UNIT
	MIN	NOM	MAX	MIN	NOM	MAX	
Supply voltage, V_{CC}	4.5	5	5.5	4.75	5	5.25	V
High-level output current, I_{OH}			−1			−2.6	mA
Low-level output current, I_{OL}			4			8	mA
Operating free-air temperature, T_A	−55		125	0		70	°C

electrical characteristics over recommended operating free-air temperature range (unless otherwise noted)

PARAMETER		TEST CONDITIONS†		SN54LS253			SN74LS253			UNIT
				MIN	TYP‡	MAX	MIN	TYP‡	MAX	
V_{IH}	High-level input voltage			2			2			V
V_{IL}	Low-level input voltage					0.7			0.8	V
V_{IK}	Input clamp voltage	V_{CC} = MIN, I_I = −18 mA				−1.5			−1.5	V
V_{OH}	High-level output voltage	V_{CC} = MIN, V_{IH} = 2 V, V_{IL} = V_{IL} max, I_{OH} = MAX		2.4	3.4		2.4	3.1		V
V_{OL}	Low-level output voltage	V_{CC} = MIN, V_{IH} = 2 V, V_{IL} = V_{IL} max	I_{OL} = 4 mA		0.25	0.4		0.25	0.4	V
			I_{OL} = 8 mA					0.25	0.5	
I_{OZ}	Off-State (high-impedance state) output current	V_{CC} = MAX, V_{IH} = 2 V	V_O = 2.7 V			20			20	μA
			V_O = 0.4 V			−20			−20	
I_I	Input current at maximum input voltage	V_{CC} = MAX, V_I = 7 V				0.1			0.1	mA
I_{IH}	High-level input current	V_{CC} = MAX, V_I = 2.7 V				20			20	μA
I_{IL}	Low-level input current	V_{CC} = MAX, V_I = 0.4 V				−0.4			−0.4	mA
I_{OS}	Short-circuit output current§	V_{CC} = MAX		−30		−130	−30		−130	mA
I_{CC}	Supply current	V_{CC} = MAX, See Note 2	Condition A		7	12		7	12	mA
			Condition B		8.5	14		8.5	14	

†For conditions shown as MIN or MAX, use the appropriate value specified under recommended operating conditions.

‡All typical values are at V_{CC} = 5 V, T_A = 25°C.

§Not more than one output should be shorted at a time, and duration for the short-circuit should exceed one second.

NOTE 2: I_{CC} is measured with the outputs open under the following conditions:
    A. All inputs grounded.
    B. Output control at 4.5 V, all inputs grounded.

switching characteristics, V_{CC} = 5 V, T_A = 25°C

PARAMETER¶	FROM (INPUT)	TO (OUTPUT)	TEST CONDITIONS	MIN	TYP	MAX	UNIT
t_{PLH}	Data	Y			17	25	ns
t_{PHL}					13	20	
t_{PLH}	Select	Y	C_L = 15 pF, R_L = 2 kΩ, See Note 3		30	45	ns
t_{PHL}					21	32	
t_{ZH}	Output Control	Y			15	28	ns
t_{ZL}					15	23	
t_{HZ}	Output Control	Y	C_L = 5 pF, R_L = 2 kΩ, See Note 3		27	41	ns
t_{LZ}					18	27	

¶ t_{PLH} ≡ Propagation delay time, low-to-high-level output
t_{PHL} ≡ Propagation delay time, high-to-low-level output
t_{ZH} ≡ Output enable time to high level
t_{ZL} ≡ Output enable time to low level
t_{HZ} ≡ Output disable time from high level
t_{LZ} ≡ Output disable time from low level

NOTE 3: Load circuit and waveforms are shown on page 3-11.

TEXAS INSTRUMENTS
INCORPORATED
POST OFFICE BOX 5012 • DALLAS, TEXAS 75222

7

schematic (each selector/multiplexer, and the common select section)

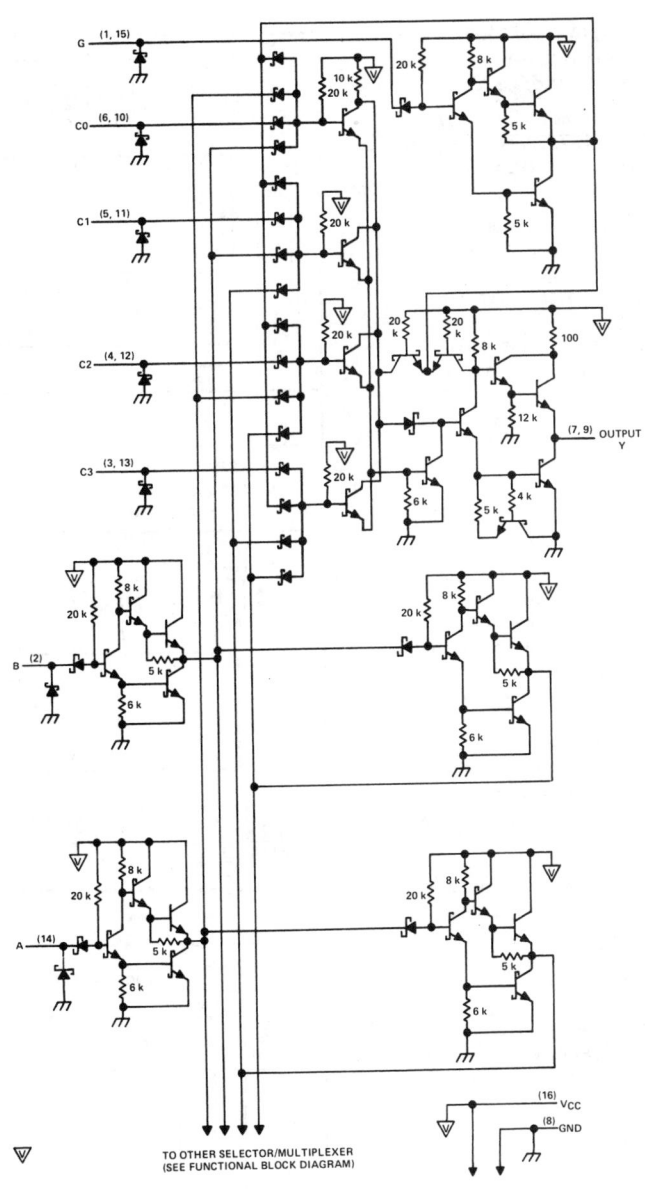

TO OTHER SELECTOR/MULTIPLEXER
(SEE FUNCTIONAL BLOCK DIAGRAM)

▽ . . . V$_{CC}$ bus

Resistor values shown are nominal and in ohms.

PRINTED IN U.S.A.

TTL
MSI

TYPES SN54LS257A, SN54LS258A, SN54S257, SN54S258,
SN74LS257A, SN74LS258A, SN74S257, SN74S258
QUADRUPLE 2-LINE-TO-1-LINE DATA SELECTORS/MULTIPLEXERS
BULLETIN NO. DL-S 7711734, OCTOBER 1976—REVISED AUGUST 1977

- Three-State Outputs Interface Directly with System Bus

- 'LS257A and 'LS258A Offer Three Times the Sink-Current Capability of the Original 'LS257 and 'LS258

- Same Pin Assignments as SN54LS157, SN74LS157, SN54S157, SN74S157, and SN54LS158, SN74LS158, SN54S158, SN74S158

- Provides Bus Interface from Multiple Sources in High-Performance Systems

	AVERAGE PROPAGATION DELAY FROM DATA INPUT	TYPICAL POWER DISSIPATION$^\diamond$
'LS257A	12 ns	60 mW
'LS258A	12 ns	60 mW
'S257	4.8 ns	320 mW
'S258	4 ns	280 mW

$^\diamond$Off state (worst case)

description

These Schottky-clamped high-performance multiplexers feature three-state outputs that can interface directly with and drive data lines of bus-organized systems. With all but one of the common outputs disabled (at a high-impedance state) the low impedance of the single enabled output will drive the bus line to a high or low logic level. To minimize the possibility that two outputs will attempt to take a common bus to opposite logic levels, the output-enable circuitry is designed such that the output disable times are shorter than the output enable times.

This three-state output feature means that n-bit (paralleled) data selectors with up to 258 sources can be implemented for data buses. It also permits the use of standard TTL registers for data retention throughout the system.

Series 54LS and 54S are characterized for operation over the full military temperature range of −55°C to 125°C; Series 74LS and 74S are characterized for operation from 0°C to 70°C.

SN54LS257A, SN54S257 . . . J OR W PACKAGE
SN74LS257A, SN74S257 . . . J OR N PACKAGE
(TOP VIEW)

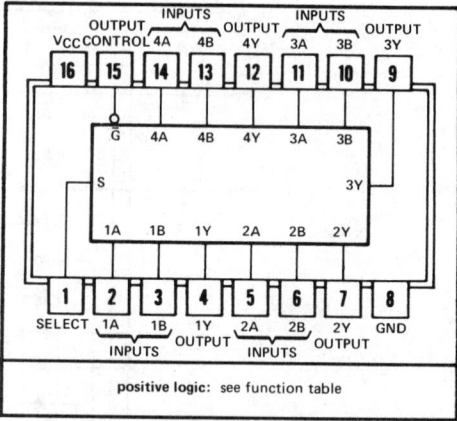

positive logic: see function table

SN54LS258A, SN54S258 . . . J OR W PACKAGE
SN74LS258A, SN74S258 . . . J OR N PACKAGE
(TOP VIEW)

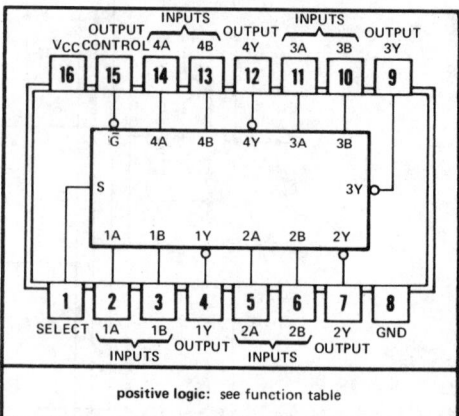

positive logic: see function table

FUNCTION TABLE

INPUTS				OUTPUT Y	
OUTPUT CONTROL	SELECT	A	B	'LS257A 'S257	'LS258A 'S258
H	X	X	X	Z	Z
L	L	L	X	L	H
L	L	H	X	H	L
L	H	X	L	L	H
L	H	X	H	H	L

H = high level, L = low level, X = irrelevant, Z = high impedance (off)

7

TEXAS INSTRUMENTS
INCORPORATED
POST OFFICE BOX 5012 • DALLAS, TEXAS 75222

functional block diagrams

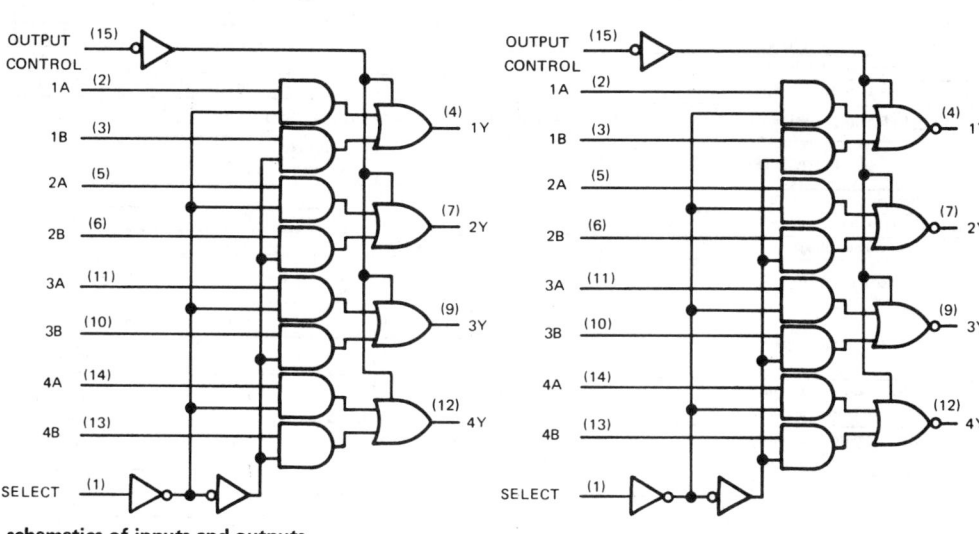

'LS257A, 'S257   'LS258A, 'S258

schematics of inputs and outputs

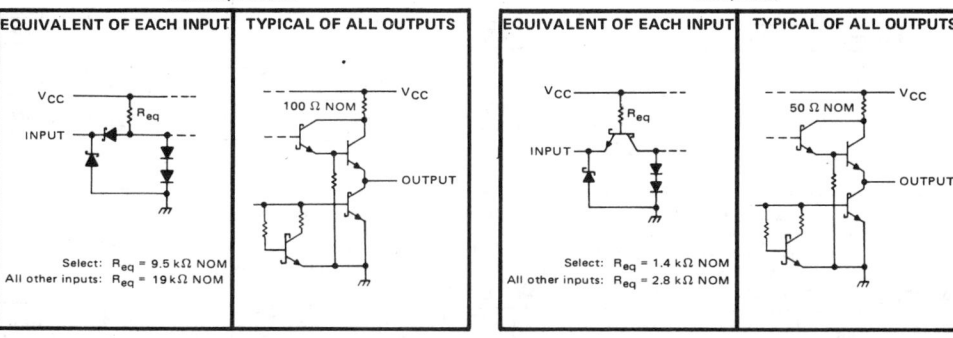

'LS257A, 'LS258A   'S257, 'S258

absolute maximum ratings over operating free-air temperature range (unless otherwise noted)

Supply voltage, V_{CC} (see Note 1) . . . . 7 V
Input voltage: 'LS257A, 'LS258A Circuits . . . . 7 V
             'S257, 'S258 Circuits . . . . 5.5 V
Off-state output voltage . . . . 5.5 V
Operating free-air temperature range: SN54LS', SN54S' Circuits . . . . $-55°C$ to $125°C$
                      SN74LS', SN74S' Circuits . . . . $0°C$ to $70°C$
Storage temperature range . . . . $-65°C$ to $150°C$

NOTE 1: Voltage values are with respect to network ground terminal.

TEXAS INSTRUMENTS
INCORPORATED
POST OFFICE BOX 5012 • DALLAS, TEXAS 75222

recommended operating conditions

	SN54LS' MIN	SN54LS' NOM	SN54LS' MAX	SN74LS' MIN	SN74LS' NOM	SN74LS' MAX	UNIT
Supply voltage, V_{CC}	4.5	5	5.5	4.75	5	5.25	V
High-level output current, I_{OH}			−1			−2.6	mA
Low-level output current, I_{OL}			12			24	mA
Operating free-air temperature, T_A	−55		125	0		70	°C

electrical characteristics over recommended operating free-air temperature range (unless otherwise noted)

PARAMETER		TEST CONDITIONS[†]		SN54LS' MIN	SN54LS' TYP[‡]	SN54LS' MAX	SN74LS' MIN	SN74LS' TYP[‡]	SN74LS' MAX	UNIT
V_{IH}	High-level input voltage			2			2			V
V_{IL}	Low-level input voltage					0.7			0.8	V
V_{IK}	Input clamp voltage	V_{CC} = MIN,	I_I = −18 mA			−1.5			−1.5	V
V_{OH}	High-level output voltage	V_{CC} = MIN, V_{IH} = 2 V, V_{IL} = V_{IL} max, I_{OH} = MAX		2.4	3.4		2.4	3.1		V
V_{OL}	Low-level output voltage	V_{CC} = MIN, V_{IH} = 2 V, V_{IL} = V_{IL} max	I_{OL} =12 mA		0.25	0.4		0.25	0.4	V
			I_{OL} = 24 mA					0.35	0.5	
I_{OZH}	Off-state output current, high-level voltage applied	V_{CC} = MAX, V_{IH} = 2 V, V_O = 2.7 V				20			20	µA
I_{OZL}	Off-state output current, low-level voltage applied	V_{CC} = MAX, V_{IH} = 2 V, V_O = 0.4 V				−20			−20	µA
I_I	Input current at	S input	V_{CC} = MAX, V_I = 7 V			0.2			0.2	mA
	maximum input voltage	Any other				0.1			0.1	
I_{IH}	High-level	S input	V_{CC} = MAX, V_I = 2.7 V			40			40	µA
	input current	Any other				20			20	
I_{IL}	Low-level	S input	V_{CC} = MAX, V_I = 0.4 V			−0.8			−0.8	mA
	input current	Any other				−0.4			−0.4	
I_{OS}	Short-circuit output current[§]		V_{CC} = MAX	−30		−130	−30		−130	mA
I_{CC}	Supply current	All outputs high	V_{CC} = MAX, See Note 2	'LS257A	6.2	10		6.2	10	mA
		All outputs low			10	16		10	16	
		All outputs off			12	19		12	19	
		All outputs high		'LS258A	4.	7		4.5	7	
		All outputs low			8.8	14		8.8	14	
		All outputs off			12	19		12	19	

[†]For conditions shown as MIN or MAX, use the appropriate value specified under recommended operating conditions.
[‡]All typical values are at V_{CC} = 5 V, T_A = 25°C.
[§]Not more than one output should be shorted at a time and duration of the short-circuit should not exceed one second.
NOTE 2: I_{CC} is measured with all outputs open and all possible inputs grounded while achieving the stated output conditions.

switching characteristics, V_{CC} = 5 V, T_A = 25°C, R_L = 667 Ω

PARAMETER[¶]	FROM (INPUT)	TO (OUTPUT)	TEST CONDITIONS	'LS257A MIN	'LS257A TYP	'LS257A MAX	'LS258A MIN	'LS258A TYP	'LS258A MAX	UNIT
t_{PLH}	Data	Any			12	18		12	18	ns
t_{PHL}					12	18		12	18	
t_{PLH}	Select	Any	C_L = 45 pF, See Note 3		14	21		14	21	ns
t_{PHL}					14	21		14	21	
t_{PZH}	Output Control	Any			20	30		20	30	ns
t_{PZL}					20	30		20	30	
t_{PHZ}	Output Control	Any	C_L = 5 pF, See Note 3		18	30		18	30	ns
t_{PLZ}					16	25		16	25	

[¶]t_{PLH} ≡ propagation delay time, low-to-high-level output
t_{PHL} ≡ propagation delay time, high-to-low-level output
t_{PZH} ≡ output enable time to high level
NOTE 3: Load circuit and waveforms are shown on page 3-11.

t_{PZL} ≡ output enable time to low level
t_{PHZ} ≡ output disable time from high level
t_{PLZ} ≡ output disable time from low level

DESIGN GOAL

TEXAS INSTRUMENTS
INCORPORATED
POST OFFICE BOX 5012 • DALLAS, TEXAS 75222

recommended operating conditions

	SN54S'			SN74S'			UNIT
	MIN	NOM	MAX	MIN	NOM	MAX	
Supply voltage, V_{CC}	4.5	5	5.5	4.75	5	5.25	V
High-level output current, I_{OH}			−2			−6.5	mA
Low-level output current, I_{OL}			20			20	mA
Operating free-air temperature, T_A	−55		125	0		70	°C

electrical characteristics over recommended operating free-air temperature range (unless otherwise noted)

PARAMETER		TEST CONDITIONS†		'S257			'S258			UNIT
				MIN	TYP‡	MAX	MIN	TYP‡	MAX	
V_{IH}	High-level input voltage			2			2			V
V_{IL}	Low-level input voltage					0.8			0.8	V
V_{IK}	Input clamp voltage	V_{CC} = MIN, I_I = −18 mA				−1.2			−1.2	V
V_{OH}	High-level output voltage	V_{CC} = MIN, V_{IH} = 2 V, V_{IL} = 0.8 V, I_{OH} = −1 mA	SN74S'	2.7			2.7			V
		V_{CC} = MIN, V_{IH} = 2 V, V_{IL} = 0.8 V, I_{OH} = MAX	SN54S'	2.4	3.4		2.4	3.4		
			SN74S'	2.4	3.2		2.4	3.2		
V_{OL}	Low-level output voltage	V_{CC} = MIN, V_{IH} = 2 V, V_{IL} = 0.8 V, I_{OL} = 20 mA				0.5			0.5	V
I_{OZH}	Off-state output current, high-level voltage applied	V_{CC} = MAX, V_{IH} = 2 V, V_O = 2.4 V				0.5			0.5	μA
I_{OZL}	Off-state output current, low-level voltage applied	V_{CC} = MAX, V_{IH} = 2 V, V_O = 0.5 V				−50			−50	μA
I_I	Input current at maximum input voltage	V_{CC} = MAX, V_I = 5.5 V				1			1	mA
I_{IH}	High-level input current	S input	V_{CC} = MAX, V_I = 2.7 V			100			100	μA
		Any other				50			50	
I_{IL}	Low-level input current	S input	V_{CC} = MAX, V_I = 0.5 V			−4			−4	mA
		Any other				−2			−2	
I_{OS}	Short-circuit output current§	V_{CC} = MAX		−40		−100	−40		−100	mA
I_{CC}	Supply current	All outputs high	V_{CC} = MAX, See Note 2		44	68		36	56	mA
		All outputs low			60	93		52	81	
		All outputs off			64	99		56	87	

†For conditions shown as MIN or MAX, use the appropriate value specified under recommended operating conditions.
‡All typical values are at V_{CC} = 5 V, T_A = 25°C.
§Not more than one output should be shorted at a time and duration of the short-circuit should not exceed one second.
NOTE 2: I_{CC} is measured with all outputs open and all possible inputs grounded while achieving the stated output conditions.

switching characteristics, V_{CC} = 5 V, T_A = 25°C, R_L = 280 Ω

PARAMETER¶	FROM (INPUT)	TO (OUTPUT)	TEST CONDITIONS	'S257			'S258			UNIT
				MIN	TYP	MAX	MIN	TYP	MAX	
t_{PLH}	Data	Any	C_L = 15 pF, See Note 4		5	7.5		4	6	ns
t_{PHL}					4.5	6.5		4	6	
t_{PLH}	Select	Any			8.5	15		8	12	ns
t_{PHL}					8.5	15		7.5	12	
t_{PZH}	Output Control	Any			13	19.5		13	19.5	ns
t_{PZL}					14	21		14	21	
t_{PHZ}	Output Control	Any	C_L = 5 pF, See Note 4		5.5	8.5		5.5	8.5	ns
t_{PLZ}					9	14		9	14	

¶ t_{PLH} ≡ propagation delay time, low-to-high-level output
t_{PHL} ≡ propagation delay time, high-to-low-level output
t_{PZH} ≡ output enable time to high level
NOTE 4: Load circuit and waveforms are shown on pages 3-10.

t_{PZL} ≡ output enable time to low level
t_{PHZ} ≡ output disable time from high level
t_{PLZ} ≡ output disable time from low level

TEXAS INSTRUMENTS
INCORPORATED
POST OFFICE BOX 5012 • DALLAS, TEXAS 75222

7-375

- **8-Bit Parallel-Out Storage Register Performs Serial-to-Parallel Conversion With Storage**
- **Asynchronous Parallel Clear**
- **Active High Decoder**
- **Enable/Disable Input Simplifies Expansion**
- **Direct Replacement for Fairchild 9334**
- **Expandable for N-Bit Applications**
- **Four Distinct Functional Modes**
- **Typical Propagation Delay Times:**

	'259	'LS259
Enable-to-Output . . .	12	17
Data-to-Output	12	18
Address-to-Output . .	16	20
Clear-to-Output	16	20

- **Fan-Out**
  I_{OL} (Sink Current)
  - '259 . . . . 16 mA
  - SN54LS259 . . . . 4 mA
  - SN74LS259 . . . . 8 mA

  I_{OH} (Source Current)
  - '259 . . . . −0.8 mA
  - 'LS259 . . . . −0.4 mA
- **Typical I_{CC}**
  - '259 . . . . 60 mA
  - 'LS259 . . . . 22 mA

SN54259, SN54LS259 . . . J OR W PACKAGE
SN74259, SN74LS259 . . . J OR N PACKAGE
(TOP VIEW)

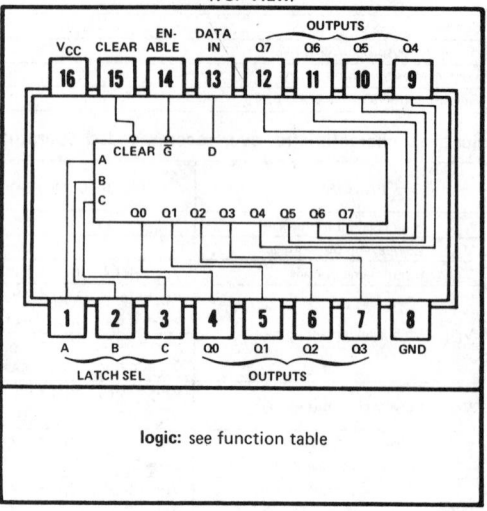

logic: see function table

description

These 8-bit addressable latches are designed for general purpose storage applications in digital systems. Specific uses include working registers, serial-holding registers, and active-high decoders or demultiplexers. They are multifunctional devices capable of storing single-line data in eight addressable latches, and being a 1-of-8 decoder or demultiplexer with active-high outputs.

Four distinct modes of operation are selectable by controlling the clear and enable inputs as enumerated in the function table. In the addressable-latch mode, data at the data-in terminal is written into the addressed latch. The addressed latch will follow the data input with all unaddressed latches remaining in their previous states. In the memory mode, all latches remain in their previous states and are unaffected by the data or address inputs. To eliminate the possibility of entering erroneous data in the latches, the enable should be held high (inactive) while the address lines are changing. In the 1-of-8 decoding or demultiplexing mode, the addressed output will follow the level of the D input with all other outputs low. In the clear mode, all outputs are low and unaffected by the address and data inputs.

FUNCTION TABLE

INPUTS		OUTPUT OF ADDRESSED LATCH	EACH OTHER OUTPUT	FUNCTION
CLEAR	$\overline{G}$			
H	L	D	Q_{i0}	Addressable Latch
H	H	Q_{i0}	Q_{i0}	Memory
L	L	D	L	8-Line Demultiplexer
L	H	L	L	Clear

LATCH SELECTION TABLE

SELECT INPUTS			LATCH ADDRESSED
C	B	A	
L	L	L	0
L	L	H	1
L	H	L	2
L	H	H	3
H	L	L	4
H	L	H	5
H	H	L	6
H	H	H	7

H ≡ high level, L ≡ low level
D ≡ the level at the data input
Q_{i0} ≡ the level of Q_i (i = 0, 1, . . . 7, as appropriate) before the indicated steady-state input conditions were established.

7

TEXAS INSTRUMENTS
INCORPORATED
POST OFFICE BOX 5012 • DALLAS, TEXAS 75222

1076

TYPES SN54259, SN54LS259, SN74259, SN74LS259 (TIM9906)
8-BIT ADDRESSABLE LATCHES

schematic of inputs and outputs

'259

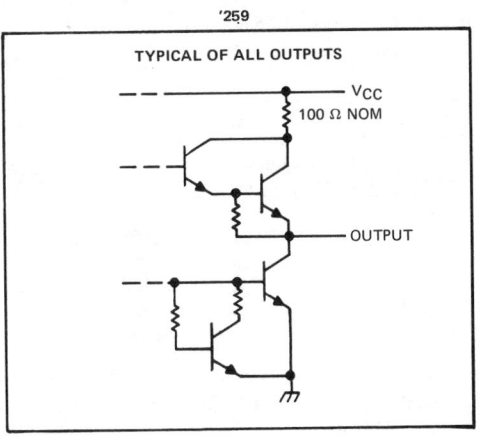

EQUIVALENT OF EACH INPUT

Latch select, data in, or clear: R_{eq} = 4 kΩ NOM
Enable: R_{eq} = 2.2 kΩ NOM

'259

TYPICAL OF ALL OUTPUTS

'LS259

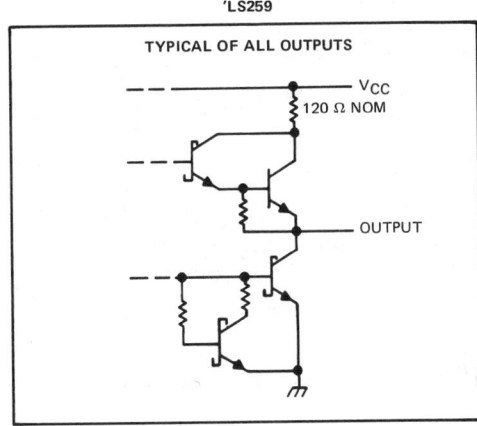

EQUIVALENT OF EACH INPUT

'LS259

TYPICAL OF ALL OUTPUTS

absolute maximum ratings over operating free-air temperature range (unless otherwise noted)

Supply voltage (see Note 1) . . . . 7 V
Input voltage: SN54259, SN74259 . . . . 5.5 V
           SN54LS259, SN74LS259 . . . . 7 V
Operating free-air temperature range: SN54259, SN54LS259 . . . . −55°C to 125°C
                  SN74259, SN74LS259 . . . . 0°C to 70°C
Storage temperature range . . . . −65°C to 150°C

NOTE 1: Voltage values are with respect to network ground terminal.

TEXAS INSTRUMENTS
INCORPORATED
POST OFFICE BOX 5012 • DALLAS, TEXAS 75222

7

recommended operating conditions

		SN54259			SN74259			UNIT
		MIN	NOM	MAX	MIN	NOM	MAX	
Supply voltage, V_{CC}		4.5	5	5.5	4.75	5	5.25	V
High-level output current, I_{OH}				−800			−800	μA
Low-level output current, I_{OL}				16			16	mA
Width of clear or enable pulse, t_w		15			15			ns
Setup time, t_{su}	Data	15↑			15↑			ns
	Address	5↑			5↑			
Hold time, t_h	Data	0↑			0↑			ns
	Address	20↑			20↑			
Operating free-air temperature, T_A		−55		125	0		70	°C

↑The arrow indicates that the rising edge of the enable pulse is used for reference.

electrical characteristics over recommended operating free-air temperature range (unless otherwise noted)

PARAMETER		TEST CONDITIONS[†]	SN54259			SN74259			UNIT
			MIN	TYP‡	MAX	MIN	TYP‡	MAX	
V_{IH}	High-level input voltage		2			2			V
V_{IL}	Low-level input voltage				0.8			0.8	V
V_{IK}	Input clamp voltage	V_{CC} = MIN, I_I = 12 mA			−1.5			−1.5	V
V_{OH}	High-level output voltage	V_{CC} = MIN, V_{IH} = 2 V, V_{IL} = 0.8 V, I_{OH} = −800 μA	2.4	3.4		2.4	3.4		V
V_{OL}	Low-level output voltage	V_{CC} = MIN, V_{IH} = 2 V, V_{IL} = 0.8 V, I_{OL} = 16 mA		0.2	0.4		0.2	0.4	V
I_I	Input current at maximum input voltage	V_{CC} = MAX, V_I = 5.5 V			1			1	mA
I_{IH}	High-level input current — Enable	V_{CC} = MAX, V_I = 2.4 V			80			80	μA
	Other inputs				40			40	
I_{IL}	Low-level input current — Enable	V_{CC} = MAX, V_I = 0.4 V			−3.2			−3.2	mA
	Other inputs				−1.6			−1.6	
I_{OS}	Short-circuit output current§	V_{CC} = MAX	−18		−57	−18		−57	mA
I_{CC}	Supply current	V_{CC} = MAX, See Note 2		60	90		60	90	mA

†For conditions shown as MIN or MAX, use the appropriate value specified under recommended operating conditions.
‡All typical values are at V_{CC} = 5 V, T_A = 25°C.
§Not more than one output should be shorted at a time.
NOTE 2: I_{CC} is measured with the inputs grounded and the outputs open.

switching characteristics, V_{CC} = 5 V, T_A = 25°C

PARAMETER	FROM (INPUT)	TO (OUTPUT)	TEST CONDITIONS	MIN	TYP	MAX	UNIT
t_{PHL}	Clear	Any Q			16	25	ns
t_{PLH}	Data	Any Q			14	24	ns
t_{PHL}			C_L = 15 pF, R_L = 400 Ω, See Note 3		11	20	
t_{PLH}	Address	Any Q			15	28	ns
t_{PHL}					17	28	
t_{PLH}	Enable	Any Q			12	20	ns
t_{PHL}					11	20	

t_{PLH} ≡ propagation delay time, low-to-high-level output
t_{PHL} ≡ propagation delay time, high-to-low-level output
NOTE 3: Load circuit is shown on page 3-10.

TEXAS INSTRUMENTS
INCORPORATED
POST OFFICE BOX 5012 • DALLAS, TEXAS 75222

7

10

recommended operating conditions

		SN54LS259 MIN	NOM	MAX	SN74LS259 MIN	NOM	MAX	UNIT
Supply voltage, V_{CC}		4.5	5	5.5	4.75	5	5.25	V
High-level output current, I_{OH}				−400			−400	μA
Low-level output current, I_{OL}				4			8	mA
Width of clear or enable pulse, t_W		15			15			ns
Setup time, t_{su}	Data	15†			15†			ns
	Address	15†			15†			
Hold time, t_h	Data	0†			0†			ns
	Address	0†			0†			
Operating free-air temperature, T_A		−55		125	0		70	°C

†The arrow indicates that the rising edge of the enable pulse is used for reference.

electrical characteristics over recommended operating free-air temperature range (unless otherwise noted)

PARAMETER		TEST CONDITIONS†	SN54LS259 MIN	TYP‡	MAX	SN74LS259 MIN	TYP‡	MAX	UNIT
V_{IH}	High level input voltage		2			2			V
V_{IL}	Low level input voltage				0.7			0.8	V
V_{IK}	Input clamp voltage	V_{CC} = MIN, I_I = −18 mA			−1.5			−1.5	V
V_{OH}	High-level output voltage	V_{CC} = MIN, V_{IH} = 2 V V_{IL} = V_{IL} max, I_{OH} = −0.4 mA	2.5	3.4		2.7	3.4		V
V_{OL}	Low-level output voltage	V_{CC} = MIN, V_{IH} = 2 V, V_{IL} = V_{IL} max, I_{OL} = 4 mA		0.25	0.4		0.25	0.4	V
		I_{OL} = 8 mA					0.35	0.5	
I_I	Input current at maximum input voltage	V_{CC} = MAX, V_I = 7 V			0.1			0.1	mA
I_{IH}	High-level input current	V_{CC} = MAX, V_I = 2.7 V			20			20	μA
I_{IL}	Low-level input current	V_{CC} = MAX, V_I = 0.4 V			−0.4			−0.4	mA
I_{OS}	Short-circuit output current§	V_{CC} = MAX	−20		−100	−20		−100	mA
I_{CC}	Supply current	V_{CC} = MAX, See Note 2		22	36		22	36	mA

†For conditions shown as MIN or MAX, use the appropriate value specified under recommended operating conditions.
‡All typical values are at V_{CC} = 5 V, T_A = 25°C.
§Not more than one output should be shorted at a time, and duration short-circuit should not exceed one second.
NOTE 2: I_{CC} is measured with the inputs grounded and the outputs open.

switching characteristics, V_{CC} = 5 V, T_A = 25°C

PARAMETER	FROM (INPUT)	TO (OUTPUT)	TEST CONDITIONS	MIN	TYP	MAX	UNIT
t_{PHL}	Clear	Any Q			17	27	ns
t_{PLH}	Data	Any Q			20	32	ns
t_{PHL}			C_L = 15 pF,		13	21	
t_{PLH}	Address	Any Q	R_L = 2 kΩ,		24	38	ns
t_{PHL}			See Note 3		18	29	
t_{PLH}	Enable	Any Q			22	35	ns
t_{PHL}					15	24	

t_{PLH} ≡ propagation delay time, low-to-high-level output
t_{PHL} ≡ propagation delay time, high-to-low-level output
NOTE 3: Load circuit is shown on page 3-11.

7

- Fast Multiplication . . . 5-Bit Product in 26 ns Typ
- Power Dissipation . . . 110 mW Typical
- Latch Outputs for Synchronous Operation
- Expandable for m-Bit-by-n-Bit Applications
- Fully Compatible with Most TTL and Other Saturated Low-Level Logic Families
- Diode-Clamped Inputs Simplify System Design

description

These low-power Schottky circuits are designed to be used in parallel multiplication applications. They perform binary multiplication in two's-complement form, two bits at a time.

The M inputs are for the multiplier bits and the B inputs are for the multiplicand. The Q outputs represent the partial product as a recoded base-4 number. This recoding effectively reduces the Wallace-tree hardware requirements by a factor of two.

The outputs represent partial products in one's-complement form generated as a result of multiplication. A simple rounding scheme using two additional gates is needed for each partial product to generate two's complement.

The leading (most-significant) bit of the product is inverted for ease in extending the sign to square (left justify) the partial-product bits.

The SN54LS261 is characterized for operation over the full military temperature range of -55°C to 125°C; the SN74LS261 for operation from 0°C to 70°C.

SN54LS261 . . . J OR W PACKAGE
SN74LS261 . . . J OR N PACKAGE
(TOP VIEW)

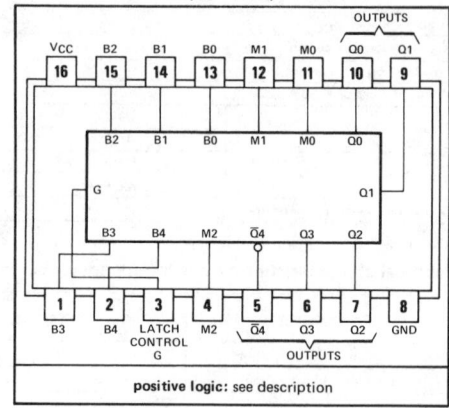

positive logic: see description

FUNCTION TABLE

INPUTS				OUTPUTS				
LATCH CONTROL G	MULTIPLIER			$\overline{Q4}$	Q3	Q2	Q1	Q0
	M2	M1	M0					
L	X	X	X	$\overline{Q4}_0$	$Q3_0$	$Q2_0$	$Q1_0$	$Q0_0$
H	L	L	L	H	L	L	L	L
H	L	L	H	$\overline{B4}$	B4	B3	B2	B1
H	L	H	L	$\overline{B4}$	B4	B3	B2	B1
H	L	H	H	$\overline{B4}$	B3	B2	B1	B0
H	H	L	L	B4	$\overline{B3}$	$\overline{B2}$	$\overline{B1}$	$\overline{B0}$
H	H	L	H	B4	$\overline{B4}$	$\overline{B3}$	$\overline{B2}$	$\overline{B1}$
H	H	H	L	B4	$\overline{B4}$	$\overline{B3}$	$\overline{B2}$	$\overline{|B1}$
H	H	H	H	H	L	L	L	L

H = high level, L = low level, X = irrelevant

$\overline{Q4}_0 \ldots Q0_0$ = The logic level of the same output before the high-to-low transition of G.

B4 . . . B0 = The logic level of the indicated multiplicand (B) input.

schematics of inputs and outputs

EQUIVALENT OF EACH INPUT	TYPICAL OF Q0, Q1, Q2, Q3 OUTPUTS	TYPICAL OF $\overline{Q4}$ OUTPUT
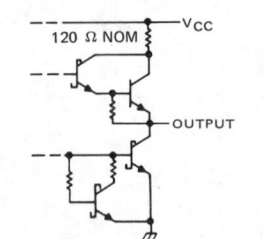 G: R_{eq} = 17 kΩ NOM; B or M2: R_{eq} = 20 kΩ NOM; M0 or MI: R_{eq} = 10 kΩ NOM	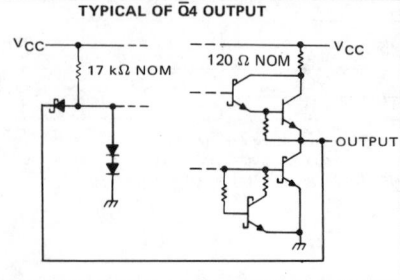	

TEXAS INSTRUMENTS
INCORPORATED
POST OFFICE BOX 5012 • DALLAS, TEXAS 75222

107

functional block diagram

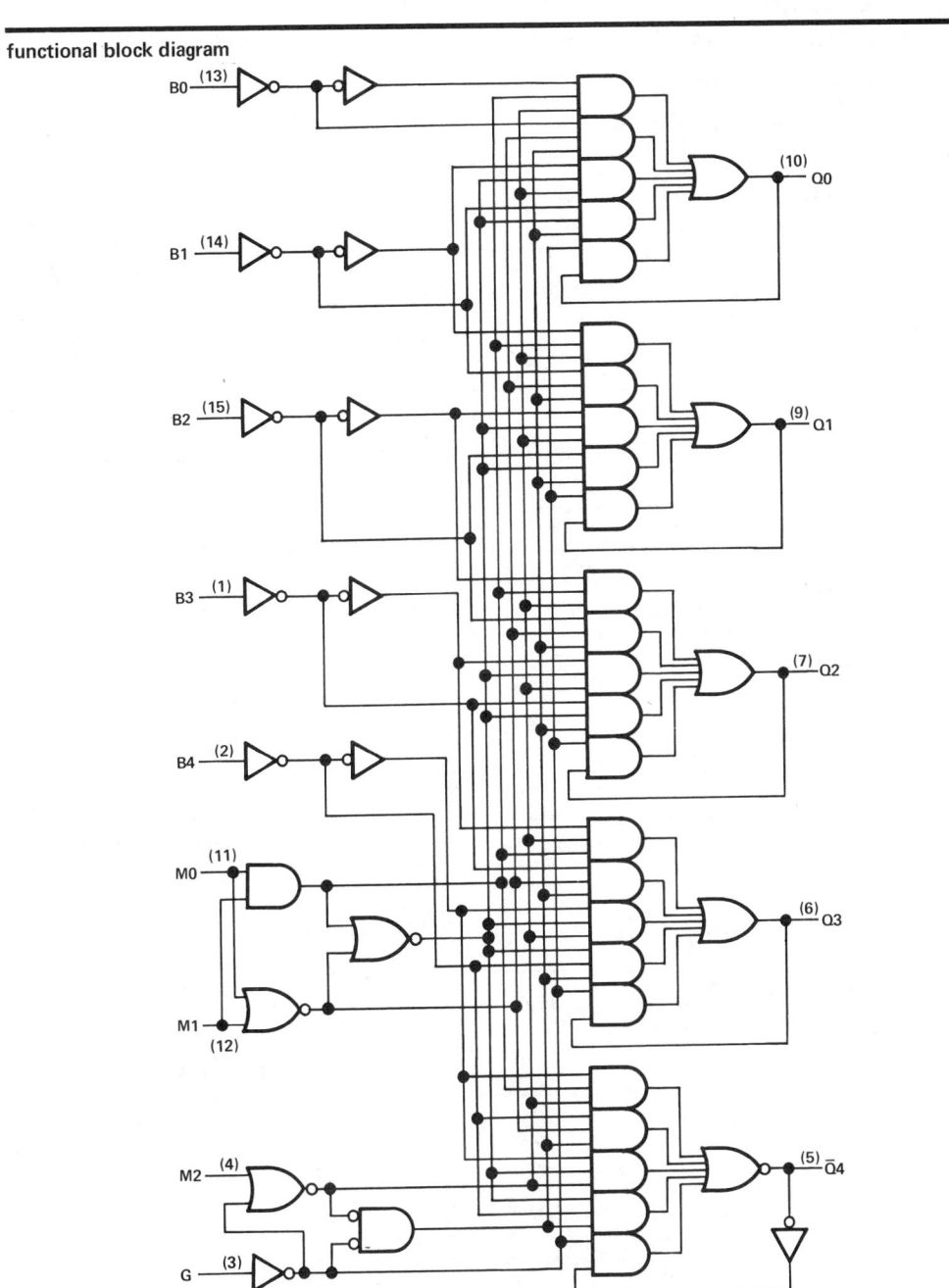

absolute maximum ratings over operating free-air temperature range (unless otherwise noted)

Supply voltage, V_{CC} (see Note 1) . . . . 7 V
Input voltage . . . . 7 V
Operating free-air temperature range: SN54LS261 . . . . -55°C to 125°C
                                       SN74LS261 . . . . 0°C to 70°C
Storage temperature range . . . . -65°C to 150°C

NOTE 1: Voltage values are with respect to network ground terminal.

recommended operating conditions

	SN54LS261			SN74LS261			UNIT
	MIN	NOM	MAX	MIN	NOM	MAX	
Supply voltage, V_{CC}	4.5	5	5.5	4.75	5	5.25	V
High-level output current, I_{OH}			-400			-400	μA
Low-level output current, I_{OL}			4			8	mA
Width of enable pulse, t_w	25			25			ns
Setup time, t_{su}	Any M input	17↓			17↓			ns
	Any B input	15↓			15↓			
Hold time, t_h	Any M input	0↓			0↓			ns
	Any B input	0↓			0↓			
Operating free-air temperature, T_A	-55		125	0		70	$^\circ$C

↓The arrow indicates that the falling edge of the enable pulse is used for reference.

electrical characteristics over recommended operating free-air temperature range (unless otherwise noted)

PARAMETER		TEST CONDITIONS†		SN54LS261			SN74LS261			UNIT
				MIN	TYP‡	MAX	MIN	TYP‡	MAX	
V_{IH}	High-level input voltage			2			2			V
V_{IL}	Low-level input voltage					0.7			0.8	V
V_{IK}	Input clamp voltage	V_{CC} = MIN,	$I_I = -18$ mA			-1.5			-1.5	V
V_{OH}	High-level output voltage	V_{CC} = MIN, V_{IH} = 2 V, $V_{IL} = V_{IL}$ max, $I_{OH} = -400\,\mu$A		2.5	3.4		2.7	3.4		V
V_{OL}	Low-level output voltage	V_{CC} = MIN, V_{IH} = 2 V, $V_{IL} = V_{IL}$ max	I_{OL} = 4 mA		0.25	0.4		0.25	0.4	V
			I_{OL} = 8 mA					0.35	0.5	
I_I	Input current at maximum input voltage	V_{CC} = MAX, V_I = 7 V	MO or MI			0.2			0.2	mA
			All others			0.1			0.1	
I_{IH}	High-level input current	V_{CC} = MAX, V_I = 2.7 V	MO or MI			40			40	μA
			All others			20			20	
I_{IL}	Low-level input current	V_{CC} = MAX, V_I = 0.4 V	MO or MI			-0.8			-0.8	mA
			All others			-0.4			-0.4	
I_{OS}	Short-circuit output current §	V_{CC} = MAX		-20		-100	-20		-100	mA
I_{CC}	Supply current	V_{CC} = MAX, All inputs at 0 V, Outputs open		22		38	20		40	mA

‡All typical values are at V_{CC} = 5 V, T_A = 25°C.
§Not more than one output should be shorted at a time and duration of the output short-circuit should not exceed one second.

switching characteristics, V_{CC} = 5 V, T_A = 25°C

PARAMETER¶	FROM (INPUT)	TO (OUTPUT)	TEST CONDITIONS	MIN	TYP	MAX	UNIT
t_{PLH}	Enable G	Any Q			22	35	ns
t_{PHL}			C_L = 15 pF, R_L = 2 kΩ, See Note 2		20	30	ns
t_{PLH}	Any M input	Any Q			25	40	ns
t_{PHL}					22	35	ns
t_{PLH}	Any B input	Any Q			27	42	ns
t_{PHL}					24	37	ns

¶t_{PLH} ≡ propagation delay time, low-to-high-level output; t_{PHL} = propagation delay time, high-to-low-level output.

NOTE 2: Load circuit and voltage waveforms are shown on page 3-11.

7

TEXAS INSTRUMENTS
INCORPORATED
POST OFFICE BOX 5012 • DALLAS, TEXAS 75222

TYPICAL APPLICATION DATA

Multiplication of the numbers 26 (multiplicand) by 29 (multiplier) in decimal, binary, and 2-bit-at-a-time-binary is shown here:

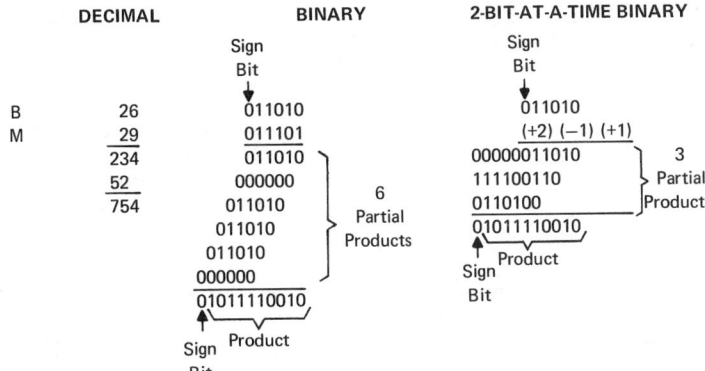

Two points should be noted in the two-bit-at-a-time-binary example above. First, in positioning the partial products beneath each other for final addition, each partial product is shifted two places to the left of the partial products above it instead of one place as is done in regular multiplication. Second, the msb of the partial product (the sign bit) is extended to the sign-bit column of the final answer.

A substantial reduction of multiplication time, cost, and power is obtained by implementing a parallel partial-product-generation scheme using a 2-bit-at-a-time algorithm, followed by a Wallace Tree summation.

Partial-product-generation rules of the algorithm are:

1. Examine two bits of multiplier M plus the next lower bit. For the first partial product (PP1) the next lower bit is zero.

$$2^{15} \quad 2^{14} \quad 2^{13} \quad 2^{12} \quad 2^{11} \quad 2^{10} \quad 2^9 \quad 2^8 \quad 2^7 \quad 2^6 \quad 2^5 \quad 2^4 \quad 2^3 \quad 2^2 \quad 2^1 \quad 2^0 \quad 0$$

PP8   PP7   PP6   PP5   PP4   PP3   PP2   PP1

TEXAS INSTRUMENTS
INCORPORATED
POST OFFICE BOX 5012 • DALLAS, TEXAS 75222

TYPICAL APPLICATION DATA

2. Generate partial product (PPi) as shown in the following table:

MULTIPLIER BITS FROM STEP 1			OPERATOR SYMBOL	TO OBTAIN PARTIAL PRODUCT
2^{2i-1}	2^{2i-2}	2^{2i-3}		
0	0	0	0	Replace multiplicand by zero
0	0	1	+1 B	Copy multiplicand
0	1	0	+1 B	Copy multiplicand
0	1	1	+2 B	Shift multiplicand left one bit
1	0	0	−2 B	Shift two's complement of multiplicand left one bit
1	0	1	−1 B	Replace multiplicand by two's complement
1	1	0	−1 B	Replace multiplicand by two's complement
1	1	1	0	Replace multiplicand by zero

3. Weight the partial products by indexing each two places left relative to the next-less-significant product.

4. Extend the most-significant bit of the partial product to the sign-bit place value of the final product.

EXAMPLE OF ALGORITHM

M = 29 = 011101   Operator Symbol   B = 26 = 011010

	Operator Symbol	
010	+1 B	00000011010
110	−1 B	111100110
011	+2 B	0110100

The summation of these partial products was shown in the 2-bit-at-a-time binary multiplication example above.

The 'LS261 generates partial products according to this algorithm with two exceptions:

1. The one's complement is generated for the cases requiring the two's complement. The two's complement can be obtained by adding one to the one's complement; this rounding can be done by using one NAND gate and one AND gate as shown in Figure B.

2. The most-significant bit is complemented to reduce the hardware required to extend the sign bit. This extension can be accomplished by adding a hard-wired logic 1 in bit position 2^{2i+15} of each partial product and also in bit position 2^{16} of the first partial product (PP1).

7

TEXAS INSTRUMENTS
INCORPORATED
POST OFFICE BOX 5012 • DALLAS, TEXAS 75222

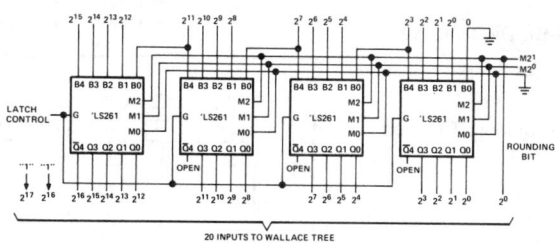

FIGURE A—FIRST PARTIAL PRODUCT, PP1

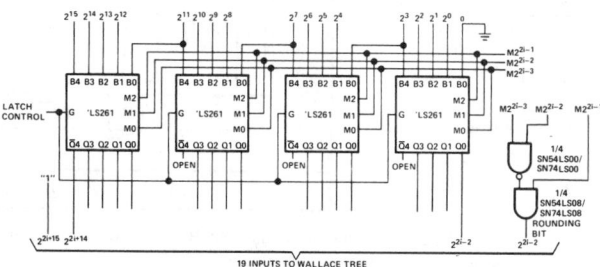

FIGURE B—OTHER PARTIAL PRODUCTS, PPi

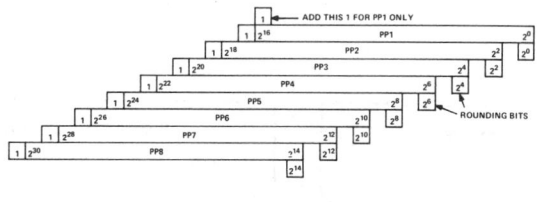

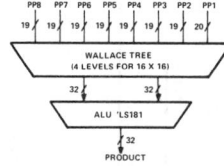

FIGURE C—MANIPULATION OF PARTIAL PRODUCTS FOR ENTRY INTO WALLACE TREE

In general, the 4 x 2 bit 'LS261 can be expanded for use in 4m x 2n bit multipliers. Partial-product generation uses m x n 'LS261s m x n ÷ 16 'LS00s, and m x n ÷ 16 'LS08s. The size of the Wallace tree and ALU requirements vary depending on the size of the problem. The count for the 16 x 16 bit multiplier is:

32	SN54LS261/SN74LS261
2	SN54LS00/SN74LS00
2	SN54LS08/SN74LS08
56	SN54LS183/SN74LS183
7	SN54LS181/SN74LS181
2	SN54S182/SN74S182

TEXAS INSTRUMENTS
INCORPORATED

POST OFFICE BOX 5012 • DALLAS, TEXAS 75222

TTL

MSI

TYPES SN54LS266, SN74LS266
QUADRUPLE 2-INPUT EXCLUSIVE-NOR GATES
WITH OPEN-COLLECTOR OUTPUTS
BULLETIN NO. DL-S 7611843, DECEMBER 1972—REVISED OCTOBER 1976

- Can Be Used as a 4-Bit Digital Comparator
- Input Clamping Diodes Simplify System Design
- Fully Compatible with Most TTL and DTL Circuits

FUNCTION TABLE

INPUTS		OUTPUT
A	B	Y
L	L	H
L	H	L
H	L	L
H	H	H

H = high level, L = low level

SN54LS266 . . . J OR W PACKAGE
SN74LS266 . . . J OR N PACKAGE
(TOP VIEW)

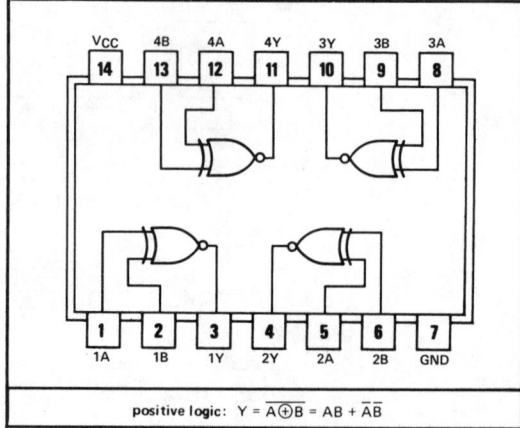

positive logic: $Y = \overline{A \oplus B} = AB + \overline{A}\,\overline{B}$

description

The 'LS266 is comprised of four independent 2-input exclusive-NOR gates with open-collector outputs. The open-collector outputs permit tying outputs together for multiple-bit comparisons.

schematics of inputs and outputs

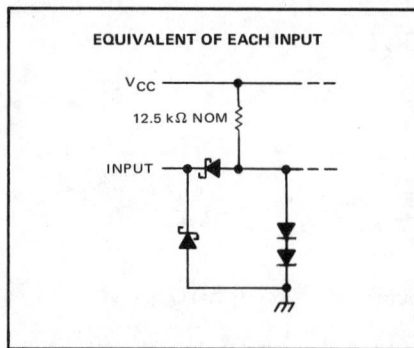

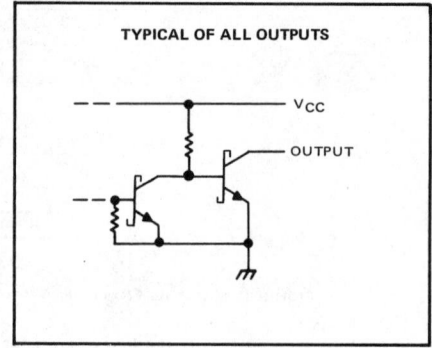

TEXAS INSTRUMENTS
INCORPORATED
POST OFFICE BOX 5012 • DALLAS, TEXAS 75222

absolute maximum ratings over operating free-air temperature range (unless otherwise noted)

Supply voltage, V_{CC} (see Note 1)	7 V
Input voltage	7 V
Operating free-air temperature range: SN54LS266	-55°C to 125°C
SN74LS266	0°C to 70°C
Storage temperature range	-65°C to 150°C

NOTE 1: Voltage values are with respect to network ground terminal.

recommended operating conditions

	SN54LS266			SN74LS266			UNIT
	MIN	NOM	MAX	MIN	NOM	MAX	
Supply voltage, V_{CC}	4.5	5	5.5	4.75	5	5.25	V
High-level output voltage, V_{OH}			5.5			5.5	V
Low-level output current, I_{OL}			4			8	mA
Operating free-air temperature, T_A	-55		125	0		70	$^\circ$C

electrical characteristics over recommended operating free-air temperature range (unless otherwise noted)

PARAMETER		TEST CONDITIONS[†]		SN54LS266			SN74LS266			UNIT
				MIN	TYP[‡]	MAX	MIN	TYP[‡]	MAX	
V_{IH}	High-level input voltage			2			2			V
V_{IL}	Low-level input voltage					0.7			0.8	V
V_{IK}	Input clamp voltage	V_{CC} = MIN,	I_I = -18 mA			-1.5			-1.5	V
I_{OH}	High-level output current	V_{CC} = MIN, V_{IH} = 2 V, V_{IL} = V_{IL} max, V_{OH} = 5.5 V				100			100	μA
V_{OL}	Low-level output voltage	V_{CC} = MIN, V_{IH} = 2 V,	I_{OL} = 4 mA	0.25		0.4	0.25		0.4	V
		V_{IL} = V_{IL} max	I_{OL} = 8 mA					0.35	0.5	
I_I	Input current at maximum input voltage	V_{CC} = MAX,	V_I = 7 V			0.2			0.2	mA
I_{IH}	High-level input current	V_{CC} = MAX,	V_I = 2.7 V			40			40	μA
I_{IL}	Low-level input current	V_{CC} = MAX,	V_I = 0.4 V			-0.8			-0.8	mA
I_{CC}	Supply current	V_{CC} = MAX,	See Note 2		8	13		8	13	mA

[†]For conditions shown as MIN or MAX, use the appropriate value specified under recommended operating conditions for the applicable type.
[‡]All typical values are at V_{CC} = 5 V, T_A = 25°C.
NOTE 2: I_{CC} is measured with one input of each gate at 4.5 V, the other inputs grounded, and the outputs open.

switching characteristics, V_{CC} = 5 V, T_A = 25°C

PARAMETER[¶]	FROM (INPUT)	TEST CONDITIONS		MIN	TYP	MAX	UNIT
t_{PLH}	A or B	Other input low	C_L = 15 pF, R_L = 2 kΩ, See Note 3		18	30	ns
t_{PHL}					18	30	
t_{PLH}	A or B	Other input high			18	30	ns
t_{PHL}					18	30	

[¶]t_{PLH} ≡ propagation delay time, low-to-high-level output
t_{PHL} ≡ propagation delay time, high-to-low-level output
NOTE 3: Load circuit and voltage waveforms are shown on page 3-11.

7

- **Contains Eight Flip-Flops with Single-Rail Outputs**
- **Buffered Clock and Direct Clear Inputs**
- **Individual Data Input to Each Flip-Flop**
- **Applications Include:**
  Buffer/Storage Registers
  Shift Registers
  Pattern Generators

SN54273, SN54LS273 . . . J PACKAGE
SN74273, SN74LS273 . . . J OR N PACKAGE

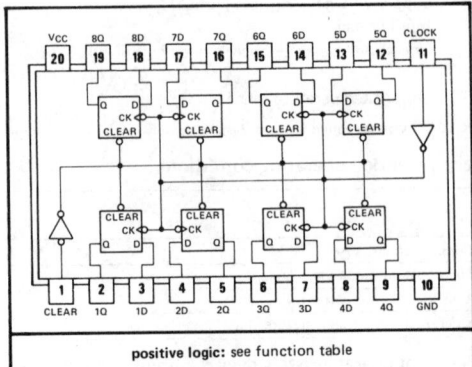

positive logic: see function table

description

These monolithic, positive-edge-triggered flip-flops utilize TTL circuitry to implement D-type flip-flop logic with a direct clear input.

Information at the D inputs meeting the setup time requirements is transferred to the Q outputs on the positive-going edge of the clock pulse. Clock triggering occurs at a particular voltage level and is not directly related to the transition time of the positive-going pulse. When the clock input is at either the high or low level, the D input signal has no effect at the output.

These flip-flops are guaranteed to respond to clock frequencies ranging from 0 to 30 megahertz while maximum clock frequency is typically 40 megahertz. Typical power dissipation is 39 milliwatts per flip-flop for the '273 and 10 milliwatts for the 'LS273.

FUNCTION TABLE
(EACH FLIP-FLOP)

INPUTS			OUTPUT
CLEAR	CLOCK	D	Q
L	X	X	L
H	↑	H	H
H	↑	L	L
H	L	X	Q_0

See explanation of function tables on page 3-8.

schematics of inputs and output

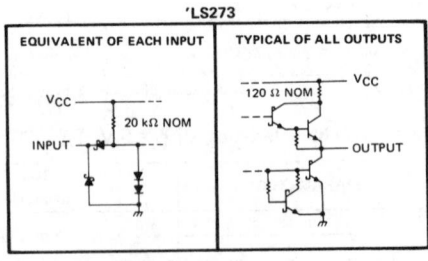

functional block diagram

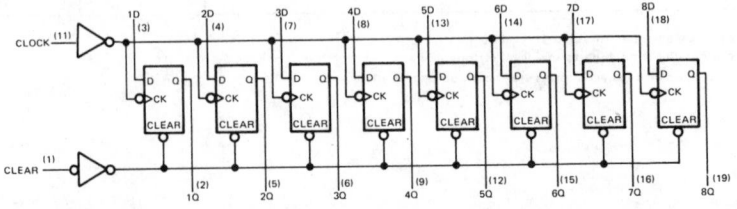

TEXAS INSTRUMENTS
INCORPORATED

POST OFFICE BOX 5012 • DALLAS, TEXAS 75222

absolute maximum ratings over operating free-air temperature range (unless otherwise noted)

Supply voltage, V_{CC} (see Note 1) . . . . 7 V
Input voltage . . . . 5.5 V
Operating free-air temperature range: SN54273 . . . . −55°C to 125°C
SN74273 . . . . 0°C to 70°C
Storage temperature range . . . . −65°C to 150°C
NOTE 1: Voltage values are with respect to network ground terminal.

recommended operating conditions

	SN54273			SN74273			UNIT
	MIN	NOM	MAX	MIN	NOM	MAX	
Supply voltage, V_{CC}	4.5	5	5.5	4.75	5	5.25	V
High-level output current, I_{OH}			−800			−800	μA
Low-level output current, I_{OL}			16			16	mA
Clock frequency, f_{clock}	0		30	0		30	MHz
Width of clock or clear pulse, t_w	16.5			16.5			ns
Set-up time, t_{su} — Data input	20†			20†			ns
Set-up time, t_{su} — Clear inactive state	25†			25†			
Data hold time, t_h	5†			5†			ns
Operating free-air temperature, T_A	−55		125	0		70	°C

†The arrow indicates that the rising edge of the clock pulse is used for reference.

electrical characteristics over recommended operating free-air temperature range (unless otherwise noted)

PARAMETER		TEST CONDITIONS†	MIN	TYP‡	MAX	UNIT
V_{IH}	High-level input voltage		2			V
V_{IL}	Low-level input voltage				0.8	V
V_{IK}	Input clamp voltage	V_{CC} = MIN, I_I = −12 mA			−1.5	V
V_{OH}	High-level output voltage	V_{CC} = MIN, V_{IH} = 2 V, V_{IL} = 0.8 V, I_{OH} = −800 μA	2.4	3.4		V
V_{OL}	Low-level output voltage	V_{CC} = MIN, V_{IH} = 2 V, V_{IL} = 0.8 V, I_{OL} = 16 mA			0.4	V
I_I	Input current at maximum input voltage	V_{CC} = MAX, V_I = 5.5 V			1	mA
I_{IH}	High-level input current — Clear	V_{CC} = MAX, V_I = 2.4 V			80	μA
	High-level input current — Clock or D				40	
I_{IL}	Low-level input current — Clear	V_{CC} = MAX, V_I = 0.4 V			−3.2	mA
	Low-level input current — Clock or D				−1.6	
I_{OS}	Short-circuit output current §	V_{CC} = MAX	−18		−57	mA
I_{CC}	Supply current	V_{CC} = MAX, See Note 2		62	94	mA

†For conditions shown as MIN or MAX, use the appropriate value specified under recommended operating conditions.
‡All typical values are at V_{CC} = 5 V, T_A = 25°C.
§Not more than one output should be shorted at a time.
NOTE 2: With all outputs open and 4.5 V applied to all data and clear inputs, I_{CC} is measured after a momentary ground, then 4.5 V, is applied to clock.

switching characteristics, V_{CC} = 5 V, T_A = 25°C

PARAMETER		TEST CONDITIONS	MIN	TYP	MAX	UNIT
f_{max}	Maximum clock frequency	C_L = 15 pF, R_L = 400 Ω, See Note 3	30	40		MHz
t_{PHL}	Propagation delay time, high-to-low-level output from clear			18	27	ns
t_{PLH}	Propagation delay time, low-to-high-level output from clock			17	27	ns
t_{PHL}	Propagation delay time, high-to-low-level output from clock			18	27	ns

NOTE 3: Load circuit and voltage waveforms are shown on page 3-10.

7

absolute maximum ratings over operating free-air temperature range (unless otherwise noted)

Supply voltage, V_{CC} (see Note 1) . . . . 7 V
Input voltage . . . . 7 V
Operating free-air temperature range: SN54LS273 . . . . −55°C to 125°C
 SN74LS273 . . . . 0°C to 70°C
Storage temperature range . . . . 65°C to 150°C

NOTE 1: Voltage values are with respect to network ground terminal

recommended operating conditions

		SN54LS273 MIN	NOM	MAX	SN74LS273 MIN	NOM	MAX	UNIT
Supply voltage, V_{CC}		4.5	5	5.5	4.75	5	5.25	V
High-level output current, I_{OH}				−400			−400	µA
Low-level output current, I_{OL}				4			8	mA
Clock frequency, f_{clock}		0		30	0		30	MHz
Width of clock or clear pulse, t_w		20			20			ns
Set-up time, t_{su}	Data input	20†			20†			ns
	Clear inactive state	25†			25†			
Data hold time, t_h		5†			5†			ns
Operating free-air temperature, T_A		−55		125	0		70	°C

†The arrow indicates that the rising edge of the clock pulse is used for reference.

electrical characteristics over recommended operating free-air temperature range (unless otherwise noted)

PARAMETER		TEST CONDITIONS†	SN54LS273 MIN	TYP‡	MAX	SN74LS273 MIN	TYP‡	MAX	UNIT
V_{IH}	High-level input voltage		2			2			V
V_{IL}	Low-level input voltage				0.7			0.8	V
V_{IK}	Input clamp voltage	V_{CC} = MIN, I_I = −18 mA			−1.5			−1.5	V
V_{OH}	High-level output voltage	V_{CC} = MIN, V_{IH} = 2 V, $V_{IL} = V_{IL}$max, I_{OH} = −400 µA	2.5	3.4		2.7	3.4		V
V_{OL}	Low-level output voltage	V_{CC} = MIN, V_{IH} = 2 V, I_{OL} = 4 mA		0.25	0.4		0.25	0.4	V
		$V_{IL} = V_{IL}$max, I_{OL} = 8 mA					0.35	0.5	
I_I	Input current at maximum input voltage	V_{CC} = MAX, V_I = 7 V			0.1			0.1	mA
I_{IH}	High-level input current	V_{CC} MAX, V_I = 2.7 V			20			20	µA
I_{IL}	Low-level input current	V_{CC} = MAX, V_I = −0.4 V			−0.4			−0.4	mA
I_{OS}	Short-circuit output current §	V_{CC} = MAX	−20		−100	−20		−100	mA
I_{CC}	Supply current	V_{CC} = MAX, See Note 2		17	27		17	27	mA

†For conditions shown as MIN or MAX, use the appropriate value specified under recommended operating conditions.
‡All typical values are at V_{CC} = 5 V, T_A = 25°C.
§Not more than one output should be shorted at a time and duration of short circuit should not exceed one second.
NOTE 2: With all outputs open and 4.5 V applied to all data and clear inputs, I_{CC} is measured after a momentary ground, then 4.5 V is applied to clock.

switching characteristics, V_{CC} = 5 V, T_A = 25°C

PARAMETER		TEST CONDITIONS	MIN	TYP	MAX	UNIT
f_{max}	Maximum clock frequency	C_L = 15 pF, R_L = 2 kΩ, See Note 4	30	40		MHz
t_{PHL}	Propagation delay time, high-to-low-level output from clear			18	27	ns
t_{PLH}	Propagation delay time, low-to-high-level output from clock			17	27	ns
t_{PHL}	Propagation delay time, high-to-low-level output from clock			18	27	ns

NOTE 4: Load circuit and voltage waveforms are shown on page 3-11.

7

TEXAS INSTRUMENTS
INCORPORATED
POST OFFICE BOX 5012 • DALLAS, TEXAS 75222

TTL

LSI

TYPES SN54LS275, SN54S274, SN54S275, SN74LS275, SN74S274, SN74S275
4-BIT-BY-4-BIT BINARY MULTIPLIER WITH 3-STATE OUTPUTS
7-BIT-SLICE WALLACE TREES WITH 3-STATE OUTPUTS
BULLETIN NO. DL-S 7612121, OCTOBER 1976

- 'S274 Provides 8-Bit Product in Typically 45 ns

- 'S274 Can Provide Sub-Multiple Products for n-Bit-by-n-Bit Binary Numbers

- 'LS275 and 'S275 Accept 7 Bit-Slice Inputs and 2 Carry Inputs for Reduction to 4 Lines in Typically 45 ns

- These High-Complexity Functions Can Reduce Package Count by Nearly 50% in Most Parallel Multiplier Designs

- When SN74S274 is Combined With SN74H183 (or SN74LS183) and Schottky Look-Ahead Adders, Multiplication Times are Typically:

    16-Bit Product in 75 ns (79 ns)
    32-Bit Product in 116 ns (132 ns)

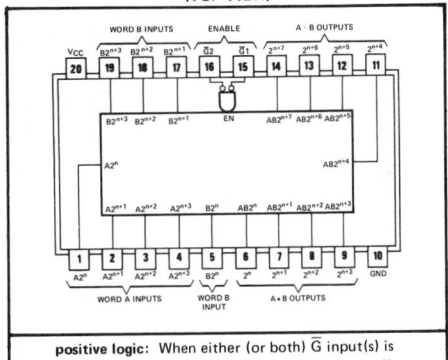

SN54S274 . . . J PACKAGE
SN74S274 . . . J OR N PACKAGE
(TOP VIEW)

positive logic: When either (or both) $\overline{G}$ input(s) is (are) high, all eight outputs are off.

description

These high-complexity Schottky-clamped TTL circuits are designed specifically to reduce the delay time required to perform high-speed parallel binary multiplication and significantly reduce package count. The 'S274 is a basic 4-bit-by-4-bit parallel multiplier in a single package, and as such, no additional components are required to obtain an 8-bit product. For word lengths longer than 4 bits, a number of 'S274 multipliers can be combined to generate sub-multiple partial products. These partial products can then be combined in Wallace trees to obtain the final product. See Typical Application Data.

The 'LS275 and 'S275 expandable bit-slice Wallace trees have been designed to accept up to seven bit-slice inputs and two carry inputs from previous slices for reduction to four lines.

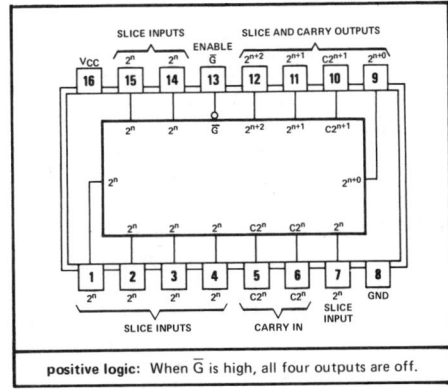

SN54LS275, SN54S275 . . . J PACKAGE
SN74LS275, SN74S275 . . . J OR N PACKAGE
(TOP VIEW)

positive logic: When $\overline{G}$ is high, all four outputs are off.

7

functional block diagram

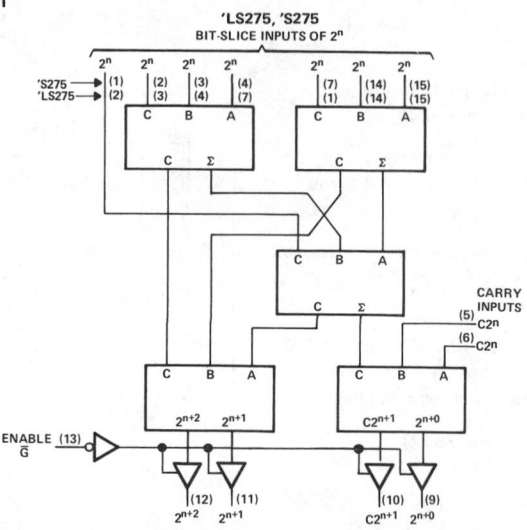

NOTE: When one of of the $C2^n$ carry inputs is not used, it must be grounded. If neither $C2^n$ carry input is used, both $C2^n$ inputs are grounded and the $C2^{n+1}$ output is normally left open.

schematics of inputs and outputs

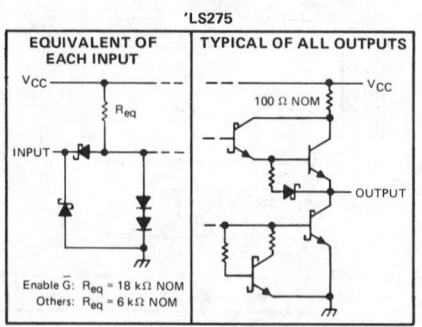

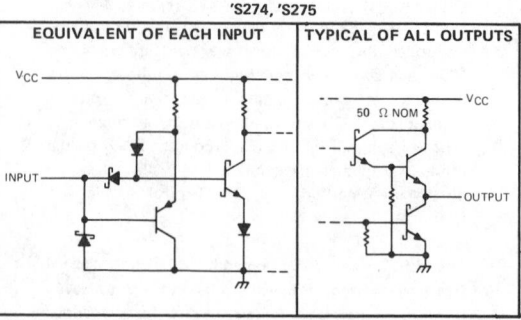

absolute maximum ratings over operating free-air temperature range (unless otherwise noted)

Supply voltage, V_{CC} (see Note 1)	7 V
Input voltage: 'LS275	7 V
'S274, 'S275	5.5 V
Off-state output voltage: 'LS275	7 V
'S274, 'S275	5.5 V
Operating free-air temperature range: SN54LS, SN54S Circuits	−55°C to 125°C
SN74LS, SN74S Circuits	0°C to 70°C
Storage temperature range	−65°C to 150°C

NOTE 1: Voltage values are with respect to network ground terminal.

TEXAS INSTRUMENTS
INCORPORATED
POST OFFICE BOX 5012 • DALLAS, TEXAS 75222

recommended operating conditions

	SN54LS275 MIN	NOM	MAX	SN74LS275 MIN	NOM	MAX	UNIT
Supply voltage, V_{CC}	4.5	5	5.5	4.75	5	5.25	V
High-level output current, I_{OH}			−1			−2.6	mA
Low-level output current, I_{OL}			12			24	mA
Operating free-air temperature, T_A	−55		125	0		70	°C

electrical characteristics over recommended operating free-air temperature range (unless otherwise noted)

PARAMETER		TEST CONDITIONS[†]	SN54LS275 MIN	TYP[‡]	MAX	SN74LS275 MIN	TYP[‡]	MAX	UNIT
V_{IH}	High-level input voltage		2			2			V
V_{IL}	Low-level input voltage				0.7			0.8	V
V_{IK}	Input clamp voltage	V_{CC} = MIN, I_I = −18 mA			−1.5			−1.5	V
V_{OH}	High-level output voltage	V_{CC} = MIN, V_{IH} = 2 V, V_{IL} = V_{IL}max I_{OH} = MAX	2.4	3.2		2.4	3.1		V
V_{OL}	Low-level output voltage	V_{CC} = MIN, V_{IH} = 2 V, V_{IL} = V_{IL}max I_{OL} = 12 mA		0.25	0.4		0.25	0.4	V
		I_{OL} = 24 mA					0.35	0.5	
I_{OZH}	Off-state output current, high-level voltage applied	V_{CC} = MAX, V_{IH} = 2 V, V_O = 2.7 V			20			20	µA
I_{OZL}	Off-state output current, low-level voltage applied	V_{CC} = MAX, V_{IH} = 2 V, V_O = 0.4 V			−20			−20	µA
I_I	Input current at maximum input voltage	Enable $\overline{G}$ — V_{CC} = MAX, V_I = 7 V			0.1			0.1	mA
		All others			0.3			0.3	
I_{IH}	High-level input current	Enable $\overline{G}$ — V_{CC} = MAX, V_I = 2.7 V			20			20	µA
		All others			60			60	
I_{IL}	Low-level input current	Enable $\overline{G}$ — V_{CC} = MAX, V_I = 0.4 V			−0.4			−0.4	mA
		All others			−1.2			−1.2	
I_{OS}	Short-circuit output current[§]	V_{CC} = MAX	−30		−130	−30		−130	mA
I_{CC}	Supply current	V_{CC} = MAX		25	40		25	40	mA

† For conditions shown as MIN or MAX, use the appropriate value specified under recommended operating conditions.
‡ All typical values are at V_{CC} = 5 V, T_A = 25°C.
§ Not more than one output should be shorted at a time and duration of the short-circuit should not exceed one second.

switching characteristics, V_{CC} = 5 V, T_A = 25°C

PARAMETER[¶]	FROM (INPUT)	TO (OUTPUT)	TEST CONDITIONS	MIN	TYP	MAX	UNIT
t_{PLH}	Any Slice or Carry	Any	C_L = 45 pF, R_L = 667 Ω, See Note 2		35	62	ns
t_{PHL}					42	66	
t_{PZH}	Enable $\overline{G}$	Any	C_L = 45 pF, R_L = 667 Ω, See Note 2		8	23	ns
t_{PZL}					13	23	
t_{PHZ}			C_L = 5 pF, R_L = 667 Ω, See Note 2		10	15	ns
t_{PLZ}					10	15	

¶ t_{PLH} ≡ Propagation delay time, low-to-high-level output
t_{PHL} ≡ Propagation delay time, high-to-low-level output
t_{PZH} ≡ Output enable time to high level
t_{PZL} ≡ Output enable time to low level
t_{PHZ} ≡ Output disable time from high level
t_{PLZ} ≡ Output disable time from low level

NOTE 2: Load circuit and voltage waveforms are shown on page 3-11.

7

TEXAS INSTRUMENTS
INCORPORATED
POST OFFICE BOX 5012 • DALLAS, TEXAS 75222

TYPES SN54S274, SN54S275, SN74S274, SN74S275
4-BIT-BY-4-BIT BINARY MULTIPLIER WITH 3-STATE OUTPUTS
7-BIT-SLICE WALLACE TREES WITH 3-STATE OUTPUTS

recommended operating conditions

	SN54S274 SN54S275			SN74S274 SN74S275			UNIT
	MIN	NOM	MAX	MIN	NOM	MAX	
Supply voltage, V_{CC}	4.5	5	5.5	4.75	5	5.25	V
High-level output current, I_{OH}			−2			−6.5	mA
Low-level output current, I_{OL}			12			12	mA
Operating free-air temperature, T_A	−55		125	0		70	°C

electrical characteristics over recommended operating free-air temperature range (unless otherwise noted)

PARAMETER		TEST CONDITIONS[†]		SN54S274 SN54S275			SN74S274 SN74S275			UNIT
				MIN	TYP[‡]	MAX	MIN	TYP[‡]	MAX	
V_{IH}	High-level input voltage			2			2			V
V_{IL}	Low-level input voltage					0.8			0.8	V
V_{IK}	Input clamp voltage	V_{CC} = MIN,	I_I = −18 mA			−1.2			−1.2	V
V_{OH}	High-level output voltage	V_{CC} = MIN, V_{IL} = 0.8 V,	V_{IH} = 2 V, I_{OH} = MAX	2.4	3.4		2.4	3.2		V
V_{OL}	Low-level output voltage	V_{CC} = MIN, V_{IL} = 0.8 V,	V_{IH} = 2 V, I_{OL} = 12 mA			0.5			0.5	V
I_{OZH}	Off-state output current, high-level voltage applied	V_{CC} = MAX, V_O = 2.4 V	V_{IH} = 2 V,			50			50	μA
I_{OZL}	Off-state output current, low-level voltage applied	V_{CC} = MAX, V_O = 0.5 V	V_{IH} = 2 V,			−50			−50	μA
I_I	Input current at maximum input voltage	V_{CC} = MAX,	V_I = 5.5 V			1			1	mA
I_{IH}	High-level input current	V_{CC} = MAX,	V_I = 2.7 V			25			25	μA
I_{IL}	Low-level input current	V_{CC} = MAX,	V_I = 0.5 V			−0.25			−0.25	mA
I_{OS}	Short-circuit output current[§]	V_{CC} = MAX		−30		−100	−30		−100	mA
I_{CC}	Supply current	V_{CC} = MAX			105	155		105	155	mA

switching characteristics over recommended ranges of T_A and V_{CC} (unless otherwise noted)

PARAMETER[¶]	FROM (INPUT)	TO (OUTPUT)	TEST CONDITIONS	SN54S274 SN54S275			SN74S274 SN74S275			UNIT
				MIN	TYP[‡]	MAX	MIN	TYP[‡]	MAX	
t_{PHL}	Any A or B ('S274), or Any Slice or Carry ('S275)	Any	C_L = 30 pF, R_L = 400 Ω, See Note 3		50	95		50	70	ns
t_{PLH}					50	95		50	70	
t_{PZH}	Any Enable	Any	C_L = 5 pF, R_L = 400 Ω, See Note 3		15	45		15	30	ns
t_{PZL}					15	45		15	30	
t_{PHZ}					10	40		10	25	ns
t_{PLZ}					10	40		10	25	

[†] For conditions shown as MIN or MAX, use the appropriate value specified under recommended operating conditions.
[‡] All typical values are at V_{CC} = 5 V, T_A = 25°C.
[§] Not more than one output should be shorted at a time and duration of the short-circuit should not exceed one second.
[¶] t_{PLH} ≡ Propagation delay time, low-to-high-level output
t_{PHL} ≡ Propagation delay time, high-to-low-level output
t_{PZH} ≡ Output enable time to high level
t_{PZL} ≡ Output enable time to low level
t_{PHZ} ≡ Output disable time from high level
t_{PLZ} ≡ Output disable time from low level
NOTE 3: Load circuit and voltage waveforms are shown on page 3-10.

TEXAS INSTRUMENTS
INCORPORATED
POST OFFICE BOX 5012 • DALLAS, TEXAS 75222

TYPES SN54LS275, SN54S274, SN54S275, SN74LS275, SN74S274, SN74S275
4-BIT-BY-4-BIT BINARY MULTIPLIER WITH 3-STATE OUTPUTS
7-BIT-SLICE WALLACE TREES WITH 3-STATE OUTPUTS

TYPICAL APPLICATION DATA

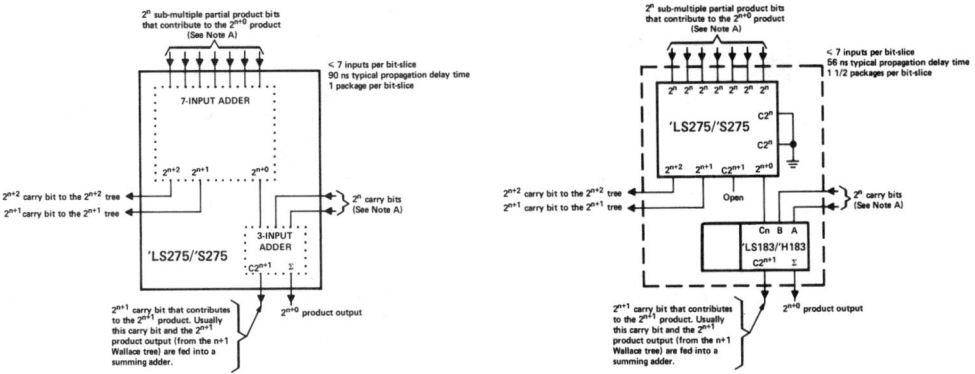

FIGURE 1—BASIC BIT-SLICE WALLACE TREE   FIGURE 2—HIGH-SPEED BIT-SLICE WALLACE TREE

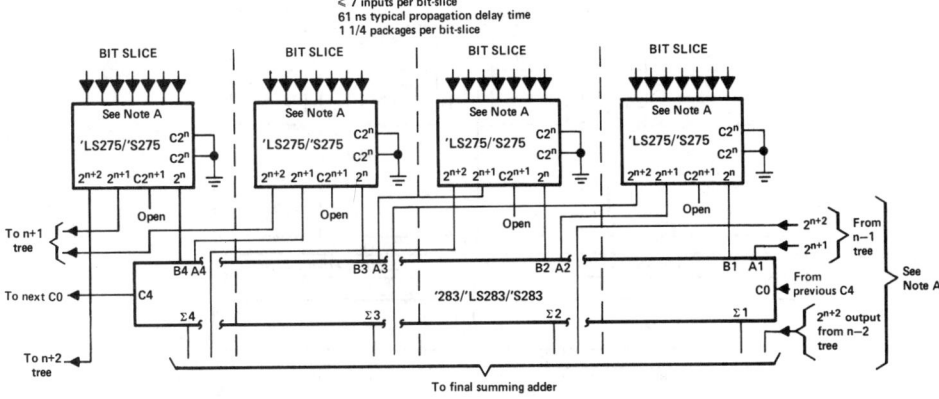

FIGURE 3—MODERATE-SPEED BIT-SLICE WALLACE TREE

NOTE A: All unused inputs must be grounded.

TEXAS INSTRUMENTS
INCORPORATED
POST OFFICE BOX 5012 • DALLAS, TEXAS 75222

TYPICAL APPLICATION DATA

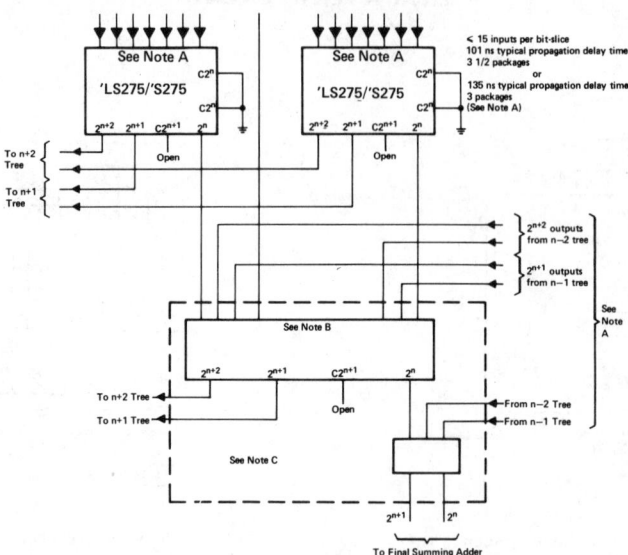

NOTES: A. Ground unused inputs.
   B. These outputs from preceding trees may go to any of the inputs of the 'LS275/'S275.
   C. The circuit within the dotted lines may be either the basic bit-slice Wallace tree or the high-speed Wallace tree. In the latter case both carry inputs of the 'LS275/'S275 must be grounded.

FIGURE 4—15-BIT-SLICE WALLACE TREE FOR 32-BIT X 32-BIT MULTIPLIER

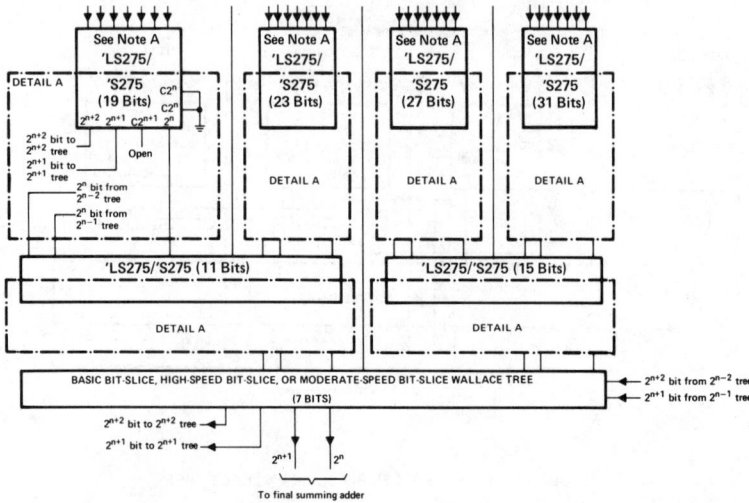

NOTES: A. Ground unused inputs.
   B. The number of bits in parentheses is the maximum number of bits this tree can combine if the remaining 'LS275/'S275 (all having a higher number in the parentheses) were not connected.

FIGURE 5—7-TO-31-BIT-SLICE WALLACE TREE FOR UP TO 64-BIT X 64-BIT MULTIPLIERS

TEXAS INSTRUMENTS
INCORPORATED
POST OFFICE BOX 5012 • DALLAS, TEXAS 75222

TYPICAL APPLICATION DATA

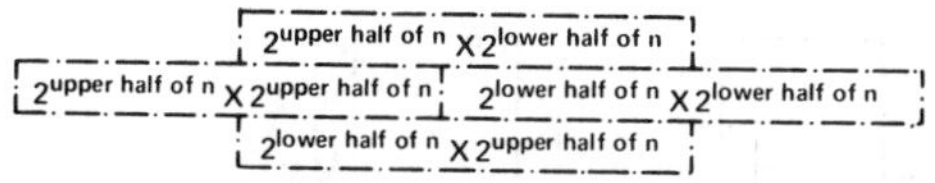

$$\begin{array}{|c|c|}
\hline
& 2^{\text{upper half of n}} \text{ X } 2^{\text{lower half of n}} \\
\hline
2^{\text{upper half of n}} \text{ X } 2^{\text{upper half of n}} & 2^{\text{lower half of n}} \text{ X } 2^{\text{lower half of n}} \\
\hline
& 2^{\text{lower half of n}} \text{ X } 2^{\text{upper half of n}} \\
\hline
\end{array}$$

NOTE A: The left-hand half of each rectangle is the portion of word one used to obtain the product shown within the rectangle. Similarly, the right-hand half of each rectangle is the portion of word two used.

FIGURE 6—UNIVERSAL METHOD OF ADDING $\frac{n}{2}$-BIT PRODUCTS TO OBTAIN AN n-BIT PRODUCT

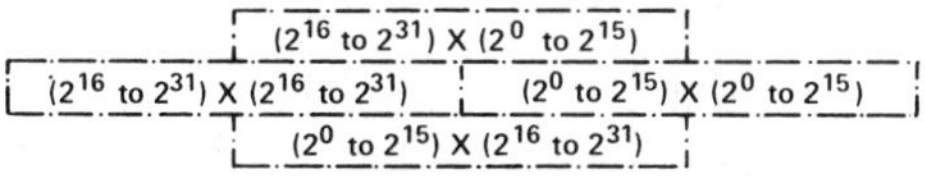

$$\begin{array}{|c|c|}
\hline
& (2^{16} \text{ to } 2^{31}) \text{ X } (2^0 \text{ to } 2^{15}) \\
\hline
(2^{16} \text{ to } 2^{31}) \text{ X } (2^{16} \text{ to } 2^{31}) & (2^0 \text{ to } 2^{15}) \text{ X } (2^0 \text{ to } 2^{15}) \\
\hline
& (2^0 \text{ to } 2^{15}) \text{ X } (2^{16} \text{ to } 2^{31}) \\
\hline
\end{array}$$

FIGURE 7—METHOD OF ADDING 32-BIT PRODUCTS TO OBTAIN A 64-BIT PRODUCT

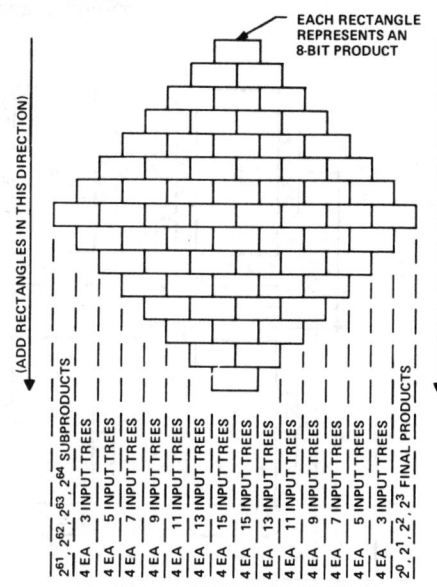

EACH RECTANGLE REPRESENTS AN 8-BIT PRODUCT

FIGURE 8—FINAL PRODUCTS AND ARRAY SUBPRODUCT ADDITIONS FOR 32-BIT X 32-BIT MULTIPLIER

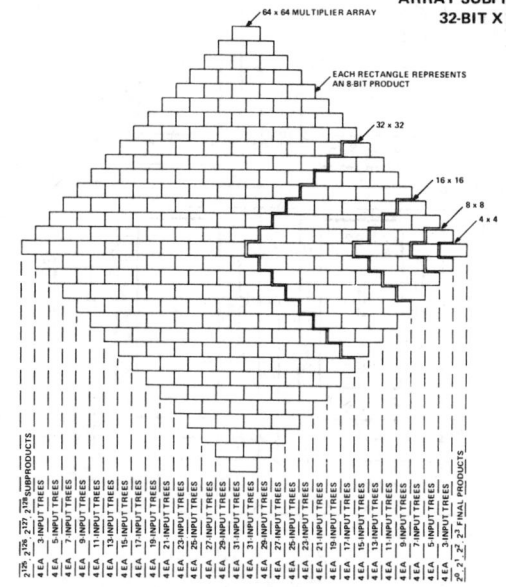

64 x 64 MULTIPLIER ARRAY

EACH RECTANGLE REPRESENTS AN 8-BIT PRODUCT

32 x 32

16 x 16

8 x 8

4 x 4

NOTE A: See Note B of Figure 6 for designing trees with any number of inputs up to 31.

FIGURE 9—ARRAY ARRANGEMENT FOR VARIOUS MULTIPLIERS INCLUDING ARRAY SUBPRODUCT ADDITIONS FOR 64-BIT X 64-BIT MULTIPLIER

TYPICAL APPLICATION DATA

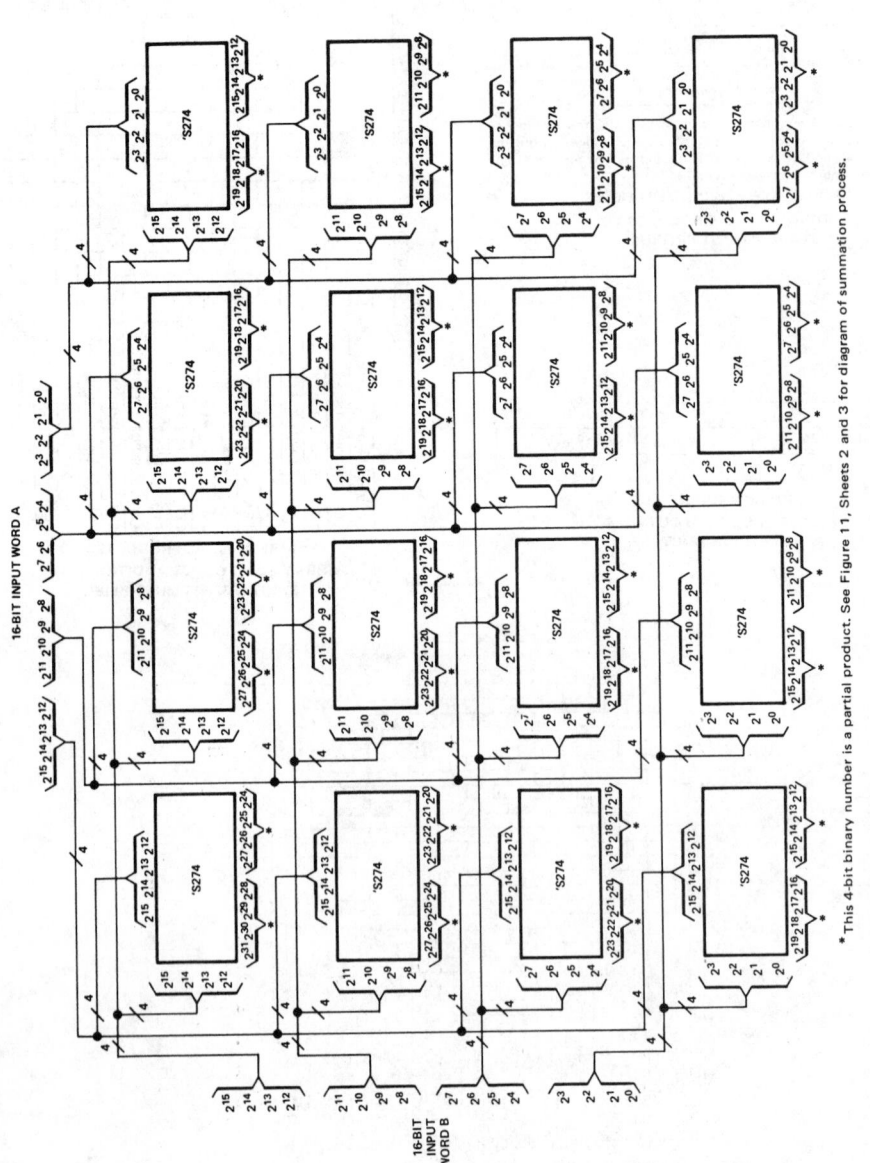

FIGURE 10—16-BIT X 16-BIT MULTIPLIER (SHEET 1 OF 3—OUTPUT CONNECTIONS)

* This 4-bit binary number is a partial product. See Figure 11, Sheets 2 and 3 for diagram of summation process.

TYPICAL APPLICATION DATA

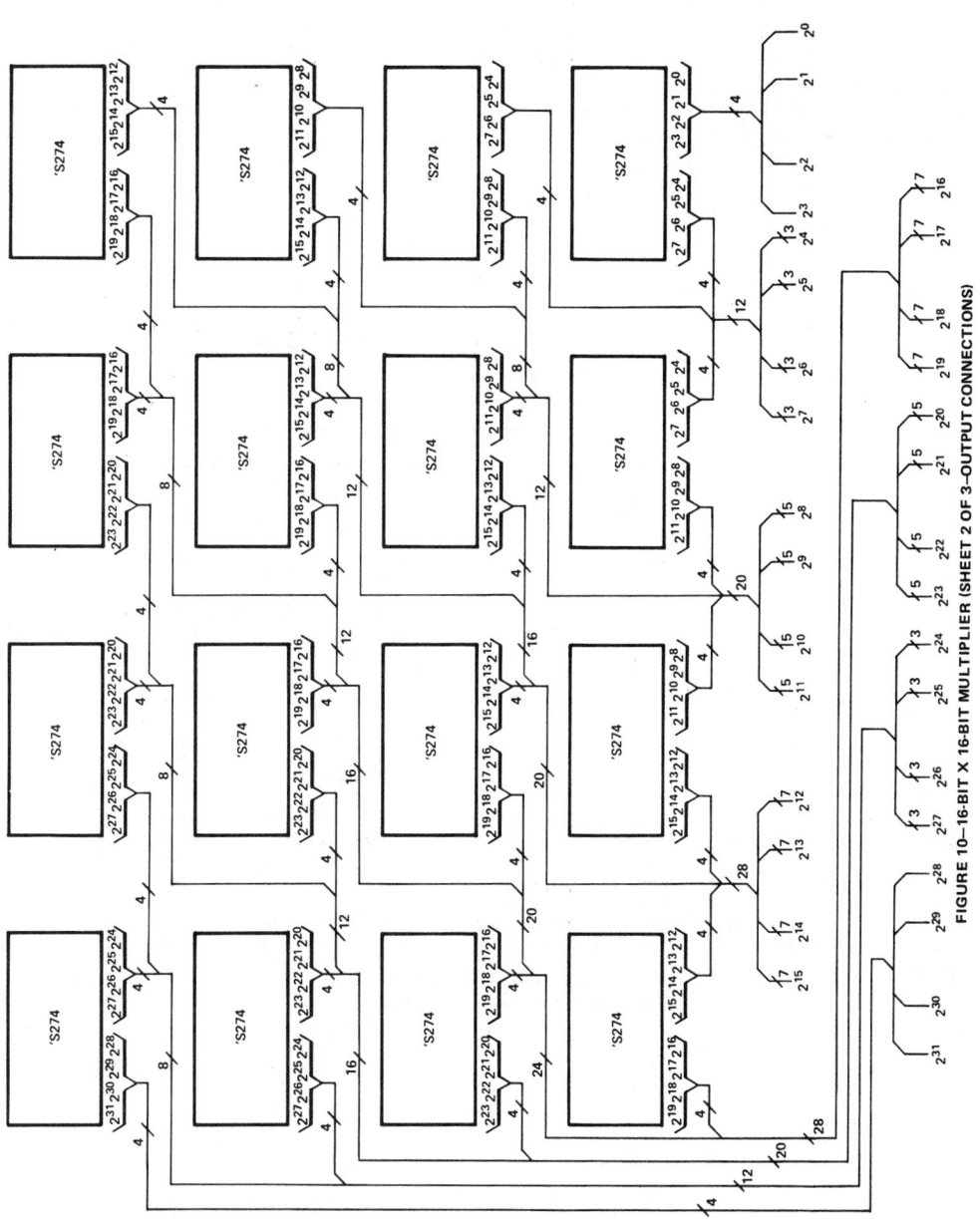

FIGURE 10—16-BIT X 16-BIT MULTIPLIER (SHEET 2 OF 3—OUTPUT CONNECTIONS)

TYPICAL APPLICATION DATA

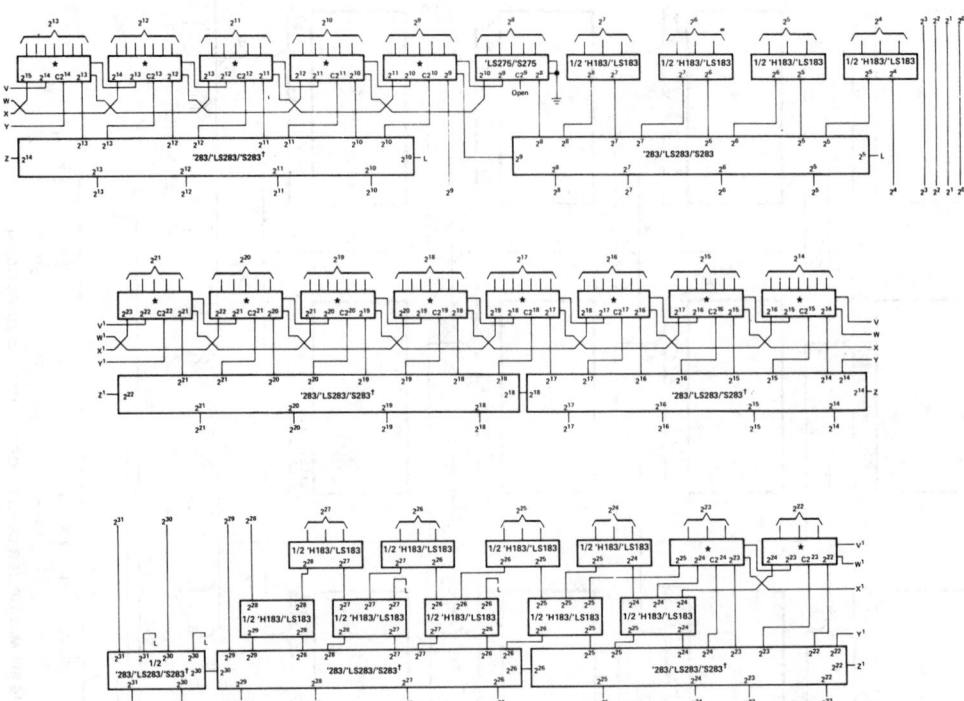

* Each starred block may be either a basic bit-slice Wallace tree ('LS275 or 'S275 only) or a high-speed bit-slice Wallace tree ('LS275 plus 1/2 'LS183 or 'S275 plus 1/2 'H183). In either case the function of the terminal is the same as the similarly located terminal of the basic bit-slice (Figure 1) or high-speed bit-slice Wallace tree (Figure 2). Also for either tree, when only five inputs of the seven-input adder of the 'LS275/'S275 are used, the remaining two inputs must be grounded. When the high-speed adder is used, the $C2^n$ inputs of the 'LS275/'S275 must be grounded.

† For improved performance SN74LS181/SN74S181 ALUs with SN74S182 look-ahead generators can be substituted for the SN74283/SN74LS283/SN74S283 adders. Typically, the multiplication time will be reduced by 18 to 32 nanoseconds.

FIGURE 10—16-BIT X 16-BIT MULTIPLIER
(SHEET 3 OF 3—SUMMING PARTIAL PRODUCTS)

TEXAS INSTRUMENTS
INCORPORATED
POST OFFICE BOX 5012 • DALLAS, TEXAS 75222

features

- Four J-$\overline{\text{K}}$ Flip-Flops in a Single Package . . . Can Reduce FF Package Count by 50%

- Separate Negative-Edge-Triggered Clocks with Hysteresis . . . Typically 200 mV

- Typical Clock Input Frequency . . . 50 MHz

- Fully Buffered Outputs

description

These quadruple TTL J-$\overline{\text{K}}$ flip-flops incorporate a number of third-generation IC features that can simplify system design and reduce flip-flop package count by up to 50%. They feature hysteresis at each clock input, fully buffered outputs, and direct clear capability, and are presettable through a buffer that also features an input hysteresis loop. The negative-edge-triggering clocks are directly compatible with earlier Series 54/74 single and dual pulse-triggered flip-flops. These circuits can be used to emulate D- or T-type flip-flops by hard-wiring the inputs, or to implement asynchronous sequential functions.

The SN54276 is characterized for operation over the full military temperature range of −55°C to 125°C; the SN74726 is characterized for operation from 0°C to 70°C.

SN54276 . . . J PACKAGE
SN74276 . . . J OR N PACKAGE
(TOP VIEW)

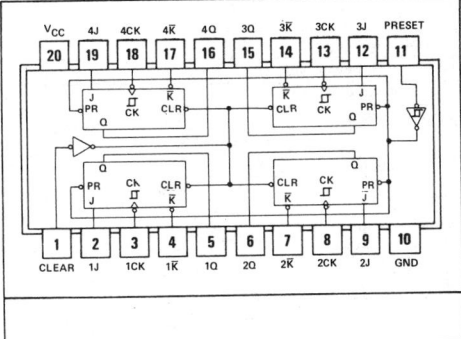

schematics of inputs and outputs

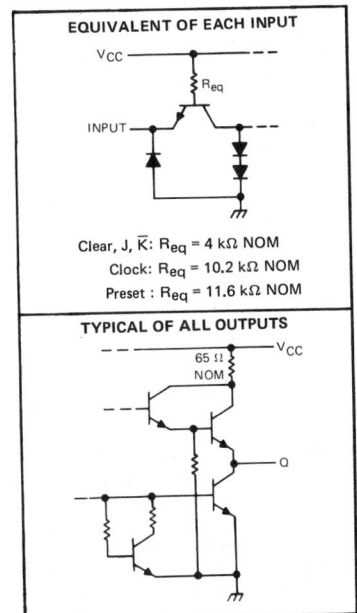

EQUIVALENT OF EACH INPUT

Clear, J, $\overline{\text{K}}$: R_{eq} = 4 kΩ NOM
Clock: R_{eq} = 10.2 kΩ NOM
Preset : R_{eq} = 11.6 kΩ NOM

TYPICAL OF ALL OUTPUTS

FUNCTION TABLE (EACH FLIP-FLOP)

COMMON INPUTS		INPUTS			OUTPUT
PRESET	CLEAR	CLOCK	J	$\overline{\text{K}}$	Q
L	H	X	X	X	H
H	L	X	X	X	L
L	L	X	X	X	H[†]
H	H	↓	L	H	Q_0
H	H	↓	H	H	H
H	H	↓	L	L	L
H	H	↓	H	L	TOGGLE
H	H	H	X	X	Q_0

†This configuration is nonstable; that is, it may not persist when preset and clear return to their inactive (high) level.

See explanation of function tables on page 3-8.

absolute maximum ratings over operating free-air temperature range (unless otherwise noted)

Supply voltage, V_{CC} (see Note 1) . . . . 7 V
Input voltage . . . . 5.5 V
Operating free-air temperature range: SN54276 . . . . −55°C to 125°C
SN74276 . . . . 0°C to 70°C
Storage temperature range . . . . −65°C to 150°C

NOTE 1: Voltage values are with respect to network ground terminal.

TYPES SN54276, SN74276
QUADRUPLE J-K FLIP-FLOPS

recommended operating conditions

		SN54276			SN74276			UNIT
		MIN	NOM	MAX	MIN	NOM	MAX	
Supply voltage, V_{CC}		4.5	5	5.5	4.75	5	5.25	V
High-level output current, I_{OH}				−800			−800	μA
Low-level output current, I_{OL}				16			16	mA
Clock frequency		0		35	0		35	MHz
Pulse width, t_W	Clock high	13.5			13.5			ns
	Clock low	15			15			
	Preset or clear low	12			12			
Setup time, t_{su}	J, K̄ inputs	3↓			3↓			ns
	Clear and preset inactive state	10↓			10↓			
Input hold time, t_h		10↓			10↓			ns
Operating free-air temperature, T_A		−55		125	0		70	°C

↓ The arrow indicates that the falling edge of the clock pulse is used for reference.

electrical characteristics over recommended operating free-air temperature range (unless otherwise noted)

	PARAMETER	TEST CONDITIONS[†]		MIN	TYP[‡]	MAX	UNIT
V_{IH}	High-level input voltage			2			V
V_{IL}	Low-level input voltage					0.8	V
V_{IK}	Input clamp voltage	V_{CC} = MIN,	I_I = −12 mA			−1.5	V
V_{OH}	High-level output voltage	V_{CC} = MIN, V_{IL} = 0.8 V,	V_{IH} = 2 V, I_{OH} = −800 μA	2.4	3.4		V
V_{OL}	Low-level output voltage	V_{CC} = MIN, V_{IL} = 0.8 V,	V_{IH} = 2 V, I_{OL} = 16 mA		0.2	0.4	V
I_I	Input current at maximum input voltage	V_{CC} = MAX,	V_I = 5.5 V			1	mA
I_{IH}	High-level input current	V_{CC} = MAX,	V_I = 2.4 V			40	μA
I_{IL}	Low-level input current	V_{CC} = MAX,	V_I = 0.4 V			−1.6	mA
I_{OS}	Short-circuit output current[§]	V_{CC} = MAX		−30		−85	mA
I_{CC}	Supply current	V_{CC} = MAX			60	81	mA

[†]For conditions shown as MIN or MAX, use the appropriate value specified under recommended operating conditions.
[‡]All typical values are at V_{CC} = 5 V, T_A = 25°C.
[§]Not more than one output should be shorted at a time.

switching characteristics, V_{CC} = 5 V, T_A = 25°C

	PARAMETER	TEST CONDITIONS	MIN	TYP	MAX	UNIT
f_{max}	Maximum clock frequency		35	50		MHz
t_{PLH}	Propagation delay time, low-to-high-level output from preset	C_L = 15 pF,		15	25	ns
t_{PHL}	Propagation delay time, high-to-low-level output from clear	R_L = 400 Ω,		18	30	ns
t_{PLH}	Propagation delay time, low-to-high-level output from clock	See Note 2		17	30	ns
t_{PHL}	Propagation delay time, high-to-low-level output from clock			20	30	ns

NOTE 2: Load circuit and voltage waveforms are shown on page 3-10.

TEXAS INSTRUMENTS
INCORPORATED
POST OFFICE BOX 5012 • DALLAS, TEXAS 75222

107

TYPES SN54278, SN74278
4-BIT CASCADABLE PRIORITY REGISTERS

BULLETIN NO. DL-S 7211729, MAY 1972–REVISED DECEMBER 1972

- Latched Data Inputs Serve as Buffer Register and Can also:
    Synchronize Data Acquisition
    "Debounce" Mechanical Switch Input

- Cascading Input P0 and Output P1 Provides "Busy"Signal Inhibiting All Lower-Order Bits

- Full TTL Compatibility

- Use for:
    Priority Interrupt
    Synchronous Priority Line Selection

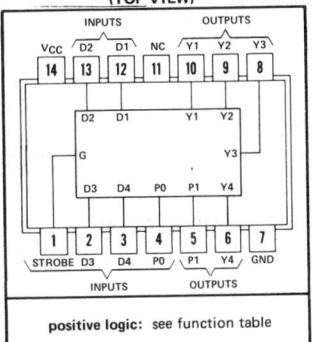

SN54278 . . . J OR W PACKAGE
SN74278 . . . J OR N PACKAGE
(TOP VIEW)

positive logic: see function table

NC—No internal connection

description

The SN54278 and SN74278 each consist of four data latches, full priority output gating, and a cascading gate. The highest-order data applied at a D latch input is transferred to the appropriate Y output while the strobe input is high, and when the strobe goes low all data is latched. The cascading input P0 is fully overriding and on the highest-order package this input must be held at a low logic level. The P1 output is intended for connection to the P0 input of the next lower-order package and will provide a "busy" (high-level) signal to inhibit all subsequent lower-order packages.

After the overriding P0 input, the order of priority is D1, D2, D3, and D4, respectively, within the package.

FUNCTION TABLE

INPUTS						INTERNAL LATCH NODES				OUTPUTS				
P0	G	D1	D2	D3	D4	$\bar{Q}1$	$\bar{Q}2$	$\bar{Q}3$	$\bar{Q}4$	Y1	Y2	Y3	Y4	P1
L	H	H	X	X	X	L	X	X	X	H	L	L	L	H
L	H	L	H	X	X	H	L	X	X	L	H	L	L	H
L	H	L	L	H	X	H	H	L	X	L	L	H	L	H
L	H	L	L	L	H	H	H	H	L	L	L	L	H	H
L	H	L	L	L	L	H	H	H	H	L	L	L	L	L
L	L	X	X	X	X	Latched when G goes low				Same function of $\bar{Q}$ nodes as on 1st 5 lines				
H	L	X	X	X	X					L	L	L	L	H
H	H	Internal $\bar{Q}$ levels are same function of D inputs as on first 5 lines								L	L	L	L	H

H = high level, L = low level, X = irrelevant

functional block diagram

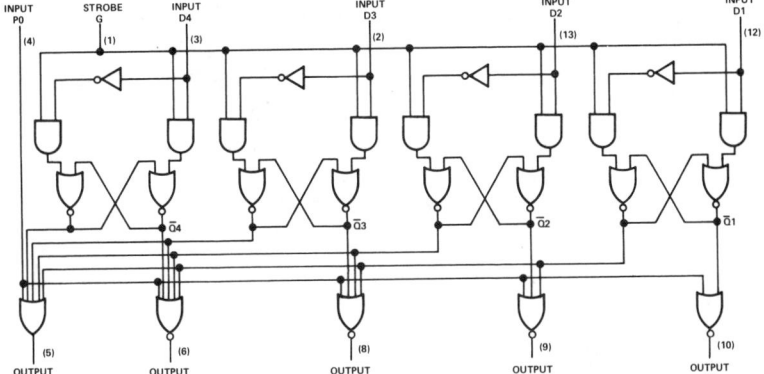

TEXAS INSTRUMENTS
INCORPORATED
POST OFFICE BOX 5012 • DALLAS, TEXAS 75222

7

absolute maximum ratings over operating free-air temperature range (unless otherwise noted)

Supply voltage, V_{CC} (see Note 1)	7 V
Input voltage	5.5 V
Interemitter voltage (see Note 2)	5.5 V
Operating free-air temperature range: SN54278 Circuits	-55°C to 125°C
SN74278 Circuits	0°C to 70°C
Storage temperature range	-65°C to 150°C

NOTES: 1. Voltage values, except interemitter voltage, are with respect to network ground terminal.

2. This is the voltage between two emitters of a multiple-emitter transistor. For this circuit, this rating applies between the strobe input and any of the four data inputs.

recommended operating conditions

	SN54278			SN74278			UNIT
	MIN	NOM	MAX	MIN	NOM	MAX	
Supply voltage, V_{CC}	4.5	5	5.5	4.75	5	5.25	V
High-level output current, I_{OH}			-800			-800	μA
Low-level output current, I_{OL}			16			16	mA
Data setup time, t_{su} (see Figure 1)	20			20			ns
Data hold time, t_h (see Figure 1)	5			5			ns
Strobe pulse width, t_w (see Figure 1)	20			20			ns
Operating free-air temperature, T_A	-55		125	0		70	$^\circ$C

electrical characteristics over recommended operating free-air temperature range (unless otherwise noted)

	PARAMETER		TEST CONDITIONS[†]		MIN	TYP	MAX	UNIT
V_{IH}	High-level input voltage				2			V
V_{IL}	Low-level input voltage						0.8	V
V_{IK}	Input clamp voltage		V_{CC} = MAX,	$I_I = -12$ mA			-1.5	V
V_{OH}	High-level output voltage		V_{CC} = MIN, V_{IH} = 2 V, V_{IL} = 0.8 V, $I_{OH} = -800\ \mu$A		2.4	3.4		V
V_{OL}	Low-level output voltage		V_{CC} = MIN, V_{IH} = 2 V, V_{IL} = 0.8 V, I_{OL} = 16 mA			0.2	0.4	V
I_I	Input current at maximum input voltage		V_{CC} = MAX,	V_I = 5.5 V			1	mA
I_{IH}	High-level input current	Any D input	V_{CC} = MAX,	V_I = 2.4 V			80	μA
		P0 input					200	
		G input					320	
I_{IL}	Low-level input current	Any D input	V_{CC} = MAX,	V_I = 0.4 V			-3.2	mA
		P0 input					-8	
		G input					-12.8	
I_{OS}	Short-circuit output current[§]	SN54278	V_{CC} = MAX		-18		-55	mA
		SN74278			-18		-57	
I_{CC}	Supply current		V_{CC} = MAX,	See Note 3		55	80	mA

[†]For conditions shown as MIN or MAX, use the appropriate value specified under recommended operating conditions for the applicable type.

[‡]All typical values are at V_{CC} = 5 V, $T_A = 25^\circ$C.

[§]Not more than one output should be shorted at a time.

NOTE 3: I_{CC} is measured with the P0 input grounded, all other inputs at 4.5 V, and outputs open.

TEXAS INSTRUMENTS
INCORPORATED

POST OFFICE BOX 5012 • DALLAS, TEXAS 75222

switching characteristics, V_{CC} = 5 V, T_A = 25°C

PARAMETER¶	FROM (INPUT)	TO (OUTPUT)	WAVEFORMS	TEST CONDITIONS	MIN	TYP	MAX	UNIT
t_{PLH}	Data	Y	A and C (with strobe high)				30	ns
t_{PHL}							39	
t_{PLH}	Data	Y	A and D (with strobe high)				38	ns
t_{PHL}							31	
t_{PLH}	Data	P1	A and E (with strobe high)	C_L = 15 pF,			46	ns
t_{PHL}				R_L = 400 Ω,			39	
t_{PLH}	Strobe	Any Y	B and C or B and D	See Figure 1			30	ns
t_{PHL}							31	
t_{PLH}	Strobe	P1	B and E				38	ns
t_{PHL}							42	
t_{PLH}	P0	P1	F and G				23	ns
t_{PHL}							30	

¶ $t_{PLH} \equiv$ propagation delay time, low-to-high-level output
$t_{PHL} \equiv$ propagation delay time, high-to-low-level output

schematics of inputs and outputs

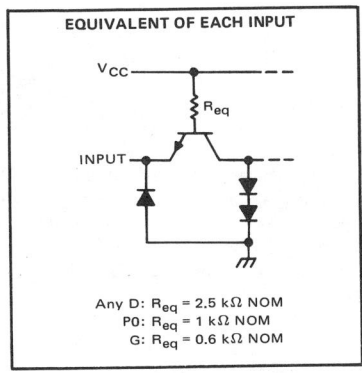

EQUIVALENT OF EACH INPUT

V_{CC}

R_{eq}

INPUT

Any D: R_{eq} = 2.5 kΩ NOM
P0: R_{eq} = 1 kΩ NOM
G: R_{eq} = 0.6 kΩ NOM

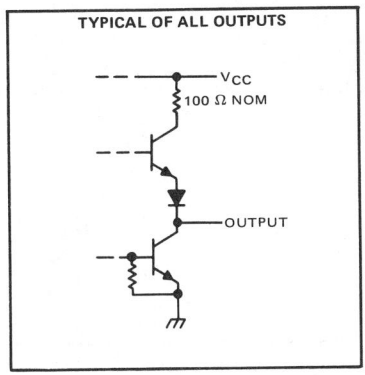

TYPICAL OF ALL OUTPUTS

V_{CC}
100 Ω NOM

OUTPUT

PARAMETER MEASUREMENT INFORMATION

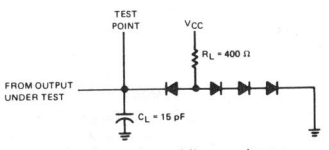

TEST POINT V_{CC}

R_L = 400 Ω

FROM OUTPUT UNDER TEST

C_L = 15 pF

C_L includes probe and jig capacitance.
All diodes are 1N3064.

LOAD CIRCUIT

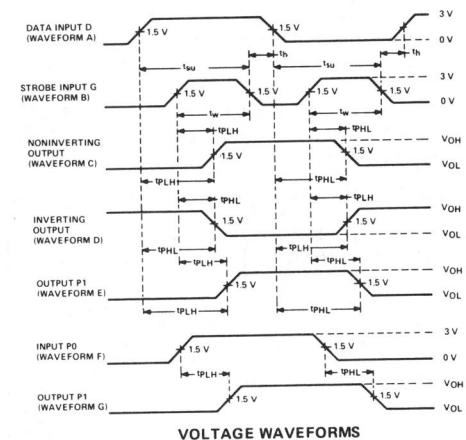

DATA INPUT D (WAVEFORM A)

STROBE INPUT G (WAVEFORM B)

NONINVERTING OUTPUT (WAVEFORM C)

INVERTING OUTPUT (WAVEFORM D)

OUTPUT P1 (WAVEFORM E)

INPUT P0 (WAVEFORM F)

OUTPUT P1 (WAVEFORM G)

VOLTAGE WAVEFORMS

NOTE: Input pulses are supplied by a generator having the following characteristics: $t_r \leqslant$ 7 ns, $t_f \leqslant$ 7 ns, PRR $\leqslant$ 1 MHz, $Z_{out} \approx$ 50 Ω.

FIGURE 1—SWITCHING TIMES

7

076

TEXAS INSTRUMENTS
INCORPORATED
POST OFFICE BOX 5012 • DALLAS, TEXAS 75222

- Generates Either Odd or Even Parity for Nine Data Lines

- Cascadable for n-Bits

- Can Be Used to Upgrade Existing Systems using MSI Parity Circuits

- Typical Data-to-Output Delay of Only 14 ns for 'S280 and 33 ns for 'LS280

- Typical Power Dissipation:
    'LS280 . . . 80 mW
    'S280 . . . 335 mW

FUNCTION TABLE

NUMBER OF INPUTS A	OUTPUTS	
THRU I THAT ARE HIGH	Σ EVEN	Σ ODD
0, 2, 4, 6, 8	H	L
1, 3, 5, 7, 9	L	H

H = high level, L = low level

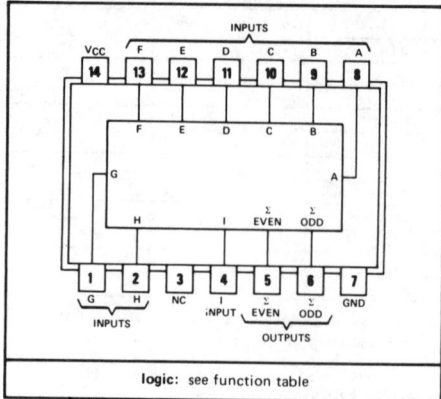

SN54LS280, SN54S280 . . . J OR W PACKAGE
SN74LS280, SN74S280 . . . J OR N PACKAGE
(TOP VIEW)

logic: see function table

NC—No internal connection

description

These universal, monolithic, nine-bit parity generators/checkers utilize Schottky-clamped TTL high-performance circuitry and feature odd/even outputs to facilitate operation of either odd or even parity application. The word-length capability is easily expanded by cascading as shown under typical application data.

Series 54LS/74LS and Series 54S/74S parity generators/checkers offer the designer a trade-off between reduced power consumption and high performance. These devices can be used to upgrade the performance of most systems utilizing the '180 parity generator/checker. Although the 'LS280 and 'S280 are implemented without expander inputs, the corresponding function is provided by the availability of an input at pin 4 and the absence of any internal connection at pin 3. This permits the 'LS280 and 'S280 to be substituted for the '180 in existing designs to produce an identical function even if 'LS280's and 'S280's are mixed with existing '180's.

These devices are fully compatible with most other TTL and DTL circuits. All 'LS280 and 'S280 inputs are buffered to lower the drive requirements to one Series 54LS/74LS or Series 54S/74S standard load, respectively.

schematics of inputs and outputs

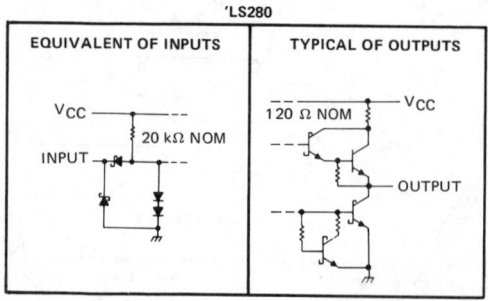

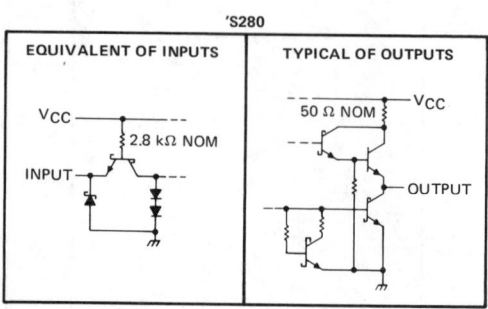

TEXAS INSTRUMENTS
INCORPORATED
POST OFFICE BOX 5012 • DALLAS, TEXAS 75222

1076

absolute maximum ratings over operating free-air temperature range (unless otherwise noted)

Supply voltage (see Note 1)	7 V
Input voltage	7 V
Operating free-air temperature range: SN54LS280	−55°C to 125°C
SN74LS280	0°C to 70°C
Storage temperature range	−65°C to 150°C

NOTE 1: Voltage values are with respect to network ground terminal.

recommended operating conditions

	SN54LS280			SN74LS280			UNIT
	MIN	NOM	MAX	MIN	NOM	MAX	
Supply voltage, V_{CC}	4.5	5	5.5	4.75	5	5.25	V
High-level output current, I_{OH}			−0.4			.4	mA
Low-level output current, I_{OL}			4			8	mA
Operating free-air temperature, T_A	−55		125	0		70	°C

electrical characteristics over recommended operating free-air temperature range (unless otherwise noted)

PARAMETER		TEST CONDITIONS[†]	SN54LS280			SN74LS280			UNIT
			MIN	TYP[‡]	MAX	MIN	TYP[‡]	MAX	
V_{IH}	High-level input voltage		2			2			V
V_{IL}	Low-level input voltage				0.7			0.8	V
V_{IK}	Input clamp voltage	V_{CC} = MIN, I_I = −18 mA			−1.5			−1.5	V
V_{OH}	High-level output voltage	V_{CC} = MIN, V_{IH} = 2 V, V_{IL} = MAX, I_{OH} = −0.4 mA	2.5	3.4		2.7	3.4		V
V_{OL}	Low-level output voltage	V_{CC} = MIN, V_{IH} = 2 V,		0.25	0.4		0.25	0.4	V
		V_{IL} = MAX					0.35	0.5	
I_I	Input current at maximum input voltage	V_{CC} = MAX, V_I = 7 V			0.1			0.1	mA
I_{IH}	High-level input current	V_{CC} = MAX, V_I = 2.7 V			20			20	μA
I_{IL}	Low-level input current	V_{CC} = MAX, V_I = 0.4 V			−0.4			−0.4	mA
I_{OS}	Short-circuit output current[§]	V_{CC} = MAX	−20		−100	−20		−100	mA
I_{CC}	Supply current	V_{CC} = MAX, See Note 2		16	27		16	27	mA

[†]For conditions shown as MIN or MAX, use the appropriate value specified under recommended operating conditions.
[‡]All typical values are at V_{CC} = 5 V, T_A = 25°C.
[§]Not more than one output should be shorted at a time and duration of the short circuit should not exceed one second.
NOTE 2: I_{CC} is measured with all inputs grounded and all outputs open.

switching characteristics, V_{CC} = 5 V, T_A = 25°C

PARAMETER[¶]	FROM (INPUT)	TO (OUTPUT)	TEST CONDITIONS	MIN	TYP	MAX	UNIT
t_{PLH}	Data	Σ Even	C_L = 15 pF, R_L = 2 kΩ, See Note 3		33	50	ns
t_{PHL}					29	45	
t_{PLH}	Data	Σ Odd			23	35	ns
t_{PHL}					31	50	

[¶]t_{PLH} ≡ propagation delay time, low-to-high-level output; t_{PHL} ≡ propagation delay time, high-to-low-level output
NOTE 3: Load circuit and voltage waveforms are shown on page 3-11.

7

TYPES SN54S280, SN74S280
9-BIT ODD/EVEN PARITY GENERATORS/CHECKERS

absolute maximum ratings over operating free-air temperature range (unless otherwise noted)

Supply voltage (see Note 1) . . . . 7 V
Input voltage . . . . 5.5 V
Operating free-air temperature range: SN54S280 . . . . −55°C to 125°C
　　　　　　　　　　　　　　　　　　SN74S280 . . . . 0°C to 70°C
Storage temperature range . . . . −65°C to 150°C

NOTE 1: Voltage values are with respect to network ground terminal.

recommended operating conditions

	SN54S280			SN74S280			UNIT
	MIN	NOM	MAX	MIN	NOM	MAX	
Supply voltage, V_{CC}	4.5	5	5.5	4.75	5	5.25	V
High-level output current, I_{OH}			−1			−1	mA
Low-level output current, I_{OL}			20			20	mA
Operating free-air temperature, T_A	−55		125	0		70	°C

electrical characteristics over recommended operating free-air temperature range (unless otherwise noted)

PARAMETER		TEST CONDITIONS[†]		MIN	TYP[‡]	MAX	UNIT
V_{IH}	High-level input voltage			2			V
V_{IL}	Low-level input voltage					0.8	V
V_{IK}	Input clamp voltage	V_{CC} = MIN, I_I = −18 mA				−1.2	V
V_{OH}	High-level output voltage	V_{CC} = MIN, V_{IH} = 2 V, V_{IL} = 0.8 V, I_{OH} = −1 mA	SN54S'	2.5	3.4		V
			SN74S'	2.7	3.4		
V_{OL}	Low-level output voltage	V_{CC} = MIN, V_{IH} = 2 V, V_{IL} = 0.8 V, I_{OL} = 20 mA				0.5	V
I_I	Input current at maximum input voltage	V_{CC} = MAX, V_I = 5.5 V				1	mA
I_{IH}	High-level input current	V_{CC} = MAX, V_I = 2.7 V				50	μA
I_{IL}	Low-level input current	V_{CC} = MAX, V_I = 0.5 V				−2	mA
I_{OS}	Short-circuit output current[§]	V_{CC} = MAX		−40		−100	mA
I_{CC}	Supply current	V_{CC} = MAX, See Note 2	SN54S280		67	99	mA
			SN74S280		67	105	
		V_{CC} = MAX, T_A = 125°C, See Note 2	SN54S280N			94	mA

[†]For conditions shown as MIN or MAX, use the appropriate value specified under recommended operating conditions.
[‡]All typical values are at V_{CC} = 5 V, T_A = 25°C.
[§]Not more than one output should be shorted at a time and duration of the short circuit should not exceed one second.
NOTE 2: I_{CC} is measured with all inputs grounded and all outputs open.

switching characteristics, V_{CC} = 5 V, T_A = 25°C

PARAMETER[¶]	FROM (INPUT)	TO (OUTPUT)	TEST CONDITIONS	MIN	TYP	MAX	UNIT
t_{PLH}	Data	Σ Even	C_L = 15 pF, R_L = 180 Ω, See Note 4		14	21	ns
t_{PHL}					11.5	18	
t_{PLH}	Data	Σ Odd			14	21	ns
t_{PHL}					11.5	18	

[¶]t_{PLH} ≡ propagation delay time, low-to-high-level output; t_{PHL} ≡ propagation delay time, high-to-low-level output
NOTE 4: Load circuit and voltage waveforms are shown on page 3-10.

7

TEXAS INSTRUMENTS
INCORPORATED
POST OFFICE BOX 5012 • DALLAS, TEXAS 75222

TYPES SN54LS280, SN54S280, SN74LS280, SN74S280
9-BIT ODD/EVEN PARITY GENERATORS/CHECKERS

functional block diagram

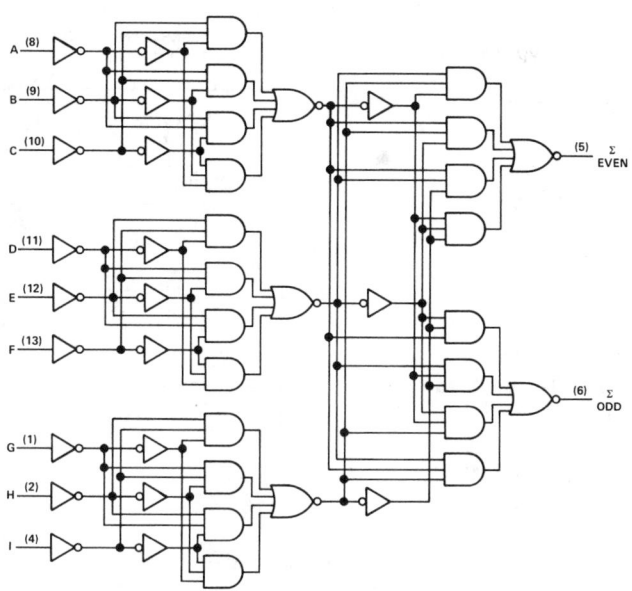

TYPICAL APPLICATION DATA

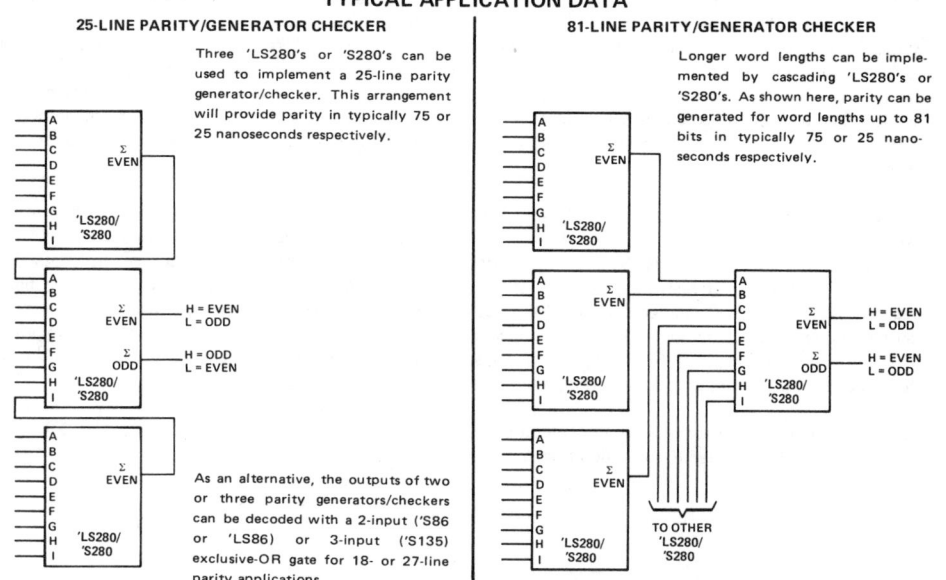

25-LINE PARITY/GENERATOR CHECKER

Three 'LS280's or 'S280's can be used to implement a 25-line parity generator/checker. This arrangement will provide parity in typically 75 or 25 nanoseconds respectively.

As an alternative, the outputs of two or three parity generators/checkers can be decoded with a 2-input ('S86 or 'LS86) or 3-input ('S135) exclusive-OR gate for 18- or 27-line parity applications.

81-LINE PARITY/GENERATOR CHECKER

Longer word lengths can be implemented by cascading 'LS280's or 'S280's. As shown here, parity can be generated for word lengths up to 81 bits in typically 75 or 25 nanoseconds respectively.

TEXAS INSTRUMENTS
INCORPORATED
POST OFFICE BOX 5012 • DALLAS, TEXAS 75222

TTL
LSI

TYPES SN54S281, SN74S281
4-BIT PARALLEL BINARY ACCUMULATORS
BULLETIN NO. DL-S 7612065, FEBRUARY 1974 – REVISED OCTOBER 1976

- Full 4-Bit Binary Accumulator in a Single Package

- 15 Arithmetic/Logic-Type Operations:
  Add
  Subtract (B–A or A–B)
  Complement
  Increment
  Transfer
  Plus 10 Other Functions

- Full Shifting Capabilities:
  Logic Shift (Left or Right)
  Arithmetic Shift (Left or Right)
  for Sign Bit Protection
  Hold
  Parallel Load

- Expandable to Handle n-Bit Words with Full Carry Look-Ahead

- Logic Mode Operation Provides Seven Boolean Functions of the Two Variables

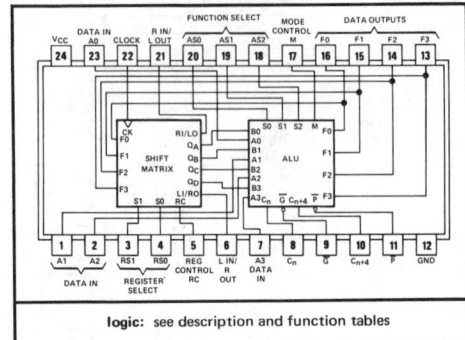

SN54S281 . . . J OR W PACKAGE
SN74S281 . . . J OR N PACKAGE
(TOP VIEW)

logic: see description and function tables

description

These Schottky-clamped four-bit accumulators integrate high-performance versions of an arithmetic logic unit/function generator and a shift/storage matrix on a single monolithic circuit bar. The arithmetic logic unit (ALU) portion, similar to the SN54S181/SN74S181 circuit, incorporates the capability to perform 16 arithmetic/logic-type operations as detailed in Table 1. The accumulator includes an exchange of subtract operands by which either A–B or B–A can be accomplished directly. The ALU is controlled by three function-select inputs (AS0, AS1, AS2) and a mode-control input (M). When the mode-control input is high, the ALU is placed in a logic mode that performs any of seven logic functions on two binary variables as detailed in Table 2. Full carry look-ahead is provided for fast, simultaneous carry generation for the full four binary bits. The carry input (C_n) and propagate and generate outputs ($\overline{P}$, $\overline{G}$) are implemented for direct use with the SN54S182/SN74S182 look-ahead carry generators. This permits systems to be implemented with the added advantage of full look-ahead across any word length to minimize the accumulator delay times. Once data is loaded into the accumulator, the typical add time with full look-ahead is 29 nanoseconds for 16-bit words.

The shift/storage matrix is analogous in its capabilities to the SN54S194/SN74S194 universal bidirectional shift register with the added advantages of multiplexed input/output (I/O) cascading lines that comprehend arithmetic shift functions having a sign bit, such as 2's complements. The matrix can be used to perform either logic or arithmetic shifts in either direction (left or right), parallel load, or hold. Control of the register is accomplished with three inputs: register control (RC) and register selection (RS0, RS1). The cascading input/output lines incorporate three-state outputs multiplexed with an input. The least-significant cascading bit is combined with the A0, F0 circuitry to provide the shift-right input and the shift-left output (RI/LO), and the most significant bit is coupled with the A3, F3 circuitry to provide the shift-left input and the shift-right output (LI/RO).

Series 54S circuits are characterized for operation over the full military temperature range of –55°C to 125°C; Series 74S circuits are characterized for operation from 0°C to 70°C.

TEXAS INSTRUMENTS
INCORPORATED
POST OFFICE BOX 5012 • DALLAS, TEXAS 75222

FUNCTION TABLES

TABLE 1—ARITHMETIC FUNCTIONS

Mode Control (M) = Low

ALU SELECTION			ACTIVE-HIGH DATA	
AS2	AS1	AS0	C_n = H (with carry)	C_n = L (no carry)
L	L	L	F_0 = L, $F_1 = F_2 = F_3$ = H	F_n = H
L	L	H	F = B MINUS A	F = B MINUS A MINUS 1
L	H	L	F = A MINUS B	F = A MINUS B MINUS 1
L	H	H	F = A PLUS B PLUS 1	F = A PLUS B
H	L	L	F = B PLUS 1	$F_n = B_n$
H	L	H	F = $\overline{B}$ PLUS 1	$\overline{F}_n = \overline{B}_n$
H	H	L	F = A PLUS 1	$F_n = A_n$
H	H	H	F = $\overline{A}$ PLUS 1	$F_n = \overline{A}_n$

TABLE 2—LOGIC FUNCTIONS

Mode Control (M) = High

Carry Input (C_n) = X (Irrelevant)

ALU SELECTION			ACTIVE-HIGH DATA FUNCTION
AS2	AS1	AS0	
L	L	L	F_n = L
L	X	H	$F_n = \overline{A_n \oplus B_n}$
L	H	L	$F_n = A_n \oplus B_n$
H	L	L	$F_n = \overline{A_n B_n}$
H	L	H	$F_n = \overline{A_n} + B_n$
H	H	L	$F_n = \overline{A_n} B_n$
H	H	H	$F_n = A_n + B_n$

TABLE 3 — SHIFT-MODE FUNCTIONS

$C_n = M = AS0 = AS1 = L$, and $AS2 = H$ ($F_n = B_n$)

FUNCTION	INPUTS BEFORE ↑									OUTPUTS AFTER ↑						
	REGISTER SELECTION RS0 RS1	REGISTER CONTROL INPUT	INPUT/ OUTPUT RI/LO	SHIFT-MATRIX INPUTS F0 F1 F2 F3				INPUT/ OUTPUT LI/RO	CLOCK INPUT	INPUT/ OUTPUT RI/LO	SHIFT-MATRIX OUTPUTS (ALU B INPUTS) Q_A Q_B Q_C Q_D				INPUT/ OUTPUT LI/RO
LOAD	L L	X	Z	f0 f1 f2 f3				Z	↑	Z	f0 f1 f2 f3				Z
LSL	L H	L	Q_A	Q_A Q_B Q_C Q_D				li	↑	Q_{Bn}	Q_{Bn} Q_{Cn} Q_{Dn} li				li
LSA	L H	H	Q_A	Q_A Q_B Q_C Q_D				li	↑	Q_{Bn}	Q_{Bn} Q_{Cn} li Q_{D0}				li
RSL	H L	L	ri	Q_A Q_B Q_C Q_D				Q_D	↑	ri	ri Q_{An} Q_{Bn} Q_{Cn}				Q_{Cn}
RSA	H L	H	ri	Q_A Q_B Q_C Q_D				Q_C	↑	ri	ri Q_{An} Q_{Bn} Q_{D0}				Q_{Bn}
HOLD	H H	X	X	Q_A Q_B Q_C Q_D				X	↑	Z	Q_{A0} Q_{B0} Q_{C0} Q_{D0}				Z
	X X	X	X	Q_A Q_B Q_C Q_D				X	L	RI/LO	Q_{A0} Q_{B0} Q_{C0} Q_{D0}				LI/RO

H = high level (steady state)
L = low level (steady state)
X = irrelevant (any input, including transitions)
Z = high impedance (output off)
↑ = transition from low to high level
f0, f1, f2, f3, ri, li = the level of steady-state conditions at F0, F1, F2, F3, RI/LO, or LI/RO respectively
Q_{A0}, Q_{B0}, Q_{C0}, Q_{D0} = the level of Q_A, Q_B, Q_C, or Q_D, respectively, before the indicated steady-state input conditions were established
Q_{An}, Q_{Bn}, Q_{Cn}, Q_{Dn} = the level of Q_A, Q_B, Q_C, or Q_D, respectively, before the most recent transition of the clock
See explanation of function tables on page 3-8.

absolute maximum ratings over operating free-air temperature range (unless otherwise noted)

Supply voltage, V_{CC} (see Note 1) . . . . 7 V
Input voltage . . . . 5.5 V
Operating free-air temperature range: SN54S281 (see Note 2) . . . . −55°C to 125°C
　　　　　　　　　　　　　　　　　　　SN74S281 . . . . 0°C to 70°C
Storage temperature range . . . . −65°C to 150°C

NOTES: 1. Voltage values are with respect to network ground terminal.
　　　　2. An SN54S281 in the W package operating at free-air temperatures above 110°C requires a heat sink that provides thermal resistance from case to free-air, $R_{\theta CA}$, of not more than 20°C/W.

7

TEXAS INSTRUMENTS
INCORPORATED
POST OFFICE BOX 5012 • DALLAS, TEXAS 75222

recommended operating conditions

		SN54S281 MIN	NOM	MAX	SN74S281 MIN	NOM	MAX	UNIT
Supply voltage, V_{CC}		4.5	5	5.5	4.75	5	5.25	V
High-level output current, I_{OH}	Any output except LI/RO and RI/LO			−1			−1	mA
	LI/RO and RI/LO			−2			−2	
Low-level output current, I_{OL}	Any output except LI/RO and RI/LO			20			20	mA
	LI/RO and RI/LO			10			10	
Clock frequency, f_{clock} (for shifting)		0		50	0		50	MHz
Width of clock pulse, $t_{w(clock)}$		8			8			ns
Data setup time with respect to clock, t_{su}		0†			0†			ns
Data hold time with respect to clock, t_h		18†			18†			ns
Operating free-air temperature, T_A (see Note 2)		−55		125	0		70	°C

†The arrow indicates that the rising edge of the clock pulse is used for reference.

NOTE 2: An SN54S281 in the W package operating at free-air temperatures above 110°C requires a heat sink that provides thermal resistance from case to free-air, $R_{\theta CA}$, of not more than 20°C/W.

electrical characteristics over recommended operating free-air temperature range (unless otherwise noted)

PARAMETER			TEST CONDITIONS†	SN54S281 MIN	TYP‡	MAX	SN74S281 MIN	TYP‡	MAX	UNIT
V_{IH}	High-level input voltage			2			2			V
V_{IL}	Low-level input voltage					0.8			0.8	V
V_{IK}	Input clamp voltage	Any input except LI/RO and RI/LO	V_{CC} = MIN, I_I = −18 mA			−1.2			−1.2	V
V_{OH}	High-level output voltage	Any output except LI/RO and RI/LO	V_{CC} = MIN, V_{IH} = 2 V,	2.5	3.4		2.7	3.4		V
		LI/RO, RI/LO	V_{IL} = 0.8 V, I_{OH} = MAX	2.4	3.4		2.4	3.4		
V_{OL}	Low-level output voltage		V_{CC} = MIN, V_{IH} = 2 V, V_{IL} = 0.8 V, I_{OL} = MAX			0.5			0.5	V
I_I	Input current at maximum input voltage		V_{CC} = MAX, V_I = 5.5 V			1			1	mA
I_{IH}	High-level input current	RS0, RS1	V_{CC} = MAX, V_I = 2.7 V, See Note 3			50			50	μA
		M, Clock				150			150	
		LI/RO, RI/LO				200			200	
		AS2				300			300	
		All others				250			250	
I_{IL}	Low-level input current	RS0, RS1, LI/RO	V_{CC} = MAX, V_I = 0.5 V See Note 3			−2			−2	mA
		RI/LO				−3			−3	
		M, Clock				−4			−4	
		AS0, AS1				−6			−6	
		All others				−8			−8	
I_{OS}	Short-circuit output current §		V_{CC} = MAX	−40		−110	−40		−110	mA
I_{CC}	Supply current		V_{CC} = MAX, T_A = 125°C	W package only		190				mA
			V_{CC} = MAX	All packages	144	230		144	230	

†For conditions shown as MIN or MAX, use the appropriate value specified under recommended operating conditions.

‡All typical values are at V_{CC} = 5 V, T_A = 25°C.

§Not more than one output should be shorted at a time and duration of the short-circuit should not exceed one second.

NOTE 3. When testing input current at the RI/LO or LI/RO terminals, the output under test must be in the high-impedance (off) state.

TEXAS INSTRUMENTS
INCORPORATED
POST OFFICE BOX 5012 • DALLAS, TEXAS 75222

1076

switching characteristics, $V_{CC} = 5$ V, $T_A = 25°C$

PARAMETER¶	FROM (INPUT)	TO (OUTPUT)	TEST CONDITIONS	MIN	TYP	MAX	UNIT
t_{PLH}	C_n	C_{n+4}			10	20	ns
t_{PHL}					10	20	
t_{PLH}	Any A	C_{n+4}			18	30	ns
t_{PHL}					18	30	
t_{PLH}	C_n	Any F			10	20	ns
t_{PHL}					10	20	
t_{PLH}	Any A	$\overline{G}$			14	24	ns
t_{PHL}					14	24	
t_{PLH}	Any A	$\overline{P}$			12	20	ns
t_{PHL}					12	20	
t_{PLH}	A_i	F_i			20	35	ns
t_{PHL}			$C_L = 15$ pF,		20	35	
t_{PLH}	A_0	RI/LO	I/O outputs: $R_L = 560$ Ω,		30	45	ns
t_{PHL}			Other outputs: $R_L = 280$ Ω,		30	45	
t_{PLH}	A_3	LI/RO	See Figure 1		30	45	ns
t_{PHL}					30	45	
t_{PLH}	F_0	RI/LO			7	11	ns
t_{PHL}					7	11	
t_{PLH}	F_3	LI/RO			7	11	ns
t_{PHL}					7	11	
t_{PLH}	Any AS	Any F or C_{n+4}			28	45	ns
t_{PHL}					28	45	
t_{PLH}	Any AS	$\overline{P}$ or $\overline{G}$			20	33	ns
t_{PHL}					20	33	
t_{PLH}	Clock	Any F			30	45	ns
t_{PHL}					30	45	
t_{PLH}	Clock	RI/LO or LI/RO			35	55	ns
t_{PHL}					35	55	

¶ t_{PLH} ≡ Propagation delay time, low-to-high-level output
t_{PHL} ≡ Propagation delay time, high-to-low-level output

7

PARAMETER MEASUREMENT INFORMATION

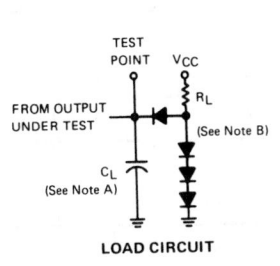

LOAD CIRCUIT

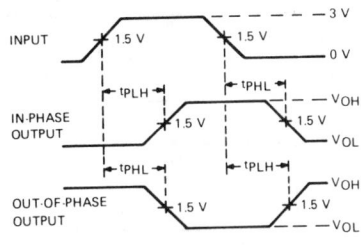

VOLTAGE WAVEFORMS

NOTES: A. Input pulse is supplied by a generator having the following characteristics: $t_r \leqslant 2.5$ ns, $t_f \leqslant 2.5$ ns, PRR $\leqslant 1$ MHz, $Z_{out} \approx 50$ Ω.
   B. C_L inlcudes probe and jig capacitance.
   C. All diodes are 1N916 or 1N3064.

FIGURE 1

TEXAS INSTRUMENTS
INCORPORATED
POST OFFICE BOX 5012 • DALLAS, TEXAS 75222

TYPES SN54S281, SN74S281
4-BIT PARALLEL BINARY ACCUMULATORS

TYPICAL APPLICATION DATA

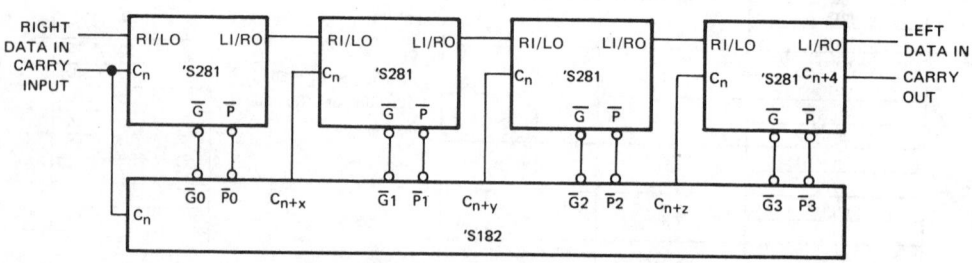

ENTER AND STORE TIME: 38 ns typical
EACH SUCCESSIVE ADDITION TO STORED DATA: 44 ns typical

**FIGURE A—16-BIT BINARY ACCUMULATOR USING FOUR SN54S281/SN74S281 CIRCUITS
IN RIPPLE-CARRY MODE**

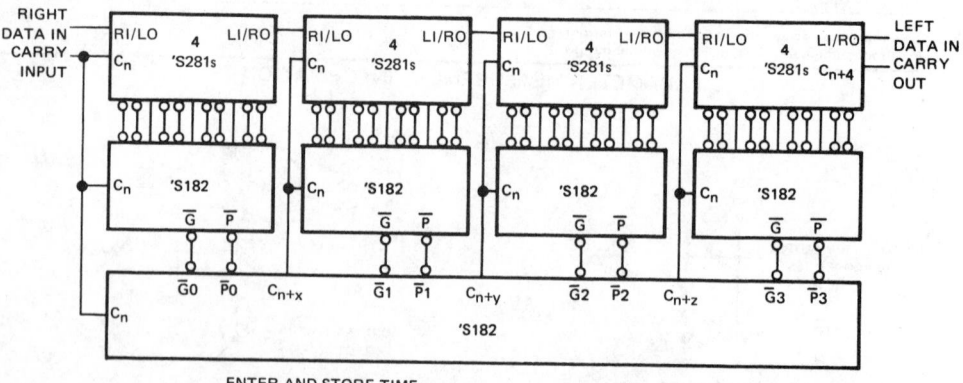

ENTER AND STORE TIME: 37 ns typical
EACH SUCCESSIVE ADDITION TO STORED DATA: 29 ns typical

**FIGURE B—16-BIT BINARY ACCUMULATOR USING FOUR SN54S281/SN74S281 CIRCUITS
AND ONE SN54S182/SN74S182 IN FULL LOOK-AHEAD CARRY MODE**

ENTER AND STORE TIME: 42 ns typical
EACH SUCCESSIVE ADDITION TO STORED DATA: 34 ns typical

**FIGURE C—64-BIT BINARY ACCUMULATOR USING 16 SN54S281/SN74S281 CIRCUITS AND
FIVE SN54S182/SN74S182 CIRCUITS FOR FULL CARRY LOOK-AHEAD**

A inputs and F outputs of 'S281 are not shown.

877

TTL
MSI

TYPES SN54283, SN54LS283, SN54S283, SN74283, SN74LS283, SN74S283
4-BIT BINARY FULL ADDERS WITH FAST CARRY

BULLETIN NO. DL-S 7611832, OCTOBER 1976

- Full-Carry Look-Ahead Across the Four Bits
- Systems Achieve Partial Look-Ahead Performance with the Economy of Ripple Carry
- Supply Voltage and Ground on Corner Pins to Simplify P-C Board Layout

TYPICAL ADD TIMES

TYPE	TWO 8-BIT WORDS	TWO 16-BIT WORDS	TYPICAL POWER DISSIPATION PER ADDER
'283	23ns	43ns	310 mW
'LS283	25ns	45ns	95 mW
'S283	15ns	30ns	510 mW

SN54283, SN54LS283 . . . J OR W PACKAGE
SN54S283 . . . J PACKAGE
SN74283, SN74LS283, SN74S283 . . . J OR N PACKAGE
(TOP VIEW)

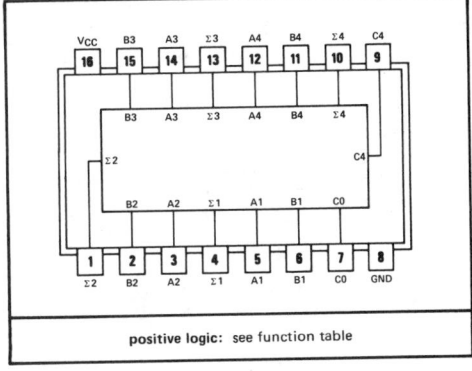

positive logic: see function table

description

The '283 and 'LS283 adders are electrically and functionally identical to the '83A and 'LS283, respectively; only the arrangement of the terminals has been changed. The 'S283 high performance versions are also functionally identical.

These improved full adders perform the addition of two 4-bit binary words. The sum (Σ) outputs are provided for each bit and the resultant carry (C4) is obtained from the fourth bit. These adders feature full internal look-ahead across all four bits generating the carry term in ten nanoseconds, typically, for the '283 and 'LS283, and 7.5 nanoseconds for the 'S283. This capability provides the system designer with partial look-ahead performance at the economy and reduced package count of a ripple-carry implementation.

The adder logic, including the carry, is implemented in its true form. End around carry can be accomplished without the need for logic or level inversion.

Series 54, Series 54LS, and Series 54S circuits are characterized for operation over the full temperature range of -55°C to 125°C. Series 74, Series 74LS, and Series 74S circuits are characterized for 0°C to 70°C operation.

FUNCTION TABLE

INPUT				OUTPUT WHEN C0 = L WHEN C2 = L			OUTPUT WHEN C0 = L WHEN C2 = H	OUTPUT WHEN C0 = H WHEN C2 = L			OUTPUT WHEN C0 = H WHEN C2 = H
A1 / A3	B1 / B3	A2 / A4	B2 / B4	Σ1 / Σ3	Σ2 / Σ4	C2 / C4	Σ1 / Σ3	Σ2 / Σ4	C2 / C4		
L	L	L	L	L	L	L	H	L	L		
H	L	L	L	H	L	L	L	H	L		
L	H	L	L	H	L	L	L	H	L		
H	H	L	L	L	H	L	H	H	L		
L	L	H	L	L	H	L	H	H	L		
H	L	H	L	H	H	L	L	L	H		
L	H	H	L	H	H	L	L	L	H		
H	H	H	L	L	L	H	H	L	H		
L	L	L	H	L	H	L	H	H	L		
H	L	L	H	H	H	L	L	L	H		
L	H	L	H	H	H	L	L	L	H		
H	H	L	H	L	L	H	H	L	H		
L	L	H	H	L	L	H	H	L	H		
H	L	H	H	H	L	H	L	H	H		
L	H	H	H	H	L	H	L	H	H		
H	H	H	H	H	H	H	H	H	H		

H = high level, L = low level

NOTE: Input conditions at A1, B1, A2, B2, and C0 are used to determine outputs Σ1 and Σ2 and the value of the internal carry C2. The values at C2, A3, B3, A4, and B4 are then used to determine outputs Σ3, Σ4, and C4.

7

TYPES SN54283, SN54LS283, SN54S283, SN74283, SN74LS283, SN74S283
4-BIT BINARY FULL ADDERS WITH FAST CARRY

functional block diagram and schematics of inputs and outputs

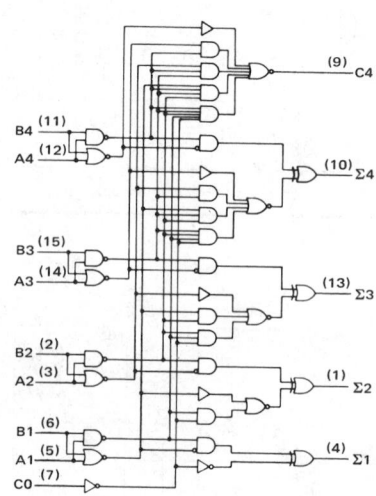

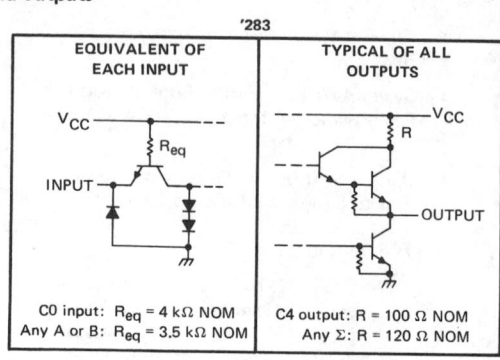

'283

EQUIVALENT OF EACH INPUT	TYPICAL OF ALL OUTPUTS

CO input: R_{eq} = 4 kΩ NOM
Any A or B: R_{eq} = 3.5 kΩ NOM

C4 output: R = 100 Ω NOM
Any Σ: R = 120 Ω NOM

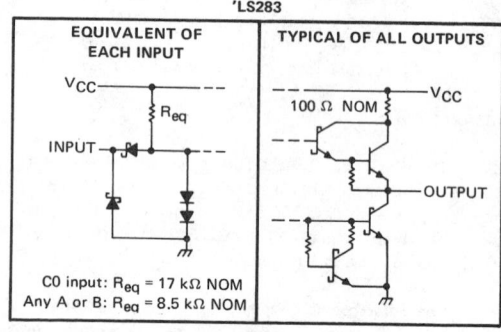

'LS283

EQUIVALENT OF EACH INPUT	TYPICAL OF ALL OUTPUTS

100 Ω NOM

CO input: R_{eq} = 17 kΩ NOM
Any A or B: R_{eq} = 8.5 kΩ NOM

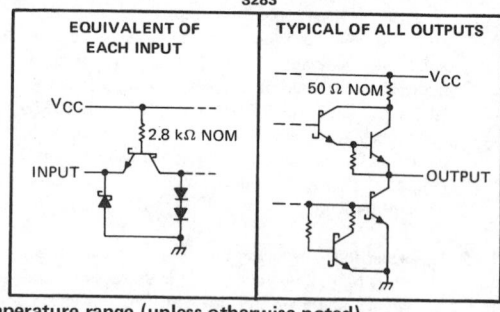

'S283

EQUIVALENT OF EACH INPUT	TYPICAL OF ALL OUTPUTS

2.8 kΩ NOM

50 Ω NOM

absolute maximum ratings over operating free-air temperature range (unless otherwise noted)

Supply voltage, V_{CC} (see Note 1) 7V
Input voltage: '283, 'S283 . . . . 5.5V
　　　　　　'LS283 . . . . 7V
Interemitter voltage (see Note 2) 5.5V
Operating free-air temperature range; SN54283, SN54LS283, SN54S283 . . . . −55°C to 125°C
　　　　　　　　　　　　　　　　　SN74283, SN74LS283, SN74S283 . . . . 0°C to 70°C
Storage temperature range . . . . −65°C to 150°C
NOTES: 1. Voltage values, except interemitter voltage, are with respect to network ground terminal.
　　　　2. This is the voltage between two emitters of a multiple-emitter transistor. This rating applies for the '283 and 'S283 only between
　　　　　the following pairs: A1 and B1, A2 and B2, A3 and B3, A4 and B4.

TEXAS INSTRUMENTS
INCORPORATED
POST OFFICE BOX 5012 • DALLAS, TEXAS 75222

1076

recommended operating conditions

		SN54283 MIN	NOM	MAX	SN74283 MIN	NOM	MAX	UNIT
Supply Voltage, V_{CC}		4.5	5	5.5	4.75	5	5.25	V
High-level output current, I_{OH}	Any output except C4			−800			−800	μA
	Output C4			−400			−400	
Low-level output current, I_{OL}	Any output except C4			16			16	mA
	Output C4			8			8	
Operating free-air temperature, T_A		−55		125	0		70	°C

electrical characteristics over recommended operating free-air temperature range (unless otherwise noted)

PARAMETER		TEST CONDITIONS[†]	SN54283 MIN	TYP[‡]	MAX	SN74283 MIN	TYP[‡]	MAX	UNIT
V_{IH}	High-level input voltage		2			2			V
V_{IL}	Low-level input voltage				0.8			0.8	V
V_{IK}	Input clamp voltage	V_{CC} = MIN, I_I = −12 mA			−1.5			−1.5	V
V_{OH}	High-level output voltage	V_{CC} = MIN, V_{IH} = 2 V, V_{IL} = 0.8 V, I_{OH} = MAX	2.4	3.6		2.4	3.6		V
V_{OL}	Low-level output voltage	V_{CC} = MIN, V_{IH} = 2 V, V_{IL} = 0.8 V, I_{OL} = MAX		0.2	0.4		0.2	0.4	V
I_I	Input current at maximum input voltage	V_{CC} = MAX, V_I = 5.5 V			1			1	mA
I_{IH}	High-level input current	V_{CC} = MAX, V_I = 2.4 V			40			40	μA
I_{IL}	Low-level input current	V_{CC} = MAX, V_I = 0.4 V			−1.6			−1.6	mA
I_{OS}	Short-circuit output current[§]	Any output except C4 — V_{CC} = MAX	−20		−55	−18		−55	mA
		Output C4	−20		−70	−18		−70	
I_{CC}	Supply current	V_{CC} = MAX, Outputs open — All B low, other inputs at 4.5 V		56			56		mA
		All inputs at 4.5 V		66	99		66	110	

[†] For conditions shown as MIN or MAX, use the appropriate value specified under recommended operating conditions.
[‡] All typical values are at V_{CC} = 5 V, T_A = 25°C.
[§] Only one output should be shorted at a time.

switching characteristics, V_{CC} = 5 V, T_A = 25°C

PARAMETER[¶]	FROM (INPUT)	TO (OUTPUT)	TEST CONDITIONS	MIN	TYP	MAX	UNIT
t_{PLH}	C0	Any Σ	C_L = 15 pF, R_L = 400 Ω, See Note 3		14	21	ns
t_{PHL}					12	21	
t_{PLH}	A_i or B_i	$Σ_i$			16	24	ns
t_{PHL}					16	24	
t_{PLH}	C0	C4	C_L = 15 pF, R_L = 780 Ω, See Note 3		9	14	ns
t_{PHL}					11	16	
t_{PLH}	A_i or B_i	C4			9	14	ns
t_{PHL}					11	16	

[¶] t_{PLH} ≡ Propagation delay time, low-to-high-level output
t_{PHL} ≡ Propagation delay time, high-to-low-level output
NOTE 3: Load circuit and voltage waveforms are shown on page 3-10.

7

TEXAS INSTRUMENTS
INCORPORATED
POST OFFICE BOX 5012 • DALLAS, TEXAS 75222

recommended operating conditions

		SN54LS283			SN74LS283			UNIT
		MIN	NOM	MAX	MIN	NOM	MAX	
Supply voltage, V_{CC}		4.5	5	5.5	4.75	5	5.25	V
High-level output current, I_{OH}				−400			−400	μA
Low-level output current, I_{OL}				4			8	mA
Operating free-air temperature, T_A		−55		125	0		70	°C

electrical characteristics over recommended operating free-air temperature range (unless otherwise noted)

PARAMETER		TEST CONDITIONS†			SN54LS283			SN74LS283			UNIT
					MIN	TYP‡	MAX	MIN	TYP‡	MAX	
V_{IH} High-level input voltage					2			2			V
V_{IL} Low-level input voltage							0.7			0.8	V
V_{IK} Input clamp voltage		V_{CC} = MIN,	$I_I = -18$ mA				−1.5			−1.5	V
V_{OH} High-level output voltage		V_{CC} = MIN, V_{IH} = 2 V, $V_{IL} = V_{IL}$ max, $I_{OH} = -400$ μA			2.5	3.4		2.7	3.4		V
V_{OL} Low-level output voltage		V_{CC} = MIN, V_{IH} = 2 V, $V_{IL} = V_{IL}$ max	I_{OL} = 4 mA			0.25	0.4		0.25	0.4	V
			I_{OL} = 8 mA						0.35	0.5	
I_I Input current at maximum input voltage	Any A or B	V_{CC} = MAX, V_I = 7 V					0.2			0.2	mA
	C0						0.1			0.1	
I_{IH} High-level input current	Any A or B	V_{CC} = MAX, V_I = 2.7 V					40			40	μA
	C0						20			20	
I_{IL} Low-level input current	Any A or B	V_{CC} = MAX, V_I = 0.4 V					−0.8			−0.8	mA
	C0						−0.4			−0.4	
I_{OS} Short-circuit output current§		V_{CC} = MAX			−20		−100	−20		−100	mA
I_{CC} Supply current		V_{CC} = MAX, Outputs open	All inputs grounded			22	39		22	39	mA
			All B low, other inputs at 4.5 V			19	34		19	34	
			All inputs at 4.5 V			19	34		19	34	

†For conditions shown as MIN or MAX, use the appropriate value specified under recommended operating conditions.
‡All typical values are at V_{CC} = 5 V, $T_A = 25°$C.
§Only one output should be shorted at a time and duration of the short-circuit should not exceed one second.

switching characteristics, V_{CC} = 5 V, $T_A = 25°$C

PARAMETER¶	FROM (INPUT)	TO (OUTPUT)	TEST CONDITIONS	MIN	TYP	MAX	UNIT
t_{PLH}	C0	Any Σ			16	24	ns
t_{PHL}					15	24	
t_{PLH}	A_i or B_i	$Σ_i$			15	24	ns
t_{PHL}			C_L = 15 pF, R_L = 2 kΩ, See Note 4		15	24	
t_{PLH}	C0	C4			11	17	ns
t_{PHL}					11	22	
t_{PLH}	A_i or B_i	C4			11	17	ns
t_{PHL}					12	17	

¶ $t_{PLH} \equiv$ Propagation delay time, low-to-high-level output
$t_{PHL} \equiv$ Propagation delay time, high-to-low-level output
NOTE 4: Load circuit and voltage waveforms are shown on page 3-11.

7

TEXAS INSTRUMENTS
INCORPORATED
POST OFFICE BOX 5012 • DALLAS, TEXAS 75222

1076

recommended operating conditions

		SN54S283			SN74S283			UNIT
		MIN	NOM	MAX	MIN	NOM	MAX	
Supply voltage, V_{CC}		4.5	5	5.5	4.75	5	5.25	V
High-level output current, I_{OH}	Any output except C4			−1			−1	mA
	Output C4			−500			−500	µA
Low-level output current, I_{OL}	Any output except C4			20			20	mA
	Output C4			10			0	
Operating free-air temperature, T_A		−55		125	0		70	°C

electrical characteristics over recommended operating free-air temperature range (unless otherwise noted)

	PARAMETER		TEST CONDITIONS[†]		MIN	TYP[‡]	MAX	UNIT
V_{IH}	High-level input voltage				2			V
V_{IL}	Low-level input voltage						0.8	V
V_{IK}	Input clamp voltage		V_{CC} = MIN,	I_I = −18 mA			−1.2	V
V_{OH}	High-level output voltage	SN54S283	V_{CC} = MIN,	V_{IH} = 2 V,	2.5	3.4		V
		SN74S283	V_{IL} = 0.8 V,	I_{OH} = MAX	2.7	3.4		
V_{OL}	Low-level output voltage		V_{CC} = MIN, V_{IL} = 0.8 V,	V_{IH} = 2 V, I_{OL} = MAX			0.5	V
I_I	Input current at maximum input voltage		V_{CC} = MAX,	V_I = 5.5 V			1	mA
I_{IH}	High-level input current		V_{CC} = MAX,	V_I = 2.7 V			50	µA
I_{IL}	Low-level input current		V_{CC} = MAX,	V_I = 0.5 V			−2	mA
I_{OS}	Short-circuit output current§	Any output except C4	V_{CC} = MAX		−40		−100	mA
		Output C4			−20		−100	
I_{CC}	Supply current		V_{CC} = MAX, Outputs open	All B low, other inputs at 4.5 V		80		mA
				All inputs at 4.5 V		95	160	

[†]For conditions shown as MIN or MAX, use the appropriate value specified under recommended operating conditions for the applicable device type.

[‡]All typical values are at V_{CC} = 5 V, T_A = 25°C.

§Only one output should be shorted at a time, and duration of the short-circuit should not exceed one second.

switching characteristics, V_{CC} = 5 V, T_A = 25°C

PARAMETER¶	FROM (INPUT)	TO (OUTPUT)	TEST CONDITIONS	MIN	TYP	MAX	UNIT
t_{PLH}	C0	Any Σ	C_L = 15 pF, R_L = 280 Ω, See Note 3		11	18	ns
t_{PHL}					12	18	
t_{PLH}	A_i or B_i	$Σ_i$			12	18	ns
t_{PHL}					11.5	18	
t_{PLH}	C0	C4	C_L = 15 pF, R_L = 560 Ω, See Note 3		6	11	ns
t_{PHL}					7.5	11	
t_{PLH}	A_i or B_i	C4			7.5	12	ns
t_{PHL}					8.5	12	

¶t_{PLH} = Propagation delay time, low-to-high-level output

t_{PHL} = Propagation delay time, high-to-low-level output

NOTE 3: Load circuit and voltage waveforms are shown on page 3-10.

7

TEXAS INSTRUMENTS
INCORPORATED
POST OFFICE BOX 5012 • DALLAS, TEXAS 75222

- **Fast Multiplication of Two Binary Numbers** 8-Bit Product in 40 ns Typical

- **Expandable for N-Bit-by-n-Bit Applications:** 16-Bit Product in 70 ns Typical 32-Bit Product in 103 ns Typical

- **Fully Compatible with Most DTL and TTL Circuits**

- **Diode-Clamped Inputs Simplify System Design**

description

These high-speed TTL circuits are designed to be used in high-performance parallel multiplication applications. When connected as shown in Figure A, these circuits perform the positive-logic multiplication of two 4-bit binary words. The eight-bit binary product is generated with typically only 40 nanoseconds delay.

This basic four-by-four multiplier can be utilized as a fundamental building block for implementing larger multipliers. For example, the four-by-four building blocks can be connected as shown in Figure B to generate submultiple partial products. These results can then be summed in a Wallace tree, and, as illustrated, will produce a 16-bit product for the two eight-bit words typically in 70 nanoseconds. SN54H183/SN74H183 carry-save adders and SN54S181/SN74S181 arithmetic logic units with the SN54S182/SN74S182 look-ahead generator are used to achieve this high performance. The scheme is expandable for implementing N X M bit multipliers.

schematics of inputs and outputs

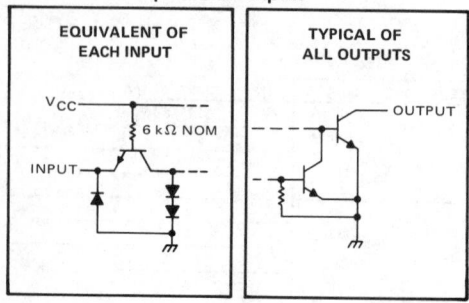

EQUIVALENT OF EACH INPUT	TYPICAL OF ALL OUTPUTS

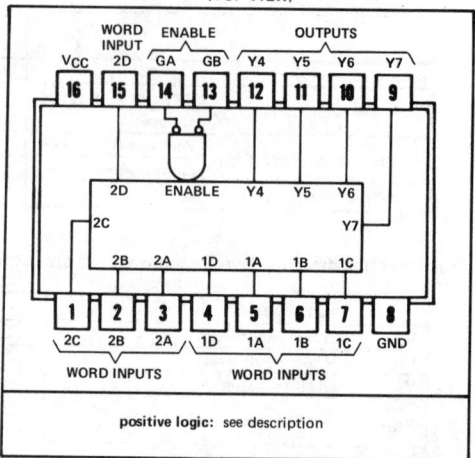

SN54284 . . . J OR W PACKAGE
SN74284 . . . J OR N PACKAGE
(TOP VIEW)

positive logic: see description

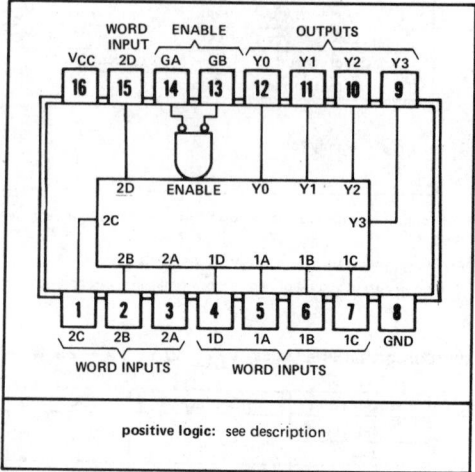

SN54285 . . . J OR W PACKAGE
SN74285 . . . J OR N PACKAGE
(TOP VIEW)

positive logic: see description

The SN54284 and SN54285 are characterized for operation over the full military temperature range of −55°C to 125°C; the SN74284 and SN74285 are characterized for operation from 0°C to 70°C.

TEXAS INSTRUMENTS
INCORPORATED
POST OFFICE BOX 5012 • DALLAS, TEXAS 75222

1076

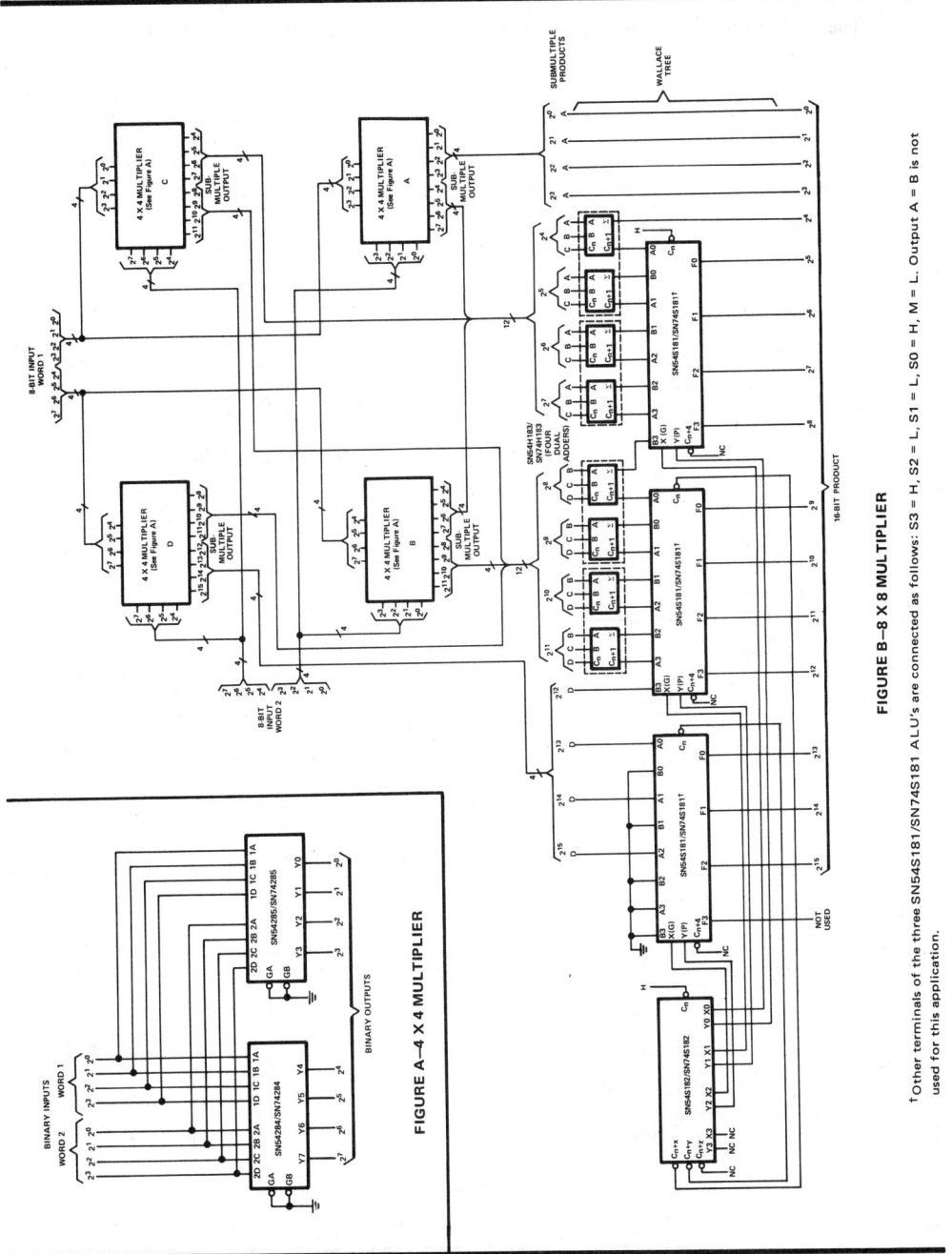

FIGURE A—4 X 4 MULTIPLIER

FIGURE B—8 X 8 MULTIPLIER

†Other terminals of the three SN54S181/SN74S181 ALU's are connected as follows: S3 = H, S2 = L, S1 = L, S0 = H, M = L. Output A = B is not used for this application.

7

TEXAS INSTRUMENTS
INCORPORATED
POST OFFICE BOX 5012 • DALLAS, TEXAS 75222

TYPES SN54284, SN54285, SN74284, SN74285
4-BIT-BY-4-BIT PARALLEL BINARY MULTIPLIERS

absolute maximum ratings over operating free-air temperature range (unless otherwise noted)

Supply voltage, V_{CC} (see Note 1)	7 V
Input voltage	5.5 V
Operating free-air temperature range: SN54' Circuits	−55°C to 125°C
SN74' Circuits	0°C to 70°C
Storage temperature range	−65°C to 150°C

NOTE 1: Voltage values are with respect to network ground terminal.

recommended operating conditions

	SN54284 SN54285			SN74284 SN74285			UNIT
	MIN	NOM	MAX	MIN	NOM	MAX	
Supply voltage, V_{CC}	4.5	5	5.5	4.75	5	5.25	V
High-level output voltage, V_{OH}			5.5			5.5	V
Low-level output current, I_{OL}			16			16	mA
Operating free-air temperature, T_A	−55		125	0		70	°C

electrical characteristics over recommended operating free-air temperature range (unless otherwise noted)

PARAMETER		TEST CONDITIONS[†]		MIN	TYP[‡]	MAX	UNIT
V_{IH}	High-level input voltage			2			V
V_{IL}	Low-level input voltage					0.8	V
V_I	Input clamp voltage	V_{CC} = MIN,	I_I = −12 mA			−1.5	V
I_{OH}	High-level output current	V_{CC} = MIN, V_{IH} = 2 V, V_{IL} = 0.8 V, V_{OH} = 5.5 V				40	µA
V_{OL}	Low-level output voltage	V_{CC} = MIN, V_{IH} = 2 V, V_{IL} = 0.8 V	I_{OL} = 12 mA			0.4	V
			I_{OL} = 16 mA			0.45	
I_I	Input current at maximum input voltage	V_{CC} = MAX, V_I = 5.5 V				1	mA
I_{IH}	High-level input current	V_{CC} = MAX, V_I = 2.4 V				40	µA
I_{IL}	Low-level input current	V_{CC} = MAX, V_I = 0.4 V				−1	mA
I_{CC}	Supply current	V_{CC} = MAX, T_A = 125°C, See Note 2	SN54284, SN54285 N package only			99	mA
		V_{CC} = MAX, See Note 2	SN54284, SN54285		92	110	
			SN74284, SN74285		92	130	

[†]For conditions shown as MIN or MAX, use the appropriate value specified under recommended operating conditions for the applicable device type.
[‡]All typical values are at V_{CC} = 5 V, T_A = 25°C.
NOTE 2: With outputs open and both enable inputs grounded, I_{CC} is measured first by selecting an output product which contains three or more high-level bits, then by selecting an output product which contains four low-level bits.

switching characteristics, V_{CC} = 5 V, T_A = 25°C

PARAMETER		TEST CONDITIONS	MIN	TYP	MAX	UNIT
t_{PLH}	Propagation delay time, low-to-high-level output from enable	C_L = 30 pF to GND, R_{L1} = 300 Ω to V_{CC}, R_{L2} = 600 Ω to GND, See Note 3		20	30	ns
t_{PHL}	Propagation delay time, high-to-low-level output from enable			20	30	
t_{PLH}	Propagation delay time, low-to-high-level output from word inputs			40	60	ns
t_{PHL}	Propagation delay time, high-to-low-level output from word inputs			40	60	

NOTE 3: Load circuit is as described above; waveforms are shown on page 3-10.

7

TTL
MSI

TYPES SN54290, SN54293, SN54LS290, SN54LS293
SN74290, SN74293, SN74LS290, SN74LS293
DECADE AND 4-BIT BINARY COUNTERS
BULLETIN NO. DL-S 7611833, MARCH 1974—REVISED OCTOBER 1976

'290, 'LS290 . . . DECADE COUNTERS
'293, 'LS293 . . . 4-BIT BINARY COUNTERS

- GND and V_{CC} on Corner Pins
  (Pins 7 and 14 Respectively)

description

The SN54290/SN74290, SN54LS290/SN74LS290, SN54293/SN74293, and SN54LS293/SN74LS293 counters are electrically and functionally identical to the SN5490A/SN7490A, SN54LS90/SN74LS90, SN5493A/SN7493A, and SN54LS93/SN74LS93, respectively. Only the arrangement of the terminals has been changed for the '290, 'LS290, '293, and 'LS293.

Each of these monolithic counters contains four master-slave flip-flops and additional gating to provide a divide-by-two counter and a three-stage binary counter for which the count cycle length is divide-by-five for the '290 and 'LS290 and divide-by-eight for the '293 and 'LS293.

All of these counters have a gated zero reset and the '290 and 'LS290 also have gated set-to-nine inputs for use in BCD nine's complement applications.

To use the maximum count length (decade or four-bit binary) of these counters, the B input is connected to the Q_A output. The input count pulses are applied to input A and the outputs are as described in the appropriate function table. A symmetrical divide-by-ten count can be obtained from the '290 and 'LS290 counters by connecting the Q_D output to the A input and applying the input count to the B input which gives a divide-by-ten square wave at output Q_A.

SN54290, SN54LS290 . . . J OR W PACKAGE
SN74290, SN74LS290 . . . J OR N PACKAGE
(TOP VIEW)

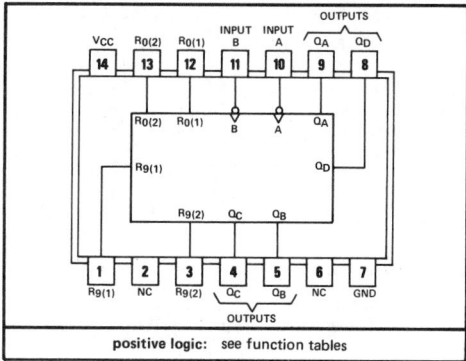

positive logic: see function tables

SN54293, SN54LS293 . . . J OR W PACKAGE
SN74293, SN74LS293 . . . J OR N PACKAGE
(TOP VIEW)

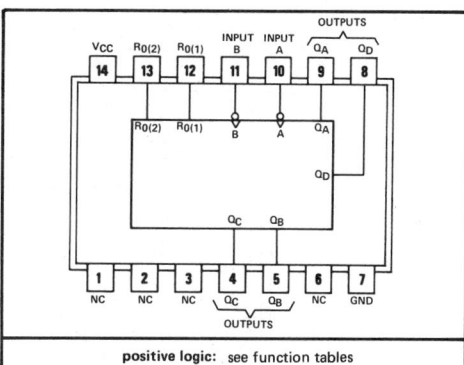

positive logic: see function tables

NC—No internal connection

7

TEXAS INSTRUMENTS
INCORPORATED
POST OFFICE BOX 5012 • DALLAS, TEXAS 75222

7-423

TYPES SN54290, SN54293, SN54LS290, SN54LS293, SN74290, SN74293, SN74LS290, SN74LS293
DECADE AND 4-BIT BINARY COUNTERS

'290, 'LS290 BCD COUNT SEQUENCE (See Note A)

COUNT	OUTPUT			
	Q_D	Q_C	Q_B	Q_A
0	L	L	L	L
1	L	L	L	H
2	L	L	H	L
3	L	L	H	H
4	L	H	L	L
5	L	H	L	H
6	L	H	H	L
7	L	H	H	H
8	H	L	L	L
9	H	L	L	H

'290, 'LS290 BI-QUINARY (5-2) (See Note B)

COUNT	OUTPUT			
	Q_A	Q_D	Q_C	Q_B
0	L	L	L	L
1	L	L	L	H
2	L	L	H	L
3	L	L	H	H
4	L	H	L	L
5	H	L	L	L
6	H	L	L	H
7	H	L	H	L
8	H	L	H	H
9	H	H	L	L

'290, 'LS290 RESET/COUNT FUNCTION TABLE

RESET INPUTS				OUTPUT			
$R_{0(1)}$	$R_{0(2)}$	$R_{9(1)}$	$R_{9(2)}$	Q_D	Q_C	Q_B	Q_A
H	H	L	X	L	L	L	L
H	H	X	L	L	L	L	L
X	X	H	H	H	L	L	H
X	L	X	L	COUNT			
L	X	L	X	COUNT			
L	X	X	L	COUNT			
X	L	L	X	COUNT			

'293, 'LS293 COUNT SEQUENCE (See Note C)

COUNT	OUTPUT			
	Q_D	Q_C	Q_B	Q_A
0	L	L	L	L
1	L	L	L	H
2	L	L	H	L
3	L	L	H	H
4	L	H	L	L
5	L	H	L	H
6	L	H	H	L
7	L	H	H	H
8	H	L	L	L
9	H	L	L	H
10	H	L	H	L
11	H	L	H	H
12	H	H	L	L
13	H	H	L	H
14	H	H	H	L
15	H	H	H	H

'293, 'LS293 RESET/COUNT FUNCTION TABLE

RESET INPUTS		OUTPUT			
$R_{0(1)}$	$R_{0(2)}$	Q_D	Q_C	Q_B	Q_A
H	H	L	L	L	L
L	X	COUNT			
X	L	COUNT			

NOTES: A. Output Q_A is connected to input B for BCD count.
B. Output Q_D is connected to input A for bi-quinary count.
C. Output Q_A is connected to input B.
D. H = high level, L = low level, X = irrelevant

functional block diagrams

'290, 'LS290

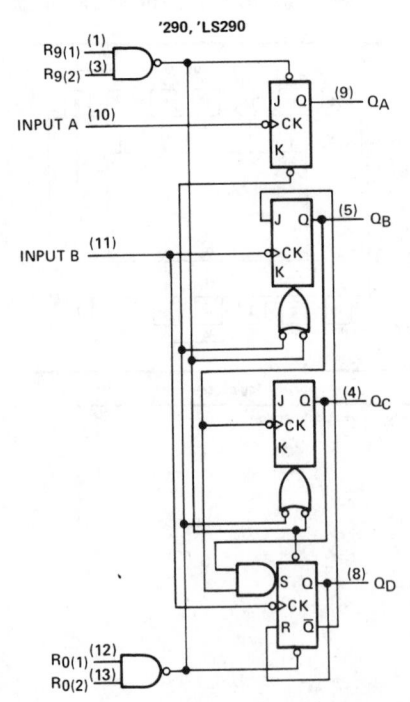

'293, 'LS293

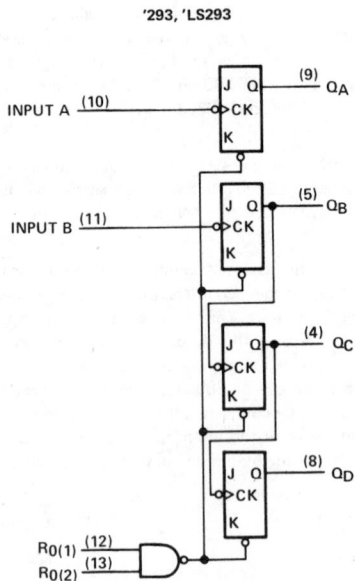

The J and K inputs shown without connection are for reference only and are functionally at a high level.

TEXAS INSTRUMENTS
INCORPORATED
POST OFFICE BOX 5012 • DALLAS, TEXAS 75222

schematics of inputs and outputs

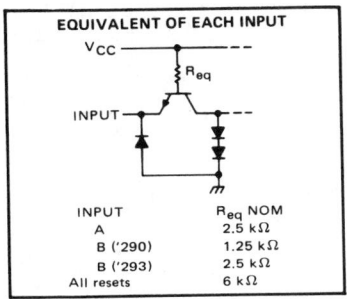

EQUIVALENT OF EACH INPUT

INPUT	R_{eq} NOM
A	2.5 kΩ
B ('290)	1.25 kΩ
B ('293)	2.5 kΩ
All resets	6 kΩ

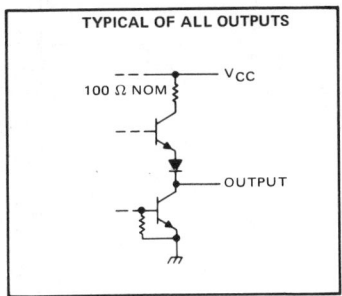

TYPICAL OF ALL OUTPUTS

100 Ω NOM

absolute maximum ratings over operating free-air temperature range (unless otherwise noted)

Supply voltage, V_{CC} (see Note 1) . . . . 7 V
Input voltage . . . . 5.5 V
Interemitter voltage (see Note 2) . . . . 5.5 V
Operating free-air temperature range: SN54' Circuits . . . . −55°C to 125°C
$\qquad\qquad\qquad\qquad\qquad\qquad\qquad$ SN74' Circuits . . . . 0°C to 70°C
Storage temperature range . . . . −65°C to 150°C

NOTES: 1. Voltage values, except interemitter voltage, are with respect to network ground terminal.
2. This is the voltage between two emitters of a multiple-emitter transistor. For these circuits, this rating applies between the two R_0 inputs, and for the '290 circuit, it also applies between the two R_9 inputs.

recommended operating conditions

		SN54'			SN74'			UNIT
		MIN	NOM	MAX	MIN	NOM	MAX	
Supply voltage, V_{CC}		4.5	5	5.5	4.75	5	5.25	V
High-level output current, I_{OH}				−800			−800	μA
Low-level output current, I_{OL}				16			16	mA
Count frequency, f_{count}	A input	0		32	0		32	MHz
	B input	0		16	0		16	
Pulse width, t_w	A input	15			15			
	B input	30			30			ns
	Reset inputs	15			15			
Reset inactive-state setup time, t_{su}		25			25			ns
Operating free-air temperature, T_A		−55		125	0		70	°C

TEXAS INSTRUMENTS
INCORPORATED
POST OFFICE BOX 5012 • DALLAS, TEXAS 75222

7

TYPES SN54290, SN54293, SN74290, SN74293
DECADE AND 4-BIT BINARY COUNTERS

REVISED AUGUST 1977

electrical characteristics over recommended operating free-air temperature range (unless otherwise noted)

PARAMETER		TEST CONDITIONS†	'290 MIN	'290 TYP‡	'290 MAX	'293 MIN	'293 TYP‡	'293 MAX	UNIT
V_{IH}	High-level input voltage		2			2			V
V_{IL}	Low-level input voltage				0.8			0.8	V
V_{IK}	Input clamp voltage	V_{CC} = MIN, I_I = −12 mA			−1.5			−1.5	V
V_{OH}	High-level output voltage	V_{CC} = MIN, V_{IH} = 2 V, V_{IL} = 0.8 V, I_{OH} = −800 µA	2.4	3.4		2.4	3.4		V
V_{OL}	Low-level output voltage	V_{CC} = MIN, V_{IH} = 2 V, V_{IL} = 0.8 V, I_{OL} = 16 mA¶		0.2	0.4		0.2	0.4	V
I_I	Input current at maximum input voltage	V_{CC} = MAX, V_I = 5.5 V			1			1	mA
I_{IH}	High-level input current — Any reset	V_{CC} = MAX, V_I = 2.4 V			40			40	µA
	A input				80			80	
	B input				120			80	
I_{IL}	Low-level input current — Any reset	V_{CC} = MAX, V_I = 0.4 V			−1.6			−1.6	mA
	A input				−3.2			−3.2	
	B input				−4.8			−3.2	
I_{OS}	Short-circuit output current § — SN54′	V_{CC} = MAX	−20		−57	−20		−57	mA
	SN74′		−18		−57	−18		−57	
I_{CC}	Supply current	V_{CC} = MAX, See Note 3		29	42		26	39	mA

†For conditions shown as MIN or MAX, use the appropriate value specified under recommended operating conditions.
‡All typical values are at V_{CC} = 5 V, T_A = 25°C.
§Not more than one output should be shorted at a time.
¶Q_A outputs are tested at I_{OL} = 16 mA plus the limit value of I_{IL} for the B input. This permits driving the B input while maintaining full fan-out capability.
NOTE 3: I_{CC} is measured with all outputs open, both R_0 inputs grounded following momentary connection to 4.5 V, and all other inputs grounded.

switching characteristics, V_{CC} = 5 V, T_A = 25°C

PARAMETER◊	FROM (INPUT)	TO (OUTPUT)	TEST CONDITIONS	'290 MIN	'290 TYP	'290 MAX	'293 MIN	'293 TYP	'293 MAX	UNIT
f_{max}	A	Q_A		32	42		32	42		MHz
	B	Q_B		16			16			
t_{PLH}	A	Q_A			10	16		10	16	ns
t_{PHL}					12	18		12	18	
t_{PLH}	A	Q_D			32	48		46	70	ns
t_{PHL}					34	50		46	70	
t_{PLH}	B	Q_B	C_L = 15 pF, R_L = 400 Ω, See Note 4		10	16		10	16	ns
t_{PHL}					14	21		14	21	
t_{PLH}	B	Q_C			21	32		21	32	ns
t_{PHL}					23	35		23	35	
t_{PLH}	B	Q_D			21	32		34	51	ns
t_{PHL}					23	35		34	51	
t_{PHL}	Set-to-0	Any			26	40		26	40	ns
t_{PLH}	Set-to-9	Q_A, Q_D			20	30				ns
t_{PHL}		Q_B, Q_C			26	40				

◊f_{max} ≡ maximum count frequency
t_{PLH} ≡ propagation delay time, low-to-high-level output
t_{PHL} ≡ propagation delay time, high-to-low-level output
NOTE 4: Load circuit and voltage waveforms are the same as those shown for the '90A and '93A, page 3-10.

7

TEXAS INSTRUMENTS
INCORPORATED
POST OFFICE BOX 5012 • DALLAS, TEXAS 75222

schematics of inputs and outputs

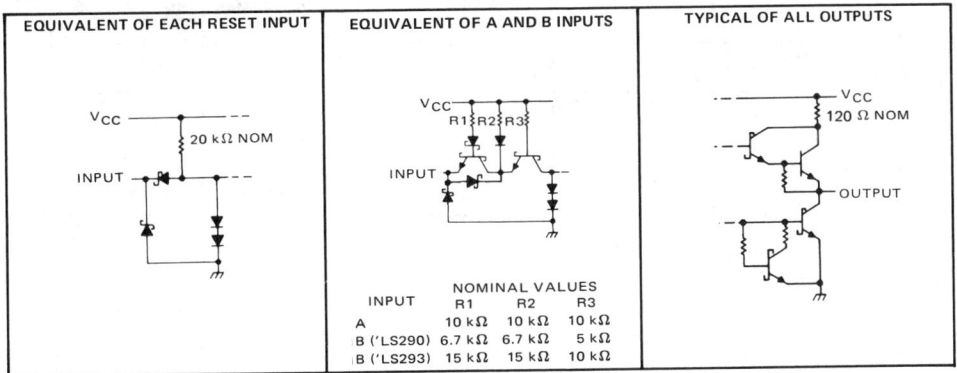

absolute maximum ratings over operating free-air temperature range (unless otherwise noted)

Supply voltage, V_{CC} (see Note 5)	7 V
Input voltage: R inputs	7 V
A and B inputs	5.5 V
Operating free-air temperature range: SN54LS290, SN54LS293	$-55°C$ to $125°C$
SN74LS290, SN74LS293	$0°C$ to $70°C$
Storage temperature range	$-65°C$ to $150°C$

NOTE 5: Voltage values are with respect to network ground terminal.

recommended operating conditions

		SN54LS'			SN74LS'			UNIT
		MIN	NOM	MAX	MIN	NOM	MAX	
Supply voltage, V_{CC}		4.5	5	5.5	4.75	5	5.25	V
High-level output current, I_{OH}				−400			−400	μA
Low-level output current, I_{OL}				4			8	mA
Count frequency, f_{count}	A input	0		32	0		32	MHz
	B input	0		16	0		16	
Pulse width, t_w	A input	15			15			ns
	B input	30			30			
	Reset inputs	15			15			
Reset inactive-state setup time, t_{su}		25			25			ns
Operating free-air temperature, T_A		−55		125	0		70	°C

TYPES SN54LS290, SN54LS293, SN74LS290, SN74LS293
DECADE AND 4-BIT BINARY COUNTERS

REVISED OCTOBER 1976

electrical characteristics over recommended operating free-air temperature range (unless otherwise noted)

PARAMETER		TEST CONDITIONS[†]		SN54LS' MIN	TYP[‡]	MAX	SN74LS' MIN	TYP[‡]	MAX	UNIT
V_{IH} High-level input voltage				2			2			V
V_{IL} Low-level input voltage						0.7			0.8	V
V_{IK} Input clamp voltage		V_{CC} = MIN,	I_I = −18 mA			−1.5			−1.5	V
V_{OH} High-level output voltage		V_{CC} = MIN, V_{IH} = 2 V, V_{IL} = V_{IL} max, I_{OH} = −400 µA		2.5	3.4		2.7	3.4		V
V_{OL} Low-level output voltage		V_{CC} = MIN, V_{IH} = 2 V, V_{IL} = V_{IL} max	I_{OL} = 4 mA[¶]		0.25	0.4		0.25	0.4	V
			I_{OL} = 8 mA[¶]					0.35	0.5	
I_I Input current at maximum input voltage	Any reset	V_{CC} = MAX, V_I = 7 V				0.1			0.1	mA
	A input					0.2			0.2	
	B of 'LS290	V_{CC} = MAX, V_I = 5.5 V				0.4			0.4	
	B of 'LS293					0.2			0.2	
I_{IH} High-level input current	Any reset	V_{CC} = MAX, V_I = 2.7 V				20			20	µA
	A input					40			40	
	B of 'LS290					80			80	
	B of 'LS293					40			40	
I_{IL} Low-level input current	Any reset	V_{CC} = MAX, V_I = 0.4 V				−0.4			−0.4	mA
	A input					−2.4			−2.4	
	B of 'LS290					−3.2			−3.2	
	B of 'LS293					−1.6			−1.6	
I_{OS} Short-circuit output current[§]		V_{CC} = MAX		−20		−100	−20		−100	mA
I_{CC} Supply current		V_{CC} = MAX, See Note 3	'LS290		9	15		9	15	mA
			'LS293		9	15		9	15	

[†]For conditions shown as MIN or MAX, use the appropriate value specified under recommended operating conditions.
[‡]All typical values are at V_{CC} = 5 V, T_A = 25°C.
[§]Not more than one output should be shorted at a time, and duration of the short-circuit should not exceed one second.
[¶]Q_A outputs are tested at specified I_{OL} plus the limit value of I_{IL} for the B input. This permits driving the B input while maintaining full fan-out capability.
NOTE 3: I_{CC} is measured with all outputs open, both R_0 inputs grounded following momentary connection to 4.5 V, and all other inputs grounded.

switching characteristics, V_{CC} = 5 V, T_A = 25°C

PARAMETER[◊]	FROM (INPUT)	TO (OUTPUT)	TEST CONDITIONS	'LS290 MIN	TYP	MAX	'LS293 MIN	TYP	MAX	UNIT
f_{max}	A	Q_A		32	42		32	42		MHz
	B	Q_B		16			16			
t_{PLH}	A	Q_A			10	16		10	16	ns
t_{PHL}					12	18		12	18	
t_{PLH}	A	Q_D			32	48		46	70	ns
t_{PHL}					34	50		46	70	
t_{PLH}	B	Q_B	C_L = 15 pF, R_L = 2 kΩ, See Note 6		10	16		10	16	ns
t_{PHL}					14	21		14	21	
t_{PLH}	B	Q_C			21	32		21	32	ns
t_{PHL}					23	35		23	35	
t_{PLH}	B	Q_D			21	32		34	51	ns
t_{PHL}					23	35		34	51	
t_{PHL}	Set-to-0	Any			26	40		26	40	ns
t_{PLH}	Set-to-9	Q_A, Q_D			20	30				ns
t_{PHL}		Q_B, Q_C			26	40				

[◊]f_{max} ≡ maximum count frequency
t_{PLH} ≡ propagation delay time, low-to-high-level output
t_{PHL} ≡ propagation delay time, high-to-low-level output
NOTE 6: Load circuit and voltage waveforms are the same as those shown for the 'LS90 and 'LS93, pages 7-80.

TEXAS INSTRUMENTS
INCORPORATED
POST OFFICE BOX 5012 • DALLAS, TEXAS 75222

TTL
MSI

TYPES SN54LS295B, SN74LS295B
4-BIT RIGHT-SHIFT LEFT-SHIFT REGISTERS
WITH 3-STATE OUTPUTS
BULLETIN NO. DL-S 7711780, OCTOBER 1976–REVISED AUGUST 1977

- 'LS295B Offers Three Times the Sink-Current Capability of 'LS295A

- Schottky-Diode-Clamped Transistors

- Low Power Dissipation . . . 80 mW Typical (Enabled)

- Applications:
  N-Bit Serial-To-Parallel Converter
  N-Bit Parallel-To-Serial Converter
  N-Bit Storage Register

SN54LS295B . . . J OR W PACKAGE
SN74LS295B . . . J OR N PACKAGE
(TOP VIEW)

logic: see function table

description

These 4-bit registers feature parallel inputs, parallel outputs, and clock, serial, mode, and output control inputs. The registers have three modes of operation:

Parallel (broadside) load
Shift right (the direction Q_A toward Q_D)
Shift left (the direction Q_D toward Q_A)

Parallel loading is accomplished by applying the four bits of data and taking the mode control input high. The data is loaded into the associated flip-flops and appears at the outputs after the high-to-low transition of the clock input. During parallel loading, the entry of serial data is inhibited.

Shift right is accomplished when the mode control is low; shift left is accomplished when the mode control is high by connecting the output of each flip-flop to the parallel input of the previous flip-flop (Q_D to input C, etc.) and serial data is entered at input D.

When the output control is high, the normal logic levels of the four outputs are available for driving the loads or bus lines. The outputs are disabled independently from the level of the clock by a low logic level at the output control input. The outputs then present a high impedance and neither load nor drive the bus line; however, sequential operation of the registers is not affected.

The SN54LS295B is characterized for operation over the full military temperature range of −55°C to 125°C; the SN74LS295B is characterized for operation from 0°C to 70°C.

FUNCTION TABLE

INPUTS							OUTPUTS			
MODE CONTROL	CLOCK	SERIAL	PARALLEL				Q_A	Q_B	Q_C	Q_D
			A	B	C	D				
H	H	X	X	X	X	X	Q_{A0}	Q_{B0}	Q_{C0}	Q_{D0}
H	↓	X	a	b	c	d	a	b	c	d
H	↓	X	Q_B†	Q_C†	Q_D†	d	Q_{Bn}	Q_{Cn}	Q_{Dn}	d
L	H	X	X	X	X	X	Q_{A0}	Q_{B0}	Q_{C0}	Q_{D0}
L	↓	H	X	X	X	X	H	Q_{An}	Q_{Bn}	Q_{Cn}
L	↓	L	X	X	X	X	L	Q_{An}	Q_{Bn}	Q_{Cn}

When the output control is low, the outputs are disabled to the high-impedance state; however, sequential operation of the registers is not affected.

†Shifting left requires external connection of Q_B to A, Q_C to B, and Q_D to C. Serial data is entered at input D.

H = high level (steady state), L = low level (steady state), X = irrelevant (any input, including transitions)
↓ = transition from high to low level.
a, b, c, d = the level of steady-state input at inputs A, B, C, or D, respectively.
Q_{A0}, Q_{B0}, Q_{C0}, Q_{D0} = the level of Q_A, Q_B, Q_C, or Q_D, respectively, before the indicated steady-state input conditions were established.
Q_{An}, Q_{Bn}, Q_{Cn}, Q_{Dn} = the level of Q_A, Q_B, Q_C, or Q_D, respectively, before the most-recent ↓ transition of the clock.

See explanation of function tables on page 3-8.

TEXAS INSTRUMENTS
INCORPORATED
POST OFFICE BOX 5012 • DALLAS, TEXAS 75222

absolute maximum ratings over operating free-air temperature range (unless otherwise noted)

Supply voltage, V_{CC} (see Note 1) . . . . 7 V
Input voltage . . . . 7 V
Operating free-air temperature range: SN54LS295B . . . . −55°C to 125°C
SN74LS295B . . . . 0°C to 70°C
Storage temperature range . . . . −65°C to 150°C

NOTE 1: Voltage values are with respect to network ground terminal.

recommended operating conditions

	SN54LS295B			SN74LS295B			UNIT
	MIN	NOM	MAX	MIN	NOM	MAX	
Supply voltage, V_{CC}	4.5	5	5.5	4.75	5	5.25	V
High-level output current, I_{OH}			−1			−2.6	mA
Low-level output current, I_{OL}			12			24	mA
Clock frequency, f_{clock}	0		20	0		20	MHz
Width of clock pulse, $t_{w(clock)}$	25			25			ns
Setup time, high-level or low-level data, t_{su}	20			20			ns
Hold time, high-level or low-level data, t_h	20			20			ns
Operating free-air temperature, T_A	−55		125	0		70	°C

electrical characteristics over recommended operating free-air temperature range (unless otherwise noted)

PARAMETER	TEST CONDITIONS†		SN54LS295B			SN74LS295B			UNIT
			MIN	TYP‡	MAX	MIN	TYP‡	MAX	
V_{IH} High-level input voltage			2			2			V
V_{IL} Low-level input voltage					0.7			0.8	V
V_{IK} Input clamp voltage	V_{CC} = MIN, I_I = −18 mA				−1.5			−1.5	V
V_{OH} High-level output voltage	V_{CC} = MIN, V_{IH} = 2 V, $V_{IL} = V_{IL}$ max, I_{OH} = MAX		2.4	3.4		2.4	3.1		V
V_{OL} Low-level output voltage	V_{CC} = MIN, V_{IH} = 2 V, $V_{IL} = V_{IL}$ max	I_{OL} = 12 mA		0.25	0.4		0.25	0.4	V
		I_{OL} = 24 mA					0.35	0.5	
I_{OZH} Off-state output current, high-level voltage applied	V_{CC} = MAX, $V_{IL} = V_{IL}$ max, V_O = 2.7 V				20			20	µA
I_{OZL} Off-state output current, low-level voltage applied	V_{CC} = MAX, V_{IH} = 2 V, V_O = 0.4 V				−20			−20	µA
I_I Input current at maximum input voltage	V_{CC} = MAX, V_I = 7 V				0.1			0.1	mA
I_{IH} High-level input current	V_{CC} = MAX, V_I = 2.7 V				20			20	µA
I_{IL} Low-level input current	V_{CC} = MAX, V_I = 0.4 V				−0.4			−0.4	mA
I_{OS} Short-circuit output current§	V_{CC} = MAX		−30		−130	−30		−130	mA
I_{CC} Supply current	V_{CC} = MAX, See Note 2	Condition A		20	29		20	29	mA
		Condition B		22	33		22	33	

†For conditions shown as MIN or MAX, use the appropriate value specified under recommended operating conditions.
‡All typical values are at V_{CC} = 5 V, T_A = 25°C.
§Not more than one output should be shorted at a time, and duration of the short-circuit should not exceed one second.
NOTE 2: I_{CC} is measured with the outputs open, the serial input and mode control at 4.5 V, and the data inputs grounded under the following conditions:
    A. Output control at 4.5 V and a momentary 3 V, then ground, applied to clock input.
    B. Output control and clock input grounded.

TEXAS INSTRUMENTS
INCORPORATED
POST OFFICE BOX 5012 • DALLAS, TEXAS 75222

switching characteristics, V_{CC} = 5 V, T_A = 25 C, R_L = 667 Ω

PARAMETER		TEST CONDITIONS	MIN	TYP	MAX	UNIT
f_{max} Maximum clock frequency			30	45		MHz
t_{PLH} Propagation delay time, low-to-high-level output		C_L = 45 pF, See Note 3		14	20	ns
t_{PHL} Propagation delay time, high-to-low-level output				19	30	ns
t_{PZH} Output enable time to high level				18	26	ns
t_{PZL} Output enable time to low level				20	30	ns
t_{PHZ} Output disable time from high level		C_L = 5 pF, See Note 3		13	20	ns
t_{PLZ} Output disable time from low level				13	20	ns

NOTE 3: Load circuit and voltage waveforms are shown on page 3-11.

functional block diagram

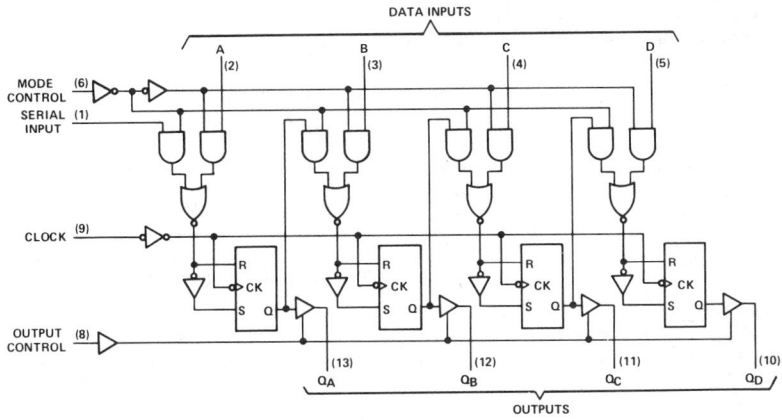

schematics of inputs and outputs

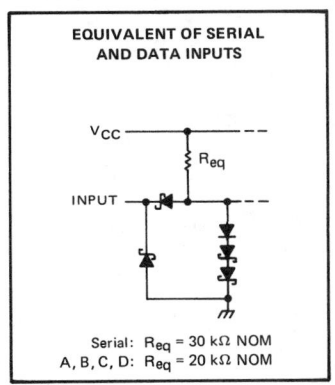

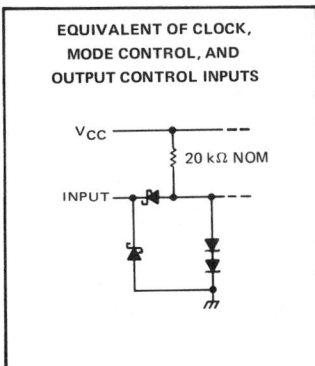

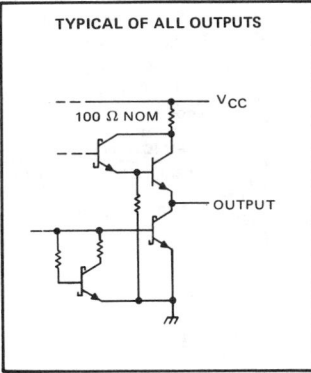

7

TEXAS INSTRUMENTS
INCORPORATED
POST OFFICE BOX 5012 • DALLAS, TEXAS 75222

TTL
MSI

TYPES SN54298, SN54LS298, SN74298, SN74LS298
QUADRUPLE 2-INPUT MULTIPLEXERS WITH STORAGE

BULLETIN NO. DL-S 7611747, MARCH 1974–REVISED OCTOBER 1976

- Selects One of Two 4-Bit Data Sources and Stores Data Synchronously with System Clock

- Applications:

   Dual Source for Operands and Constants in Arithmetic Processor; Can Release Processor Register Files for Acquiring New Data

   Implement Separate Registers Capable of Parallel Exchange of Contents Yet Retain External Load Capability

   Universal Type Register for Implementing Various Shift Patterns; Even Has Compound Left-Right Capabilities

description

These monolithic quadruple two-input multiplexers with storage provide essentially the equivalent functional capabilities of two separate MSI functions (SN54157/SN74157 or SN54LS157/SN74LS157 and SN54175/SN74175 or SN54LS175/SN74LS175) in a single 16-pin package.

When the word-select input is low, word 1 (A1, B1, C1, D1) is applies to the flip-flops. A high input to word select will cause the selection of word 2 (A2, B2, C2, D2). The selected word is clocked to the output terminals on the negative-going edge of the clock pulse.

Typical power dissipation is 195 milliwatts for the '298 and 65 milliwatts for the 'LS298. SN54298 and SN54LS298 are characterized for operation over the full military temperature range of −55°C to 125°C; SN74298 and SN74LS298 are characterized for operation from 0°C to 70°C.

SN54298, SN54LS298 . . . J OR W PACKAGE
SN74298, SN74LS298 . . . J OR N PACKAGE
(TOP VIEW)

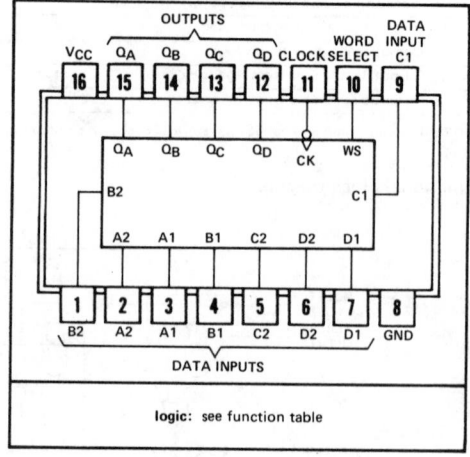

logic: see function table

FUNCTION TABLE

INPUTS		OUTPUTS			
WORD SELECT	CLOCK	Q_A	Q_B	Q_C	Q_D
L	↓	a1	b1	c1	d1
H	↓	a2	b2	c2	d2
X	H	Q_{A0}	Q_{B0}	Q_{C0}	Q_{D0}

H = high level (steady state)
L = low level (steady state)
X = irrelevant (any input, including transitions)
↓ = transition from high to low level
a1, a2, etc. = the level of steady-state input at A1, A2, etc.
Q_{A0}, Q_{B0}, etc. = the level of Q_A, Q_B, etc. entered on the most-recent ↓ transition of the clock input.

functional block diagram

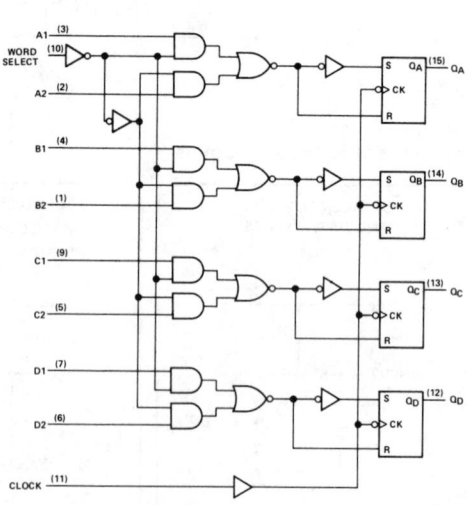

⎓⊸ . . . Dynamic input activated by a transition from a high level to a low level

schematics of inputs and outputs

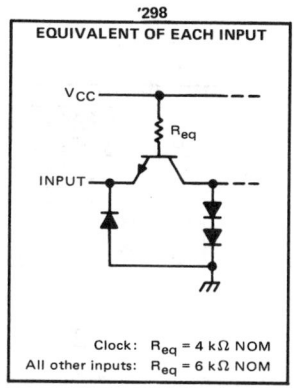

'298
EQUIVALENT OF EACH INPUT

Clock: R_{eq} = 4 kΩ NOM
All other inputs: R_{eq} = 6 kΩ NOM

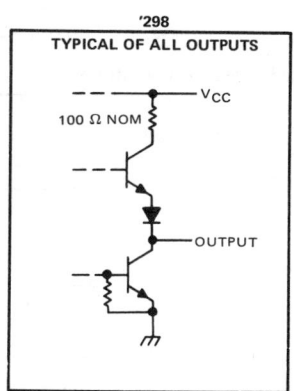

'298
TYPICAL OF ALL OUTPUTS

100 Ω NOM

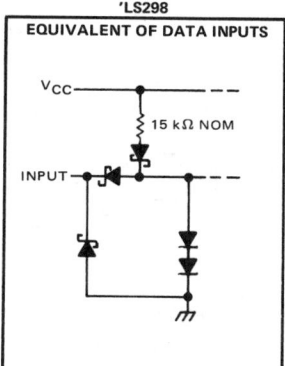

'LS298
EQUIVALENT OF DATA INPUTS

15 kΩ NOM

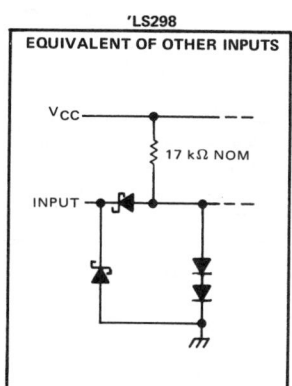

'LS298
EQUIVALENT OF OTHER INPUTS

17 kΩ NOM

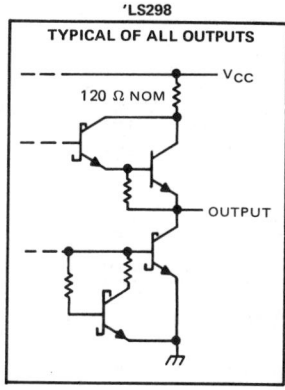

'LS298
TYPICAL OF ALL OUTPUTS

120 Ω NOM

7

absolute maximum ratings over operating free-air temperature range (unless otherwise noted)

Supply voltage, V_{CC} (see Note 1) . . . . 7 V
Input voltage . . . . 5.5 V
Operating free-air temperature range: SN54298 . . . . −55°C to 125°C
SN74298 . . . . 0°C to 70°C
Storage temperature . . . . −65°C to 150°C

NOTE 1: Voltage values are with respect to network ground terminal.

recommended operating conditions

		SN54298			SN74298			UNIT
		MIN	NOM	MAX	MIN	NOM	MAX	
Supply voltage, V_{CC}		4.5	5	5.5	4.75	5	5.25	V
High-level output current, I_{OH}				−800			−800	µA
Low-level output current, I_{OL}				16			16	mA
Width of clock pulse, high or low level, t_w		20			20			ns
Setup time, t_{su}	Data	15			15			ns
	Word select	25			25			
Hold time, t_h	Data	5			5			ns
	Word select	0			0			
Operating free-air temperature, T_A		−55		125	0		70	°C

electrical characteristics over recommended operating free-air temperature range (unless otherwise noted)

PARAMETER		TEST CONDITIONS†	MIN	TYP‡	MAX	UNIT
V_{IH}	High-level input voltage		2			V
V_{IL}	Low-level input voltage				0.8	V
V_{IK}	Input clamp voltage	V_{CC} = MIN, I_I = −12 mA			−1.5	V
V_{OH}	High-level output voltage	V_{CC} = MIN, V_{IH} = 2 V, V_{IL} = 0.8 V, I_{OH} = −800 µA	2.4	3.2		V
V_{OL}	Low-level output voltage	V_{CC} = MIN, V_{IH} = 2 V, V_{IL} = 0.8 V, I_{OL} = 16 mA			0.4	V
I_I	Input current at maximum input voltage	V_{CC} = MAX, V_I = 5.5 V			1	mA
I_{IH}	High-level input current	V_{CC} = MAX, V_I = 2.4 V			40	µA
I_{IL}	Low-level input current	V_{CC} = MAX, V_I = 0.4 V			−1.6	mA
I_{OS}	Short-circuit output current§	V_{CC} = MAX SN54298	−20		−57	mA
		SN74298	−18		−57	
I_{CC}	Supply current	V_{CC} = MAX, See Note 2		39	65	mA

†For conditions shown as MIN or MAX, use the appropriate value specified under recommended operating conditions.
‡All typical values are at V_{CC} = 5 V, T_A = 25°C.
§Not more than one output should be shorted at a time.
NOTE 2: With all outputs open and all inputs except clock low, I_{CC} is measured after applying a momentary 4.5 V, followed by ground, to the clock input.

switching characteristics, V_{CC} = 5 V, T_A = 25°C

PARAMETER		TEST CONDITIONS	MIN	TYP	MAX	UNIT
t_{PLH}	Propagation delay time, low-to-high-level output	C_L = 15 pF, R_L = 400 Ω, See Note 3		18	27	ns
t_{PHL}	Propagation delay time, high-to-low-level output			21	32	

NOTE 3: Load circuit and waveforms are shown on page 3-10.

TEXAS INSTRUMENTS
INCORPORATED
POST OFFICE BOX 5012 • DALLAS, TEXAS 75222

absolute maximum ratings over operating free-air temperature range (unless otherwise noted)

Supply voltage, V_{CC} (see Note 1) . . . . 7 V

Input voltage . . . . 7 V

Operating free-air temperature range: SN54LS298 . . . . $-55°$C to $125°$C

SN74LS298 . . . . $0°$C to $70°$C

Storage temperature range . . . . $-65°$C to $150°$C

NOTE 1: Voltage values are with respect to network ground terminal.

recommended operating conditions

		SN54LS298			SN74LS298			UNIT
		MIN	NOM	MAX	MIN	NOM	MAX	
Supply voltage, V_{CC}		4.5	5	5.5	4.75	5	5.25	V
High-level output current, I_{OH}				−400			−400	μA
Low-level output current, I_{OL}				4			8	mA
Width of clock pulse, high or low level, t_w		20			20			ns
Setup time, t_{su}	Data	15			15			ns
	Word select	25			25			
Hold time, t_h	Data	5			5			ns
	Word select	0			0			
Operating free-air temperature, T_A		−55		125	0		70	°C

electrical characteristics over recommended operating free-air temperature range (unless otherwise noted)

PARAMETER		TEST CONDITIONS[†]		SN54LS298			SN74LS298			UNIT
				MIN	TYP[‡]	MAX	MIN	TYP[‡]	MAX	
V_{IH}	High-level input voltage			2			2			V
V_{IL}	Low-level input voltage					0.7			0.8	V
V_{IK}	Input clamp voltage	V_{CC} = MIN,	I_I = −18 mA			−1.5			−1.5	V
V_{OH}	High-level output voltage	V_{CC} = MIN, V_{IH} = 2 V, $V_{IL} = V_{IL}$ max, I_{OH} = −400 μA		2.5	3.4		2.7	3.4		V
V_{OL}	Low-level output voltage	V_{CC} = MIN, V_{IH} = 2 V, $V_{IL} = V_{IL}$ max	I_{OL} = 4 mA		0.25	0.4		0.25	0.4	V
			I_{OL} = 8 mA					0.35	0.5	
I_I	Input current at maximum input voltage	V_{CC} = MAX,	V_I = 7 V			0.1			0.1	mA
I_{IH}	High-level input current	V_{CC} = MAX,	V_I = 2.7 V			20			20	μA
I_{IL}	Low-level input current	V_{CC} = MAX,	V_I = 0.4 V			−0.4			−0.4	mA
I_{OS}	Short-circuit output current[§]	V_{CC} = MAX		−20		−100	−20		−100	mA
I_{CC}	Supply current	V_{CC} = MAX,	See Note 2		13	21		13	21	mA

[†]For conditions shown as MIN or MAX, use the appropriate value specified under recommended operating conditions.

[‡]All typical values are at V_{CC} = 5 V, T_A = 25°C.

[§]Not more than one output should be shorted at a time, and duration of the short-circuit should not exceed one second.

NOTE 2: With all outputs open and all inputs except clock low, I_{CC} is measured after applying a momentary 4.5 V, followed by ground, to the clock input.

switching characteristics, V_{CC} = 5 V, T_A = 25°C

PARAMETER		TEST CONDITIONS	MIN	TYP	MAX	UNIT
t_{PLH}	Propagation delay time, low-to-high-level output	C_L = 15 pF, R_L = 2 kΩ, See Note 4		18	27	ns
t_{PHL}	Propagation delay time, high-to-low-level output			21	32	

NOTE 4: Load circuit and waveforms are shown on page 3-11.

7

TYPICAL APPLICATION DATA

This versatile multiplexer/register can be connected to operate as a shift register that can shift N-places in a single clock pulse.

The following figure illustrates a BCD shift register that will shift an entire 4-bit BCD digit in one clock pulse.

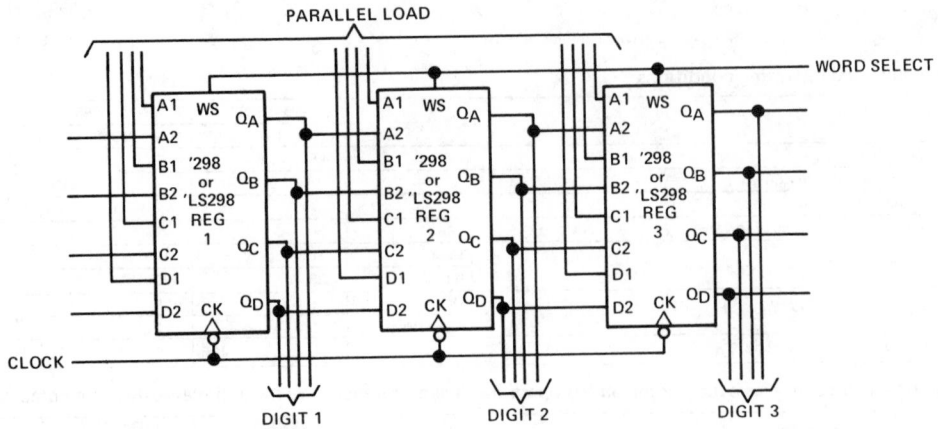

When the word-select input is high and the registers are clocked, the contents of register 1 is transferred (shifted) to register 2 and etc. In effect, the BCD digits are shifted one position. In addition, this application retains a parallel-load capability which means that new BCD data can be entered in the entire register with one clock pulse. This arrangement can be modified to perform the shifting of binary data for any number of bit locations.

Another function that can be implemented with the '298 or 'LS298 is a register that can be designed specifically for supporting multiplier or division operations. The example below is a one place/two-place shift register.

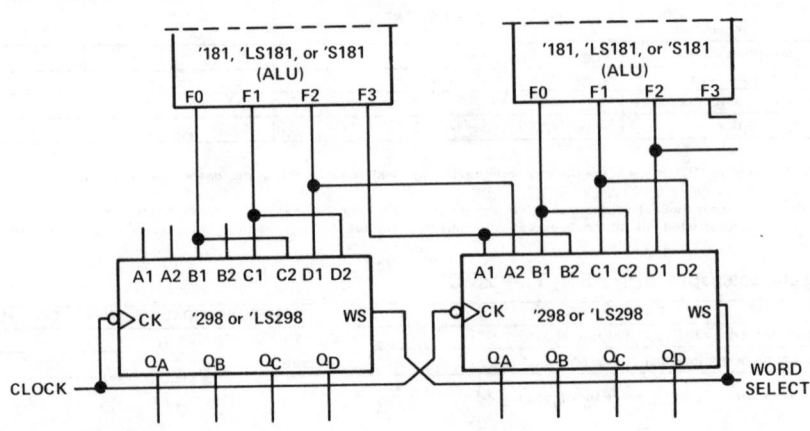

When word select is low and the register is clocked, the outputs of the arithmetic/logic units (ALU's) are shifted one place. When word select is high and the registers are clocked, the data is shifted two places.

TEXAS INSTRUMENTS
INCORPORATED
POST OFFICE BOX 5012 • DALLAS, TEXAS 75222

TTL
LSI

TYPES SN54LS299, SN54S299, SN74LS299, SN74S299
8-BIT UNIVERSAL SHIFT/STORAGE REGISTERS

BULLETIN NO. DL–S 7712115, MARCH 1974–REVISED AUGUST 1977

- Multiplexed Inputs/Outputs Provide Improved Bit Density

- Four Modes of Operation:
  Hold (Store)   Shift Left
  Shift Right   Load Data

- Operates with Outputs Enabled or at High Z

- 3-State Outputs Drive Bus Lines Directly

- Can Be Cascaded for N-Bit Word Lengths

- SN54LS323 and SN74LS323 Are Similar But Have Synchronous Clear

- Applications:
  Stacked or Push-Down Registers.
  Buffer Storage, and
  Accumulator Registers

TYPE	GUARANTEED SHIFT (CLOCK) FREQUENCY	TYPICAL POWER DISSIPATION
'LS299	35 MHz	175 mW
'S299	50 MHz	700 mW

SN54LS299, SN54S299 . . . J PACKAGE
SN74LS299, SN74S299 . . . J OR N PACKAGE
(TOP VIEW)

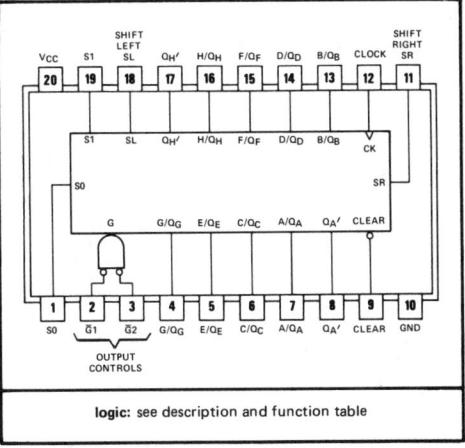

logic: see description and function table

description

These Schottky TTL eight-bit universal registers feature multiplexed inputs/outputs to achieve full eight bit data handling in a single 20-pin package. Two function-select inputs and two output-control inputs can be used to choose the modes of operation listed in the function table.

Synchronous parallel loading is accomplished by taking both function-select lines, S0 and S1, high. This places the three-state outputs in a high-impedance state, which permits data that is applied on the input/output lines to be clocked into the register. Reading out of the register can be accomplished while the outputs are enabled in any mode. A direct overriding input is provided to clear the register whether the outputs are enabled or off.

FUNCTION TABLE

MODE	INPUTS								INPUTS/OUTPUTS								OUTPUTS	
	CLEAR	FUNCTION SELECT		OUTPUT CONTROL		CLOCK	SERIAL		A/Q_A	B/Q_B	C/Q_C	D/Q_D	E/Q_E	F/Q_F	G/Q_G	H/Q_H	$Q_{A'}$	$Q_{H'}$
		S1	S0	$\overline{G1}†$	$\overline{G2}†$		SL	SR										
Clear	L	X	L	L	L	X	X	X	L	L	L	L	L	L	L	L	L	L
	L	L	X	L	L	X	X	X	L	L	L	L	L	L	L	L	L	L
Hold	H	L	L	L	L	X	X	X	Q_{A0}	Q_{B0}	Q_{C0}	Q_{D0}	Q_{E0}	Q_{F0}	Q_{G0}	Q_{H0}	Q_{A0}	Q_{H0}
	H	X	X	L	L	X	X	X	Q_{A0}	Q_{B0}	Q_{C0}	Q_{D0}	Q_{E0}	Q_{F0}	Q_{G0}	Q_{H0}	Q_{A0}	Q_{H0}
Shift Right	H	L	H	L	L	↑	X	H	H	Q_{An}	Q_{Bn}	Q_{Cn}	Q_{Dn}	Q_{En}	Q_{Fn}	Q_{Gn}	H	Q_{Gn}
	H	L	H	L	L	↑	X	L	L	Q_{An}	Q_{Bn}	Q_{Cn}	Q_{Dn}	Q_{En}	Q_{Fn}	Q_{Gn}	L	Q_{Gn}
Shift Left	H	H	L	L	L	↑	H	X	Q_{Bn}	Q_{Cn}	Q_{Dn}	Q_{En}	Q_{Fn}	Q_{Gn}	Q_{Hn}	H	Q_{Bn}	H
	H	H	L	L	L	↑	L	X	Q_{Bn}	Q_{Cn}	Q_{Dn}	Q_{En}	Q_{Fn}	Q_{Gn}	Q_{Hn}	L	Q_{Bn}	L
Load	H	H	H	X	X	↑	X	X	a	b	c	d	e	f	g	h	a	h

†When one or both output controls are high the eight input/output terminals are disabled to the high-impedance state; however, sequential operation or clearing of the register is not affected.

a . . . h = the level of the steady-state input at inputs A through H, respectively. These data are loaded into the flip-flops while the flip-flop outputs are isolated from the input/output terminals. See explanation of function tables on page 3-8.

TEXAS INSTRUMENTS
INCORPORATED
POST OFFICE BOX 5012 • DALLAS, TEXAS 75222

TYPES SN54LS299, SN54S299, SN74LS299, SN74S299
8-BIT UNIVERSAL SHIFT/STORAGE REGISTERS

functional block diagram

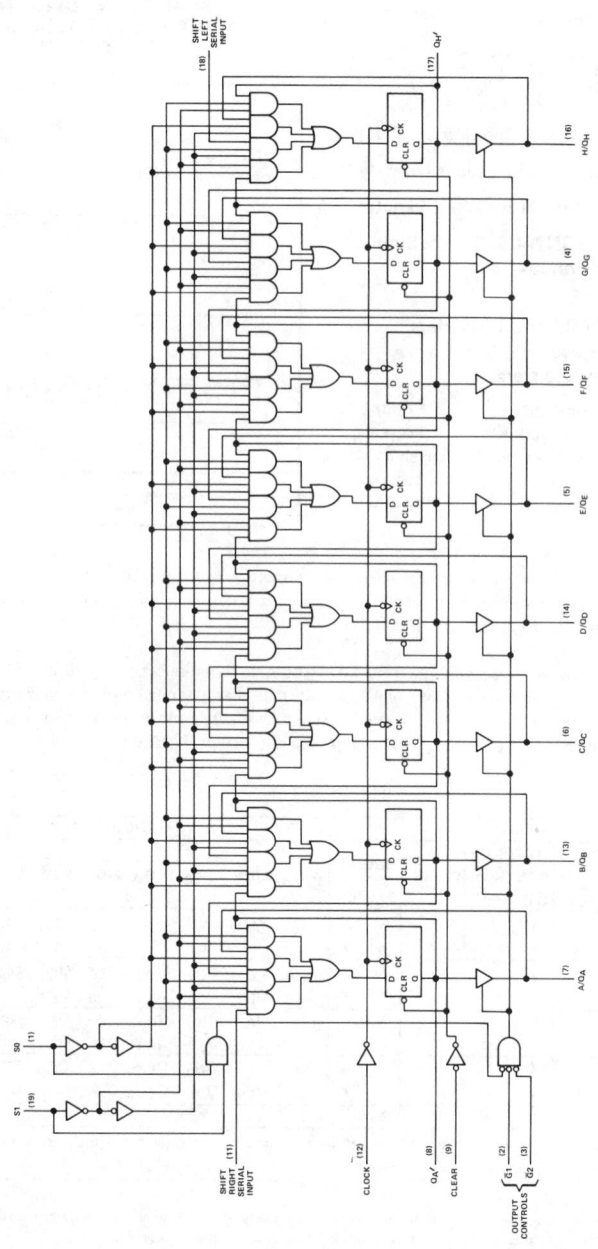

TEXAS INSTRUMENTS
INCORPORATED
POST OFFICE BOX 5012 • DALLAS, TEXAS 75222

schematics of inputs and outputs

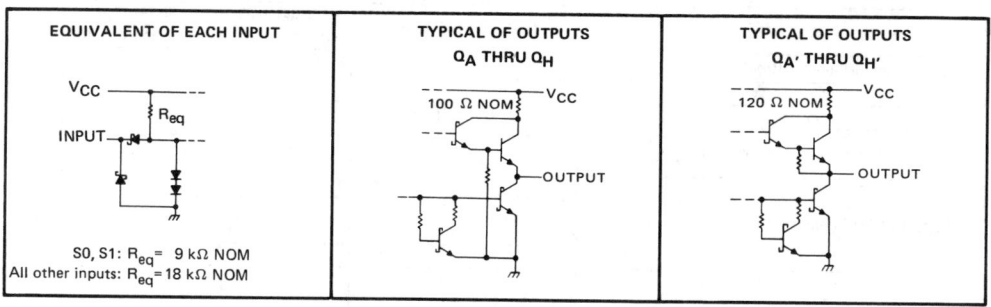

EQUIVALENT OF EACH INPUT	TYPICAL OF OUTPUTS Q_A THRU Q_H	TYPICAL OF OUTPUTS $Q_{A'}$ THRU $Q_{H'}$

S0, S1: R_{eq} = 9 kΩ NOM
All other inputs: R_{eq} = 18 kΩ NOM

absolute maximum ratings over operating free-air temperature range (unless otherwise noted)

Supply voltage, V_{CC} (see Note 1) . . . . 7 V
Input voltage . . . . 7 V
Off-state output voltage . . . . 7 V
Operating free-air temperature range: SN54LS299 . . . . −55°C to 125°C
　　　　　　　　　　　　　　　　　　　SN74LS299 . . . . 0°C to 70°C
Storage temperature . . . . −65°C to 150°C

NOTE 1: Voltage values are with respect to network ground terminal.

recommended operating conditions

		SN54LS299			SN74LS299			UNIT
		MIN	NOM	MAX	MIN	NOM	MAX	
Supply voltage, V_{CC}		4.5	5	5.5	4.75	5	5.25	V
High-level output current, I_{OH}	Q_A thru Q_H			−1			−2.6	mA
	$Q_{A'}$ or $Q_{H'}$			−0.4			−0.4	
Low-level output current, I_{OL}	Q_A thru Q_H			12			24	mA
	$Q_{A'}$ or $Q_{H'}$			4			8	
Clock frequency, f_{clock}		0		35	0		35	MHz
Width of clock pulse, $t_{w(clock)}$	Clock high	20			20			ns
	Clock low	20			20			
Width of clear pulse, $t_{w(clear)}$	Clear low	20			20			ns
Setup time, t_{su}	Select	10†			10†			ns
	High-level data◇	20†			20†			
	Low-level data◇	20†			20†			
	Clear inactive-state	20†			20†			
Hold time, t_h	Select	10†			10†			ns
	Data◇	0†			0†			
Operating free-air temperature, T_A		−55		125	0		70	°C

◇Data includes the two serial inputs and the eight input/output data lines.

TEXAS INSTRUMENTS
INCORPORATED
POST OFFICE BOX 5012 • DALLAS, TEXAS 75222

7-439

electrical characteristics over recommended operating free-air temperature range (unless otherwise noted)

PARAMETER		TEST CONDITIONS[†]		SN54LS299			SN74LS299			UNIT
				MIN	TYP[‡]	MAX	MIN	TYP[‡]	MAX	
V_{IH} High-level input voltage				2			2			V
V_{IL} Low-level input voltage						0.7			0.8	V
V_{IK} Input clamp voltage		V_{CC} = MIN,	I_I = −18 mA			−1.5			−1.5	V
V_{OH} High-level output voltage	Q_A thru Q_H	V_{CC} = MIN, V_{IH} = 2 V,		2.4	3.2		2.4	3.1		V
	Q_A' or Q_H'	V_{IL} = V_{IL}max, I_{OH} = MAX		2.7	3.4		2.7	3.4		
V_{OL} Low-level output voltage	Q_A thru Q_H	V_{CC} = MIN, V_{IH} = 2 V, V_{IL} = V_{IL}max	I_{OL} = 12 mA		0.25	0.4		0.25	0.4	V
			I_{OL} = 24 mA					0.35	0.5	
	Q_A' or Q_H'		I_{OL} = 4 mA		0.25	0.4		0.25	0.4	
			I_{OL} = 8 mA					0.35	0.5	
I_{OZH} Off-state output current, high-level voltage applied	Q_A thru Q_H	V_{CC} = MAX, V_{IH} = 2 V, V_O = 2.7 V				40			40	µA
I_{OZL} Off-state output current, low-level voltage applied	Q_A thru Q_H	V_{CC} = MAX, V_{IH} = 2 V, V_O = 0.4 V				−400			−400	µA
I_I Input current at maximum input voltage	S0, S1	V_{CC} = MAX	V_I = 7 V			200			200	µA
	A thru H		V_I = 5.5 V			100			100	
	Any other		V_I = 7 V			100			100	
I_{IH} High-level input current	A thru H, S0, S1	V_{CC} = MAX, V_I = 2.7 V				40			40	µA
	Any other					20			20	
I_{IL} Low-level input current	S0, S1	V_{CC} = MAX, V_I = 0.4 V				−0.8			−0.8	mA
	Any other					−0.4			−0.4	
I_{OS} Short-circuit output current[§]	Q_A thru Q_H	V_{CC} = MAX		−30		−130	−30		−130	mA
	Q_A' or Q_H'			−20		−100	−20		−100	
I_{CC} Supply current		V_{CC} = MAX			35	60		35	60	mA

[†]For conditions shown as MIN or MAX, use the appropriate value specified under recommended operating conditions.
[‡]All typical values are at V_{CC} = 5 V, T_A = 25°C.
[§]Not more than one output should be shorted at a time and duration of the short-circuit should not exceed one second.

switching characteristics, V_{CC} = 5 V, T_A = 25°C

PARAMETER[¶]	FROM (INPUT)	TO (OUTPUT)	TEST CONDITIONS	MIN	TYP	MAX	UNIT
f_{max}			See Note 2	35	50		MHz
t_{PLH}	Clock	Q_A' or Q_H'	C_L = 15 pF, R_L = 2 kΩ, See Note 2		15	25	ns
t_{PHL}					15	25	
t_{PHL}	Clear	Q_A' or Q_H'			20	35	ns
t_{PLH}	Clock	Q_A thru Q_H	C_L = 45 pF, R_L = 665 Ω, See Note 2		15	25	ns
t_{PHL}					15	25	
t_{PHL}	Clear	Q_A thru Q_H			20	35	ns
t_{PZH}	$\overline{G}1, \overline{G}2$	Q_A thru Q_H			20	35	ns
t_{PZL}					20	35	
t_{PHZ}	$\overline{G}1, \overline{G}2$	Q_A thru Q_H	C_L = 5 pF, R_L = 665 Ω, See Note 2		15	25	ns
t_{PLZ}					15	25	

[¶] f_{max} ≡ maximum clock frequency
t_{PLH} ≡ propagation delay time, low-to-high-level output.
t_{PHL} ≡ propagation delay time, high-to-low-level output
t_{PZH} ≡ output enable time to high level
t_{PZL} ≡ output enable time to low level
t_{PHZ} ≡ output disable time from high level
t_{PLZ} ≡ output disable time from low level
NOTE 2: For testing f_{max}, all outputs are loaded simultaneously, each with C_L and R_L as specified for the propagation times. See load circuits and waveforms on page 3-11.

TEXAS INSTRUMENTS
INCORPORATED
POST OFFICE BOX 5012 • DALLAS, TEXAS 75222

schematics of inputs and outputs

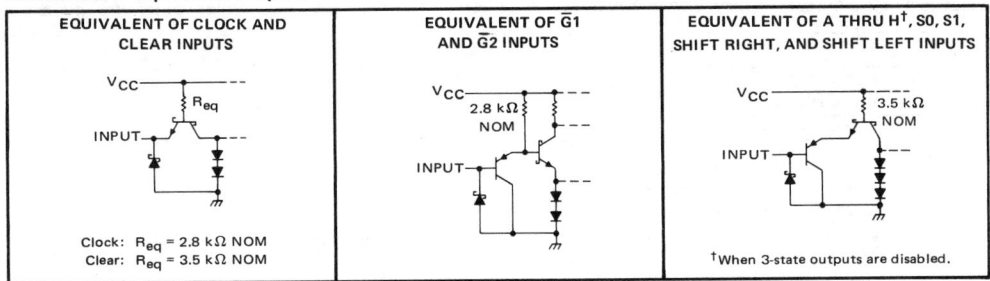

| EQUIVALENT OF CLOCK AND CLEAR INPUTS | EQUIVALENT OF $\overline{G}1$ AND $\overline{G}2$ INPUTS | EQUIVALENT OF A THRU H[†], S0, S1, SHIFT RIGHT, AND SHIFT LEFT INPUTS |

Clock: R_{eq} = 2.8 kΩ NOM
Clear: R_{eq} = 3.5 kΩ NOM

2.8 kΩ NOM

3.5 kΩ NOM

[†]When 3-state outputs are disabled.

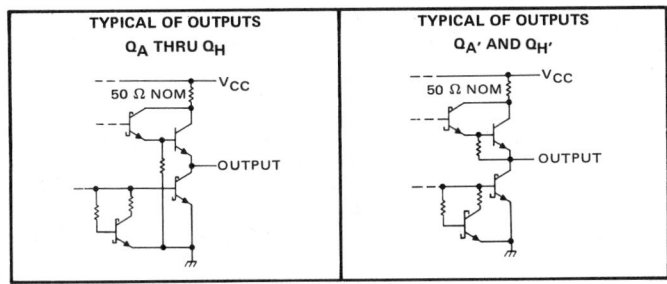

| TYPICAL OF OUTPUTS Q_A THRU Q_H | TYPICAL OF OUTPUTS $Q_{A'}$ AND $Q_{H'}$ |

50 Ω NOM

50 Ω NOM

absolute maximum ratings over operating free-air temperature range (unless otherwise noted)

Supply voltage, V_{CC} (see Note 1) . . . . 7 V
Input voltage . . . . 5.5 V
Off-state output voltage . . . . 5.5 V
Operating free-air temperature range: SN54S299 (see Note 2) . . . . −55°C to 125°C
SN74S299 . . . . 0°C to 70°C
Storage temperature . . . . −65°C to 150°C

NOTES 1: Voltage values are with respect to network ground terminal.

recommended operating conditions

		SN54S299			SN74S299			UNIT
		MIN	NOM	MAX	MIN	NOM	MAX	
Supply voltage, V_{CC}		4.5	5	5.5	4.75	5	5.25	V
High-level output current, I_{OH}	Q_A thru Q_H			−2			−6.5	mA
	$Q_{A'}$ or $Q_{H'}$			−0.5			−0.5	
Low-level output current, I_{OL}	Q_A thru Q_H			20			20	mA
	$Q_{A'}$ or $Q_{H'}$			6			6	
Clock frequency, f_{clock}		0		50	0		50	MHz
Width of clock pulse, $t_{w(clock)}$	Clock high	10			10			ns
	Clock low	10			10			
Width of clear pulse, $t_{w(clear)}$	Clear low	10			10			ns
Setup time, t_{su}	Select	15↑			15↑			ns
	High-level data◊	7↑			7↑			
	Low-level data◊	5↑			5↑			
	Clear inactive-state	10↑			10↑			
Hold time, t_h	Select	5↑			5↑			ns
	Data◊	5↑			5↑			
Operating free-air temperature, T_A		−55		125	0		70	°C

◊Data includes the two serial inputs and the eight input/output data lines.

TEXAS INSTRUMENTS
INCORPORATED
POST OFFICE BOX 5012 • DALLAS, TEXAS 75222

7

electrical characteristics over recommended operating free-air temperature range (unless otherwise noted)

PARAMETER		TEST CONDITIONS[†]	MIN	TYP[‡]	MAX	UNIT
V_{IH}	High-level input voltage		2			V
V_{IL}	Low-level input voltage				0.8	V
V_{IK}	Input clamp voltage	V_{CC} = MIN, I_I = −18 mA			−1.2	V
V_{OH}	High-level output voltage	Q_A thru Q_H V_{CC} = MIN, V_{IH} = 2 V,	2.4	3.2		V
		$Q_{A'}$ or $Q_{H'}$ V_{IL} = 0.8 V, I_{OH} = MAX	2.7	3.4		
V_{OL}	Low-level output voltage	V_{CC} = MIN, V_{IH} = 2 V, V_{IL} = 0.8 V, I_{OL} = MAX			0.5	V
I_{OZH}	Off-state output current, high-level voltage applied	Q_A thru Q_H V_{CC} = MAX, V_{IH} = 2 V, V_O = 2.4 V			100	µA
I_{OZL}	Off-state output current, low-level voltage applied	Q_A thru Q_H V_{CC} = MAX, V_{IH} = 2 V, V_O = 0.5 V			−250	µA
I_I	Input current at maximum input voltage	V_{CC} = MAX, V_I = 5.5 V			1	mA
I_{IH}	High-level input current	A thru H, S0, S1 V_{CC} = MAX, V_I = 2.7 V			100	µA
		Any other			50	
I_{IL}	Low-level input current	Clock or clear V_{CC} = MAX, V_I = 0.5 V			−2	mA
		Any other			−250	µA
I_{OS}	Short-circuit output current[§]	Q_A thru Q_H V_{CC} = MAX	−40		−100	mA
		$Q_{A'}$ or $Q_{H'}$	−20		−100	
I_{CC}	Supply current	V_{CC} = MAX		140	225	mA

[†] For conditions shown as MIN or MAX, use the appropriate value specified under recommended operating conditions.
[‡] All typical values are at V_{CC} = 5 V, T_A = 25°C.
[§] Not more than one output should be shorted at a time and duration of the short-circuit should not exceed one second.

switching characteristics, V_{CC} = 5 V, T_A = 25°C

PARAMETER[¶]	FROM (INPUT)	TO (OUTPUT)	TEST CONDITIONS	MIN	TYP	MAX	UNIT
f_{max}			See Note 2	50	70		MHz
t_{PLH}	Clock	$Q_{A'}$ or $Q_{H'}$	C_L = 15 pF, R_L = 1 kΩ, See Note 2		12	20	ns
t_{PHL}					13	20	
t_{PHL}	Clear	$Q_{A'}$ or $Q_{H'}$			14	21	ns
t_{PLH}	Clock	Q_A thru Q_H	C_L = 45 pF, R_L = 280 Ω, See Note 2		15	21	ns
t_{PHL}					15	21	
t_{PHL}	Clear	Q_A thru Q_H			16	24	ns
t_{PZH}	$\overline{G}1, \overline{G}2$	Q_A thru Q_H			10	18	ns
t_{PZL}					12	18	
t_{PHZ}	$\overline{G}1, \overline{G}2$	Q_A thru Q_H	C_L = 5 pF, R_L = 280 Ω, See Note 3		7	12	ns
t_{PLZ}					7	12	

[¶] f_{max} ≡ maximum clock frequency
t_{PLH} ≡ propagation delay time, low-to-high-level output.
t_{PHL} ≡ propagation delay time, high-to-low-level output
t_{PZH} ≡ output enable time to high level
t_{PZL} ≡ output enable time to low level
t_{PHZ} ≡ output disable time from high level
t_{PLZ} ≡ output disable time from low level
NOTE 3: For testing f_{max}, all outputs are loaded simultaneously, each with C_L and R_L as specified for the propagation times. See load circuits and waveforms on page 3-10.

7

TEXAS INSTRUMENTS
INCORPORATED
POST OFFICE BOX 5012 • DALLAS, TEXAS 75222

TTL
LSI

TYPES SN54LS323, SN74LS323
8-BIT UNIVERSAL SHIFT/STORAGE REGISTERS

BULLETIN NO. DL-S 7612462, OCTOBER 1976

- **Multiplexed Inputs/Outputs Provide Improved Bit Density**

- **Four Modes of Operation:**
  Hold (Store)   Shift Left
  Shift Right   Load Data

- **Operates with Outputs Enabled or at High Z**

- **3-State Outputs Drive Bus Lines Directly**

- **Can Be Cascaded for N-Bit Word Lengths**

- **Typical Power Dissipation . . . 175 mW**

- **Guaranteed Shift (Clock) Frequency . . . 35 MHz**

- **Applications:**
  Stacked or Push-Down Registers,
  Buffer Storage, and
  Accumulator Registers

- **SN54LS299 and SN74LS299 Are Similar But Have Direct Overriding Clear**

SN54LS323 . . . J PACKAGE
SN74LS323 . . . J OR N PACKAGE
(TOP VIEW)

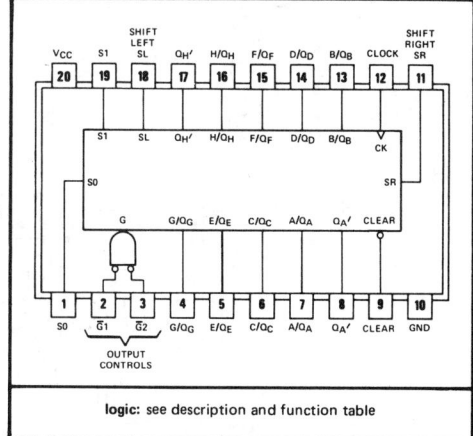

logic: see description and function table

description

These Low-Power Schottky eight-bit universal registers feature multiplexed inputs/outputs to achieve full eight-bit data handling in a single 20-pin package. Two function-select inputs and two output-control inputs can be used to choose the modes of operation listed in the function table. Synchronous parallel loading is accomplished by taking both function-select lines, S0 and S1, high. This places the three-state outputs in a high-impedance state, which permits data that is applied on the input/output lines to be clocked into the register. Reading out of the register can be accomplished while the outputs are enabled in any mode. The clear function is synchronous and a low level at the clear input clears the register on the next low-to-high transition of the clock.

FUNCTION TABLE

MODE	INPUTS							INPUTS/OUTPUTS								OUTPUTS	
	CLEAR	FUNCTION SELECT		OUTPUT CONTROL		CLOCK	SERIAL		A/Q$_A$	B/Q$_B$	C/Q$_C$	D/Q$_D$	E/Q$_E$	F/Q$_F$	G/Q$_G$	H/Q$_H$	Q$_A$'	Q$_H$'
		S1	S0	$\overline{G1}$†	$\overline{G2}$†		SL	SR										
Clear	L	X	L	L	L	↑	X	X	L	L	L	L	L	L	L	L	L	L
	L	L	X	L	L	↑	X	X	L	L	L	L	L	L	L	L	L	L
Hold	H	L	L	L	L	X	X	X	Q$_{A0}$	Q$_{B0}$	Q$_{C0}$	Q$_{D0}$	Q$_{E0}$	Q$_{F0}$	Q$_{G0}$	Q$_{H0}$	Q$_{A0}$	Q$_{H0}$
	H	X	X	L	L	L	X	X	Q$_{A0}$	Q$_{B0}$	Q$_{C0}$	Q$_{D0}$	Q$_{E0}$	Q$_{F0}$	Q$_{G0}$	Q$_{H0}$	Q$_{A0}$	Q$_{H0}$
Shift Right	H	L	H	L	L	↑	X	H	H	Q$_{An}$	Q$_{Bn}$	Q$_{Cn}$	Q$_{Dn}$	Q$_{En}$	Q$_{Fn}$	Q$_{Gn}$	H	Q$_{Gn}$
	H	L	H	L	L	↑	X	L	L	Q$_{An}$	Q$_{Bn}$	Q$_{Cn}$	Q$_{Dn}$	Q$_{En}$	Q$_{Fn}$	Q$_{Gn}$	L	Q$_{Gn}$
Shift Left	H	H	L	L	L	↑	H	X	Q$_{Bn}$	Q$_{Cn}$	Q$_{Dn}$	Q$_{En}$	Q$_{Fn}$	Q$_{Gn}$	Q$_{Hn}$	H	Q$_{Bn}$	H
	H	H	L	L	L	↑	L	X	Q$_{Bn}$	Q$_{Cn}$	Q$_{Dn}$	Q$_{En}$	Q$_{Fn}$	Q$_{Gn}$	Q$_{Hn}$	L	Q$_{Bn}$	L
Load	H	H	H	X	X	↑	X	X	a	b	c	d	e	f	g	h	a	h

†When one or both output controls are high the eight input/output terminals are disabled to the high-impedance state; however, sequential operation or clearing of the register is not affected.

a . . . h = the level of the steady-state input at inputs A through H, respectively. These data are loaded into the flip-flops while the flip-flop outputs are isolated from the input/output terminals. See explanation of function tables on page 3-8.

schematics of inputs and outputs, absolute maximum ratings, recommended operating conditions, and electrical characteristics

Same as SN54LS299 and SN74LS299, see page 7-439.

TEXAS INSTRUMENTS
INCORPORATED
POST OFFICE BOX 5012 • DALLAS, TEXAS 75222

TYPES SN54LS323, SN74LS323
8-BIT UNIVERSAL SHIFT/STORAGE REGISTERS

functional block diagram

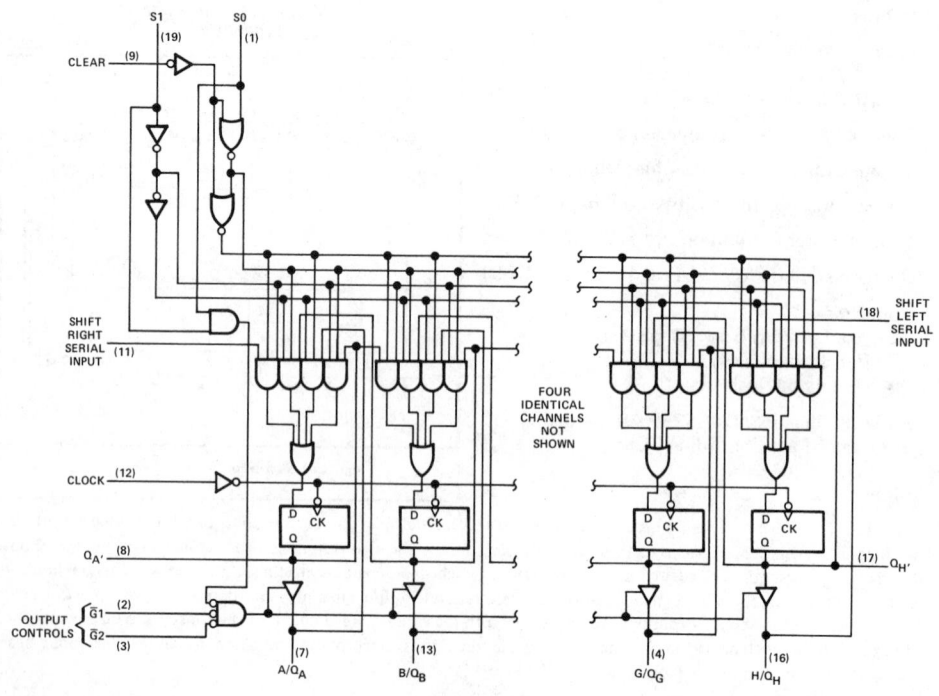

INPUTS/OUTPUTS NOT SHOWN:
(6) C/Q_C   (5) E/Q_E
(14) D/Q_D   (15) F/Q_F

switching characteristics, $V_{CC} = 5$ V, $T_A = 25°$ C

PARAMETER¶	FROM (INPUT)	TO (OUTPUT)	TEST CONDITIONS	MIN	TYP	MAX	UNIT
f_{max}			See Note 1	35	50		MHz
t_{PLH}	Clock	$Q_{A'}$ or $Q_{H'}$	$C_L = 15$ pF, $R_L = 2$ kΩ, See Note 1		15	25	ns
t_{PHL}					15	25	
t_{PLH}	Clock	Q_A thru Q_H			15	25	ns
t_{PHL}			$C_L = 45$ pF, $R_L = 665$ Ω, See Note 1		15	25	
t_{PZH}	$\overline{G}1, \overline{G}2$	Q_A thru Q_H			20	35	ns
t_{PZL}					20	35	
t_{PHZ}	$\overline{G}1, \overline{G}2$	Q_A thru Q_H	$C_L = 5$ pF, $R_L = 665$ Ω, See Note 1		15	25	ns
t_{PLZ}					15	25	

¶$f_{max} \equiv$ maximum clock frequency
$t_{PLH} \equiv$ propagation delay time, low-to-high-level output
$t_{PHL} \equiv$ propagation delay time, high-to-low-level output
$t_{PZH} \equiv$ output enable time to high level
$t_{PZL} \equiv$ output enable time to low level
$t_{PHZ} \equiv$ output disable time from high level
$t_{PLZ} \equiv$ output disable time from low level
NOTE 1: For testing f_{max}, all outputs are loaded simultaneously, each with C_L and R_L as specified for the propagation times. See load
circuits and waveforms on page 3-11.

DESIGN GOAL

TEXAS INSTRUMENTS
INCORPORATED
POST OFFICE BOX 5012 • DALLAS, TEXAS 75222

TTL
MSI

TYPES SN54LS324 THRU SN54LS327, SN74LS324 THRU SN74LS327 VOLTAGE-CONTROLLED OSCILLATORS

BULLETIN NO. DL-S 7612472, OCTOBER 1976

- 'LS325, 'LS326 and 'LS327 Have Two Independent VCO's in a Single Package
- Output Frequency Set by Single External Component:
    Crystal for High-Stability Fixed-Frequency Operation
    Capacitor for Fixed- or Variable-Frequency Operation
- Separate Supply Voltage Pins for Isolation of Frequency Control Inputs and Oscillators from Output Circuitry
- Highly Stable Operation over Specified Temperature and/or Supply Voltage Ranges

description

With the exception of 'LS324, all of these devices feature two independent voltage-controlled oscillators (VCO) in a single monolithic chip. The 'LS324, 'LS325 and 'LS326 have complementary outputs. The output frequency of each VCO is established by a single external component, either a capacitor or a crystal, in combination with the voltage-sensitive inputs, one for frequency control and on the 'LS324, another one for frequency range. These inputs can be used to vary the output frequency by changing the voltage applied to them. These highly stable oscillators can be set to operate at any frequency typically between 0.12 Hz and 30 MHz. With 2 volts applied to the frequency control input and also to the range input of the 'LS324, the output frequency can be approximated as follows:

$$f_o = \frac{1 \times 10^{-4}}{C_{ext}}$$

where: f_o = output frequency in hertz

C_{ext} = external capacitance in farads.

These devices can operate from a single 5-volt supply. However, one set of supply-voltage and ground pins (V_{CC} and GND) is provided for the enable, synchronization-gating, and output sections, and a separate set ($\ominus V_{CC}$ and $\ominus$GND) is provided for the oscillator and associated frequency-control circuits so that effective isolation can be accomplished in the system. Disabling either VCO of the 'LS325 and 'LS327 can be accomplished by removing the appropriate $\ominus V_{CC}$. An enable input is provided on the 'LS324 and 'LS326. While this input is low, the output is enabled. While the enable input is high, Y is high and $\overline{Y}$ is low.

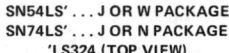

SN54LS'...J OR W PACKAGE
SN74LS'...J OR N PACKAGE
'LS324 (TOP VIEW)

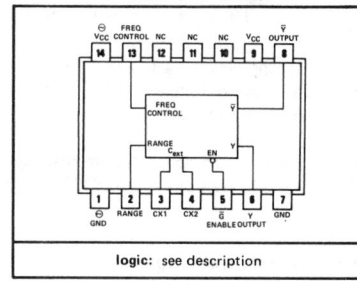

logic: see description

'LS325 (TOP VIEW)

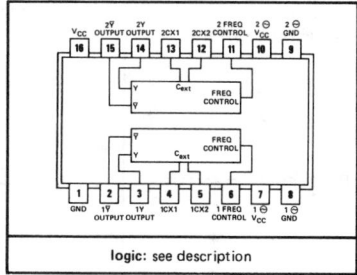

logic: see description

'LS326 (TOP VIEW)

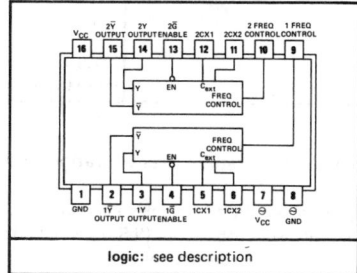

logic: see description

'LS327 (TOP VIEW)

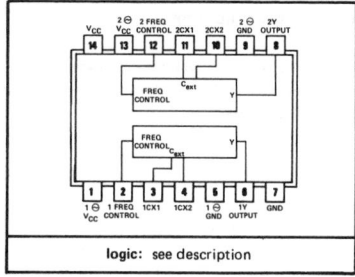

logic: see description

7

TEXAS INSTRUMENTS
INCORPORATED
POST OFFICE BOX 5012 • DALLAS, TEXAS 75222

TYPES SN54LS324 THRU SN54LS327, SN74LS324 THRU SN74LS327
VOLTAGE-CONTROLLED OSCILLATORS

description (continued)

The internal oscillator runs continuously even while the output is disabled via the enable input. The enable input is one standard load, and it and the buffered output operate at standard Schottky-clamped TTL levels.

The pulse synchronization-gating section ensures that the first output pulse is neither clipped nor extended. Duty cycle of the square-wave output is fixed at approximately 50 percent. Simultaneous operation of both VCO's in the same package is not recommended.

The SN54LS324 thru SN54LS327 are characterized for operation over the full military temperature range of -55°C to 125°C; the SN74LS324 thru SN74LS327 are characterized for operation from 0°C to 70°C.

schematics of inputs and outputs

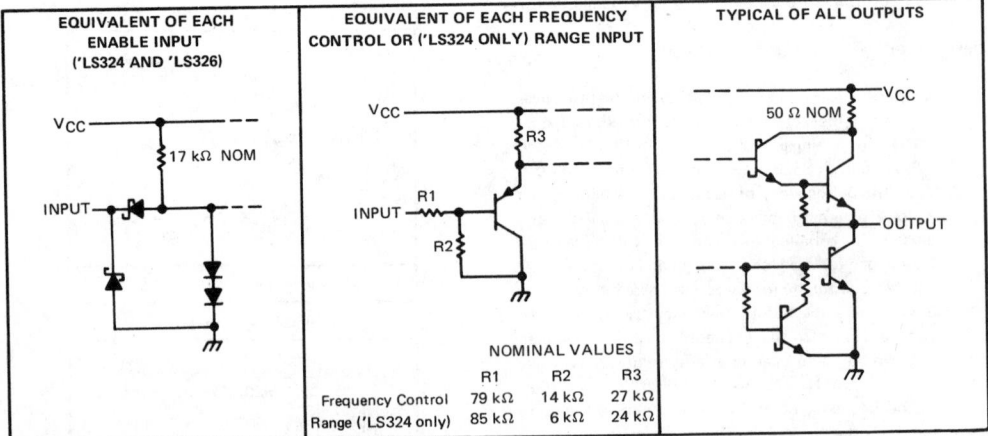

	NOMINAL VALUES		
	R1	R2	R3
Frequency Control	79 kΩ	14 kΩ	27 kΩ
Range ('LS324 only)	85 kΩ	6 kΩ	24 kΩ

absolute maximum ratings over operating free-air temperature range (unless otherwise noted)

Supply voltage, V_{CC} (see Notes 1 and 2) . . . . 7 V
Input voltage: Enable input ('LS324 and 'LS326) . . . . 7 V
            Frequency control or range input . . . . V_{CC}
Operating free-air temperature range: SN54LS' Circuits . . . . -55°C to 125°C
                       SN74LS' Circuits . . . . 0°C to 70°C
Storage temperature range . . . . -65°C to 150°C

NOTES: 1. Voltage values are with respect to the appropriate ground terminal.
        2. Throughout this data sheet, the symbol V_{CC} is used for the voltage applied to both the V_{CC} and $\ominus V_{CC}$ terminals, unless otherwise noted.

TEXAS INSTRUMENTS
INCORPORATED
POST OFFICE BOX 5012 • DALLAS, TEXAS 75222

recommended operating conditions

		SN54LS'			SN74LS'			UNIT
		MIN	NOM	MAX	MIN	NOM	MAX	
Supply voltage, V_{CC}		4.5	5	5.5	4.75	5	5.25	V
Input voltage at frequency control or range input, $V_{I(freq)}$ or $V_{I(rng)}$ ▲		0		5	0		5	V
High-level output current, I_{OH}				−1.2			−1.2	mA
Low-level output current, I_{OL}				12			24	mA
Output frequency (enabled), f_o		1			1			Hz
				20			20	MHz
Operating free-air temperature, T_A		−55		125	0		70	°C

electrical characteristics over recommended operating free-air temperature range (unless otherwise noted)

PARAMETER		TEST CONDITIONS[†]		SN54LS'			SN74LS'			UNIT
				MIN	TYP[‡]	MAX	MIN	TYP[‡]	MAX	
V_{IH}	High-level input voltage at enable[♦]			2			2			V
V_{IL}	Low-level input voltage at enable[♦]					0.7			0.8	V
V_{IK}	Input clamp voltage at enable[♦]	V_{CC} = MIN, I_I = −18 mA				−1.5			−1.5	V
V_{OH}	High-level output voltage	V_{CC} = MIN, V_{IH} = 2 V, I_{OH} = −1.2 mA, See Note 3		2.5	3.4		2.7	3.4		V
V_{OL}	Low-level output voltage	V_{CC} = MIN, ⊖V_{CC} open $V_{IL} = V_{IL}$ max	I_{OL} = 12 mA	0.25	0.4		0.25	0.4		V
			I_{OL} = 24 mA				0.35	0.5		
I_I	Input current — Freq control or range ▲	V_{CC} = MAX	V_I = 5 V		50	250		50	250	μA
			V_I = 1 V		10	50		10	50	
I_I	Input current at maximum input voltage — Enable[♦]	V_{CC} = MAX, V_I = 7 V				0.1			0.1	mA
I_{IH}	High-level input current — Enable[♦]	V_{CC} = MAX, V_I = 2.7 V				20			20	μA
I_{IL}	Low-level input current — Enable[♦]	V_{CC} = MAX, V_I = 0.4 V				−0.4			−0.4	mA
I_{OS}	Short-circuit output current[§]	V_{CC} = MAX		−40		−225	−40		−225	mA
I_{CC}	Supply current, total into V_{CC} and ⊖V_{CC} pins	V_{CC} = Max See Note 4	'LS324, 'LS326		18	30		18	30	mA
			'LS325, 'LS327		30	50		30	50	

[†] For conditions shown as MIN or MAX, use the appropriate value specified under recommended operating conditions.
[‡] All typical values are at V_{CC} = 5 V, T_A = 25°C.
[§] Not more than one output should be shorted at a time and duration of the short-circuit should not exceed one second.
[♦] The characteristics involving an enable input are applicable to 'LS324 and 'LS326 only.

NOTES: 3. V_{OH} is measured for Y outputs by connecting a 1-kΩ resistor from CX1 to V_{CC} and another 1-kΩ resistor from CX2 to GND. This procedure is reversed for testing V_{OH} of $\bar{Y}$ outputs (not applicable to 'LS327). That is, a 1-kΩ resistor is connected from CX2 to V_{CC} and another 1-kΩ resistor from CX1 to GND. During the V_{OH} tests of 'LS324 and 'LS326, the enable pin should be at V_{IL} max.
  4. For 'LS324 and 'LS326, I_{CC} is measured with the outputs disabled and open, and ⊖ V_{CC} = MAX. For 'LS325 and 'LS327, I_{CC} is measured with one ⊖ V_{CC} = MAX, and with the other ⊖ V_{CC} and outputs open.

switching characteristics, V_{CC} = 5 V (unless otherwise noted), R_L = 667 Ω, C_L = 45 pF, T_A = 25°C

PARAMETER		TEST CONDITIONS		MIN	TYP	MAX	UNIT
f_o	Output frequency	C_{ext} = 2 pF	$V_{I(freq)}$ = 5 V, $V_{I(rng)}$ = 0 V	20	30		MHz
			$V_{I(freq)}$ = 0 V, $V_{I(rng)}$ = 5 V	11	20		
f_o	Output frequency (crystal controlled)	⊖V_{CC} = 3 V, $V_{I(freq)}$ = $V_{I(rng)}$ = 0 V		10	20		MHz
	Output duty cycle	C_{ext} = 8.3 pF to 500 μF			50%		
t_{PHL}	Propagation delay time, high-to-low-level output from enable	f_o ⩾ 1 Hz			30+*		ns

▲ The range input is provided only on the 'LS324.
* The delay will typically be 30 ns pulse up to one period of one cycle (i.e. 30 ns + $\frac{1 \times 10^9}{f_o(Hz)}$ ns) depending upon the timing of the enable pulse with respect to the signal generated by the internal oscillator.

076

7

TTL
MSI

TYPES SN54LS348, SN74LS348 (TIM9908)
8-LINE-TO-3-LINE PRIORITY ENCODERS
WITH 3-STATE OUTPUTS
BULLETIN NO. DL-S 7712469, OCTOBER 1976—REVISED AUGUST 1977

- **3-State Outputs Drive Bus Lines Directly**
- **Encodes 8 Data Lines to 3-Line Binary (Octal)**
- **Applications Include:**
  N-Bit Encoding
  Code Converters and Generators
- **Typical Data Delay . . . 15 ns**
- **Typical Power Dissipation . . . 60 mW**

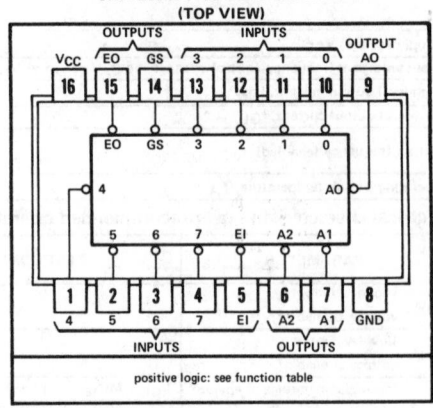

SN54LS348 . . . J OR W PACKAGE
SN74LS348 . . . J OR N PACKAGE
(TOP VIEW)

description

These TTL encoders feature priority decoding of the inputs to ensure that only the highest-order data line is encoded. The 'LS348 circuits encode eight data lines to three-line (4-2-1) binary (octal). Cascading circuitry (enable input EI and enable output EO) has been provided to allow octal expansion. Outputs A0, A1, and A2 are implemented in three-state logic for easy expansion up to 64 lines without the need for external circuitry. See Typical Application Data.

functional block diagram

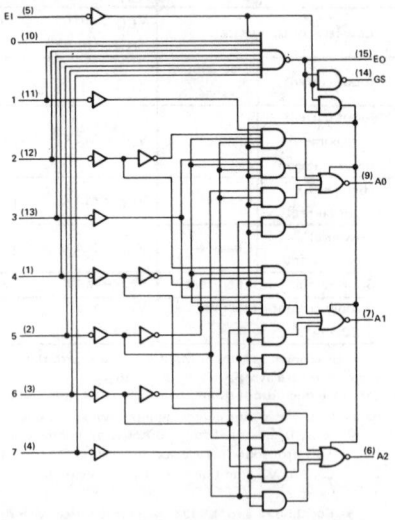

FUNCTION TABLE

INPUTS									OUTPUTS				
EI	0	1	2	3	4	5	6	7	A2	A1	A0	GS	EO
H	X	X	X	X	X	X	X	X	Z	Z	Z	H	H
L	H	H	H	H	H	H	H	H	Z	Z	Z	H	L
L	X	X	X	X	X	X	X	L	L	L	L	L	H
L	X	X	X	X	X	X	L	H	L	L	H	L	H
L	X	X	X	X	X	L	H	H	L	H	L	L	H
L	X	X	X	X	L	H	H	H	L	H	H	L	H
L	X	X	X	L	H	H	H	H	H	L	L	L	H
L	X	X	L	H	H	H	H	H	H	L	H	L	H
L	X	L	H	H	H	H	H	H	H	H	L	L	H
L	L	H	H	H	H	H	H	H	H	H	H	L	H

H = high logic level, L = low logic level, X = irrelevant
Z = high-impedance state

schematic of inputs and outputs

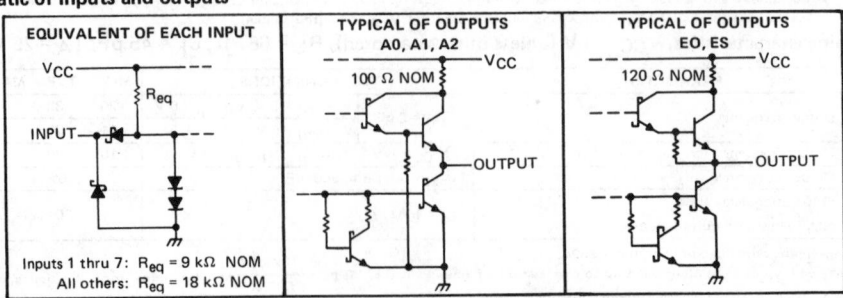

EQUIVALENT OF EACH INPUT	TYPICAL OF OUTPUTS A0, A1, A2	TYPICAL OF OUTPUTS EO, ES

Inputs 1 thru 7: R_{eq} = 9 kΩ NOM
All others: R_{eq} = 18 kΩ NOM

877

7-448

TYPES SN54LS348, SN74LS348 (TIM9908)
8-LINE-TO-3-LINE PRIORITY ENCODERS WITH 3-STATE OUTPUTS

REVISED AUGUST 1977

absolute maximum ratings over operating free-air temperature range (unless otherwise noted)

Supply voltage, V_{CC} (see Note 1) . . . . 7 V
Input voltage . . . . 7 V
Operating free-air temperature range: SN54LS348 . . . . −55°C to 125°C
SN74LS348 . . . . 0°C to 70°C
Storage temperature range . . . . −65°C to 150°C

NOTE 1: Voltage values are with respect to network ground terminal.

recommended operating conditions

		SN54LS348			SN74LS348			UNIT
		MIN	NOM	MAX	MIN	NOM	MAX	
Supply voltage, V_{CC}		4.5	5	5.5	4.75	5	5.25	V
High-level output current, I_{OH}	A0, A1, A2			−1			−2.6	mA
	EO, GS		−400			−400		µA
Low-level output current, I_{OL}	A0, A1, A2			12			24	mA
	EO, GS			4			8	mA
Operating free-air temperature, T_A		−55		125	0		70	°C

electrical characteristics over recommended operating free-air temperature range (unless otherwise noted)

PARAMETER		TEST CONDITIONS†		SN54LS348			SN74LS348			UNIT
				MIN	TYP‡	MAX	MIN	TYP‡	MAX	
V_{IH}	High-level input voltage			2			2			V
V_{IL}	Low-level input voltage					0.7			0.8	V
V_{IK}	Input clamp voltage	V_{CC} = MIN,	I_I = −18 mA			−1.5			−1.5	V
V_{OH}	High-level output voltage	A0, A1, A2	V_{CC} = MIN, V_{IH} = 2 V, $V_{IL} = V_{IL}$max	I_{OH} = −1 mA	2.4	3.1					V
				I_{OH} = −2.6 mA				2.4	3.1		
		EO, GS		I_{OH} = −400 µA	2.5	3.4		2.7	3.4		
V_{OL}	Low-level Output voltage	A0, A1, A2	V_{CC} = MIN, V_{IH} = 2 V, $V_{IL} = V_{IL}$max	I_{OL} = 12 mA		0.25	0.4		0.25	0.4	V
				I_{OL} = 24 mA					0.35	0.5	
		EO, GS		I_{OL} = 4 mA		0.25	0.4		0.25	0.4	
				I_{OL} = 8 mA					0.35	0.5	
I_{OZ}	Off-State (high-impedance state) output current	A0, A1, A2	V_{CC} = MAX, V_{IH} = 2 V	V_O = 2.7 V			20			20	µA
				V_O = 0.4 V			−20			−20	
I_I	Input current at maximum input voltage	Inputs 1 thru 7	V_{CC} = MAX, V_I = 7 V				0.2			0.2	mA
		All other inputs					0.1			0.1	
I_{IH}	High-level input current	Inputs 1 thru 7	V_{CC} = MAX, V_I = 2.7 V				40			40	µA
		All other inputs					20			20	
I_{IL}	Low-level input current	Inputs 1 thru 7	V_{CC} = MAX, V_I = 0.4 V				−0.8			−0.8	mA
		All other inputs					−0.4			−0.4	
I_{OS}	Short-circuit output current§	Outputs A0, A1, A2	V_{CC} = MAX		−30		−130	−30		−130	mA
		Outputs EO, GS			−20		−100	−20		−100	
I_{CC}	Supply current	V_{CC} = MAX, See Note 2	Condition 1		13	25		13	25	mA
			Condition 2		12	23		12	23	

NOTE 2: I_{CC} (condition 1) is measured with inputs 7 and EI grounded, other inputs and outputs open. I_{CC} (condition 2) is measured with all inputs and outputs open.

†For conditions shown as MIN or MAX, use the appropriate value specified under recommended operating conditions.
‡All typical values are at V_{CC} = 5 V, T_A = 25°C.
§Not more than one output should be shorted at a time.

TEXAS INSTRUMENTS
INCORPORATED
POST OFFICE BOX 5012 • DALLAS, TEXAS 75222

TYPES SN54LS348, SN74LS348 (TIM9908)
8-LINE-TO-3-LINE PRIORITY ENCODERS WITH 3-STATE OUTPUTS
REVISED AUGUST 1977

switching characteristics, V_{CC} = 5 V, T_A = 25°C

PARAMETER¶	FROM (INPUT)	TO (OUTPUT)	WAVEFORM	TEST CONDITIONS	MIN	TYP	MAX	UNIT
t_{PLH}	0 thru 7	A0, A1, or A2	In-phase output	C_L = 45 pF, R_L = 667 Ω, See Note 3		11	17	ns
t_{PHL}						20	30	
t_{PLH}	0 thru 7	A0, A1, or A2	Out-of-phase output			23	35	ns
t_{PHL}						23	35	
t_{PZH}	EI	A0, A1, or A2				25	39	ns
t_{PZL}						24	41	
t_{PLH}	0 thru 7	EO	Out-of-phase output	C_L = 15 pF R_L = 2 kΩ, See Note 3		11	18	ns
t_{PHL}						26	40	
t_{PLH}	0 thru 7	GS	In-phase output			38	55	ns
t_{PHL}						9	21	
t_{PLH}	EI	GS	In-phase output			11	17	ns
t_{PHL}						14	36	
t_{PLH}	EI	EO	In-phase output			17	21	ns
t_{PHL}						25	40	
t_{PHZ}	EI	A0, A1, or A2		C_L = 5 pF R_L = 667 Ω		18	27	ns
t_{PLZ}						23	35	

¶ t_{PLH} = propagation delay time, low-to-high-level output
 t_{PHL} = propagation delay time, high-to-low-level output
 t_{PZH} = output enable time to high level
 t_{PZL} = output enable time to low level
 t_{PHZ} = output disable time from high level
 t_{PLZ} = output disable time from low level
NOTE 3: Load circuits and waveforms are shown on page 3-11.

TYPICAL APPLICATION DATA

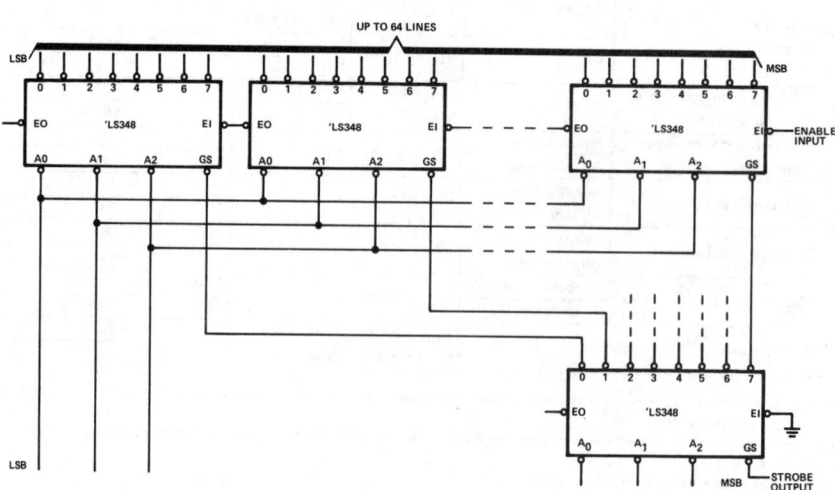

FIGURE 1—PRIORITY ENCODER WITH UP TO 64 INPUTS.

TEXAS INSTRUMENTS
INCORPORATED
POST OFFICE BOX 5012 • DALLAS, TEXAS 75222

- **Dual 8-Line-to-1-Line Multiplexer That Can Replace Two SN54151, SN74151 Multiplexers in Some Applications**

- **Four Common Data Lines Permit Simultaneous Interdigitation with Parallel-to-Serial Conversion**

- **4-Bit Organization Is Easily Adapted to Handle Binary or BCD**

- **Three-State Outputs Can Be Connected Directly to System Bus Lines**

- **Enable Input Controls Impedance Levels of the 12 Data Inputs and Two Outputs**

description

The SN74351 comprises two 8-line-to-1-line data selectors/multiplexers with full decoding on one monolithic chip. Symmetrically switching, complementary decode generators minimize decoder skew during changes at the select inputs and ensure that potentially erroneous effects are minimized at the data outputs. Four data inputs are exclusive to each multiplexer and four are common to both. A common enable input is provided which, when high, causes both outputs to assume the high-impedance (off) state and simultaneously diverts the majority of the input current, which reduces the load significantly on the data input drivers. A low logic level at the enable input activates both outputs so that each will assume the complement of the level of the selected input.

N
DUAL-IN-LINE PACKAGE (TOP VIEW)

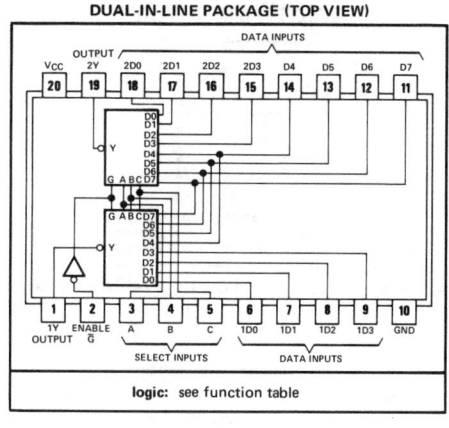

logic: see function table

functional block diagram

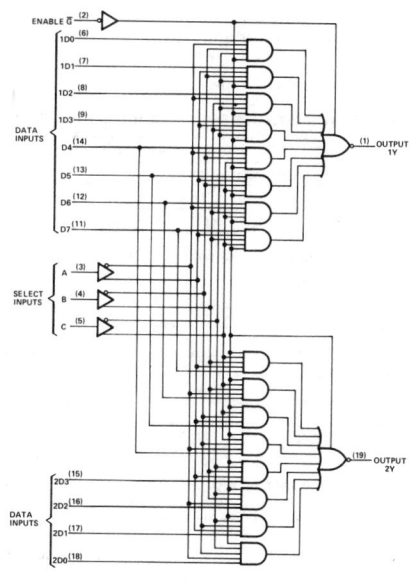

FUNCTION TABLE

INPUTS			OUTPUTS	
ENABLE	SELECT			
$\overline{G}$	C	B	A	1Y	2Y
H	X	X	X	Z	Z
L	L	L	L	$\overline{1D0}$	$\overline{2D0}$
L	L	L	H	$\overline{1D1}$	$\overline{2D1}$
L	L	H	L	$\overline{1D2}$	$\overline{2D2}$
L	L	H	H	$\overline{1D3}$	$\overline{2D3}$
L	H	L	L	$\overline{D4}$	$\overline{D4}$
L	H	L	H	$\overline{D5}$	$\overline{D5}$
L	H	H	L	$\overline{D6}$	$\overline{D6}$
L	H	H	H	$\overline{D7}$	$\overline{D7}$

H = high level, L = low level, X = irrelevant
Z = high impedance (off)
$\overline{1D0}, \overline{1D1}, \ldots \overline{D7}$ = The complement of the level of the respective D input

TEXAS INSTRUMENTS
INCORPORATED
POST OFFICE BOX 5012 • DALLAS, TEXAS 75222

TYPE SN74351
DUAL DATA SELECTOR/MULTIPLEXER WITH 3-STATE OUTPUTS

REVISED OCTOBER 1976

schematics of inputs and outputs

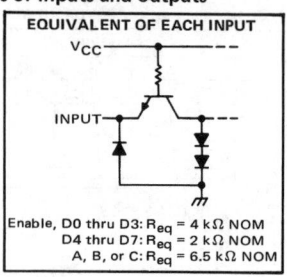

EQUIVALENT OF EACH INPUT

Enable, D0 thru D3: R_{eq} = 4 kΩ NOM
D4 thru D7: R_{eq} = 2 kΩ NOM
A, B, or C: R_{eq} = 6.5 kΩ NOM

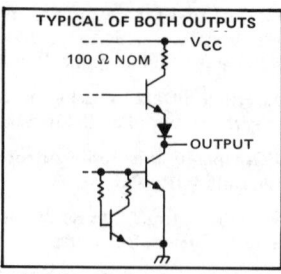

TYPICAL OF BOTH OUTPUTS

100 Ω NOM

absolute maximum ratings over operating free-air temperature range (unless otherwise noted)

Supply voltage, V_{CC} (see Note 1)	7 V
Input voltage	5.5 V
Operating free-air temperature range	0°C to 70°C
Storage temperature range	−65°C to 150°C

NOTE 1: Voltage values are with respect to network ground terminal.

recommended operating conditions

	MIN	NOM	MAX	UNIT
Supply voltage, V_{CC}	4.75	5	5.25	V
High-level output current, I_{OH}			−0.8	mA
Low-level output current, I_{OL}			16	mA
Operating free-air temperature, T_A	0		70	°C

electrical characteristics over recommended operating free-air temperature range (unless otherwise noted)

	PARAMETER		TEST CONDITIONS		MIN	TYP‡	MAX	UNIT
V_{IH}	High-level input voltage				2			V
V_{IL}	Low-level input voltage						0.8	V
V_{IK}	Input clamp voltage		V_{CC} = MIN,	I_I = −12 mA			−1.5	V
V_{OH}	High-level output voltage		V_{CC} = MIN, V_{IH} = 2 V, V_{IL} = 0.8 V, I_{OH} = −0.8 mA		2.4	3.4		V
V_{OL}	Low-level output voltage		V_{CC} = MIN, V_{IH} = 2 V, V_{IL} = 0.8 V, I_{OL} = 16 mA			0.2	0.4	V
I_{OZH}	Off-state output current, high-level voltage applied		V_{CC} = MAX, V_{IH} = 2 V, V_O = 2.4 V				40	µA
I_{OZL}	Off state output current, low level voltage applied		V_{CC} = MAX, V_{IH} = 2 V, V_O = 0.4 V				−40	µA
I_I	Input current at maximum input voltage		V_{CC} = MAX, V_I = 5.5 V				1	mA
I_{IH}	High-level input current	Enable, any select, any D0 thru D3	V_{CC} = MAX, V_I = 2.4 V				40	µA
		D4 thru D7					80	
I_{IL}	Low-level input current	Enable, any select, any D0 thru D3	V_{CC} = MAX, V_I = 0.4 V				−1.6	mA
		D4 thru D7					−3.2	
		Any D	V_{CC} = MAX, V_I = 0.5, $V_{I(enable)}$ = 2 V				−40	µA
I_{OS}	Short-circuit output current§		V_{CC} = MAX		−18		−55	mA
I_{CC}	Supply current		V_{CC} = MAX, See Note 2			44	66	mA

†For conditions shown as MIN or MAX, use the appropriate value specified under recommended operating conditions.
‡All typical values are at V_{CC} = 5 V, T_A = 25°C.
§Not more than one output should be shorted at a time.
NOTE 2: I_{CC} is measured with the enable input grounded, other inputs and both outputs open.

TEXAS INSTRUMENTS
INCORPORATED
POST OFFICE BOX 5012 • DALLAS, TEXAS 75222

1076

switching characteristics, $V_{CC} = 5$ V, $T_A = 25°C$

PARAMETER¶	FROM (INPUT)	TO (OUTPUT)	TEST CONDITIONS	MIN	TYP	MAX	UNIT
t_{PLH}	A, B, or C	Y			20	30	ns
t_{PHL}					20	30	
t_{PLH}	Any D	Y	$C_L = 50$ pF, $R_L = 400\ \Omega$, See Note 3		10	22	ns
t_{PHL}					10	22	
t_{ZH}	$\overline{G}$	Y			18	33	ns
t_{ZL}					20	33	
t_{HZ}	$\overline{G}$	Y	$C_L = 5$ pF, $R_L = 400\ \Omega$, See Note 3		6	20	ns
t_{LZ}					10	20	

¶ $t_{PLH} \equiv$ propagation delay time, low-to-high-level output
$t_{PHL} \equiv$ propagation delay time, high-to-low-level output
$t_{ZH} \equiv$ output enable time to high level
$t_{ZL} \equiv$ output enable time to low level
$t_{HZ} \equiv$ output disable time from high level
$t_{LZ} \equiv$ output disable time from low level
NOTE 3: Load circuit and voltage waveforms are shown on page 3-10.

TYPICAL APPLICATION DATA

This application illustrates how common data can be interdigitated onto two serial data lines. It is useful for transmitting prefixes, suffixes, addresses, or similar functions.

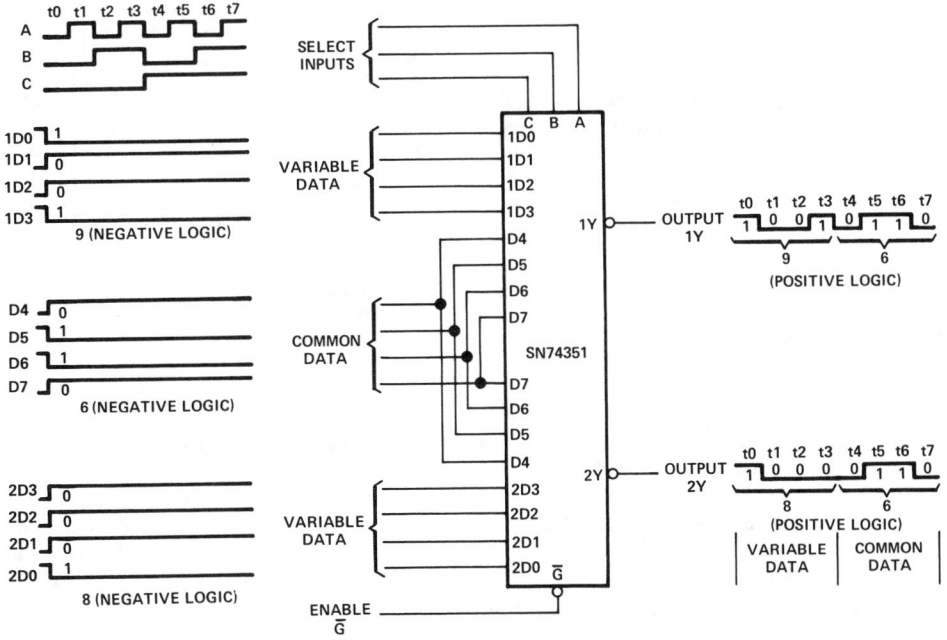

TEXAS INSTRUMENTS
INCORPORATED
POST OFFICE BOX 5012 • DALLAS, TEXAS 75222

- Inverting Versions of SN54LS153, SN74LS153
- Schottky-Diode-Clamped Transistors
- Permits Multiplexing from N lines to 1 line
- Performs Parallel-to-Serial Conversion
- Typical Average Propagation Delay Times:
  Data Input to Output . . . 15 ns
  Strobe Input to Output . . . 19 ns
  Select Input to Output . . . 22 ns
- Fully Compatible with most TTL and DTL Circuits
- Low Power Dissipation . . . 31 mW Typical (Enabled)
- Inverted Data

SN54LS352 . . . J OR W PACKAGE
SN74LS352 . . . J OR N PACKAGE
(TOP VIEW)

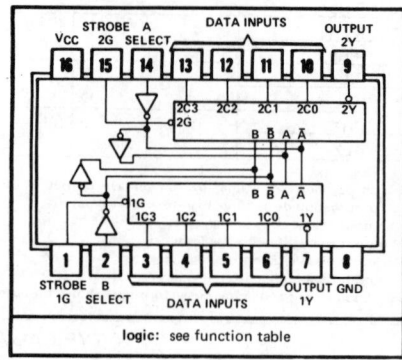

logic: see function table

description

Each of these Schottky-clamped data selectors/-multiplexers contains inverters and drivers to supply fully complementary, on-chip, binary decoding data selection to the AND-OR-invert gates. Separate strobe inputs are provided for each of the two four-line sections.

FUNCTION TABLE

SELECT INPUTS		DATA INPUTS				STROBE	OUTPUT
B	A	C0	C1	C2	C3	G	Y
X	X	X	X	X	X	H	H
L	L	L	X	X	X	L	H
L	L	H	X	X	X	L	L
L	H	X	L	X	X	L	H
L	H	X	H	X	X	L	L
H	L	X	X	L	X	L	H
H	L	X	X	H	X	L	L
H	H	X	X	X	L	L	H
H	H	X	X	X	H	L	L

Select inputs A and B are common to both sections.
H = high level, L = low level, X = irrelevant

absolute maximum ratings over operating free-air temperature range (unless otherwise noted)

Supply voltage, V_{CC} (see Note 1) . . . . 7 V
Input voltage . . . . 7 V
Operating free-air temperature range: SN54LS352 . . . . −55°C to 125°C
　　　　　　　　　　　　　　　　　　SN74LS352 . . . . 0°C to 70°C
Storage temperature range . . . . −65°C to 150°C

NOTE 1: Voltage values are with respect to network ground terminal.

TEXAS INSTRUMENTS
INCORPORATED
POST OFFICE BOX 5012 • DALLAS, TEXAS 75222

functional block diagram

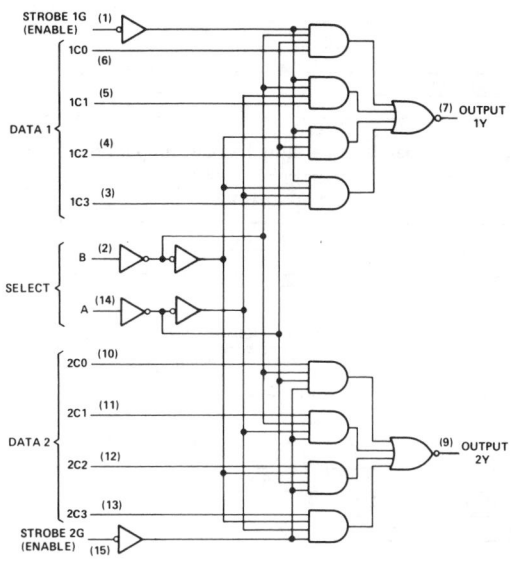

schematics of inputs and outputs

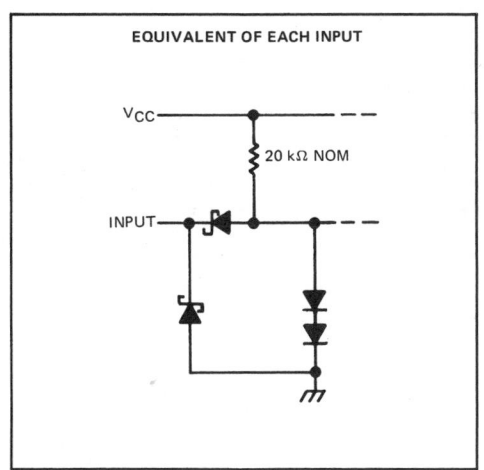

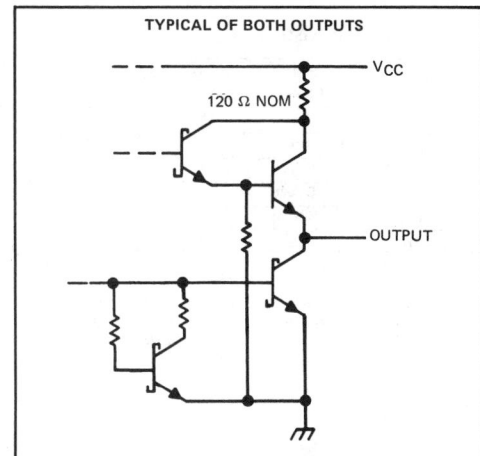

1076

recommended operating conditions

	SN54LS352			SN74LS352			UNIT
	MIN	NOM	MAX	MIN	NOM	MAX	
Supply voltage, V_{CC}	4.5	5	5.5	4.75	5	5.25	V
High-level output current, I_{OH}			−400			−400	μA
Low-level output current, I_{OL}			4			8	mA
Operating free-air temperature, T_A	−55		125	0		70	°C

electrical characteristics over recommended operating free-air temperature range (unless otherwise noted)

PARAMETER	TEST CONDITIONS†		SN54LS352			SN74LS352			UNIT
			MIN	TYP‡	MAX	MIN	TYP‡	MAX	
V_{IH} High-level input voltage			2			2			V
V_{IL} Low-level input voltage					0.7			0.8	V
V_{IK} Input clamp voltage	V_{CC} = MIN, I_I = −18 mA				−1.5			−1.5	V
V_{OH} High-level output voltage	V_{CC} = MIN, V_{IH} = 2 V, V_{IL} = V_{IL} max, I_{OH} = −400 μA		2.5	3.4		2.7	3.4		V
V_{OL} Low-level output voltage	V_{CC} = MIN, V_{IH} = 2 V, V_{IL} = V_{IL} max	I_{OL} = 4 mA		0.25	0.4		0.25	0.4	V
		I_{OL} = 8 mA					0.35	0.5	
I_I Input current at maximum input voltage	V_{CC} = MAX, V_I = 7 V				0.1			0.1	mA
I_{IH} High-level input current	V_{CC} = MAX, V_I = 2.7 V				20			20	μA
I_{IL} Low-level input current	V_{CC} = MAX, V_I = 0.4 V				−0.4			−0.4	mA
I_{OS} Short-circuit output current§	V_{CC} = MAX		−20		−100	−20		−100	mA
I_{CCL} Supply current, output low	V_{CC} = MAX, See Note 2			6.2	10		6.2	10	mA

†For conditions shown as MIN or MAX, use the appropriate value specified under recommended operating .
‡All typical values are at V_{CC} = 5 V, T_A = 25°C.
§Not more than one output should be shorted at a time, and duration of the short-circuit should not exceed one second.
NOTE 2: I_{CCL} is measured with the outputs open and all inputs grounded.

switching characteristics, V_{CC} = 5 V, T_A = 25°C

PARAMETER¶	FROM (INPUT)	TO (OUTPUT)	TEST CONDITIONS	MIN	TYP	MAX	UNIT
t_{PLH}	Data	Y			13	20	ns
t_{PHL}	Data	Y	C_L = 15 pF, R_L = 2 kΩ, See Note 3		17	26	ns
t_{PLH}	Select	Y			19	29	ns
t_{PHL}	Select	Y			25	38	ns
t_{PLH}	Strobe	Y			16	24	ns
t_{PHL}	Strobe	Y			21	32	ns

¶ t_{PLH} ≡ propagation delay time, low-to-high-level output
  t_{PHL} ≡ propagation delay time, high-to-low-level output
NOTE 3:   Load circuits and voltage waveforms are shown on page 3-11.

TEXAS INSTRUMENTS
INCORPORATED
POST OFFICE BOX 5012 • DALLAS, TEXAS 75222

TYPES SN54LS353, SN74LS353
DUAL 4-LINE-TO-1-LINE DATA SELECTORS/MULTIPLEXERS
WITH 3-STATE OUTPUTS

BULLETIN NO. DL-S 7612464, OCTOBER 1976

- Inverting Versions of SN54LS253, SN74LS253
- Schottky-Diode-Clamped Transistors
- Permits Multiplexing from N Lines to 1 Line
- Performs Parallel-to-Serial Conversion
- Typical Average Propagation Delay Times:
  Data Input to Output . . . 12 ns
  Control Input to Output . . . 16 ns
  Select Input to Output . . . 21 ns
- Fully Compatible with Most TTL and DTL Circuits
- Low Power Dissipation . . . 35 mW Typical (Enabled)
- Inverted Data

SN54LS353 . . . J OR W PACKAGE
SN74LS353 . . . J OR N PACKAGE
(TOP VIEW)

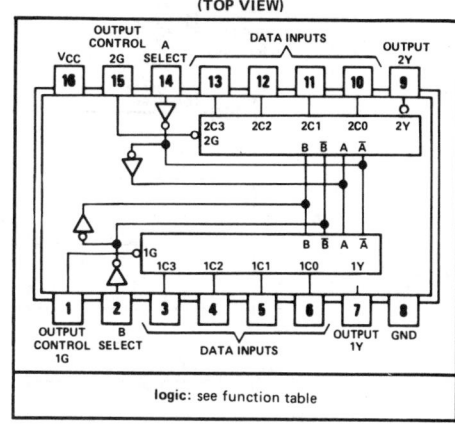

logic: see function table

description

Each of these Schottky-clamped data selectors/multiplexers contains inverters and drivers to supply fully complementary, on-chip, binary decoding data selection to the AND-OR-invert gates. Separate output control inputs are provided for each of the two four-line sections.

The three-state outputs can interface with and drive data lines of bus-organized systems. With all but one of the common outputs disabled (at a high-impedance state) the low-impedance of the single enabled output will drive the bus line to a high or low logic level.

logic

FUNCTION TABLE

SELECT INPUTS		DATA INPUTS				OUTPUT CONTROL	OUTPUT
B	A	C0	C1	C2	C3	G	Y
X	X	X	X	X	X	H	Z
L	L	L	X	X	X	L	H
L	L	H	X	X	X	L	L
L	H	X	L	X	X	L	H
L	H	X	H	X	X	L	L
H	L	X	X	L	X	L	H
H	L	X	X	H	X	L	L
H	H	X	X	X	L	L	H
H	H	X	X	X	H	L	L

Select inputs A and B are common to both sections.

H = high level, L = low level, X = irrelevant, Z = high impedance (off)

absolute maximum ratings over operating free-air temperature range (unless otherwise noted)

Supply voltage, V_{CC} (see Note 1) . . . . 7 V
Input voltage . . . . 7 V
Off-state output voltage . . . . 5.5 V
Operating free-air temperature range: SN54LS353 . . . . -55°C to 125°C
 SN74LS353 . . . . 0°C to 70°C
Storage temperature range . . . . -65°C to 150°C

NOTE 1: Voltage values are with respect to network ground terminal.

TEXAS INSTRUMENTS
INCORPORATED
POST OFFICE BOX 5012 • DALLAS, TEXAS 75222

TYPES SN54LS353, SN74LS353
DUAL 4-LINE-TO-1-LINE DATA SELECTORS/MULTIPLEXERS
WITH 3-STATE OUTPUTS

functional block diagram

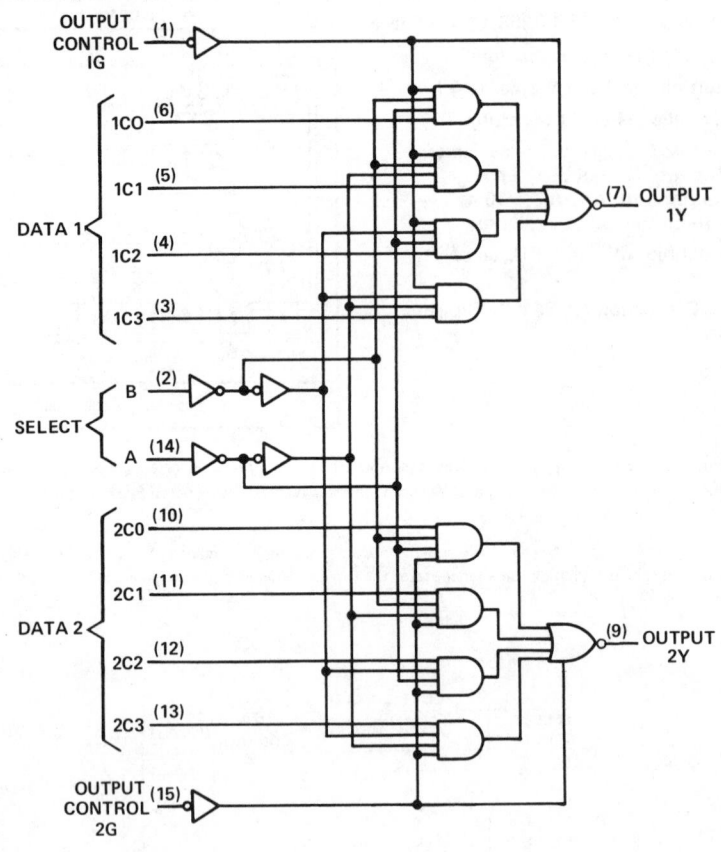

schematics of inputs and outputs

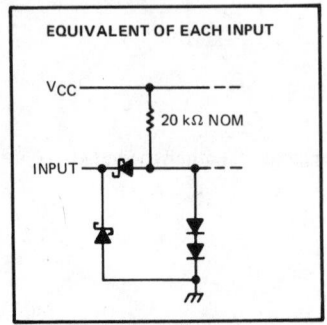

EQUIVALENT OF EACH INPUT

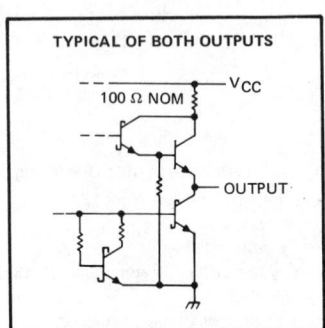

TYPICAL OF BOTH OUTPUTS

TEXAS INSTRUMENTS
INCORPORATED
POST OFFICE BOX 5012 • DALLAS, TEXAS 75222

107

recommended operating conditions

	SN54LS353			SN74LS353			UNIT
	MIN	NOM	MAX	MIN	NOM	MAX	
Supply voltage, V_{CC}	4.5	5	5.5	4.75	5	5.25	V
High-level output current, I_{OH}			−1			−2.6	mA
Low-level output current, I_{OL}			4			8	mA
Operating free-air temperature, T_A	−55		125	0		70	°C

electrical characteristics over recommended operating free-air temperature range (unless otherwise noted)

	PARAMETER	TEST CONDITIONS[†]		SN54LS353			SN74LS353			UNIT
				MIN	TYP[‡]	MAX	MIN	TYP[‡]	MAX	
V_{IH}	High-level input voltage			2			2			V
V_{IL}	Low-level input voltage					0.7			0.8	V
V_{IK}	Input clamp voltage	V_{CC} = MIN, I_I = −18 mA				−1.5			−1.5	V
V_{OH}	High-level output voltage	V_{CC} = MIN, V_{IH} = 2 V, V_{IL} = V_{IL} max, I_{OH} = MAX		2.4	3.4		2.4	3.1		V
V_{OL}	Low-level output voltage	V_{CC} = MIN, V_{IH} = 2 V, V_{IL} = V_{IL} max	I_{OL} = 4 mA		0.25	0.4		0.25	0.4	V
			I_{OL} = 8 mA					0.35	0.5	
I_{OZ}	Off-State (high-impedance state) output current	V_{CC} = MAX, V_{IH} = 2 V	V_O = 2.7 V			20			20	μA
			V_O = 0.4 V			−20			−20	
I_I	Input current at maximum input voltage	V_{CC} = MAX, V_I = 7 V				0.1			0.1	mA
I_{IH}	High-level input current	V_{CC} = MAX, V_I = 2.7 V				20			20	μA
I_{IL}	Low-level input current	V_{CC} = MAX, V_I = 0.4 V				−0.4			−0.4	mA
I_{OS}	Short-circuit output current [§]	V_{CC} = MAX		−30		−130	−30		−130	mA
I_{CC}	Supply current	V_{CC} = MAX, See Note 2	Condition A		7	12		7	12	mA
			Condition B		8.5	14		8.5	14	

[†]For conditions shown as MIN or MAX, use the appropriate value specified under recommended operating conditions.

[‡]All typical values are at V_{CC} = 5 V, T_A = 25°C.

[§]Not more than one output should be shorted at a time, and duration of the short-circuit should not exceed one second.

NOTE 2: I_{CC} is measured with the outputs open under the following conditions:
      A. All inputs grounded.
      B. Output control at 4.5 V, all inputs grounded.

switching characteristics, V_{CC} = 5 V, T_A = 25°C

PARAMETER[¶]	FROM (INPUT)	TO (OUTPUT)	TEST CONDITIONS	MIN	TYP	MAX	UNIT
t_{PLH}	Data	Y			11	25	ns
t_{PHL}					13	20	
t_{PLH}	Select	Y	C_L = 15 pF, R_L = 2 kΩ, See Note 3		20	45	ns
t_{PHL}					21	32	
t_{PZH}	Output Control	Y			11	23	ns
t_{PZL}					15	23	
t_{PHZ}	Output Control	Y	C_L = 5 pF, R_L = 2 kΩ, See Note 3		27	41	ns
t_{PLZ}					12	27	

[¶] t_{PLH} ≡ Propagation delay time, low-to-high-level output
  t_{PHL} ≡ Propagation delay time, high-to-low-level output
  t_{PZH} ≡ Output enable time to high level
  t_{PZL} ≡ Output enable time to low level
  t_{PHZ} ≡ Output disable time from high level
  t_{PLZ} ≡ Output disable time from low level

NOTE 3: Load circuit and waveforms are shown on page 3-11.

7

TEXAS INSTRUMENTS
INCORPORATED
POST OFFICE BOX 5012 • DALLAS, TEXAS 75222

- Clock Generator/Driver for The TMS 9900 or Other Microprocessors
- High-Level 4-Phase Outputs
- Complementary TTL 4-Phase Outputs
- Self-Contained Oscillator Can be Crystal or Capacitor Controlled
- External Oscillator Can Be Used
- Clocked D-Type Flip-Flop With Schmitt-Trigger Input For Reset Signal Synchronization

SN74LS362 . . . J OR N PACKAGE
(TOP VIEW)

		XTAL 2	XTAL 1	OSC IN	OSC OUT	$\overline{\phi}2$ TTL	$\overline{\phi}1$ TTL	V_{DD}	$\phi 1$	$\phi 2$
	V_{CC} 20	19	18	17	16	15	14	13	12	11

XTAL 2	XTAL 1	OSC IN	OSC OUT	$\overline{\phi}2$ TTL	$\overline{\phi}1$ TTL		$\phi 1$		
TANK 1								$\phi 2$	
TANK 2		FFQ	FFD	$\overline{\phi}4$ TTL	$\overline{\phi}3$ TTL	$\phi 3$	$\phi 4$		

TANK 1	TANK 2	GND 1	FFQ	FFD	$\overline{\phi}4$ TTL	$\overline{\phi}3$ TTL	$\phi 3$	$\phi 4$	GND 2
1	2	3	4	5	6	7	8	9	10

description

The 'LS362 consists of an oscillator, divide-by-four counter, a second divide-by-four counter with gating to generate four clock phases, high-level (12-volt) output drivers, low-level (5-volt) complementary output drivers, and a D-type flip-flop controlled by an external signal and the $\phi 3$ clock. The four high-level clock phases provide clock inputs to a TMS 9900 microprocessor. The four complementary TTL-level clocks can be used to time memory or other logic functions in a TMS 9900 computer system. The D-type flip-flop can be used to provide (for example) a reset signal to a TMS 9900, timed by $\phi 3$, on receipt of an input to the FFD input from power turn-on or a manual switch closure. Other applications are possible. A safety feature has been incorporated in the ϕ outputs such that if an open occurs in the V_{CC} supply common to 'LS362 and TMS 9900, the ϕ outputs will go low thus protecting the TMS 9900.

The frequency of the internal oscillator can be established by a quartz crystal or capacitor and LC circuit. Either a fundamental or overtone crystal may be used. The LC circuit connected to the tank inputs selects the desired crystal overtone or establishes the internal oscillator frequency when a capacitor is used instead of a crystal. An LC circuit must always be used at the tank inputs when using the internal oscillator. An external oscillator can be used, if desired, see "Applications Information" for details.

typical phase relationships of inputs and outputs (OSC is internal)

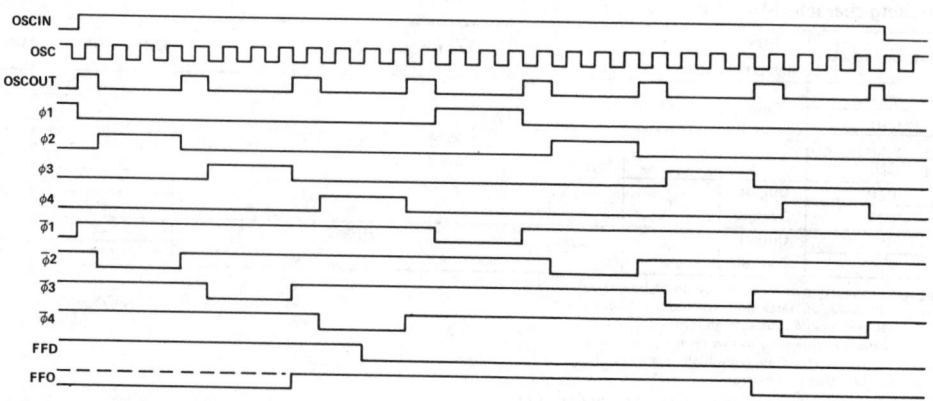

TEXAS INSTRUMENTS
INCORPORATED
POST OFFICE BOX 5012 • DALLAS, TEXAS 75222

877

functional block diagram

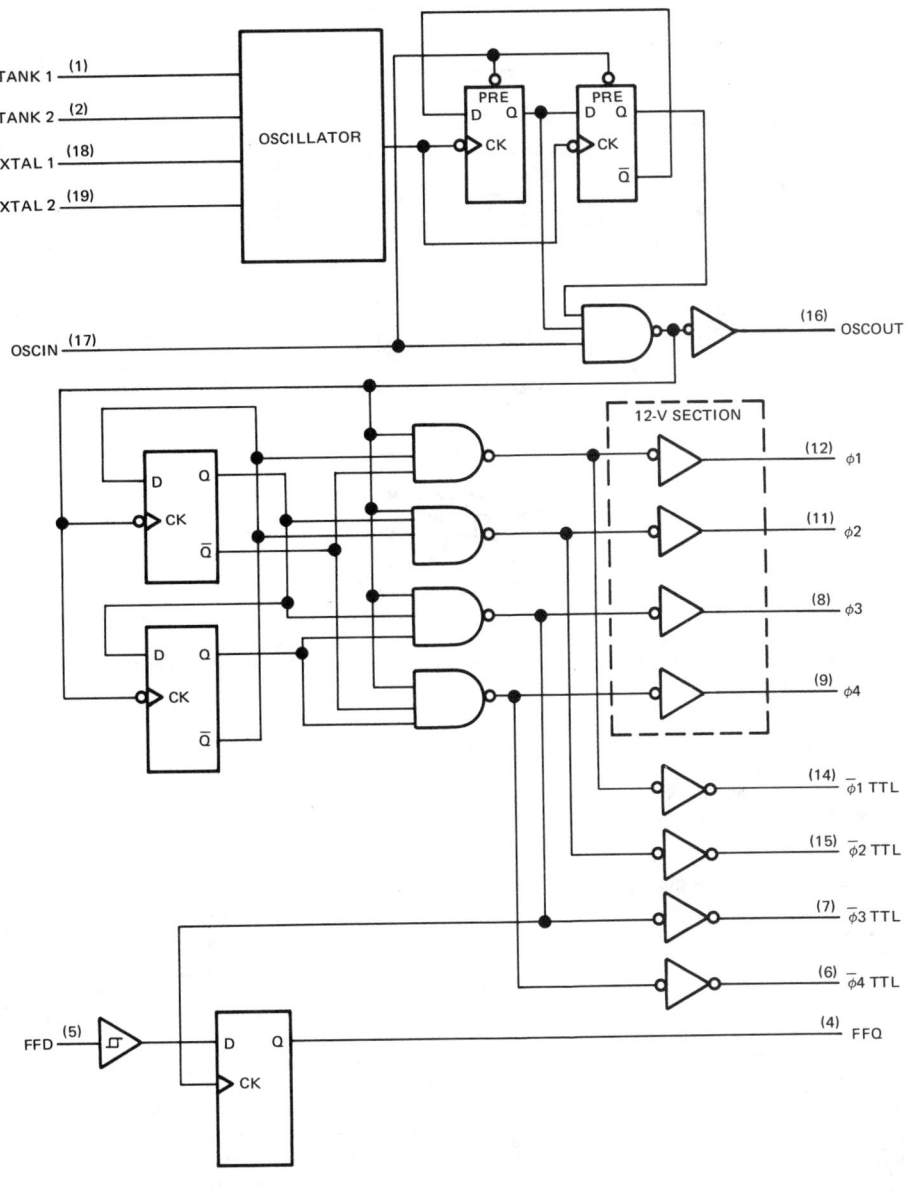

TEXAS INSTRUMENTS
INCORPORATED
POST OFFICE BOX 5012 • DALLAS, TEXAS 75222

TYPE SN74LS362 (TIM9904)
FOUR-PHASE CLOCK GENERATOR/DRIVER

schematics of inputs and outputs

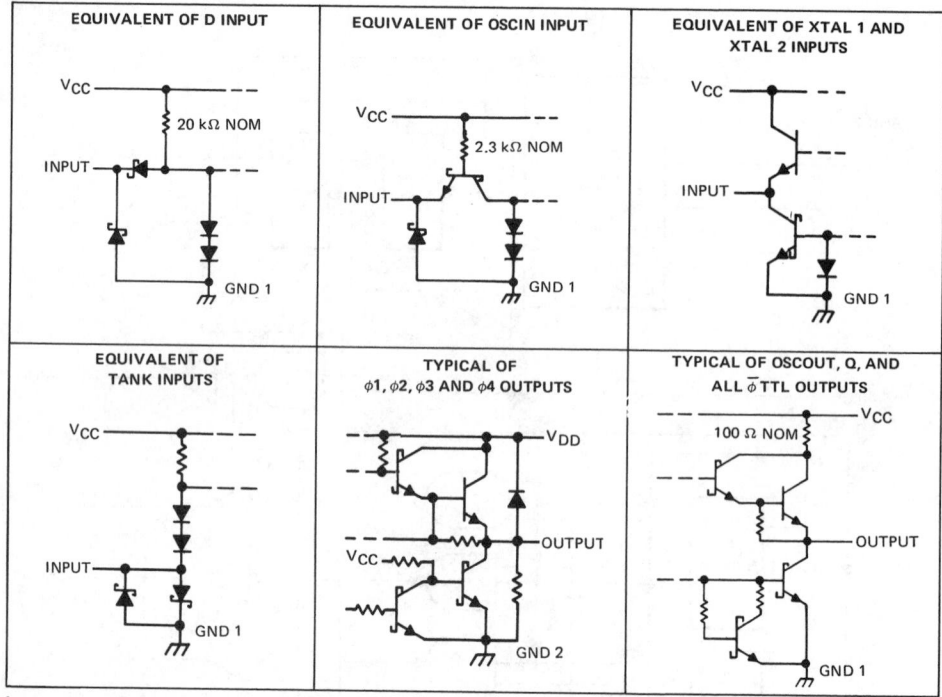

absolute maximum ratings over operating free-air temperature range (unless otherwise noted)

Supply voltage: V_{CC} (see Note 1) . . . . 7 V
$\qquad$ V_{DD} (see Note 1) . . . . 13 V
Input voltage: OSCIN . . . . 5.5 V
$\qquad$ FFD . . . . −0.5 V to 7 V
Operating free-air temperature range . . . . 0°C to 70°C
Storage temperature range . . . . −65°C to 150°C

NOTE 1: Voltage values are with respect to the network ground terminals connected together.

recommended operating conditions

		MIN	NOM	MAX	UNIT
Supply voltages	V_{CC}	4.75	5	5.25	V
	V_{DD}	11.4	12	12.6	V
High-level output current, I_{OH}	$\phi1, \phi2, \phi3, \phi4$			−100	μA
	All others			−400	μA
Low-level output current, I_{OL}	$\phi1, \phi2, \phi3, \phi4$			4	mA
	All others			8	mA
Internal oscillator frequency, f_{osc}			48	54	MHz
External oscillator pulse width, $t_{w(osc)}$		25			ns
Setup time, FFD input (with respect to falling edge of $\phi3$), t_{su}		50			ns
Hold time, FFD input (with respect to falling edge of $\phi3$), t_h		−30			ns
Operating free-air temperature, T_A		0		70	°C

TEXAS INSTRUMENTS
INCORPORATED
POST OFFICE BOX 5012 • DALLAS, TEXAS 75222

877

electrical characteristics over recommended operating free-air temperature range (unless otherwise noted)

PARAMETER			TEST CONDITIONS		MIN	TYP‡	MAX	UNIT
V_{IH}	High-level input voltage				2			V
V_{IL}	Low-level	FFD					0.5	V
	input voltage	OSCIN					0.8	
$V_{T+} - V_{T-}$	Hysteresis	FFD			0.4	0.8		V
V_{IK}	Input clamp voltage		V_{CC} = 4.75 V, V_{DD} = 11.4 V, I_I = −18 mA				−1.5	V
V_{OH}	High-level	$\phi1, \phi2, \phi3, \phi4$	V_{CC} = 4.75 V,	I_{OH} = −100 μA	V_{DD}−2	V_{DD}−1.5	V_{DD}	V
	output voltage	Other outputs	V_{DD} = 11.4 V to 12.6 V	I_{OH} = −400 μA	2.7	3.4		
V_{OL}	Low-level	$\phi1, \phi2, \phi3, \phi4$	V_{CC} = 4.75 V, V_{DD} = 11.4 V	I_{OL} = 4 mA		0.25	0.4	
	output voltage	Other outputs		I_{OL} = 4 mA		0.25	0.4	mA
				I_{OL} = 8 mA		0.35	0.5	
I_I	Input current at	FFD	V_{CC} = 5.25 V, V_{DD} = 12.6 V	V_I = 7 V			0.1	mA
	maximum input voltage	OSCIN		V_I = 5.5 V			0.3	
I_{IH}	High-level	FFD	V_{CC} = 5.25 V, V_{DD} = 12.6 V, V_I = 2.7 V				20	μA
	input current	OSCIN					60	
I_{IL}	Low-level	FFD	V_{CC} = 5.25 V, V_{DD} = 12.6 V, V_I = 0.4 V				−0.4	mA
	input current	OSCIN					−3.2	
I_{OS}	Short-circuit output current‡	All except $\phi1, \phi2, \phi3, \phi4$	V_{CC} = 5.25 V		−20		−100	mA
I_{CC}	Supply current from V_{CC}		V_{CC} = 5.25 V, FFD and OSCIN at GND, Outputs open			105	175	mA
I_{DD}	Supply current from V_{DD}		V_{CC} = 5.25 V, V_{DD} = 12.6 V, FFD and OSCIN at GND, Outputs open			12	20	mA

† All typical values are at V_{CC} = 5 V, V_{DD} = 12 V, T_A = 25°C.

‡ Not more than one output should be shorted at a time, and duration of the short-circuit should not exceed one second. Outputs $\phi1, \phi2, \phi3$, and $\phi4$ do not have short-circuit protection.

switching characteristics, T_A = 25°C, V_{CC} = 5 V, V_{DD} = 12 V, f_{osc} = 48 MHz, see figure 1

PARAMETER		TEST CONDITIONS	MIN	TYP	MAX	UNIT
f_{out}	Output frequency, any ϕ or $\overline{\phi}$ TTL			3		MHz
f_{out}	Output frequency, OSCOUT			12		MHz
$t_{c(\phi)}$	Cycle time, any ϕ output			333		ns
$t_{r(\phi)}$	Rise time, any ϕ output		5		20	ns
$t_{f(\phi)}$	Fall time, any ϕ output		5		20	ns
$t_{w(\phi)}$	Pulse width, any ϕ output high		40			ns
$t_{\phi1L, \phi2H}$	Delay time, $\phi1$ low to $\phi2$ high		0	5	15	ns
$t_{\phi2L, \phi3H}$	Delay time, $\phi2$ low to $\phi3$ high		0	5	15	ns
$t_{\phi3L, \phi4H}$	Delay time, $\phi3$ low to $\phi4$ high		0	5	15	ns
$t_{\phi4L, \phi1H}$	Delay time, $\phi4$ low to $\phi1$ high	Output loads:	0	5	15	ns
$t_{\phi1H, \phi2H}$	Delay time, $\phi1$ high to $\phi2$ high	$\phi1, \phi3, \phi4$: 100 pF to GND	70	83		ns
$t_{\phi2H, \phi3H}$	Delay time, $\phi2$ high to $\phi3$ high	$\phi2$: 200 pF to GND	70	83		ns
$t_{\phi3H, \phi4H}$	Delay time, $\phi3$ high to $\phi4$ high	Others: R_L = 2 kΩ,	70	83		ns
$t_{\phi4H, \phi1H}$	Delay time, $\phi4$ high to $\phi1$ high	C_L = 15 pF	70	83		ns
$t_{\phi H, \overline{\phi} TL}$	Delay time, ϕ_n high to $\overline{\phi}_n$ TTL low	See Note 2		−8		ns
$t_{\phi L, \overline{\phi} TH}$	Delay time, ϕ_n low to $\overline{\phi}_n$ TTL high			−19		ns
$t_{\phi3L, QH}$	Delay time, $\phi3$ low to FFQ output high			−7		ns
$t_{\phi3L, QL}$	Delay time, $\phi3$ low to FFQ output low			−12		ns
$t_{\phi L, OSOH}$	Delay time, ϕ low to OSCOUT high			−5		ns
$t_{\phi H, OSOL}$	Delay time, FFQ high to OSCOUT low			−13		ns

NOTE 2: Use load circuit for bi-state totem-pole outputs, page 3-11.

TEXAS INSTRUMENTS
INCORPORATED
POST OFFICE BOX 5012 • DALLAS, TEXAS 75222

TYPE SN74LS362 (TIM9904)
FOUR-PHASE CLOCK GENERATOR/DRIVER

PARAMETER MEASUREMENT INFORMATION

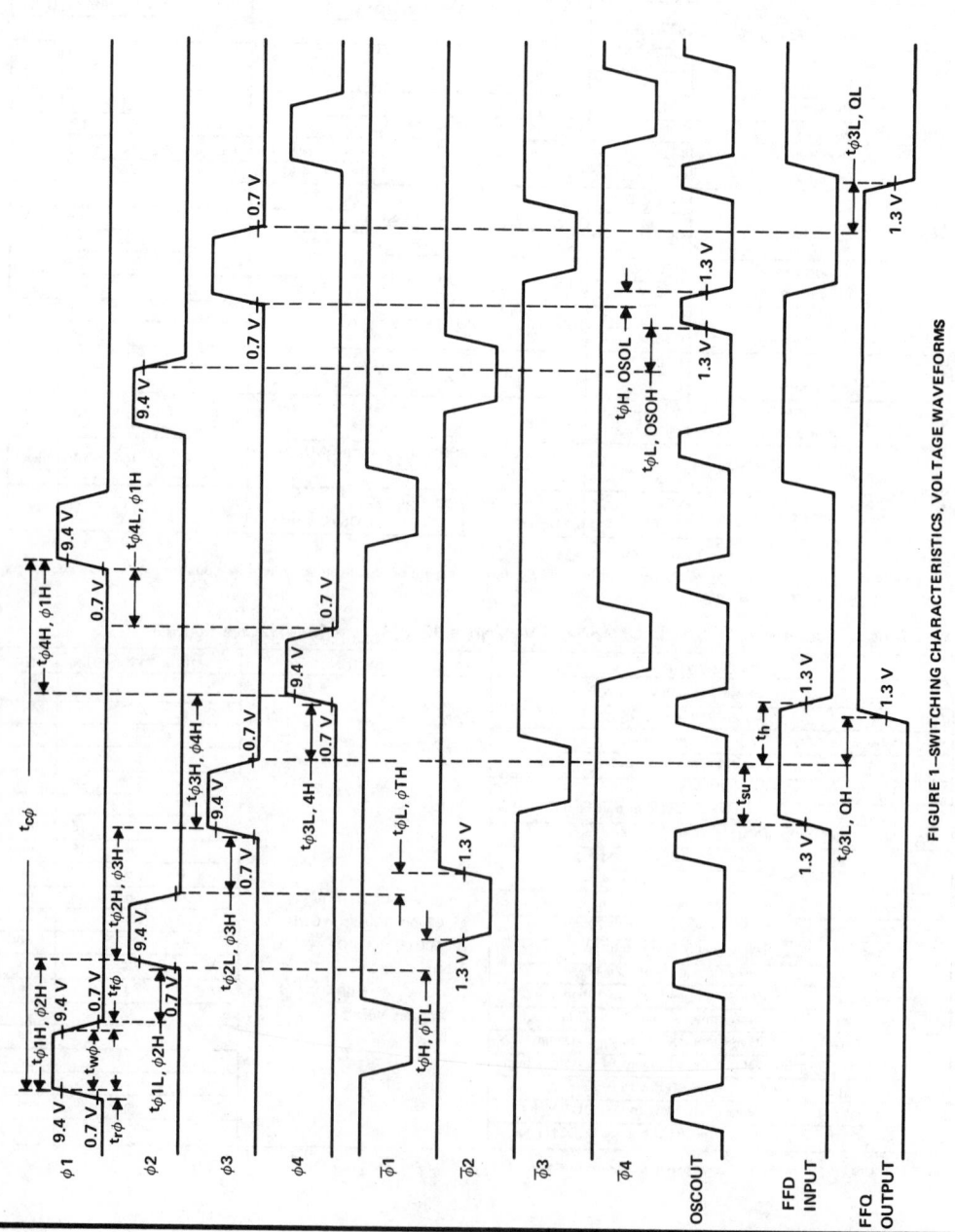

FIGURE 1—SWITCHING CHARACTERISTICS, VOLTAGE WAVEFORMS

TEXAS INSTRUMENTS
INCORPORATED
POST OFFICE BOX 5012 • DALLAS, TEXAS 75222

1076

APPLICATION INFORMATION

Figure 2 shows the 'LS362 connected to a TMS9900. The oscillator is shown operating with a quartz crystal and an LC circuit connected to the tank terminals.

For operation of the TMS 9900 microprocessor at 3 MHz, the frequency reference will need a resonant frequency of 48 MHz (16 x 3 MHz). A quartz crystal used as a frequency reference should be made for series-mode operation with a resistance in the 20- to 75-ohm range and be capable of a minimum of 2 mW power dissipation. Typical frequency tolerance is ±0.005%. For 48-MHz operation a third-overtone crystal is used. The inductance L connected across the tank terminals should be 0.47 μH ± 10%, and the capacitance C (including board capacity) should be 22 pF ± 5%. The LC circuit should be tuned to the third-overtone crystal frequency for best results. A 0.1-μF capacitor can be substituted for the quartz crystal. With a capacitor rather than a crystal, the LC tuned circuit establishes the operating frequencies. LC component values for operation at any frequency can be computed from $f_{osc} = 1/(2\pi\sqrt{LC})$ where f_{osc} is the oscillator frequency, L is the inductance value in henries, and C is the capacitance value in farads.

When the internal oscillator is being used, OSCIN should be connected to V_{CC} through a resistor (1 kΩ nominal) and an LC tank circuit must be connected to the tank inputs. An external oscillator can be used by connecting it to OSCIN and disabling the internal oscillator by connecting the crystal terminals to V_{CC} and leaving the tank inputs open. An external oscillator must have a frequency four times the desired output clock frequency and a 25% duty cycle. See Figure 3.

The first low-level external clock pulse will preset the divide-by-four counter, allowing the external oscillator signal to directly drive the phase generator. Figure 3 is a timing diagram illustrating operation with an external oscillator.

Resistors between $\phi 1$, $\phi 2$, $\phi 3$, and $\phi 4$ outputs of the 'LS362 and the corresponding clock input terminals of the TMS 9900 should be in the 10- to 20-ohm range (See Figure 2). Their purpose is to minimize overshoot and undershoot. The required resistance value is dependent on circuit layout. Clock signal interconnections should be as short as possible.

The D-type flip-flop associated with pins FFD and FFQ can be used to provide a power-on reset and a manual reset to the TMS 9900 as shown in Figure 4. A Schmitt-trigger circuit driving the D input generates a fast-rising waveform when the input voltage rises to a specific value. At power turn-on, voltage across the 0.1 μF capacitor in Figure 4 will rise towards V_{CC}. This circuit provides a delay that resets the TMS 9900 after V_{CC} has stabilized. An optional manual reset switch can be connected to the delay circuit for resetting the TMS 9900 at any time. The TMS 9900 HOLD signal could alternately be actuated by FFD.

The ground terminals GND1 and GND2 should be connected together and to system ground.

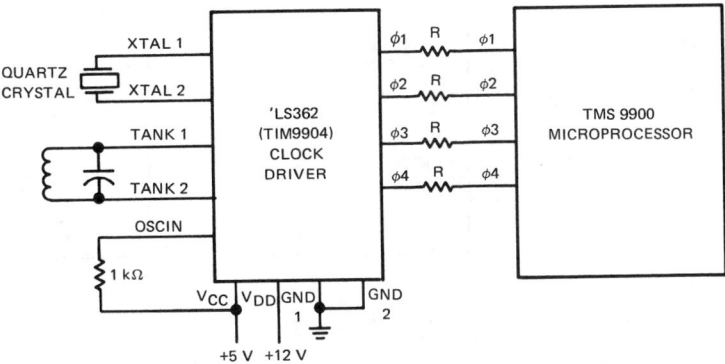

FIGURE 2—'LS362 CRYSTAL-CONTROLLED OPERATION

TEXAS INSTRUMENTS
INCORPORATED
POST OFFICE BOX 5012 • DALLAS, TEXAS 75222

TYPE SN74LS362 (TIM9904)
FOUR-PHASE CLOCK GENERATOR/DRIVER

APPLICATION INFORMATION

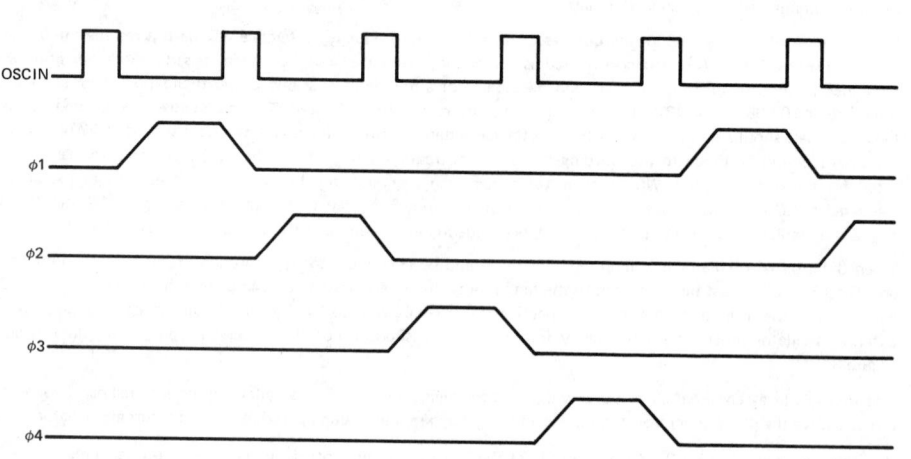

FIGURE 3—EXTERNAL OSCILLATOR TIMING

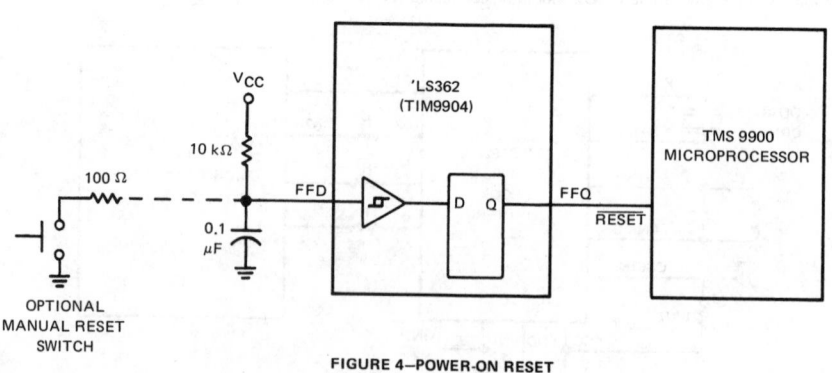

FIGURE 4—POWER-ON RESET

TEXAS INSTRUMENTS
INCORPORATED
POST OFFICE BOX 5012 • DALLAS, TEXAS 75222

TTL
MSI

TYPES SN54LS363, SN54LS364, SN74LS363, SN74LS364
OCTAL D-TYPE TRANSPARENT LATCHES AND
EDGE-TRIGGERED FLIP-FLOPS
BULLETIN NO. DL-S 7612466, OCTOBER 1976

- High V$_{OH}$ . . . 3.65 V Min (74LS')
- Choice of 8 Latches or 8 D-Type Flip-Flops In a Single Package
- 3-State Bus-Driving Outputs
- Full Parallel-Access for Loading and Reloading
- Buffered Control Inputs
- Clock/Enable Input Has Hysteresis to Improve Noise Rejection and P-N-P Inputs To Reduce D-C Loading
- SN54LS373/SN74LS373 and SN54LS374/ SN74LS374 Are Similar But Have Standard V$_{OH}$ of 2.4 V Min

SN54LS363 . . . J PACKAGE
SN74LS363 . . . J OR N PACKAGE
(TOP VIEW)

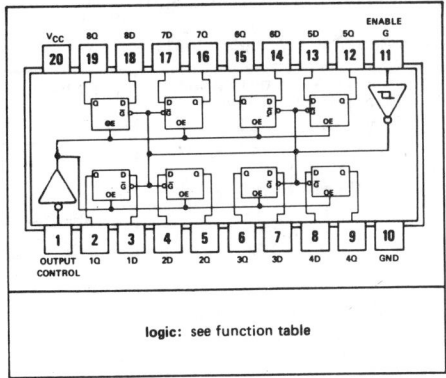

logic: see function table

'LS363
FUNCTION TABLE

OUTPUT CONTROL	ENABLE G	D	OUTPUT
L	H	H	H
L	H	L	L
L	L	X	Q$_0$
H	X	X	Z

'LS364
FUNCTION TABLE

OUTPUT CONTROL	CLOCK	D	OUTPUT
L	↑	H	H
L	↑	L	L
L	L	X	Q$_0$
H	X	X	Z

See explanation of function tables on page 3-8.

SN54LS364 . . . J PACKAGE
SN74LS364 . . . J OR N PACKAGE
(TOP VIEW)

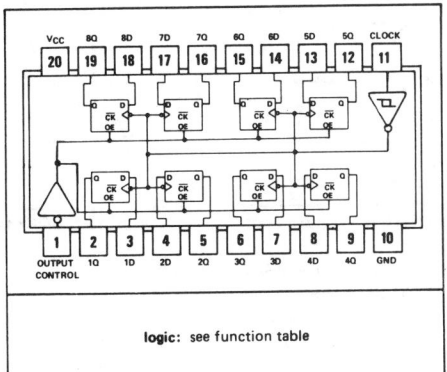

logic: see function table

description

These 8-bit registers feature totem-pole three-state outputs designed specifically for driving highly-capacitive or relatively low-impedance loads. The high-impedance third state and increased high-logic-level drive provide these registers with the capability of being connected directly to and driving the bus lines in a bus-organized system without need for interface or pull-up components. They are particularly attractive for implementing buffer registers, I/O ports, bidirectional bus drivers, and working registers.

The eight latches of the 'LS363 are transparent D-type latches meaning that while the enable (G) is high the Q outputs will follow the data (D) inputs. When the enable is taken low the outputs will be latched at the level of the data that was setup.

The eight flip-flops of the 'LS364 are edge-triggered D-type flip-flops. On the positive transition of the clock the Q output will be set to the logic state that was setup at the D input. The 'LS363 is particularly useful for interfacing to MOS logic where a higher than normal V$_{OH}$ level is desirable such as that required by the TMS 8080A microprocessor.

Schmitt-trigger buffered inputs at the enable ('LS363) and clock ('LS364) lines simplify system design as ac and dc noise rejection is improved by typically 400 mV due to the input hysteresis. A buffered output control input can be used to place the eight outputs in either a normal logic state (high or low logic levels) or a high-impedance state. In the high-impedance state the outputs neither load nor drive the bus line significantly.

1076

TEXAS INSTRUMENTS
INCORPORATED
POST OFFICE BOX 5012 • DALLAS, TEXAS 75222

TYPES SN54LS363, SN54LS364, SN74LS363, SN74LS364 OCTAL D-TYPE TRANSPARENT LATCHES AND EDGE-TRIGGERED FLIP-FLOPS

functional block diagram

Same as SN54LS373/SN74LS373 and SN54LS374/SN74LS374

schematics of inputs and outputs

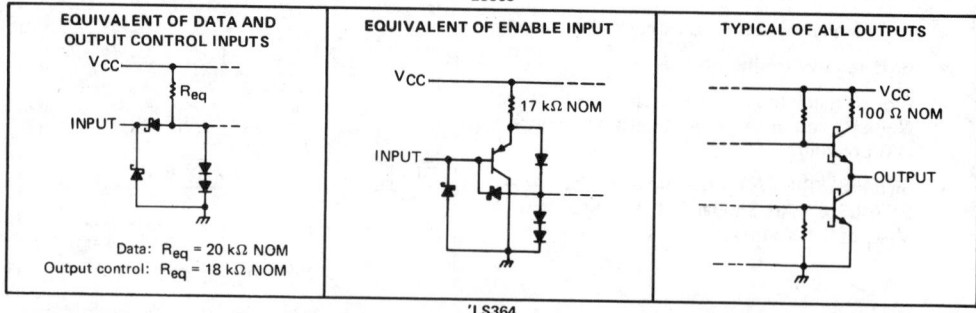

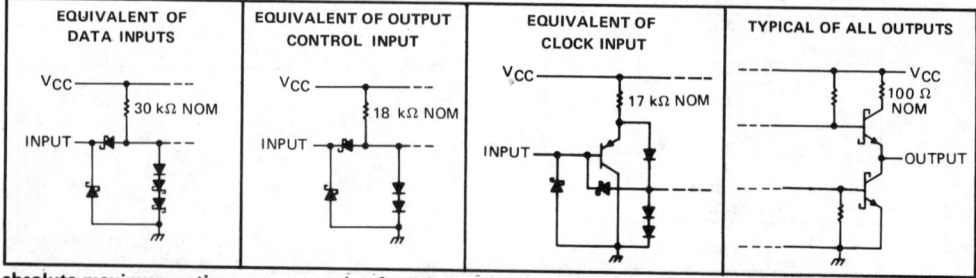

absolute maximum ratings over operating free-air temperature range (unless otherwise noted)

Supply voltage, V_{CC} (see Note 1) . . . . 7 V
Input voltage . . . . 7 V
Off-state output voltage . . . . 7 V
Operating free-air temperature range: SN54LS' . . . . −55°C to 125°C
                              SN74LS' . . . . 0°C to 70°C
Storage temperature range . . . . −65°C to 150°C

NOTE 1: Voltage values are with respect to network ground terminal.

recommended operating conditions

		SN54LS'			SN74LS'			UNIT
		MIN	NOM	MAX	MIN	NOM	MAX	
Supply voltage, V_{CC}		4.5	5	5.5	4.75	5	5.25	V
High-level output voltage, V_{OH}				5.5			5.5	V
High-level output current, I_{OH}				−1			−2.6	mA
Width of clock/enable pulse, t_w	High	15			15			ns
	Low	15			15			
Data setup time, t_{su}	'LS363	0↓			0↓			ns
	'LS364	20↑			20↑			
Data hold time, t_h	'LS363	10↓			10↓			ns
	'LS364	0↑			0↑			
Operating free-air temperature, T_A		−55		125	0		70	°C

↑↓ The arrow indicates the transition of the clock/enable input used for reference: ↑ for the low-to-high transition, ↓ for the high-to-low transition.

7-468

TEXAS INSTRUMENTS
INCORPORATED
POST OFFICE BOX 5012 • DALLAS, TEXAS 75222

1076

TYPES SN54LS363, SN54LS364, SN74LS363, SN74LS364
OCTAL D-TYPE TRANSPARENT LATCHES AND
EDGE-TRIGGERED FLIP-FLOPS

electrical characteristics over recommended operating free-air temperature range (unless otherwise noted)

PARAMETER		TEST CONDITIONS†		SN54LS' MIN	TYP‡	MAX	SN74LS' MIN	TYP‡	MAX	UNIT
V_{IH}	High-level input voltage			2			2			V
V_{IL}	Low-level input voltage					0.7			0.8	V
V_{IK}	Input clamp voltage	V_{CC} = MIN, I_I = −18 mA				−1.5			−1.5	V
V_{OH}	High-level output voltage	V_{CC} = MIN, V_{IH} = 2 V, V_{IL} = V_{IL}max, I_{OH} = MAX		3.45			3.65			V
V_{OL}	Low-level output voltage	V_{CC} = MIN, V_{IH} = 2 V, V_{IL} = V_{IL}max	I_{OL} = 12 mA		0.25	0.4		0.25	0.4	V
			I_{OL} = 24 mA					0.35	0.5	
I_{OZH}	Off-state output current, high-level voltage applied	V_{CC} = MAX, V_{IH} = 2 V, V_O = 3.65 V				20			20	μA
I_{OZL}	Off-state output current, low-level voltage applied	V_{CC} = MAX, V_{IH} = 2 V, V_O = 0.4 V				−20			−20	μA
I_I	Input current at maximum input voltage	V_{CC} = MAX, V_I = 7 V				0.1			0.1	mA
I_{IH}	High-level input current	V_{CC} = MAX, V_I = 2.7 V				20			20	μA
I_{IL}	Low-level input current	V_{CC} = MAX, V_I = 0.4 V				−400			−400	μA
I_{OS}	Short-circuit output current§	V_{CC} = MAX		−30		−130	−30		−130	mA
I_{CC}	Supply current	V_{CC} = MAX, Output control at 4.5 V			42	70		42	70	mA

†For conditions shown as MIN or MAX, use the appropriate value specified under recommended operating conditions.
‡All typical values are at V_{CC} = 5 V, T_A = 25°C.
§Not more than one output should be shorted at a time and duration of the short circuit should not exceed one second.

switching characteristics, V_{CC} = 5 V, T_A = 25°C

PARAMETER	FROM (INPUT)	TO (OUTPUT)	TEST CONDITIONS	'LS363 MIN	TYP	MAX	'LS364 MIN	TYP	MAX	UNIT
f_{max}							35	50		MHz
t_{PLH}	Data	Any Q	C_L = 45 pF, R_L = 667 Ω, See Notes 2 and 3		15	23				ns
t_{PHL}					18	27				
t_{PLH}	Clock or enable	Any Q			19	30		21	33	ns
t_{PHL}					24	36		22	34	
t_{PZH}	Output Control	Any Q			16	28		16	28	ns
t_{PZL}					22	36		22	36	
t_{PHZ}	Output Control	Any Q	C_L = 5 pF, R_L = 667 Ω, See Note 3		12	20		10	18	ns
t_{PLZ}					16	25		14	24	

NOTES: 2. Maximum clock frequency is tested with all outputs loaded.
3. See load circuits and waveforms on page 3-11.

f_{max} ≡ maximum clock frequency
t_{PLH} ≡ propagation delay time, low-to-high-level output
t_{PHL} ≡ propagation delay time, high-to-low-level output
t_{PZH} ≡ output enable time to high level
t_{PZL} ≡ output enable time to low level
t_{PHZ} ≡ output disable time from high level
t_{PLZ} ≡ output disable time from low level

7

TEXAS INSTRUMENTS
INCORPORATED
POST OFFICE BOX 5012 • DALLAS, TEXAS 75222

TYPES SN54LS363, SN54LS364, SN74LS363, SN74LS364
OCTAL D-TYPE TRANSPARENT LATCHES AND
EDGE-TRIGGERED FLIP-FLOPS

TYPICAL APPLICATION DATA

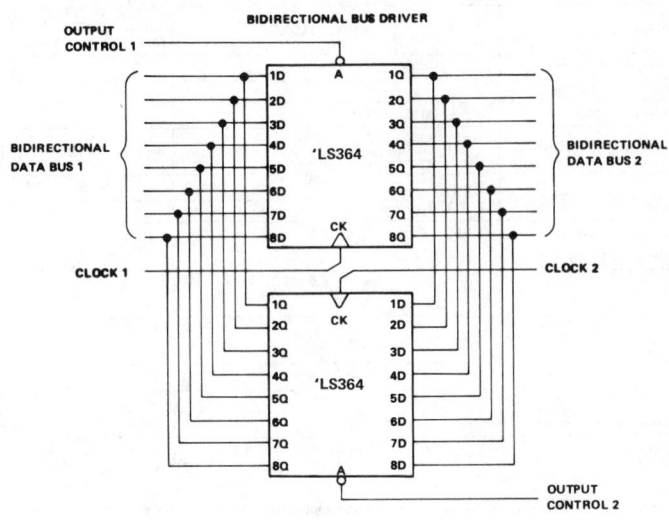

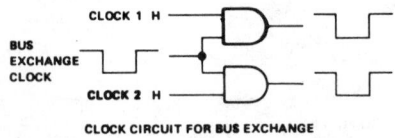

CLOCK CIRCUIT FOR BUS EXCHANGE

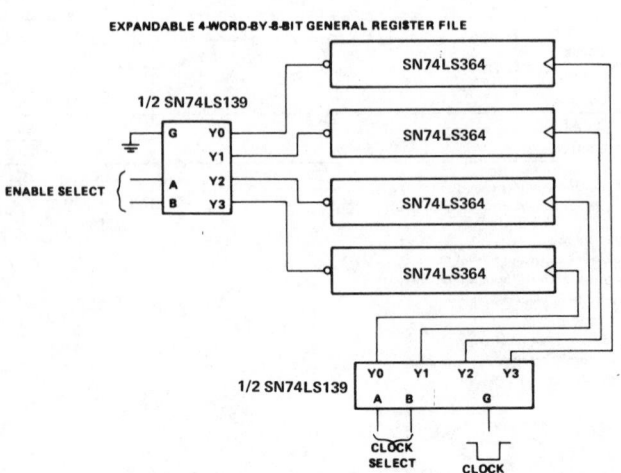

EXPANDABLE 4-WORD-BY-8-BIT GENERAL REGISTER FILE

TEXAS INSTRUMENTS
INCORPORATED
POST OFFICE BOX 5012 • DALLAS, TEXAS 75222

**TTL
MSI**

TYPES SN54LS373, SN54LS374, SN54S373, SN54S374, SN74LS373, SN74LS374, SN74S373, SN74S374
OCTAL D-TYPE TRANSPARENT LATCHES AND EDGE-TRIGGERED FLIP-FLOPS
BULLETIN NO. DL-S 7712350, OCTOBER 1976–REVISED AUGUST 1977

- **Choice of 8 Latches or 8 D-Type Flip-Flops In a Single Package**
- **3-State Bus-Driving Outputs**
- **Full Parallel-Access for Loading**
- **Buffered Control Inputs**
- **Clock/Enable Input Has Hysteresis to Improve Noise Rejection**
- **P-N-P Inputs Reduce D-C Loading on Data Lines ('S373 and 'S374)**
- **SN54LS363 and SN74LS364 Are Similar But Have Higher V_{OH} For MOS Interface**

SN54LS373, SN54S373 . . . J PACKAGE
SN74LS373, SN74S373 . . . J OR N PACKAGE
(TOP VIEW)

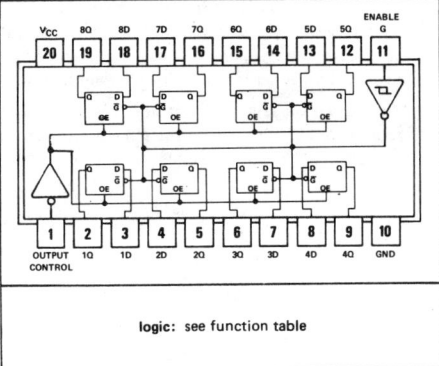

logic: see function table

**'LS373, 'S373
FUNCTION TABLE**

OUTPUT CONTROL	ENABLE G	D	OUTPUT
L	H	H	H
L	H	L	L
L	L	X	Q_0
H	X	X	Z

SN54LS374, SN54S374 . . . J PACKAGE
SN74LS374, SN74S374 . . . J OR N PACKAGE
(TOP VIEW)

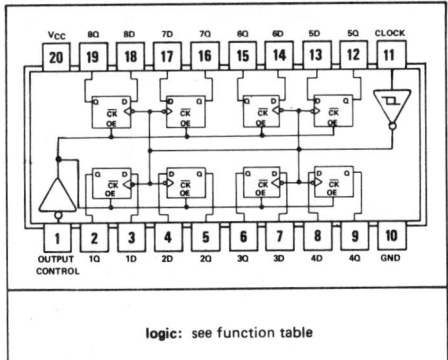

logic: see function table

**'LS374, 'S374
FUNCTION TABLE**

OUTPUT CONTROL	CLOCK	D	OUTPUT
L	↑	H	H
L	↑	L	L
L	L	X	Q_0
H	X	X	Z

See explanation of function tables on page 3-8.

7

description

These 8-bit registers feature totem-pole three-state outputs designed specifically for driving highly-capacitive or relatively low-impedance loads. The high-impedance third state and increased high-logic-level drive provide these registers with the capability of being connected directly to and driving the bus lines in a bus-organized system without need for interface or pull-up components. They are particularly attractive for implementing buffer registers, I/O ports, bidirectional bus drivers, and working registers.

The eight latches of the 'LS373 and 'S373 are transparent D-type latches meaning that while the enable (G) is high the Q outputs will follow the data (D) inputs. When the enable is taken low the output will be latched at the level of the data that was setup.

TEXAS INSTRUMENTS
INCORPORATED
POST OFFICE BOX 5012 • DALLAS, TEXAS 75222

TYPES SN54LS373, SN54LS374, SN54S373, SN54S374, SN74LS373, SN74LS374, SN74S373, SN74S374 OCTAL D-TYPE TRANSPARENT LATCHES AND EDGE-TRIGGERED FLIP-FLOPS

description (continued)

The eight flip-flops of the 'LS374 and 'S374 are edge-triggered D-type flip-flops. On the positive transition of the clock, the Q outputs will be set to the logic states that were setup at the D inputs.

Schmitt-trigger buffered inputs at the enable/clock lines simplify system design as ac and dc noise rejection is improved by typically 400 mV due to the input hysteresis. A buffered output control input can be used to place the eight outputs in either a normal logic state (high or low logic levels) or a high-impedance state. In the high-impedance state the outputs neither load nor drive the bus lines significantly.

The output control does not affect the internal operation of the latches or flip-flops. That is, the old data can be retained or new data can be entered even while the outputs are off.

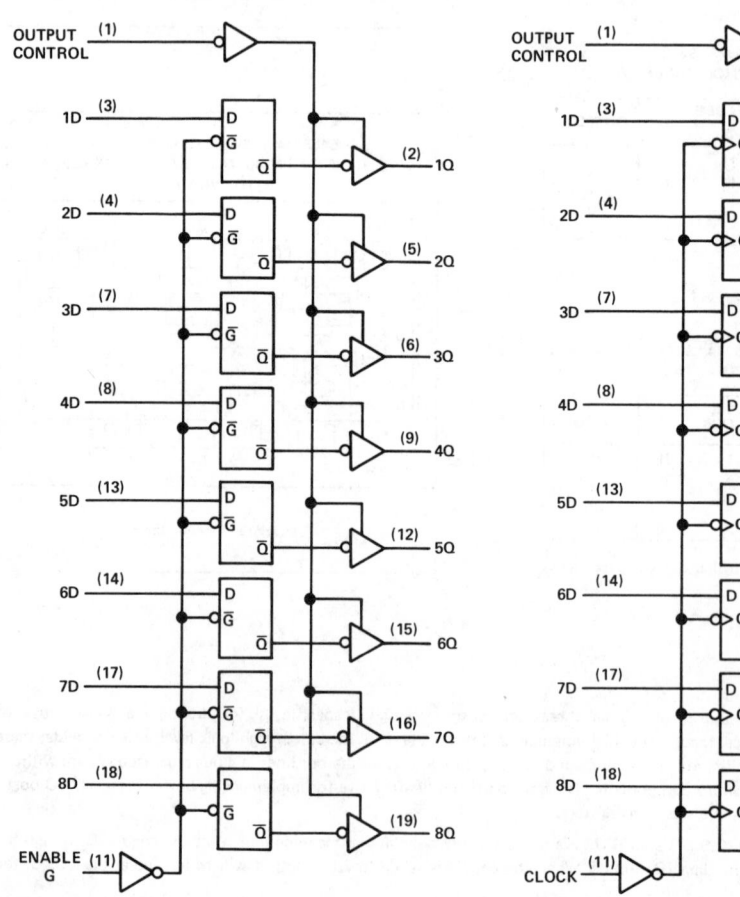

'LS373, 'S373
TRANSPARENT LATCHES

'LS374, 'S374
POSITIVE-EDGE-TRIGGERED FLIP-FLOPS

TEXAS INSTRUMENTS
INCORPORATED
POST OFFICE BOX 5012 • DALLAS, TEXAS 75222

TYPES SN54LS373, SN54LS374, SN74LS373, SN74LS374
OCTAL D-TYPE TRANSPARENT LATCHES AND
EDGE-TRIGGERED FLIP-FLOPS

schematic of inputs and outputs

'LS373

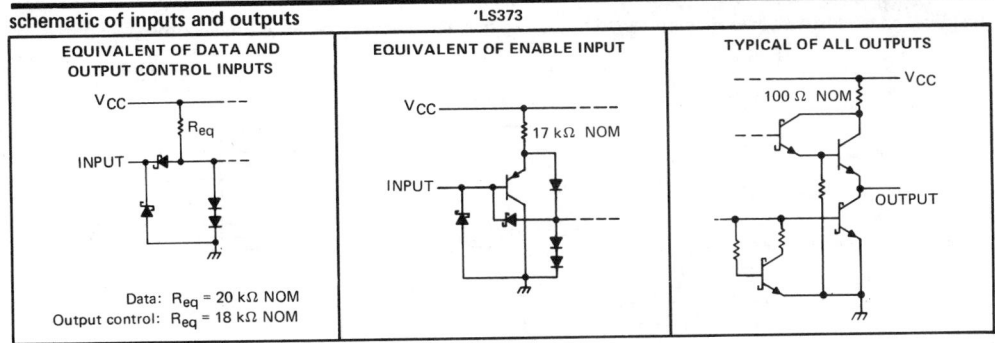

'LS374

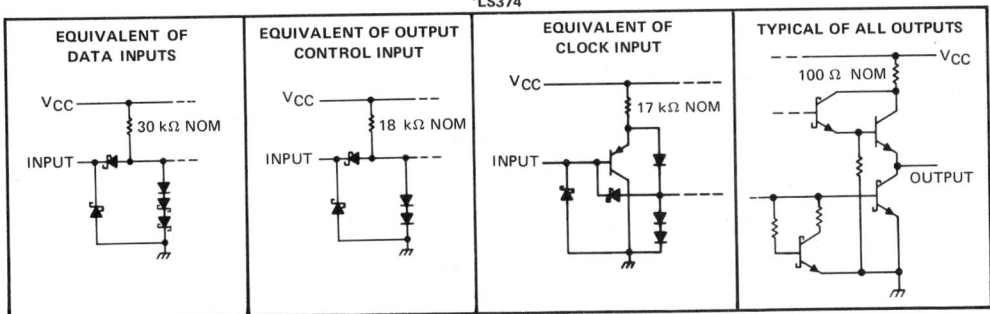

absolute maximum ratings over operating free-air temperature range (unless otherwise noted)

Supply voltage, V_{CC} (see Note 1) . . . . 7 V
Input voltage . . . . 7 V
Off-state output voltage . . . . 7 V
Operating free-air temperature range: SN54LS' . . . . −55°C to 125°C
                                       SN74LS' . . . . 0°C to 70°C
Storage temperature range . . . . −65°C to 150°C

NOTE 1: Voltage values are with respect to network ground terminal.

recommended operating conditions

		SN54LS'			SN74LS'			UNIT
		MIN	NOM	MAX	MIN	NOM	MAX	
Supply voltage, V_{CC}		4.5	5	5.5	4.75	5	5.25	V
High-level output voltage, V_{OH}				5.5			5.5	V
High-level output current, I_{OH}				−1			−2.6	mA
Width of clock/enable pulse, t_w	High	15			15			ns
	Low	15			15			
Data setup time, t_{su}	'LS373	0↓			0↓			ns
	'LS374	20↑			20↑			
Data hold time, t_h	'LS373	10↓			10↓			ns
	'LS374	0↑			0↑			
Operating free-air temperature, T_A		−55		125	0		70	°C

↑↓ The arrow indicates the transition of the clock/enable input used for reference: ↑ for the low-to-high transition, ↓ for the high-to-low transition.

electrical characteristics over recommended operating free-air temperature range (unless otherwise noted)

PARAMETER		TEST CONDITIONS[†]		SN54LS'			SN74LS'			UNIT
				MIN	TYP[‡]	MAX	MIN	TYP[‡]	MAX	
V_{IH}	High-level input voltage			2			2			V
V_{IL}	Low-level input voltage					0.7			0.8	V
V_{IK}	Input clamp voltage	V_{CC} = MIN, I_I = −18 mA				−1.5			−1.5	V
V_{OH}	High-level output voltage	V_{CC} = MIN, V_{IH} = 2 V, $V_{IL} = V_{IL}$max, I_{OH} = MAX		2.4	3.4		2.4	3.1		V
V_{OL}	Low-level output voltage	V_{CC} = MIN, V_{IH} = 2 V, $V_{IL} = V_{IL}$max	I_{OL} = 12 mA		0.25	0.4		0.25	0.4	V
			I_{OL} = 24 mA					0.35	0.5	
I_{OZH}	Off-state output current, high-level voltage applied	V_{CC} = MAX, V_{IH} = 2 V, V_O = 2.7 V				20			20	μA
I_{OZL}	Off-state output current, low-level voltage applied	V_{CC} = MAX, V_{IH} = 2 V, V_O = 0.4 V				−20			−20	μA
I_I	Input current at maximum input voltage	V_{CC} = MAX, V_I = 7 V				0.1			0.1	mA
I_{IH}	High-level input current	V_{CC} = MAX, V_I = 2.7 V				20			20	μA
I_{IL}	Low-level input current	V_{CC} = MAX, V_I = 0.4 V				−0.4			−0.4	mA
I_{OS}	Short-circuit output current[§]	V_{CC} = MAX		−30		−130	−30		−130	mA
I_{CC}	Supply current	V_{CC} = MAX, Output control at 4.5 V	'LS373		24	40		24	40	mA
			'LS374		27	40		27	40	

[†] For conditions shown as MIN or MAX, use the appropriate value specified under recommended operating conditions.
[‡] All typical values are at V_{CC} = 5 V, T_A = 25°C.
[§] Not more than one output should be shorted at a time and duration of the short circuit should not exceed one second.

switching characteristics, V_{CC} = 5 V, T_A = 25°C

PARAMETER	FROM (INPUT)	TO (OUTPUT)	TEST CONDITIONS	'LS373			'LS374			UNIT
				MIN	TYP	MAX	MIN	TYP	MAX	
f_{max}							35	50		MHz
t_{PLH}	Data	Any Q	C_L = 45 pF, R_L = 667 Ω, See Notes 2 and 3		12	18				ns
t_{PHL}					12	18				
t_{PLH}	Clock or enable	Any Q			20	30		15	28	ns
t_{PHL}					18	30		19	28	
t_{PZH}	Output Control	Any Q			15	28		20	28	ns
t_{PZL}					25	36		21	28	
t_{PHZ}	Output Control	Any Q	C_L = 5 pF, R_L = 667 Ω, See Note 3		12	20		12	20	ns
t_{PLZ}					15	25		14	25	

NOTES: 2. Maximum clock frequency is tested with all outputs loaded.
3. See load circuits and waveforms on page 3-11.

f_{max} ≡ maximum clock frequency
t_{PLH} ≡ propagation delay time, low-to-high-level output
t_{PHL} ≡ propagation delay time, high-to-low-level output
t_{PZH} ≡ output enable time to high level
t_{PZL} ≡ output enable time to low level
t_{PHZ} ≡ output disable time from high level
t_{PLZ} ≡ output disable time from low level

7

TEXAS INSTRUMENTS
INCORPORATED
POST OFFICE BOX 5012 • DALLAS, TEXAS 75222

TYPES SN54S373, SN54S374, SN74S373, SN74S374
OCTAL D-TYPE TRANSPARENT LATCHES AND EDGE-TRIGGERED FLIP-FLOPS

schematic of inputs and outputs

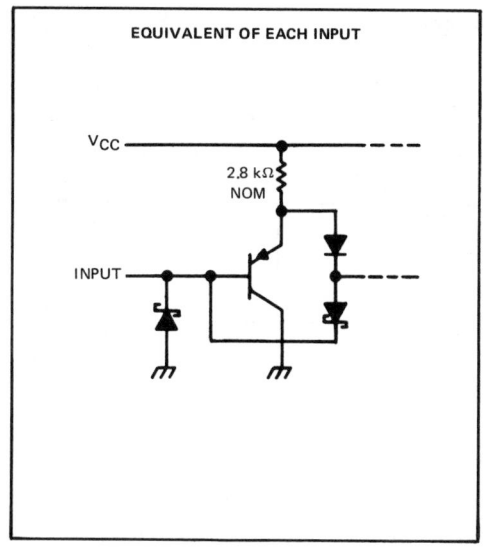

EQUIVALENT OF EACH INPUT

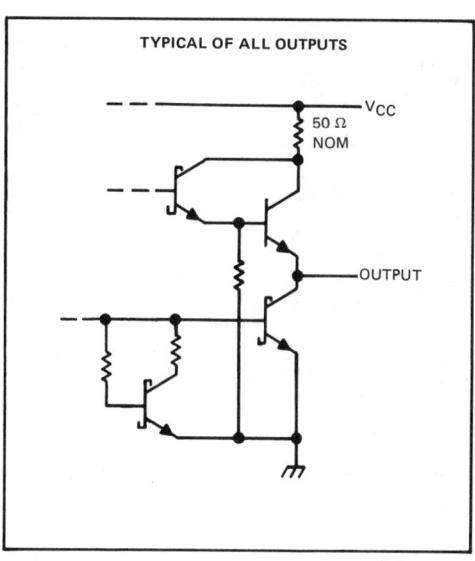

TYPICAL OF ALL OUTPUTS

absolute maximum ratings over operating free-air temperature range (unless otherwise noted)

Supply voltage, V_{CC} (see Note 1) . . . . 7 V
Input voltage . . . . 5.5 V
Off-state output voltage . . . . 5.5 V
Operating free-air temperature range: SN54S' . . . . -55°C to 125°C
                                  SN74S' . . . . 0°C to 70°C
Storage temperature range . . . . -65°C to 150°C

NOTE 1: Voltage values are with respect to network ground terminal.

recommended operating conditions

		SN54S'			SN74S'			UNIT
		MIN	NOM	MAX	MIN	NOM	MAX	
Supply voltage, V_{CC}		4.5	5	5.5	4.75	5	5.25	V
High-level output voltage, V_{OH}				5.5			5.5	V
High-level output current, I_{OH}				-2			-6.5	mA
Width of clock/enable pulse, t_W	High	6			6			ns
	Low	7.3			7.3			
Data setup time, t_{su}	'S373	$0\downarrow$			$0\downarrow$			ns
	'S374	$5\uparrow$			$5\uparrow$			
Data hold time, t_h	'S373	$10\downarrow$			$10\downarrow$			ns
	'S374	$2\uparrow$			$2\uparrow$			
Operating free-air temperature, T_A		-55		125	0		70	$^\circ$C

$\uparrow\downarrow$ The arrow indicates the transition of the clock/enable input used for reference: $\uparrow$ for the low-to-high transition, $\downarrow$ for the high-to-low transition.

TEXAS INSTRUMENTS
INCORPORATED
POST OFFICE BOX 5012 • DALLAS, TEXAS 75222

electrical characteristics over recommended operating free-air temperature range (unless otherwise noted)

PARAMETER		TEST CONDITIONS[†]		MIN	TYP[‡]	MAX	UNIT
V_{IH}	High-level input voltage			2			V
V_{IL}	Low-level input voltage					0.8	V
V_{IK}	Input clamp voltage	V_{CC} = MIN,	I_I = −18 mA			−1.2	V
V_{OH}	High-level output voltage — SN54S'	V_{CC} = MIN,	V_{IH} = 2 V,	2.4	3.4		V
	SN74S'	V_{IL} = 0.8 V,	I_{OH} = MAX	2.4	3.1		
V_{OL}	Low-level output voltage	V_{CC} = MIN, V_{IL} = 0.8 V,	V_{IH} = 2 V, I_{OL} = 20 mA			0.5	V
I_{OZH}	Off-state output current, high-level voltage applied	V_{CC} = MAX, V_O = 2.4 V	V_{IH} = 2 V,			50	µA
I_{OZL}	Off-state output current, low-level voltage applied	V_{CC} = MAX, V_O = 0.5 V	V_{IH} = 2 V,			−50	µA
I_I	Input current at maximum input voltage	V_{CC} = MAX,	V_I = 5.5 V			1	mA
I_{IH}	High-level input current	V_{CC} = MAX,	V_I = 2.7 V			50	µA
I_{IL}	Low-level input current	V_{CC} = MAX,	V_I = 0.5 V			−250	µA
I_{OS}	Short-circuit output current[§]	V_{CC} = MAX		−40		−100	mA
I_{CC}	Supply current	V_{CC} = MAX	'S373		105	160	mA
			'S374		90	140	

[†] For conditions shown as MIN or MAX, use the appropriate value specified under recommended operating conditions.
[‡] All typical values are at V_{CC} = 5 V, T_A = 25°C.
[§] Not more than one output should be shorted at a time and duration of the short circuit should not exceed one second.

switching characteristics, V_{CC} = 5 V, T_A = 25°C

PARAMETER	FROM (INPUT)	TO (OUTPUT)	TEST CONDITIONS	'S373			'S374			UNIT
				MIN	TYP	MAX	MIN	TYP	MAX	
f_{max}							75	100		MHz
t_{PLH}	Data	Any Q	C_L = 15 pF, R_L = 280 Ω, See Notes 2 and 4		5	9				ns
t_{PHL}					9	13				
t_{PLH}	Clock or enable	Any Q			7	14		8	15	ns
t_{PHL}					12	18		11	17	
t_{PZH}	Output Control	Any Q			8	15		8	15	ns
t_{PZL}					11	18		11	18	
t_{PHZ}	Output Control	Any Q	C_L = 5 pF, R_L = 280 Ω, See Note 3		6	9		5	9	ns
t_{PLZ}					8	12		7	12	

NOTES: 2. Maximum clock frequency is tested with all outputs loaded.
4. See load circuits and waveforms on page 3-10.

f_{max} ≡ maximum clock frequency
t_{PLH} ≡ propagation delay time, low-to-high-level output
t_{PHL} ≡ propagation delay time, high-to-low-level output
t_{PZH} ≡ output enable time to high level
t_{PZL} ≡ output enable time to low level
t_{PHZ} ≡ output disable time from high level
t_{PLZ} ≡ output disable time from low level

7

TENTATIVE DATA

This page provides tentative information on a new product. Texas Instruments reserves the right to change specifications for this product in any manner without notice.

TEXAS INSTRUMENTS
INCORPORATED
POST OFFICE BOX 5012 • DALLAS, TEXAS 75222

TYPICAL APPLICATION DATA

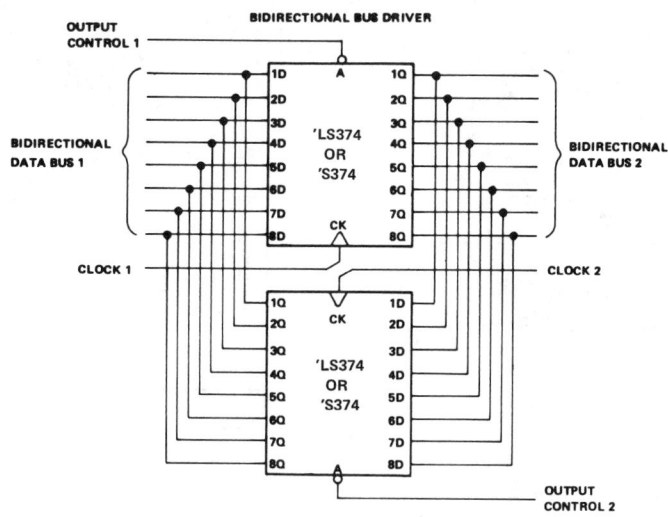

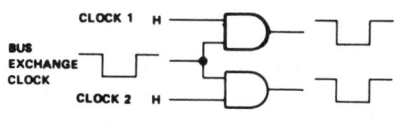

CLOCK CIRCUIT FOR BUS EXCHANGE

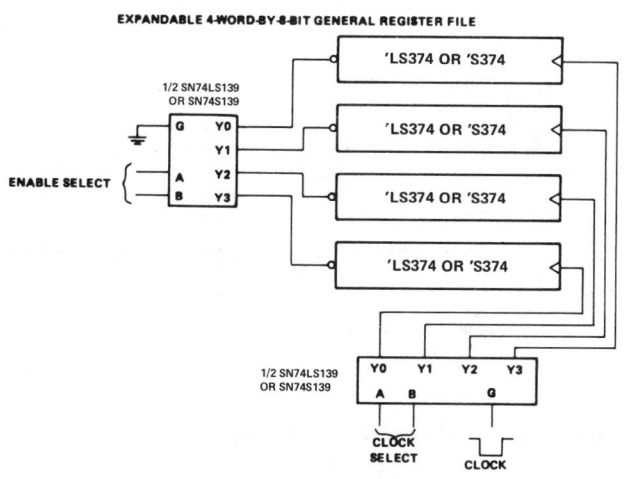

TEXAS INSTRUMENTS
INCORPORATED
POST OFFICE BOX 5012 • DALLAS, TEXAS 75222

● **Supply Voltage and Ground on Corner Pins To Simplify P-C Board Layout**

logic

FUNCTION TABLE
(EACH LATCH)

INPUTS		OUTPUTS	
D	G	Q	$\bar{Q}$
L	H	L	H
H	H	H	L
X	L	Q_0	$\bar{Q}_0$

H = high level, L = low level, X = irrelevant
Q_0 = the level of Q before the high-to-low transition of G.

SN54LS375 . . . J OR W PACKAGE
SN74LS375 . . . J OR N PACKAGE
(TOP VIEW)

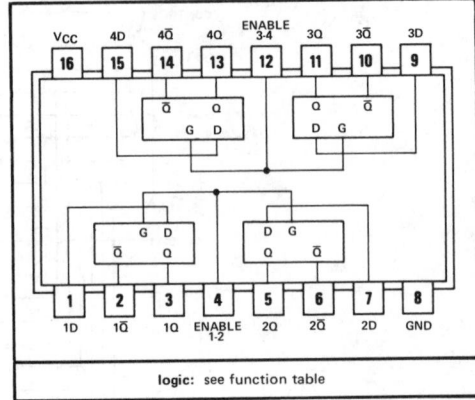

logic: see function table

functional block diagram (each latch)

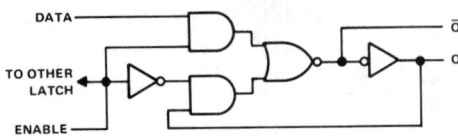

description

The SN54LS375 and SN74LS375 bistable latches are electrically and functionally identical to the SN54LS75 and SN74LS75, respectively. Only the arrangement of the terminals has been changed in the SN54LS375 and SN74LS375.

These latches are ideally suited for use as temporary storage for binary information between processing units and input/output or indicator units. Information present at a data (D) input is transferred to the Q output when the enable (G) is high and the Q output will follow the data input as long as the enable remains high. When the enable goes low, the information (that was present at the data input at the time the transition occurred) is retained at the Q output until the enable goes high.

These circuits are completely compatible with all popular TTL or DTL families. All inputs are diode-clamped to minimize transmission-line effects and simplify system design. The SN54LS375 is characterized for operation over the full military temperature range of −55°C to 125°C; SN74LS375 is characterized for operation from 0°C to 70°C.

schematics of inputs and outputs

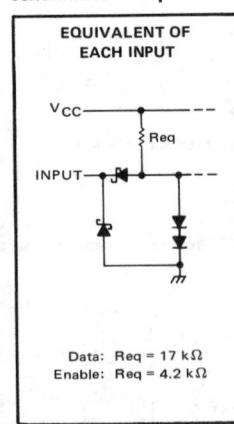

EQUIVALENT OF EACH INPUT

Data: Req = 17 kΩ
Enable: Req = 4.2 kΩ

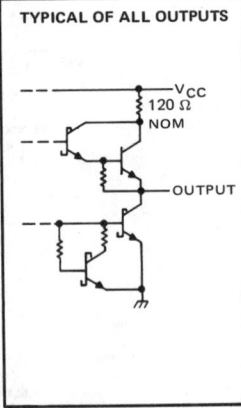

TYPICAL OF ALL OUTPUTS

absolute maximum ratings over operating free-air temperature range (unless otherwise noted)

Supply voltage, V_{CC} (see Note 1) . . . . 7 V
Input voltage . . . . 7 V
Operating free-air temperature range: SN54LS375 . . . . −55°C to 125°C
SN74LS375 . . . . 0°C to 70°C
Storage temperature range . . . . −65°C to 150°C

NOTE 1: Voltage values are with respect to network ground terminal.

recommended operating conditions, electrical characteristics, and switching characteristics

Same as SN54LS75 and SN74LS75, see page 7-39.

TEXAS INSTRUMENTS
INCORPORATED
POST OFFICE BOX 5012 ● DALLAS, TEXAS 75222

- Four J-K̄ Flip-Flops in a Single Package . . . Can Reduce FF Package Count by 50%
- Common Positive-Edge-Triggered Clocks with Hysteresis . . . Typically 200 mV
- Fully Buffered Outputs
- Typical Clock Input Frequency . . . 45 MHz

SN54376 . . . J OR W PACKAGE
SN74376 . . . J OR N PACKAGE
(TOP VIEW)

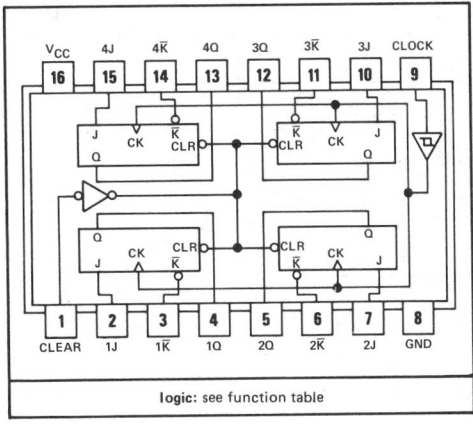

logic: see function table

description

These quadruple TTL J-K̄ flip-flops incorporate a number of third-generation IC features that can simplify system design and reduce flip-flop package count by as much as 50%. They feature hysteresis at the clock input, fully buffered outputs, and direct clear capability. The positive-edge-triggered SN54376 and SN74376 are directly compatible with most Series 54/74 MSI registers.

The SN54376 is characterized for operation over the full military temperature range of −55°C to 125°C; the SN74376 is characterized for operation from 0°C to 70°C.

schematics of inputs and outputs

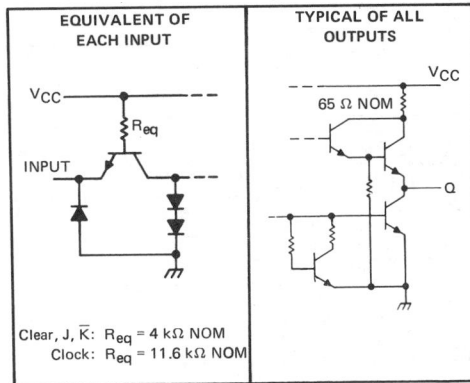

Clear, J, K̄: R_{eq} = 4 kΩ NOM
Clock: R_{eq} = 11.6 kΩ NOM

Resistor values shown are nominal and in ohms

FUNCTION TABLE (EACH FLIP-FLOP)

COMMON INPUTS		INPUTS		OUTPUT
CLEAR	CLOCK	J	K̄	Q
L	X	X	X	L
H	↑	L	H	Q_0
H	↑	H	H	H
H	↑	L	L	L
H	↑	H	L	TOGGLE
H	L	X	X	Q_0

See explanation of function tables on page 3-8.

absolute maximum ratings over operating free-air temperature range (unless otherwise noted)

Supply voltage, V_{CC} (see Note 1) . . . . 7 V
Input voltage . . . . 5.5 V
Operating free-air temperature range: SN54376 . . . . −55°C to 125°C
　　　　　　　　　　　　　　　　　　SN74376 . . . . 0°C to 70°C
Storage temperature range . . . . −65°C to 150°C

NOTE 1: Voltage values are with respect to network ground terminal.

recommended operating conditions

		SN54376			SN74376			UNIT
		MIN	NOM	MAX	MIN	NOM	MAX	
Supply voltage, V_{CC}		4.5	5	5.5	4.75	5	5.25	V
High-level output current, I_{OH}				−800			−800	µA
Low-level output current, I_{OL}				16			16	mA
Clock frequency		0		30	0		30	MHz
Pulse width, t_w	Clock high	22			22			ns
	Clock low	12			12			
	Preset or clear low	12			12			
Setup time, t_{su}	J, $\overline{\text{K}}$ inputs	0↑			0↑			ns
	Clear inactive state	10↑			10↑			
Input hold time, t_h		20↑			20↑			ns
Operating free-air temperature, T_A		55		125	0		70	°C

↑↓The arrow indicates the edge of the clock pulse used for reference: ↑ for the rising edge, ↓ for the falling edge.

electrical characteristics over recommended operating free-air temperature range (unless otherwise noted)

	PARAMETER	TEST CONDITIONS[†]	MIN	TYP[‡]	MAX	UNIT
V_{IH}	High-level input voltage		2			V
V_{IL}	Low-level input voltage				0.8	V
V_{IK}	Input clamp voltage	V_{CC} = MIN, I_I = −12 mA			−1.5	V
V_{OH}	High-level output voltage	V_{CC} = MIN, V_{IH} = 2 V, V_{IL} = 0.8 V, I_{OH} = −800 µA	2.4	3.4		V
V_{OL}	Low-level output voltage	V_{CC} = MIN, V_{IH} = 2 V, V_{IL} = 0.8 V, I_{OL} = 16 mA		0.2	0.4	V
I_I	Input current at maximum input voltage	V_{CC} = MAX, V_I = 5.5 V			1	mA
I_{IH}	High-level input current	V_{CC} = MAX, V_I = 2.4 V			40	µA
I_{IL}	Low-level input current	V_{CC} = MAX, V_I = 0.4 V			−1.6	mA
I_{OS}	Short-circuit output current[§]	V_{CC} = MAX	−30		−85	mA
I_{CC}	Supply current	V_{CC} = MAX		52	74	mA

[†]For conditions shown as MIN or MAX, use the appropriate value specified under recommended operating conditions.
[‡]All typical values are at V_{CC} = 5 V, T_A = 25°C.
[§]Not more than one output should be shorted at a time.

switching characteristics, V_{CC} = 5 V, T_A = 25°C

	PARAMETER	TEST CONDITIONS	MIN	TYP	MAX	UNIT
f_{max}	Maximum clock frequency	C_L = 15 pF, R_L = 400 Ω, See Note 2	30	45		MHz
t_{PHL}	Propagation delay time, high-to-low-level output from clear			17	30	ns
t_{PLH}	Propagation delay time, low-to-high-level output from clock			22	35	ns
t_{PHL}	Propagation delay time, high-to-low-level output from clock			24	35	ns

NOTE 2: Load circuit and voltage waveforms are shown on page 3-10.

TEXAS INSTRUMENTS
INCORPORATED
POST OFFICE BOX 5012 • DALLAS, TEXAS 75222

TYPES SN54LS377, SN54LS378, SN54LS379, SN74LS377, SN74LS378, SN74LS379
OCTAL, HEX, AND QUAD D-TYPE FLIP-FLOPS WITH ENABLE

BULLETIN NO. DL-S 7612474, OCTOBER 1976

- 'LS377 and 'LS378 Contain Eight and Six Flip-Flops, Respectively, with Single-Rail Outputs

- 'LS379 Contains Four Flip-Flops with Double-Rail Outputs

- Individual Data Input to Each Flip-Flop

- Applications Include:
  Buffer/Storage Registers
  Shift Registers
  Pattern Generators

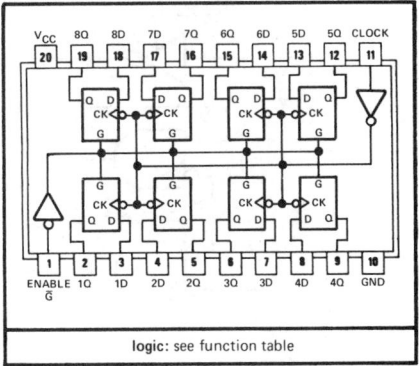

SN54LS377 . . . J PACKAGE
SN74LS377 . . . J OR N PACKAGE
(TOP VIEW)

logic: see function table

description

These monolithic, positive-edge-triggered flip-flops utilize TTL circuitry to implement D-type flip-flop logic with an enable input. The 'LS377, 'LS378, and 'LS379 devices are similar to 'LS273, 'LS174, and 'LS175, respectively, but feature a common enable instead of a common clear.

Information at the D inputs meeting the setup time requirements is transferred to the Q outputs on the positive-going edge of the clock pulse if the enable input $\overline{G}$ is low. Clock triggering occurs at a particular voltage level and is not directly related to the transition time of the positive-going pulse. When the clock input is at either the high or low level, the D input signal has no effect at the output. The circuits are designed to prevent false clocking by transitions at the $\overline{G}$ input.

These flip-flops are guaranteed to respond to clock frequencies ranging from 0 to 30 MHz while maximum clock frequency is typically 40 megahertz. Typical power dissipation is 10 milliwatts per flip-flop.

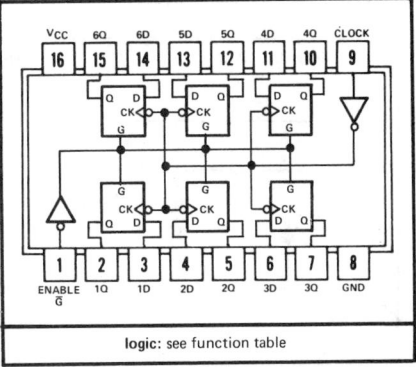

SN54LS378 . . . J OR W PACKAGE
SN74LS378 . . . J OR N PACKAGE
(TOP VIEW)

logic: see function table

FUNCTION TABLE
(EACH FLIP-FLOP)

INPUTS			OUTPUTS	
$\overline{G}$	CLOCK	DATA	Q	$\overline{Q}$
H	X	X	Q_0	$\overline{Q}_0$
L	↑	H	H	L
L	↑	L	L	H
X	L	X	Q_0	$\overline{Q}_0$

See explanation of function tables on page 3-8.

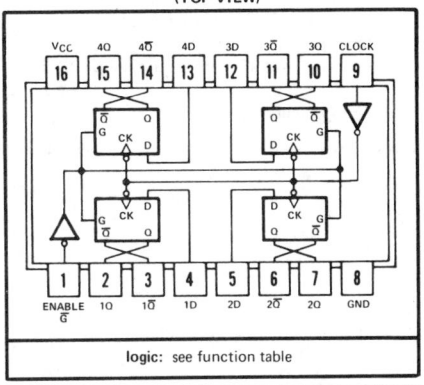

SN54LS379 . . . J OR W PACKAGE
SN74LS379 . . . J OR N PACKAGE
(TOP VIEW)

logic: see function table

7

TEXAS INSTRUMENTS
INCORPORATED
POST OFFICE BOX 5012 • DALLAS, TEXAS 75222

TYPES SN54LS377, SN54LS378, SN54LS379, SN74LS377, SN74LS378, SN74LS379
OCTAL, HEX, AND QUAD D-TYPE FLIP-FLOPS WITH ENABLE

functional block diagram

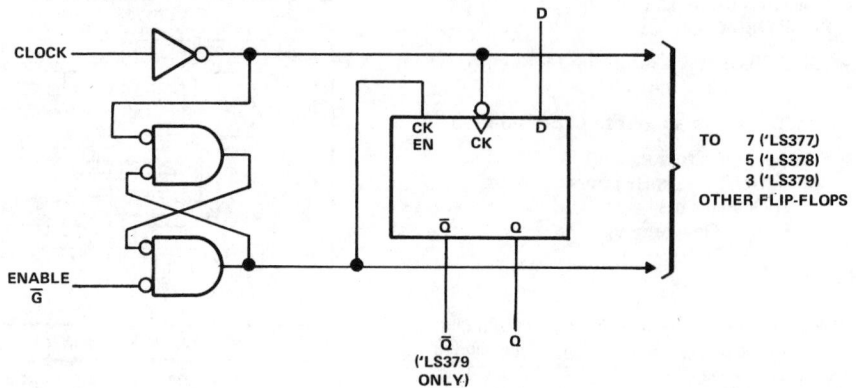

schematics of inputs and outputs

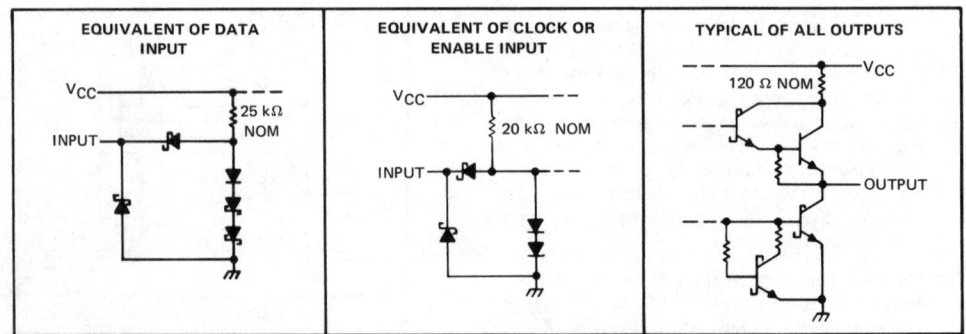

absolute maximum rating over operating free-air temperature range (unless otherwise noted)

Supply voltage, V_{CC} (see Note 1) . . . . 7 V
Input voltage . . . . 7 V
Operating free-air temperature range: SN54LS' . . . . −55°C to 125°C
    SN74LS' . . . . 0°C to 70°C
Storage temperature range . . . . −65°C to 150°C

NOTE 1: Voltage values are with respect to network ground terminal.

TEXAS INSTRUMENTS
INCORPORATED
POST OFFICE BOX 5012 • DALLAS, TEXAS 75222

recommended operating conditions

		SN54LS' MIN	SN54LS' NOM	SN54LS' MAX	SN74LS' MIN	SN74LS' NOM	SN74LS' MAX	UNIT
Supply voltage, V_{CC}		4.5	5	5.5	4.75	5	5.25	V
High-level output current, I_{OH}				−400			−400	μA
Low-level output current, I_{OL}				4			8	mA
Clock frequency, f_{clock}		0		30	0		30	MHz
Width of clock or clear pulse, t_w		20			20			ns
Setup time, t_{su}	Data input	20†			20†			ns
	Enable active-state	25†			25†			
	Enable inactive-state	10†			10†			
Hold time, t_h	Data and enable	5†			5†			ns
Operating free-air temperature, T_A		−55		125	0		70	°C

†The arrow indicates that the rising edge of the clock pulse is used for reference.

electrical characteristics over recommended operating free-air temperature range (unless otherwise noted)

PARAMETER		TEST CONDITIONS†		SN54LS' MIN	SN54LS' TYP‡	SN54LS' MAX	SN74LS' MIN	SN74LS' TYP‡	SN74LS' MAX	UNIT
V_{IH}	High-level input voltage			2			2			V
V_{IL}	Low-level input voltage					0.7			0.8	V
V_{IK}	Input clamp voltage	V_{CC} = MIN,	I_I = −18 mA			−1.5			−1.5	V
V_{OH}	High-level output voltage	V_{CC} = MIN, V_{IL} = V_{IL} max,	V_{IH} = 2 V, I_{OH} = −400 μA	2.5	3.5		2.7	3.5		V
V_{OL}	Low-level output voltage	V_{CC} = MIN, V_{IL} = V_{IL} max	V_{IH} = 2 V, I_{OL} = 4 mA		0.25	0.4		0.25	0.4	V
			I_{OL} = 8 mA					0.35	0.5	
I_I	Input current at maximum input voltage	V_{CC} = MAX,	V_I = 7 V			0.1			0.1	mA
I_{IH}	High-level input current	V_{CC} = MAX,	V_I = 2.7 V			20			20	μA
I_{IL}	Low-level input current	V_{CC} = MAX,	V_I = 0.4 V			−0.4			−0.4	mA
I_{OS}	Short-circuit output current§	V_{CC} = MAX		−20		−100	−20		−100	mA
I_{CC}	Supply current	V_{CC} = MAX,	See Note 2 'LS377		17	28		17	28	mA
			'LS378		13	22		13	22	mA
			'LS379		9	15		9	15	mA

† For conditions shown as MIN or MAX, use the appropriate value specified under recommended operating conditions.
‡ All typical values are at V_{CC} = 5 V, T_A = 25°C.
§ Note more than one input should be shorted at a time, and duration of the short-circuit should not exceed one second.
NOTE 2: With all outputs open and ground applied to all data and enable inputs, I_{CC} is measured after a momentary ground, then 4.5 V, is applied to clock.

switching characteristics, V_{CC} = 5 V, T_A = 25°C

PARAMETER		TEST CONDITIONS	MIN	TYP	MAX	UNIT
f_{max}	Maximum clock frequency	C_L = 15 pF,	30	40		MHz
t_{PLH}	Propagation delay time, low-to-high-level output from clock	R_L = 2 kΩ		17	27	ns
t_{PHL}	Propagation delay time, high-to-low-level output from clock	See Note 3		18	27	ns

NOTE 3: Load circuit and voltage waveforms are shown on page 3-11.

7

TEXAS INSTRUMENTS
INCORPORATED
POST OFFICE BOX 5012 • DALLAS, TEXAS 75222

PIN DESIGNATIONS

DESIGNATION	PIN NOS.	FUNCTION
A3, A2, A1, A0	17, 19, 1, 3	WORD A INPUTS
B3, B2, B1, B0	16, 18, 2, 4	WORD B INPUTS
S2, S1, S0	7, 6, 5	FUNCTION-SELECT INPUTS
C_n	15	CARRY INPUT FOR ADDITION, INVERTED CARRY INPUT FOR SUBTRACTION
F3, F2, F1, F0	12, 11, 9, 8	FUNCTION OUTPUTS
$\overline{P}$	14	INVERTED CARRY PROPAGATE OUTPUT
$\overline{G}$	13	INVERTED CARRY GENERATE OUTPUT
V_{CC}	20	SUPPLY VOLTAGE
GND	10	GROUND

SN54S381 . . . J PACKAGE
SN74S381 . . . J OR N PACKAGE
(TOP VIEW)

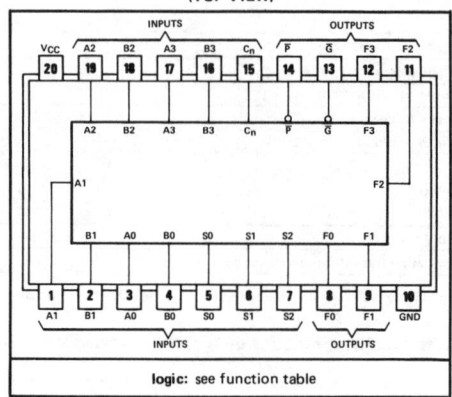

logic: see function table

- A Fully Parallel 4-Bit ALU in 20-Pin Package for 0.300-Inch Row Spacing

- Ideally Suited for High-Density Economical Processors

- Parallel Inputs and Outputs and Full Look-Ahead Provide System Flexibility

- Arithmetic and Logic Operations Selected Specifically to Simplify System Implementation:
  A Minus B
  B Minus A
  A Plus B
  and Five Other Functions

- Schottky-Clamped for High Performance
  16-Bit Add Time . . . 26 ns Typ Using Look-Ahead
  32-Bit Add Time . . . 34 ns Typ Using Look-Ahead

FUNCTION TABLE

SELECTION			ARITHMETIC/LOGIC
S2	S1	S0	OPERATION
L	L	L	CLEAR
L	L	H	B MINUS A
L	H	L	A MINUS B
L	H	H	A PLUS B
H	L	L	A $\oplus$ B
H	L	H	A + B
H	H	L	AB
H	H	H	PRESET

H = high level, L = low level

description

The 'S381 is a Schottky TTL arithmetic logic unit (ALU)/function generator that performs eight binary arithmetic/logic operations on two 4-bit words as shown in the function table. These operations are selected by the three function-select lines (S0, S1, S2). A full carry look-ahead circuit is provided for fast, simultaneous carry generation by means of two cascade outputs ($\overline{P}$ and $\overline{G}$) for the four bits in the package. The method of cascading SN54182/SN74182 or SN54S182/SN74S182 look-ahead carry generators with these ALU's to provide multi-level full carry look-ahead is illustrated under typical applications data for the '182 and 'S182. The typical addition times shown above illustrate the short delay time required for addition of longer words when full look-ahead is employed. The exclusive-OR, AND, or OR function of two Boolean variables is provided without the use of external circuitry. Also, the outputs can be either cleared (low) or preset (high) as desired.

functional block diagram and schematics of inputs and outputs

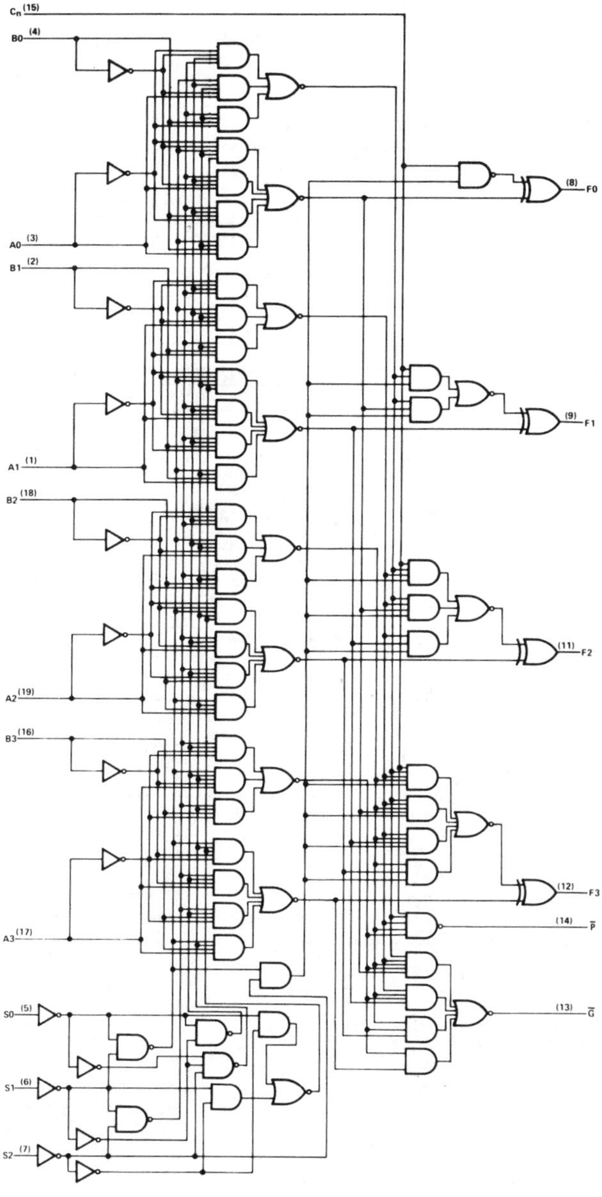

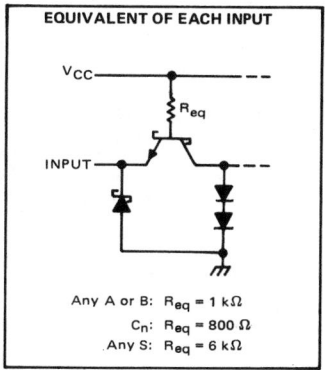

EQUIVALENT OF EACH INPUT

V_{CC}

R_{eq}

INPUT

Any A or B: $R_{eq} = 1 \text{ k}\Omega$
C_n: $R_{eq} = 800 \ \Omega$
Any S: $R_{eq} = 6 \text{ k}\Omega$

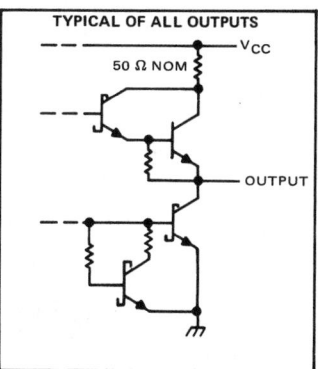

TYPICAL OF ALL OUTPUTS

V_{CC}

50 Ω NOM

OUTPUT

7

absolute maximum ratings over operating free-air temperature range (unless otherwise noted)

Supply voltage, V_{CC} (see Note 1) . . . . 7 V

Input voltage . . . . 5.5 V

Interemitter voltage (see Note 2) . . . . 5.5 V

Operating free-air temperature range: SN54S381 . . . . −55°C to 125°C

SN74S381 . . . . 0°C to 70°C

Storage free-air temperature range . . . . −65°C to 150°C

NOTES: 1. Voltage values, except interemitter voltage, are with respect to network ground terminal.
2. This is the voltage between two emitters of a multiple-emitter transistor. For this circuit, this rating applies to each A input in conjunction with its respective B input; for example A0 with B0, etc.

recommended operating conditions

	SN54S381			SN74S381			UNIT
	MIN	NOM	MAX	MIN	NOM	MAX	
Supply voltage, V_{CC}	4.5	5	5.5	4.75	5	5.25	V
High-level output current, I_{OH}			−1			−1	mA
Low-level output current, I_{OL}			20			20	mA
Operating free-air temperature, T_A	−55		125	0		70	°C

electrical characteristics over recommended operating free-air temperature range (unless otherwise noted)

PARAMETER		TEST CONDITIONS†		MIN	TYP‡	MAX	UNIT
V_{IH}	High-level input voltage			2			V
V_{IL}	Low-level input voltage					0.8	V
V_{IK}	Input clamp voltage	V_{CC} = MIN,	I_I = −18 mA			−1.2	V
V_{OH}	High-level output voltage	SN54S381	V_{CC} = MIN, V_{IH} = 2 V,	2.4	3.4		V
		SN74S381	V_{IL} = 0.8 V, I_{OH} = −1 mA	2.7	3.4		
V_{OL}	Low-level output voltage		V_{CC} = MIN, V_{IH} = 2 V, V_{IL} = 0.8 V, I_{OL} = 20 mA			0.5	V
I_I	Input current at maximum input voltage		V_{CC} = MAX, V_I = 5.5 V			1	mA
I_{IH}	High-level input current	Any S input	V_{CC} = MAX, V_I = 2.7 V			50	µA
		C_n				250	
		All others				200	
I_{IL}	Low-level input current	Any S input	V_{CC} = MAX, V_I = 0.5 V			−2	mA
		C_n				−8	
		All others				−6	
I_{OS}	Short-circuit output current§		V_{CC} = MAX	−40		−100	mA
I_{CC}	Supply current		V_{CC} = MAX		105	160	mA

†For conditions shown as MIN or MAX, use the appropriate value specified under recommended operating conditions.
‡All typical values are at V_{CC} = 5 V, T_A = 25°C.
§Not more than one output should be shorted at a time.

switching characteristics, V_{CC} = 5 V, T_A = 25°C

PARAMETER¶	FROM (INPUT)	TO (OUTPUT)	TEST CONDITIONS	MIN	TYP	MAX	UNIT
t_{PLH}	C_n	Any F			10	17	ns
t_{PHL}					10	17	
t_{PLH}	Any A or B	$\overline{G}$			12	20	ns
t_{PHL}					12	20	
t_{PLH}	Any A or B	$\overline{P}$	C_L = 15 pF, R_L = 280 Ω, See Note 3		11	18	ns
t_{PHL}					11	18	
t_{PLH}	A_i or B_i	F_i			18	27	ns
t_{PHL}					16	25	
t_{PLH}	Any S	Any			18	30	ns
t_{PHL}					18	30	

¶t_{PLH} ≡ propagation delay time, low-to-high-level output
t_{PHL} ≡ propagation delay time, high-to-low-level output
NOTE 3: Load circuit and voltage waveforms are shown on page 3-10.

TEXAS INSTRUMENTS
INCORPORATED
POST OFFICE BOX 5012 • DALLAS, TEXAS 75222

TTL
MSI

TYPES SN54LS386, SN74LS386
QUADRUPLE 2-INPUT EXCLUSIVE-OR GATES
BULLETIN NO. DL-S 7612118, MARCH 1974—REVISED OCTOBER 1976

- Electrically Identical to SN54LS86/SN74LS86
- Mechanically Identical to SN54L86/SN74L86
- Total Average Propagation Delay Times . . . 10 ns
- Typical Total Power Dissipation . . . 30.5 mW

SN54LS386 . . . J OR W PACKAGE
SN74LS386 . . . J OR N PACKAGE
(TOP VIEW)

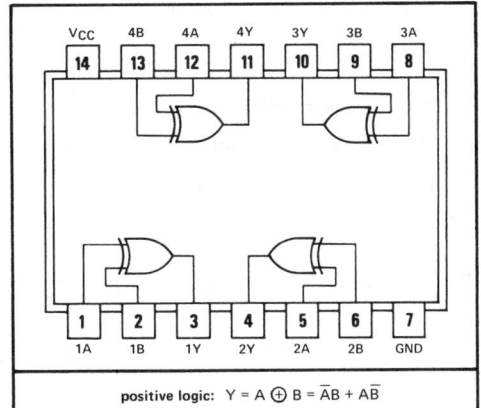

positive logic: $Y = A \oplus B = \overline{A}B + A\overline{B}$

FUNCTION TABLE
(EACH GATE)

INPUTS		OUTPUT
A	B	
L	L	L
L	H	H
H	L	H
H	H	L

H = high level
L = low level

schematics of inputs and outputs

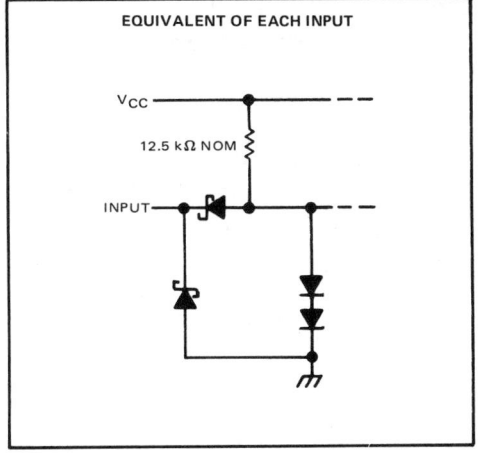

EQUIVALENT OF EACH INPUT

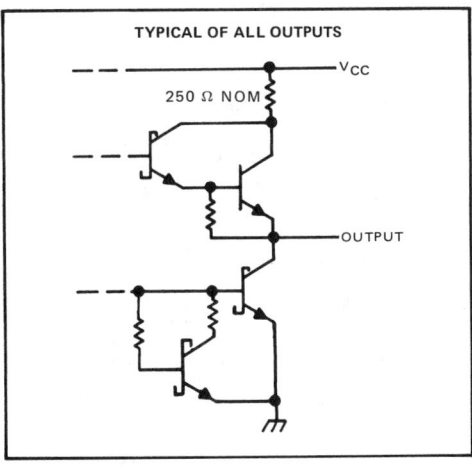

TYPICAL OF ALL OUTPUTS

TYPES SN54LS386, SN74LS386
QUADRUPLE 2-INPUT EXCLUSIVE-OR GATES

REVISED OCTOBER 1976

absolute maximum ratings over operating free-air temperature range (unless otherwise noted)

Supply voltage, V_{CC} (see Note 1)	7 V
Input voltage	7 V
Operating free-air temperature range: SN54LS386	$-55°C$ to $125°C$
SN74LS386	$0°C$ to $70°C$
Storage temperature range	$-65°C$ to $150°C$

NOTE 1: Voltage values are with respect to network ground terminal.

recommended operating conditions

	SN54LS386			SN74LS386			UNIT
	MIN	NOM	MAX	MIN	NOM	MAX	
Supply voltage, V_{CC}	4.5	5	5.5	4.75	5	5.25	V
High-level output current, I_{OH}			−400			−400	μA
Low-level output current, I_{OL}			4			8	mA
Operating free-air temperature, T_A	−55		125	0		70	°C

electrical characteristics over recommended operating free-air temperature range (unless otherwise noted)

PARAMETER	TEST CONDITIONS[†]		SN54LS386			SN74LS386			UNIT
			MIN	TYP[‡]	MAX	MIN	TYP[‡]	MAX	
V_{IH} High-level input voltage			2			2			V
V_{IL} Low-level input voltage					0.7			0.8	V
V_{IK} Input clamp voltage	V_{CC} = MIN,	$I_I = -18$ mA			−1.5			−1.5	V
V_{OH} High-level output voltage	V_{CC} = MIN, V_{IH} = 2 V, $V_{IL} = V_{IL}$ max, $I_{OH} = -400$ μA		2.5	3.4		2.7	3.4		V
V_{OL} Low-level output voltage	V_{CC} = MIN. V_{IH} = 2 V, $V_{IL} = V_{IL}$ max	I_{OL} = 4 mA		0.25	0.4		0.25	0.4	V
		I_{OL} = 8 mA					0.35	0.5	
I_I Input current at maximum input voltage	V_{CC} = MAX,	V_I = 7 V			0.2			0.2	mA
I_{IH} High-level input current	V_{CC} = MAX,	V_I = 2.7 V			40			40	μA
I_{IL} Low-level input current	V_{CC} = MAX,	V_I = 0.4 V			−0.8			−0.8	mA
I_{OS} Short-circuit output current[§]	V_{CC} = MAX		−6		−40	−5		−42	mA
I_{CC} Supply current	V_{CC} = MAX,	See Note 2		6.1	10		6.1	10	mA

[†]For conditions shown as MIN or MAX, use the appropriate value specified under recommended operating conditions.
[‡]All typical values are at V_{CC} = 5 V, $T_A = 25°C$.
[§]Not more than one output should be shorted at a time.
NOTE 2: I_{CC} is measured with the inputs grounded and the outputs open.

switching characteristics, V_{CC} = 5 V, $T_A = 25°C$

PARAMETER[¶]	FROM (INPUT)	TEST CONDITIONS		MIN	TYP	MAX	UNIT
t_{PLH}	A or B	Other input low	C_L = 15 pF, R_L = 2 kΩ, See Note 3		12	23	ns
t_{PHL}					10	17	
t_{PLH}	A or B	Other input high			20	30	ns
t_{PHL}					13	22	

[¶]t_{PLH} ≡ propagation delay time, low-to-high-level output
t_{PHL} ≡ propagation delay time, high-to-low-level output
NOTE 3: Load circuit and voltage waveforms are shown on page 3-11.

7

TEXAS INSTRUMENTS
INCORPORATED
POST OFFICE BOX 5012 • DALLAS, TEXAS 75222

TTL

TYPES SN54390, SN54LS390, SN54393, SN54LS393, SN74390, SN74LS390, SN74393, SN74LS393
DUAL 4-BIT DECADE AND BINARY COUNTERS
BULLETIN NO. DL-S 7612099, OCTOBER 1976

- Dual Versions of the Popular '90A, 'LS90 and '93A, 'LS93

- '390, 'LS390. . .Individual Clocks for A and B Flip-Flops Provide Dual ÷2 and ÷5 Counters

- '393, 'LS393. . .Dual 4-Bit Binary Counter with Individual Clocks

- All Have Direct Clear for Each 4-Bit Counter

- Dual 4-Bit Versions Can Significantly Improve System Densities by Reducing Counter Package Count by 50%

- Typical Maximum Count Frequency . . . 35 MHz

- Buffered Outputs Reduce Possibility of Collector Commutation

SN54390, SN54LS390 . . . J OR W PACKAGE
SN74390, SN74LS390 . . . J OR N PACKAGE
(TOP VIEW)

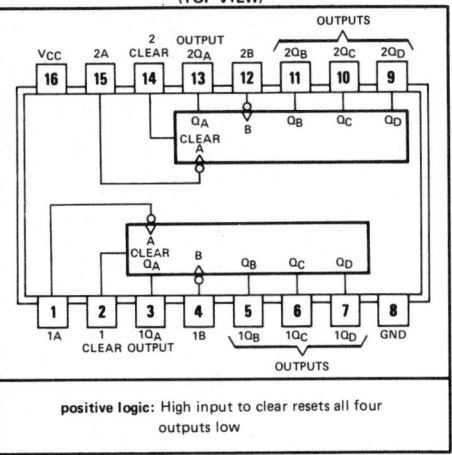

positive logic: High input to clear resets all four outputs low

description

Each of these monolithic circuits contains eight master-slave flip-flops and additional gating to implement two individual four-bit counters in a single package. The '390 and 'LS390 incorporate dual divide-by-two and divide-by-five counters, which can be used to implement cycle lengths equal to any whole and/or cumulative multiples of 2 and/or 5 up to divide-by-100. When connected as a bi-quinary counter, the separate divide-by-two circuit can be used to provide symmetry (a square wave) at the final output stage. The '393 and 'LS393 each comprise two independent four-bit binary counters each having a clear and a clock input. N-bit binary counters can be implemented with each package providing the capability of divide-by-256. The '390, 'LS390, '393, and 'LS393 have parallel outputs from each counter stage so that any submultiple of the input count frequency is available for system-timing signals.

Series 54 and Series 54LS circuits are characterized for operation over the full military temperature range of −55°C to 125°C; Series 74 and Series 74LS circuits are characterized for operation from 0°C to 70°C.

SN54393, SN54LS393 . . . J OR W PACKAGE
SN74393, SN54LS393 . . . J OR N PACKAGE
(TOP VIEW)

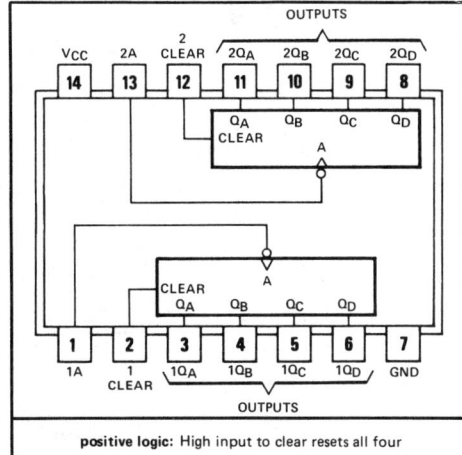

positive logic: High input to clear resets all four outputs low

7

TEXAS INSTRUMENTS
INCORPORATED
POST OFFICE BOX 5012 • DALLAS, TEXAS 75222

TYPES SN54390, SN54LS390, SN54393, SN54LS393, SN74390, SN74LS390, SN74393, SN74LS393
DUAL 4-BIT DECADE AND BINARY COUNTERS

FUNCTION TABLES

'390, 'LS390 BCD COUNT SEQUENCE (EACH COUNTER) (See Note A)

COUNT	OUTPUT			
	Q_D	Q_C	Q_B	Q_A
0	L	L	L	L
1	L	L	L	H
2	L	L	H	L
3	L	L	H	H
4	L	H	L	L
5	L	H	L	H
6	L	H	H	L
7	L	H	H	H
8	H	L	L	L
9	H	L	L	H

'390, 'LS390 BI-QUINARY (5-2) (EACH COUNTER) (See Note B)

COUNT	OUTPUT			
	Q_A	Q_D	Q_C	Q_B
0	L	L	L	L
1	L	L	L	H
2	L	L	H	L
3	L	L	H	H
4	L	H	L	L
5	H	L	L	L
6	H	L	L	H
7	H	L	H	L
8	H	L	H	H
9	H	H	L	L

'393, 'LS393 COUNT SEQUENCE (EACH COUNTER)

COUNT	OUTPUT			
	Q_D	Q_C	Q_B	Q_A
0	L	L	L	L
1	L	L	L	H
2	L	L	H	L
3	L	L	H	H
4	L	H	L	L
5	L	H	L	H
6	L	H	H	L
7	L	H	H	H
8	H	L	L	L
9	H	L	L	H
10	H	L	H	L
11	H	L	H	H
12	H	H	L	L
13	H	H	L	H
14	H	H	H	L
15	H	H	H	H

NOTES: A. Output Q_A is connected to input B for BCD count.
B. Output Q_D is connected to input A for bi-quinary count.
C. H = high level, L = low level.

functional block diagrams

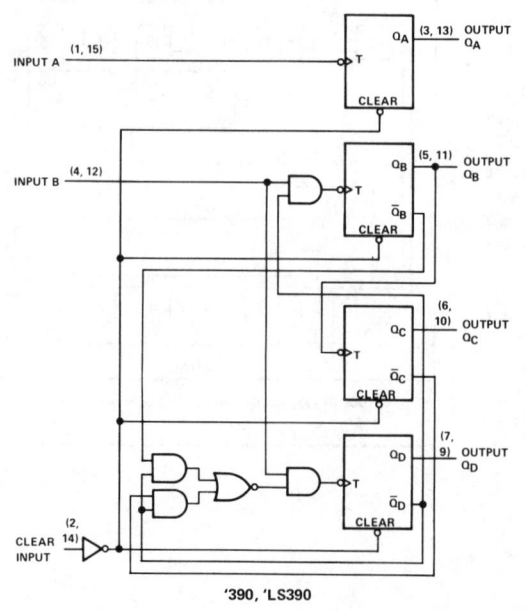

'390, 'LS390

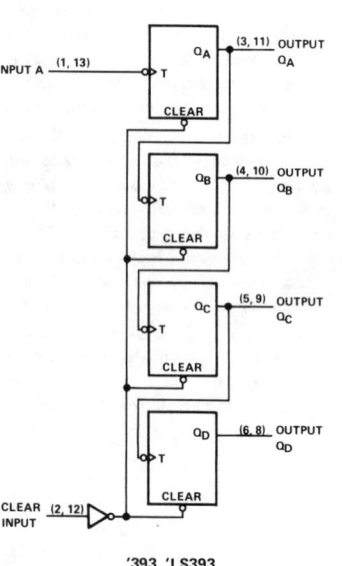

'393, 'LS393

TEXAS INSTRUMENTS
INCORPORATED
POST OFFICE BOX 5012 • DALLAS, TEXAS 75222

schematics of inputs and outputs

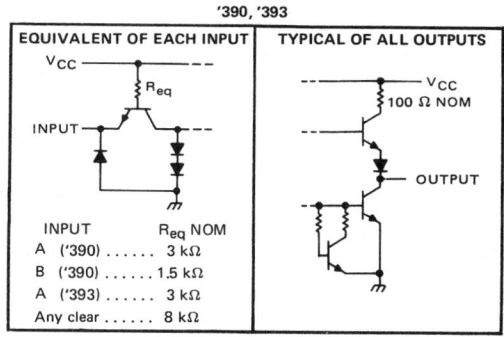

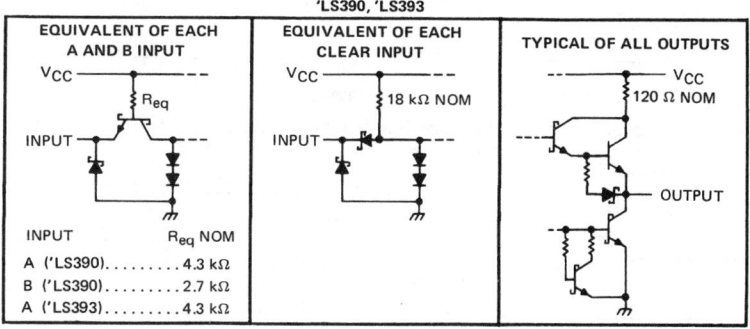

TEXAS INSTRUMENTS
INCORPORATED
POST OFFICE BOX 5012 • DALLAS, TEXAS 75222

TYPES SN54390, SN54393, SN74390, SN74393
DUAL 4-BIT DECADE AND BINARY COUNTERS

absolute maximum ratings over operating free-air temperature range (unless otherwise noted)

Supply voltage, V_{CC} (see Note 1) . . . . 7 V
Input voltage . . . . 5.5 V
Operating free-air temperature range: SN54390, SN54393 . . . . -55°C to 125°C
SN74390, SN74393 . . . . 0°C to 70°C
Storage temperature range . . . . -65°C to 150°C

NOTE 1: Voltage values are with respect to network ground terminal.

recommended operating conditions

		SN54390 SN54393			SN74390 SN74393			UNIT
		MIN	NOM	MAX	MIN	NOM	MAX	
Supply voltage, V_{CC}		4.5	5	5.5	4.75	5	5.25	V
High-level output current, I_{OH}				-800			-800	μA
Low-level output current, I_{OL}				16			16	mA
Count frequency, f_{count}	A input	0		25	0		25	MHz
	B input	0		20	0		20	
Pulse width, t_w	A input high or low	20			20			ns
	B input high or low	25			25			
	Clear high	20			20			
Clear inactive-state setup time, t_{su}		25↓			25↓			ns
Operating free-air temperature, T_A		-55		125	0		70	$^\circ$C

↓ The arrow indicates that the falling edge of the clock pulse is used for reference.

electrical characteristics over recommended operating free-air temperature range (unless otherwise noted)

PARAMETER		TEST CONDITIONS†	'390			'393			UNIT
			MIN	TYP‡	MAX	MIN	TYP‡	MAX	
V_{IH}	High-level input voltage		2			2			V
V_{IL}	Low-level input voltage				0.8			0.8	V
V_{IK}	Input clamp voltage	V_{CC} = MIN, I_I = -12 mA			-1.5			-1.5	V
V_{OH}	High-level output voltage	V_{CC} = MIN, V_{IH} = 2 V, V_{IL} = 0.8 V, I_{OH} = -800 μA	2.4	3.4		2.4	3.4		V
V_{OL}	Low-level output voltage	V_{CC} = MIN, V_{IH} = 2 V, V_{IL} = 0.8 V, I_{OL} = 16 mA¶		0.2	0.4		0.2	0.4	V
I_I	Input current at maximum input voltage	V_{CC} = MAX, V_I = 5.5 V			1			1	mA
I_{IH}	High-level input current	Clear	V_{CC} = MAX, V_I = 2.4 V			40			40	μA
		Input A				80			80	
		Input B				120				
I_{IL}	Low-level input current	Clear	V_{CC} = MAX, V_I = 0.4 V			-1			-1	mA
		Input A				-3.2			-3.2	
		Input B				-4.8				
I_{OS}	Short-circuit output current§	V_{CC} = MAX	SN54'	-20		-57	-20		-57	mA
			SN74'	-18		-57	-18		-57	
I_{CC}	Supply current	V_{CC} = MAX, See Note 2		42	69		38	64	mA

†For conditions shown as MIN or MAX, use the appropriate value specified under recommended operating conditions.
‡All typical values are at V_{CC} = 5 V, T_A = 25°C.
¶The Q_A outputs of the '390 are tested at I_{OL} = 16 mA plus the limit value for I_{IL} for the B input. This permits driving the B input while maintaining full fan-out capability.
§Not more than one output should be shorted at a time.
NOTE 2: I_{CC} is measured with all outputs open, both clear inputs grounded following momentary connection to 4.5 V, and all other inputs grounded.

7

TEXAS INSTRUMENTS
INCORPORATED
POST OFFICE BOX 5012 • DALLAS, TEXAS 75222

switching characteristics, V_{CC} = 5 V, T_A = 25°C

PARAMETER¶	FROM (INPUT)	TO (OUTPUT)	TEST CONDITIONS	'390 MIN	'390 TYP	'390 MAX	'393 MIN	'393 TYP	'393 MAX	UNIT
f_{max}	A	Q_A		25	35		25	35		MHz
	B	Q_B		20	30					
t_{PLH}	A	Q_A			12	20		12	20	ns
t_{PHL}					13	20		13	20	
t_{PLH}	A	Q_C of '390	C_L = 15 pF,		37	60		40	60	ns
t_{PHL}		Q_D of '393	R_L = 400 Ω,		39	60		40	60	
t_{PLH}	B	Q_B	See Note 3		13	21				ns
t_{PHL}			and		14	21				
t_{PLH}	B	Q_C	Figure 1		24	39				ns
t_{PHL}					26	39				
t_{PLH}	B	Q_D			13	21				ns
t_{PHL}					14	21				
t_{PHL}	Clear	Any			24	39		24	39	ns

¶ f_{max} ≡ maximum count frequency
t_{PLH} ≡ propagation delay time, low-to-high-level output
t_{PHL} ≡ propagation delay time, high-to-low-level output
NOTE 3: Load circuit is shown on page 3-10.

PARAMETER MEASUREMENT INFORMATION

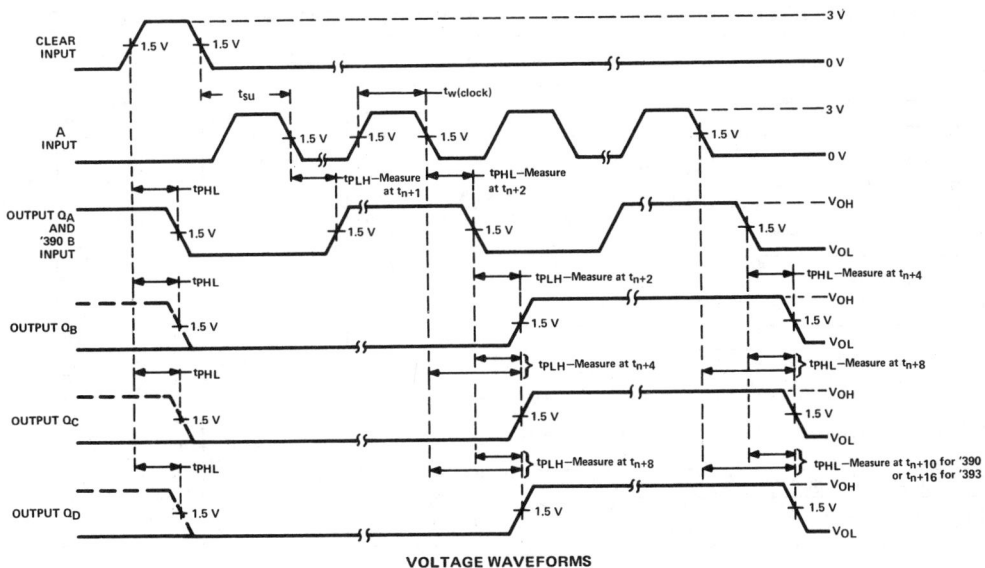

VOLTAGE WAVEFORMS

NOTE A: Input pulses are supplied by a generator having the following characteristics t_r ⩽ 5 ns, t_f ⩽ 5 ns, PRR = 1 MHz, duty cycle = 50%, Z_{out} ≈ 50 ohms.

FIGURE 1

TYPES SN54LS390, SN54LS393, SN74LS390, SN74LS393
DUAL 4-BIT DECADE AND BINARY COUNTERS

absolute maximum ratings over operating free-air temperature range (unless otherwise noted)

Supply voltage, V_{CC} (see Note 1) . . . . 7 V
Clear input voltage . . . . 7 V
Any A or B clock input voltage . . . . 5.5 V
Operating free-air temperature range: SN54LS390, SN54LS393 . . . . −55°C to 125°C
SN74LS390, SN74LS393 . . . . 0°C to 70°C
Storage temperature range . . . . −65°C to 150°C
NOTE 1: Voltage values are with respect to network ground terminal.

recommended operating conditions

			SN54LS390 SN54LS393			SN74LS390 SN74LS393			UNIT
			MIN	NOM	MAX	MIN	NOM	MAX	
Supply voltage, V_{CC}			4.5	5	5.5	4.75	5	5.25	V
High-level output current, I_{OH}					−400			−400	µA
Low-level output current, I_{OL}					4			8	mA
Count frequency, f_{count}	A input		0		25	0		25	MHz
	B input		0		20	0		20	
Pulse width, t_W	A input high or low		20			20			ns
	B input high or low		25			25			
	Clear high		20			20			
Clear inactive-state setup time, t_{su}			25↓			25↓			ns
Operating free-air temperature, T_A			−55		125	0		70	°C

↓ The arrow indicates that the falling edge of the clock pulse is used for reference.

electrical characteristics over recommended operating free-air temperature range (unless otherwise noted)

PARAMETER			TEST CONDITIONS[†]		SN54LS'			SN74LS'			UNIT
					MIN	TYP[‡]	MAX	MIN	TYP[‡]	MAX	
V_{IH}	High-level input voltage				2			2			V
V_{IL}	Low-level input voltage						0.7			0.8	V
V_{IK}	Input clamp voltage		V_{CC} = MIN,	I_I = −18 mA			−1.5			−1.5	V
V_{OH}	High-level output voltage		V_{CC} = MIN, V_{IH} = 2 V, V_{IL} = V_{IL}max, V_{OH} = −400 µA		2.5	3.4		2.7	3.4		V
V_{OL}	Low-level output voltage		V_{CC} = MIN, V_{IH} = 2 V, V_{IL} = 0.8 V,	I_{OL} = 4 mA¶		0.25	0.4		0.25	0.4	V
				I_{OL} = 8 mA¶					0.35	0.5	
I_I	Input current at maximum input voltage	Clear	V_{CC} = MAX	V_I = 7 V			0.1			0.1	mA
		Input A		V_I = 5.5 V			0.2			0.2	
		Input B					0.4			0.4	
I_{IH}	High-level input current	Clear	V_{CC} = MAX, V_I = 2.7 V				20			20	µA
		Input A					40			40	
		Input B					80			80	
I_{IL}	Low-level input current	Clear	V_{CC} = MAX, V_I = 0.4 V				−0.4			−0.4	mA
		Input A					−1.6			−1.6	
		Input B					−2.4			−2.4	
I_{OS}	Short-circuit output current§		V_{CC} = MAX		−20		−100	−20		−100	mA
I_{CC}	Supply current		V_{CC} = MAX, See Note 2	'LS390		15	26		15	26	mA
				'LS393		15	26		15	26	

†For conditions shown as MIN or MAX, use the appropriate value specified under recommended operating conditions.
‡All typical values are at V_{CC} = 5 V, T_A = 25°C.
¶The Q_A outputs of the 'LS390 are tested at I_{OL} = MAX plus the limit value for I_{IL} for the clock B input. This permits driving the clock B input while maintaining full fan-out capability.
§Not more than one output should be shorted at a time, and duration of the short-circuit should not exceed one second.
NOTE 2: I_{CC} is measured with all outputs open, both clear inputs grounded following momentary connection to 4.5 V, and all other inputs grounded.

TEXAS INSTRUMENTS
INCORPORATED
POST OFFICE BOX 5012 • DALLAS, TEXAS 75222

7

1076

TYPES SN54LS390, SN54LS393, SN74LS390, SN74LS393
DUAL 4-BIT DECADE AND BINARY COUNTERS

switching characteristics, V_{CC} = 5 V, T_A = 25°C

PARAMETER¶	FROM (INPUT)	TO (OUTPUT)	TEST CONDITIONS	'LS390 MIN	'LS390 TYP	'LS390 MAX	'LS393 MIN	'LS393 TYP	'LS393 MAX	UNIT
f_{max}	A	Q_A		25	35		25	35		MHz
	B	Q_B		20	30					
t_{PLH}	A	Q_A			12	20		12	20	ns
t_{PHL}					13	20		13	20	
t_{PLH}	A	Q_C of 'LS390	C_L = 15 pF,		37	60		40	60	ns
t_{PHL}		Q_D of 'LS393	R_L = 2 kΩ,		39	60		40	60	
t_{PLH}	B	Q_B	See Note 4 and Figure 2		13	21				ns
t_{PHL}					14	21				
t_{PLH}	B	Q_C			24	39				ns
t_{PHL}					26	39				
t_{PLH}	B	Q_D			13	21				ns
t_{PHL}					14	21				
t_{PHL}	Clear	Any			24	39		24	39	ns

¶ f_{max} ≡ maximum count frequency
t_{PLH} ≡ propagation delay time, low-to-high-level output
t_{PHL} ≡ propagation delay time, high-to-low-level output
NOTE 4: Load circuit is shown on page 3-11.

PARAMETER MEASUREMENT INFORMATION

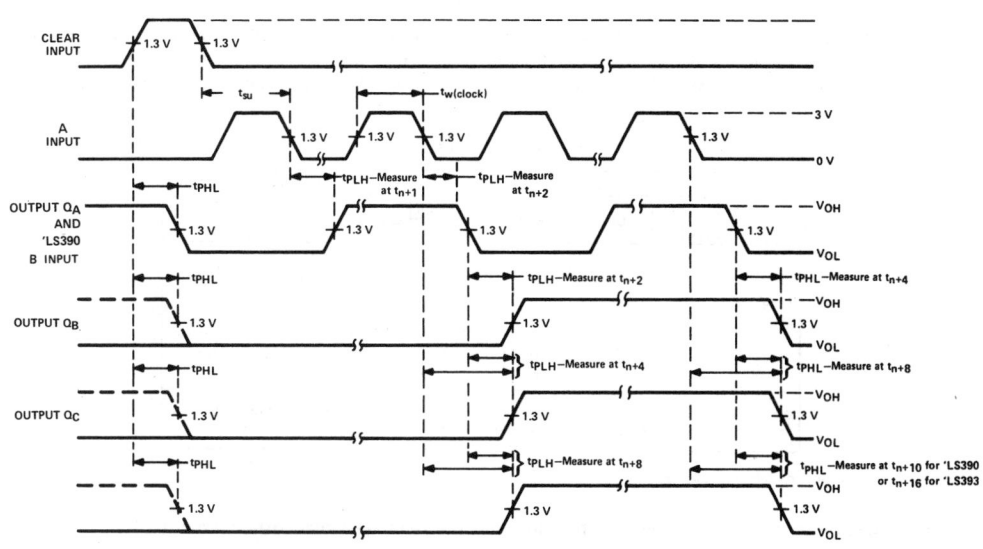

VOLTAGE WAVEFORMS

NOTE A: Input pulses are supplied by a generator having the following characteristics t_r ≤ 15 ns, t_f ≤ 6 ns, PRR = 1 MHz, duty cycle = 50%, Z_{out} ≈ 50 ohms.

1076

TEXAS INSTRUMENTS
INCORPORATED
POST OFFICE BOX 5012 • DALLAS, TEXAS 75222

TYPES SN54LS395A, SN74LS395A
4-BIT CASCADABLE SHIFT REGISTERS WITH 3-STATE OUTPUTS

BULLETIN NO. DL-S 7712114, OCTOBER 1976–REVISED AUGUST 1977

- Three-State, 4 Bit, Cascadable, Parallel-In, Parallel-Out Registers

- 'LS395A Offers Three Times the Sink-Current Capability of 'LS395

- Low Power Dissipation . . . 75 mW Typical (Enabled)

- Applications:
  N-Bit Serial-To-Parallel Converter
  N-Bit Parallel-To-Serial Converter
  N-Bit Storage Register

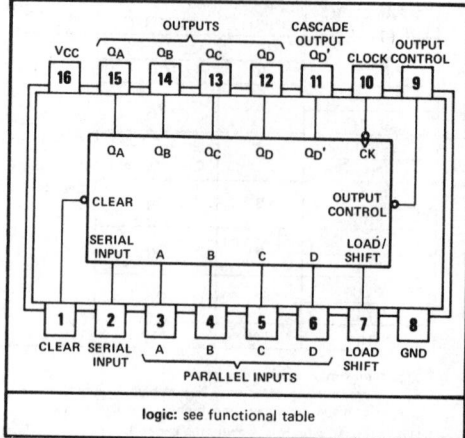

SN54LS395A . . . J OR W PACKAGE
SN74LS395A . . . J OR N PACKAGE
(TOP VIEW)

logic: see functional table

description

These 4-bit registers feature parallel inputs, parallel outputs, and clock, serial, load/shift, output control and direct overriding clear inputs.

Shifting is accomplished when the load/shift control is low. Parallel loading is accomplished by applying the four bits of data and taking the load/shift control input high. The data is loaded into the associated flip-flops and appears at the outputs after the high-to-low transition of the clock input. During parallel loading, the entry of serial data is inhibited.

When the output control is low, the normal logic levels of the four outputs are available for driving the loads or bus lines. The outputs are disabled independently from the level of the clock by a high logic level at the output control input. The outputs then present a high impedance and neither load nor drive the bus line; however, sequential operation of the registers is not affected. During the high-impedance mode, the output at Q_D' is still available for cascading.

FUNCTION TABLE

INPUTS								3-STATE OUTPUTS				CASCADE OUTPUT
CLEAR	LOAD/SHIFT CONTROL	CLOCK	SERIAL	\multicolumn{4}{c}{PARALLEL}						
				A	B	C	D	Q_A	Q_B	Q_C	Q_D	Q_D'
L	X	X	X	X	X	X	X	L	L	L	L	L
H	H	H	X	X	X	X	X	Q_{A0}	Q_{B0}	Q_{C0}	Q_{D0}	Q_{D0}
H	H	↓	X	a	b	c	d	a	b	c	d	d
H	L	H	X	X	X	X	X	Q_{A0}	Q_{B0}	Q_{C0}	Q_{D0}	Q_{D0}
H	L	↓	H	X	X	X	X	H	Q_{An}	Q_{Bn}	Q_{Cn}	Q_{Cn}
H	L	↓	L	X	X	X	X	L	Q_{An}	Q_{Bn}	Q_{Cn}	Q_{Cn}

When the output control is high, the 3-state outputs are disabled to the high-impedance state; however, sequential operation of the registers and the output at Q_D' are not affected.

See explanation of function tables on page 3-8.

absolute maximum ratings over operating free-air temperature range (unless otherwise noted)

Supply voltage, V_{CC} (see Note 1)	7 V
Input voltage	7 V
Operating free-air temperature range: SN54LS395A	−55°C to 125°C
SN74LS395A	0°C to 70°C
Storage temperature range	−65°C to 150°C

NOTE 1: Voltage values are with respect to network ground terminal.

TEXAS INSTRUMENTS
INCORPORATED
POST OFFICE BOX 5012 • DALLAS, TEXAS 75222

recommended operating conditions

		SN54LS395A			SN74LS395A			UNIT
		MIN	NOM	MAX	MIN	NOM	MAX	
Supply voltage, V_{CC}		4.5	5	5.5	4.75	5	5.25	V
High-level output current, I_{OH}	Q_A, Q_B, Q_C, Q_D			−1			−2.6	mA
	Q_D'			−400			−400	μA
Low-level output current, I_{OL}	Q_A, Q_B, Q_C, Q_D			12			24	mA
	Q_D'			4			8	mA
Clock frequency, f_{clock}		0		25	0		25	MHz
Width of clock pulse, $t_{w(clock)}$		25			25			ns
Setup time, high-level or low-level data, t_{su}		20			20			ns
Hold time, high-level or low-level data, t_h		10			10			ns
Operating free-air temperature, T_A		−55		125	0		70	°C

electrical characteristics over recommended operating free-air temperature range (unless otherwise noted)

PARAMETER		TEST CONDITIONS[†]			SN54LS395A			SN74LS395A			UNIT
					MIN	TYP[‡]	MAX	MIN	TYP[‡]	MAX	
V_{IH}	High-level input voltage				2			2			V
V_{IL}	Low-level input voltage						0.7			0.8	V
V_{IK}	Input clamp voltage	V_{CC} = MIN,	I_I = −18 mA				−1.5			−1.5	V
V_{OH}	High-level output voltage	V_{CC} = MIN, V_{IH} = 2 V, V_{IL} = V_{IL} max, I_{OH} = MAX	Q_A, Q_B, Q_C, Q_D		2.4	3.4		2.4	3.1		V
			Q_D'		2.5	3.4		2.7	3.4		V
V_{OL}	Low-level output voltage	V_{CC} = MIN, V_{IL} = V_{IL} max, V_{IH} = 2 V	Q_A, Q_B, Q_C, Q_D I_{OL} = 12 mA			0.25	0.4		0.25	0.4	V
			I_{OL} = 24 mA						0.35	0.5	
			Q_D' I_{OL} = 4 mA			0.25	0.4		0.25	0.4	V
			I_{OL} = 8 mA						0.35	0.5	
I_{OZH}	Off-state output current, high-level voltage applied	V_{CC} = MAX, V_O = 2.7 V	V_{IH} = 2 V, Q_A, Q_B, Q_C, Q_D				20			20	μA
I_{OZL}	Off-state output current, low-level voltage applied	V_{CC} = MAX, V_O = 0.4 V	V_{IH} = 2 V, Q_A, Q_B, Q_C, Q_D				−20			−20	μA
I_I	Input current at maximum input voltage	V_{CC} = MAX,	V_I = 7 V				0.1			0.1	mA
I_{IH}	High-level input current	V_{CC} = MAX,	V_I = 2.7 V				20			20	μA
I_{IL}	Low-level input current	V_{CC} = MAX,	V_I = 0.4 V				−0.4			−0.4	mA
I_{OS}	Short-circuit output current[§]	V_{CC} = MAX	Q_A, Q_B, Q_C, Q_D		−30		−130	−30		−130	mA
			Q_D'		−20		−100	−20		−100	mA
I_{CC}	Supply current	V_{CC} = MAX,	See Note 2	Condition A		22	34		22	34	mA
				Condition B		21	31		21	31	

[†] For conditions shown as MIN or MAX, use the appropriate value specified under recommended operating conditions.

[‡] All typical values are at V_{CC} = 5 V, T_A = 25°C.

[§] Not more than one output should be shorted at a time, and duration of the short-circuit should not exceed one second.

NOTE 2: I_{CC} is measured with the outputs open, the serial input and mode control at 4.5 V, and the data inputs grounded under the following conditions:

    A. Output control at 4.5 V and a momentary 3 V, then ground, applied to clock input.

    ·B. Output control and clock input grounded.

TEXAS INSTRUMENTS
INCORPORATED
POST OFFICE BOX 5012 • DALLAS, TEXAS 75222

TYPES SN54LS395A, SN74LS395A
4-BIT CASCADABLE SHIFT REGISTERS WITH 3-STATE OUTPUTS

REVISED AUGUST 1977

switching characteristics, $V_{CC} = 5$ V, $T_A = 25°C$

	PARAMETER	TEST CONDITIONS	MIN	TYP	MAX	UNIT
f_{max}	Maximum clock frequency	See Note 3,	30	45		MHz
t_{PHL}	Propagation delay time, high-to-low-level output from clear	Q_A, Q_B, Q_C, Q_D outputs:		22	35	ns
t_{PLH}	Propagation delay time, low-to-high-level output	$R_L = 667$ Ω, $C_L = 45$ pF		15	30	ns
t_{PHL}	Propagation delay time, high-to-low-level output			20	30	ns
t_{PZH}	Output enable time to high level	Q_D' output:		15	25	ns
t_{PZL}	Output enable time to low level	$R_L = 2$ kΩ, $C_L = 15$ pF		17	25	ns
t_{PHZ}	Output disable time from high level	$C_L = 5$ pF,		11	17	ns
t_{PLZ}	Output disable time from low level	See Note 3		12	20	ns

NOTE 3: Load circuit and voltage waveforms are shown on page 3-11.

functional block diagram

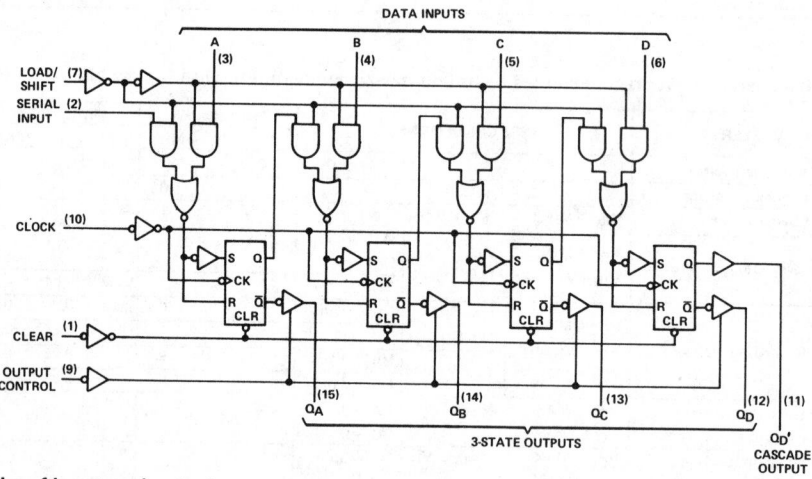

schematics of inputs and outputs

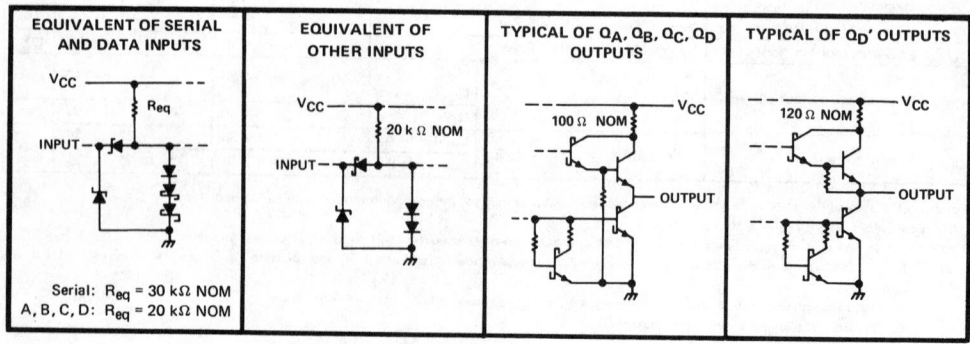

7

TEXAS INSTRUMENTS
INCORPORATED
POST OFFICE BOX 5012 • DALLAS, TEXAS 75222

87

TYPES SN54LS398, SN54LS399
SN74LS398, SN74LS399
QUADRUPLE 2-INPUT MULTIPLEXERS WITH STORAGE

BULLETIN NO. DL-S 7712465, OCTOBER 1976—REVISED AUGUST 1977

- Double-Rail Outputs on 'LS398

- Single-Rail Outputs on 'LS399

- 'LS398 is Similar to 'LS298,
  Which Has Inverted Clock

- Selects One of Two 4-Bit Data Sources
  and Stores Data Synchronously with System Clock

- Applications:
  Dual Source for Operands and Constants
  in Arithmetic Processor; Can Release
  Processor Register Files for Acquiring
  New Data

  Implement Separate Registers Capable of
  Parallel Exchange of Contents Yet Retain
  External Load Capability

  Universal Type Register for Implementing
  Various Shift Patterns; Even Has Compound
  Left-Right Capabilities

SN54LS398 . . . J OR W PACKAGE
SN74LS398 . . . J OR N PACKAGE
(TOP VIEW)

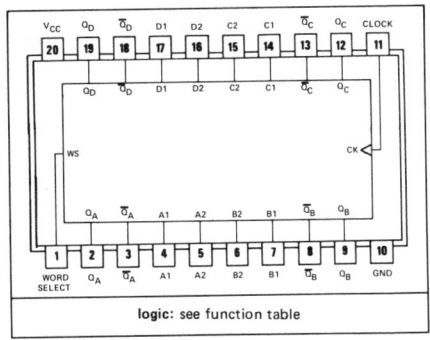

logic: see function table

SN54LS399 . . . J OR W PACKAGE
SN74LS399 . . . J OR N PACKAGE
(TOP VIEW)

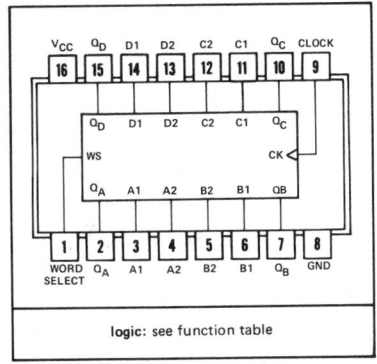

logic: see function table

description

These monolithic quadruple two-input multiplexers
with storage provide essentially the equivalent functional capabilities of two separate MSI functions
(SN54LS157/SN74LS157 and SN54LS175/
SN74LS175) in a single 16-pin or 20-pin package.

When the word-select input is low, word 1 (A1, B1,
C1, D1) is applied to the flip-flops. A high input to
word select will cause the selection of word 2 (A2,
B2, C2, D2). The selected word is clocked to the
output terminals on the positive-going edge of the
clock pulse.

Typical power dissipation is 37 milliwatts.
SN54LS398 and SN54LS399 are characterized for
operation over the full military range of −55°C to
125°C, SN74LS398 and SN74LS399 are characterized for operation from 0°C to 70°C.

FUNCTION TABLE

INPUTS		OUTPUTS			
WORD SELECT	CLOCK	Q_A	Q_B	Q_C	Q_D
L	↑	a1	b1	c1	d1
H	↑	a2	b2	c2	d2
X	L	Q_{A0}	Q_{B0}	Q_{C0}	Q_{D0}

See explanation of function tables on page 3-8.

TEXAS INSTRUMENTS
INCORPORATED
POST OFFICE BOX 5012 • DALLAS, TEXAS 75222

TYPES SN54LS398, SN54LS399, SN74LS398, SN74LS399
QUADRUPLE 2-INPUT MULTIPLEXERS WITH STORAGE

functional block diagram

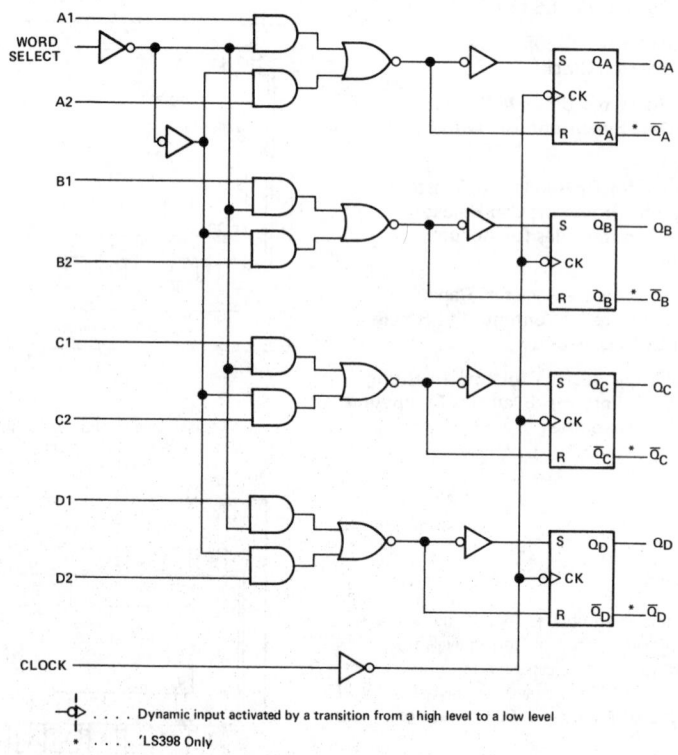

⎯◁— . . . . Dynamic input activated by a transition from a high level to a low level

* . . . . 'LS398 Only

schematics of inputs and outputs

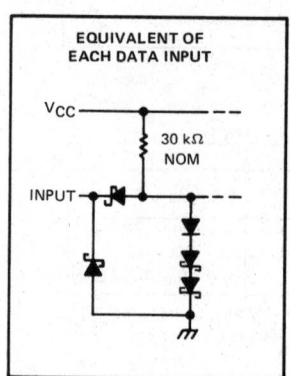

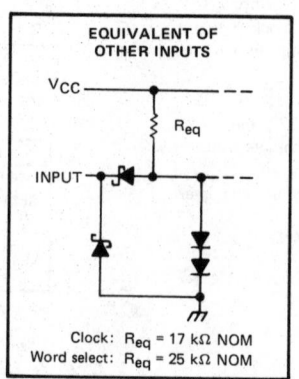

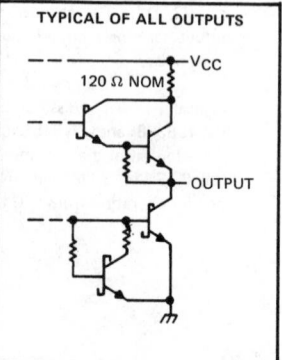

TEXAS INSTRUMENTS
INCORPORATED
POST OFFICE BOX 5012 • DALLAS, TEXAS 75222

1076

TYPES SN54LS398, SN54LS399, SN74LS398, SN74LS399
QUADRUPLE 2-INPUT MULTIPLEXERS WITH STORAGE

absolute maximum ratings over operating free-air temperature range (unless otherwise noted)

Supply voltage, V_{CC} (see Note 1) . . . . 7 V
Input voltage . . . . 7 V
Operating free-air temperature range: SN54LS' . . . . $-55°$C to $125°$C
　　　　　　　　　　　　　　　　　SN74LS' . . . . $0°$C to $70°$C
Storage temperature range . . . . $-65°$C to $150°$C

NOTE 1: Voltage values are with respect to network ground terminal.

recommended operating conditions

		SN54LS'			SN74LS'			UNIT
		MIN	NOM	MAX	MIN	NOM	MAX	
Supply voltage, V_{CC}		4.5	5	5.5	4.75	5	5.25	V
High-level output current, I_{OH}				−400			−400	µA
Low-level output current, I_{OL}				4			8	mA
Width of clock pulse, high or low level, t_W		20			20			ns
Setup time, t_{su}	Data	20			20			ns
	Word select	25			25			
Hold time, t_h	Data	0			0			ns
	Word select	0			0			
Operating free-air temperature, T_A		−55		125	0		70	°C

electrical characteristics over recommended operating free-air temperature range (unless otherwise noted)

PARAMETER		TEST CONDITIONS†		SN54LS'			SN74LS'			UNIT
				MIN	TYP‡	MAX	MIN	TYP‡	MAX	
V_{IH}	High-level input voltage			2			2			V
V_{IL}	Low-level input voltage					0.7			0.8	V
V_{IK}	Input clamp voltage	V_{CC} = MIN,	I_I = −18 mA			−1.5			−1.5	V
V_{OH}	High-level output voltage	V_{CC} = MIN, V_{IH} = 2 V, $V_{IL} = V_{IL}$max	$I_{OH} = -400\,\mu A$	2.5	3.4		2.7	3.4		V
V_{OL}	Low-level output voltage	V_{CC} = MIN, V_{IH} = 2 V, $V_{IL} = V_{IL}$max	I_{OL} = 4 mA	0.25	0.4		0.25	0.4		V
			I_{OL} = 8 mA					0.35	0.5	
I_I	Input current at maximum input voltage	V_{CC} = MAX,	V_I = 7 V			0.1			0.1	mA
I_{IH}	High-level input current	V_{CC} = MAX,	V_I = 2.7 V			20			20	µA
I_{IL}	Low-level input current	V_{CC} = MAX,	V_I = 0.4 V			−0.4			−0.4	mA
I_{OS}	Short-circuit output current§	V_{CC} = MAX		−20		−100	−20		−100	mA
I_{CC}	Supply current	V_{CC} = MAX,	See Note 2		7.3	13		7.3	13	mA

† For conditions shown as MIN or MAX, use the appropriate value specified under recommended operating conditions.
‡ All typical values are at V_{CC} = 5 V, T_A = 25°C.
§ Not more than one output should be shorted at a time, duration of the short-circuit should not exceed one second
NOTE 2: With all outputs open and all inputs except clock low, I_{CC} is measured after applying a momentary 4.5 V, followed by ground, to the clock input.

switching characteristics, V_{CC} = 5 V, T_A = 25°C

PARAMETER		TEST CONDITIONS	MIN	TYP	MAX	UNIT
t_{PLH}	Propagation delay time, low-to-high-level output	C_L = 15 pF, R_L = 2 kΩ, See Note 3		18	27	ns
t_{PHL}	Propagation delay time, high-to-low-level output			21	32	

NOTE 3: Load circuit and waveforms are shown on page 3-11.

TEXAS INSTRUMENTS
INCORPORATED
POST OFFICE BOX 5012 • DALLAS, TEXAS 75222

7

TTL
MSI

TYPES SN54S412, SN74S412 (TIM8212)
MULTI-MODE BUFFERED LATCHES

BULLETIN NO. DL-S 7512351, OCTOBER 1975

- **P-N-P Inputs and 3-State Outputs Maximize I/O and Data Bus Capabilities**
- **Data Latch Transparency Permits Asynchronous or Latched Receiver Modes**
- **Mode and Select Inputs Permit Storing With Outputs Enabled or Disabled**
- **Strobe-Controlled Flag Flip-Flop Indicates Status or Interrupt**
- **Asynchronous Clear Sets All Eight Data Lines Low and Initializes Status Flag**
- **High-Level Output Voltage, Typically 4 V, Drives Most MOS Functions Directly**
- **Direct Replacement for Intel 3212 or 8212**

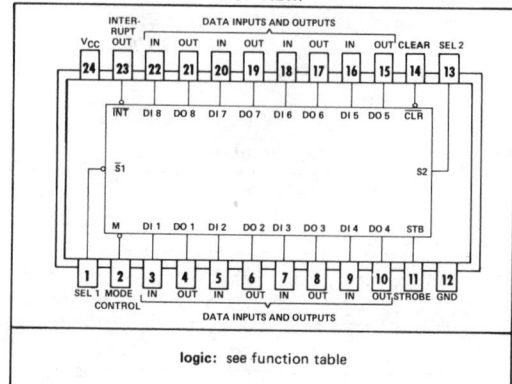

SN54S412 . . . J PACKAGE
SN74S412 . . . J OR N PACKAGE
(TOP VIEW)

logic: see function table

description

This high-performance eight-bit parallel expandable buffer register incorporates package and mode selection inputs and an edge-triggered status flip-flop designed specifically for implementing bus-organized input/output ports. The three-state data outputs can be connected to a common data bus and controlled from the appropriate select inputs to receive or transmit data. An integral status flip-flop provides package busy or request interrupt commands. The outputs, with a 4-volt typical high-level voltage, are compatible for driving low-threshold MOS directly.

DATA LATCHES

The eight data latches are fully transparent when the internal gate enable, G, input is high and the outputs are enabled (OE = H). Latch transparency is selected by the mode control (M), select ($\overline{S1}$ and S2), and the strobe (STB) inputs and during transparency each data output (DO_i) follows its respective data input (DI_i). This mode of operation can be terminated by clearing, de-selecting, or holding the data latches. See data latches function table.

MODE SELECTION

An input mode or an output mode is selectable from this single input line. In the input mode, MD = L, the eight data latch inputs are enabled when the strobe is high regardless of device selection. If selected during an input mode, the outputs will follow the data inputs. When the strobe input is taken low, the latches will store the most-recently setup data.

In the output mode, M = H, the output buffers are enabled regardless of any other control input. During the output mode the content of the register is under control of the select ($\overline{S1}$ and S2) inputs. See data latches function table.

STATUS FLIP-FLOP

The status flip-flop provides a low-level output signal when:

a. the package is selected

b. a strobe input is received.

This status signal can be used to indicate that the register is busy or to initiate an interrupt type command.

TEXAS INSTRUMENTS
INCORPORATED
POST OFFICE BOX 5012 • DALLAS, TEXAS 75222

1076

functional block diagram

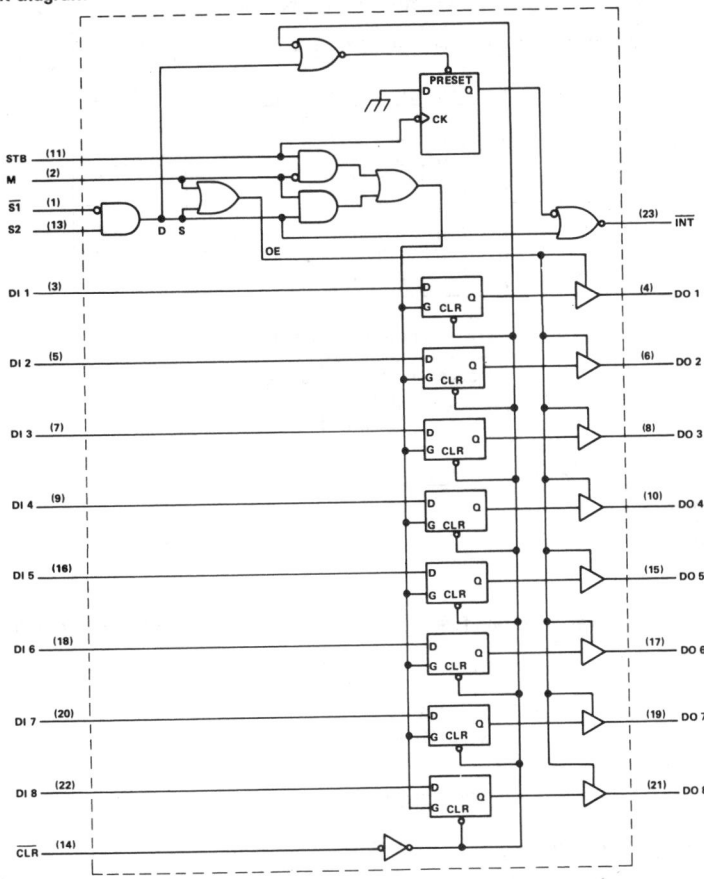

schematics of inputs and outputs

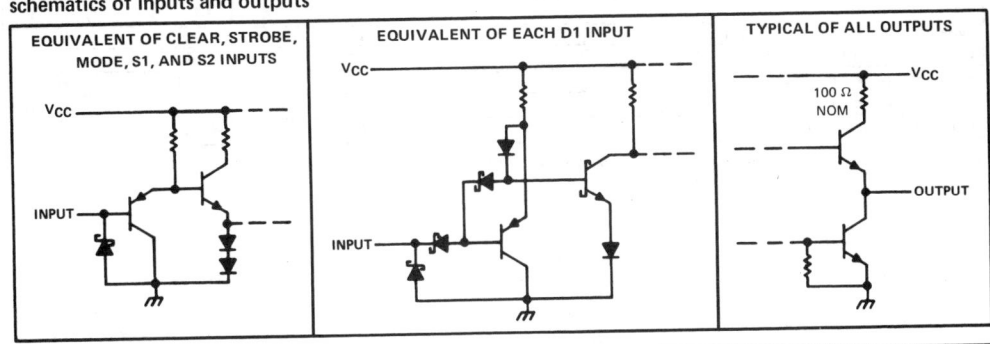

| EQUIVALENT OF CLEAR, STROBE, MODE, S1, AND S2 INPUTS | EQUIVALENT OF EACH D1 INPUT | TYPICAL OF ALL OUTPUTS |

7

TEXAS INSTRUMENTS
INCORPORATED
POST OFFICE BOX 5012 • DALLAS, TEXAS 75222

DATA LATCHES FUNCTION TABLE

FUNCTION	CLEAR	M	$\overline{S1}$	S2	STB	DATA IN	DATA OUT
Clear	L	H	H	X	X	X	L
	L	L	L	H	L	X	L
De-select	X	L	X	L	X	X	Z
	X	L	X	H	X	X	Z
Hold	H	H	H	L	X	X	Q_O
	H	L	L	H	L	X	Q_O
Data Bus	H	H	L	H	X	L	L
	H	H	L	H	X	H	H
Data Bus	H	L	L	H	H	L	L
	H	L	L	H	H	H	H

STATUS FLIP-FLOP FUNCTION TABLE

CLEAR	$\overline{S1}$	S2	STB	$\overline{INT}$
L	H	X	X	H
L	X	L	X	H
H	X	X	↓	L
H	L	H	X	L

H ≡ high level (steady state)
L ≡ low level (steady state)
X ≡ irrelevant (any input, including transitions)
Z ≡ high impedance (off)
↓ ≡ transition from low to high level

absolute maximum ratings over operating free-air temperature range (unless otherwise noted)

Supply voltage, V_{CC} (see Note 1) . . . . 7 V
Input voltage . . . . 5.5 V
Operating free-air temperature range: SN54S412 . . . . −55°C to 125°C
SN74S412 . . . . 0°C to 70°C
Storage temperature range . . . . −65°C to 150°C

NOTE 1: Voltage values are with respect to network ground terminal.

recommended operating conditions

		SN54S412 MIN	NOM	MAX	SN74S412 MIN	NOM	MAX	UNIT
Supply voltage, V_{CC}		4.5	5	5.5	4.75	5	5.25	V
Pulse width, t_W	STB or $\overline{S1} \cdot S2$	25			25			ns
(see Figures 1, 2, and 4)	Clear low	25			25			
Setup time, t_{su} (see Figure 3)		15↓			15↓			ns
Hold time, t_h (see Figures 1 and 3)		20↓			20↓			ns
Operating free-air temperature, T_A		−55		125	0		70	°C

↓ The arrow indicates that the falling edge of the clock pulse is used for reference.

TEXAS INSTRUMENTS
INCORPORATED
POST OFFICE BOX 5012 • DALLAS, TEXAS 75222

electrical characteristics over recommended operating free-air temperature range (unless otherwise noted)

PARAMETER		TEST CONDITIONS†	SN54S412 MIN	SN54S412 TYP‡	SN54S412 MAX	SN74S412 MIN	SN74S412 TYP‡	SN74S412 MAX	UNIT
V_{IH}	High-level input voltage		2			2			V
V_{IL}	Low-level input voltage				0.85			0.85	V
V_{IK}	Input clamp voltage	V_{CC} = MIN; I_I = −18 mA			−1.2			−1.2	V
V_{OH}	High-level output voltage	V_{CC} = MIN, V_{IH} = 2 V, V_{IL} = 0.8 V, I_{OH} = −1 mA	3.65	4		3.65	4		V
V_{OL}	Low-level output voltage	V_{CC} = MIN, V_{IH} = 2 V, V_{IL} = 0.8 V — I_{OL} = 15 mA			0.45			0.45	V
		I_{OL} = 20 mA			0.5			0.5	
I_{OZH}	Off-state output current, high-level voltage applied — DO 1 thru DO 8	V_{CC} = MAX, V_O = 2.4 V			50			50	μA
I_{OZL}	Off-state output current, low-level voltage applied — DO 1 thru DO 8	V_{CC} = MAX, V_O = 0.5 V			−50			−50	μA
I_I	Input current at maximum input voltage	V_{CC} = MAX, V_I = 5.5 V			1			1	mA
I_{IH}	High-level input current	V_{CC} = MAX, V_I = 5.25 V			20			10	μA
I_{IL}	Low-level input current — $\overline{S}1$	V_{CC} = MAX, V_I = 0.4 V			−1			−1	mA
	Low-level input current — M				−0.75			−0.75	
	Low-level input current — All others				−0.25			−0.25	
I_{OS}	Short-circuit output current §	V_{CC} = MAX	−20		−65	−20		−65	mA
I_{CC}	Supply current	V_{CC} = MAX, see Note 2		82			82	130	mA

† For conditions shown as MIN or MAX, use the appropriate value specified under recommended operating conditions.

‡ All typical values are at V_{CC} = 5 V, T_A = 25°C.

§ Not more than one output should be shorted at a time.

NOTE 2: I_{CC} is measured with all outputs open, clear input at 4.5 V, and all other inputs grounded.

switching characteristics, V_{CC} = 5 V, T_A = 25°C

PARAMETER	FROM	TO	FIGURE	TEST CONDITIONS	MIN	TYP	MAX	UNIT
t_{PLH}	STB, $\overline{S}1$, or S2	Any DO	1	C_L = 30 pF, See Note 3		18	27	ns
t_{PHL}						15	25	
t_{PHL}	$\overline{CLR}$	Any DO	2			18	27	ns
t_{PLH}	DI_i	DO_i	3			12	20	ns
t_{PHL}						10	20	
t_{PLH}	$\overline{S}1$ or S2	$\overline{INT}$	4	C_L = 30 pF, See Note 3		12	20	ns
t_{PHL}	STB	$\overline{INT}$	4			16	25	
t_{ZH}	$\overline{S}1$, S2, or M	Any DO	5	C_L = 30 pF, See Note 3		21	35	ns
t_{ZL}						25	40	
t_{HZ}	$\overline{S}1$, S2, or M	Any DO	5	C_L = 5 pF, See Note 3		9	20	ns
t_{LZ}						12	20	

$t_{PLH} \equiv$ propagation delay time, low-to-high-level output
$t_{PHL} \equiv$ propagation delay time, high-to-low-level output
$t_{ZH} \equiv$ output enable time to high level
$t_{ZL} \equiv$ output enable time to low level
$t_{HZ} \equiv$ output disable time from high level
$t_{LZ} \equiv$ output disable time from low level

NOTE 3: Load circuit and voltage waveforms are shown on page 3-10.

TYPES SN54S412, SN74S412 (TIM8212)
MULTI-MODE BUFFERED LATCHES

PARAMETER MEASUREMENT INFORMATION

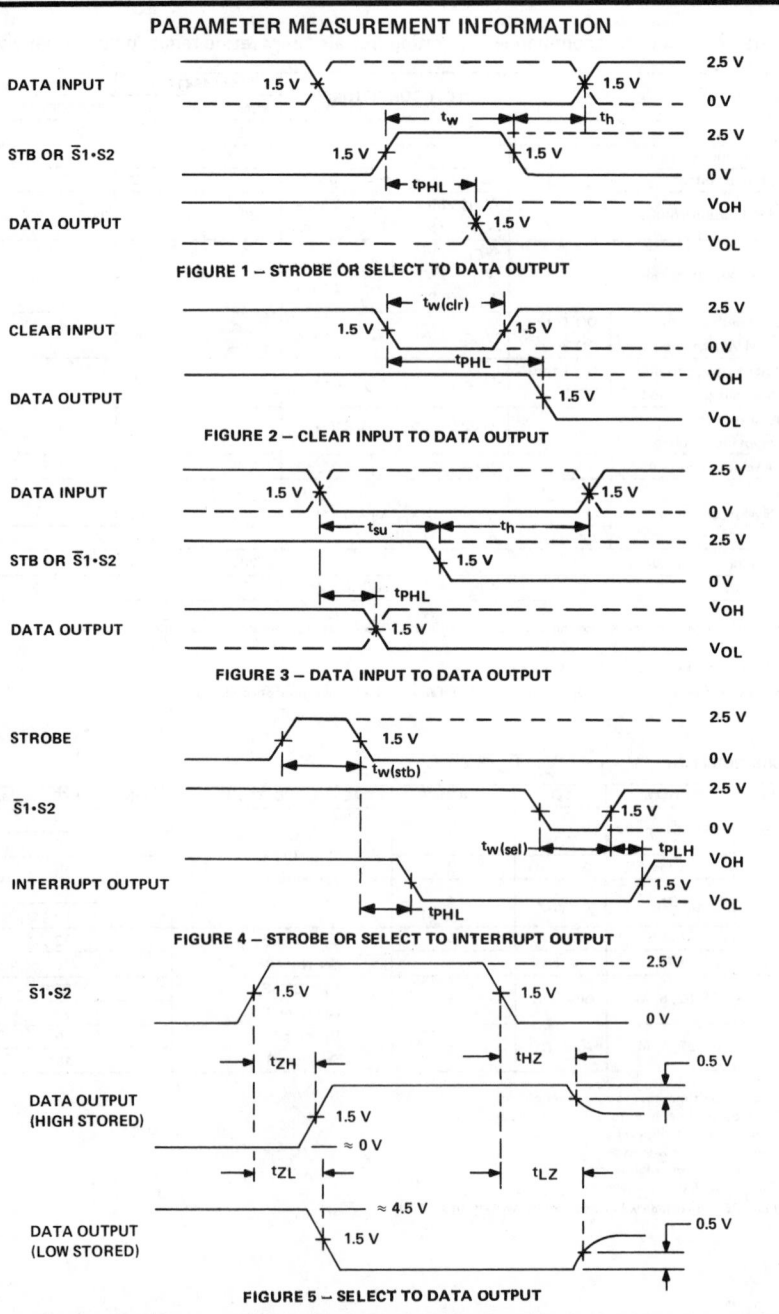

FIGURE 1 – STROBE OR SELECT TO DATA OUTPUT

FIGURE 2 – CLEAR INPUT TO DATA OUTPUT

FIGURE 3 – DATA INPUT TO DATA OUTPUT

FIGURE 4 – STROBE OR SELECT TO INTERRUPT OUTPUT

FIGURE 5 – SELECT TO DATA OUTPUT

TEXAS INSTRUMENTS
INCORPORATED
POST OFFICE BOX 5012 • DALLAS, TEXAS 75222

1075

TTL
MSI

TYPE SN74LS424 (TIM8224)
TWO-PHASE CLOCK GENERATOR/DRIVER

BULLETIN NO. DL-S 7712475, OCTOBER 1976—REVISED AUGUST 1977

- Designed to be Interchangeable With Intel 8224

- Single-Chip Clock Driver With Self-Contained Oscillator

- Specifically Designed to Drive All 8080A Microprocessors

description

This clock generator is capable of driving 12-volt lines. It contains a crystal-controlled oscillator, a divide-by-nine clock phase generator, two high-level drivers, and auxiliary circuitry.

The internal oscillator is designed to operate with fundamental-mode crystals, or with overtone-mode crystals when using a parallel-tuned circuit connected to the tank terminal, pin 13. The oscillator output appears on pin 12 and drives the divide-by-nine counter. The ÷9 clock phase generator output consists of phases $\phi2$ for driving MOS inputs and $\phi2$ TTL for driving TTL. Three other TTL outputs, status strobe, reset, and ready, are coupled to the divide-by-nine counter. A sync input from the 8080A is AND'ed with $\phi1A$ to produce the status strobe. The power-on reset also generates the status strobe signal through an output NOR gate. The reset input works on a voltage-level basis by use of a Schmitt

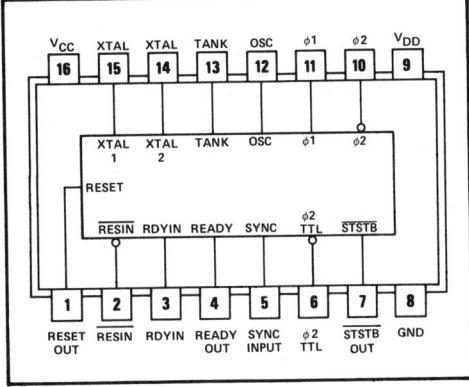

J OR N PACKAGE
(TOP VIEW)

trigger. A rising voltage waveform is triggered at a particular voltage. A synchronized ready output is obtained by clocking with a $\phi2$ signal.

The SN74LS424 is characterized for operation over the temperature range of $0°C$ to $70°C$.

functional block diagram

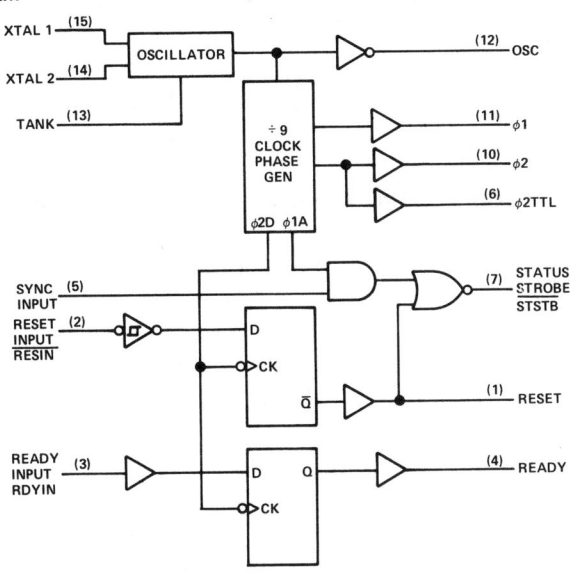

TEXAS INSTRUMENTS
INCORPORATED
POST OFFICE BOX 5012 • DALLAS, TEXAS 75222

TYPE SN74LS424 (TIM8224)
TWO-PHASE CLOCK GENERATOR/DRIVER

schematics of inputs and outputs

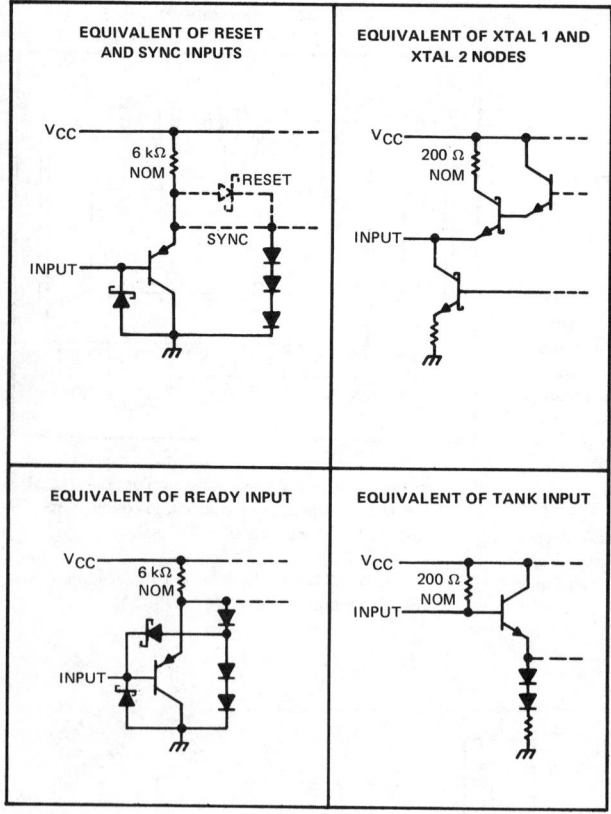

EQUIVALENT OF RESET AND SYNC INPUTS

EQUIVALENT OF XTAL 1 AND XTAL 2 NODES

EQUIVALENT OF READY INPUT

EQUIVALENT OF TANK INPUT

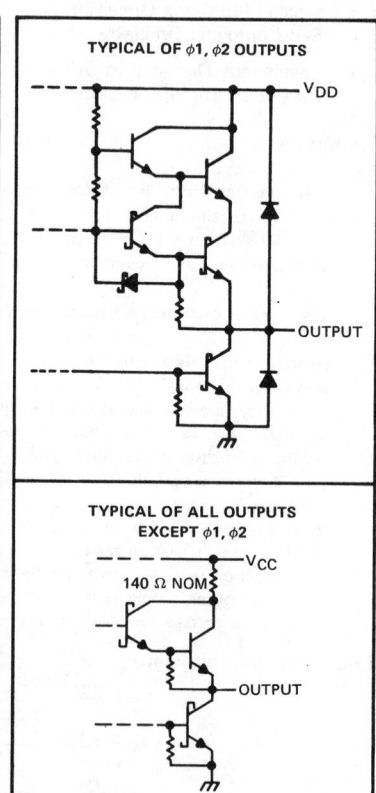

TYPICAL OF φ1, φ2 OUTPUTS

TYPICAL OF ALL OUTPUTS EXCEPT φ1, φ2

absolute maximum ratings over operating free-air temperature range (unless otherwise noted)

Supply voltage, V_{CC} (see Note 1)	7 V
Supply voltage, V_{DD}	17 V
Input voltages (sync, reset, ready)	7 V
Operating free-air temperature range, T_A	0°C to 70°C
Storage temperature range	−65°C to 150°C

NOTE 1: Voltage values are with respect to network ground terminal.

TEXAS INSTRUMENTS
INCORPORATED
POST OFFICE BOX 5012 • DALLAS, TEXAS 75222

1076

recommended operating conditions

	MIN	NOM	MAX	UNIT
Supply voltage, V_{CC}	4.75	5	5.25	V
Supply voltage, V_{DD}	11.4	12	12.6	V
Ready input setup time, t_{su}(RDYIN)	$50 - \dfrac{4t_c}{9}$			ns
Ready input hold time, t_h(RDYIN)	$\dfrac{4t_c}{9}$			ns
Operating free-air temperature range, T_A	0	25	70	°C

electrical characteristics over recommended operating free-air temperature range (unless otherwise noted)

PARAMETER			TEST CONDITIONS		MIN	TYP[‡]	MAX	UNIT
V_{IH}	High-level input voltage	Reset input			2.6			V
		All others			2			
V_{IL}	Low-level input voltage						0.8	V
$V_{T+} - V_{T-}$	Hysteresis	Reset input			0.25			V
V_{IK}	Input clamp voltage		V_{CC} = 4.75 V, V_{DD} = 11.4 V	I_I = −5 mA			−1	V
				I_I = −18 mA			−1.5	
V_{OH}	High-level output voltage	$\phi 1, \phi 2$	V_{CC} = 4.75 V, V_{DD} = 11.6 V	I_{OH} = −100 μA	9.4	10.4		V
		Ready, reset			3.6	3.9		
		Others		I_{OH} = −1 mA	2.4	3.1		
V_{OL}	Low-level output voltage	$\phi 1, \phi 2$, reset, status strobe	V_{CC} = 4.75 V, V_{DD} = 11.4 V	I_{OL} = 2.5 mA		0.2	0.45	V
		$\phi 2$ TTL, osc		I_{OL} = 15 mA		0.25	0.45	
I_I	Input current at maximum input voltage		V_{CC} = 5.25 V, V_{DD} = 12.6 V, V_I = 7 V				100	μA
I_{IH}	High-level input current		V_{CC} = 5.25 V, V_{DD} = 12.6 V, V_I = 5.25 V				10	μA
I_{IL}	Low-level input current		V_{CC} = 5.25 V, V_{DD} = 12.6 V, V_I = 0.4 V				−0.25	mA
I_{OS}	Short-circuit circuit current[§]	All except $\phi 1, \phi 2$	V_{CC} = 5 V, V_{DD} = 12 V		−10		−60	mA
I_{CC}	Supply current from V_{CC}		V_{CC} = 5.25 V, V_{DD} = 12 V			70	115	mA
I_{DD}	Supply current from V_{DD}		V_{DD} = 12.6 V, V_{CC} = 5 V,	See Note 2		6	12	mA
C_i	Input capacitance		V_{CC} = 5 V, V_{DD} = 12 V, V_I = 2.5 V, f = 1 MHz,	See Note 2			8	pF

[‡]All typical values are at V_{CC} = 5 V, V_{DD} = 12 V, T_A = 25°C.
[§]Not more than one output should be shorted at a time. $\phi 1$ and $\phi 2$ do not have short-circuit protection.
NOTE 2: I_{CC} and I_{DD} are measured with outputs disabled and open.

7

TYPE SN74LS424 (TIM8224)
TWO-PHASE CLOCK GENERATOR/DRIVER

REVISED AUGUST 1977

switching characteristics, V_{CC} = 5 V, V_{DD} = 12 V, T_A = 25°C, see figure 1

PARAMETER		TEST CONDITIONS	MIN	TYP	MAX	UNIT
f_{max}	Maximum oscillator frequency		27			MHz
$t_{c(osc)}$	Oscillator cycle time			$\frac{t_c}{9}$†		ns
$t_{w(\phi 1)}$	Pulse width, $\phi 1$ high	$\phi 1$ and $\phi 2$:	$\frac{2t_c}{9} - 20$			ns
$t_{w(\phi 2)}$	Pulse width, $\phi 2$ high	C_L = 20 pF to 110 pF, See Figure 2	$\frac{5t_c}{9} - 35$			ns
$t_{w(SS)}$	Pulse width, status strobe low	$\phi 2$ TTL:	$\frac{t_c}{9} - 15$			ns
$t_{r(\phi)}$	Rise time, clock outputs	C_L = 30 pF, R1 = 300 Ω,			20	ns
$t_{f(\phi)}$	Fall time, clock outputs	R2 = 600 Ω, See Figure 3			20	ns
$t_{\phi 1L,\phi 2H}$	Delay time, $\phi 1$ low to $\phi 2$ high	Status Strobe:	0			ns
$t_{\phi 2L,\phi 1H}$	Delay time, $\phi 2$ low to $\phi 1$ high	C_L = 15 pF, R1 = 2 kΩ,	$\frac{2t_c}{9} - 30$			ns
$t_{\phi 1H,\phi 2H}$	Delay time, $\phi 1$ high to $\phi 2$ high	R2 = 4 kΩ, See Figure 3	$\frac{2t_c}{9}$		$\frac{2t_c}{9} + 20$	ns
$t_{\phi 2,\phi 2T}$	Delay time, $\phi 2$ to $\phi 2$ TTL	OSC, Ready, Reset: C_L = 10 pF, R1 = 2 kΩ,	-5		15	ns
$t_{\phi 2H,SSL}$	Delay time, $\phi 2$ high to status strobe low	R2 = 4 kΩ, See Figure 3	$\frac{6t_c}{9} - 50$		$\frac{6t_c}{9}$	ns
$t_{RV,\phi 2L}$	Delay time, ready or reset output valid to phase 2 low		$\frac{4t_c}{9} - 25$			ns

† $t_c \equiv t_{c(\phi 1)} = t_{c(\phi 2)}$

EXAMPLE: switching times for f_{osc} = 20 MHz ($t_{c(\phi 1)} = t_{c(\phi 2)}$ = 450 ns)

PARAMETER		TEST CONDITIONS	MIN	TYP	MAX	UNIT
f_{osc}	Oscillator frequency			20		MHz
$t_{c(osc)}$	Oscillator cycle time			50		ns
$t_{w(\phi 1)}$	Pulse width, $\phi 1$ high		80			ns
$t_{w(\phi 2)}$	Pulse width, $\phi 2$ high		215			ns
$t_{w(SS)}$	Pulse width, status strobe		35			ns
$t_{\phi 1L,\phi 2H}$	Delay time, $\phi 1$ low to $\phi 2$ high	Same as above	0			ns
$t_{\phi 2L,\phi 1H}$	Delay time, $\phi 2$ low to $\phi 1$ high		70			ns
$t_{\phi 1H,\phi 2H}$	Delay time, $\phi 1$ high to $\phi 2$ high		100		120	ns
$t_{\phi 2H,SSL}$	Delay time, $\phi 2$ high to status strobe low		250		300	ns
$t_{RV,\phi 2L}$	Delay time, ready or reset output valid to $\phi 2$ low		175			ns

7

TEXAS INSTRUMENTS
INCORPORATED
POST OFFICE BOX 5012 • DALLAS, TEXAS 75222

PARAMETER MEASUREMENT INFORMATION

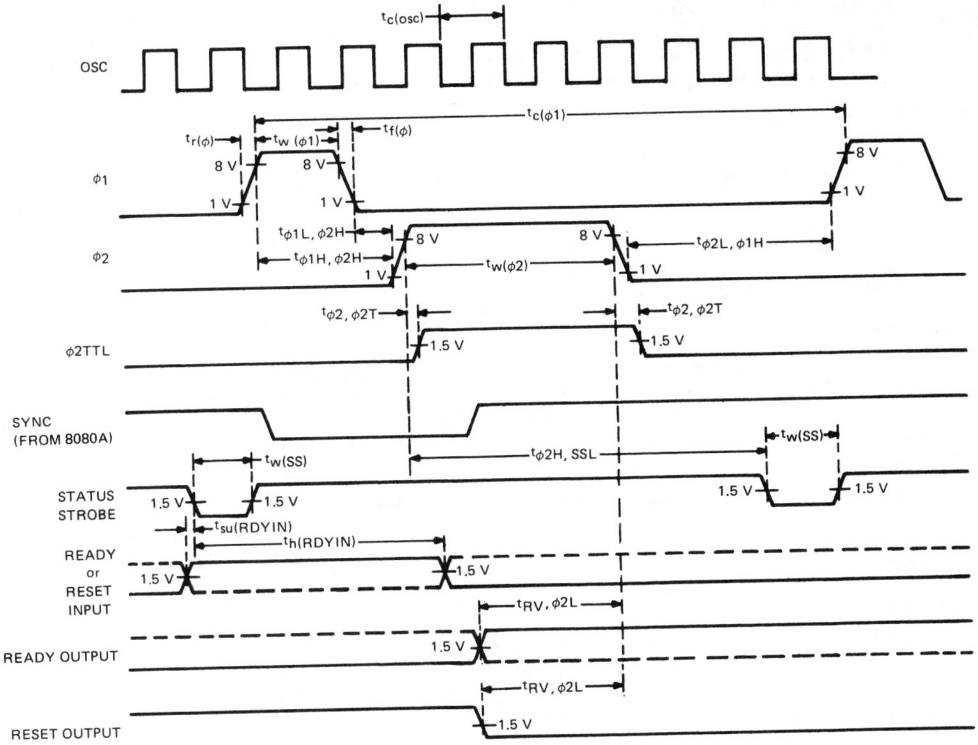

OSC

$t_{c(osc)}$

$\phi 1$

$t_{c(\phi 1)}$

$t_{r(\phi)}$ $t_{w(\phi 1)}$ $t_{f(\phi)}$

8 V 8 V

1 V 1 V

8 V

1 V

$\phi 2$

$t_{\phi 1L, \phi 2H}$ 8 V 8 V $t_{\phi 2L, \phi 1H}$

$t_{\phi 1H, \phi 2H}$ 1 V $t_{w(\phi 2)}$ 1 V

$\phi 2$TTL

$t_{\phi 2, \phi 2T}$ $t_{\phi 2, \phi 2T}$

1.5 V 1.5 V

SYNC
(FROM 8080A)

$t_{\phi 2H, SSL}$ $t_{w(SS)}$

STATUS
STROBE

$t_{w(SS)}$ 1.5 V 1.5 V

1.5 V 1.5 V

READY
or
RESET
INPUT

$t_{su(RDYIN)}$

$t_{h(RDYIN)}$

1.5 V 1.5 V

READY OUTPUT

$t_{RV, \phi 2L}$

1.5 V

RESET OUTPUT

$t_{RV, \phi 2L}$

1.5 V

NOTE: Transistion times, pulse widths, and interpulse relationships are distorted in this diagram in order to define various intervals, See Figure 5
for correct relative relationships.

VOLTAGE WAVEFORMS

FIGURE 1

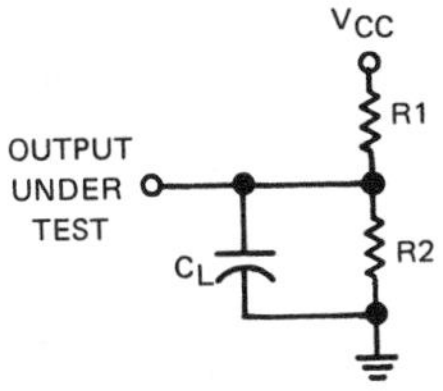

V_{CC}

R1

OUTPUT
UNDER
TEST

C_L R2

LOAD CIRCUIT

FIGURE 2

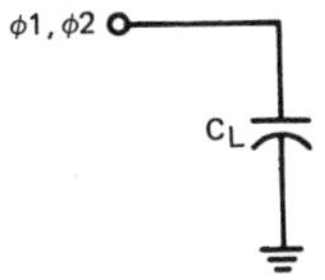

$\phi 1, \phi 2$

C_L

LOAD CIRCUIT

FIGURE 3

7

TYPE SN74LS424 (TIM8224)
TWO-PHASE CLOCK GENERATOR/DRIVER

TYPICAL APPLICATION DATA

The 'LS424 is a single-chip clock generator/driver for 8080A CPU's, furnishing three clocks (ϕ1, ϕ2 and ϕ2 TTL), status strobe, reset, and ready signals. The 'LS424 contains a crystal-controlled oscillator, a divide-by-nine counter, two high-level drivers, and several auxiliary logic functions. Figure 4 is a functional block diagram of the SN74LS424. Figure 5 shows the relationship between ϕ1, ϕ2, and the oscillator frequency period.

oscillator

A high order of clock frequency stability is provided by use of an external quartz crystal to set the oscillator frequency which is nine times the operating frequency of the 8080A. The quartz crystal is operated in a series-resonant mode. A fundamental-mode crystal requires no auxiliary circuitry, but an overtone-mode crystal requires an ac-coupled parallel-resonant circuit to be connected to the tank connection (pin 13). The parallel-resonant circuit, tuned to the oscillator frequency, compensates for the lower Q of the overtone-mode crystal. The required size of the circuit components can be calculated from $f = 1/2\pi\sqrt{LC}$ where f is the oscillator frequency, L is inductance value, and C is capacitance value. Figure 6 shows an ac-coupled parallel-tuned circuit used with the SN74LS424.

clock phase generator

The divide-by-nine clock phase generator contains a divide-by-nine counter, logic required to shape the clock pulses as shown under parameter measurement information, gates and flip-flops to generate auxiliary signals, and output drivers. The divide-by-nine counter waveforms are combined with gates to form a ϕ1 pulse with a width of two periods of the oscillator frequency, repeating at intervals of nine oscillator periods. Similarly, the ϕ2 pulse, having a width of five oscillator frequency periods, is formed lagging the ϕ1 pulse by two oscillator periods.

ϕ1 and ϕ2 outputs are provided by high-level drivers for direct connection to the 8080A CPU. ϕ2 TTL is derived in a manner similar to ϕ1 and ϕ2, but the output driver output is at TTL voltage levels. The ϕ2 TTL pulse width is the same as ϕ2. A ϕ2 TTL application is clocking in direct memory access activities. Figure shows the 'LS424 connected to an 8080A, quartz crystal, and LC circuits.

status strobe

The 8080A CPU puts status information on its data bus at the beginning of each machine cycle that defines the nature of the machine operation for that cycle. A sync signal from the 8080A is gated by an internal timing signal (ϕ1A) and becomes a status strobe to notify system components that the status data is present on 8080A status output lines. The status strobe signal connects directly to the 'S428 system controller.

The status strobe signal is alternatively generated by the reset input. An external RC series network connected to V_{CC} and the reset input will provide a rising voltage waveform when V_{CC} is turned on. An internal Schmitt trigger circuit generates a sharp, fast-rising waveform when the reset input reaches a particular voltage value. The Schmitt trigger is connected to the D input of a flip-flop clocked by ϕ2D. When power is turned on, the combination of internal and external circuitry will produce a status strobe signal. A manual reset switch can be connected as in figure 6 to the RC network to produce reset and status strobe signals for the 8080A.

The ready signal indicates to the 8080A that an external device has completed transfer of data to or from the data bus. A ready signal input to the 'LS424 drives the D input of a flip-flop clocked by an internal ϕ2D signal. Timing requirements of the 8080A machine cycle are met by the synchronization with the system clocks provided by the flip-flop. This implementation saves about 200 ns of system time during memory cycles (as contrasted with generating a "wait request" within the 8080A's MOS logic) since the bipolar logic of the 'LS424 has much less delay.

TEXAS INSTRUMENTS
INCORPORATED
POST OFFICE BOX 5012 • DALLAS, TEXAS 75222

TYPICAL APPLICATION DATA

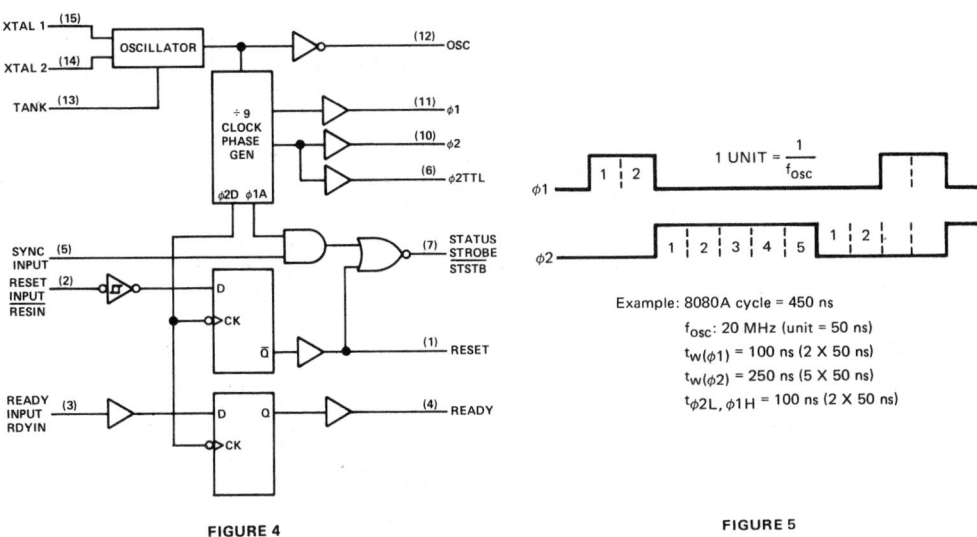

FIGURE 4

FIGURE 5

Example: 8080A cycle = 450 ns

f_{osc}: 20 MHz (unit = 50 ns)

$t_{w(\phi 1)}$ = 100 ns (2 X 50 ns)

$t_{w(\phi 2)}$ = 250 ns (5 X 50 ns)

$t_{\phi 2L, \phi 1H}$ = 100 ns (2 X 50 ns)

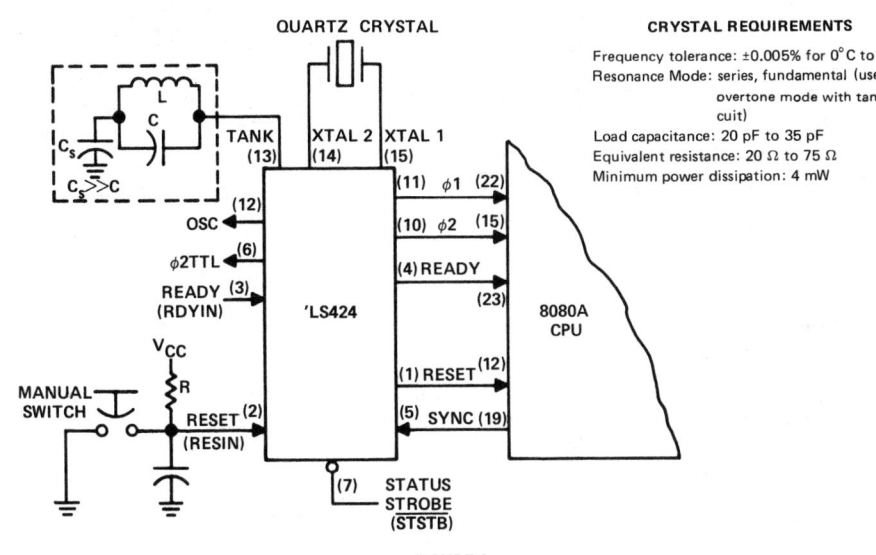

QUARTZ CRYSTAL

CRYSTAL REQUIREMENTS

Frequency tolerance: ±0.005% for 0°C to 70°C

Resonance Mode: series, fundamental (use 3rd overtone mode with tank circuit)

Load capacitance: 20 pF to 35 pF

Equivalent resistance: 20 Ω to 75 Ω

Minimum power dissipation: 4 mW

FIGURE 6

TEXAS INSTRUMENTS
INCORPORATED
POST OFFICE BOX 5012 • DALLAS, TEXAS 75222

- Designed to Be Interchangeable with Intel 8228 and 8238

PIN DESIGNATIONS

DESIGNATION	PIN NOS.	FUNCTION
D0 thru D7	15, 17, 12, 10, 6, 19, 21, 8	BIDIRECTIONAL DATA PORT (TO TMS 8080A)
DB0 thru DB7	13, 16, 11, 9, 5, 18, 20, 7	BIDIRECTIONAL DATA PORT (TO SYSTEM BUS)
I/OR	25	READ OUTPUT TO I/O (ACTIVE LOW)
IO/W	27	WRITE OUTPUT TO I/O (ACTIVE LOW)
MEMR	24	READ OUTPUT TO MEMORY (ACTIVE LOW)
MEMW	26	WRITE OUTPUT TO MEMORY (ACTIVE LOW)
DBIN	4	INPUT TO INDICATE TMS 8080A IS IN INPUT MODE (ACTIVE HIGH)
INTA	23	INTERRUPT ACKNOWLEDGE OUTPUT (ACTIVE LOW)
HLDA	2	HOLD ACKNOWLEDGE INPUT (ACTIVE HIGH) FROM TMS 8080A
WR	3	INPUT TO INDICATE TMS 8080A IS IN WRITE MODE (ACTIVE LOW)
BUSEN	22	SYSTEM DATA PORT ENABLE INPUT (ACTIVE LOW)
STSTB	1	SYNCHRONIZING STATUS STROBE INPUT FROM SN74LS424 (TIM8224)
VCC	28	SUPPLY VOLTAGE (5 V)
GND	14	GROUND

N PACKAGE
(TOP VIEW)

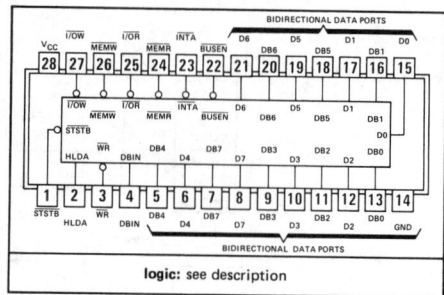

logic: see description

functional block diagram

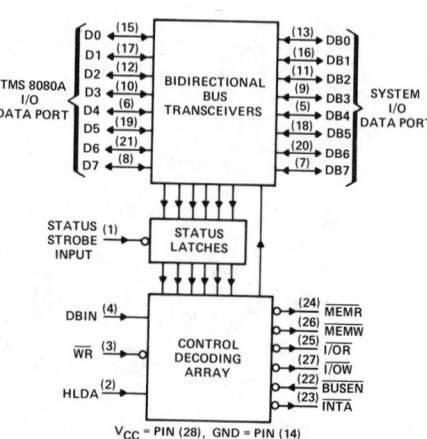

V_{CC} = PIN (28), GND = PIN (14)

description

These monolithic Schottky-clamped TTL system controllers are designed specifically to provide bus-driving and peripheral-control capabilities for interfacing memory and I/O devices with the 8080A in small to medium-large microcomputer systems.

A bidirectional eight-bit parallel bus driver is provided that isolates the 8080A bus from the memory and I/O data bus allowing the system designed to utilize cost-effective memory and peripheral devices while obtaining the maximum efficiency from the microprocessor. The TTL system drivers also provide increased fan-out with a lower impedance that enhances noise margins on the system bus.

Implementation of the status latches and control decoding array of the SN74S428/SN74S438 provides for using either a single-level interrupt vector RST7 for small systems, or multiple-byte call instructions for systems needing unlimited interrupt levels.

TENTATIVE DATA SHEET

TEXAS INSTRUMENTS
INCORPORATED
POST OFFICE BOX 5012 • DALLAS, TEXAS 75222

description (continued)

With respect to the system clocks, the SN74S438 is configured to generate an advanced response for I/O or memory write output signals to further simplify peripheral control implementation of complex systems. See Figure 3.

8-bit parrallel bus transceiver

The 8-bit parallel bus transceiver buffers the 8080A data bus from the memory and I/O system bus by providing one port (DO through D7) to interface with the 8080A and another port (DBO through DB7) to interface with the system devices. The 8080A side of the transceiver is designed specifically to interface with the microprocessor data bus ensuring not only that the processor output drive capabilities are adequate, but also that the inputs are driven with enhanced noise margins. The system bus side features high fan-out buffers designed to drive a number of system devices simultaneously and directly. The system port is rated to sink ten milliamperes of current and to source one milliampere of current at standard low-threshold voltage levels.

Status lines from the 8080A instruction-status decoder and the system bus enable input (BUSEN) provide complete transceiver directional and enable control to ensure integrity of both the processor data and the system bus data.

status latches

During the beginning of each machine cycle, the six status latches receive status information from the 8080A data bus indicating the type of operation that will be performed. When the $\overline{\text{STSTB}}$ input goes low, the latches store the status data and generate the signals needed to enable and sequence the memory and I/O control outputs. The status words and types of machine cycles are enumerated in Table A.

TABLE A – STATUS WORDS

STATUS WORD	8080A STATUS OUTPUT								TYPE OF MACHINE CYCLE	'S428/'S438 COMMAND GENERATED
	D0	D1	D2	D3	D4	D5	D6	D7		
1	L	H	L	L	L	H	L	H	Instruction fetch	$\overline{\text{MEMR}}$
2	L	H	L	L	L	L	L	H	Memory read	$\overline{\text{MEMR}}$
3	L	L	L	L	L	L	L	L	Memory write	$\overline{\text{MEMW}}$
4	L	H	H	L	L	L	L	H	Stack read	$\overline{\text{MEMR}}$
5	L	L	H	L	L	L	L	L	Stack write	$\overline{\text{MEMW}}$
6	L	H	L	L	L	L	H	L	Input read	$\overline{\text{I/OR}}$
7	L	L	L	L	H	L	L	L	Output write	$\overline{\text{I/OW}}$
8	H	H	L	L	L	H	L	L	Interrupt acknowledge	$\overline{\text{INTA}}$
9	L	H	L	H	L	L	L	H	Halt acknowledge	NONE
10	H	H	L	H	L	H	L	L	Interrupt acknowledge at halt	$\overline{\text{INTA}}$
	INTA	$\overline{\text{WO}}$	STACK	HLTA	OUT	M1	INP	MEMR		
			STATUS INFORMATION							

decoding array

The decoding array receives enabling commands from the status latches and sequencing commands from the 8080A and generates memory and I/O read/write commands and an interrupt acknowledgement.

7

TEXAS INSTRUMENTS
INCORPORATED
POST OFFICE BOX 5012 • DALLAS, TEXAS 75222

TYPES SN74S428(TIM8228), SN74S438(TIM8238)
CONTROLLER AND BUS DRIVER FOR 8080A SYSTEMS

description (continued)

The read commands (MEMR, I/OR) and the interrupt acknowledgement (INTA) are derived from the status bit(s) and the data bus input mode (DBIN) signal. The write commands (MEMW, I/OW) are derived from the status bit(s) and the write mode (WR) signal. (See Table A.) All control commands are active low to simplify interfacing with memory and I/O controllers.

The interrupt acknowledgement (INTA) command output is actually a dual function pin. As an output, its function is to provide the INTA command to the memory and I/O peripherals as decoded from the status inputs and latches. When CALL is used as an interrupt instruction, the SN74S428/SN74S428 generates the proper sequence of control signals. Additionally, the terminal includes high-threshold decoding logic that permits it to be biased through a one-kilohm series resistor to the 12-volt supply to implement an interrupt structure that automatically inserts an RST7 instruction on the bus when the DBIN input is active and an interrupt is acknowledged. This capability provides a single-level interrupt vector with minimal hardware.

The asynchronous bus enable (BUSEN) input to the decoding array is a control signal that protects the system bus. The system bus can be accessed and driven from the SN74S428/SN74S428 controller only when the BUSEN input is at a low voltage level.

absolute maximum ratings over operating free-air temperature range (unless otherwise noted)

Supply voltage, V_{CC} (see Note 1) . . . . 7 V
Input voltage . . . . 7 V
Operating free-air temperature range . . . . $0°C$ to $70°C$
Storage temperature range . . . . $-65°C$ to $150°C$

NOTE 1: Voltage values are with respect to network ground terminal.

recommended operating conditions

		MIN	NOM	MAX	UNIT
Supply voltage, V_{CC}		4.75	5	5.25	V
High-level output current, I_{OH}	D0 thru D7			−10	μA
	All others			−1	mA
Low-level output current, I_{OL}	D0 thru D7			2	mA
	All others			10	
Status strobe pulse width, $t_{w(STSTB)}$ (see Figure 3)		22			ns
Setup time, t_{su} (see Figure 3)	Status inputs D0 thru D7	8			ns
	System bus inputs to HLDA	10			
Hold time, t_h (see Figure 3)	Status inputs D0 thru D7	5			ns
	System bus inputs to HLDA	20			
Operating free-air temperature, T_A		0		70	°C

TEXAS INSTRUMENTS
INCORPORATED
POST OFFICE BOX 5012 • DALLAS. TEXAS 75222

electrical characteristics over recommended operating free-air temperature range (unless otherwise noted)

PARAMETER		TEST CONDITIONS		MIN	TYP‡	MAX	UNIT
V_{IH}	High-level input voltage			2			V
V_{IL}	Low-level input voltage					0.8	V
V_{IK}	Input clamp voltage	V_{CC} = MIN,	I_I = −5 mA			−1	V
V_{OH}	High-level output voltage	D0 thru D7	V_{CC} = MIN, V_{IH} = 2 V,	3.6	4		V
		All other outputs	V_{IL} = 0.8 V, I_{OH} = MAX	2.4			
V_{OL}	Low-level output voltage		V_{CC} = MIN, V_{IH} = 2 V, V_{IL} = 0.8 V, I_{OL} = MAX			0.45	V
I_{OZH}	Off-state output current, high-level voltage applied		V_{CC} = MAX, V_O = 5.25 V			100	µA
I_{OZL}	Off-state output current, low-level voltage applied		V_{CC} = MAX, V_O = 0.45 V			−100	µA
I_{IH}	High-level input current	INTA	V_{CC} = MIN, See Figure 1			5	mA
		D0 thru D7	V_{CC} = MAX, V_I = 5.25 V			20	µA
		All other inputs				100	
I_{IL}	Low-level input current	D2 or D6	V_{CC} = MAX, V_I = 0.45 V			−750	µA
		STSTB				−500	
		All other inputs				−250	
I_{OS}	Short-circuit output current§		V_{CC} = MAX	−15		−90	mA
I_{CC}	Supply current		V_{CC} = MAX		140	190	mA

†For conditions shown as MIN or MAX, use the appropriate value specified under recommended operating conditions.
‡All typical values are at V_{CC} = 5 V, T_A = 25°C.
§Not more than one output should be shorted at a time.

switching characteristics, V_{CC} = 5 V, T_A = 25°C, see figure 3

PARAMETER¶	FROM (INPUT)	TO (OUTPUT)	TEST CONDITIONS		MIN	TYP	MAX	UNIT
t_{PD}	D0 thru D7	DB0 thru DB7	C_L = 100 pF,	See Figure 2	5		40	ns
t_{PD}	DB0 thru DB7	D0 thru D7	C_L = 25 pF,	See Figure 2			30	ns
t_{PHL}	STSTB	INTA, I/OR, MEMR, I/OW, MEMW	C_L = 100 pF,	See Figure 2	20		60	ns
t_{PD}	WR	I/OW, MEMW			5		45	ns
t_{PLH}	DBIN	INTA, I/OR, MEMR					30	ns
t_{PLH}	HLDA	INTA, I/OR, MEMR					25	ns
t_{PZX}	DBIN	D0 thru D7	C_L = 25 pF,	See Figure 2			45	ns
t_{PXZ}	DBIN	D0 thru D7					45	ns
t_{PZX}	STSTB, BUSEN	DB0 thru DB7	C_L = 100 pF,	See Figure 2			30	ns
t_{PXZ}	BUSEN	DB0 thru DB7					30	ns

¶ t_{PD} ≡ propagation delay time
t_{PHL} ≡ propagation delay time, high-to-low-level output
t_{PLH} ≡ propagation delay time, low-to-high-level output
t_{PZX} ≡ output enable time from high-impedance state
t_{PXZ} ≡ output disable time to high-impedance state

7

TEXAS INSTRUMENTS
INCORPORATED
POST OFFICE BOX 5012 • DALLAS, TEXAS 75222

TYPES SN74S428(TIM8228), SN74S438(TIM8238)
CONTROLLER AND BUS DRIVER FOR 8080A SYSTEMS

PARAMETER MEASUREMENT INFORMATION

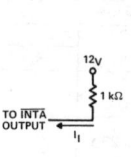

FIGURE 1—INTA INPUT CURRENT
TEST CIRCUIT

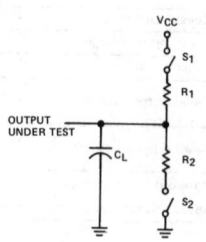

FIGURE 2—SWITCHING CHARACTERISTICS
LOAD CIRCUIT

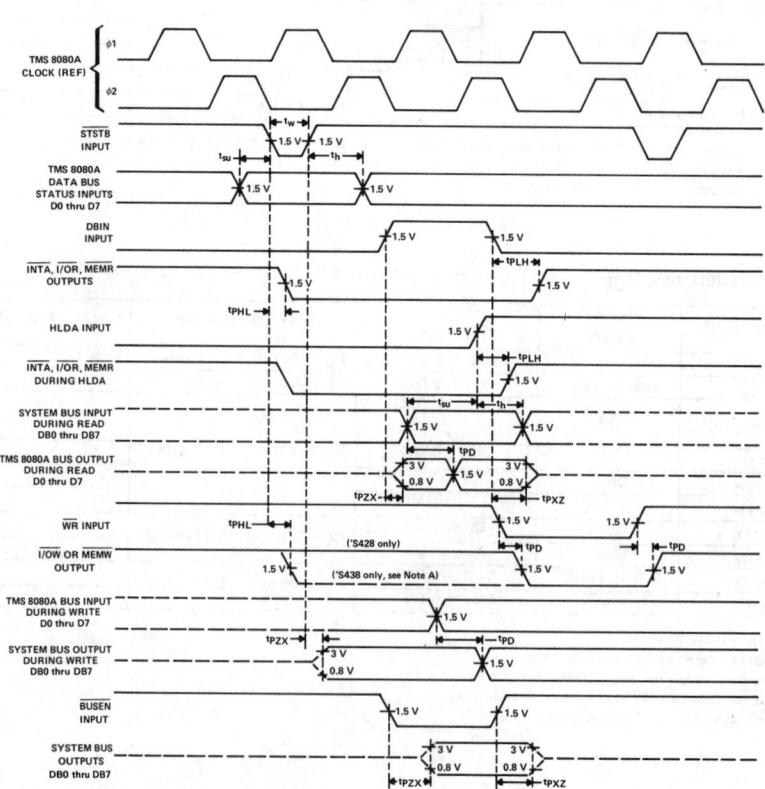

NOTE A: Advanced response of I/OW or MEMW for the SN74S438 is indicated by the dashed line.

FIGURE 3—VOLTAGE WAVEFORMS

7

TEXAS INSTRUMENTS
INCORPORATED
POST OFFICE BOX 5012 • DALLAS, TEXAS 75222

TYPICAL APPLICATION DATA

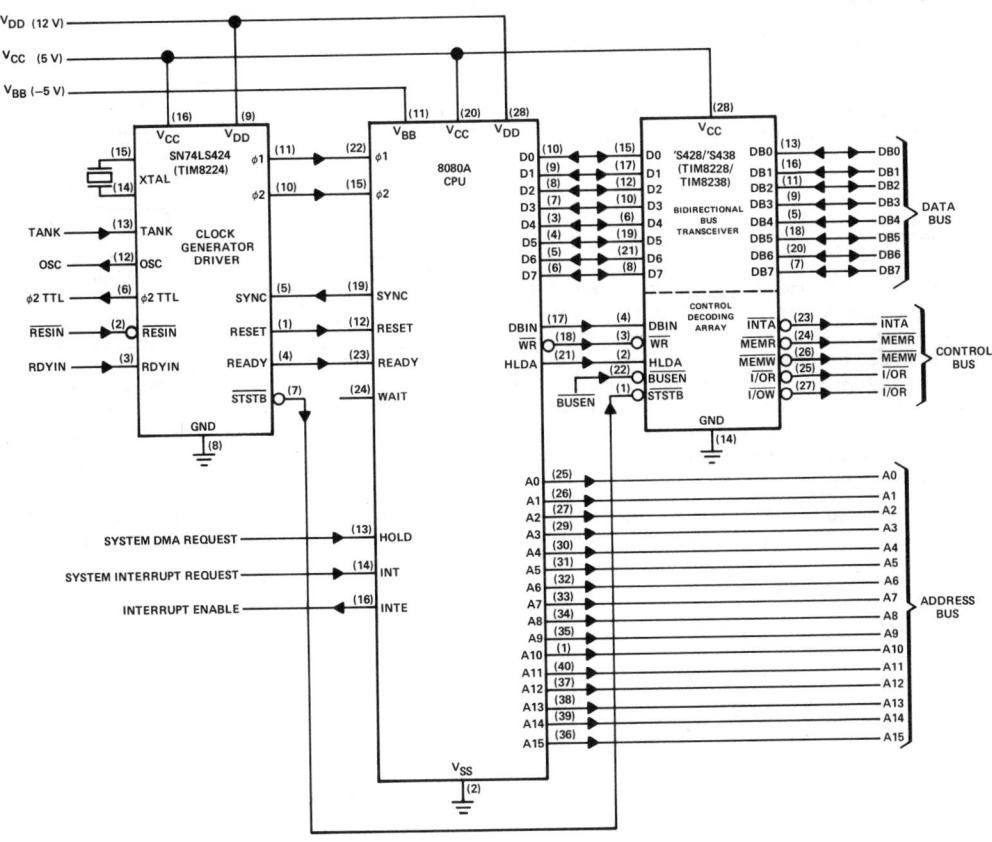

FIGURE 4—SYSTEM INTERFACING WITH CENTRAL PROCESSING UNIT

TEXAS INSTRUMENTS
INCORPORATED
POST OFFICE BOX 5012 • DALLAS, TEXAS 75222

TYPES SN54490, SN54LS490, SN74490, SN74LS490
DUAL 4-BIT DECADE COUNTERS

BULLETIN NO. DL-S 7612089, OCTOBER 1976

- Dual Versions of Popular SN5490A, SN54LS90, SN7490A, and SN74LS90 Counters

- Individual Clock, Direct Clear, and Set-to-9 Inputs for Each Decade Counter

- Dual Counters Can Significantly Improve System Densities as Package Count Can Be Reduced by 50%

- Maximum Count Frequency . . . 35 MHz Typical

- Buffered Outputs Reduce Possibility of Collector Commutation

SN54490 . . . J OR W PACKAGE
SN74490 . . . J OR N PACKAGE
(TOP VIEW)

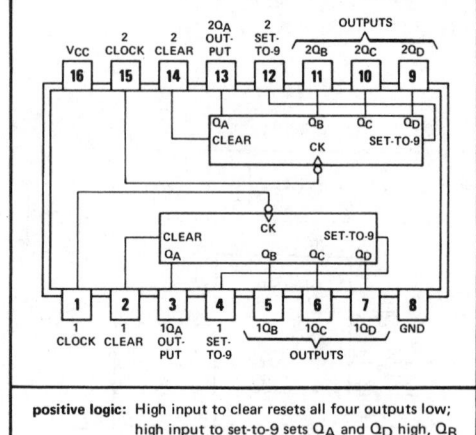

positive logic: High input to clear resets all four outputs low; high input to set-to-9 sets Q_A and Q_D high, Q_B and Q_C low.

description

Each of these monolithic circuits contains eight master-slave flip-flops and additional gating to implement two individual 4-bit decade counters in a single package. Each decade counter has individual clock, clear, and set-to-9 inputs. BCD count sequences of any length up to divide-by-100 may be implemented with a single '490 or 'LS490. Buffering on each output is provided to ensure that susceptibility to collector commutation is reduced significantly. All inputs are diode-clamped to reduce the effects of line ringing. The counters have parallel outputs from each counter stage so that submultiples of the input count frequency are available for system timing signals.

The SN54490 and SN54LS490 are characterized for operation over the full military temperature range of $-55°$C to $125°$C; the SN74490 and SN74LS490 are characterized for use in industrial systems operating from $0°$C to $70°$C.

BCD COUNT SEQUENCE
(EACH COUNTER)

COUNT	OUTPUT			
	Q_D	Q_C	Q_B	Q_A
0	L	L	L	L
1	L	L	L	H
2	L	L	H	L
3	L	L	H	H
4	L	H	L	L
5	L	H	L	H
6	L	H	H	L
7	L	H	H	H
8	H	L	L	L
9	H	L	L	H

CLEAR/SET-TO-9
FUNCTION TABLE
(EACH COUNTER)

INPUTS		OUTPUTS			
CLEAR	SET-TO-9	Q_A	Q_B	Q_C	Q_D
H	L	L	L	L	L
L	H	H	L	L	H
L	L	COUNT			

H = high level, L = low level

TEXAS INSTRUMENTS
INCORPORATED
POST OFFICE BOX 5012 • DALLAS, TEXAS 75222

10

schematics of inputs and outputs

'490

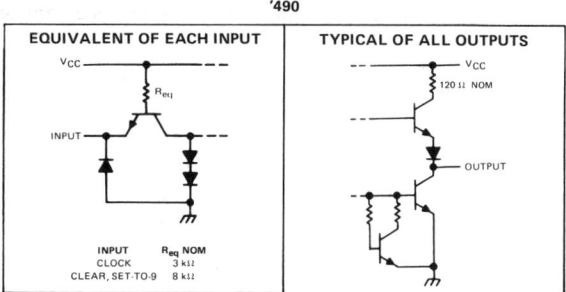

'LS490

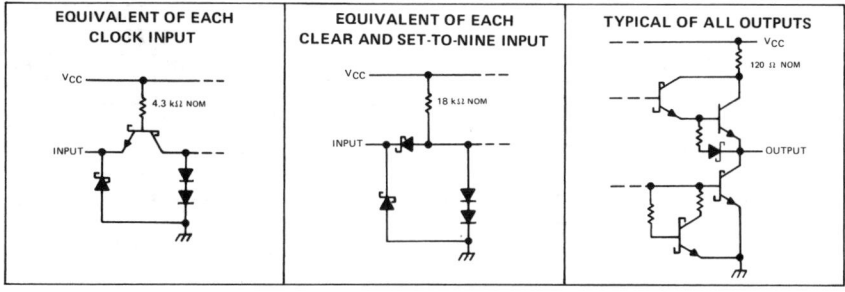

functional block diagram (each counter)

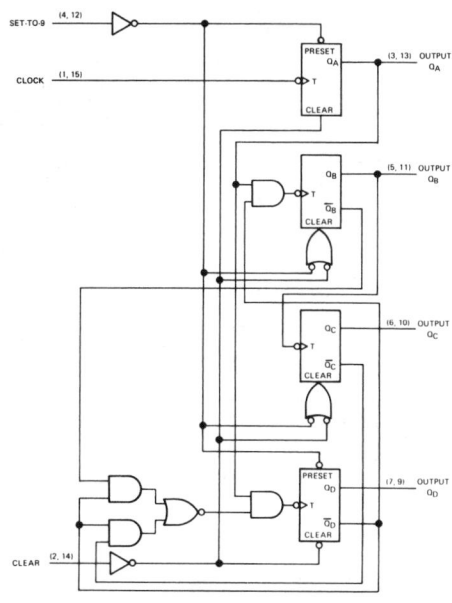

7

TEXAS INSTRUMENTS
INCORPORATED
POST OFFICE BOX 5012 • DALLAS, TEXAS 75222

TYPES SN54490, SN74490
DUAL 4-BIT DECADE COUNTERS

absolute maximum ratings over operating free-air temperature range (unless otherwise noted)

Supply voltage, V_{CC} (see Note 1) . . . . 7 V
Input voltage . . . . 5.5 V
Operating free-air temperature range: SN54490 . . . . −55°C to 125°C
SN74490 . . . . 0°C to 70°C
Storage temperature range . . . . −65°C to 150°C

NOTE 1: Voltage values are with respect to network ground terminal.

recommended operating conditions

	SN54490			SN74490			UNIT
	MIN	NOM	MAX	MIN	NOM	MAX	
Supply voltage, V_{CC}	4.5	5	5.5	4.75	5	5.25	V
High-level output current, I_{OH}			−800			−800	µA
Low-level output current, I_{OL}			16			16	mA
Count frequency, f_{count}	0		25	0		25	MHz
Pulse width, t_W (any input)		20			20		ns
Clear or set-to-9 inactive-state setup time, t_{su}	25↓			25↓			ns
Operating free-air temperature, T_A	−55		125	0		70	°C

↓The arrow indicates that the falling edge of the clock pulse is used for reference.

electrical characteristics over recommended operating free-air temperature range (unless otherwise noted)

PARAMETER		TEST CONDITIONS[†]		MIN	TYP[‡]	MAX	UNIT
V_{IH} High-level input voltage				2			V
V_{IL} Low-level input voltage						0.8	V
V_{IK} Input clamp voltage		V_{CC} = MIN, I_I = −12 mA				−1.5	V
V_{OH} High-level output voltage		V_{CC} = MIN, V_{IH} = 2 V, V_{IL} = 0.8 V, I_{OH} = −800 µA		2.4	3.4		V
V_{OL} Low-level output voltage		V_{CC} = MIN, V_{IH} = 2 V, V_{IL} = 0.8 V I_{OL} = 16 mA			0.2	0.4	V
I_I Input current at maximum input voltage		V_{CC} = MAX, V_I = 5.5 V				1	mA
I_{IH} High-level input current	Clear, set-to-9	V_{CC} = MAX, V_I = 2.4 V				40	µA
	Clock					80	
I_{IL} Low-level input current	Clear, set-to-9	V_{CC} = MAX, V_I = 0.4 V				−1	mA
	Clock					−3.2	
I_{OS} Short-circuit output current[§]		V_{CC} = MAX	SN54490	−20		−57	mA
			SN74490	−18		−57	
I_{CC} Supply current		V_{CC} = MAX, See Note 2			45	70	mA

†For conditions shown as MIN or MAX, use the appropriate value specified under recommended operating conditions.
‡All typical values are at V_{CC} = 5 V, T_A = 25°C.
§Not more than one output should be shorted at a time.
NOTE 2: I_{CC} is measured with all outputs open, both clear inputs grounded following momentary connection to 4.5 V, and all other inputs grounded.

TEXAS INSTRUMENTS
INCORPORATED
POST OFFICE BOX 5012 • DALLAS, TEXAS 75222

switching characteristics, V_{CC} = 5 V, T_A = 25°C

PARAMETER¶	FROM (INPUT)	TO (OUTPUT)	TEST CONDITIONS	MIN	TYP	MAX	UNIT
f_{max}	Clock	Q_A		25	35		MHz
t_{PLH}	Clock	Q_A			12	20	ns
t_{PHL}					13	20	
t_{PLH}	Clock	Q_B, Q_D			24	39	ns
t_{PHL}			C_L = 15 pF, R_L = 400 Ω,		26	39	
t_{PLH}	Clock	Q_C	See Figure 1 and Note 3		32	54	ns
t_{PHL}					36	54	
t_{PHL}	Clear	Any			24	39	ns
t_{PLH}	Set-to-9	Q_A, Q_D			24	39	ns
t_{PHL}		Q_B, Q_C			20	36	

¶ f_{max} ≡ maximum count frequency
t_{PLH} ≡ propagation delay time, low-to-high-level output
t_{PHL} ≡ propagation delay time, high-to-low-level output
NOTE 3: Load circuit is shown on page 3-10.

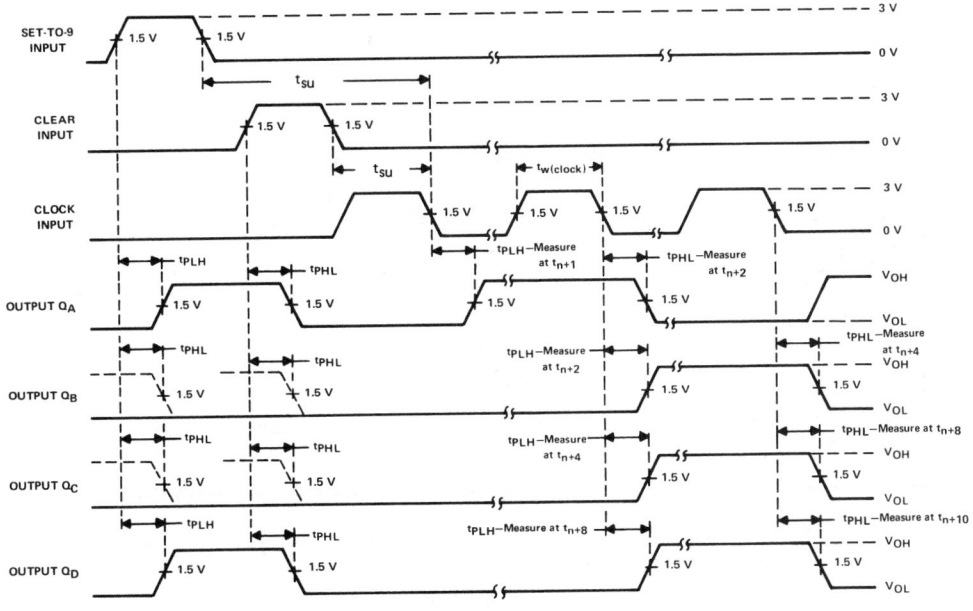

VOLTAGE WAVEFORMS

NOTES: A. Input pulses are supplied by a generator having the following characteristics: t_r ≤ 5 ns, t_f ≤ 5 ns, PRR = 1 MHz, duty cycle = 50%, Z_{out} ≈ 50 ohms.

FIGURE 1

TEXAS INSTRUMENTS
INCORPORATED
POST OFFICE BOX 5012 • DALLAS, TEXAS 75222

absolute maximum ratings over operating free-air temperature range (unless otherwise noted)

Supply voltage, V_{CC} (see Note 1) . . . . 7 V
Clear and set-to-9 input voltage . . . . 7 V
Clock input voltage . . . . 5.5 V
Operating free-air temperature range: SN54LS490 . . . . -55°C to 125°C
                                  SN74LS490 . . . . 0°C to 70°C
Storage temperature range . . . . -65°C to 150°C

NOTE 1: Voltage values are with respect to network ground terminal.

recommended operating conditions

		SN54LS490			SN74LS490			UNIT
		MIN	NOM	MAX	MIN	NOM	MAX	
Supply voltage, V_{CC}		4.5	5	5.5	4.75	5	5.25	V
High-level output current, I_{OH}				−400			−400	μA
Low-level output current, I_{OL}				4			8	mA
Count frequency, f_{count}		0		25	0		25	MHz
Pulse width, t_w (any input)		20			20			ns
Clear or set-to-9 inactive-state setup time, t_{su}		25↓			25↓			ns
Operating free-air temperature, T_A		−55		125	0		70	°C

↓The arrow indicates that the falling edge of the clock pulse is used for reference.

electrical characteristics over recommended operating free-air temperature range (unless otherwise noted)

PARAMETER			TEST CONDITIONS[†]		SN54LS490			SN74LS490			UNIT
					MIN	TYP[‡]	MAX	MIN	TYP[‡]	MAX	
V_{IH}	High-level input voltage				2			2			V
V_{IL}	Low-level input voltage						0.7			0.8	V
V_{IK}	Input clamp voltage		V_{CC} = MIN,	I_I = −1 mA			−1.5			−1.5	V
V_{OH}	High-level output voltage		V_{CC} = MIN, V_{IL} = V_{IL}max	V_{IH} = 2 V,	2.5	3.4		2.7	3.4		V
V_{OL}	Low-level output voltage		V_{CC} = MIN, V_{IH} = 2 V, V_{IL} = V_{IL}max	I_{OL} = 4 mA		0.25	0.4		0.25	0.4	V
				I_{OL} = 8 mA					0.35	0.5	
I_I	Input current at maximum input voltage	Clear, set-to-9	V_{CC} = MAX,	V_I = 7 V			0.1			0.1	mA
		Clock		V_I = 5.5 V			0.2			0.2	
I_{IH}	High-level input current	Clear, set-to-9	V_{CC} = MAX,	V_I = 2.7 V			20			20	μA
		Clock					40			40	
I_{IL}	Low-level input current	Clear, set-to-9	V_{CC} = MAX,	V_I = 0.4 V			−0.4			−0.4	mA
		Clock					−1.6			−1.6	
I_{OS}	Short-circuit output current[§]		V_{CC} = MAX		−20		−100	−20		−100	mA
I_{CC}	Supply current		V_{CC} = MAX,	See Note 2		15	26		15	26	mA

[†]For conditions shown as MIN or MAX, use the appropriate value specified under recommended operating conditions.
[‡]All typical values are at V_{CC} = 5 V, T_A = 25°C.
[§]Not more than one output should be shorted at a time, and duration of the short-circuit should not exceed one second.
NOTE 2: I_{CC} is measured with all outputs open, both clear inputs grounded following momentary connection to 4.5 V, and all other inputs grounded.

TEXAS INSTRUMENTS
INCORPORATED
POST OFFICE BOX 5012 • DALLAS, TEXAS 75222

7

switching characteristics, V_{CC} = 5 V, T_A = 25°C

PARAMETER¶	FROM (INPUT)	TO (OUTPUT)	TEST CONDITIONS	MIN	TYP	MAX	UNIT
f_{max}	Clock	Q_A		25	35		MHz
t_{PLH}	Clock	Q_A			12	20	ns
t_{PHL}					13	20	
t_{PLH}	Clock	Q_B, Q_D	C_L = 15 pF, R_L = 2 kΩ		24	39	ns
t_{PHL}			See Figure 2 and Note 4		26	39	
t_{PLH}	Clock	Q_C			32	54	ns
t_{PHL}					36	54	
t_{PHL}	Clear	Any			24	39	ns
t_{PLH}	Set-to-9	Q_A, Q_D			24	39	ns
t_{PHL}		Q_B, Q_C			20	36	

¶ f_{max} ≡ maximum count frequency
t_{PLH} ≡ propagation delay time, low-to-high-level output
t_{PHL} ≡ propagation delay time, high-to-low-level output
NOTE 4: Load circuit is shown on page 3-11.

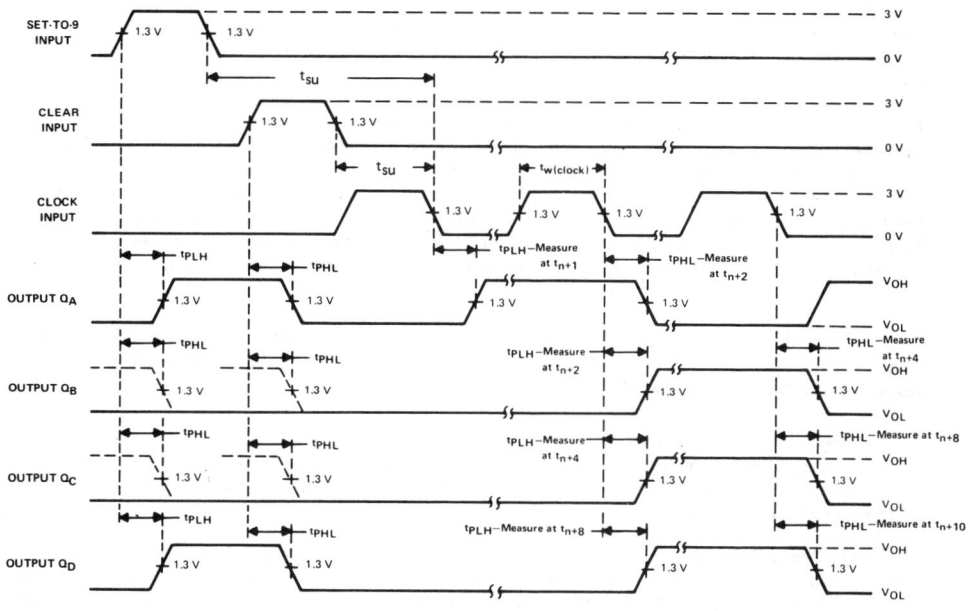

VOLTAGE WAVEFORMS

NOTES: A. Input pulses are supplied by a generator having the following characteristics: t_r ≤ 15 ns, t_f ≤ 6 ns, PRR = 1 MHz, duty cycle = 50%, Z_{out} ≈ 50 ohms.

FIGURE 2

7

TEXAS INSTRUMENTS
INCORPORATED
POST OFFICE BOX 5012 • DALLAS, TEXAS 75222

TYPES SN54LS670, SN74LS670
4-BY-4 REGISTER FILES WITH 3-STATE OUTPUTS

BULLETIN NO. DL-S 7612122, MARCH 1974–REVISED OCTOBER 1976

- Separate Read/Write Addressing Permits Simultaneous Reading and Writing

- Fast Access Times . . . Typically 20 ns

- Organized as 4 Words of 4 Bits

- Expandable to 512 Words of n-Bits

- For Use as:

    Scratch-Pad Memory

    Buffer Storage between Processors

    Bit Storage in Fast Multiplication Designs

- 3-State Outputs

- SN54LS170 and SN74LS170 Are Similar But Have Open-Collector Outputs

SN54LS670 . . . J OR W PACKAGE
SN74LS670 . . . J OR N PACKAGE
(TOP VIEW)

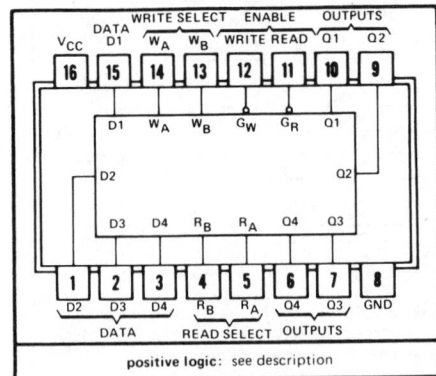

positive logic: see description

description

The SN54LS670 and SN74LS670 MSI 16-bit TTL register files incorporate the equivalent of 98 gates. The register file is organized as 4 words of 4 bits each and separate on-chip decoding is provided for addressing the four word locations to either write-in or retrieve data. This permits simultaneous writing into one location and reading from another word location.

Four data inputs are available which are used to supply the 4-bit word to be stored. Location of the word is determined by the write-address inputs A and B in conjunction with a write-enable signal. Data applied at the inputs should be in its true form. That is, if a high-level signal is desired from the output, a high-level is applied at the data input for that particular bit location. The latch inputs are arranged so that new data will be accepted only if both internal address gate inputs are high. When this condition exists, data at the D input is transferred to the latch output. When the write-enable input, G_W, is high, the data inputs are inhibited and their levels can cause no change in the information stored in the internal latches. When the read-enable input, G_R, is high, the data outputs are inhibited and go into the high-impedance state.

The individual address lines permit direct acquisition of data stored in any four of the latches. Four individual decoding gates are used to complete the address for reading a word. When the read address is made in conjunction with the read-enable signal, the word appears at the four outputs.

This arrangement—data-entry addressing separate from data-read addressing and individual sense line—eliminates recovery times, permits simultaneous reading and writing, and is limited in speed only by the write time (27 nanoseconds typical) and the read time (24 nanoseconds typical). The register file has a nondestructive readout in that data is not lost when addressed.

All inputs except read enable and write enable are buffered to lower the drive requirements to one Series 54LS/74LS standard load, and input-clamping diodes minimize switching transients to simplify system design. High-speed, double-ended AND-OR-INVERT gates are employed for the read-address function and have high-sink-current, three-state outputs. Up to 128 of these outputs may be wire-AND connected for increasing the capacity up to 512 words. Any number of these registers may be paralleled to provide n-bit word length.

The SN54LS670 characterized for operation over the full military temperature range of −55°C to 125°C; the SN74LS670 is characterized for operation from 0°C to 70°C.

TEXAS INSTRUMENTS
INCORPORATED
POST OFFICE BOX 5012 • DALLAS, TEXAS 75222

logic

WRITE FUNCTION TABLE (SEE NOTES A, B, AND C)

WRITE INPUTS			WORD			
W_B	W_A	G_W	0	1	2	3
L	L	L	Q = D	Q_0	Q_0	Q_0
L	H	L	Q_0	Q = D	Q_0	Q_0
H	L	L	Q_0	Q_0	Q = D	Q_0
H	H	L	Q_0	Q_0	Q_0	Q = D
X	X	H	Q_0	Q_0	Q_0	Q_0

READ FUNCTION TABLE (SEE NOTES A AND D)

READ INPUTS			OUTPUTS			
R_B	R_A	G_R	Q1	Q2	Q3	Q4
L	L	L	W0B1	W0B2	W0B3	W0B4
L	H	L	W1B1	W1B2	W1B3	W1B4
H	L	L	W2B1	W2B2	W2B3	W2B4
H	H	L	W3B1	W3B2	W3B3	W3B4
X	X	H	Z	Z	Z	Z

NOTES: A. H = high level, L = low level, X = irrelevant, Z = high impedance (off)
B. (Q = D) = The four selected internal flip-flop outputs will assume the states applied to the four external data inputs.
C. Q_0 = the level of Q before the indicated input conditions were established.
D. W0B1 = The first bit of word 0, etc.

functional block diagram

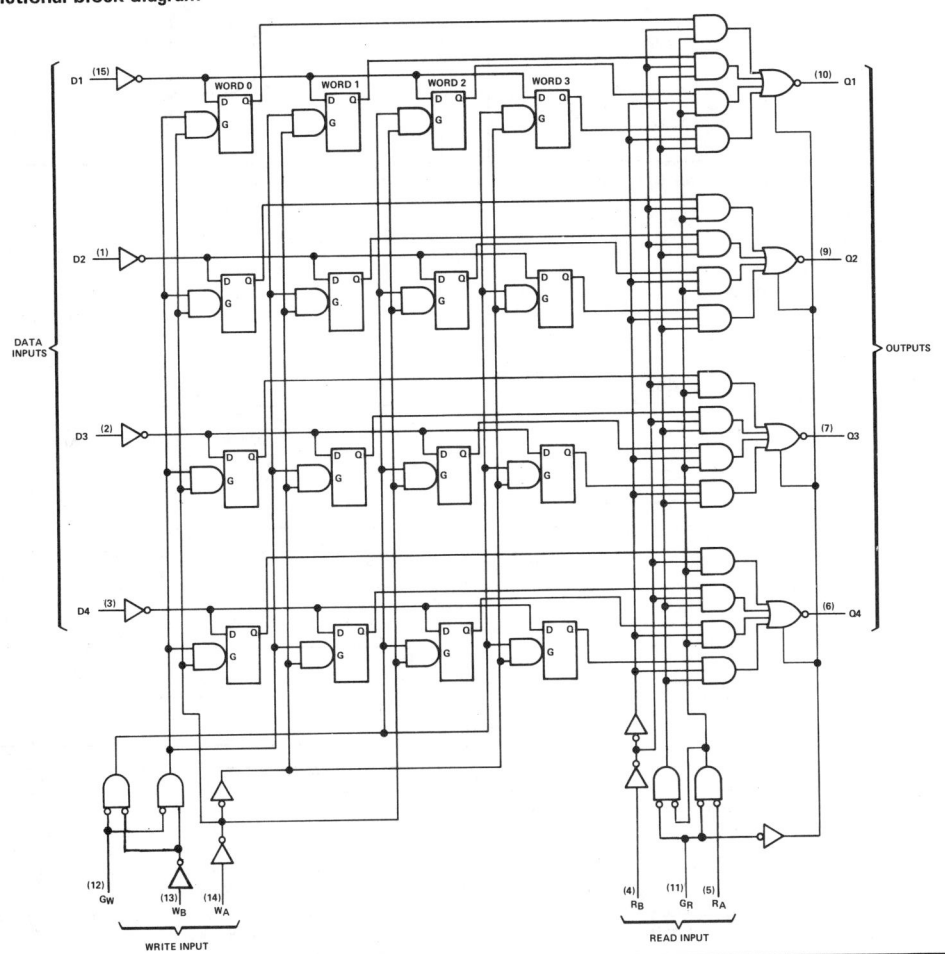

TEXAS INSTRUMENTS
INCORPORATED
POST OFFICE BOX 5012 • DALLAS, TEXAS 75222

TYPES SN54LS670, SN74LS670
4-BY-4 REGISTER FILES WITH 3-STATE OUTPUTS

schematics of inputs and outputs

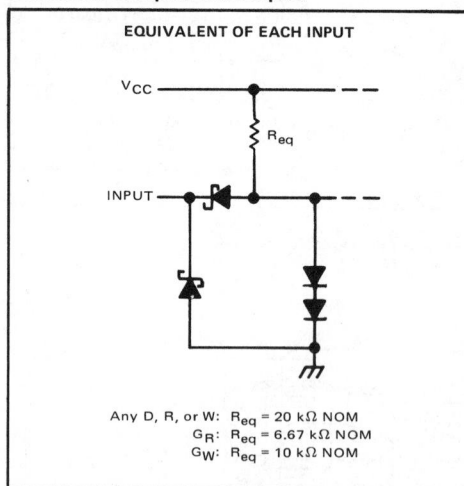

EQUIVALENT OF EACH INPUT

Any D, R, or W: R_{eq} = 20 kΩ NOM
G_R: R_{eq} = 6.67 kΩ NOM
G_W: R_{eq} = 10 kΩ NOM

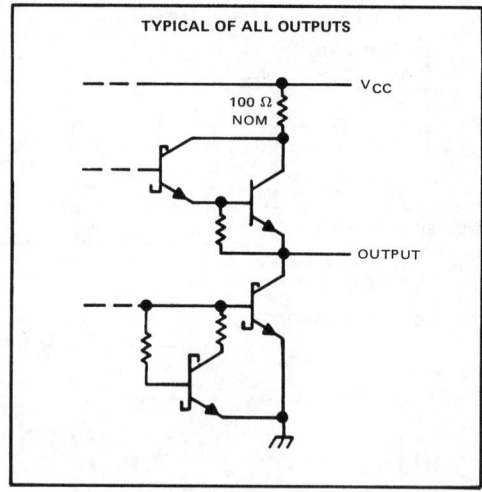

TYPICAL OF ALL OUTPUTS

absolute maximum ratings over operating free-air temperature range (unless otherwise noted)

Supply voltage, V_{CC} (see Note 1) . . . . 7 V
Input voltage . . . . 7 V
Off-state output voltage . . . . 5.5 V
Operating free-air temperature range: SN54LS670 . . . . −55°C to 125°C
                                      SN74LS670 . . . . 0°C to 70°C
Storage temperature range . . . . −65°C to 150°C

recommended operating conditions

		SN54LS670			SN74LS670			UNIT
		MIN	NOM	MAX	MIN	NOM	MAX	
Supply voltage, V_{CC}		4.5	5	5.5	4.75	5	5.25	V
High-level output current, I_{OH}				−1			−2.6	mA
Low-level output current, I_{OL}				4			8	mA
Width of write-enable or read-enable pulse, t_w		25			25			ns
Setup times, high- or low-level data (see Figure 2)	Data input with respect to write enable, $t_{su(D)}$	10			10			ns
	Write select with respect to write enable, $t_{su(W)}$	15			15			ns
Hold times, high- or low-level data (see Note 2 and Figure 2)	Data input with respect to write enable, $t_{h(W)}$	15			15			ns
	Write select with respect to write enable, $t_{h(D)}$	5			5			ns
Latch time for new data, t_{latch} (see Note 3)		25			25			ns
Operating free-air temperature range, T_A		−55		125	0		70	°C

NOTES: 1. Voltage values are with respect to network ground terminal.
2. Write-select setup time will protect the data written into the previous address. If protection of data in the previous address is not required, $t_{su(W)}$ can be ignored as any address selection sustained for the final 30 ns of the write-enable pulse and during $t_{h(W)}$ will result in data being written into that location. Depending on the duration of the input conditions, one or a number of previous addresses may have been written into.
3. Latch time is the time allowed for the internal output of the latch to assume the state of new data. See Figure 2. This is important only when attempting to read from a location immediately after that location has received new data.

TEXAS INSTRUMENTS
INCORPORATED
POST OFFICE BOX 5012 • DALLAS, TEXAS 75222

electrical characteristics over recommended operating free-air temperature range (unless otherwise noted)

PARAMETER		TEST CONDITIONS†			SN54LS670 MIN	SN54LS670 TYP‡	SN54LS670 MAX	SN74LS670 MIN	SN74LS670 TYP‡	SN74LS670 MAX	UNIT
V_{IH}	High-level input voltage				2			2			V
V_{IL}	Low-level input voltage						0.7			0.8	V
V_{IK}	Input clamp voltage	V_{CC} = MIN,	I_I = −18 mA				−1.5			−1.5	V
V_{OH}	High-level output voltage	V_{CC} = MIN, V_{IH} = 2 V, $V_{IL} = V_{IL}$ max	I_{OH} = −1 mA		2.4	3.4					V
			I_{OH} = −2.6 mA					2.4	3.1		
V_{OL}	Low-level output voltage	V_{CC} = MIN, V_{IH} = 2 V, $V_{IL} = V_{IL}$ max	I_{OL} = 4 mA			0.25	0.4		0.25	0.4	V
			I_{OL} = 8 mA						0.35	0.5	
I_{OZH}	Off-state output current, high-level voltage applied	V_{CC} = MAX,	V_{IH} = 2 V,	V_O = 2.7 V			20			20	µA
I_{OZL}	Off-state output current, low-level voltage applied	V_{CC} = MAX,	V_{IH} = 2 V,	V_O = 0.4 V			−20			−20	µA
I_I	Input current at maximum input voltage	V_{CC} = MAX, V_I = 7 V	Any D, R, or W				0.1			0.1	mA
			G_W				0.2			0.2	
			G_R				0.3			0.3	
I_{IH}	High-level input current	V_{CC} = MAX, V_I = 2.7 V	Any D, R, or W				20			20	µA
			G_W				40			40	
			G_R				60			60	
I_{IL}	Low-level input current	V_{CC} = MAX	Any D, R, or W				−0.4			−0.4	mA
			G_W				−0.8			−0.8	
			G_R				−1.2			−1.2	
I_{OS}	Short-circuit output current§	V_{CC} = MAX			−30		−130	−30		−130	mA
I_{CC}	Supply current	V_{CC} = MAX,	See Note 4			30	50		30	50	mA

†For conditions shown as MIN or MAX, use the appropriate value specified under recommended operating conditions.
‡All typical values are at V_{CC} = 5 V, T_A = 25°C.
§Not more than one output should be shorted at a time, and duration of the short-circuit should not exceed one second.
NOTE 4: Maximum I_{CC} is guaranteed for the following worst-case conditions: 4.5 V is applied to all data inputs and both enable inputs, all address inputs are grounded and all outputs are open.

switching characteristics, V_{CC} = 5 V, T_A = 25°C

PARAMETER¶	FROM (INPUT)	TO (OUTPUT)	TEST CONDITIONS	MIN	TYP	MAX	UNIT
t_{PLH}	Read select	Any Q	C_L = 15 pF, R_L = 2 kΩ, See Figures 1 and 2		23	40	ns
t_{PHL}					25	45	
t_{PLH}	Write enable	Any Q	C_L = 15 pF, R_L = 2 kΩ, See Figures 1 and 3		26	45	ns
t_{PHL}					28	50	
t_{PLH}	Data	Any Q			25	45	ns
t_{PHL}					23	40	
t_{PZH}	Read enable	Any Q	C_L = 15 pF, R_L = 2 kΩ, See Figures 1 and 4		15	35	ns
t_{PZL}					22	40	
t_{PHZ}			C_L = 5 pF, R_L = 2 kΩ, See Figures 1 and 4		30	50	ns
t_{PLZ}					16	35	

¶ t_{PLH} ≡ propagation delay time, low-to-high-level output
t_{PHL} ≡ propagation delay time, high-to-low-level output
t_{PZH} ≡ output enable time to high level
t_{PZL} ≡ output enable time to low level
t_{PHZ} ≡ output disable time from high level
t_{PLZ} ≡ output disable time from low level

7

PARAMETER MEASUREMENT INFORMATION

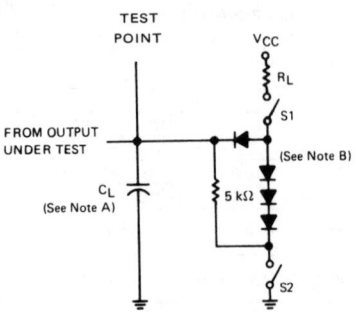

LOAD CIRCUIT

NOTES: A. C_L includes probe and jig capacitance.
         B. All diodes are 1N916 or 1N3064.

FIGURE 1

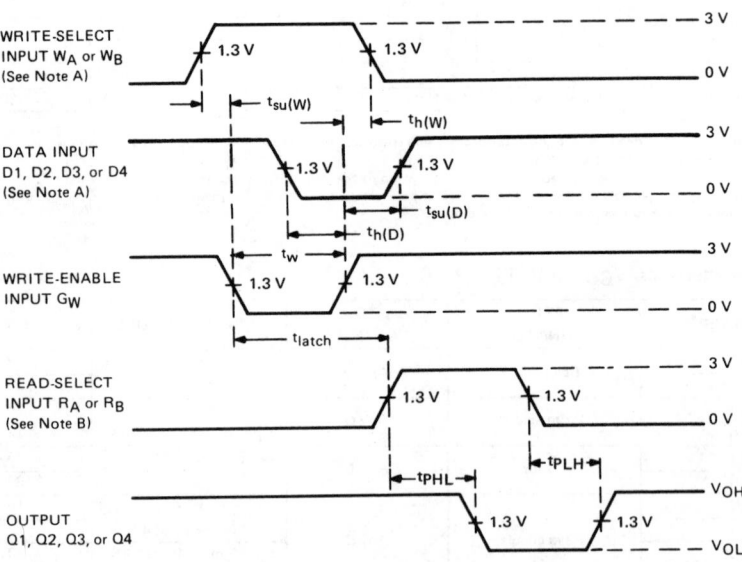

VOLTAGE WAVEFORMS (S1 AND S2 ARE CLOSED)

NOTES: A. High-level input pulses at the select and data inputs are illustrated; however, times associated with low-level pulses are measured from the same reference points.
         B. When measuring delay times from a read-select input, the read-enable input is low.
         C. Input waveforms are supplied by generators having the following characteristics: PRR ≤ 2 MHz, $Z_{out} \approx$ 50 Ω, duty cycle ≤ 50%, t_r ≤ 15 ns, t_f ≤ 6 ns.

FIGURE 2

TEXAS INSTRUMENTS
INCORPORATED
POST OFFICE BOX 5012 • DALLAS, TEXAS 75222

PARAMETER MEASUREMENT INFORMATION

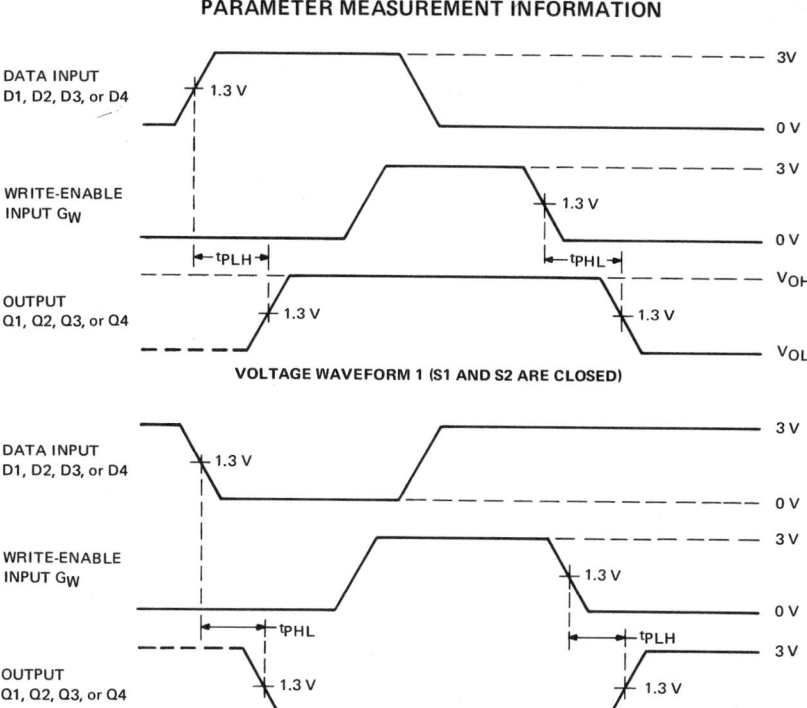

VOLTAGE WAVEFORM 1 (S1 AND S2 ARE CLOSED)

VOLTAGE WAVEFORM 2 (S1 AND S2 ARE CLOSED)

NOTES: A. Each select address is tested. Prior to the start of each of the above tests both write and read address inputs are stabilized with $W_A = R_A$ and $W_B = R_B$. During the test G_R is low.
B. Input waveforms are supplied by generators having the following characteristics: PRR $\leqslant$ 1 MHz, $Z_{out} \approx 50\ \Omega$, duty cycle $\leqslant$ 50%, $t_r \leqslant$ 15 ns, $t_r \leqslant$ 6 ns.

FIGURE 3

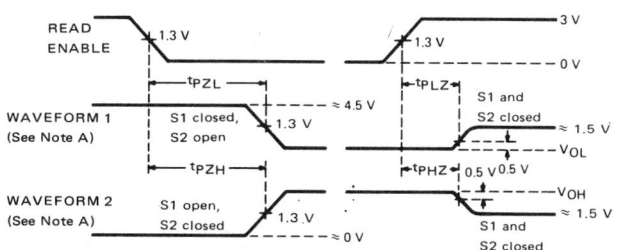

VOLTAGE WAVEFORMS
ENABLE AND DISABLE TIMES, THREE-STATE OUTPUTS

NOTES: A. Waveforms 1 is for an output with internal conditions such that the output is low except when disabled by the read-enable input.
Waveform 2 is for an output with internal conditions such that the output is high except when disabled by the read-enable input.
B. When measuring delay times from the read-enable input, both read-select inputs have been established at steady states.
C. Input waveforms are supplied by generators having the following characteristics: PRR $\leqslant$ 1 MHz, $Z_{out} \approx 50\ \Omega$, duty cycle $\leqslant$ 50%, $t_r \leqslant$ 15 ns, $t_r \leqslant$ 6 ns.
FIGURE 4

7

TEXAS INSTRUMENTS
INCORPORATED
POST OFFICE BOX 5012 • DALLAS, TEXAS 75222

JAN MIL-M-38510
Integrated Circuits

MIL-M-38510 AND MIL-STD-883
Military High-Reliability Integrated Circuits

The Texas Instruments MIL-M-38510 and MIL-STD-883 programs offer several options designed to meet system cost, reliability, lead time, and contract requirements. The following are the key features of the options available for MIL-M-38510 and MIL-STD-883 Class B applications:

JAN-Processed TI SNJ

■ Produced under MIL-M-38510 guidelines with all chips manufactured in a DESC-certified front end facility
■ Fully tested per MIL-STD-883 method 5004 Class B
■ Includes device types covered by MIL-M-38510 part numbers and circuits not yet covered by MIL numbers
■ Electrical and mechanical characteristics per TI data sheets
■ Marked with 38510 part numbers where applicable
■ Each lot includes Certificate of Conformance and Group A Summary Report
■ Approximately one-half the cost of JAN-Qualified IC's

SNC/MACH-IV (883B)

■ Cost effective — approximately one-third the cost of JAN-Qualified IC's
■ Produced under MIL-M-38510 guidelines with all chips manufactured in a DESC-certified front end facility
■ Tested per MIL-STD-883 method 5004 Class B and TI 38510/MACH-IV specification, Section 9 of this catalog
■ Tested per MIL-STD-883 method 5004 Class B and TI 38510/MACH-IV specification, Section 9 of this catalog
■ Electrical and mechanical characteristics per TI data sheets
■ Available in broad product spectrum including SSI, MSI, and LSI, both bipolar and MOS

JAN-Qualified

■ Qualified per MIL-M-38510 Class B
■ Produced per MIL-STD-883 and MIL-M-38510 Class B and appropriate slash sheets
■ Produced in DESC-certified domestic production facility
■ Applicable devices and packages

PRODUCT	A	C	D	E	F	G	I	J	L	T	V	W
SERIES 54 TTL	X	X	X	X				X	X			
SERIES 54H TTL	X	X	X	X								
SERIES 54L TTL *										X		
SERIES 54LS TTL	X	X	X	X				X	X			
SERIES 54S TTL	X	X	X	X				X	X			
LINEAR CONTROL	X					X	X					
SERIES 55 INTERFACE	X		X									
MOS LSI										X	X	X
LEAD FINISH B	X	X	X	X				X	X		X	X
LEAD FINISH C/D						X	X			X		

* PER MIL-M-0038510B, Class S.

8

TEXAS INSTRUMENTS
INCORPORATED
POST OFFICE BOX 5012 • DALLAS, TEXAS 75222

How to Order

See Tables I, II and III for device, package and lead-finish cross-reference.

• JAN-Processed/TI SNJ

	Device type covered by 38510 part number:		Device type not covered by 38510 part number:	
Device	SN5400J	883 Class B	Device	SN54LS298J	883 Class B
Order	SNJ5400J			SNJ54LS298J	
Marking	{ SNJ5400J { 38510/00104BCB		Marking	{ SNJ54LS298J { 38510B	

• SNC/MACH-IV

Device	SNC5400J	883 Class B
Order	SNC5400J	
Marking	SNC5400J	

• JAN-Qualified

Device	SN5400J	883 Class B
Order	JM38510/00104BCB	
Marking	JM38510/00104BCB	

Table I Part Numbers

EXAMPLE: 5400 TTL NAND gate in ceramic dual-in-line package to 883 Class B with standard tin-plated leads.

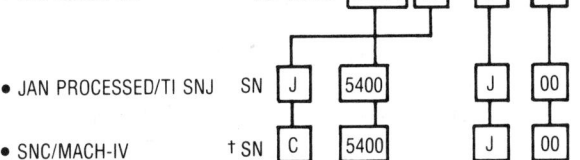

• JAN QUALIFIED   JM 38510/ [00104] [B]   [C]   [B]

• JAN PROCESSED/TI SNJ   SN [J] [5400]   [J] [00]

• SNC/MACH-IV   † SN [C] [5400]   [J] [00]

MIL-STD-883
CLASS B SCREENING ONLY

MIL-M-38510 SLASH SHEET
AND DEVICE TYPE
SEE TABLE II & III

CASE OUTLINE

JAN	PACKAGE	SNJ SNC/MACH-IV
A	1/4" x 1/4" FLAT-14	U/FB
B/T*	1/4" x 1/8" FLAT-14	T
C	DIP-14	J
D	1/4" x 3/8" FLAT-14	W
E	DIP-16	J
F	1/4" x 3/8" FLAT-16	W/SB
G	TO-99	L
H	1/4" x 1/4" FLAT-10	U
I	TO-100	L
J	DIP-24	J
K	3/8" x 5/8" FLAT-24	W
L	3/8" x 1/2" FLAT-24	W
V	DIP-18	JR §
W	DIP-22	JR §
X	TO-5	—
Y	TO-3	—
Z	1/4" X 3/8" FLAT-24	—

LEAD FINISH

JAN	TYPE	SNJ SNC/MACH-IV
A	SOLDER DIP	10
B	TIN-PLATE	00
C/D*	GOLD-PLATE	00'
X	OPTIONAL **	

*Per MIL-M-0038510B, Class S.

**Finish B or C at TI's option. Devices will
be marked B or C as applicable.

†Prefix designation for MOS/LSI is "SMC."

§ R denotes temperature range.

Screening — Class B

SCREEN	JAN QUALIFIED		SNJ JAN PROCESSED		SNC MACH-IV	
	METHOD	RQMT	METHOD	RQMT	METHOD	RQMT
Internal Visual (Precap)	2010.2 Cond B and 38510	100%	2010.2 Cond B and 38510	100%	2010.2 Cond B and 38510	100%
Stabilization Bake	1008.1 24 hrs min test Cond C	100%	1008.1 24 hrs min test Cond C	100%	1008.1 24 hrs min test Cond C	100%
Temperature Cycling	1010.1 Cond C	100%	1010.1 Cond C	100%	1010.1 Cond C	100%
Constant Acceleration	2001.1 Cond E (min) in Y_1 plane	100%	2001.1 Cond E (min) in Y_1 plane	100%	2001.1 Cond E (min) in Y_1 plane	100%
Seal (a) Fine (b) Gross	1014.1	100%	1014.1	100%	1014.1 (cond C_1)	100%
Interim Electrical	JAN slash-sheet electrical specifications	As applicable	TI data sheet electrical specifications	As applicable	TI data sheet electrical specifications	As applicable
Burn-in test	1015.1 160 hrs @ 125°C min	100%	1015.1 160 hrs @ 125°C min	100%	1015.1 160 hrs @ 125°C min	100%
Final Electrical Tests (a) Static tests (1) 25°C (Subgroup 1, table 1, 5005.3)	JAN slash-sheet electrical specifications	100%	TI data sheet electrical specifications	100%	TI data sheet electrical specifications	100%
(2) Max and min rated op. temperature (subgroups 2 and 3, table 1, 5005.3)		100%		100%		100% Note 1
(b) Dynamic tests and switching tests 25°C (subgroup 4 and 9, table 1, 5005.3)		100%		100%		
(c) Functional test 25°C (subgroup 7, table 1, 5005.3)		100%		100%		100%
Qualification or quality conformance inspection	5005.3 Class B	per 38510	5005.3 Class B	per 38510 Note 2	5005.3 Class B	per 38510 Note 2
External Visual	2009.1	100%	2009.1	100%	2009.1	100%

NOTES: 1. Temperature guardband test may be used in lieu of 100% test for digital bipolar only.
2. Group A per 5005.3. Generic data available for groups B, C, and D.

For MIL-M-38510/MIL-STD-883 Class A/S

For critical space and satellite applications, SAMSO Class S JAN-Qualified TTL flat pack devices are available per MIL-M-0038510B including:

CIRCUIT TYPE	JAN NO.
SN54L00T	JM38510/02004STD
SN54L01T	JM38510/02006STD
SN54L02T	JM38510/02701STD
SN54L04T	JM38510/02005STD
SN54L10T	JM38510/02003STD
SN54L20T	JM38510/02002STD
SN54L30T	JM38510/02001STD
SN54L51T	JM38510/04101STD

CIRCUIT TYPE	JAN NO.
SN54L54T	JM38510/04104STD
SN54L71T	JM38510/02101STD
SN54L74T	JM38510/02105STD
SN54L78T	JM38510/02104STD
SN54L86T	JM38510/02601STD
SN54L91T	JM38510/02806STD
SN54L95T	JM38510/02801STD
SN54L121T	JM38510/04201STD
SN54L122T	JM38510/04202STD
SN54L164T	JM38510/02802STD
SN5400T	JM38510/00104STD
SN5401T	JM38510/00107STD

CIRCUIT TYPE	JAN NO.
SN5402T	JM38510/00401STD
SN5404T	JM38510/00105STD
SN5410T	JM38510/00103STD
SN5420T	JM38510/00102STD
SN5440T	JM38510/00301STD
SN5472T	JM38510/00201STD
SN5473T	JM38510/00202STD
SN5474T	JM38510/00205STD
SN5493T	JM38510/01302STD
SN5495T	JM38510/00901STD
SN54121T	JM38510/01201STD
SN54H00T	JM38510/02304STD

TEXAS INSTRUMENTS
INCORPORATED
POST OFFICE BOX 5012 • DALLAS, TEXAS 75222

TABLE I. JAN INTEGRATED CIRCUITS AND CIRCUIT-TYPE CROSS-REFERENCE

JAN /NO.	CKT TYPE	JAN /NO.	CKT TYPE	JAN /NO.	CKT TYPE	JAN /NO.	CKT TYPE
00101	5430	01307	5490	03001	15930	06005	10507‡
00102	5420	01308	54192	03002	15935	06006	10509‡
00103	5410	01309	54193	03003	15936	06101	10531‡
00104	5400	01310†	54196	03004	15946	06102	10631‡
00105	5404	01311†	54197	03005	15962	06103	10576‡
00106	5412	01312†	54177	03101	15932	06104	10535‡
00107	5401	01401	54150	03102	15944	06201	10504
00108	5405	01402	9312‡	03103	15957	06202	10597
00109	5403	01403	54153	03104	15958	07001	54S00
00201	5472	01404	9309	03105	15933	07002	54S03
00202	5473	01405	54157	03201	15951	07003	54S04
00203	54107	01406	54151	03301	15945	07004	54S05
00204	5476	01501	5475	03302	15948	07005	54S10
00205	5474	01502	5477	03303	15950	07006	54S20
00206	5470	01503	54116	03304	9094	07007	54S22
00207	5479‡	01504	9314‡	03501	MH0026	07008	54S30
00301	5440	01601	5408	04001	54H50	07009	54S133
00302	5437	01602	5409	04002	54H51	07010	54S134
00303	5438	01701	54174	04003	54H53	07101	54S74
00401	5402	01702	54175	04004	54H54	07102	54S112
00402	5423	01703†	54173	04005	54H55	07103	54S113
00403	5425	01801	54170	04101	54L51	07104	54S114
00404	5427	01901	54180	04102	54L54	07105	54S174
00501	5450	02001	54L30	04103	54L55	07106	54S175
00502	5451	02002	54L20	04104♦	54L54	07201	54S40
00503	5453	02003	54L10	04201	54L121	07301	54S02
00504	5454	02004	54L00	04202	54L122	07401	54S51
00601	5482	02005	54L04	04301	93L18	07402	54S64
00602	5483	02006	54L01/54L03	04401	93L24	07403	54S65
00603	9304‡	02101	54L71	04501†	93L14	07501	54S86
00604	5480	02102	54L72	04502†	93L08	07502	54S135
00701	5486	02103	54L73	04601	93L09	07601†	54S194
00801	5406	02104	54L78	04602	93L12	07602†	54S195
00802	5416	02105	54L74	04603	93L22	07701†	54S138
00803	5407	02201	54H72	05001	4011A	07702†	54S139
00804	5417	02202	54H73	05002	4012A	07703†	54S280
00805	5426	02203	54H74	05003	4023A	07801	54S181
00901	5495	02204	54H76	05101	4013A	07802	54S182
00902	5496	02205	54H101	05102	4027A	07901	54S151
00903	54164	02206	54H103	05201	4000A	07902	54S153
00904	54165	02301	54H30	05202	4001A	07903	54S157
00905	54194	02302	54H20	05203	4002A	07904	54S158
00906	54195	02303	54H10	05204	4025A	07905	54S251
00907†	9300‡	02304	54H00	05301	4007A	07906	54S257
00908†	9328	02305	54H04	05302	4019A	07907	54S258
00909†	54198	02306	54H01	05303	4030A	08001	54S11
00910†	54166	02307	54H22	05401	4008A	08002	54S15
01001	5442	02401	54H40	05501	4009A	08003†	54S08
01002	5443	02501	54L90	05502	4010A	08004†	54S09
01003	5444	02502	54L93	05503	4049A	08101	54S140
01004	5445	02503	54L193	05504	4050A	08201	54S85
01005	54145	02504	93L10	05505	4041A	10101	uA741
01006	5446	02505	93L16	05601	4017A	10102	uA747
01007	5447	02601	54L86	05602	4018A	10103	LM101A
01008	5448	02701	54L02	05603	4020A	10104	LM108A
01009	5449	02801	54L95	05604	4022A	10105	LH2101A
01101	54181	02802	54L164	05605	4024A	10106	LH2108A
01102	54182	02803	93L28‡	05701	4006A	10107	LM118
01201	54121	02804	93L00	05702	4014A	10201	uA723
01202	54122	02805	76L70	05703	4015A	10202†	LM104
01203	54123	02806♦	54L91	05704	4021A	10203†	LM105
01204	9601	02901	54L42	05705	4031A	10301	uA710
01205	9602	02902	54L43	05706	4034A	10302	uA711
01301	5492	02903	54L44	05801†	4016A	10303	LM106
01302	5493	02904	54L46	06001	10501‡	10304	LM111
01303	54160	02905	54L47	06002	10502‡	10305†	LM2111
01304	54163	02906	76L42A	06003	10505‡	10401	55107
01305	54162	02907	93L01	06004	10506‡	10402	55108
01306	54161						

NOTE: Only the basic JAN and commercial numbers are shown.

† Slash sheets not released as of date of this publication.

‡ Not recommended for new designs.

♦ Class S only.

TABLE I. JAN INTEGRATED CIRCUITS AND CIRCUIT-TYPE CROSS-REFERENCE

JAN. /NO.	CKT TYPE	JAN. /NO.	CKT TYPE	JAN. /NO.	CKT TYPE	JAN. /NO.	CKT TYPE
10403	55114	15802	9317	30104	54LS113	31001	54LS11
10404	55115	15901	9300	30105	54LS114	31002	54LS15
10405	55113	15902	9328	30106	54LS174	31003	54LS21
10406	7831	16001	9334	30107	54LS175	31004	54LS08
10407	7832	16101	5432	30108	54LS107	31101	54LS85
10501†	uA733	16201	5428	30109	54LS109	31201†	54LS83A
10601	LM102‡	20101	54186 (PROM 512)	30110	54LS76	31202†	54LS283
10602	LM110	20102	MCM5304‡	30201	54LS40	31301	54LS13
10603†	LM2110	20103†	IM5603A	30202	54LS37	31302	54LS14
10701	LM109	20201†	IM5603 (PROM 1024)	30203	54LS38	31303	54LS132
10702†	LM140-12	20202†	IM5623	30204	54LS28	31401†	54LS123
10703†	LM140-15	20301†	AM27S10	30301	54LS02	31402†	54LS221
10704†	LM140-24	20302†	AM27S11	30302	54LS27	31403†	54LS122
10801	3018A	20401†	IM5604	30303	54LS266	31501†	54LS90
10802	3045	20402†	IM5624	30401	54LS51	31502†	54LS160
10901†	SE555	20501†	HHX7620-8	30402	54LS54	31503†	54LS161
10902†	SE556	20502†	HMX7621-8	30501	54LS32	31504†	54LS168
15001	5485	20601†	HMX7640-8	30502	54LS86	31505†	54LS169
15101	5413	20602†	HMX7641-8	30601†	54LS194	31506†	54LS192
15102	5414	23001†	93410 (256 RAM)	30602†	54LS195	31507†	54LS193
15103	54132	23002†	93411 (256 RAM)	30603†	54LS95	31508†	54LS191
15201	54154	23003†	93421	30604†	54LS96	31509†	54LS190
15202	54155	23501	TMS4060 (4K RAM)	30605†	54LS164	31510†	54LS92
15203	54156	23502	TMS4050 (4K RAM)	30606†	54LS295	31511†	54LS162
15204	8250	23503	TMS4060 (4K RAM)	30607†	54LS395	31512†	54LS163
15205	8251	23504	TMS4050 (4K RAM)	30701†	54LS138	31513†	54LS190
15206	8252	30001	54LS00	30702†	54LS139	31601†	54LS75
15301	54125	30002	54LS03	30703†	54LS42	31602†	54LS279
15302	54126	30003	54LS04	30704†	54LS47	31701†	54LS124
15401†	54120	30004	54LS05	30801	54LS181	31702†	54LS324
15501	54H08	30005	54LS10	30901†	54LS151	31801†	54LS261
15502	54H11	30006	54LS12	30902†	54LS153	31901†	54LS670
15503	54H21	30007	54LS20	30903†	54LS157	32001†	54LS196
15601	54147	30008	54LS22	30904†	54LS158	32002†	54LS197
15602	54148	30009	54LS30	30905†	54LS251	32003†	54LS290
15603	9318‡	30101	54LS73	30906†	54LS257	32004†	54LS293
15701	9338	30102	54LS74	30907†	54LS258	32102†	54LS26
15801	9321	30103	54LS112	30908†	54LS253		

NOTE: Only the basic JAN and commercial numbers are shown.

† Slash sheets not released as of date of this publication.

‡ Not recommended for new designs.

TEXAS INSTRUMENTS
INCORPORATED
POST OFFICE BOX 5012 • DALLAS, TEXAS 75222

TABLE II. CIRCUIT-TYPE AND JAN INTEGRATED CIRCUITS CROSS-REFERENCE

TTL 54 SERIES

CKT TYPE	JAN /NO.
5400	00104
5401	00107
5402	00401
5403	00109
5404	00105
5405	00108
5406	00801
5407	00803
5408	01601
5409	01602
5410	00103
5412	00106
5413	15101
5414	15102
5416	00802
5417	00804
5420	00102
5423	00402
5425	00403
5426	00805
5427	00404
5428	16201
5430	00101
5432	16101
5437	00302
5438	00303
5440	00301
5442	01001
5443	01002
5444	01003
5445	01004
5446	01006
5447	01007
5448	01008
5449	01009
5450	00501
5451	00502
5453	00503
5454	00504
5470	00206
5472	00201
5473	00202
5474	00205
5475	01501
5476	00204
5477	01502
5480	00604
5482	00601
5483	00602
5485	15001
5486	00701
5490	01307
5492	01301
5493	01302
5495	00901
5496	00902
54107	00203
54116	01503
54120	15401†
54121	01201
54122	01202
54123	01203
54125	15301
54126	15302

CKT TYPE	JAN /NO.
54132	15103
54145	01005
54147	15601
54148	15602
54150	01401
54151	01406
54153	01403
54154	15201
54155	15202
54156	15203
54157	01405
54160	01303
54161	01306
54162	01305
54163	01304
54164	00903
54165	00904
54166	00910†
54173	01703†
54174	01701
54175	01702
54177	01312†
54180	01901
54181	01101
54182	01102
54186	20101
54192	01308
54193	01309
54194	00905
54195	00906
54196	01310†
54197	01311†
54198	00909†

TTL 54H SERIES

CKT TYPE	JAN /NO.
54H00	02304
54H01	02306
54H04	02305
54H08	15501
54H10	02303
54H11	15502
54H20	02302
54H21	15503
54H22	02307
54H30	02301
54H40	02401
54H50	04001
54H51	04002
54H53	04003
54H54	04004
54H55	04005
54H72	02201
54H73	02202
54H74	02203
54H76	02204
54H101	02205
54H103	02206

TTL 54L SERIES

CKT TYPE	JAN /NO.
54L00	02004
54L01	02006
54L02	02701
54L03	02006
54L04	02005
54L10	02003
54L20	02002
54L30	02001
54L42	02901
54L43	02902
54L44	02903
54L46	02904
54L47	02905
54L51	04101
54L54	04102
54L54	04104♦
54L55	04103
54L71	02101
54L72	02102
54L73	02103
54L74	02105
54L78	02104
54L86	02601
54L90	02501
54L91	02806♦
54L93	02502
54L95	02801
54L121	04201
54L122	04202
54L164	02802
54L193	02503

TTL 54LS SERIES

CKT TYPE	JAN /NO.
54LS00	30001
54LS02	30301
54LS03	30002
54LS04	30003
54LS05	30004
54LS08	31004
54LS10	30005
54LS11	31001
54LS12	30006
54LS13	30301
54LS14	31302
54LS15	31002
54LS20	30007
54LS21	31003
54LS22	30008
54LS26	32102†
54LS27	30302
54LS28	30204
54LS30	30009
54LS32	30501
54LS37	30202

CKT TYPE	JAN /NO.
54LS38	30203
54LS40	30201
54LS42	30703†
54LS47	30704†
54LS51	30401
54LS54	30402
54LS73	30101
54LS74	30102
54LS75	31601†
54LS76	30110
54LS83A	31201
54LS85	31101
54LS86	30502
54LS90	31501†
54LS92	31511†
54LS93	31502†
54LS95	30603†
54LS96	30604†
54LS107	30108
54LS109	30109
54LS112	30103
54LS113	30104
54LS114	30105
54LS122	31403†
54LS123	31401†
54LS124	31701†
54LS132	31303
54LS138	30701†
54LS139	30702†
54LS151	30901†
54LS153	30902†
54LS157	30903†
54LS158	30904†
54LS160	31503†
54LS161	31504†
54LS162	31510†
54LS163	31512†
54LS164	30605†
54LS168	31505†
54LS169	31506†
54LS174	30106
54LS175	30107
54LS181	30801
54LS190	31509†
54LS191	31513†
54LS192	31507†
54LS193	31508†
54LS194	30601†
54LS195	30602†
54LS196	32001†
54LS197	32002†
54LS221	31402†
54LS251	30905†
54LS253	30908†
54LS257	30906†
54LS258	30907†
54LS261	31801†
54SL266	30303
54LS279	31602†
54LS283	31202†
54LS290	32003†
54LS293	32004†
54LS295	30606†
54LS324	31702†
54LS395	30607†
54LS670	31901†

NOTE: Only the basic JAN and commercial numbers are shown.

†Slash sheets not released as of the date of this publication.

‡Not recommended for new designs.

♦Class S only.

TABLE II. CIRCUIT-TYPE AND JAN INTEGRATED CIRCUITS CROSS-REFERENCE

TTL 54S SERIES

CKT TYPE	JAN /NO.
54S00	07001
54S02	07301
54S03	07002
54S04	07003
54S05	07004
54S08	08003†
54S09	08004†
54S10	07005
54S11	08001
54S15	08002
54S20	07006
54S22	07007
54S30	07008
54S40	07201
54S51	07401
54S64	07402
54S65	07403
54S74	07101
54S85	08201
54S86	07501
54S112	07102
54S113	07103
54S114	07104
54S133	07009
54S134	07010
54S135	07502
54S138	07701†
54S139	07702†
54S140	08101
54S151	07901
54S153	07902
54S157	07903
54S158	07904
54S174	07105
54S175	07106
54S181	07801
54S182	07802
54S194	07601†
54S195	07602†
54S251	07905
54S257	07906
54S258	07907
54S280	07703†

MOS LSI

CKT TYPE	JAN /NO.
TMS4050	23502 (4K RAM)
TMS4050	23504 (4K RAM)
TMS4060	23501 (4K RAM)
TMS4060	23503 (4K RAM)

CMOS 54H SERIES

CKT TYPE	JAN /NO.
4000A	05201
4001A	05202
4002A	05203
4006A	05701
4007A	05301
4008A	05401
4009A	05501
4010A	05502
4011A	05001
4012A	05002
4013A	05101
4014A	05702
4015A	05703
4016A	05801†
4017A	05601
4018A	05602
4019A	05302
4020A	05603
4021A	05704
4022A	05604
4023A	05003
4024A	05605
4025A	05204
4027A	05102
4030A	05303
4031A	05705
4034A	05706
4041A	05505
4049A	05503
4050A	05504

LINEAR CONTROL SERIES

CKT TYPE	JAN /NO.
LM101A	10103
LM104	10202†
LM105	10203†
LM106	10303
LM108A	10104
LM109	10701
LM111	10304
LM118	10107
LM140-12	10702†
LM140-15	10703†
LM140-21	10704†
SE555	10901†
SE556	10902†
uA710	10301
uA711	10302
uA723	10201
uA733	10501†
uA741	10101
uA747	10102

LINEAR INTERFACE SERIES

CKT TYPE	JAN /NO.
55107	10401
55108	10402
55113	10405
55114	10403
55115	10404

NOTE: Only the basic JAN and commercial numbers are shown.

†Slash sheets not released as of date of this publication.

TEXAS INSTRUMENTS
INCORPORATED
POST OFFICE BOX 5012 • DALLAS, TEXAS 75222

38510/MACH IV

**High-Reliability Microelectronics
Procurement Specifications**

MIL-STD-883

CONTENTS

9

REVISIONS

CLASSIFICATION (MAJOR/MINOR)	DATE CODE EFFECTIVITY	LTR	DESCRIPTION	DATE	APPROVED
Major	7040	A	Incorporate MIL-M-38510 and Revision Notice 2 of MIL-STD-883	8/15/70	T.S. J Adams
Major	7239	B	Incorporate Revision Notice 3 and 4 of MIL-STD-883 and Revision A of MIL-STD-38510	9/1/72	
Major	7401	C	Incorporate revised Level IV (SNH) processing with inclusion of recorded electrical data with delta requirements; incorporate technological criteria in Table III for precap of complex circuits.	1/1/74	
Minor	7518	D	Incorporate Revision A of MIL-STD-883 and provisions for MOS LSI and CMOS devices	4/15/75	
Minor	7628	E	Incorporate Revision C of MIL-M-38510 and MIL-STD-883 Revision A, Notice 2	6/15/76	

UNLESS OTHERWISE SPECIFIED
DIMENSIONS ARE IN INCHES
TOLERANCES:
ANGLES ± 1°
3 PLACE DECIMAL ±.010
2 PLACE DECIMAL ±.02
INTERPRET DWG. IN
ACCORDANCE WITH STD.
DESCRIBED IN MIL-STD-100
MATERIAL:

DR C.E. Smith   DATE 9/22/69
CHK
ENGR
QUALITY CONTROL
QRA MGR.

TEXAS INSTRUMENTS
INCORPORATED
SEMICONDUCTOR CIRCUITS DIVISION DALLAS, TEXAS

TITLE **MICROELECTRONICS, HIGH RELIABILITY PROCUREMENT SPECIFICATION (MIL-STD 38510/883)**

DESIGN ACTIVITY RELEASE
DEPARTMENT MANAGER, TXL
CIRCUITS DIVISION MANAGER

SIZE A	CODE IDENT NO. 01295	DRAWING NO. 38510/MACH IV PROGRAM
SCALE	REV D	SHEET

38510/MACH IV PROCUREMENT SPECIFICATION

38510/MACH IV PROGRAM

1.0 SCOPE

1.1 This specification establishes standards for materials, workmanship, performance capabilities, identification, and processing of high-reliability monolithic integrated circuits.

1.2 Intent

The intent of this document is such as to recognize that quality and reliability are *built* into, not *tested* into, a product. There is no specification or screening procedure that can substitute for inherent, built-in reliability. However, it must be realized that irrespective of lot quality, there will always be some small percentage of devices that are subject to early failure (infant mortality). A well engineered screening procedure will eliminate most, if not all, of these early failures. Secondly, the screening and acceptance testing described herein will also serve to demonstrate, with a high degree of statistical confidence, that the required levels of quality and reliability have, in fact, been built into the product.

2.0 APPLICABLE DOCUMENTS

2.1 The following specifications and standards, of the issue in effect on the date of invitation for bids or request for proposal, form a part of this specification to the extent specified herein:

2.2 Specifications

Military

MIL-M-55565   Microcircuits, Packaging of
MIL-M-38510   Microcircuits devices, general specification for

TEXAS INSTRUMENTS
INCORPORATED
POST OFFICE BOX 5012 • DALLAS, TEXAS 75222

2.3   Standards

Military

MIL-STD-105	Sampling Procedures and Tables for Inspection by Attributes
MIL-STD-883	Test Methods and Procedures for Microelectronics
MIL-STD-790	Reliability Assurance Program for Electronic Parts Specification
MIL-STD-1276	Leads, Weldable, for Electronic Components Parts
MIL-STD-1313	Microelectronics Terms and Definitions

Detail Specifications

SNXXXX (Bipolar) TMSXXXX (MOS LSI) TFXXXX (CMOS)	Detail Specification for a Particular Part Type (e.g., Manufacturer's Data Sheet)

2.4   Precedence of Documents

For the purpose of interpretation, in case of any conflicts, the following order of precedence shall apply:

a)   Purchase Order   —The purchase order shall have precedence over any referenced specification.

b)   Detail Specification   —The detail specification shall have precedence over this specification and other referenced specifications.

c)   This Specification   —This specification shall have precedence over all referenced specifications.

d)   Referenced Specifications   —Referenced Specifications shall apply to the extent specified herein.

2.5   Federal and/or military specifications and standards required shall be obtained from the usual government sources.

9

3.0   GENERAL REQUIREMENTS

The individual item requirements shall be as specified herein and in accordance with the applicable detail specification. In the event of any conflict between the requirements of this specification and the detail specification, the latter shall govern. The static and dynamic electrical performance requirements of the integrated circuits plus absolute maximum ratings and test methods shall be as specified in the detail specifications.

3.1.1   Definitions

a)   LTPD   Lot Tolerance Percent Defective shall be as defined by MIL-M-38510.

b) λ Lambda, stated in percent per 1000 hours as defined by MIL-M-38510.

c)   MRN   Minimum reject number as defined by MIL-M-38510.

d)   Production   For the purpose of this specification, a production
     Lot   lot shall be defined per MIL-M-38510.

e)   Inspection   An inspection lot shall be as defined in
     Lot   MIL-M-38510.

f)   C   Acceptance number as defined by MIL-M-38510.

3.1.2   Terms and Definitions

Terms and definitions shall be as defined in MIL-STD-1313.

3.1.3   Classification of Requirements

The requirements for the integrated circuits are classified herein as follows:

Requirement	Paragraph
Process Conditioning, Testing and Screening	3.2
Qualification	3.3
Design and Construction	3.4

TEXAS INSTRUMENTS
INCORPORATED
POST OFFICE BOX 5012 • DALLAS, TEXAS 75222

Marking of Integrated Circuits	3.5
Product Assurance	3.6
Workmanship	3.7
Performance Capabilities	3.8
Quality and Reliability Assurance Program Plan	3.9

3.2   Process Conditioning, Testing and Screening

Three levels of screening and quality assurance for integrated circuits are provided for in this specification. Process conditioning, testing and screening shall be as specified in 4.3 and the applicable figure for the appropriate quality assurance level stated on the purchase order and defined as follows:

SCREENING LEVEL	PART NUMBER PREFIX			APPLICABLE FLOW CHART
	BIPOLAR	CMOS	MOS LSI	
38510/883 Class A (Level IV)	SNH	Not Avail.	Not Avail.	Figure 4
38510/883 Class B (Level III)	SNC	TFC		Figure 3
			SMC	Figure 2
38510/883 Class C (Level I)	SNM	TFM	Not Avail.	Figure 1

3.3   Qualification

Vendor qualification for delivery of integrated circuits to this specification shall be as specified in paragraph 4.2.

3.4   Design and Construction

Integrated circuit design and construction shall be in accordance with the requirements specified herein and in the applicable detail specification.

3.4.1   Topography

Integrated circuits furnished under this specification shall have topography information available for review by procuring activity. The information made available shall provide sufficient data for thorough circuit design, application, performance, and failure analysis studies.

3.4.1.1   Monolithic Die Topography

An enlarged photograph or drawing (to scale) with a minimum magnification of 80 times the die (chip) size showing the topography of elements formed on the silicon monolithic die shall be available for review. This shall be identified with the specific detail integrated circuit part-type in which it is used and the applicable detail specification.

38510/MACH IV PROCUREMENT SPECIFICATION

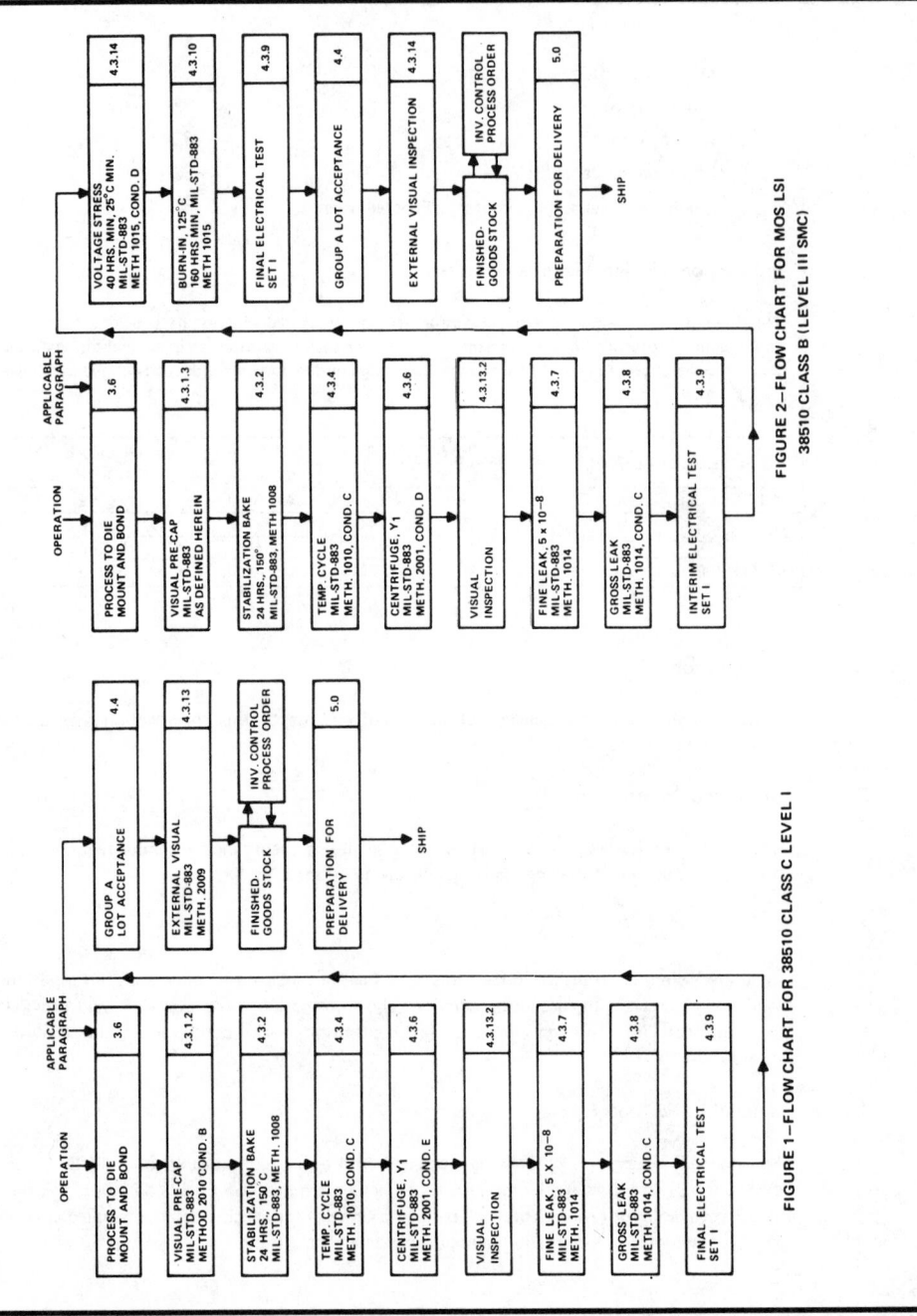

FIGURE 2—FLOW CHART FOR MOS LSI
38510 CLASS B (LEVEL III SMC)

FIGURE 1—FLOW CHART FOR 38510 CLASS C LEVEL I

TEXAS INSTRUMENTS
INCORPORATED
POST OFFICE BOX 5012 • DALLAS, TEXAS 75222

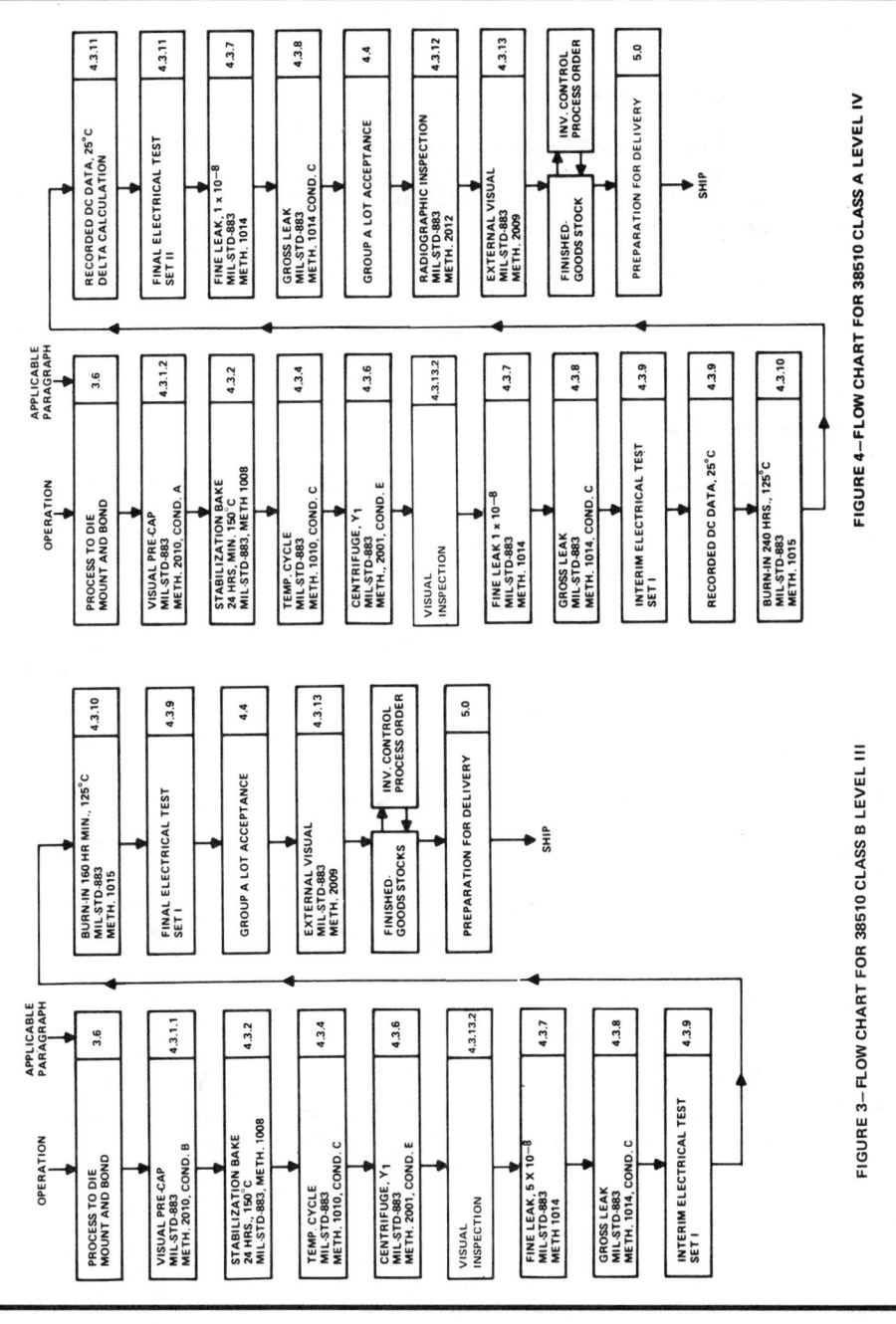

FIGURE 4—FLOW CHART FOR 38510 CLASS A LEVEL IV

FIGURE 3—FLOW CHART FOR 38510 CLASS B LEVEL III

3.4.1.2   Die Intraconnection Pattern

An enlarged photograph or drawing (to scale) with a minimum magnification of 80 times the die (chip) size showing the specific intraconnection pattern utilized to intraconnect the elements in the circuit. This shall be in the same scale as the die topography 3.4.1.1 so that the elements utilized and those not being used can easily be determined.

3.4.2   Materials

Materials shall be inherently non-nutrient to fungus and shall not blister, crack, outgas, soften, flow or exhibit other immediate or latent defects that adversely affect storage, operation or environmental capabilities of integrated circuits.

3.4.2.1   Material Selection

Materials selected for use in the construction of the integrated circuits shall be chosen for maximum suitability for the application. This shall include consideration of the best balance for:

a)   Electrical performance

b)   Thermal compatibility and conductivity

c)   Chemical stability including resistance to deleterious interactions with other materials

d)   Metallurgical stability with respect to adjacent materials and change in crystal configuration

e)   Maximum stability with regard to continued uniform performance through the specified environmental conditions and life.

3.4.2.2   Foreign Materials

No lacquer, grease, paste, desiccant or other similar foreign encapsulant or coating material shall be included in the circuit enclosure nor applied to any part of the internal circuit assembly.

3.4.3   Mechanical

3.4.3.1   Case

Each integrated circuit shall be securely mounted and hermetically sealed within a case designed and constructed to conform to the outline and physical dimensions shown in the detailed specification.

TEXAS INSTRUMENTS
INCORPORATED
POST OFFICE BOX 5012 • DALLAS, TEXAS 75222

3.4.3.2   Interconnections

Interconnections within the integrated circuit case shall be minimized and there shall be no wire crossovers. Circuit intraconnections by means of wire jumpers shall not be used. (See Note 6.2)

3.4.3.3   Leads

Lead material, construction, and outline shall be as specified on the detail specification and shall be capable of meeting the solderability test of MIL-STD-883, Method 2003. (See note 6.4).

3.4.3.3.1   Lead Size

Lead outline and dimensions shall be as specified in the detail specification.

3.4.3.3.2   Lead Surface Condition

Leads shall be free of the following defects over their entire length when inspected under a minimum of 4X magnification:

a)   Foreign materials adhering to the leads such as paint, film, deposits and dust. Where adherence of such foreign materials is in question, leads may be subjected to a clean, contaminant-free (e.g., oil, dust, etc.), filtered air stream (suction or expulsion) of 88 feet per second maximum, or a wash/rinse as necessary and reinspected.

b)   Nicks, cuts, scratches or other surface defacing defects which expose the base metal.

3.4.3.3.3   Lead Straightness

Leads shall be aligned within a 0.050-inch diameter, 0.050-inch length cylinder concentric to the point of lead emergence from the case and the X-axis (the axis parallel to the lead axis). Along the remaining lead length, there shall be no unspecified bend whose radius is less than 0.10 inch and no twist whose angle is greater than $30°$ (ribbon leads, only).

3.4.3.3.4   Preformed Leads

Preformed leads, when specified, shall be in accordance with the detail specification. The part number of the integrated circuit shall remain as specified in the applicable detail specification or purchase order, the applicable suffix designation shall appear on the purchase order but shall not be marked on the device.

9

3.4.3.3.5 Carriers (Mech-Pak Carrier)

Carrier-matrix assemblies consisting of individually mounted integrated circuits shall be furnished when so specified by purchase order. The individual carriers shall have provisions for use with automatic test equipment contacts. Devices supplied "clipped-out" of the Mech-Pak Carrier shall be supplied in the Barnes Carrier type 029-188 or equivalent. (Applicable to Flat Packs only.)

3.5 Marking of Integrated Circuits

3.5.1 Legibility

All marking shall be permanent in nature and remain legible when subjected to specified operating, storage, and environmental requirements. All markings shall be insoluble in standard solvents such as trichlorethylene, water and xylene.

3.5.2 Marking Details

Marking of the integrated circuits shall be located as follows unless otherwise specified in the detail specification:

a) TO-99, TO-100, and similar "can" cases shall be marked on the top of the case. Where space limitations exist, the side of the case may be used.

b) Flat Packs shall be marked on the top of the case. Where space limitation exists, the bottom of the package may be utilized as necessary. As a minimum the top of the package shall show the manufacturer's identification mark or symbol, the device part number, date code, and pin 1 orientation mark (where applicable).

c) Dual-in-line plug-in packages shall be marked in the same manner as flat packs.

3.5.3 Required Device Marking

a) Index point indicating the starting point for numbering of leads shall be as indicated in the detail specification. The indexing point may be a tab, color dot, or other suitable indicator.

b) Manufacturer's identification mark or symbol.

c) A lot date code indicating the week of initial submission for screening or inspection. The date code shall be as follows:

1) EIA four-digit date code, the first two numbers shall be the last two digits of the year, the last two numbers shall indicate the calendar week.

TEXAS INSTRUMENTS
INCORPORATED
POST OFFICE BOX 5012 • DALLAS, TEXAS 75222

2) EIA three-digit date code (when limited by space available), the first number shall be the last digit of the year, the last two numbers shall indicate the calendar week.

d) Manufacturer's part number defining circuit type and applicable MIL-STD-883 screening level and MIL-M-38510 product assurance level as defined in paragraph 3.2.

e) Individual device serial number is required for Class A (SNH).

f) A dot to indicate acceptance by Radiographic inspection.

NOTE:

When a color dot is used to identify pin one, the radiographic inspection acceptance dot shall be placed on the bottom of the package.

g) Country of origin shall be per U.S. Customs codes.

3.6 Product Assurance

The manufacturer shall establish and maintain a reliability assurance program that complies with the basic intent of MIL-STD-790. Furthermore, it is intended that each integrated circuit delivered shall be free of any defect in design, material, manufacturing process, testing and handling, which would degrade or otherwise limit its performance when used within the specified limits.

3.6.1 Visual and Mechanical Examination

Integrated circuits shall be examined to verify that material, design, construction, physical dimensions, marking and workmanship are in accordance with the specified acceptance criteria.

3.6.2 Test Equipment

The manufacturer shall prepare and maintain a current list, by name and drawing number or other unique identification, of test equipment used in the manufacturing and testing of devices submitted for acceptance inspection under this specification. This list shall be made available to the procuring activity representative upon request.

3.6.3 Process Controls

Each integrated circuit shall be constructed by manufacturing processes which are under the surveillance of the manufacturer's Quality Control department. The processes shall be monitored and controlled by use of statistical techniques in accordance with published specifications and procedures. The manufacturer shall prepare and maintain suitable documentation (such as quality control manuals, inspection instructions, control charts, etc.) covering all phases of incoming part and material inspection and in-process inspections required to assure that product quality meets the requirements of this specification. The procuring activity may verify, with the permission of and in the company of the manufacturer's designated representative, that suitable documentation exists and is being applied. Information designated as proprietary by the manufacturer will be made available to the procuring activity or its representative only with the written permission of the manufacturer.

Process control is recognized as being vital to the concept of "built-in" quality. The process control program shall include a scanning electron microscope (SEM) monitor program for evaluating the metal integrity over oxide step and oxide step contour. The SEM analysis will be defined in a Quality & Reliability Assurance document.

3.6.4   Production Changes

The manufacturer shall advise the procuring activity of the time at which any major change(s) in production or QC methods or documentation become effective during the period of device production for delivery against any given purchase order referencing this specification.

3.7   Workmanship

Integrated circuits shall be manufactured and processed in a careful and workmanlike manner, in accordance with the production processes, workmanship instructions, inspection and test procedures, and training aids prepared by the manufacturer in fulfillment of the reliability assurance program established by paragraph 3.6.

3.7.1   Personnel Certification

The manufacturer shall be responsible for training, testing and certification of personnel involved in producing integrated circuits. Training shall be commensurate and consistent with the requirements of this specification and in conformance to the basic intent of MIL-STD-790. Training aids in the form of satisfactory criteria shall be available for operator and inspector review at any time.

3.7.2   Personnel Evaluation

The supplier shall maintain a continuous evaluation of the proficiency of personnel concerned with production and inspection. Retraining of an operator or inspector shall be required when this evaluation establishes that a degree of proficiency necessary to meet the requirements of this specification is not being exercised.

TEXAS INSTRUMENTS
INCORPORATED
POST OFFICE BOX 5012 • DALLAS, TEXAS 75222

3.7.3 Rework provisions

3.7.3.1 Rework

All rework on micorcircuits manufactured under this specification shall be accomplished in accordance with paragraph 3.7.1 of MIL-M-38510 as defined herein.

3.7.3.2 Rebonding

Rebonding shall be in accordance with MIL-M-38510, as defined herein (see Note 6.5)

3.8 Performance Capabilities

The integrated circuits delivered to this specification shall be designed to be capable of meeting the environmental requirements specified in Table II. The manufacturer need not perform these tests specifically for the contract or specification, but shall provide data which demonstrates the ability of the integrated circuits to pass the environmental tests. The data shall have been generated on devices from the same generic family as the circuits being supplied to this specification, and the package configuration shall be the same as for the delivered parts (i.e., Flat Pack, TO-100, etc.).

3.9 Quality and Reliability Assurance Program Plan

The manufacturer shall establish and implement a Quality and Reliability Assurance Program Plan that meets the intent of MIL-M-38510, Appendix A. Submission of the program plan to the procuring activity shall not be a requirement of this specification; however, the program plan shall be maintained by the manufacturer and shall be available for review by the procuring activity.

4.0   QUALITY ASSURANCE PROVISIONS

4.1   Responsibility for Inspection

Unless otherwise specified in the contract or purchase order, the manufacturer is responsible for the performance of all inspection requirements specified herein. Except as otherwise specified, the manufacturer may utilize his own facilities or any commercial laboratory acceptable to the procuring activity. The procuring activity may, at its discretion, perform any of the inspections set forth in the specification where such inspections are deemed necessary to assure supplies and services conform to prescribed requirements.

4.1.1   Inspection and Testing Procedures Coverage

Inspection and testing processes and procedures prepared in fulfillment of the reliability assurance program established per paragraph 3.6 shall be prescribed by clear, complete and current instructions. These instructions shall assure inspection and test of materials, work in process and completed integrated circuits as required by this specification. In addition, criteria for approval and rejection of materials and integrated circuits shall be included.

4.1.2   Inspection at Point of Delivery

The procuring activity may, at its discretion, reinspect any or all of the delivered parts excluding Groups B, C, and D destructive samples as defined by MIL-STD-883. All parts found to be defective, excluding devices exhibiting damage from use, may be returned to the manufacturer at the manufacturer's expense.

4.1.3   Inspection Records

The manufacturer shall maintain a reliability data and records library. This library shall have on file, for review by the procuring activity, records of examination, qualification test results, variables data (when required) and all other pertinent data generated on devices manufactured to this specification.

4.1.4   Control of Procurement Sources

The manufacturer shall be responsible for assuring that all supplies and services conform to this specification, the detail specification and the manufacturer's procurement requirements.

TEXAS INSTRUMENTS
INCORPORATED
POST OFFICE BOX 5012 • DALLAS, TEXAS 75222

4.1.4.1   Manufacturer's Receiving Inspection

Purchased supplies shall be subjected to inspection after receipt as necessary to ensure conformance to contract requirements. In selecting sampling plans, consideration shall be given to the controls exercised by the procurement source and evidence of sustained quality conformance.

4.1.4.2   The manufacturer shall provide procedures for withholding from use all incoming supplies pending completion of required tests or receipt of necessary certification or test records and their evaluation.

4.1.4.3   The manufacturer shall initiate corrective action with the procurement source depending upon the nature and frequency of receipt of nonconforming supplies.

4.1.5   Procuring Activity Quality Assurance Representative

The procuring activity, may, at its discretion, place quality assurance representatives in the manufacturer's plant as deemed necessary to assure conformance to contract requirements in any non-proprietary phase of design, fabrication, processing, inspection, and testing of the integrated circuits being produced. The manufacturer shall provide reasonable facilities and assistance for the safety and convenience of such personnel in the performance of their duties. Inspection and test procedures shall be made available for review by the quality assurance representative.

4.2   Qualification and Quality Conformance Inspection

4.2.1   Qualification

When specifically called out and funded on the purchase order or contract, the manufacturer's specific device qualification shall be based on compliance with the quality conformance test per Table III for MOS LSI devices. Qualification for other technologies shall be per Table I except that the testing will be to one LTPD level tighter than as defined in Table B-I of MIL-M-38510. For 38510 Class A (Level IV), qualification shall be per MIL-STD-883, Method 5005, Table IIa.

4.2.1.2   Procedures and Definitions

4.2.1.2.1 Sampling Procedure

Device selection for the qualification procedure of 4.2.1 shall be based on a random sampling technique and will be selected from a generic family.

9

4.2.1.2.2 Generic Family

Electrically and structurally similar devices shall be said to comprise a generic family (e.g., TTL) if they meet the following criteria:

a)   Are designed with the same basic circuit-element configuration such as TTL, TTL Schottky, DTL, CMOS, MOS metal-gate, or MOS silicon-gate, and differ only in the number or complexity of specified circuits that they contain. Generic family for linear circuits is defined by circuit function (e.g., op amp, comparator, etc.).

b)   Are designed for the same supply, bias and signal voltage, and for input/output capability with each other under an established set of loading rules.

c)   Are enclosed in housings (packages) of the same basic construction (e.g., hermetically sealed flat packages, dual-in-line ceramic, dual-in-line plastic) and outline, differing only in the number of active housing terminals included and/or utilized.

4.2.2   Quality Conformance Inspection

Quality conformance inspections (Groups B, C, and D) are per Tables I and II. Table II shall apply to MOS LSI and Table I to other technologies.

a)   When specifically called out and funded on the purchase order or contract, the manufacturer shall perform the quality conformance inspections (Groups B, C, and D) on a lot-by-lot basis.

b)   The manufacturer shall, upon request, make available for review the following generic quality conformance inspection and data:

Group B — To be performed every six weeks on each package type (a different number of pins constitutes a different package) at each assembly location.

Group C — To be performed every three months on each generic family as defined in 4.2.1.2.2a and b.

Group D — To be performed every six months on each package type (a different number of pins constitutes a different package) at each assembly location.

4.2.2.1   Lot Acceptance Sampling

Statistical sampling for quality conformance inspections shall be in accordance with MIL-M-38510 Table B-I.

Group B samples shall be selected from sublots that have successfully completed all of the 100% processing steps specified on the applicable process flow chart.

TEXAS INSTRUMENTS
INCORPORATED
POST OFFICE BOX 5012 • DALLAS, TEXAS 75222

4.2.2.2   Resubmission of Failed Lots

When any lot (paragraph 4.2.2.a) submitted for quality conformance inspection fails any subgroup requirement, it may be resubmitted a maximum of one time for that particular subgroup. This additional submission is permitted, provided an analysis is performed to determine the failure mechanism for each reject device in the subgroup, and that it is determined that the failures are due to one of the following:

a)   Testing error resulting in electrical damage to devices

b)   A defect that can effectively be removed by rescreening the lot

c)   Random defects that do not reflect poor basic device designs or poor workmanship.

4.2.2.3   Early Shipments

When quality conformance inspection is being performed for a specific contract or purchase order, the accepted Group A devices that are awaiting shipment pending successful completion of Groups B, C, and D shall be stored and controlled by Quality Assurance. Under no circumstances shall such parts be shipped prior to the successful completion of the Group B tests.

4.2.2.4   Groups B, C, and D Test Data

All lot-by-lot data generated by Groups B, C, and D testing when specifically called out and funded on the purchase order, shall accompany the initial shipment of devices. This data shall consist, at a minimum, of the following:

a)   Attributes data for Group B. Endpoints for the subgroups are visual per the applicable MIL-STD-883 test method.

b)   Attributes data for Groups C and D. Endpoints for each subgroup are electrical test parameters as defined in Tables I and II.

4.2.2.5   Precedure in Case of Test Equipment Failure or Operator Error

Where an integrated circuit is believed to have failed as a result of faulty test equipment or operator error, the failure shall be entered in the test record which shall be retained for review along with a complete explanation verifying why the failure is believed to be invalid. If it is determined that the failure is invalid, a replacement integrated circuit from the same inspection lot may be added to the sample. The replacement integrated circuit shall be subjected to all those tests to which the discarded integrated circuit was submitted prior to its failure, and any remaining specified test to which the discarded integrated circuit was not subjected prior to its failure.

4.3   Quality Assurance Processing, Methods and Procedures

This section establishes the test methods and conditions to be used for the 100% processing (screening) requirements specified by the applicable process flow chart.

4.3.1   Precap Visual Inspection

Each microcircuit shall be required to pass the appropriate precap visual inspection defined as follows. Precap Lot Acceptance shall be per paragraph 4.6.

4.3.1.1   38510 Class C (Level I) and 38510 Class B (Level III) devices shall be visually inspected in accordance with MIL-STD-883, Method 2010, Condition B.

4.3.1.2   38510A Class A (Level IV) devices (designated for NASA type applications) shall be visually inspected in accordance with MIL-STD-883, Method 2010, Condition A. (See notes 6.1.1.1 and 6.1.1.2.) (See notes under 6.1.2 for MOS LSI devices.)

4.3.1.3   Complex MSI and LSI circuits as defined in MIL-STD-883, Method 5004, paragraph 3.3 may be precap inspected per MIL-STD-883, Method 5004, paragraph 3.3.1 for 38510 Class B (Level III) and paragraph 3.3.2 for 38510 Class C (Level I).

4.3.2   Stabilization Bake

The purpose of this test is to determine the effect on microelectronic devices of baking at elevated temperatures without electrical stress applied. Test shall be performed in accordance with MIL-STD-883, Method 1008, Condition C.

4.3.3   Thermal Shock

The purpose of this test is to determine the resistance of the device to sudden exposure to extreme changes in temperature. Test shall be performed in accordance with MIL-STD-883, Method 1011, Condition A.

4.3.4   Temperature Cycle

This test is conducted for the purpose of determining the resistance of a part to exposures to extremes of high and low temperatures, and to the effect of alternate exposures to these extremes, such as would be experienced when equipment or parts are transferred to and from heated shelters in arctic areas. Test shall be performed in accordance with MIL-STD-883, Method 1010, Condition C, for a minimum of 10 cycles. For MSI and LSI comples devices as defined in MIL-STD-883, Method 5004, paragraph 3.3, 50 cycles may be used in lieu of alternate pre-cap visual inspection criteria.

4.3.5   (Deleted)

4.3.6   Centrifuge (Constant Acceleration)

The centrifuge test is used to determine the effects on microelectronics devices of a centrifugal force. This test is designed to indicate structural and mechanical weaknesses not necessarily detected in shock and vibration tests. Test shall be performed in accordance with MIL-STD-883, Method 2002, Condition E for devices having 20 or less pins and Condition D for those having more than 20 pins.

TEXAS INSTRUMENTS
INCORPORATED
POST OFFICE BOX 5012 • DALLAS, TEXAS 75222

4.3.7 **Fine Leak Test**

Each integrated circuit for 38510 Class C (Level I), 38510 Class B (Level III), and 38510 Class A (Level IV) screens shall be subject to a fine leak test in accordance with paragraph 4.3.7.1 or 4.3.7.2. The method shall be optional providing it is consistent with and capable of detecting the specified leak rate of the applicable process flow chart.

4.3.7.1 **Helium Leak Test**

Helium leak test shall be performed in accordance with MIL-STD-883, Method 1014, Condition A.

4.3.7.2 **Radiflo Leak Test**

Radiflo leak test shall be performed in accordance with MIL-STD-883, Method 1014, Condition B. Krypton 85 bomb pressure and dwell time are a function of the radioactivity level and shall be selected so as to conform to the equations given in Condition B.

4.3.8 **Gross-Leak Test**

Each integrated circuit for 38510 Class C (Level I), 38510 Class B, (Level III) and 38510 Class A (Level IV) screens shall be subjected to the appropriate gross-leak test of paragraph 4.3.8.1 or 4.3.8.2, or an approved equivalent. The manufacturer may, at his option, perform gross-leak testing after the Set I Electrical Tests of paragraph 4.3.9.

4.3.8.1 When specifically called out and funded on the purchase order or contract, units will be bombed 2 hours minimum at 30 psig in FC-78, or equivalent. Units will then be immersed in FC-40 or equivalent at +125°C ±5°C for 30 seconds minimum and observed for for a definite stream of bubbles, more than two large bubbles, or an attached bubble that grows in size, per MIL-STD-883, Method 1014, Condition C2.

4.3.8.2 Units will be immersed in FC-40 or equivalent at +125°C ± 5°C for 30 seconds minimum and observed for a definite stream of bubbles, or more than two large bubbles per MIL-STD-883, Method 1014, Condition C1.

4.3.9 **Final Electrical Test (Set I)**

Each integrated circuit shall be required to pass the electrical requirements of the data sheet. The manufacturer shall also perform such additional testing necessary to assure the parts will meet the temperature extreme limits. MOS LSI memory devices will be 100% tested both at 25°C and at high temperature. Linear circuits will be 100% dc tested at high and low temperatures and 25°C.

When specifically called out and funded on the purchase order or contract, the manufacturer shall perform subgroups 2, 3, and 4 of paragraph 4.4 in accordance with Method 5004 of MIL-STD-883.

4.3.10   Burn-In

The burn-in screen is performed for the purpose of eliminating marginal devices and early-life failures. Device biasing shall be in accordance with MIL-STD-883 Method 1015, Conditions A, D, or E for Digital Circuits and Conditions B, C, or D for Linear Circuits. For 38510 Class B (Level III) devices, equivalent test conditions using the time/temperature acceleration factor of Condition F between the temperature range of 125°C to 150°C may be used. For 38510 Class B (Level III) MSI and LSI complex devices as defined in MIL-STD-883 paragraph 3.3.1, a 240 hour burn-in in lieu of alternate pre-cap visual inspection criteria per MIL-STD-883, Method 5004, paragraph 3.3.1 may be used.

4.3.11   Final Electrical Test (Set II)

Each 38510 Class A (Level IV) integrated circuit shall be required to pass the electrical requirements of the detail specifications. The following tests shall be performed as a minimum: dc parameters at maximum and minimum rated temperatures, and switching parameters at 25°C. In addition, each bipolar device shall have critical 25°C dc electrical parameters read and recorded by serial number and shall pass the following delta requirements:

PARAMETER	DELTA LIMIT
V_{OL}	±10% of detail specification limit
V_{OH}	±10% of detail specification limit
I_{IL}	±10% of detail specification limit
I_{IH}	±10% of detail specification limit

CMOS recorded parameters and delta limits will be defined by the manufacturer as required.

One copy of the pre-burn-in and post-burn-in recorded data with delta calculations shall be shipped with each lot. Data will not be available for the metal flat pack (T). See MIL-M-0038510, Class S. The manufacturer may, when deemed necessary, elect to perform additional electrical testing over and above the requirements stated herein.

4.3.12   Radiographic Inspection (X-Ray)

Test shall be performed in accordance with MIL-STD-883, Method 2012. X-ray may be performed at any point after serialization at the manufacturer's option (see note 6.3).

4.3.13   External Visual Inspection

4.3.13.1 The purpose of this examination is to verify that materials, construction, marking, and general workmanship are as specified. Examination shall be in accordance with MIL-STD-883, Method 2009.

TEXAS INSTRUMENTS
INCORPORATED
POST OFFICE BOX 5012 • DALLAS, TEXAS 75222

4.3.13.2 Visual inspection will be performed for catastrophic failures. Catastrophic failures are defined as missing leads, broken packages, and damaged lids.

4.3.14 Voltage Stress

Selected n-channel MOS LSI devices will be voltage stressed for 40 hours minimum at 25°C min per MIL-STD-883 Method 1015, Condition D.

4.4 Group A Conformance

Group A conformance shall consist of the electrical parameters in the manufacturer's data sheet. If an inspection lot is made up of a collection of sublots, each sublot shall conform to Group A, as specified.

SUBGROUP	LTPD (%)			
	LEVEL I 38510C	LEVEL II	LEVEL III 38510B	LEVEL IV 38510A
Subgroup 1 25°C, dc	5	7	5	5
Subgroup 2 High Temperature, dc	10	10	7	5
Subgroup 3 Low Temperature, dc	10	10	7	5
Subgroup 4 Dynamic and Switching Tests @ 25°C	10	10	7	5

NOTES: Functional tests included in dc tests.
MOS LSI devices will be lot accepted at 25°C and high temperature.
The LTPD's of subgroups 1 and 2 will apply.

4.5 Certification

The manufacturer shall include a certificate of compliance with each shipment of parts if requested on the purchase order. This certificate shall indicate that all specified tests and requirements of this specification have been made or met, and that the lot of devices (identified by lot and/or batch number) is acceptable. The certificate shall bear the name and signature of the manufacturer's Quality Control representative, the date of acceptance or signing, and any pertinent notes as applicable.

4.6 Precap Lot Acceptance

After each precap inspection the lot of devices shall be sampled by quality control and inspected for the specified visual criteria.

9

TABLE 1
QUALITY CONFORMANCE TEST (GROUPS B, C, D)

TEST	METHOD	MIL-STD-883 CONDITION	CLASSES B, C LTPD

GROUP B 1/

Subgroup 1 Physical dimensions	2016		2 devices (no failures)
Subgroup 2 a. Resistance to solvents	2015		3 devices (no failures)
b. Internal visual and mechanical	2014	Failure criteria from design and construction requirements of applicable procurement document.	1 device (no failures)
c. Bond strength 2/ (1) Thermocompression (2) Ultrasonic or wedge	2011	(1) Test condition D (2) Test condition D	15
Subgroup 3 Solderability 3/	2003	Soldering temperature of $260 \pm 10^{\circ}$C.	15

1. Electrical reject devices from the same inspection lot may be used for all subgroups when end-point measurements are not required.
2. Test samples for bond strength may, at the manufacturer's option unless otherwise specified, be randomly selected following internal visual (precap) inspection specified in method 5004, prior to sealing.
3. All devices submitted for solderability test must have been through the temperature/time exposure specified for burn-in. The LTPD for solderability test applies to the number of leads inspected except in no case shall less than 3 devices be used to provide the number of leads required.

GROUP C (Die Related Tests)

Subgroup 1 Operating life test End point electrical parameters	1005	Test condition to be specified (1000 hours) As specified in the applicable device specification	5
Subgroup 2 Temperature cycling	1010	Test condition C	15
Constant acceleration	2001	Test condition E min. (see 3) Y_1 axis followed by one other axis X or Z.	
Seal (a) Fine (b) Gross 2/	1014	As applicable	
Visual examination	1/		
End-point electrical parameters		As specified in the applicable device specification	

1. Visual examination shall be in accordance with method 1010.
2. When fluorocarbon gross-leak testing is utilized, test condition C_2 shall apply as minimum.

TEXAS INSTRUMENTS
INCORPORATED
POST OFFICE BOX 5012 • DALLAS, TEXAS 75222

TABLE 1
QUALITY CONFORMANCE TEST (GROUPS B, C, D)
(continued)

| TEST | MIL-STD-883 | | CLASSES B, C LTPD |
	METHOD	CONDITION	

GROUP D (Package Related Test)

TEST	METHOD	CONDITION	CLASSES B, C LTPD
Subgroup 1			
Physical dimensions	2016		15
Subgroup 2 [1]			
Lead integrity	2004	Test condition B2 (lead fatigue)	15
Seal	1014	As applicable	
(a) Fine [2]			
(b) Gross [3]			
Subgroup 3 [4]			
Thermal shock	1011	Test condition B as a minimum, 15 cycles minimum.	15
Temperature cycling	1010	Test condition C, 100 cycles minimum.	
Moisture resistance	1004		
Seal	1014	As applicable	
(a) Fine [2]			
(b) Gross [3]			
Visual examination	[5]		
End point electrical parameters		As specified in the applicable device specification.	
Subgroup 4 [4]			
Mechanical shock	2002	Test condition B	15
Vibration variable frequency	2007	Test condition A	
Constant acceleration	2001	Test condition E (see 3)	
Seal	1014	As applicable	
(a) Fine [2]			
(b) Gross [3]			
Visual examination	[6]		
End point electrical parameters	5005	Subgroups 1, 2, 3, and 7.	
Subgroup 5 [1]			
Salt atmosphere	1009	Test condition A. Omit initial conditioning	15
Visual examination	[7]		

1. Electrical reject devices from the same production lot may be used for samples.
2. Condition A or B per paragraph 3.7 herein.
3. When fluorocarbon gross leak testing is utilized; test condition C2 shall apply as minimum.
4. Devices used in subgroup 3, "Thermal and Moisture Resistance", may be used in subgroup 4, "Mechanical".
5. Visual examination shall be in accordance with method 1010 or 1011 at a magnification of 5X to 10X.
6. Visual examination shall be performed in accordance with method 2007 for evidence of defects or damage to case, leads, or seals resulting from testing (not fixturing). Such damages shall constitute a failure.
7. Visual examination shall be in accordance with paragraph 3.3.1 of method 1009.

9

TABLE II
QUALITY CONFORMANCE TEST
MOS LSI CIRCUIT

TEST	MIL-STD-883 METHOD	CONDITIONS	LTPD
Subgroup 1			
Temperature Cycle	1010	Condition C	
Constant Acceleration	2001	Condition D[1], Y_1 Plane	
Electrical End Points	5005	Subgroup 1	15
Subgroup 2			
Operating Life	1005	Condition D, 500 Hrs. Minimum	
Electrical End Points	5005	Subgroup 1	10

1. Condition D for packages with more than 20 pins. Condition E for packages with 20 pins or less.

TEXAS INSTRUMENTS
INCORPORATED
POST OFFICE BOX 5012 • DALLAS, TEXAS 75222

TABLE III
MANUFACTURER'S QUALIFICATION PROCEDURE
MOS LSI CIRCUITS

TEST	MIL-STD-883		CLASSES B, C
	METHOD	CONDITION	LTPD

GROUP B

Subgroup 1 Physical dimensions	2016		2 devices (no failures)
Subgroup 2 a. Resistance to solvents	2015		3 devices (no failures)
b. Internal visual and mechanical	2014	Failure criteria from design and construction requirements of applicable procurement document.	1 device (no failures)

c. Bond strength2/
   (1) Thermocompression
   (2) Ultrasonic or wedge
	2011	(1) Test condition D
		(2) Test condition D
			15

Subgroup 3 Solderability3/	2003	Soldering temperature of $260 \pm 10^\circ$C.	15

1. Electrical reject devices from the same inspection lot may be used for all subgroups when end-point measurements are not required.
2. Test samples for bond strength may, at the manufacturer's option unless otherwise specified, be randomly selected following internal visual (precap) inspection specified in method 5004, prior to sealing.
3. All devices submitted for solderability test must have been through the temperature/time exposure specified for burn-in. The LTPD for solderability test applies to the number of leads inspected except in no case shall less than 3 devices be used to provide the number of leads required.

GROUP C (Die Related Tests)

Subgroup 1
   Operating life test
   End point electrical parameters
     Subgroups 1, 2, 3, and 7
	1005
	5005
		$T_A = 85^\circ$C, 1000 hours minimum	5

Subgroup 2
   Temperature cycling
   Constant acceleration
	1010
	2001
		Test condition C
		Test condition E for package with $<$ 20 pins
		Test condition D for packages with $\geqslant$ 20 pins
		Y_1 axis followed by one other axis X or Z.
			15

Seal
   (a) Fine
   (b) Gross2/
   Visual examination
   End-point electrical
   parameters
	1014
	
	1/
		As applicable
		
		As specified in the applicable device specification	

1. Visual examination shall be in accordance with method 1010.
2. When fluorocarbon gross-leak testing is utilized, test condition C_2 shall apply as minimum.

TABLE III
MANUFACTURER'S QUALIFICATION PROCEDURE
MOS LSI CIRCUITS
(continued)

TEST	MIL-STD-883		CLASSES B, C
	METHOD	CONDITION	LTPD

GROUP D (Package Related Test)

Subgroup 1			
Physical dimensions	2016		15
Subgroup 21/			
Lead integrity	2004	Test condition B2 (lead fatigue)	15
Seal	1014	As applicable	
(a) Fine2/			
(b) Gross3/			
Subgroup 34/			
Thermal shock	1011	Test condition B as a minimum, 15 cycles minimum	15
Temperature cycling	1010	Test condition C, 100 cycles minimum.	
Moisture resistance	1004		
Seal	1014	As applicable	
(a) Fine2/			
(b) Gross3/			
Visual examination	2/ 5/		
End point electrical parameters		As specified in the applicable device specifications.	
Subgroup 44/			
Mechanical shock	2002	Test condition B	15
Vibration variable frequency	2007	Test condition A	
Constant acceleration	2001	Test condition E (see 3)	
Seal	1014	As applicable	
(a) Fine2/			
(b) Gross3/			
Visual examination	3/ 6/		
End point electrical parameters	5005	Subgroups 1, 2, 3, and 7.	
Subgroup 51/			
Salt atmosphere	1009	Test condition A. Omit initial conditioning	15
Visual examination	5/ 7/		

1. Electrical reject devices from the same production lot may be used for samples.
2. Condition A or B per paragraph 3.7 herein.
3. When fluorocarbon gross leak testing is utilized; test condition C2 shall apply as minimum.
4. Devices used in subgroup 3, "Thermal and Moisture Resistance", may be used in subgroup 4, "Mechanical".
5. Visual examination shall be in accordance with method 1010 or 1011 at a magnification of 5X to 10X.
6. Visual examination shall be performed in accordance with method 2007 for evidence of defects or damage to case, leads, or seals resulting from testing (not fixturing). Such damages shall constitute a failure.
7. Visual examination shall be in accordance with paragraph 3.3.1 of method 1009.

TEXAS INSTRUMENTS
INCORPORATED
POST OFFICE BOX 5012 • DALLAS, TEXAS 75222

5.0 PREPARATION FOR DELIVERY

5.1 Final Visual Shipping Inspection

Each lot of microcircuits and its associated documentation shall be sampled by Quality Control and visually inspected for the following:

- a) Scratched, nicked or bent leads
- b) Damaged header (packages)
- c) All test data specified in section 4.0
- d) Certificate of Compliance as specified in section 4.0
- e) All other pertinent documentation required and specified by this specification.

5.2 Packing Requirements

Parts shall be packed in containers of the type, size, and kind commonly used which will ensure acceptance by common carriers and safe delivery at the destination and in accordance with MIL-M-55565, Level C, bulk pack. The containers shall be clearly marked with manufacturer's name or symbol.

5.3 Preservation and Package Identification

The package shall be marked with the following:

The country of origin if other than U.S.A.

Procuring activity parts number

Purchase order number

Material nomenclature

Quantity

Lot number

Date code

This information shall appear on the label or shall be directly marked on each container. Method is optional.

6.0 NOTES

6.1 Precap Visual Method 2010

The following criteria may be in conflict with the circuit design topology and construction techniques of some microcircuit manufacturers. Where such a conflict does exist, the inspection criteria listed herein may be waived. (Reference paragraph 3.0 of MIL-STD-883, Method 2010).

6.1.1   Preseal Visual Inspection, Test Condition B [38510 Class B (Level III) and 38510 Class C (Level I)].

6.1.1.1 Paragraph 3.2: a 20-PSI minimum blow-off prior to seal will be performed to meet the intent of a controlled environment.

6.1.1.2 For titanium-tungsten, gold, titanium-tungsten multilayered systems, the underlying metal is defined as the bottom titanium tungsten and the top layer is defined as gold.

6.1.2   Preseal Visual Inspection for MOS LSI devices (38510 Class B, level III SMC). When the alternate screening option of paragraph 3.3 of Method 5004 is applied, the following additional items are applicable:

6.1.2.1 Internal visual, Method 2010, Condition B: In addition to the changes indicated by paragraph 3.3.1 of Method 5004, the following additional clarifications and deletions are applicable as reflected in MIL-M-38510/235:

   a)   Metallization inspection shall be applicable to the top layer metal conductor (i.e., Al) and need not include "underlying conductors" such as poly-silicon.

   b)   Omit paragraphs 3.2.1.1 (b) through 3.2.1.1 (e), 3.2.1.2 (b) through 3.2.1.2 (e) and 3.2.3 (e) (Items 3.2.1.1 (f) and 3.2.3 (g) do not apply).

6.2   Interconnections

Circuit interconnections (metallization pattern) shall be designed so that no properly fabricated connection shall experience a current density greater than 5×10^5 amperes/cm^2, including allowances for worst-case conductor composition, normal production tolerances on design dimensions, and nominal thickness at critical areas such as contact windows.

6.3   X-Ray Method 2012

Paragraph 3.9.2.2a(2) and (3) delete and replace with: "Cause for rejection shall be a single void in the bar attachment material opening two adjacent sides and exceeding 50% of the length of one side and 100% of the length of the other side."

6.4   Salt Atmosphere Test, Method 1009

Where package design considerations necessitate (such as 0.75-inch tip-to-tip metal flat packs), there may be a conformal coating applied prior to the salt atmosphere test.

6.5   Rebonding

Attempts to bond where only impressions have been made in the metal and where the bond did not make a physical attachment to the pad or post shall not be considered evidence of rebonding.

9

TEXAS INSTRUMENTS
INCORPORATED
POST OFFICE BOX 5012 • DALLAS, TEXAS 75222

IC Sockets
and
Interconnection Panels

IC SOCKETS AND INTERCONNECTION PANELS

Texas Instruments lines of off-the-shelf interconnection products are designed specifically to meet the performance needs of volume commercial applications. They provide both the economy of a standard product line and performance features developed after many year's experience with custom designs. Foremost among these is our ability to selectively bond a wrought gold stripe at the contact point. No waste. Reduced cost. Reliable contacts.

Wrought Gold Contact

Plate a contact with gold and you get a better contact. More reliable, longer lasting. Increase the gold, you improve the contact. But gold is precious, so improved performance has to be costly — right? Wrong. Because now you can get the gold only where it is needed — at the point of contact.

How? With selective metallurgical bonding; a gold stripe inlay. Not porous plating, but durable wrought gold bonded to the contact by the same technology used to produce clad coins and thermostat metals.

Texas Instruments, Attleboro, Massachusetts, is the world's largest producer of these multimetal systems. We also know our way around electronics. The result? A full line of reliable, low cost, interconnection systems featuring an extra measure of gold where it's needed. Premium performance at no premium in price.

IC Sockets

Texas Instruments family of IC sockets includes every type and size in common use today, and as wide a choice of contact materials as you'll find anywhere. Choose from open or closed entry *wire-wrapped*[†] sockets, standard or low profile solder tail sockets, cable plugs, and component platforms. Sizes from 8 to 40 pins.

IC Panels

To match the industry's broadest line of IC sockets TI offers one of the industry's widest selections of off-the-shelf socket panel products. Logic panels. Logic cards. Accessories. Add TI's custom design capability and wire wrapping for full service.

Additional information including pricing and delivery quotations may be obtained from your nearest TI Distributor, TI Representative, or:

> Texas Instruments Incorporated
> Connector Systems Department
> MS 2-16
> Attleboro, Massachusetts 02703
> Telephone: (617) 222-2800
> TELEX: ABORA927708

10

[†] Registered trademark of Gardner-Denver

LOW PROFILE SOCKETS

SOLDER TAIL

C-93 SERIES GOLD-CLAD CONTACTS
C-83 SERIES TIN-PLATED CONTACTS

- Universal mounting and packaging
- Anti-wicking wafer
- Stand-off tabs on base for solder flush
- Redundant contact points for low contact resistance, high reliability and repetitive insertion
- Closed entry construction

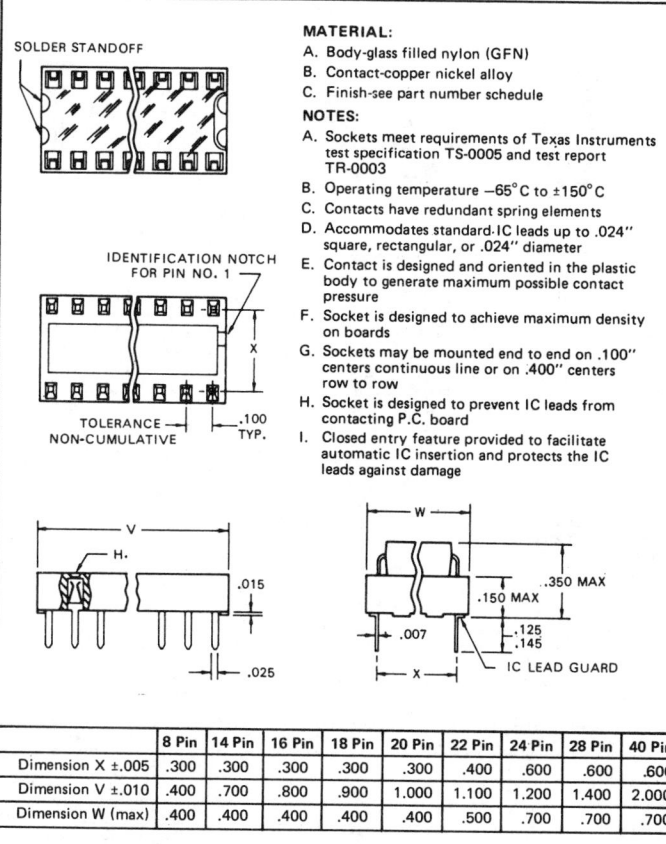

SOLDER STANDOFF

IDENTIFICATION NOTCH
FOR PIN NO. 1

X

TOLERANCE
NON-CUMULATIVE

.100
TYP.

V

H.

.015

.025

W

.350 MAX
.150 MAX

.007

.125
.145

X

IC LEAD GUARD

MATERIAL:

A. Body-glass filled nylon (GFN)
B. Contact-copper nickel alloy
C. Finish-see part number schedule

NOTES:

A. Sockets meet requirements of Texas Instruments test specification TS-0005 and test report TR-0003
B. Operating temperature −65°C to ±150°C
C. Contacts have redundant spring elements
D. Accommodates standard IC leads up to .024" square, rectangular, or .024" diameter
E. Contact is designed and oriented in the plastic body to generate maximum possible contact pressure
F. Socket is designed to achieve maximum density on boards
G. Sockets may be mounted end to end on .100" centers continuous line or on .400" centers row to row
H. Socket is designed to prevent IC leads from contacting P.C. board
I. Closed entry feature provided to facilitate automatic IC insertion and protects the IC leads against damage

PART NO. SCHEDULE

BLACK BODY

	NOMEX ANTI-WICKING WAFER	
Pins	C-93 SERIES	C-83 SERIES
8	C930810	C830810
14	C931410	C831410
16	C931610	C831610
18	C931810	C831810
20	C932010	C832010
22	C932210	C832210
24	C932410	C832410
28	C932810	C832810
40	C934010	C934010

CONTACT FINISH
C-93 SERIES:
100 microinch minimum gold stripe inlay
C-83 SERIES:
200 microinch minimum bright tin plate

10

	8 Pin	14 Pin	16 Pin	18 Pin	20 Pin	22 Pin	24 Pin	28 Pin	40 Pin
Dimension X ±.005	.300	.300	.300	.300	.300	.400	.600	.600	.600
Dimension V ±.010	.400	.700	.800	.900	1.000	1.100	1.200	1.400	2.000
Dimension W (max)	.400	.400	.400	.400	.400	.500	.700	.700	.700

STANDARD PROFILE SOCKET

SOLDER TAIL
C-82 SERIES PLATED CONTACTS • C-92 SERIES GOLD CLAD CONTACTS

WIRE WRAP
C-81 SERIES PLATED CONTACTS • C-91 SERIES GOLD CLAD CONTACTS

- Designed for low cost, reliable, high density production packaging
- Universal mounting and packaging capabilities
- 8 to 40 pin lead configurations
- Contacts accommodate .015" through .024" rectangular or round dual-in-line leads
- Wire wrap posts held to true position of .015" providing a true position of .020" on boards for efficient automatic wire wrapping

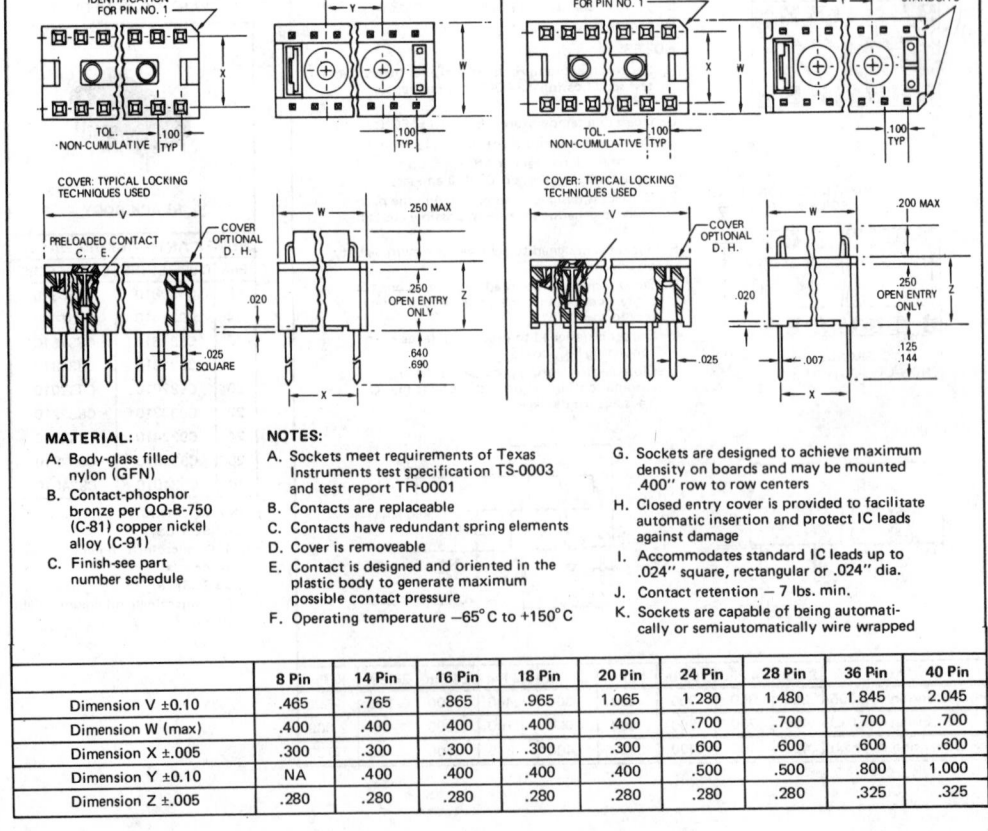

MATERIAL:

A. Body-glass filled nylon (GFN)

B. Contact-phosphor bronze per QQ-B-750 (C-81) copper nickel alloy (C-91)

C. Finish-see part number schedule

NOTES:

A. Sockets meet requirements of Texas Instruments test specification TS-0003 and test report TR-0001

B. Contacts are replaceable

C. Contacts have redundant spring elements

D. Cover is removeable

E. Contact is designed and oriented in the plastic body to generate maximum possible contact pressure

F. Operating temperature −65°C to +150°C

G. Sockets are designed to achieve maximum density on boards and may be mounted .400" row to row centers

H. Closed entry cover is provided to facilitate automatic insertion and protect IC leads against damage

I. Accommodates standard IC leads up to .024" square, rectangular or .024" dia.

J. Contact retention — 7 lbs. min.

K. Sockets are capable of being automatically or semiautomatically wire wrapped

	8 Pin	14 Pin	16 Pin	18 Pin	20 Pin	24 Pin	28 Pin	36 Pin	40 Pin
Dimension V ±0.10	.465	.765	.865	.965	1.065	1.280	1.480	1.845	2.045
Dimension W (max)	.400	.400	.400	.400	.400	.700	.700	.700	.700
Dimension X ±.005	.300	.300	.300	.300	.300	.600	.600	.600	.600
Dimension Y ±0.10	NA	.400	.400	.400	.400	.500	.500	.800	1.000
Dimension Z ±.005	.280	.280	.280	.280	.280	.280	.280	.325	.325

WIRE WRAP

		OPEN ENTRY	CLOSED ENTRY
PART NUMBER SCHEDULE			
Contact Finish	Pins	Black Body	Black Cover
Series C-81 200-400 microinch min tin per MIL-T-10727	8	C810854	C810804
	14	C811454	C811404
	16	C811654	C811604
	18	C811854	C811804
	20	C812054	C812004
	24	C812454	C812404
	28	C812854	C812804
	36		C813604
	40		C814004
Series C-91 50 microinch min gold stripe inlay	8	C910850	C910800
	14	C911450	C911400
	16	C911650	C911600
	18	C911450	C911400
	20	C912050	C911800
	24	C912450	C912000
	28	C912850	C912800
	36		C913600
	40		C914000

SOLDER TAIL

		OPEN ENTRY	CLOSED ENTRY
PART NUMBER SCHEDULE			
Contact Finish	Pins	Black Body	Black Cover
Series C-82 30 microinch min gold per MIL-G-45204 over 50 microinch min nickel per QQ-N-290	8	C820850	C820800
	14	C821450	C821400
	16	C821650	C821600
	18	C821850	C821800
	24	C822450	C822400
	28	C822850	C822800
	36		C823600
	40		C824000
Series C-82 50 microinch min gold per MIL-G-45204 over 100 microinch min nickel per QQ-N-290	8	C820852	C820802
	14	C821452	C821402
	16	C821652	C821602
	18	C821852	C821802
	24	C822452	C822402
	28	C822852	C822802
	36		C823602
	40		C824002
Series C-82 200-400 microinch min tin per MIL-T-10727	8	C820854	C820804
	14	C821454	C821404
	16	C821654	C821604
	18	C821854	C821604
	24	C822454	C822404
	28	C822854	C822804
	36		C823604
	40		C824004
Series C-92 100-microinch min gold stripe inlay	8	C920850	C920800
	14	C921450	C921400
	16	C921650	C921600
	18	C921850	C921800
	24	C922450	C922400
	28	C922850	C922800
	36		C923600
	40		C924000

SOCKET PANELS

STANDARD
D4 SERIES

- **180 position panel or multiples of 30 position with 14 or 16 position socket pattern**
- **I/O — 4 rows with 13 pins per row or 3 - 14 pin sockets**
- **Low cost standard hardware**
- **Available in 98 standard series**
- **Off-the-shelf availability**

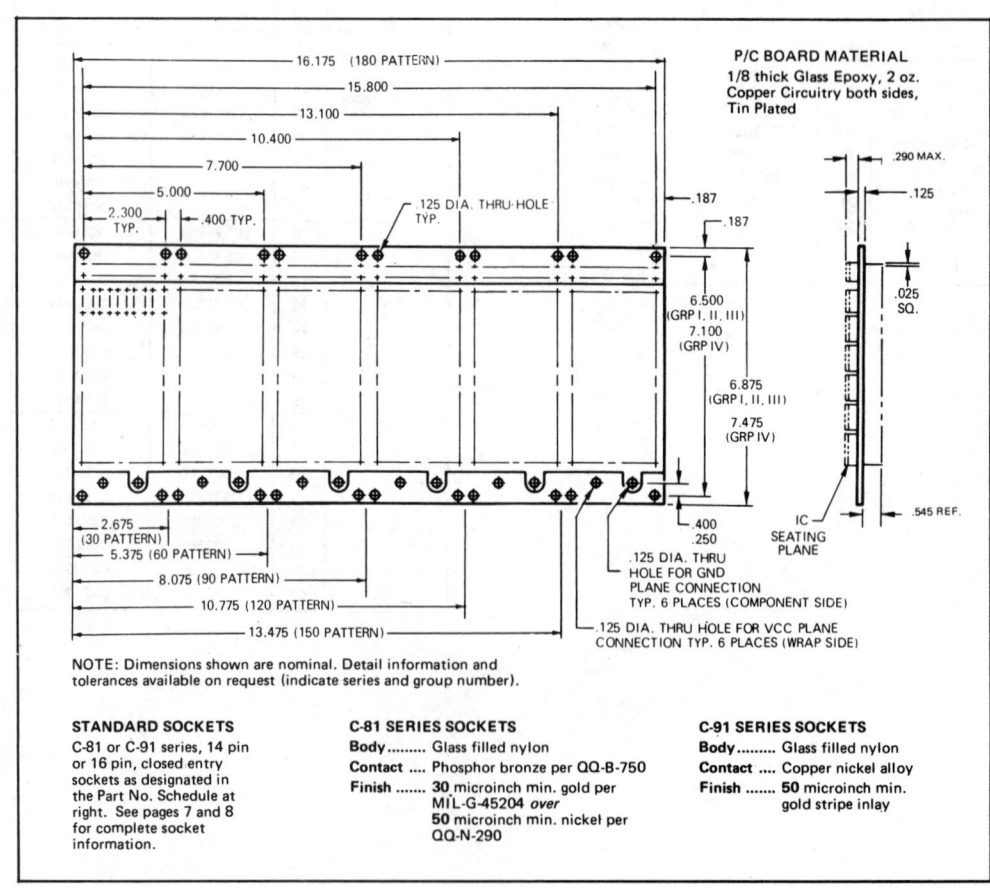

P/C BOARD MATERIAL
1/8 thick Glass Epoxy, 2 oz. Copper Circuitry both sides, Tin Plated

NOTE: Dimensions shown are nominal. Detail information and tolerances available on request (indicate series and group number).

STANDARD SOCKETS
C-81 or C-91 series, 14 pin or 16 pin, closed entry sockets as designated in the Part No. Schedule at right. See pages 7 and 8 for complete socket information.

C-81 SERIES SOCKETS
Body .... Glass filled nylon
Contact .... Phosphor bronze per QQ-B-750
Finish .... **30** microinch min. gold per MIL-G-45204 *over* **50** microinch min. nickel per QQ-N-290

C-91 SERIES SOCKETS
Body .... Glass filled nylon
Contact .... Copper nickel alloy
Finish .... **50** microinch min. gold stripe inlay

10

STANDARD PANEL PART NO. SCHEDULE —D4 Series

Group No.	I/O Option	Sockets Per Panel	C-81 Sockets	C-91 Sockets
Group I **14 Pin** PIN 14 .... VCC PIN 7 ...... GRD	SOCKETS	30	D411211	D411231
		60	D411212	D411232
		90	D411213	D411233
		120	D411214	D411234
		150	D411215	D411235
		180	D411216	D411236
	FEED-THRU PINS	30	D411411	D411431
		60	D411412	D411432
		90	D411413	D411433
		120	D411414	D411434
		150	D411415	D411435
		180	D411416	D411436
Group II **14 Pin** PIN V ...... VCC PIN G ...... GRD	SOCKETS	30	D434211	D434231
		60	D434212	D434232
		90	D434213	D434233
		120	D434214	D434234
		150	D434215	D434235
		180	D434216	D434236
	FEED-THRU PINS	30	D434411	D434431
		60	D434412	D434432
		90	D434413	D434433
		120	D434414	D434434
		150	D434415	D434435
		180	D434416	D434436
Group III **16 Pin** PIN 16 .... VCC PIN 8 ...... GRD	SOCKETS	30	D423211	D423231
		60	D423212	D423232
		90	D423213	D423233
		120	D423214	D423234
		150	D423215	D423235
		180	D423216	D423236
	FEED-THRU PINS	30	D423411	D423431
		60	D423412	D423432
		90	D423413	D423433
		120	D423414	D423434
		150	D423415	D423435
		180	D423416	D423436
Group IV **16 Pin** PIN V ...... VCC PIN G ...... GRD	SOCKETS	30	D444211	D444231
		60	D444212	D444232
		90	D444213	D444233
		120	D444214	D444234
		150	D444215	D444235
		180	D444216	D444236
	FEED-THRU PINS	30	D444411	D444431
		60	D444412	D444432
		90	D444413	D444433
		120	D444414	D444434
		150	D444415	D444435
		180	D444416	D444436

10

SOCKET CARDS

STANDARD
DO2 SERIES

- Low Cost
- 14 - 16 pin socket pattern —
  60 position
- Standard ground and power pin
  commitment
- 8 standard designs
- Mates with dual 60 position edge
  connector

P/C BOARD MATERIAL
1/16 and 1/8 thick Glass Epoxy, 2 oz. Copper Circuitry both sides, Tin Plated

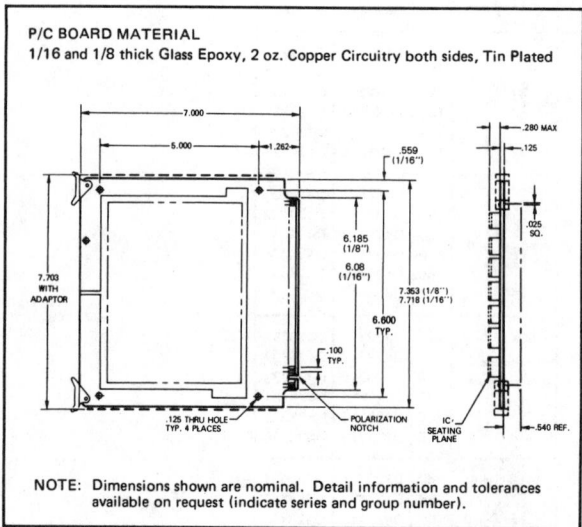

NOTE: Dimensions shown are nominal. Detail information and tolerances
available on request (indicate series and group number).

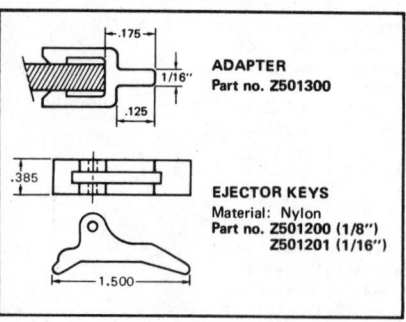

ADAPTER
Part no. Z501300

EJECTOR KEYS
Material: Nylon
Part no. Z501200 (1/8")
Z501201 (1/16")

DO Series
MULTIPURPOSE CARD PART NO. SCHEDULE

I/O	
Board Thk.	Part No.
1/16"	Z012510
1/8"	Z011510

DO2 Series
STANDARD CARD PART NO. SCHEDULE

Group No.	Board Thk.	C-81 Sockets	C-91 Sockets
Group I 14 Pin PIN 14 .... VCC PIN 7 ..... GRD	1/16"	D022110	D022130
	1/8"	D021110	D021130
Group II 14 Pin PIN V ..... VCC PIN G ..... GRD	1/16"	D022310	D022330
	1/8"	D021310	D021330
Group III 16 Pin PIN 16 .... VCC PIN 8 ..... GRD	1/16"	D022210	D022230
	1/8"	D021210	D021230
Group IV 16 Pin PIN V ..... VCC PIN G ..... GRD	1/16"	D022410	D022430
	1/8"	D021410	D021430

10